Ramsay's

Catalogue of

MODEL TOYS

13TH EDITION

Originator
John Ramsay

Editor: Denise Burrows

Email: DeniseBurrows@warnersgroup.co.uk

Consultant technical editor: John King

1st Edition published 1983
2nd Edition published 1986
3rd Edition published 1988
3rd Edition Update published 1989
4th Edition published 1991
5th Edition published 1993
6th Edition published 1995
7th Edition published 1997
8th Edition published 1999
9th Edition published 2001
10th Edition published 2003
11th Edition published 2005
12th Edition published 2007
13th Edition published 2009

Copyright © 2009 Warners Group Publications plc

ISBN: 978-0-9559626-4-6

Original design by John King
Origination by Warners Group Publications plc, West Street, Bourne, Lincs PE10 9PH
Printed by Warners Midlands plc, Bourne, Lincs

Models featured on the front cover: Courtesy of Vectis Auctions

Taken from the Simply Dinky 15 auction on 19th May 2009: Scarce issue Dinky No 905 Foden Flat Truck with chains, 2nd type cab, mid blue cab, chassis and Supertoy hubs, pale grey back, riveted back, in near mint condition, in mint striped Supertoy box. Sold for £4,800

Taken from the Matchbox auction on 26th February 2009: Matchbox Regular Wheels No 62c-1 Mercury Cougar, cream, white interior, chrome hubs with black tyres, in near mint condition, in near mint type E4 colour picture box with correct illustration. Sold for £4,400

Taken from the Corgi Toys auction on 21st April 2009: Corgi No 349 Morris Mini Minor 'Pop Art – Mostest', orangey red, lemon interior, cast hubs, in excellent plus condition, superb example of a harder issue to find, in excellent correct issue carded colour picture box. Sold for £1,500

Contents

Preface

FROM childhood days I was an avid collector of GB postage stamps and my specialised collection was built on the information contained in the Stanley Gibbons' stamp catalogues. These not only listed the variations available but also provided a price guide.

In the 1970s my interests changed and I became a keen toy collector. However, when I looked for a Stanley Gibbons type of catalogue on British model toys to help me, I could not find one. Consequently I started compiling detailed reference information purely for my own information.

Eventually fate took a hand when a printer friend persuaded me to publish my efforts and the 1st edition of John Ramsay's *British Diecast Model Toys Catalogue* was published in 1983. It was not perfect but leastways it was a start.

The Dinky Toys listings in subsequent editions were greatly improved by Dr Cecil Gibson, author of the *History of British Dinky Toys* when he provided direct access to his archives. Similarly the other model listings were greatly improved over the years by the invaluable help and encouragement received from Roger Mazillius, Robert Newson, Mike and Sue Richardson, Hugo Marsh, Ray Strutt, Brian Goodall and staff at Vectis Auctions, John King and David Cooke plus many others from the UK and around the world.

As the originator, publisher and editor of the catalogue, one my greatest concerns was always securing the long-term future of the publication.

Consequently on my retirement I was delighted when Warners Group Publications, the publishers of *Diecast Collector* and *Collectors Gazette* magazines, took over the publishing, compiling and editing of the catalogue. I feel the catalogue's future could not be in better hands.

I have no doubt that this new 13th edition will have built on the past editions and will prove to be of great help to both collectors and the trade alike.

John Ramsay

Introduction

WELCOME to the 13th edition of the *British Diecast Model Toys Catalogue*, brought to you by Warners Group Publications, publishers of *Collectors Gazette* and *Diecast Collector*.

During the summer of 2007, and nearly 25 years after the launch of the first edition, Warners took over publishing responsibility for this catalogue. The work involved in compiling the 12th edition continued to be done by John Ramsay and John King but this 13th update has been wholly compiled by staff at Warners along with a team of 'experts and enthusiasts' from the field.

Updating and revision of the 13th edition

The 13th edition model listings have, where applicable, been completely revised and improved and this catalogue includes many new items never before listed.

A huge amount of time and effort has been put into updating this edition, with new full-colour pictures throughout. Due to time constraints and the enormity of the task, some sections, readers will notice, have been thoroughly revised with many new variations and models listed, while other sections await such detailed attention. We are hoping to fully update these remaining sections in the 14th edition and any help with future amendments and revisions would be gratefully received by the editor.

We have provided a selection of colour pictures throughout the guide and we hope this brand new feature will assist readers to identify models with ease. Sourcing these pictures has largely been done by individual contributors and we are proud to say that most of the illustrations used are new to this edition. We have appreciated the help too of a number of auction houses in providing illustrative material direct to the editor.

The 'Market Price Range' prices have been revised and amended by a team of experts giving readers a 'guide' to model prices at the time of going to press. Variations will occur from auction to auction and readers will appreciate it is impossible to give an exact price for each model. Therefore we advise to use these prices merely as a guide and to bear in mind that market fluctuations will affect these published prices.

The future

It is the new publisher's intention to grow the publication and achieve even greater accuracy in the 14th edition. We have therefore set up a forum on our website: www.ramsays-british-diecast.co.uk (part of the Collector's Club of Great Britain) to give readers the facility to update the editor directly of any amendments. We welcome all comments and suggestions on ways to improve the next edition.

And finally...

We would like to thank everyone involved for their quite remarkable achievements in this update and for helping to make this guide a vital reference material for all serious diecast collectors. A big 'thank you' to everyone who has contributed, whether it be as a major source of information, providing new illustrative material or merely offering words of encouragement when required, we really are grateful to you all, so thank you. Until the next time...

Useful Contacts/Collectors' Clubs

GENERAL
United Kingdom
Collectors Club of Great Britain
Website: www.collectors-club-of-great-britain.co.uk

USA
Diecast Car Collectors Club
Website: www.diecast.org

Canada
Canadian Toy Collectors Society
Website: www.ctcs.org

Netherlands
Nederlandse Algemene Miniatuur Auto Club
Website: www.namac.nl

CORGI CLASSICS
United Kingdom
Corgi Collector Club
Susan Pownall
Westwood Industrial Estate, Margate, Kent CT9 4JX.
Website: www.corgi.co.uk

Australia
Hobbyco Club, Queen Victoria Building, 429-481
George Street, Sydney NSW 2000.
E-mail: info@hobbyco.com.au
Tel: (02) 9264 4877.
Website: www.hobbyco.com.au

New Zealand
New Zealand Model Vehicle Club
NZMVC Inc, PO Box 1356, Dunedin, New Zealand.
Website: www.nzmvc.in-nz.com

USA
Corgi Collector Club, c/o Corgi Classics Inc, Suite
205, 430W, Erie Street, Chicgao IL60610.

Canada
Corgi Collector Club, 4461, Highway No 7,
Unionville, Ontario L3R 1M1.

MATCHBOX
United Kingdom
The Matchbox International Collectors
Association (MICA)
Kevin McGimpsey, MICA, PO Box 120,
Deeside CH5 3HE.
Tel: 01244 539414. Fax: 01244 303335.
E-mail: kevin@matchboxclub.com

USA
Bay Area Matchbox Collectors Association
PO Box 1534, San Jose, California 95109-1534.
E-mail: staff@bamca.org
Website:www.bamca.org

Illinois Matchbox Collector's Club
Bob Neumann, Club Secretary, PO Box 1582,
Bridgeview, Illinois 60455.
Tel: 630-257-0579.

E-mail: neuelectro@email.com
Website: home.comcast.net/~rneumann25/imcc.html

DINKY
United Kingdom
The Dinky Toys Collectors Association
DTCA, PO Box 60, Norwich NR4 7WB.
Website: www.dtca.org.uk
E-mail: info@dtca.org.uk

Dinky Collector
Website: www.dinkycollector.com
Tel: 01473 274367.
E-mail: info@dinkycollector.com

Argentina
Dinky Mania
Website: http://xoomer.virgilio.it/hectorluis

Germany
Dinky Toys Germany
Website: www.dinkytoys.de
E-mail: information@dinkytoys.de

France
Club Dinky France
BP 5117, 14079 Caen, Cedex 5, France.

Australia
Dinky News – Australia
Bruce Hoy, PO Box 249 Aspley,
Queensland 4034, Australia.
Tel/Fax: +61-7-3264-4227.
E-mail: dinkynews@yahoo.com.au

Switzerland
Dinky Toys Switzerland
Website: www.dinkytoys.ch

LLEDO DAYS-GONE AND VANGUARDS
Lledo Collectors Club
Website: www.collectfair.co.uk/lledoshuffle

EXCLUSIVE FIRST EDITIONS
Exclusive First Editions Collectors Association
32 Woodall Road, Enfield, London EN3 4LG.
Website: www.exclusivefirsteditions.com
Tel: 020 8344 6720. Fax: 020 8344 6723.

OXFORD DIECAST
Oxford Diecast Collectors Club
Website: www.oxforddiecast.co.uk
E-mail: sales@oxforddiecast.co.uk

WILLIAM BRITAIN
W Britain Collectors Club
Website: www.wbritaincollectorsclub.com
Tel: 01403 241177.

HORNBY
Hornby Collectors Club
Website: www.hornby.com
Tel: 01843 233525.

TRI-ANG MINIC
Tri-ang Minic Ships
Website: www.triangminicships.com

Tri-ang Model Railways
Website: www.tri-ang.co.uk

LONE STAR
Lone Star
Website: www.lone-star-diecast-bk.com
E-discussion group: Treble-0-
Gauge@yahoogroups.com

MECCANO
International Society of Meccanomen
Website: www.internationalmeccanomen.org.uk

United Kingdom
West London Meccano Society
E-mail: enquiries@wlms.org.uk

Meccano Society of Scotland
Website: www.meccanoscotland.org.uk
Secretary Mr A M J Hutchings. Tel: 0131 663 1568.

North East Meccano Society
Website: www.northeastmeccanosociety.com
E-mail: timroylance-1@blocksetter.co.uk

Meccano Web Ring
Website: www.melright.com/meccring

The East Anglian Meccano Set
Website: www.starman.co.uk/teams
Secretary Dennis Remnant.
E-mail: dennis-millcot@supanet.com

Henley Society of Meccano Engineers
Website: www.hsme.org.uk

Telford & Ironbridge Meccano Society
Website: www.tims.org.uk

New Zealand
Auckland Meccano Guild
Website: www.amg.nzmeccano.com

Canada
Canadian Modeling Association for Meccano &
Allied Systems
Website: www.cmamas.ca

Netherlands
Dutch Meccano Guild
Website: www.meccanogilde.nl

South Africa
Johannesburg Meccano Hobbyists
www.mecworld.co.za
Secretary Andrea Kattan.
E-mail: andrea.kattan@liblink.co.za

Official Company Acknowledgments

The names CORGI TOYS, CARS OF THE '50s, CORGITRONICS, CORGIMATICS, HUSKY, JUNIORS and ROCKETS are all acknowledged as trademarks of Corgi Classics Ltd. BRITAINS is acknowledged as the trademark of Britains Ltd. The name TRI-ANG is acknowledged as a trademark of Hornby Hobbies Ltd, Margate, Kent. The names MATCHBOX, MODELS of YESTERYEAR, DINKY TOYS and SUPERFAST are acknowledged as trademarks of Mattel Inc USA. The name MECCANO is acknowledged as the trademark of MECCANO S.N., 73, rue Henri Barbusse, 92586 Clichy Cedex, France.

Acknowledgments

T HE editor would like to thank the following collectors, enthusiasts, auctioneers and traders who very kindly took the time and trouble to provide updated information and photographs of new entries and colour variations in this edition. The editor would also like to thank those contributors who provided technical support and encouragement throughout the process of publication. A full list of previous contributors can be found on page 4 of the 12th edition and in this issue in relevant sections.

AE Dowse
Alwyn Brice
Andrew Reed
Aston's Auctioneers
Bonhams
Brian Salter
Chris Aston
Christie's
Collectoys
Cottees

David Boxall
Dave Phillips
Dreweatts
Graham Hamilton
Jan Oldenhuis
Jason Preistley
John King
John Ramsay
Lacy Scott & Knight
Lloyd Thomas

Loma Kaufman
Marilyn Swain
Mike Ennis
Phil Silvester
Philip Hill
Rob Tysall
Special Auction Services
Stephen Beardmore
Stephen Yates
Tony Wright

Vectis Auctions
Wallis & Wallis
Warwick & Warwick

Grateful thanks must also go to Andrianna Curtis for design and layout (and never ending patience!).

Abbreviations

A
A.E.C.	Associated Equipment Company
AA	Anti-aircraft
A.A.	Automobile-Association
ABC-TV	Associated British Cinemas (Television)
A.F.S.	Auxiliary Fire Service
AG	Amber glass
AMC	American Motor Corporation
APC	Armoured Personnel Carrier
artic.	articulated
ATV	Associated Television

B
BA	British Airways
BAC	British Airways Corporation
BB	Black base
BBC	British Broadcasting Corporation
BE	Black engine
BEA	British European Airways
BG	Blue glass
bhp	brake horsepower
BLMC	British Leyland Motor Corporation
BMC	British Motor Corporation
BMW	Bayrische Motoren-Werke
B.O.A.C.	British Overseas Airways
BP	British Petroleum
BPR	Black plastic rollers
BPT	Black plastic tyres
BPW	Black plastic wheels
BR	British Railways
BRM	British Racing Motors
BRS	British Road Services
B.S.M.	British School of Motoring
BT	Black tyres
BW	Black wheels
BWW	Black WhizzWheels

C
CA	Crimped axles
CE	Chrome engine
CG	Clear glass
CLE	Certificated Limited Edition
cv	chevaux-vapeur. (a measure of power; translated into English, it literally means 'horse-steams')
CW	Clear windows
C.W.S.	Co-operative Wholesale Society
cwt.	hundred-weight
CWW	Chrome WhizzWheels

D
DCMT	Die Casting Machine Tools
DH	De Havilland
Dk.	Dark (shade of colour)
DUKW	An amphibious military vehicle developed by General Motors in WWII. The letters are not initials or an abbreviation - just part of an early drawing office reference.

E
EEC	European Economic Community
e.g.	exempli gratia (= 'for example')
EMI	Electrical & Musical Industries
ER	Elizabetha Regina, (E II R, Queen Elizabeth II)
ERF	Edwin Richard Foden
Est.	Established (or estimate/d)

F
Fiat	(or FIAT) Fabbrica Italiana Automobile Torino
fig(s)	figure(s)

G
GB	Green box, or Grey base
GB	Grey base
G.B.	Great Britain
GER	Great Eastern Railway
GG	Green glass
GMC	General Motors Corporation
GP	Grand Prix
GPO	General Post Office
GPR	Grey plastic rollers
GPW	Grey plastic wheels
GR	Georgius Rex
GRRT	Grey rubber tracks
GRT	Green rubber tracks
GS	Gift Set
GSP	Gift Set price
GTO	Gran Turismo Omologato
GTV	Gran Turismo Veloce
GW	Green windows
GWR	Great Western Railway

H
HM	His/Her Majesty
HMS	His/Her Majesty's Ship
H.M.V.	'His Masters Voice'
hp	horse-power
H.W.M.	Hersham & Walton Motors

I
ICI	Imperial Chemical Industries
int.	interior
INTER	(or INTL) International
I.O.M.	Isle of Man

J
JB	James Bond
JCB	Joseph C. Bamford

K
KBPW	Knobbly black plastic wheels
K.D.F.	Kraft durch Freude
KGPW	Knobbly grey plastic wheels
K.L.G.	Kenelm Lee Guinness
K.L.M.	Koninklijke Luchtvaart Maatschappij NV (Dutch airline)

L
L.A.P.D.	Los Angeles Police Department
LE	Limited Edition
l/h	left hand
LM	Le Mans
LMS	London Midland & Scottish Railway
LNER	London & North Eastern Railway
LNWR	London & North Western Railway
Lt.	Light (shade of colour)
Ltd.	Limited Liability Company
LWB	Long wheel-base

M
MB	Matchbox
Met.	Metallic
MG	Make of car, ('Morris Garages')
M.I.C.A.	Matchbox International Collectors Association
mm.	millimetres
MOY	Models of Yesteryear
MPR	Market Price Range
MR	Metal rollers
MW	Metal wheels

N
N	North
NAAFI	Navy, Army & Air Force Institutes
N.A.S.A.	National Aeronautics & Space Administration
NB	nota bene ('mark well')
NCO	Non-Commissioned Officer
NGPP	No guide price at present
nhp	(or n.h.p.) nominal horsepower
No.	Number
NPP	No price possible
NS	(or n/s) Nearside
NW	Narrow wheels

O
OPH	Orange plastic hubs
OG	Orange glass
OS	(or o/s) Offside

P
PB	Propeller blade(s)
PB	Purple base
PG	Purple glass
PH	Plastic hubs
P.I.	Private Investigator
PLC	Public Limited Company
PO	Post Office
PP	Packing piece(s), or plated parts
PSV	Public service vehicle
PSW	Plastic steering wheel
P.T.T.	Postes-Telephones-Telegraphes

R
RA	Rounded axles
RAC	Royal Automobile Club
RACO	Rear axle has cut-out

(continued)
RAF	Royal Air Force
R.C.M.P.	Royal Canadian Mounted Police
r/h	right hand
RHD	Right-hand drive
RM	Routemaster (bus)
RN(s)	Racing or Rally number(s)
RNLI	Royal National Lifeboat Institution
RPH	Red plastic hubs

S
S	South
SB	Silver base
SBPW	Smooth black plastic wheels
SBRW	Solid black rubber wheels
SBX	Special box
SE	Silver engine
SGPW	Smooth grey plastic wheels
SPH	Silver plastic hubs
SPK	Speed Kings
SPW	Silver plastic wheels
SR	Southern Railway
SRAB	Straight rear axle bar
ST	Silver trim
St.	Saint or Street
SW	Steering wheel
SWB	Short wheel-base
SWRW	Solid white rubber wheels

T
TDF	Tour de France
TK	Type of Bedford truck
TP	Twin Pack
TS	'Touring Secours'
TT	Two-tone (or Tourist Trophy)
TV	Television
TW	Tinted windows

U
UB	Unboxed, or Unpainted base
UK	United Kingdom
UN	United Nations
US	United States (of America)
USA	United States of America
USAAF	United States Army Air Force
USAF	United States Air Force
USS	United Space Starship
UW	Unpainted wheels

V
VW	Volkswagen

W
W	West
WB	Window box, or White base
WW	WhizzWheels (Corgi), wide wheels
WW	'Wire' wheels

Y
YB	Yellow box, or Yellow base
YMCA	Young Men's Christian Association

Market Price Range (MPR) grading system

BASED on the findings of the Market Surveys undertaken since 1983 virtually all the models have been given a 'Market Price Range'. The price gap between the lower and higher figures indicates the likely price range a collector should expect to pay for the model.

Models qualifying for a price at the top end of the range could include:
- boxed models where both the model and the box are in pristine condition;
- a scarce or unusual colour;
- an unusual component such as special wheels;
- a model with pristine decals where this is unusual;
- a model in an unusual or special box; and
- a model priced by a trader who disagrees with the price range quoted in the catalogue (which is only a guide).

PRICES FOR MODELS IN LESS THAN MINT BOXED CONDITION

Many boxed models seen for sale fail to match up to the exacting standards on which the Market Price Range has been based, having slight model or box damage. In these instances models may be priced at 50% to 60% of the Market Price Range shown, and this is particularly relevant when a model is common. Boxed models with considerable damage or models lacking their original box will be priced much lower.

Note: It cannot be over-emphasised that irrespective of the price guidance provided by this catalogue, collectors should not always expect to see prices asked within the price ranges shown. Traders will ask a price based on their trading requirements and will NOT be governed by any figures shown in this catalogue, nor could they be reasonably expected to do so.

MODELS NOT GIVEN A MARKET PRICE RANGE

It has not been possible to give every model a price range and these exceptions are as follows:

NPP No Price Possible

This is shown alongside models never encountered in the survey or about which there is doubt as to their actual issue, even though a model may have been pictured in a catalogue. Readers will appreciate that unlike postage stamps or coins, no birth records are available in respect of all the diecast models designed or issued.

NGPP No Grading Possible at Present

Price grading may not be possible at present because:

i) The model or gift set is particularly rare and has not come to market in recent times. Consequently, no price grading has been shown as the compiler believes that to attempt one would be carrying rarity and value assessment into the realms of pure guesswork. As and when information becomes available concerning these rarities it will be included in the catalogue.

ii) The model may have been recently introduced or announced in the model press or in a manufacturer's own literature, but a price has not yet been suggested or communicated to us.

GSP Gift Set Price

If a model forms part of a set (and is not available separately) the price range will be shown against the entry in the relevant Gift Set section and will refer to the complete set.

DESCRIPTION OF MODEL COLOURS

The descriptions of the various colours used to describe model colour variations have been derived from the following sources:
i) Manufacturers' colour descriptions.
ii) Colours commonly used and known to refer to certain models over a period of many years
iii) Colours which we, in consultation with the trade or specialist collectors, decide most closely describes a previously unrecorded genuine colour variation
iv) Colours given a model by an bonafide auction house. If this model is a previously unrecorded colour variation we will include the variation in future catalogue listings provided that:
    a) the auctioneers are themselves satisfied that the model is genuine and not a repaint; and
    b) specialist dealers and collectors who view the model are satisied that the colour variation is genuine and is not a repaint.

SCARCE COLOURS AND VARIATIONS

Collectors or traders who know of other variations which they believe warrant a separate listing are invited to forward this information to the Editor together with any supporting evidence.

AUCTION PRICE REALISATIONS

Prices of common models sold are often less than the Market Price Range figures shown. In many instances, the models have been purchased by the trade who will add their own mark-up.

Classifying the condition of models and boxes

THE condition of a model and its accompanying box does, of course, have a direct bearing on its value which makes accurate condition grading a matter of key importance.

Unlike other collecting hobbies, such as stamps or coins, no one universal grading system is used to classify the condition of models and boxes. Nevertheless, whilst several versions exist, there are really two main systems of condition classification in the UK as follows:

1) THE 'SPECIFIC CONDITION' GRADING SYSTEM

The following example is fairly typical of the types of descriptions and gradings seen on mail order lists.

M	**Mint**	**AM**	**Almost Mint**
VSC	**Very Slightly Chipped**	**SC**	**Slightly Chipped**
C	**Chipped**	**VC**	**Very Chipped**

If a model is described as mint boxed, the condition of its box is not normally separately described. However, it is expected to be in first class and as near original condition as is possible, bearing in mind the age of the model concerned.

If a box is damaged the flaws are usually separately described. This method has always seemed to work out quite well in practice, for all reputable dealers automatically offer a 'Sale or Return if not satisfied' deal to their clients, which provides the necessary safeguard against the misrepresentation of the model's condition. The compiler would stress that the foregoing is only an example of a mail order condition grading system and stricter box grading definitions are known to exist.

2) THE 'GENERAL CONDITION' GRADING SYSTEM

This method is often used by auctioneers although it is also to be seen used on the occasional mail order list.

M **Mint**	**E** **Excellent**	**G** **Good**
F **Fair**	**P** **Poor**	

Usually these gradings are separately applied to describe firstly, the condition of the model and, secondly, the condition of the box. From our observations and purely for guidance purposes, we would suggest the following descriptions approximately represent the different grades.

MODEL CONDITION GRADINGS

1 MINT (M) The model must be complete and as fresh, new and original in appearance as when first received from the manufacturers.

2 EXCELLENT (E) The model is almost in mint condition and is only barred from that classification by having a few slight flaws, eg, slight paintwork chipping in unimportant areas.

3 GOOD (G) The model is in a complete and original condition and retains an overall collectable appearance despite having a few chips or rubbed paintwork.

4 FAIR (F) The model may not be in its original state having, for example, a broken bumper, replacement radiator or windscreen, or it may have signs of metal fatigue. The paintwork may be faded, well chipped, retouched or repainted. There may be signs of rust. Unless the model is rare it is in a barely collectable condition.

5 POOR (P) The model may be damaged, incomplete, repainted, altered, metal fatigued, or have a rusted baseplate or heavily chipped paintwork, etc. Unless the model is rare it has little real value to a collector other than as a candidate for a complete restoration or use as spares.

BOX CONDITION GRADINGS

1 MINT (M) The box must be complete both inside and out and contain all the original packing materials, manufacturer's leaflet and box labels. It should look as fresh, new and original in appearance as when first received from the manufacturers.

2 EXCELLENT (E) The box is in almost mint condition but is only barred from that classification by just the odd minor blemish, eg, there may be slight damage to the display labels caused by bad storage. The original shop price label may have been carelessly removed and caused slight damage. The cover of a bubble pack may be cracked or there may be very slight soiling, etc.

3 GOOD (G) The box is complete both inside and out, and retains an overall attractive collectable appearance. Furthermore, despite showing a few signs of wear and tear, it does not appear 'tired'.

4 FAIR (F) The box will have a 'tired' appearance and show definite signs of wear and tear. It may be incomplete and not contain the original packing materials or leaflets. In addition it may not display all the exterior identification labels or they may be torn or soiled or a box-end flap may be missing or otherwise be slightly damaged. In this condition, unless the model is particularly rare, it will not add much to the model's value.

5 POOR (P) The box will show considerable signs of wear and tear. It will almost certainly be badly damaged, torn, incomplete or heavily soiled and in this condition, unless it is very rare, is of little value to a collector.

Model and box valuation guidelines

The research has produced the following comparative price information concerning the values of both unboxed models and separate boxes in the various condition classifications.

The guidelines have been based on the 'General Condition' grading system as described in the previous section. The percentage value ranges are designed to reflect the relatively higher values of the rarer models and boxes.

RARE MODELS AND SETS

The exceptions to the guidelines are in respect of rare models or boxes, or models seldom found in first class condition, such as some pre-war models. In these situations rarity commands a premium and the asking price or the price realised at auction will certainly reflect it.

Note: The same model may have been issued in two or more types of box (Yesteryears, for example). The model in the earlier box is usually (though not always) the more valuable.

UNBOXED MODEL CONDITION	% VALUE OF MINT BOXED MODEL
Mint	50% - 60%
Excellent	40% - 50%
Good	20% - 40%
Fair	10% - 20%
Poor	0% - 10%

BOX CONDITION	%VALUE OF MINT BOXED MODEL
Mint	40% - 50%
Excellent	30% - 40%
Good	20% - 30%
Fair	10% - 20%
Poor	0% - 10%

Buying and selling models

SELLING MODELS TO THE TRADE

THE model value figures produced by the price grading system always refer to the likely *asking prices* for models. They have been prepared solely to give collectors an idea of the amount they might reasonably expect to pay for a particular model. The figures given are *not* intended to represent the price which will be placed on a model when it is offered for sale to a dealer. This is hardly surprising bearing in mind that the dealer is carrying all the expense of offering his customers a collecting service which costs money to maintain.

Collectors should not, therefore, be surprised when selling models to the trade to receive offers which may appear somewhat low in comparison with the figures shown in the catalogue. Dealers are always keen to replenish their stocks with quality items and will as a result normally make perfectly fair and reasonable offers for models. Indeed, depending on the particular models offered to them, the actual offer made may well at times exceed the levels indicated in the Catalogue which are only *guidelines* and not firm figures.

One last point: when selling models to the trade, do get quotations from two or three dealers, especially if you have rare models to sell.

BUYING AND SELLING MODELS AT AUCTION

Collectors wishing to acquire or dispose of models are recommended to contact auctioneers advertising in this catalogue and ask for their terms of trade. Most have their own websites where much information may be obtained concerning rates of commission and forthcoming auction dates, etc.

Catalogue omissions

ACCURATE birth records do not exist in respect of all the diecast models issued. Therefore, whilst every effort has been made to provide comprehensive information, it is inevitable that collectors will have knowledge of models which have not been included. Consequently the Editor will be pleased to receive details of these models in order that they may be included in future editions. Naturally, supporting evidence regarding authenticity will be required.

This catalogue has been prepared solely for use as a reference book and guide to the rarity and asking prices of diecast model toys.

Whilst every care has been taken in compiling the catalogue, neither the Editor nor the Publisher can accept any responsibility whatsoever for any financial loss which may occur as a result of its use.

The Metal in the Model
John King

The process of casting

Collectable cast metal models are made mostly of lead or of a zinc alloy. Casting molten metal in a mould is an established engineering process.

Some forms of casting have changed little since early man discovered how to make arrow heads from iron or bronze. The chosen metal is simply heated to the point at which it becomes liquid and is poured into a container and allowed to cool. It then solidifies and makes a near-perfect three-dimensional mirror image of its container. This is called gravity casting since the metal enters all parts of the mould under its own weight. Lead toy soldiers were often made by gravity casting as it was a quick and cheap way of producing toys.

Developments in casting

Slush casting was a development suitable for larger items in non-ferrous metals. Since the molten metal cools rapidly on entering the mould it can start to solidify before reaching the extremities resulting in incomplete castings. By tilting and turning the mould the metal can be slushed around it to cover all surfaces. The finished item may have a depression at the back and would not be of even thickness. The process is often used for cheap brass door-knockers or crude metal ornaments.

To overcome the 'flat-back' problem, a method of joining two (sometimes more) moulds was devised, using hinges or sliding jigs. This allowed a complete casting to be made with one pouring and released when solid by opening the mould halves. Castings from multi-part moulds can easily be identified by the presence of a join line (along the roof of a model car or the back of a model horse, for instance).

Hollow casting

Another problem for producers was the sheer amount of metal required to make solid castings. A logical step towards using less metal and improving the product was the development of hollow casting. Several makers used this process here and in America but the masters of this art must be Britains Ltd whose delightful hollow cast figures were available

for decades. The technique is developed from slush casting but uses a closed rotating mould. A small amount of molten metal is deposited evenly over just the mould surface, producing a lighter model of fairly uniform thickness. Entry and exit ports are required as the metal must actually flow through the mould. One result is the rather obvious 'hole in the head' appearance on some figures!

Centrifugal casting

In centrifugal casting the metal also flows through the mould but produces a solid casting. The mould is in two halves, each half on the surface of a disc. The discs are placed together to close the mould.

Molten metal is poured in at the centre and the discs spun till sufficient centrifugal force drags the metal through to exit points at the rim. The process was originally developed by the jewellery trade and was really only suitable for smaller solid items such as cheap base castings for ear-rings and brooches. Suppliers of spare parts for Dinky or Corgi models have successfully developed it in recent times, however, and find it a useful way of making chain posts for Foden lorries or additional parts for Code-3 models.

Die casting

None of the casting methods described so far could be considered an exact science. Molten metal in adequate amounts was all that was required to obtain a basic casting. But with the desire to make more accurate models on a commercial scale came the need for more detailed moulds and improved control over the flow of metal.

An alloy was also required that had different qualities of flow-rate, and expansion and contraction characteristics. It needed to be stable under pressure and to exit cleanly from the mould. Pressure diecasting was thus developed as a technically precise process, one that was reliable and controllable and could be automated and adapted to the demands of industry. The system has two important differences from previous processes – the volume of metal required is decided before use, and it is forced into the mould (a steel die) under pressure. The alloy best suited to the production of model vehicles

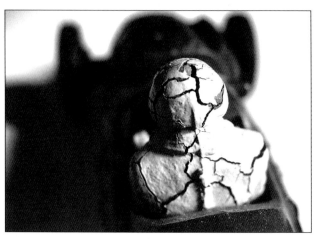

Self-inflicted wounds. The driver figure is an extension of the baseplate component in the Crescent range of racing cars. In this example of a Connaught model, the base has expanded, cracked and is shedding paint. The driver is racing to an early finish as the deterioration is even more extensive higher up in the casting. Believe it or not, this is actually a mint model that has never been played with!

would typically consist of 95 percent zinc, 3.5 percent aluminium and 1.5 percent copper. A trace of magnesium is usually added to the mix to improve flow and handling characteristics. Trade names for the alloy are 'Mazak' in the UK and 'Zamak' in America and France.

Other alloys have been used for various reasons: The Dinky Toys 581 Horse Box and 749 Vulcan Bomber are examples of models cast almost entirely in aluminium. Pewter and white metal are zinc alloys with a high tin or lead content, hence their increased softness or weight. Virtually instant solidification takes place in the mould when the Mazak enters.

After the casting

When castings are removed from their moulds they must be fettled to remove flash. This is often done by rolling several together in a rotating drum that also contains stones (or ball bearings), water and detergent. Dinky, Corgi and Lesney castings were particularly free of flash as the dies were of such a high standard. Consequently, fettling times for them were usually down to a couple of minutes, but could extend to ten minutes when necessary.

Next, castings are sorted and rejects returned to the foundry for re-melting. Acceptable castings are degreased and primed for automatic spray painting, followed by drying and hardening (at temperatures often above 200°F). Subsequent spraying covers smaller areas (two-tone finishes for instance) while mask spraying applies details like radiators and lights. Models are then tampo printed if required before final assembly, inspection and packing.

Cracks in the casting

Casting deterioration, so often a problem with pre-war Dinky Toys, is due to the presence of remarkably small amounts of impurities in the alloy. As little as 0.008 percent of lead or 0.006 percent of cadmium can upset the chemical balance sufficiently to give rise to inter-granular or inter-crystalline corrosion.

The impurities attach themselves to grains of the alloy, altering their electro-chemical relationship which becomes increasingly unstable when humidity levels rise. Moisture, always present in the air, acts as an electrolyte - like the acid in a car battery. Minute electrical currents carry chemicals between crystals within the alloy, altering its structure. The corrosion thus formed (along with changes in temperature) keeps pushing the crystals apart, expanding and cracking the casting. Wheels and other simple castings suffer most because of re-used metal contaminated by lead sweepings. Complex castings demand clean alloy that will flow into the areas of finer detail, so are usually less affected. Ships and aircraft models are often a problem as they are simpler and less detailed castings.

Wartime production was the most vulnerable, since shortages of materials meant using whatever materials were to hand, however inferior. For this reason, the Spitfire Fund Badge is notably difficult to find in good condition, while some Dinky aeroplanes are too big for the box that once held them so snugly!

There is, unfortunately, no cure for the problem – usually but incorrectly called metal fatigue – but at least it is possible to arrest the effects of the corrosion. If the model is kept in a dry unchanging environment, preferably at a temperature above 20°C, the condition will remain stable. Models that have deformed cannot be reset or straightened, but broken parts can be glued back in place using a cyano-acrylate adhesive ('SuperGlue').

Reassuringly, models produced since the War seem hardly to suffer at all from this problem, though some from the 1940s and early 1950s have a certain brittleness and will shatter if dropped onto a hard surface. This effect has been observed with early DCMT-produced toys, Major Models, and Crescent's racing car range, for example.

Caution with your casting

Be warned. . . that nice soft paper you lovingly wrapped your treasured models in may not be acid-free. Even if it is acid-free, it can still attract moisture from the air to rust axles and baseplates with which it has contact. It may be doing more damage than it prevents, especially in a draughty loft. Why not keep your models in a nice display cabinet in the living room – and enjoy your investment!

Sailing into stormy waters. The greatest concern for models afflicted with metal deterioration is with pre-war Dinky Toys. Some 28 Series Delivery Vans and the rarer aircraft models are especially vulnerable. Nevertheless, while condition is always of paramount importance, collectors with a realistic approach do still seem to want to acquire the rarest models and will settle for the best condition available. Fortunately, many examples are still to be found in excellent collectable condition, unlike the model of Dinky Toys 52 'Queen Mary' shown here.

Photo: John King

Bonhams
1793

Toys and Trains at Auction

Bonhams holds four specialist toy sales a year at both our London and Midland salesrooms. These auctions feature a wide range of diecast toys from 'mint and boxed' examples to mixed played with lots, and our sales regularly feature famous manufacturers such as: Dinky, Corgi, Matchbox, Spot-on and European Diecast.

If you are considering selling either individual items of merit or an entire collection why not contact us for a free and confidential auction valuation and competitive proposal of sale.

Enquiries
Leigh Gotch
+44 (0) 8700 273 628
leigh.gotch@bonhams.com

Kegan Harrison
+44 (0)1564 732 971
kegan.harrison@bonhams.com

Catalogue
+44 (0) 1666 502 200
subscriptions@bonhams.com

Illustrated:
Corgi 1110 'Dutch issue'
Shell Benzeen-Tolueen-Xyleen Bedford
'S' tankers in original box
Sold for £4,320

Bonhams
Montpelier Street
London SW7 1HH
+44 (0) 20 7393 3900
+44 (0) 20 7393 3905 fax
www.bonhams.com/toys

London · New York · Paris · San Francisco · Los Angeles · Hong Kong · Melbourne · Dubai   www.bonhams.com

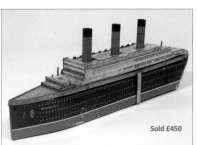

Love collecting? Then you will love Diecast Collector

Benbros and Zebra Toys

The following history and listings of Benbros and Zebra models have been provided by Robert Newson and Mike Ennis.

Benbros was started in the late 1940s by brothers Jack and Nathan Benenson, at Walthamstow in north-east London. They first called themselves 'Benson Bros' and made diecast toys and lead figures (some of which are marked 'Benson'). The name Benbros was adopted in 1951. One of their best known diecast toys was a miniature coronation coach, copied from the Moko-Lesney coach. Their range of large diecast toys was expanded during the 1950s with re-issues of various Timpo Toys, for which Benbros

had acquired the dies. The miniature 'TV Series' was introduced in late 1954, packed in individual boxes which resembled a 1950s television set. By 1956 there were 24 models in the TV Series, and soon after this the packaging was changed to red and yellow 'Mighty Midget' boxes. The Mighty Midgets were available up to 1965.

The Zebra Series was introduced in the 1960s in an attempt to update the range with better features and more accurate models. However, toy production was discontinued when Benbros was taken over in 1965.

Benbros 'TV Series' and 'Mighty Midgets'

Model and details	MPR

Although most models have the words 'Benbros', 'Made in England' or both some are without. Wheels are metal painted or unpainted also Silver or Black plastic wheels on later models. Base plates - 1st type are a push fit, 2nd type are riveted and have strengthened bumpers. Military models, some versions have a dark brownish colour tint to the green.

Benbros TV models

1 Horse Drawn Hay Cart
Green cart with red stays and wheels, Brown horse man either Brown or Blue ... **£25-35**

2 Horse Drawn Log Cart
With man and log, 'Made in England' under horse, log being a length of wooden dowel.. **£25-35**

3 A.A. Motorcycle and Sidecar
Yellow sidecar and windscreen, Black bike with tan coloured rider. 'Made in England' under sidecar, some models have AA badge cast on windscreen **£40-50**

4 Stage Coach (with four horses)
'KANSAS STAGE' cast on side, separate driver on some, 'BENBROS' on later models, issued in various colours **£40-50**

5 Horse Drawn Gipsy Caravan
Issued in various colours for both the roof and body. No makers name on model, brown horse **£100-150**

6 Horse Drawn Milk Cart
Yellow or Lt. Blue cart, Milkman & horse two seperate or cast-in churns, 'BENBROS' on later models. Early models issued in plain box with line drawing **£70-100**

7 Three-wheeled Electric Milk Trolley
Blue or Orange Cart, 'EXPRESS DAIRY' cast in, White crates and white milkman **£40-50**

8 Foden Tractor and Log Trailer
Green, Red or Orange Tractor unit with Red or Yellow trailer with Wooden dowel as log.. **£70-100**

9 Dennis Fire Engine
Red with separate wheeled escape ladder. Ladder Lt. Brown metallic with either open rungs and filled in. Also issued with unpainted ladder **£20-40**

10 Crawler Bulldozer
Body and wheels in Orange or Yellow with either Yellow or Red blades fitted with green rubber tracks **£70-100**

11 Crawler Tractor with Hay Rake
Tractor same as No.10, Rake yellow or Red. No makers name on model.............. **£40-70**

12 Army Scout Car
Matt or Gloss Green with driver cast in or seperate.. **£25-35**

13 Austin Champ
Dark Green with driver cast in or seperate .. **£20-30**

14 Centurion Tank
Similar colours to No's. 12 & 13. With green rubber tracks **£10-15**

15 Vespa Scooter
Issued in various colours, with Red rider, some have either their goggles, boots and gauntlets painted black **£50-90**

16 Streamlined Express Loco
Issued in various colours, 'BENBROS MADE IN ENGLAND' cast underneath. No.17 on cab (TV series only)............ **£20-30**

16 Chevrolet Nomad Station Wagon
Issued as a 'Mighty Midget' model only. In various colours, with or without silver flash. Early models have push fit base, later have riveted **£20-40**

17 Crawler Tractor with Disc Harrow
Same tractor as no. 11. Harrow Red or Yellow. **£30-40**

18 Hudson Tourer
Issued in various colours, 1st or 2nd base either painted or unpainted **£15-25**

19 Crawler Tractor and Trailer
Same Tractor as nos. 11 and 17. No maker's name on model. Green rubber tracks. Green or red trailer....................... **£30-60**

20 Foden 8-wheel Flat Lorry
Various colours some two tone issued with all types of wheels................................. **£70-90**

21 Foden 8-wheel Open Lorry
Various colours some two tone, issued with all types of wheels................................. **£70-90**

22 ERF Petrol Tanker
Similar to Matchbox 11a.Issued in various colours, 'Esso' logo to one side, Orange and Red models are without logo. (Boxes shows tanker with 'Shell logo).................. **£60-80**

23 Box Van (Two types)

AEC Cab, Issued in various colours for cab & chassis, plain with no logos. Open rear end. Bedford S type cab, red, some with 'Dunlop' logo **£40-50**

24 Field Gun.
Solid wheels. No maker's name on model. Firing mechanism **£10-15**

25 Spyker
Pink or Silver with black chassis Red wheels. One version both body, chassis and wheels in Silver.................................. **£15-25**

26 1904 Vauxhall 5 hp
Yellow or Silver with black chassis, Red wheels. One version both body, chassis and wheels in Silver **£15-25**

27 1906 Rolls-Royce
Various colours with Black chassis & Red wheels **£20-40**

28 Foden 8-wheel Flat Lorry with Chains
Various colours with the chains cast as part of the body. Box incorrectly has picture of a 4 wheeled AEC lorry........................... **£60-80**

29 RAC Motorcycle and Sidecar
Black motorcycle, Blue sidecar & rider, separate windscreen, sidecar with 'RAC' cast on front. **£20-35**

30 Army Box Van (Two types)
AEC Cab, green some with a Black/Yellow squadron square. Bedford Cab. Green, some have a Red/Yellow squadron square.**£40-50**

31 Covered Lorry (Two types)
AEC version in Green, Blue or Red, with unpainted metal wheels. Bedford version Blue, Red, Beige with Red trim with unpainted wheels, Lt. Blue version with Black plastic wheels. Both have Cast metal 'canvas' tilt **£40-50**

32 Compressor Lorry (two types)
AEC Cab, and compressor Yellow, or Lt. Brown cab and chassis with Yellow compressor. Bedford Cab, all Yellow or Beige, some with Red trim........................ **£40-50**

33 Crane Lorry (two types)
AEC Cab version was issued in various different colours for the Cab/Chassis and Crane. The Bedford cab version issued in various colours but the whole model being the same colour **£20-30**

34 A.A. Land Rover
Yellow with 'AA ROAD SERVICE' cast on both sides, open rear **£20-30**

35 Army Land Rover
Military-Green body and wheels, open rear end, red/yellow squadron logo on some models **£20-30**

36 Royal Mail Land Rover
Red body and wheels, open back, 'ROYAL
MAIL E-II-R' cast on both sides **£30-60**

37 Wolseley Six-Eighty Police Car
Black or silver with Red roof loudspeaker
cast into roof. Some black models have
separate loudspeakers.............................. **£30-40**

38 Daimler Ambulance
Off-White (civilian) and Dark Green
(military) with Red Cross on roof, some
military have it also on the rear. **£20-40**

39 Bedford Milk Float
Orange or Red body, White crates. **£20-30**

40 American Ford Convertible
Lt. Blue, Yellow with 1st type base, Green
Silver and Blue models with 2nd type base.
Red version can be found with both......... **£20-30**

41 Army Hudson Tourer
Matt or Gloss Green with the red/Yellow
squadron badge, with either 1st or 2nd base. **£20-30**
Box has image of Chevrolet Station Wagon .

42 Army Dispatch Motorcycle and Sidecar
Same Castings as Nos. 3 and 29, in Military
Green. Still with the 'RAC' and 'AA' cast
into sidecar.. **£15-25**

43-48 Bedford Articulated vehicles
Bedford 'S' type cab for model No's 43-48
issued in various colours with all wheel types.

43 Bedford Articulated Box Van
Lt. Blue, Yellow, Blue and Beige.
'Dunlop' transfers on some models......... **£20-30**

44 Bedford Articulated Crane Lorry
Blue, Yellow, Red or Cream. The box is
labelled 'Articulated Wagon' with illustration
showing such a vehicle with a load of
wooden planks. The model illustrated was
not produced **£25-35**

45 Bedford Articulated Timber Lorry
Beige model has a smooth floor other
colours a ribbed version all with log
(wooden dowel)... **£20-30**

46 Bedford Articulated Petrol Tanker
Red 'Esso' logo on one side only on some
models **£30-40**

47 Bedford Articulated Dropside Lorry
Beige, Lt. Blue, Blue or Red. The Beige
model as a separate tailboard, the other
has it cast in. Box description 'Articulated
Wagon'.. **£30-40**

48 Bedford Articulated Lorry with Chains
Beige with Red trim, with ribbed or
smooth floor, Beige, Lt. Blue and Red model
have a ribbed floor. The chains are cast in
the model. Box description 'Articulated
Flat Truck with drawing of lorry without
chains **£30-40**

49 Karrier Bantam Bottle Lorry
Yellow with logo 'Drink Coca-Cola' logos
on side and back. Black plastic wheels.
Some of them have 'MADE IN ENGLAND'
cast under cab roof.................................... **£60-80**

50 RAC Land Rover
Blue, 'RAC ROAD SERVICE' cast into
body, open rear. No box has been
discovered for this model so the No. 50
is not confirmed .... **No price recorded**

Benbros Zebra Toys

Zebra Toys were introduced in the early 1960s and were manufactured along with the existing production of large scale Benbros vehicles. Zebra Toys were packaged in distinctive black and white striped boxes. Most of the models had jewelled headlights and some also had windows and plastic interiors. The AA and RAC Mini Vans apparently had not been introduced when toy production by Benbros came to an end in 1965. They do not appear on a trade price list dated January 1965 but a small number of these models (probably a trial run) were sold off with the remaining toy stocks and are now in the hands of collectors.

In the following list, numbers in brackets are those shown on Zebra boxes. The other numbers are cast on the models themselves. There seems to be no connection between the two numbering systems! These models are rare in today's market.

Model and details	MPR
100 (16) Ready Mixed Concrete Lorry Red Foden cab/chassis, Beige or Yellow barrel..............	**£100-125**
101 (36) Railway Articulated Van Maroon Scammel Scarab Unit, with Pale Orange or Mustard coloured tilt with 'BRITISH RAILWAYS' logo.........................	**£80-110**
103 (10) Jaguar 'E'-type Metallic Light Green, Light Blue or Light Brown..........................	**£130-150**
Royal Coach Silver or Gold Coach with 'ER' cast on doors, eight white horses out riders	**£40-80**
104 (30) Routemaster Bus London Transport Bus on Route 6, *'Fina Petrol goes a long way'* logo on side. Early models with metal wheels, later versions with various coloured plastic.	**£80-110**
106 (34) Heinkel Bubble Car Red, Yellow interior and Yellow plastic wheels. Also in Blue	**£180-220**
107 (27) Daimler Ambulance Cream body, jewelled headlights, small Red cross on side..............	**£70-100**
--- (20) Bedford Cattle Transporter Red cab/chassis, Light Brown body, Blue plastic wheels.	**£70-100**
--- Fork Lift Truck Lansing Bagnall Rapide 2000, Red body, ...	**£50-80**
--- Field Gun 'BENBROS' cast in........................	**£15-20**

Bubble Car

AUSTIN MINI VANS

Model and details	MPR
--- (60) Austin Mini Van 'AA' Yellow, 'AA PATROL SERVICE', logo to sides, and roof sign, AA Logo to doors. Yellow plastic wheels. Opening side and rear doors	**£150-200**
--- -- Austin Mini Van 'RAC' Blue 'RAC' opening side and rear doors	**£150-200**

MOTOR CYCLES (Triumph)

--- (1) Police Patrol Motorcycle Brown finish, plastic rider, 'ENT 303' cast on front, mudguard.	**£50-65**
--- Rally Motorcycle Rally version of Police model.......	**£30-45**
--- (3) Army Despatch Motorcycle Military Green version of Police model	**£30-45**
--- (4) Telegraph Boy Motorcycle Red version of Police model........	**£30-45**
--- (52) 'RAC' Motorcycle & Sidecar	

Model and details	MPR
Black bike, Blue sidecar with RAC logo on front, blue plastic rider .	**£70-100**
--- (6) 'A.A.' Motorcycle & Sidecar Black bike, Yellow sidecar with AA logo to side front, brown plastic rider	**£200-250**

Police Motorbike

Daimler Ambulance, cream, with black interior.

'Qualitoys' and Other Benbros Model Vehicles

This list includes all the other vehicles in the Benbros range, mostly large scale items. Many carried the name 'Qualitoy' as well as 'Benbros', and most were individually boxed. Dating of these models is quite difficult, since there were few contemporary advertisements, and the only catalogues known are trade price lists for 1964 and 1965. The Timpo re-issues were probably no earlier than 1952, and the various motorcycles were introduced in late 1955.

Coronation Coach with 8 horses
Similar to the Zebra model £30-40
State Landau with 4 horses
With four horses and Two footmen. 'MADE IN ENGLAND' cast under coach £30-40
Father Christmas & Sleigh
Metallic green or blue sleigh, Father Christmas figure with four reindeer £40-70
Cinderella Coach
Orange Pumpkin shape Coach with driver and footman, four white horses £100-150
Covered Wagon
Green wagon, cloth canopy, Yellow wheels, Cowboy, with 4 Hollow Cast Bullocks. 'MADE IN ENGLAND' cast in lengthwise. Re-issue of model by L.Brooks (Toys) Ltd which had diecast Bullocks £80-90

Buffalo Bill's wagon

Buffalo Bill's Covered Wagon
Blue wagon with red shafts, or Green wagon with Yellow shafts, both with Yellow wheels, canvas top with illustration. Cowboy with whip, 4 horses £60-90
Roman Chariot
Gold Chariot with Roman figure, two White horses £90-120
Farm Cart
Light Green or Yellow Cart with farmer and horse. (Re-issue of Timpo model) £40-60

Log Carrier

Water Wagon
Lt. Green wagon, brown horse (Re-issue of Timpo model) £40-60
Log Wagon
Horse Drawn wagon, issued in various colours, brown horse £40-60

Stephenson's Rocket

Stephenson's Rocket
Metallic Bronze coloured loco with Grey cylinders and wheels. Green tender with water barrel, also issued in other colours.. £60-80

Caterpillar Tractor
Copy of Lesney model, issued in various colours, 4 inches long £40-60

Qualitoys Bulldozer

Caterpillar Bulldozer
Red with Black blade, or Metallic Blue with Red or Yellow blade, Rubber tracks. Copy of early Lesney Model 5½ inches long. £80-110
Caterpillar Excavator
Orange with Green shovel, or Metallic Blue with Red shovel, with either Red or Green driver, rubber tracks. £80-110
Ferguson Tractor
Issued in various colours, no name on model, with driver also in various colours £150-200
Ferguson Tractor
Fitted with Cab and Shovel, with driver, issued in various colours............ £150-200
Ferguson Tractor
With Log Trailer, driver, Tractor in various colours £80-110
Ferguson Tractor with Roller
Tractor in various colours with driver, Yellow trailer with former Timpo horse drawn roller £150-200
Ferguson Tractor with Harrow
Tractor in various colours with driver, Yellow or Red trailer with former Timpo horse drawn Harrow. £150-200
Dumper Lorry
Copy of Dinky Toys model(965). Metallic Blue cab/chassis, Yellow or Orange tipper.................................... £220-260
Muir Hill Dump Truck
Issued in various colours with driver.......... £60-100

A101 Army Land Rover & Field Gun
Open Land Rover, two cast figures separate windscreen, metal wheels with rubber tyres. Gun marked 'BENBROS' solid rubber tyres. Both in Matt dark green £125-175
A102 Mobile Anti-Aircraft Gun
Silver twin Gun mounted on Green Dodge flat lorry with Red/Yellow logo on door.............................. £150-200
A103 Mobile Radar
Silver Radar aerial mounted on green Dodge Flat lorry £150-200

Qualitoys Mobile Searchlight

A104 Mobile Searchlight
Green Searchlight mounted on Green Dodge flat lorry with Red/Yellow logo on door.. £150-200
A105 Armoured Car & Field Gun
Dark Green or Brownish-Green. Field gun same as Model A101. .... £80-110

Benbros Army Lorry

A106 Army Covered Lorry
Green AEC lorry 'SUNDERLAND' cast in door with green cloth tilt £125-175
A107 Army Land Rover
Matt Dark Green, Black roof, Casting as A101, opening side and rear doors..... £60-100
A110 Army Articulated Low-Loader & Field Gun
Matt Dark Green Low-load as 221, Field Gun as no.101 but with metal hubs and rubber tyres £40-60
220 AEC Flat Lorry with chains
Red Cab and chassis. Other collours also issued £150-200
221 Articulated Low Loader
Red or Green cab, with Red, Yellow or metallic Green trailer. No name on model. Reissue of Timpo Model £40-60

223 Land Rover
Red, Black roof. 'ROYAL MAIL E-II-R' cast on sides. Opening doors, 2 cast figures £60-100

224 Articulated Tanker
Red or Orange cab, with Green or metallic Green, Yellow tank 'MOTOR OIL ESSO PETROL' logo £80-110
Green cab, Red tank, 'SHELL PETROL' logo £80-110
Light Green cab, Red tank, 'UNITED DAIRIES' logo £80-110

Qualitoys AEC Dropside Lorry

225 AEC Dropside Lorry
Red cab/chassis, light Green or Blue body £100-150
Green cab/chassis, Green body, dark Green hubs £125-175

226 Petrol Tanker
Red cab/chassis with Red or Yellow tank. Green cab/chassis with Yellow tank '*Motor Oil Esso Petrol*' logo or '*Fina Petrol Goes a Long Way*' logo. Re-issue of Timpo model £100-150

227 AEC Flat Lorry
Red cab/chassis, light green, Blue or Cream body, 'SUNDERLAND' cast on cab doors. Re-issue of Timpo model £100-150

228 AEC Lorry with Tilt
AEC Dropside lorry as 225 with plain cloth tilt £125-175

--- Forward Control Box Van
Timpo re-issue. Green cab/chassis, Light Green or Red body. 'PICKFORDS REMOVALS' logo £100-150
Red cab/chassis and body £40-60
Red cab/chassis and body, 'CHIVERS JELLIES' logo £100-150

--- Articulated Box Van
Timpo re-issue. Red or Green cab with Green, Red or Cream trailer 'LYONS TEA' logo £100-150
Red cab with Green trailer, 'UNITED DAIRIES' logo £100-150
Light Green cab with Red or Orange trailer, 'BISHOP & SONS DEPOSITORIES LTD' £125-175

A.A. Land Rover
Yellow, some with Black roof, 'AA ROAD SERVICE' cast into side and roof sign. (Same casting as 107 & 223) £125-175

310 Ruston-Bucyrus 10-RB Crane
Maroon/Yellow body, Dark Green chassis and jib, rubber tracks. 'BENBROS' cast underneath £80-110

311 Ruston-Bucyrus 10-RB Excavator
As 310 with Bucket in place of Hook £80-110

AEC Lorry and Ruston-Bucyrus Crane
Red cab and chassis, Yellow body. 'SUNDERLAND' cast in doors. Crane as 310 model £300-400

AEC Lorry with Ruston-Bucyrus Excavator
Red cab and chassis, Yellow body. 'SUNDERLAND' cast on cab sides. Crane as no.311 model £300-400

A.A. Motorcycle Patrol
Black motorbike with fixed forks, Yellow windscreen with plastic glazing. Yellow sidecar. AA badge cast in both sidecar and windscreen.Metal rider, 'TTC 147' cast number plate £100-150

Qualitoys AA Motorbike

A.A. Motorcycle Patrol
Black motorbike with moveable forks, Yellow cast windscreen. Yellow sidecar. AA badge cast in both sidecar and windscreen. Plastic rider. 'TTC 147' cast number plate £100-150

RAC Motorcycle Patrol
Black motorbike with moveable forks, Blue cast windscreen. Blue sidecar. AA badge cast in both sidecar and windscreen. Plastic rider. 'TTC 147' cast number plate £100-150

Solo Motorcycle with Rider Boy
Red cycle and metal rider

Army Despatch Rider - Khaki cycle and rider

Rally Rider - Green or Green cycle, Blue or Red metal rider. All cycle with fixed forks and 'TTC147' cast number plates. Later models were silver coloured with steerable forks, no cast No. £40-60

Motorcycle and Sidecar
'Express Window Service' Black/Cream, Blue rider with cap £100-150

Benbros Salesman's Sample Set.
Plain Red box with 7 chrome/black TV model No.s 16 (Station Wagon), 18, 25, 26, 27, 37 and 40 .... £250-350

Britains Ltd

Britains Vehicles, Guns and Novelties, 1880–1916

BRITAINS VEHICLES, GUNS and NOVELTIES, 1880–1916

by James Opie

Although Britains is famous for manufacturing toy soldiers, it is not so widely known that they had produced toy vehicles before they made their first soldier. In one of their catalogues pre-dating toy soldier production, there are large and small Road Rollers, and probably manufactured even before these are a much larger and cruder Road Roller and Steam Crane, mostly built of tinplate (uncatalogued), and a Rotary Railway Express (uncatalogued), which was a lead diecast floor toy rather than a toy train. All came boxed.

Dating in all probability from 1890 or earlier, the diecast Road Rollers can lay claim to be the earliest attributable catalogued British diecast toys.

> **The London Road Roller** c.1890 to 1895 ....
> **£2,500-4,000**
> **The Miniature Road Roller** c.1890 to 1916 ....
> **£750-1,000**
> **The Rotary Railway Express** c.1891 to 1894 ....
> **£3,000-5,000**

The next group of models, diecast from lead alloy with steel and wire pins, springs, axles and ammunition, were the early guns and vehicles to accompany toy soldier production from 1895 to 1916. In fact, the first Britains spring gun was incorporated in a model soldier with a hollow rifle barrel and a steel spring set just behind the breech, so that a protruding piece of wire could be flicked through.

Set 28 included a three part mountain gun which loaded onto mules, set 39 was a Royal Horse Artillery set with a field gun and limber, and set 79 had the same gun as set 28, slightly modified with a wire towing eye to join to a small limber pulled by eight sailors. Set 144 used the same gun as set 39 with a modified limber as a Royal Field Artillery set. Sets 145 and 146 included a diecast lead four wheel general purpose wagon. Sets 125 and 126 were Royal Horse Artillery sets made in a smaller size with a gun and limber, the gun from which, slightly modified without its towing hole, was also used in sets 148 and 149, and in small size second grade displays 04, 05 amd 06. Perhaps the most famous gun of all, the 4.7 inch Naval Gun, was at first sold without a catalogue number. This was the gun used by H.G. Wells in his book 'Little Wars'. The field gun from set 39 was also available separately in an un-numbered box entitled 'Royal Artillery Gun.'

In 1906, Britains introduced a horse-drawn four wheel general service waggon, which was used in sets 145 and 146. In 1914, Britains produced their first civilian vehicle which was part of their standard scale figure range, the Boy Scout Trek Cart, two of which were included in both set 180 and in set 181. This would probably have been predated by the Coster's Barrow, which is almost the right scale, but produced as part of the novelty range

As the majority of these guns and vehicles came as part of sets, I will give both the price of the boxed sets and the price of the individual guns and vehicles when found separately.

> **Set 28 Mountain Artillery** (oval base men), 1895-1908.. **£350-500**
> **Set 28 Mountain Artillery** (square base men), 1908-1916 .... **£250-350**
> **Mountain Artillery Gun** (eight spoke wheels), 1895-1916.. **£30-50**
> **Set 39 Royal Horse Artillery** (shafted limber), 1896-1906.. **£1,500-2,000**
> **Gun** with bucket seats **and Shafted Limber**, 1896-1906... **£250-400**
> **Set 39 Royal Horse Artillery** (centre pole limber), 1906-1916.. **£800-1,000**
> **Gun and Centre Pole Limber**, 1906-1916 ......
> **£80-100**
> **Royal Artillery Gun** (boxed, no catalogue number), 1896-1916............................. **£120-150**
> **4.7 inch Naval Gun** (boxed, no catalogue number), 1896-1916...............................**£80-100**
> **Set 79 Royal Navy Landing Party** (oval base men), 1897-1916 .... **£600-800**
> **Landing Party Gun and Limber**, 1897-1916......
> **£100-150**
> **Set 125 Royal Horse Artillery**, full dress, small size, 1902-1916 .... **£600-800**
> **Set 126 Royal Horse Artillery**, field dress, small size, 1902-1916 .... **£600-800**
> Small size **Gun and Limber**, grey finish (from set 125), 1902-1916 .... **£100-150**
> Small size **Gun and Limber**, khaki (from set 126), 1902-1916.. **£100-150**
> **Set 144 Royal Field Artillery**, bucket seats, 1906-1916...................................... **£1,500-2,000**
> **Gun** with bucket seats and **Centre Pole Limber**, 1906-1916.. **£300-400**
> **Set 145 Royal Army Medical Corps Four Horse Ambulance Waggon**, 1906-1916 .... **£400-500**
> **Set 146 Army Service Corps Two Horse Waggon**, 1906-1916.. **£300-400**
> Four wheel **General Service Waggon**, 1906-1916
> **£60-90**
> **Set 148 Royal Lancaster Regiment Game Set**, with gun, 1907-1916 .... **£6,000-7,000**
> **Set 149 American Soldiers Game Set**, with gun 1907-1916...................................... **£6,000-7,000**

> **Set 04 British Army Encampment**, small size, 1910-1916................................... **£400-500**
> **Set 05 British Army Encampment**, small size, 1910-1916................................... **£500-600**
> **Set 06 British Army Encampment**, small size, 1910-1916................................... **£600-700**
> Small size **Gun**, without towing hole, 1907-1916..
> **£80-100**
> **Set 180, Boy Scout Display** with two trek carts, 1914-1916................................... **£800-1,000**
> **Set 181, large Boy Scout Display** with two trek carts, 1914-1916 ....**£3,000-4,000**
> **Trek Cart with Boy Scout**, 1914-1916.. **£150-200**

Novelties 1900–1916

Probably from around 1900 or even before, Britains produced cast alloy novelty toys. Exact dates of production are unknown. Those listed below (unboxed except where specified) were in the 1915 catalogue, but had no catalogue number quoted. The catalogue also stated 'Miscellaneous castings. Jockeys, Bicycles, Warships, Yachts, etc., in several qualities and sizes for Race Games, &c.'

> **Tea Pot**, gilt, 1900-1916............................**£20-30**
> **Coffee Pot**, gilt, 1900-1916.......................**£20-30**
> **Kettle**, gilt or black, 1900-1916.................**£20-30**
> **Rocking Chair**, 1900-1916.........................**£30-40**
> **Tea and Coffee Set**, gilt, boxed, 1900-1916..............
> **£200-300**
> **Saucepan**, black, with lid, bright metal, 1900-1916 ....**£30-40**
> **Boiler with Lid**, copper, gilt or black, 1900-1916 .....
> **£20-30**
> **Coal Vase with Tongs**, copper, gilt or black, 1900-1916 ....**£25-40**
> **Watering Pot**, red, 1900-1916 ....**£20-30**
> **Kettle on Stand**, gilt, 1900-1916................**£35-50**
> **Large boxed Kitchen Set** with kettles, 1900-1916 ... **£300-500**
> **Small boxed Kitchen Set** with kettle, 1900-1916.....
> **£200-300**
> **Baby's Chair**, 1900-1916..........................**£40-60**
> **Push Chair**, 1900-1916 ....**£35-50**
> **Coster's Barrow**, blue or gold, 1900-1916 **£40-60**
> **Kitchen Steps**, 1900-1916.........................**£30-40**
> **Football Association Cup**, silver or gilt, 1904-1916 .... **£750-1,000**

Boy Scout Display Set comprising Scout Master, 2 x Scouts signalling, 8 x Scouts walking with poles, 1 x Scout kneeling with hatchet, 2 x Scouts climbing trees, 2 x Scouts to pull Trek Cart, tree & gate, 3 x pieces of fencing & ladder.

Britains Motor Vehicles

By Mike Richardson

Most people are aware of the military vehicles made by Britains both before the War and after in 1/32 scale to go with their soldiers, but not so many are acquainted with the contemporary civilian models. Some of these models are only colour variations of the military versions, for example the 59F 'Four-wheeled Lorry with Driver' in the farm series is the same as 1335 'Lorry, Army, Four-wheeled type' but painted in a smart duotone colour scheme instead of khaki. Other models are only available in the civilian type, usually for the good reason that the army could not possibly have a use for a militarised version. A good example of this would be 1656 'John Cobb's Railton Wonder Car' (or 'Railton Mobil Special' as we know it!).

Britains are our oldest toy company which is still in business having been started in 1860 although the first of the famous toy soldiers did not appear until 1890. This still means over a hundred years continuous toy manufacture, surely a record. The motor lorry models appeared in late 1932 and were based on the Albion army lorries of the time with the familiar 'square' cab design which was to be a hallmark of the Britains lorries until the end of the decade. The range of 4, 6 and 10-wheel farm lorries are still illustrated in the 1940 catalogue. After the War the cab was brought up to date by a

change to a more rounded Fordson type, not nearly so attractive.

The military ambulance was also used in civilian versions, a cream 'Corporation' and a blue 'Volunteer Corps' as alternative liveries to the khaki army one. The rarest version of this model is the red and black 'Royal Mail' van which was sold for a short time towards the end of the production run.

There are three civilian cars, a 'Two-seater Coupé' and two 'Sports Model Open Tourers' in the pre-war production. The coupé and the open sports car without driver and passenger do not have military equivalents, but when the open sports car has people in it then it is either a 'Mobile Police Car with 2 Officers' (finished in green with black wings), or a 'Staff Car with 2 Officers' as the military offering. The occupants of the car are legless and their lower regions are covered with a tartan rug - how nice for them on cold days! After the War there was a one-piece casting version of the staff car and police car without the separate grilles of the pre-war models and these were rather plain by comparison.

The final group of models consists of the superb record cars 'Bluebird' and 'Railton Special'. These came out in the late 1930s and each is over 6 inches long. The Bluebird was produced in three versions; a) with fully detailed removable chassis, b) without this part, and c) a slightly smaller one

(just over 5 inches), without underside detail. The Railton Mobil Special always had the removable chassis and was available painted silver for 1s.6d. or chrome plated for 2s.6d.

After the War two new farm tractor models appeared, a couple of Fordson Majors produced with the active co-operation of the Ford Motor Company. These are excellent models both finished in the correct shade of dark blue and with the name 'Fordson' applied to the front and sides of the radiator. One version has standard wheels but the other (rarer) one had the spiked or 'spud' wheels used on heavy ground.

All these models are to the same scale as the soldiers (1/32), but there is also a similar range in '00' gauge (1/76 scale) to go with model railways. The smaller models date mainly from the post-war era although a sports car and a fastback saloon were seen pre-war. The small scale trucks have a Fordson cab similar to the later large scale farm and army lorries.

The large scale pre-war models are very collectable and prices are consequently very high for rare items in excellent condition and with original lovely boxes. Some few years ago a batch of replicas of the coupé were made here in England so exercise care when buying this model. Spare parts are, or have been available for most of these toys to enable repairs to be carried out.

Britains Motor Vehicles (pre-war issues)

The models were constructed of a lead based alloy and the main body parts were hollow cast. However, parts such as wings and running boards were diecast individually by hand. The Market Price Range figures refer to boxed models in excellent condition. Pre-war lorry models have a 'square nose' bonnet shape.

Civilian vehicles

59 F   **Four-wheeled Tipping Lorry with Driver**
Square nose, back and doors open, rubber tyres, 6"...**£400-500**

60 F   **Six-wheeled Tipping Lorry with Driver**
Two-tone Blue square nose body, White cab roof, back and doors open, White rubber tyres, 6"..............................**£150-200**

61 F   **Ten-wheeled Lorry with Driver**
Square nose, back and doors open, rubber tyres **£200-250**

90 F   **Builders Lorry**
As 59 F plus builders name on side.
'DAVIS ESTATES LTD BUILDERS OF HOMES'......................................**£4,000-5,000**

91F and 92F Builders Lorry
As 60F and 61F plus builders name on side. .
....**£4,000-5,000**

1398   **Sports Model Open Tourer**

Military vehicles

Early issues of lorry and truck models in the ranges 1333 - 1433 and 1641 - 1643 had 'square' fronts, (post-war issues had 'rounded' fronts).

1321   **Armoured Car with Gun**
Military Green, solid metal wheels**£100-125**

1333   **Lorry, Army, Caterpillar Type with Driver**
Military Green finish, rubber tyres, 6" ....
....**£150-200**

1334   **Four-wheeled Tipper Lorry with Driver** ......
....**£150-200**

1335   **Lorry, Army, Six-wheeled Type with Driver**
Military Green finish, rubber tyres, 6" ....
....**£150-200**

Cream body, Black chassis and wheels, White rubber tyres, 4.25" **£750-1,000**

1399   **Two-Seater Coupé** (fitted bumpers)
Cream body, Tan roof, wings and running-boards, White hubs, White tyres, 4.5". (Also in other colours).....................**£1,000-1,250**

1413   **Mobile Police Car with two Officers**
2-piece casting, Green body, Black wings, White tyres, 4.75". (Also in other colours) ......
....**£600-700**

1470   **The Royal Household Set**
Coronation State Coach, King George VI plus the Queen with twelve attendants..........
....**£300-500**

1513   **Volunteer Corps 'AMBULANCE' with Driver, Wounded Man and Stretcher**
Blue body, Red/White cross, White tyres.......
....**£1,000-1,250**

1514   **Corporation Type Motor 'AMBULANCE'**

1392   **Autogiro**
Military Green, RAF roundels, pilot, three rotor blades.................................... **£750-950**

1432   **Tender, Army, Covered, Ten-wheeled (with Driver)**
Military Green finish, White rubber tyres, 6" .
....**£150-200**

1433   **Tender, Army, Covered, Ten-wheeled Caterpillar Type (with Driver)** Military Green finish, White rubber tyres, 6" **£150-200**

1448   **Staff Car**
Military Green car with 2 Staff Officers, White rubber tyres, 4"....................**£350-450**

with Driver, Wounded Man and Stretcher
Cream body, Red/White cross, White tyres ...
....**£900-1,100**

1552   **'ROYAL MAIL' Van with Driver**
Post-Office Red body, Black bonnet, 'GR' plus crown design, White tyres ....
....**£1,600-2,000**

---   **1924 Wembley Exhibition Locomotive**
Bronze finished diecast locomotive on plinth with '1924 Wembley Exhibition,' '240 tons - largest locomotive in the world' NGPP

2024   **Light Goods Van with Driver**
Various colours, 'BRITAINS LTD' logo ....
....**£600-800**

2045   **Clockwork Van** (c1938)
Various colours, driver, opening rear doors. In Red box with Dark Yellow picture label.....
....**£900-1,200**

1641   **Underslung Heavy Duty Lorry (18 wheels) with Driver**
Military Green finish, 10" **£350-450**

1641   **Underslung Heavy Duty Lorry (18 wheels) with Driver**
with 1749 Mounted Barrage Balloon Winch...
.... **£900-1,100**

1642   **Underslung Heavy Duty Lorry (18 wheels) with Driver with Mounted Searchlight**,
Military Green finish, 10" **£350-450**

1643   **Underslung Heavy Duty Lorry (18 wheels) with Driver with Mounted Anti-Aircraft Gun** (small) **£350-450**

1643   **Underslung Heavy Duty Lorry (18 wheels) with Driver with Mounted Anti-Aircraft Gun** (large) **£600-800**

Britains Military Vehicles and Guns (post-war issues)

Military vehicles

Post-war issues of lorry and truck models in the ranges 1334 - 1433 and 1641 - 1643 had 'rounded' cabs, (pre-war issues had 'square' cabs).

1334 Four-wheeled Army Lorry with Tipping Body
('rounded' cab) with Driver, 6" long **£150-200**

1335 Six-wheeled Army Lorry with Tipping Body
('rounded' cab) with Driver, 6" long.............
....**£150-200**

1433 Covered Army Tender
('rounded' cab) Caterpillar type with Driver, 6"...**£150-200**

1448 Army Staff Car
1st issue: White tyres, with General (red/kahki cap) and Driver, 4" long **£350-450**
2nd issue: Black tyres, General (all-kahki cap) and Driver..**£350-450**

Army Ambulance [2nd 1948-56 version], comprising round nosed Ambulance with black treaded rubber tyres, opening driver's door and post war white cross roundels.

1512 RAMC Army Ambulance
3rd version, split windscreen, driver, stretcher, patient **£200-250**

1791 Royal Corps of Signals Motor Cycle Dispatch Rider
sold unboxed.....................................**£25-35**

1791-DB Royal Corps of Signals Motor Cycle Dispatch Riders
Four motorcycles with revolving wheels in display box...NGPP

1832 Lorry and Gun Set.
10 wheel Lorry and 2 pdr. anti-aircraft gun, driver, box **£150-200**

1876 Bren Gun Carrier with Driver, Gunner and 2nd Guard
Carden-Vickers type suspension cast-in, separate gun, 3½" **£75-125**

1877 Beetle Lorry and Driver **£65-75**

1879 'OO' gauge Lorry with Trailer and Hydrogen Cylinders
Military Green, solid wheels, red cylinders ...
....NGPP

1897 RAMC Motor Ambulance Set (18 pieces)
With Driver, Orderlies, Nurses, Stretcher and Wounded ....NGPP

2048 Military Set
1877, 2041 and 2026 Gun **£150-175**

2150 Centurion Tank
Military Green **£300-400**
Matt Green **£175-200**
Dark green finish, US star to turret. **£80-100**

2154 Centurion Tank, Desert Warfare
Sand colour finish. Box has illustrated label .
....**£225-275**

2156 Centurion Tank
Desert warfare finish **£400-500**

2175 Centurion Tank. Self propelled 155mm gun, Matt Olive **£150-200**

Guns and equipment

1201 Gun of the Royal Artillery
with shells, to fire with or without Amorce cap. 5.75" long ....NGPP

1263 Gun of the Royal Artillery
with shells, to fire with or without Amorce cap. 3.75" long ....NGPP

1264 4.7 inch Naval Gun (mounted for field operations),
with shells, to fire with or without Amorce cap. 7.75" long ....NGPP

1292 Gun of the Royal Artillery
with shells, to fire with or without Amorce cap. 4.75" long ....NGPP

2026 25-pounder Gun Howitzer
with shells, to fire with or without Amorce cap. 4" long ....NGPP

1639 Army Range Finder (for all classes of Artillery) a tripod mounted rangefinder with Operator..NGPP

1640 Searchlight
with full movements, uses 3 volt torch battery. 2.5" high ....NGPP

1715 25-pounder (40 mm.) Light Anti-Aircraft Gun
'firing a metal shell with great accuracy'. Base 2" in diameter ....NGPP

1717 Mobile Unit 25-pounder
Light A.A. Gun (1715) on 4-wheel screw-jack chassis, 4.5"..NGPP

1718 Searchlight
1640 on mobile screw-jack chassis, uses 3v battery. 4.5" long ....NGPP

1726 Howitzer Limber (Lead). In Red box, Yellow label..**£50-60**

1728 Predictor, with Operator
Aircraft position predictor on a stand, for A.A defence ....NGPP

1729 Height Finder, with Operator
tripod mounted instrument for use with Predictor ....NGPP

1731 Spotting Chair (Swivelling)
'with Man to lie down' (Service Dress, Shrapnel Helmet)................................NGPP

1749 Balloon and Winch (1939-).
Silver balloon, mooring ropes, box**£750-950**

1757 Barrage Balloon Unit
1641 Lorry + 1640 Barrage Balloon and Winch..**£200-300**

2052DB Anti-Aircraft Unit (15 pieces)
with usual personnel, 2 x 1728, 1 x 1729, 1 x (1639), 1 x 1731, 1 x 1640, Mobile A.A. Gun (1717) ....NGPP

? 18 inch Heavy Howitzer.
3 sprung shells, 6 lead shells, instructions, red box **£150-200**

2107 18 inch Howitzer.
1960s, wheeled, 11 plastic shells, plus loader, box...**£150-175**

Britains 'Farm' Series (post-war issues)

Motor-driven farm vehicles

59F 19?? Farm Tipping Lorry with Driver,
Light Green or Blue, round nose, 4 wheels, 6" long...**£200-250**

127F 19?? Fordson 'MAJOR' Tractor with Driver,
fitted with spade-end wheels . **£200-250**
In prototype Green, unboxed. **£400-500**

128F 19?? Fordson 'MAJOR' Tractor with Driver,
with rubber-tyred wheels **£175-225**

129F 1955 Timber Trailer with real log
Adjustable body. 8" .... NGPP

130F 1955 Trailer with Racks (Tipping Hay Cart)
Two wheels, body tips, tailboard drops. 4.5"... NGPP

135F 1955 Disc Harrow
2.5" ('Can be coupled in pairs to make tandem harrows, or to 136 F to make combination roller-harrow') **£40-50**

136F 1955 Roller
2.25". (See 135 F)......................**£40-50**

137F 1955 Clockwork Set
Fordson Major Tractor with Driver, Mechanical Trailer (2041) + Tipping Hay Cart (130 F). 13.25"................**£400-500**

138F 1955 Four-Farrow Tractor Plough
(3-position adjustment of front wheel-arms possible) **£70-90**

139F 1955 Clockwork Set (Fordson Major Tractor with Driver and Mechanical Trailer (2041). 8.5" **£225-275**

171F 19?? Fordson Power Major Tractor and Trailer
Blue/Orange Tractor, spiked wheels, red/black driver, Orange/Green Trailer, 2 racks, implements **£500-600**

? ? Fordson Power Major Tractor.
Blue body, Orange wheels, an example given 'With the compliments of the Ford Motor Co Ltd'. on wooden plinth ....
....**£300-400**

The following were all supplied in cellophane fronted landscape boxes.
NB Some of the same model numbers were used twice for different models.

Britains Fordson Major Tractor - mid blue body, orange hubs, red and silver plastic hubs, figure driver.

8715 ? Fordson E27N Tractor.
Henry Ford figure and display stand, boxed...**£75-85**

9324 ? County 1884 Tractor.
Black/white with electric motor in box....
....**£125-150**

9515 1980-85 Volvo BM Valmet 805 Tractor,
red/black **£35-45**

9517 1980-85 Massey-Ferguson MF2680 Double Rear wheeled Tractor,
red/white **£45-55**

9518 1980-85 Renault TX145-14 Turbo Tractor,
orange/black/white **£30-40**

9520 1965-70 Fordson Major Tractor with Driver,
cast metal wheels, plastic outset lights.....................................**£100-125**

9520 1980-85 Massey-Ferguson MF2680 Tractor,
red/white **£40-50**

9521 ? County 1884 Tractor.
Yellow/grey, no power, driver, box ...
....**£125-150**

9522 1970-80 Massey-Ferguson 595 Tractor
with safety cab, red body, silver cab .
....**£40-60**

9522 1980-85 Renault Double Rear Wheeled Tractor, orange/white..........**£40-45**

9523 1980-85 **Ford TW20 Tractor**, blue/white .....
....................................**£35-45**
9524 1970-80 **Ford 6600 Tractor**, blue/white,
blue driver..................**£60-70**
9525 1980-85 **Mercedes-Benz Tractor**, yellow/
black **£35-45**
9525 ? **Fordson Super Major** **£125-150**
9525 ? **Fordson New Major Tractor**.
Bright blue, plastic rear hubs ....
....................................**£150-175**
9526 1965-70 **Ford Super Major '5000' Tractor**
with spade end wheels, dark blue ...
....................................**£100-125**
9526 1970-80 **Deutz DX 110 Tractor**, green/black
....................................**£40-50**
9527 1965-70 **Ford Super Major '5000' Tractor**
with rubber tyres, dark blue ....
....................................**£100-125**
9527 1970-80 **Fiat Half-Track Tractor**, red/black,
beige driver.........................**£45-55**
9528 1970-80 **Fiat Tractor**, red/black **£30-40**

*Britains No 9529 Massey Ferguson 135 Tractor - red,
white, brown, silver plastic hubs, figure driver.*

9529 1965-70 **Massey-Ferguson 135 Tractor**
with safety cab, red/white ...**£65-75**
9529 1970-80 **Massey-Ferguson Tractor with
Cab**, dark blue/white............**£60-70**

Britains Land Rover with Horse Box and Pony figure.

9529 1980-85 **Massey-Ferguson MF2680 Double
Rear Wheeled Tractor**, red/grey .....
....................................**£45-55**
9530 1980-85 **Deutz Eight Wheeled Tractor**,
green/black............................**£35-45**
9568 ? **Animal Transporter**. Farm Cart
with cow, box **£150-175**

*Britains No 9569 Mercedes Unimog - green cab, black
chassis, pale elmon back, bright yellow hubs, figure driver.*

9569 1970-80 **Unimog Tractor/Lorry**, green/
yellow..................**£30-40**
9570 1970-80 **Massey-Ferguson 760 Combine
Harvester**,
red with driver.................. **£100-130**
9571 1970-80 **Farm Land-Rover**, 'BRITAINS
FARM' **£30-35**

*Britains No 9571 Land Rover 'Britains Farm' - blue,
white canopy, beige plastic hubs, figure driver.*

9572 1970-80 **Massey-Ferguson 595 Tractor** with
Front Loader, yellow with red front
loader **£100-130**
9575 1980-85 **'New Holland' Combine Harvester**,
yellow..........................**£25-35**
9576 1970-80 **Farm Land-Rover**, blue with cream
canopy **£25-35**
9580 1980-85 **Magirus Deutz Iveco Animal
Transporter**,
dark blue cab, red/grey back **£25-35**
9581 1980-85 **Unimog Breakdown Truck**, white/
orange/red **£15-25**
9582 1980-85 **Magirus Deutz Iveco Flatbed
Transporter**,
white cab, grey back **£25-35**
9583 1980-85 **Magirus Deutz Iveco Tipper Truck**,
yellow/black **£20-30**
9581 1980-85 **Unimog Breakdown Truck
'Recovery Service'**...............**£20-30**
9584 1970-80 **Ford Tractor and Front Loader** ....
....................................**£45-55**
9584 1980-85 **Ford Tractor** with front loader **£40-50**
9585 1980-85 **Fiat Tractor and Vacuum Tanker** ....
....................................**£40-50**
9586 1980-85 **Volvo Tractor and Trailer** **£45-55**
9587 1980-85 **Massey-Ferguson Tractor and Rear
Dump**.............................**£45-55**
9588 1980-85 **Ford Tractor and Rotary Manure
Spreader**........................**£45-55**
9589 1980-85 **Deutz Tractor and Implements Set**
.... **£100-125**
9591 1970-80 **Massey-Ferguson 595 Tractor and
2 Wheeled Trailer**,
red/white tractor with green/yellow
trailer......................**£65-75**
9591 1980-85 **Fiat Tractor and Implements Set** ....
.... **£100-125**
9595 1970-80 **Massey-Ferguson 595 Tractor**
and Front Loader,red/white .**£60-70**
9596 1965-70 **Ford Super Major '5000' Tractor Set**,
Ford Tractor plus nine implements ..
.... **£100-150**
9596 1980-85 **Deutz Tractor and Manure Spreader**
....................................**£45-55**
9597 1970-80 **Massey-Ferguson 595 Tractor and
8 Wheeled Trailer**,
red/white **£65-75**
9597 1980-85 **Ford Tractor and 8 wheeled trailer**
....................................**£50-60**
9597 1980-85 **Mercedes-Benz Tractor with
Tipper Hopper** **£40-50**
9598 1980-85 **Massey-Ferguson MF2680 Tractor
and Trailer**...........................**£45-55**
9599 1980-85 **Farm Tractor and Implements Set** .
.... **£100-125**

*Britains No 9676 Land Rover - greyish blue, orange
interior with figure driver, beige hubs.*

9630 1965-70 **Ford Super Major '5000' Tractor**
with cab and Shawnee-Poole Rear
Dump Set..............................**£85-95**
9670 1965-70 **Dumper**, red with yellow wheels
and blue driver.......................**£20-25**
9676 c1968 **LWB Land Rover**,
Sage green, driver, early sleeve box.......
.... **£400-500**

Horse-drawn farm vehicles

4 F 1955 **Tumbrel Cart with Farm Hand & Horse**
with removable Hay Racks &
Backboard. 7.25" **£100-150**
5 F 1955 **Farm Waggon with Farm Hand**
plus two Horses, removable Backboard.
9.25".......................... **£100-150**
6 F 1955 **General Purpose Plough**
with Farm Hand & two Horses. 10.75" ...
.... **£100-150**
8 F 1955 **Farm Rake with Driver & Horse**
with lever operated Rake. 5.75"**£200-300**
9 F 1955 **Farm Roller with Farm Hand & Horse**
5" long **£100-150**
12 F 1955 **Timber Waggon with Farm Hand &
two Horses**
with real log load. 11.75" **£170-200**
20 F 1955 **Farmers' Gig with Horse & Farmer**
Backboard drops. (Reins not supplied).
5.25".......................... **£125-150**
40 F 1955 **Farm Cart & Horse**
5" long **£75-95**
45 F 1955 **Milk Float & Horse**
(Churns No.588 were recommended
but not supplied with this model). 5"
long.......................... **£100-150**
126 F1955 **Horse Drawn Farm Cart**
5" long **£75-95**
131 F1955 **Horse Drawn Milk Float**
with Milkman & two Churns. 5"**£100-150**
142 F1955 **Single Horse General Purpose Plough**
with Ploughman. 10.25" **£100-150**

'Clockwork' series

2041 **Clockwork Unit** (2-wheeled trailer)
'Will last 1 1/2 minutes when fully wound
and capable of driving any other vehicle
20-30 feet' **£45-55**
2045 **Clockwork Van**
Finished in various colours with
'BRITAINS LTD' logo **£500-700**

'Motor & Road' series (civilian vehicles)

1428 **Road Signs Set**
Fifteen road signs and a Policeman**£300-350**
2024 **Light Goods Van with Driver**
various colours, opening doors, 'Britains
Ltd' logos, 6" long...................NGPP
Set No 641 Civilian Motorcycle and Sidecar.
Red Sidecar, Dark Brown motorcyclist,
White/Red lady on pillion,
child with yellow/Green hat in sidecar.......
.... **£900-1,100**
Set No 641 As above, but Grey Sidecar, Brown
Motorcyclist Yellow/Black lady, child in
Red.....................**£700-900**
653 Civilian Motorcycle/Rider.
Red Motorcycle with Dark Grey Rider ....
....................................**£400-500**
**Post-War U.S. Milk Tanker Lorry
'Milk - America's Health Kick'**.
Special issue - Yellow, Silver Tank, White
hubs.................................**£200-250**
9610 Land Rover 'Police', boxed **£30-40**

Autogiro and Record Cars (1:43 scale)

1392   Autogiro
Blue body, (other colours are known) including Military Green with pilot and three detachable rotor blades **£750-950**

?   Bluebird Record Car, 1938. (Napier-Campbell) Malcolm Campbell's car, lift-off body, detailed engine, White tyres **£125-150**

1656   Napier Railton, 1938, John Cobb's car, '350.20 mph World Land Speed Record'. Painted **£150-200**

1658   Napier Railton, As 1656, but chromium-plated ....NGPP

'Circus' series

'Mammoth Circus Roundabout'
Six horses (Black, Brown, White) plus riders, Green, Red and Yellow Carousel canopy. Lead and card construction. Circa 1910.........
....**£2,000-3,000**

Set No. 1444 Mammoth Circus Display.
In special box (pre-war only). Blue Circus Ring, Clowns, Ringmaster, rare Cowboy with Lasso, Liberty horse, Elephants and Circus Performers......................**£4,000-5,000**

'The Flying Trapeze' Set (No. 1141)
High wire act with balancing clown and suspended girl trapeze artiste, twirling paper parasol, wire and card winder, marbled patterned box. 1936-39 ......**£1,500-2,500**

354B and 359B. 4 clowns in red, with elephant and hoop ....**£45 each**

448B Lion Tamer. Plus lion and tub **£50-60**
447B Boxing Clown **£50-75**
447B Boxing Kangaroo **£50-75**
450B Performing Elephant. no details .. **£100-150**
Elephant Ride Set.
Brown elephant (rubber trunk, red blanket on back), 2 children, keeper, howdah, box ....
.... **£150-200**

Railway items

Set No. 1R Railway Station Staff Set (post war only).
21 items tied to card including Man with Pipe, Lady with Umbrella, Guard, Military Policeman, Station Master and Timetable, 3 Porters/barrows/luggage, box.... **£900-1,100**

Set No. 158 Complete Railway Station.
24 items tied in original box **£700-800**

Set No. 333 Railway Station Staff.
6 figures- Porters with trunks etc. in box........
....**£600-700**

Set No. 1256 O Gauge Railway Set.
17 items items tied to card, boxed **£500-600**

Miscellaneous sets

Set 4 Miniature Household.
12 Pots and Pans etc. tied in box... **£600-800**

Set MB 20 Miniature Garden Set.
In box **£200-250**

Set 16G Miniature Gardening Series.
Flower beds/flowers etc, plus listing **£300-400**

Set MG 26 Miniature Garden Set.
Large quantity of items, boxed **£1,500-1,750**

Petrol pumps, etc

Each of the pumps 1v - 7v has a cast delivery nozzle attached by a flexible hose to the rotating top arm.

1v	'SHELL'	£65-75
2v	'B.P.'	£65-75
3v	'ESSO'	£65-75
4v	'MOBILGAS'	£65-75
5v	'NATIONAL BENZOLE'	£65-75
6v	'FINA'	£65-75

7v   'DOMINION' Petrol Pumps.
3 pumps on plinth.........................**£200-250**

9v   'CASTROL' Oil Cabinet,
sliding front / 3 pumps. 1.75" high. ..NGPP

101v   Stand with Three Pumps
'SHELL', 'B.P.' and 'NATIONAL BENZOLE' pumps a base plus oil cabinet and operator......................................**£100-150**

Set 38F Farm Set (small edition). 12 farm animals etc. in box **£100-125**

Set 134F Model Farm Set.
Post War, 2 Fordson Tractors, plus log trailer, hay wagon and other farm equipment...........
....**£2,500-3,000**

Set 145 Royal Army Medical Corps.
Horse Drawn Ambulance, 1906. Collar harness, four horses, 2 riders, wagon and 2 men.............................. **£500-750**

Set No. 433 Round-Wing Royal Air Force Monoplane.
Red, with Pilot and RAF roundels, boxed.......
....**£9,000-11,000**

Set 1288 Royal Marines Band.
1933 version, Drum Major and 20 men..........
.... **£400-600**

Set 1316 Salvation Army Band and Escort Set.
Fifteen piece band in blue uniforms with Bandmaster, Standard Bearer, Four Females and four Officers **£5,000-6,000**

Set 1317 Salvation Army Band.
23 Bandsmen (red uniforms) + Bandmaster (Blue uniform) **£1,500-1,750**

Set 1475 Historical Series Set.
18 Beefeaters etc., strung in box.... **£100-125**

Set 1477 Queen Elizabeth Set
Queen and George VI, 1953 Coronation Coach, Horses, Royal Household, Marching Horseguards etc.....................**£1,500-2,000**

Set 1495 Painter's Set.
3 White/Black men with one red ladder. Tied in box **£400-450**

Set No 1654 Snow White and the Seven Dwarfs.
Names of Dwarfs on backing card and pictures of Dwarfs on box lid...**£1,400-1,600**

1968 Ex-Factory Prototype Sample.
Un-issued Farm Series , blue tractor, three figures, four animals, box.........**£1,500-1,750**

1939 'Lambeth Walk' Dancing Couple.
Man in Brown bowler hat and suit with Green shirt, Girl in Yellow jacket and Purple skirt **£1,000-1,200**

2034   Prairie Schooner with Pioneer Driver and Wife, Covered.
Green/red wagon, white tin cover, four horses, all strung on card in box ... **£250-350**

2073 'R.A.F. On the March' Set.
7 Airmen/Rifles plus Officer/Sword, box ....
.... **£100-120**

Set 5819 Coronation Set presented at Britains Centenary Dinner in 1993.

102v   Stand with Three Pumps
'ESSO', 'MOBILGAS' and 'FINA' pumps a base plus oil cabinet and operator**£175-225**

103v   Stand with Three Pumps
'SHELL', 'ESSO' and 'MOBILGAS' pumps a base plus oil cabinet and operator . **£200-250**

?   'Regent' Petrol Pump. Apparently never issued .... NPP

?   Petrol Pump Attendant and 'POWER' Pump.
Cream/Red overalls, 'Power' Pump **£80-90**

?   Petrol Pump Attendant and 'SHELL' Pump.
Brown/Green overalls, 'Shell' Pump**£80-90**

?   Rare 'Fina' Petrol Pumps Set.
Three 'Fina' Pumps on plinth, boxed**£500-750**

9689   Garage Set.
'Shell', 'BP' and 'National' on plinth, boxed .
....**£300-400**

One of limited edition of 85, original box with menu. (QE II)........................ **£200-250**

9402 State Landau
with instructions, Queen, Prince Philip, 6 grey horses, 3 drivers, 2 footmen, traces, figures tied in box **£100-150**

'Nestle's Home Farm'.
Variant of Home Farm Set 1F. Contents are the same but with the 'Nestle's World Cow' substituted for the standard cow. This is the only set known to exist............ **£1,750-2,000**

Trade Box 222.
One dozen 'Nestles' 'Map of the World' cows
.... **£700-800**

Set 3/228 Bahamas Police Band.
25 piece band, boxed **£3,000-4,000**

Set 2186 Bahamas Police Band.
1959/60 only, Band Master and 25 men.........
....**£2,500-3,000**

Rare Britains & C.F. Eckhardt CIV Army Service Supply Column.
Four-horse collar harness. Supply wagon with ASC tilt and 8 ASC crates, 9 escort at the trail, 1 officer, oval bases, unboxed.................................**£2,000-2,500**

Miscellaneous figures, etc

Felix the Cat.
Black/white cat on hind legs **£200-300**

587 Village Idiot.
Dark Blue Smock, Brown Trousers (other colours seen).................................. **£175-200**

Army Service Supply Column.
2 Four-Horse Wagons, 13 soldiers**£2,000-2,500**

London Road Roller c.1800's.
Red/Green/Gold, wood box **£2,000-3,000**

'Everton' Football Team.
Tied to card in box...................... **£900-1,100**

'Liverpool' Football Team.
With Players, Referee, Linesman, Goal Post, Corner Flags - boxed **£1,000-1,250**

Set 809 Cricketer.
Circa 1910, cricket whites / red cap, moveable arms **£175-225**

A Cricketer.
In Whites, Blue cap...................... **£150-250**

1934 Pro. Cococubs Series 'Jonathan'
Boy eating Cadbury's chocolate **£175-225**

The FA Cup. Very rare - shown in pre-WW 1 Britains Catalogues **£750-1,000**

Britains 'Lilliput' series

1:76 scale models manufactured under license by Horton (Toys and Games) Ltd., Reno Works, Middlesbrough, England.

This once very extensive series of OO railway compatible miniatures started its life as sets of figures and accessories manufactured exclusively for Trix Twin Railways from 1937 onwards. Just before WWII the first vehicles appeared, both military types. Post war the T.T.R. connection remained for a while, but as the decade changed to the 1950s, Britains introduced the first civilian vehicles. Also new were farm livestock, farm folk, and the Lilliput title was coined.

The vehicular range had quite a makeover in 1956 with new state of the art wheels, and a useful number of new castings. Military vehicles now found favour again and formed quite a large section. However, alongside the phasing out of lead in all toy production, the whole Lilliput range was discontinued after 1960.

Many items were scaled down versions of Britains standard 1:32 scale series. Vehicles always came individually boxed, each individually designed in the earlier years. From 1956 onwards it was just two sizes of generic open fronted display boxes with the details on the end. Only the vehicles are listed here, together with any sets that contained them.

Farm vehicles

Four of the six early Lilliput vehicles that were available from 1950. Left to Right, LV/604, 605, 602, and 603. The silver plastic wheels on the car are earlier production than the lead ones on the lorry.

LV/604 Fordson Tractor – Ford Blue (shades), Orange wheels, always with driver with various waistcoat colours. **£45-55**

LV/605 Milk Float – always with Brown Van Horse, Separate standing milkman, omitted from 1956. Mid Blue, White shaft ends and nearboards, cream wheels Bright Blue, Red shaft ends and nearboards, off white wheels................... **£45-55**

LV/606 Tumbrel Cart with hay racks – always with Brown cart horse. Separate standing carter, omitted from 1956. Green (shades). Red wheels, off white racks........ .... **£45-55**

Civilian vehicles

LV/601 Open Sports Car – not based on any identified prototype, No.1.32 scale counterpart. Three wheel types, earliest is Silver or Grey plastic from 1950, followed by lead, and from 1956 Red plastic wheel with Black tyre. Permutations are legion, with seats either Tan, Brown, Maroon, or Black. To keep it simple therefore,
Known colour combinations –
Single colours – Cream; Light green; Grass Green; Almond Green;Red; Light Blue.
Chassis/Body combinations – Black/Red or Cream; Red/Cream; Cream/Red or Grass Green. **£50-60**

Later 1950s Lilliput vehicles, right to left, LV/607, 609, 614, and 619, plus the Telegraph Boy LB/548 from a few years earlier. The Tractor unit is in the lightest of three distinct shades of brown.

LV/602 Saloon Car – Same comments apply as LV/601, except of course no seats.
Single colours – Cream; Light Blue; Red; White; Grass Green; Bright Blue; Yellow
Chassis/Body combinations – Black/Yellow, Red, Blue, Lemon Cream, or Grass Green, Red/

Rich Cream or Light Green. **£50-60**

LV/603 Articulated Lorry – based on pre-war (just) Kew Dodge. Large 1:32 sized version came later than Lilliput. Same comment re-wheels as LV601/2. Worth being aware that method of painting trailer and rear deck varies. Trailer does not detach, second colour is deck.
Navy Blue/Deep Rich Cream or Grey Green; Dark Blue/Grey; Red/Deep Cream, Grey or Grey Green; Mid Green/Deep Cream, Pinkish Cream, Grey, or Grey Green; Light Green/Grey; Light Blue/Grey; Dark Green/Greenish Light Grey; Red Brown/Grey/Green Trailer; Cream/Grey/Red Trailer; Brown/Grey/Red Trailer. **£50-60**

LV/608 3 Ton Civilian Lorry (Big Bedford).
Open rear body, no 1:32 scale equivalent. Earlier castings have two open windows in rear of cab. Colours - Cab and chassis / rear body.
Bright Apple Green/Red; Black/Yellow; Red/Bright Blue... **£40-50**

LV/614 Articulated Truck (Fordson Thames).
Trailer lifts off easily, too easily, so front and rear combinations open to "Mix and Match". So, separately – Tractor units – three fairly distinct shades that could be described as Fawn Brown, Red Brown and Chocolate Brown.
Trailers – Either Sky or Bright Mid Blue, Mid or Dark Green. Any pairing. **£40-50**
Complete Unit, Cream throughout. **£100-150**

LV/616 1½ ton Civilian Truck (Fordson Thames).
Same three Browns for the cab and chassis as LV/614 are probably possible. Rear body either Pale Green, Yellow, or Red...................... **£35-45**

LV/617 Local Authority Ambulance (Fordson Thames).
Light Cream (No Red Crosses). **£90-110**

LV/619 Post Office Royal Mail Van (Fordson Thames).................................£110-130

Early military vehicles

Lead castings, including wheels, usually all assembled before painting. Colour – mostly the earlier Khaki Brownish Green shade much favoured by Britains Pre-War. Introduced late 1930s, early Post-War production almost certain. Lift-off lid boxes with illustrated labels.

1855 Miniature Barrage Balloon Unit.
Six wheeled lorry (Kew Dodge) with operating winch and lead Silver Balloon................ **£90-130**
1879 Hydrogen Cylinder Lorry and Trailer
Four wheeled lorry and matching trailer, each with cast cylinder load.
All Red Hydrogen Cylinders. **£90-130**
Silver Cylinders with Red end. **£120-150**

Later 1950s military vehicles

All wheeled vehicles had Military Green plastic wheels with Black tyres. Most production was in a not particularly authentic gloss shade of Bronze

Green. This was later changed to a more suitable semi-matt NATO Green. Shades of both can vary.

LV/607 3-ton Army Truck (Big Bedford)
with plastic rear body cover. Early versions have two windows in the rear of cab. No. 1:32 scale equivalent.
With or without U.S. star in circle on cab roof. **£40-50**

LV/609 Austin Champ, with detachable metal top. **£40-50**

LV/610 Centurion Tank, usually with Silver to Gun Barrel end. NATO Green only. With or without U.S. star in circle on turret top. **£30-40**

LV/611 Sexton Self-Propelled Gun. No. 1:32 scale version. **£40-50**

LV/612 1½ ton Army Truck (Fordson Thames). With or without U.S. star (no circle) on cab roof or door. **£30-40**

LV/613 1½ ton Covered Army Truck – as LV/613 but with plastic cover to rear body.......... **£40-50**

LV/615 Saracen Armoured Personnel Carrier. No. 1:32 Scale equivalent. **£30-40**

LV/618 Army Ambulance (Fordson Thames). **£50-60**

LV/620 3-ton Open Army Truck (Big Bedford) – as LV/607 but without rear cover............. **£30-40**

Motorcycles

Solo machines, always with lead wheels.
LB/536 – Civilian – Black Bike, Green Fuel Tank, Grey or Pale Fawn Rider. **£30-40**
LB/548 Telegraph Boy – Red Bike, Midnight Blue Rider with Red Uniform details................ **£50-60**
LB/550 Speed Cop – Black Bike, Midnight Blue Rider.. **£30-40**

Sets containing vehicles

LV/SA "OO" and "HO" Gauge Vehicle Set.
The six early 1950's Vehicles in one display box, items strung to base card. Saloon and open car, both horse drawn vehicles and attendants, Tractor with Driver, Articulated Lorry. **£250-300**

L/7 Farm Display Box – 28 pieces with Farm Figures and Animals. Small items loose with dividers, a few strung to backing card.
Four vehicles held by cut-outs. Tractor and both Horse-drawn Vehicles with relevant figures, saloon car. **£350-450**

L/11 Railway Display Box – 43 pieces including all the Railway Figures and Accessories, some in multiple. Small items and Six of the vehicles loose with dividers, a few items strung to backing card. Eight vehicles – Saloon and Open Cars, 3-ton Farm Wagon (Big Bedford), two articulated lorries (Dodge), Austin Champ, Civilian and Speed Cop Motorcycles...**£600-800**

L/15 Centurion Tank with Infantry – Action display window. Carton with Eight figures. Shown in 1960 catalogue, never issued? ... NGPP

Britains 'Racing Colours of Famous Owners'

Ref. / Owner / horse colour / Jockey's colours	MPR
RC1 H.M. The King Brown Black cap, Purple silks with Gold hoop. **£200-250**	
RC2 Lord Astor GreyPink cap, Grey/Blue silks with diagonal Pink stripe **£200-250**	
RC3 Lord Derby Brown White cap, Black silks........ **£200-250**	
RC6 Lord Roseberry Grey Pink cap, Green silks with Pink hoops.. .... **£200-250**	

Ref. / Owner / horse colour / Jockey's colours	MPR
RC12 Mr J.V. Rank Grey Dark Blue cap, Yellow silks with Blue squares **£150-200**	
RC63 The Aga Khan Brown Brown cap, Green silks with Brown hoops.. **£150-200**	
RC64 Dorothy Paget Brown Yellow cap/Blue bands, Blue silks/ Yellow hoops............................... **£200-250**	
RC67 Mr H.J. Joel Brown Red cap, Black silks **£150-200**	

Ref. / Owner / horse colour / Jockey's colours	MPR
RC82 Princess Elizabeth Brown Black cap, Red /Black hoops **£175-225**	
RC83 Winston S. Churchill Brown Brown cap, Pink/Brown silks**£200-250**	
RC142 Duke of Norfolk Brown Red cap with Blue quartering, Blue silks **£200-250**	
RC144 Msr. M. Boussac Brown Grey cap, Orange silks....... **£150-200** **Salesman's Sample Card of Jockeys** in racing colours and horses .... NGPP	

Britains Catalogues

1905 Catalogue (1972 Copy Edition).
Oblong format (21cm x 16.5cm).
Monochrome Reprint Edition,
19 pages,Originally signed by Dennis Britain.
.... **£30-40**
1949 Export Edition Catalogue.
USA - 34 pages in the 1930's style **£80-120**
1952 'Clockwork Series' Supplement.
Lists all vehicles and sets with clockwork.......
.... **£70-80**
1952 Britains 'Lilliput' 'World of Models' Catalogue.
20cm x 15cm. 11 pages **£80-90**
1952 'SP Fort Range Series' Supplement.
Folding single sheet with the Fort range**£40-50**
1953 Coronation Souvenir Supplement.
Colour and monochrome booklet **£60-70**
1953 'Pots and Pans' Supplement.

2 page colour illustrated leaflet.......... **£50-60**
1955 Pocket Edition - 110th Edition.
128 pages, black/white, buff covers ... **£65-75**
1957 'New Lines' Catalogue (Oblong).
28 pages with Centurion Tank on cover**£70-80**
1958 Britains 'Herald' Catalogue.
Monochrome illustrated 3 page catalogue .....
.... **£75-100**
1958 'New Lines' Supplement.
20 pages, 'New Additions', cameo photograph
of William Britain (1828 -1906) on cover ....
.... **£80-90**
1959 'Crown' and 'New Crown' Range.
Oblong (20 x 15cm), 16 pages booklet**£50-60**
1961 Catalogue, Price List, Order Form.
84 pages (landscape), some colour pages ......
.... **£80-120**

1962 Catalogue.
Large landscape format. 88 black/white
pages, colour cover **£100-140**
1963 Catalogue
Large landscape format. 72 pages + Price List
and Order Form.............................. **£80-120**
1964 Catalogue.
Large landscape format. 64 pages + Price List
and Order Form.............................. **£80-120**
1973 Trade Catalogue.
24 pages in full colour showing the range of
products **£30-45**
Herald Miniatures Ltd. 1957 Catalogue.
Plus 'New Lines 1957' leaflet.......... **£250-300**
Britains Herald Catalogue 1959.
'1st combined catalogue by the new Co'.........
.... **£200-250**

Britains Motor Cycles 1965–1975

Most have plastic saddles, plated engines and
'jewelled' headlights, and are packed in display boxes.

*Britains Motorcycles including No 9683 Drag Racing
Machine, Challenger and
No 9684 2-piece Speedway Racers.*

9640 Two Go-Karts, yellow/black or red/black .....
.... NGPP
9650 Speedway Set. Four differently coloured
Speedway bikes............................. **£100-125**
9666 Motor Cycle Boxed Set with 3 different
motor cycles.................................**£80-100**
9695 BMW with Policeman, white with black/
white rider **£70-90**
9696 BMW with Civilian, blue with white/blue
rider **£70-90**
9671 Racing Norton, yellow with red/green rider .
.... **£70-90**

9674 Chopper Trike, yellow/gold/black..... NGPP
9677 Long Fork Chopper, red with blue rider ......
.... NGPP
9679 German Army Motor Cycle, khaki ...**£70-90**
9680 'Chopper' Motor Cycle, black with pink rder
.... NGPP
9681 German Army B.M.W. Combination, khaki,
two blue riders..............................**£70-90**
9682 U.S. Army Motor Cycle, black with khaki
rider **£70-90**
9683 Drag Motor Cycle, gold with grey rider ....
.... NGPP
9684 Speedway Motor Cycles, silver with black
riders .... NGPP
9685 Lambretta Scooter, red/white scooter, blue
and red riders................................**£80-100**
White/blue scooter, orange/brown rider,
blue passenger **£100-125**
9687 Honda. Red/White/Silver bike, Black/Blue/
White rider **£70-90**
9688 BMW, Silver bike, Black rider, '8', Blue
helmet...**£70-90**
Black bike, Brown rider, Grey soft hat**£70-90**
9689 Harley-Davidson, red/white 'Buzz' with
red/blue/yellow rider....................**£70-90**
Red/Silver bike with 'Buzz' on panniers,
Tan/Blue/White rider.........................**£70-90**
9690 Triumph Thunderbird 650cc, red with
blue/brown/red rider.........................**£70-90**

Green bike, black seat **£70-90**
Metallic blue bike, black seat **£80-100**
9691 Gieves Challenger with Rider, green with
blue/brown rider **£70-90**
Green bike, yellow/black rider **£70-90**
9692 Harley-Davidson Electra Glide. White bike,
black seat.
brown/grey Rider 'U.S.Sheriff' on panniers...
....**£70-90**
9693 Honda Benly 125cc, red with black/blue/
yellow rider **£80-100**
9694 B.M.W. 600cc, Black/silver with black/blue
rider **£80-100**
9696 Triumph Speed Twin with Rider, yellow/
blue with black rider **£70-90**
Maroon/blue, black rider................... **£70-90**
9697 Triumph Thunderbird Police Patrol , white
with black or dark blue police rider,
loudhailer **£70-90**
9698 Dispatch Rider on Triumph Motor Cycle,
black bike, black/green rider............. **£70-90**
Green/chrome bike, military green rider
with armbands................................**£70-90**
9698/2 MV-Augusta Motor Cycle,
red '7', green/yellow or white/blue rider ....
.... NGPP
9699 BMW Racing Combination, red/yellow with
two black riders .... NGPP

Chad Valley

The Chad Valley company (makers of board games and wooden toys) produced tinplate toy vehicles from 1932 incorporating the year of manufacture in the registration number on the number plates.

Their first 'Wee-Kin' diecast toy vehicles were produced around 1949 and had 'CV 1949' as the registration number. They were fitted with a key-wound clockwork motor and were designed more as toys than models having generic titles like 'Open Lorry' or 'Fire Engine'. The cars issued between 1951 and 1954 as Rootes Group promotionals are much better attempts at models and were sold at Rootes Group

garages as well as normal toy shops. The tractors produced from 1952 are particularly fine and well detailed models. The years shown below indicate the periods in which Chad Valley offered them for sale though not all the toys were available for the whole of the period and some were still in the shops well after production ceased in 1956.

(This introduction to Chad Valley was written by Sue Richardson who also provided the basic listing. Additional listing information came from the Cecil Gibson archives and John G. Butler of Berkhampstead, Herts plus more updates from Mike Ennis.)

Diecast Clockwork Toys and Model Vehicles

220 1949-53 **Razor Edge Saloon**. Various colours, silver trim, Blue illustrated box, 1:43 scale **£160-200**
221 1949-53 **Traffic Control Car**. Casting as 220, Blue, plus Loudspeaker....**£100-150**
222 1949-53 **'POLICE' Car**. Same casting as 220, black with police roof sign, Blue illustrated box. **£125-175**
223 1949-53 **Track Racer**. Various metallic colours. Known race numbers 0, 1, 2, 7, 8 ....**£150-200**

Buses

224 1949-53 **Double Decker Bus**. Red, Green, Light blue. Some examples have a coloured stripe between decks (1:76 scale) **£175-225**
225 1949-53 **Open Lorry**. Green cab/chassis brown back.......................**£160-200**
  Open Lorry. Cream Cab/chassis silver back.........................**£160-200**
226 1949-53 **Low-Loader**. Green with red back with load of three wooden plain cases **£100-150**
227 1949-53 **Timber Wagon**. Red Cab/Chassis, Blue back, wooden logs....**£110-160**
228 1949-53 **Cable Layer**. Red cab/Chassis green back red string as cable **£175-210**
229 1949-53 **Breakdown Lorry**. Green cab/chassis Grey towing crane...................**£100-130**
230 1949-53 **Milk Lorry**. Cream open back lorry with 8 milk churns................**£150-200**
231 1949-53 **Fire Engine**. Red body, silver trim, blue illustrated box..............**£125-175**
232 1949-53 **Tower Repair Wagon**. Green Cab/Chassis grey tower also red cab/chassis grey tower **£180-240**
233 1949-53 **Milk Tanker**. Blue or Green cab/chassis with White tank 'Milk' **£100-150**

234 1949-53 **Petrol Tanker**. Red Cab/chassis Grey tank Red 'Petrol'....................**£100-150**
  Petrol Tanker. Red with Grey tank, 'Regent' Red, White and Blue striped logo **£200-250**
239 1949-53 **Dust Cart**. Green with grey tinplate sliding side panels...............**£180-240**

247 Fork Lift Truck and 239 Dust Cart

--- 1951-54 **Guy Van**. Dark Blue / Cream, tinplate doors, *'Lyons Ice Cream Cadby Hall London W11'*.**£200-275**
502 1951-54 **Guy Van**. Red body, Blue hubs, tinplate doors, Red *'Chad Valley'* logo **£200-275**
  1951-54 **Guy Van**. Blue body, Grey hubs, tinplate doors Red *'Chad Valley'* logo **£200-275**
502 1951-54 **Guy Van**. Green body, tinplate doors, Yellow *'Guy Motors Ltd, Commercial Vehicle Manufacturers'* **£240-275**

Wee Kin Toy Guy Van

551 **Midget Coach**. In various colours, Black wheels, clockwork motor, illustrated Tan and White box **£65-100**
  Midget Van. Red, Black wheels, clockwork motor, illustrated Tan and White Box....................**£65-100**
  Midget Van Esso. Blue with White and Red 'Esso' logo. Black wheels, clockwork motor, illustrated Tan and White box..............**£65-100**

Other Issues (with or without motor)

Hillman Minx Saloon

---	1950-55	**Hillman Minx Saloon**......**£100-125**
---	1950-55	**Humber Super Snipe**, blue / grey body **£90-120**
---	1950-55	**Guy Truck** **£80-120**
---	1950-55	**Sunbeam Racer** **£100-125**
---	1950-55	**Humber Hawk**.................**£100-125**
---	1950-55	**Rolls-Royce Razor Edge Saloon** **£100-125**
---	1950-55	**Routemaster London Bus**£125-150
---	1950-55	**Commer Avenger Coach £100-125**
---	1950-55	**Guy Truck 'LYONS ICE CREAM'**..... ....**£350-500**
---	1950-55	**Sunbeam-Talbot Saloon**, metallic pale brown.....................**£100-125**
---	1950-55	**Guy Milk Tanker**, blue /cream, 'MILK'..................................**£200-300**
---	1950-55	**Guy Cable Lorry**..............**£100-150**
---	1950-55	**Guy Petrol Tanker 'REGENT PETROL'** **£300-400**
---	1950-55	**Guy 'FIRE' Engine** **£300-400**
---	1950-55	**Guy Container Lorry**.......**£100-150**
---	1950-55	**Guy Refuse Lorry**.............**£100-150**

Tractors

Fordson Major Tractor

9235 1952 **Fordson Major E27N.** Dark Blue body, Orange wheels, rubber tyres (two types of tread on rear), steering, towbar with pin, clockwork wound by starting handle. (Scale 1:16) Illustrated box or plain box with small label **£300-400**

1955 **Fordson Major E27N.** Red and Yellow with driver, clockwork, (Scale 1:43) boxed. Made under licence by 'Raybro & Sturdy Products S.A.', Johannesburg, South Africa, (model marked 'Chad Valley GB') **£300-400**

1954 **Fordson Major DDN.** Mid-Blue body, Orange wheels, rubber tyres, working steering, lifting bonnet, towbar/pin, hydraulic lift at rear (detachable centre arm), clockwork wound through rear hub. (Scale 1:16) Illustrated box or plain box with small label **£300-400**
Orange body, Red wheels, as above, .. illustrated box **£1,500-1,750**
Static version: As above but without clockwork operation. Illustrated box or plain box with small label.
The word 'working' is deleted from all sides of box **£500-600**
Chrome version: Static version in chrome plate, wooden plinth with some. Ploughing trophy or Ford presentation model? **£500-600**

9503 1950-55 **Fordson E27N.** Yellow, Black wheels, Red Hubs driver with cap in various colours. Simple 3 inch long model. Clockwork **£100-150**

1953 **Ford Dexta.** Mid-Blue, Orange wheels, radiator panels and 'Fordson Dexta', not steerable,

rubber tyres, hook, (Scale 1:16) Illustrated box **£550-650**

1955 **Ferguson.** Green, Red wheels, 'Ferguson' on side, steering, hook, (Scale 1:16) Illustrated box inscribed 'Ferguson'. Promotional **£900-1,000**
Grey body, Grey wheels, hydraulic lift at rear **£800-1,000**

Small Ferguson Tractor

1950-55 **Massey Ferguson Tractor**, with or without motor **£400-600**
1950-55 **Fordson Major Tractor**, Red or Blue, motor in some **£400-600**
Bright Yellow/Orange, Red wheels, key, boxed.................... **£1,750-2,250**

Rootes Group Promotional Models
(scale 1:43)

236 1949-53 **The Hillman Minx Saloon.** Grey or Metallic Dark Blue body. Maroon illustration box. **£100-140**

237 1949-53 **The Humber Super Snipe Saloon.** Various Metallic Colours**£100-140**

238 1949-53 **The Sunbeam-Talbot** Light Blue or Metallic Dark Green. Base has wording 'A Rootes Group Product' plus usual CV marks **£140-180**

240 1949-53 **Commer Avenger Coach.** Blue, Red or Green body with flash, (1:76 scale) Fitted with 'Autostop' mechanism. Maroon Illustrated box................................... **£125-175**

242 1951-54 **Commer Articulated Truck.** Red cab and trailer with 'Commer Hands' on side of trailer **£150-200**

Stacatruc

247 **Stacatruc.** Fork Lift Truck, Light blue with yellow fork lift. Fitted with 'Autostop', made under license by Raybro & Sturdy Products of Johannesburg **£150-200**

507 1949-53 **The Humber Hawk.** Metallic Dark Blue, Green, or mid-Green............. .... **£125-175**

Tractor in blue, burnt orange front and rear hubs with black tyres.

Humber Super Snipe and Commer Avenger Coach.

Sunbeam Talbot and Humber Hawk, both Rootes Group products.

The firm of Charbens & Co was started around 1928 by the brothers Charles and Benjamin Reid and was based at Hornsey Road, Holloway, London N7. One of the brothers earlier had worked for Britains. At first they made hollow-cast lead military, civilian and farm related figures, and horse drawn vehicles were also produced in the 1930s. The production in the 1930s was mainly non-military models. After the war, zinc diecasting was introduced, but very few of the pre-war models were reissued, although a range of military figures was increased. Zinc castings by Charbens very often have metal failure as a result of contamination from the lead that was still used extensively in the factory.

Charbens had connections with other companies and produced models for Taylor & Barrett, John Hill and others, while some of the models were sold under the trade name of Salco.

Model numbers were allocated around 1954, so items which had already been withdrawn, are not numbered. Dates of issue have been taken from catalogues or adverts, but inevitably are incomplete. Most pre-war items have 'RD' cast in; most post-war items have 'CHARBENS' cast underneath. Most were boxed.

The 'Old Crocks' series of miniatures was introduced in 1955 with the issue of 12 models, by 1960, some 34 models were listed. After 1967 all vehicle models were deleted from the catalogue except for a few items included in sets with plastic figures. Production of figures was discontinued in 1973.

Pre-war Issues (part hollow-cast, part diecast construction)

Model and details	MPR

Goat Cart with Girl
Blue or red cart and girl, brown or white goat, yellow 6-spoke wheels **£100-150**

Charbens Gipsy Caravan

Horse Drawn Gypsy Caravan
Blue/white caravan with white horse, yellow wheels (smaller at front) plus orange/black seated Gypsy woman with baby, standing man, washing + line, cooking pot **£750-1,000**
Horse Drawn Farm Wagon
Green/yellow 4 wheel wagon with two hay racks, brown carthorse, cream/black carter figure. **£125-150**
Horse Drawn Hay (or Tumbril) Cart
Yellow/green cart, grey/black or brown horse, yellow/brown figure, boxed **£100-125**
Horse-Drawn Roller
Green/yellow roller brown driver and horse.. **£100-125**
Horse-Drawn Log Wagon
Yellow, red wheels, with man, 2 tandem horses, wooden dowel as log, cream card box **£125-150**
Governess's Cart (two wheels).
Yellow/black, cream/red or brown/black cart, 2 children, donkey, zoo-keeper figure .. **£100-125**
Llama Ride
Same as Governess Cart with Llama , four Children and Zookeeper. .... **£100-125.**
Horse-Drawn Cape Cart (two wheels).
Enclosed green body with white roof , or all blue, brown horse, mid-blue figure.. **£80-100**
Pony and Cart
Blue Cart, red 12 spoked red wheels Brown pony... **£90-110**

Pony and Milk Cart (two wheels).
Yellow/red cart with 'PURE MILK' cast in. Brown horse, milkman figure (see 25)... **£80-100**
Horse-Drawn Coal Cart (four wheels).
Black cart, coalman and sack, white/orange horse, 12-spoke wheels, 6 spare sacks **£300-400**
Horse Drawn Pitch Boiler
White Horse, Black Wagon Brown box with white label **£200-300**

Railway Wagon

Horse-Drawn Railway Wagon (four wheels)
Grey/red open wagon, driver, 'London Midland Scottish Railway' cast into side, white horse **£400-600**
Horse Drawn Tip Cart
Similar to Hay Cart without the Raves first issued 1929............................ **£100-125**
Horse-Drawn Milk Float (four wheels)
Orange/white body with 'UNITED DAIRIES', PASTEURISED MILK' and 'CREAM' logo. 8-spoke wheels with rubber tyres, brown or white horse, white/blue milkman with bottle **£200-300**
Horse-Drawn Milk Float (four wheels).
Mid-blue, 'EXPRESS DAIRY', 'PURE MILK', 'BUTTER & EGGS', white shafts, brown horse, 8-spoke wheels, rubber tyres, white/blue milkman holding bottle **£250-350**
Horse-Drawn Baker's Wagon
Red with yellow wheels, with baker and basket 'T. SMITH' on roof............. **£600-800**
Horse Drawn Coffee Stall (four wheels).
Brown stall, silver chimney, brown/white horse, tea urn and crockery **£300-400**

Horse Drawn Organ Grinder's Cart (two wheels)
Brown/yellow organ, grey donkey, red monkey with mug, brown/green organ-grinder... **£175-225**
Coster Cart with Donkey
Green/yellow cart, solid sides, grey donkey, costermonger figure (see 24 below)...... **£100-125**

Coffee Stall

Motorcycle Policeman
Unpainted bike, with or without green petrol tank dark blue, RD cast in petrol tank **£40-60**
Police Motor Cycle and Sidecar
Unpainted bike, rider and passenger in dk blue, dk blue sidecar, RD cast in petrol tank **£40-60**

Soap Box Racer

Soap Box Racer
Solid cast brown base, four red wheels (six spokes), Cub Scout pushing, Cub Scout rider + another **£400-600**

Road Workers Set
Horse Roller (green/orange/brown), orange and black tar boiler truck with 6-spoke wheels, plus 4 workmen, a nightwatchman, hut, brazier, 'Road up' sign, pipe, 2 barriers............. **£250-350**

Rodeo Set
Cowboys on horseback, with lasso, bucking Bronco with hat in the air, rearing longhorn Steers, ...**NPP**

Jack's Band
Nine assorted musicians with instruments plus conductor, dressed full evening dress or pink jackets boxed set...................... **£400-600**

Musical Trio Set
Pianist, Piano, Cellist and Violinist, ... **£200-300**

Hiker's Set

'The Hiker's Camp Set'
Green metal tent ('The Hikery'), male hiker resting, male hiker walking with backpack and stick, female hiker walking with backpack and stick, female hiker reading a book, 2 plates, 2 cups. Brown card box with b/w picture label on lid **£750-1,000**

Gamekeeper with Dog
Gamekeeper with cap and shotgun, brown/white dog with bird in mouth Also issued with some Hiker Sets **£100-125**

Windmill

Windmill
Green base, beige Mill body with red Cap, 4 brown tinplate sales................... **£150-175**

Road Bridge

Road Bridge
Two diecast sections beige side walls Red pillars and arch ring with green Railings **£100-150**

Cyclist and Bike
Cream cyclist and unpainted Bike ....**NPP**

Circus Clown Set
Clowns on Stilts, Clown on Unicycle, Clown climbing Ladder, Clown standing, Policeman clown **£150-200**

Circus Single Figures
Liberty Horses, Performing Elephants, Seal with Balls, Strongman, Boxing Midgets, Acrobats, Parrot, Dog, Ringmaster each:. **£25-30**

Trapeze Artists Set
Two Artists on Wire - unboxed.............. **£250-300**

Performing Animals Set
2 elephants with tubs, ringmaster and seal with ball on nose............................ **£300-400**

'Mimic Series' Circus Set
boxed Includes Clowns, Performers, etc.
.... **£900-1,100**

Elephant Set

'Performing Elephant' Set
Ringmaster with whip, elephant with tub, Boxed **£250-350**

Circus Clown.
Clown in top hat and tails climbing ladder in green... **£250-350**

Acrobat
Doing handstand on a chair **£100-150**

'Fairy on Horse'
Equestrienne in orange dress, white horse **£100-150**

Flower Seller
Seated female figure with bunch of flowers, separate casting of basket of flowers..... **£100-125**

Other diecast models

Ambulance
3-1/2 inch long Cream with gold and red trim Red Cross cast in door........................... **£200-300**

Large Racing Car
4 inch long dark green or red including wheels large fuel cap on rear. 'Mimic Toy made in England' cast underneath ....**NGPP**

Coupe
4 inch long dark red, silver trim 'Mimic Toy' cast under bonnet ....**NGPP**

Small Racing Car
3-1/2 inch long, blue, red or dk green, driver in white, 'Mimic Toy RD England Charbens' cast underneath....................................**NGPP**

Blue Bird Racing Car
5 inch long, dk blue crossed flags on nose 'Charbens made in England' cast in body **£150-200**

Aeroplane
4-1/4 inch long, green or red with silver tail, tan coloured pilot 'Mimic Toy England' cast underneath..**NGPP**

Ambulance with man at rear
Dark blue, dark green or brown. With figure of man standing at the Rear step.......... **£100-150**

Armoured Car
Dark brown or brown/green camouflage Including wheels, ... **£20-30**

Petrol Tanker
Yellow, dk blue, red or green all with black and gold trim **£80-110**

Fire Engine.
Red with white and gold trim, cast-in driver in red or blue uniform, separate ladder, rubber tyres................. **£200-300**

Car and Caravan.
Saloon car red, green or yellow with black wings and gold trim, Two tone coloured Caravan yellow/orange, yellow/green, and green/blue, joined with twisted wire. ... **£200-300**

Motor Van
4-1/4 inch long Lt Brown with green tilt, metal hubs with rubber tyres. No name. **£100-150**

Breakdown Lorry
Listed in a Catalogue, not known if it was issued ....**NGPP**

Tootsietoy copies

It is understood that the earliest Charbens Motor Vehicles were copies of the American Tootsietoy items. The known ones are listed below. The Mack Trucks had either RD or Mimic Toy cast underneath.

Mack Stake Truck
3-1/4 inch long green cab/chassis, red stake body and black wheels **£100-120**

Mack Anti-Aircraft Truck
2-3/4 inch long, olive brown cab/chassis, black gun mount, silver gun. **£100-150**

Mack Searchlight Truck
Same body as Anti-Aircraft Truck red Searchlight mounted on a black base.. **£100-150**

Renault Tank
Olive brown or dk blue unpainted wheels white rubber tracks **£80-100**

Caterpillar Tractor
3-1/4 inch long, red unpainted wheels white rubber tracks 'Mimic Toy England' cast underneath..................................... **£150-200**

Post-war Issues

(Early models issued in trade boxes but some later model in their own box. Dates approximate).

1 45-60 **Horse-Drawn Log Wagon**
Yellow, red wheels, with man, 2 tandem horses, wooden log, cream card box .. **£150-200**

2 45-67 **Horse-Drawn Roller**
Yellow with green or red roller, with horse and man (seated)......................... **£80-100**

3 45-67 **Horse-drawn Grass Cutter.**
Yellow, red wheels, unpainted cutter, with horse and man (seated) **£150-200**

4 46-67 **Horse-drawn Two-wheel Farm Wagon with Raves** Green wagon, yellow shafts and wheels **£200-250**

5 46-67 **Horse-drawn Four-wheel Farm Wagon with Raves** Green wagon, yellow shafts and wheels **£200-250**

6 46-67 **Tractor with Driver**
Red with metal wheels.......................... **£125-150**
Orange with Lt Blue metal or plastic wheels **£125-150**
Blue with solid black rubber wheels ... **£200-275**
Red Plastic body Lt blue metal wheels . **£90-120**

7 46-62 **Horse-drawn Van with Man.**
Blue with cream upper, metal wheels, labels: 'HOVIS BREAD' or 'PURE MILK' **£350-450**
Orange with light brown upper, rubber wheels, 'HOVIS BREAD' labels............ **£300-400**

8 46-62 **Tipper Lorry**
Red or blue cab/chassis, cream tipper **£40-60**
Dk green Cab/chassis, yellow tipper **£40-60**
Orange cab/chassis, yellow tipper Red hubs ....**NGPP**

9 48-62 **Motor Coach**
Various colours, some with paper
destination boards £150-200

10 to 14 **Light Vans**
Two castings known. The first was a small
boxy van with no rear windows.
The second (from the early 1950s)
was larger and more rounded, resembling a
Ford E83W, with two rear windows.

10 46-60 **Royal Mail Van**
Red, 2nd casting with black bonnet,
'ROYAL MAIL', 'G-VI-R' paper labels.... £100-125

11 46-62 **'AMBULANCE'**
Cream, Red Cross (paper labels) £100-125

12 46-62 **'Carter Paterson' Van**
Dark green, 'CARTER PATERSON'
paper labels £100-125

13 46-60 **'Police' Van**
Dark blue, 'POLICE GR' paper labels . £100-125

14 46-62 **Post Office Telephones Van**
Green, with or without black mudguards,
metal or plastic wheels 'POST OFFICE
TELEPHONES' on paper labels £100-125

15 47-62 **Fire Engine and Wheeled Escape**
Red or orange-red, unpainted ladders,
three firemen and hose......................... £100-125

16 47-67 **Covered Wagon with Four Horses**
and Driver. Green or red wagon, yellow
wheels, cloth canopy, metal shaft and
horses. Red box, full-colour label £100-125
Orange wagon, plastic shaft / horses .. £100-125

17 50-67 **Tractor and Log Trailer with Driver**
Tractor as No.6, Trailer as No.1 but drawbar
in place of shafts.................................. £150-200

18 50-62 **Tractor and Grass Cutter with
two Drivers**
Tractor as No.6, Trailer modified
from No.3 .... £100-150

Tractor and Reaper

19 50-67 **Tractor and Reaper with two
Drivers**
Tractor as No.6, green Reaper (yellow
or red metal blades) or light blue Reaper
(red plastic blades), or all plastic. £150-200

20 54-67 **Mobile Crane**
Red body, green chassis, unpainted or
yellow jib £100-120
Orange body, lt.blue chassis, yellow jib .. £100-150

Dumper Truck

21 54-67 **Muir-Hill Dumper with Driver**
Beige or orange with green or yellow
dumper £70-90
Red with yellow plastic dumper £60-70

Travelling Zoo Set

22 54-67 **Travelling Zoo**
Elephant towing two cages with two lions,
two polar bears, man. Red chassis,
unpainted cages, yellow roofs, metal or
plastic animals..................................... £150-200
With orange chassis, light blue cages,
yellow roofs... £125-150

23 55-58 **Water Pistol**
No details £5-10

24 54-55 **Costermonger's Cart**
Dark green cart, solid sides, red or
yellow wheels, donkey, man and basket £40-60

25 55 **Horse-drawn Milk Cart**
Yellow with red wheels, 'PURE MILK'
labels. With man and churn................. £125-150

26 54-62 **Armoured Car**
Khaki, metal wheels, plastic aerial £30-40
Desert Sand body, rubber no aerial £40-60

Large Tractor

27 55-67 **Large Tractor**
Cast in two halves. Red with
yellow wheels or orange with
light blue wheels £150-200

28 54-67 **Diesel Road Roller**
Green or pale green, red wheels,
unpainted flywheel £80-100

29 54-62 **Mincer**
Toy kitchen equipment...............................£5-10

Scammel Mech Horse GWR

30 55 **Scammell Mechanical Horse and Trailer**
Blue with 'LNER' labels, or dark
brown cab with beige trailer and
'GWR' labels... £90-120

Cable Lorry

31 55-62 **Articulated Low-loader
with Cable Drum**
Red, green or blue cab, yellow trailer
Red cradle unpainted drum £80-100

32 55-62 **Alfa-Romeo Racing Car**
Hollow-cast lead, red, rubber wheels
Copy of Dinky Toys 232 .... £50-75

33 55-62 **Cooper-Bristol Racing Car**
Hollow-cast lead, green, rubber wheels
Copy of Dinky Toys 233 .... £50-75

34 55-62 **Ferrari Racing Car**
Hollow-cast lead, blue body, yellow
nose, rubber wheels. Copy of Dinky
Toys 234 .... £50-75

35 54-67 **Horse-drawn Log Wagon**
As No.1 but single horse £50-75

36 50-55 **3-wheel Pedestrian Electric Van**
Dark blue, 'PURE MILK' or 'EXPRESS
DAIRIES' printed on sides; milkman,
crate/bottles £160-200
Orange, 'HOVIS' on sides, man,
tray of loaves.. £160-200
Orange and yellow no name with
Bread delivery man.............................. £160-200

Horse Transporter

36 57-62 **Maudslay Horse Box**
Dark red, 'HORSE TRANSPORT' printed
on sides, with horse and driver............ £160-200
'NEWMARKET HORSEBOX'
Green/Red body.................................... £160-200

36 1967 **Steam Roller Large scale**
Light or dark green body, red 12-spoke
wheels, red roller, black chimney,
card box.. £300-400

37 60-62 **Articulated Low-loader with
Rocket Missile**
Dark green cab/trailer, orange/black
missile launcher. No makers name £90-120

38 55-60 **'Shoot and Save' Money Box**
Savings bank, with gun (catapult) to fire
coin into bank.. £90-120

39 1955 **Telephone Kiosk**
Red kiosk with opening door,
unpainted phone...................................... £15-20

40 55 **Fire Engine with Ladder and Firemen**
Red body, five firemen unpainted
2-part ladder.. £90-120

41 1955 **Fireplace**
Dolls house item £5-10

1955   **Model Soldier Set**
Motorcycle Dispatch Rider and four
Soldiers with rifles in action postions.
In red box with inner label 'Charbens
Toys World Wide Series Made in
England' ....**NGPP**

1946-60**Petrol Tanker**
Roughly made, red, blue with silver trim
Silver hose and black filler caps 'Charbens
Made in England' cast underneath **£40-60**

1948   **Station Wagon**
4 inch long Lt brown with dk brown bonnet
and mudguards, spare wheel at the rear.
'Charbens Made in England' cast underneath
.... **£40-60**

        Saloon Car 'Javelin'
5-1/2 inch long red or green with silver
trim Saloon Car, has 'Javelin' cast
under bonnet, black wheels **£40-60**

445 1955   **'Auto Race Set' 'Andover series'**
Made only for the Flare Import Corporation,
230 Fifth Ave., New York. Contains 3 (Dinky
style) racing cars, 6 mechanics, man with
chequered flag. 43mm scale, hollow-cast.
Card box has Formula I race scene
on colour label......................................**£300-400**

'Big Show' Circus Set
boxed. US issue with Clowns, etc. **£900-1,100**
Large scale Wolf
Walking wolf figure **£40-60**
Trade Pack with Six Scammell
Articulated Dropside Lorries **£300-350**
Horse Drawn Farm Hay Wagon
Green/Red with 2 racks, horse,
2 land girls, boxed **£200-250**
Walking Barrow Boy
Clockwork.Man in long green
coat pushing two wheeled blue/yellow
handcart with orange trunk **£100-150**

Barrow Boy

Post-war aircraft
Rather crude lead models with tinplate Props

Bristol Blenheim Bomber (late 40's)
3-1/2 inch long, dk blue or green with silver
cockpit and nose, paper RAF roundels
'Charbens' cast underside ....**NGPP**

Hawker Hurricane (late 40's)
3 inch long dark green, 'Charbens & Co
underside Allied Forces Star on each
wing   ....**NGPP**

Post-war 'Old Crocks', Military Models and 'Miniature Lorries', etc

'OLD CROCKS' series
1 **1904 Darracq.** Dark Blue, Red or
  Orange, open 2-seater **£10-20**
2 **1904 Spyker.** Yellow 4-seater open car..... **£10-20**

Old Crocks Old Bill Bus

3 **1914 'Old Bill' Bus.** 2-piece casting, or
  single casting + separate top deck,
  Red or Orange **£10-20**
4 **1907 Ford Model T**
  2-piece casting, tin chassis, Dark Blue...... **£10-20**
  Single casting, no separate chassis,
  Dark Blue **£10-20**
5 **1907 Vauxhall.**
  Green open 2-seater **£10-20**
6 **1906 De Dion Bouton.**
  Light Green or Violet open 2-seater **£10-20**
7 **1898 Panhard.**
  Light Green or Brown 2-seater **£10-20**

8 **1906 Rolls-Royce Silver Ghost.**
  Silver 4-seater open car............................. **£10-20**
9 **1903 Standard 6hp.**
  Dark Red or Maroon with Beige roof........ **£10-20**
10 **1902 Wolseley.**
  Light Blue 4-seater open car..................... **£10-20**
11 **1908 Packard Runabout.**
  Light Green open 2-seater **£10-20**
12 **1905 Vauxhall Hansom Cab.**
  Orange/Beige **£10-20**
13 **1900 Straker Flat Steam Lorry.**
  Light Green, packing case......................... **£10-20**
  1900 Straker Lowside Steam Lorry.
  Light Blue, three barrels........................... **£10-20**
14 **Stephenson's 'Rocket' Locomotive.**
  Yellow / Black.. **£10-20**
15 **Tender for 'Rocket',** colours as 14 .... **£10-20**
16 **1909 Albion.**
  Dark or Light Blue open truck.................. **£10-20**
17 **1912 Rover.**
  Orange 2-seater open sports **£10-20**
18 **1911 Mercedes-Benz.**
  Dark Green open 2-seater......................... **£10-20**
19 **Bedford Horse-Box.**
  Brown, 'HORSE TRANSPORT' cast
  on sides, 'H.G. IVORY' on tailgate............ **£15-25**
20 **1910 Lanchester.**
  Light Blue 4-seater sports **£10-20**
21 **1922 Morris Cowley.**
  Beige 2-seater open **£10-20**
22 **1900 Daimler.** Maroon 2-seater................ **£10-20**
23 **1904 Autocar.**
  Dark Blue, open 3-wheeler **£10-20**

24 **1870/80 Grenville Steam Carriage.**
  Green or Light Green **£10-20**
25 **1905 Napier.**
  Violet or Purple 2-seater racer.................. **£10-20**
26 **Fire Engine and Escape.**
  Red or Orange... **£10-20**
27 **Articulated Breakdown Lorry.**
  Dark Green cab, Light Blue trailer,
  Orange crane... **£10-20**
28 **Mercer Runabout.**
  Dark Blue or Green 2-seater sports......... **£10-20**

MILITARY MODELS
30 **Searchlight on 4-wheel Trailer.**
  Green and Silver **£10-20**
31 **Twin Bofors Gun on Trailer.**
  Green and Silver **£10-20**
32 **Radar Scanner on Trailer.**
  Green and Silver **£10-20**
33 **Field Gun on Trailer.**
  Green and Silver **£10-20**
34 **Rocket Gun on Trailer.**
  Green and Silver **£10-20**
35 **Armoured Car.** Green **£10-20**

'MINIATURE LORRIES'
  Listed in 1960 catalogue but not issued.
40 **Articulated Tanker**....................................**NPP**
41 **Articulated Lorry**.....................................**NPP**
42 **Six-wheeled Lorry**...................................**NPP**
43 **Six-wheeled Tanker** ....**NPP**

Salco Series

Mickey's Fire Brigade
Red fire engine with unpainted ladder,
5 painted Mickey Mouse figures.
All card picture box **£750-1,000**

Mickey and Minnies' Piano
Cream piano with operating handle,
Mickey and Minnie Mouse figures.
Black/Blue/Yellow/White all
card picture box......................................**£200-300**

Mickey and Minnies' Barrel Organ
Red organ with Yellow wheels,

Mickey and Minnie Mouse figures.
All card picture box **£200-300**

Milk Cart with Pluto and Donald Duck
(no details) **£200-300**

'Mickey and Minnie on the River'
Green boat, 2 seats,
Mickey and Minnie figures **£750-1,000**

'Mickey and Donald's Garden' Set
Blue wheelbarrow, spade, rake.Boxed **£750-1,000**

Donald Duck's Dairy
A cart with Donald and Pluto.
Yellow / red / blue / white **£300-450**

Horse-drawn Brewer's Dray
Light Blue dray with Yellow detachable
brewery sign marked 'TOY TOWN BREWERS',
six unpainted barrels, black bowler-hatted
driver and brown horse...........................**£300-400**

Window Cleaner (boxed)
'Toyland Series'. Green/brown cleaner, red
bike, yellow sidecar, ladder, bucket....... **£300-400**

Corgi Toys were launched in 1956 by the Mettoy Company which had itself been founded in Northampton by Phillip Ullmann in 1933. The 'Mettoy' name was derived from the first three letters of 'Metal' plus 'toy' – the company's main product range being composed of lithographed metal toys. In 1948 Mettoy produced its first cast metal toys and called them 'Castoys'. The Castoys models contained a clockwork motor and when the first Corgi Toys models were introduced they also contained a mechanism. This, plus the introduction of window glazing, gave Corgi a competitive edge against its great rivals, Dinky Toys.

Corgi Toys were named after the Welsh breed of dogs and this logo will be found on virtually all the Corgi packaging. The models were produced in Swansea by Mettoy Playcraft Ltd, hence baseplates are marked 'Made in Gt. Britain'.

The development of the Corgi Toys product range was largely instigated by Howard Fairbairn, a Mettoy company director. Prior to his director appointment, he had been Head of Development at the Birmingham Aluminium Casting Co and had considerable diecasting experience. The first truly Corgi Toys product was No 200 Ford Consul in 1956.

Corgi has always been famed for its model innovations. This was especially true when it was able to promote its models as 'the ones with windows'. Additionally, greater realism was achieved over time with, for example, better detailing of its wheel hubs.

Corgi introduced various model ranges which have stood the test of time. Today, virtually all the Corgi models produced in the 1950s and 1960s are highly sought after. In particular, models such as the range of 'Monte Carlo' Minis, the Gift Sets, Farm Tractors and the 'Chipperfield's Circus' items are very collectable. In addition, television and film related models such as Batman, James Bond and similar models command a very high price at auction.

In 1983, the Mettoy company went into receivership and Corgi Toys became the subject of a management buy-out. From this time, the emphasis changed from the mass-production of toy vehicles to mainly the development of authentic limited edition models aimed at adult collectors – the 'Corgi Classics' range. Regrettably these items fall outside the scope of this publication. However, collectors requiring information on Corgi Classics are recommended to join the Corgi Collectors Club.

The editor wishes to thank all who have contributed to these greatly revised listings.

Corgi Toys Identification

Often referred to as 'the ones with windows', Corgi Toys were the first manufacturer to produce models with that refinement. Some of its first models also had a mechanical motor. Spring suspension was introduced from 1959 and, in 1960, the first diecast model to have an opening bonnet. The first models were based on real cars of the period. Similarly, with the launch of the 'Corgi Major Toys' in 1959, models of real commercial vehicles were available and competed with the Dinky 'Supertoys' range.

In the 1960s Corgi produced many successful film and TV-related models. Probably the best remembered was the James Bond Aston Martin which sold in huge quantities in the autumn of 1965. Indeed, such is the popularity of the model that various versions have been marketed over the last 40 years and are still available to the present day!

Corgi introduced many new features in the 1960s such as: jewelled headlights, an opening bonnet revealing a detailed engine, an opening boot to store a spare wheel, self-centering steering, and ruby rear lights, to name but a few. Innovations were frequent and imaginative throughout the 1960s. Further examples include the 'Golden Jacks' built-in jacking system, which enabled models to have 'take-off' wheels. A 'Trans-O-Lites' system was also introduced, whereby light rays were captured and fed through prisms to illuminate the headlights. 'WhizzWheels' and the slightly larger scale of 1:42 were introduced in the 1970s.

All these aspects influenced Corgi sales and boosted its popularity. Models were continually upgraded and given new features, such as suspension, interiors or even a new colour scheme, in order to enhance their desirability. Models were used in a new way – perhaps as part of a gift set. Cars could be included in the 'load' for a car transporter, while other vehicles became the towing unit such as the Land Rover in Gift Set 17, the Ferrari Racing Set.

Two of the major influences upon the value of the toys continue to be related to the condition and the quantities produced. Some Corgi Toys were simply not as sought after by children when they were first issued. These would have been manufactured in smaller quantities and are often the more valuable items to collect. One might deduce that the more obscure or unusual colour used for a model would have affected how many were sold at the time of release. This would also have influenced the withdrawal date of any vehicle. Some of the very rare items were only produced for one or two years and in low quantities.

A good example of this is the Heavy Equipment Transporter No 1135. Released in 1965 and withdrawn in 1966, it recorded 28,000 sales. In contrast, the Ferrari Berlinetta 250 Le Mans Car No 314, was also released in 1965 but withdrawn in 1972 with recorded sales of 1,598,000 (+1969 sales). Both these models appear on page 166 in *The Great Book of Corgi*. The Berlinetta's mint and boxed value in this 13th edition is cited as £60-70, whereas the Heavy Transporter with red interior, boxed and in mint condition is listed as £450-500. Some vehicles, which may have been less popular as toys are now highly sought after as rare collectables.

A market strategy favoured by Corgi was the launching of a replica model car simultaneously with the real car. To date simultaneous launches have occurred with Austin Metro, Ford Escort, Triumph Acclaim, Ford Sierra and the MG Maestro 1600, which is a unique record. Corgi was the first diecast manufacturer to introduce the dimensions of light, sound and movement into its models by using the micro-chip in its 'Corgitronic' range. The models 'come alive', for example, by just pushing down on the rear axle or, in the case of the Road Repair Unit, by pressing the workman to activate the pneumatic drill sound. Others (like the Sonic Corgi Truck) can be operated from a remote control handset.

Some early Corgi Toys were produced in either the normal form or with a friction-type flywheel motor. Exceptions were the sports cars and trucks which could not be converted to take the flywheel. The mechanisms were not robust and were phased out in 1959.

Model boxes often contain much more than just the basic model. Prices shown in the catalogue assume that not only is the model in pristine condition, but that it is accompanied by all the original additional contents. These can include extra card packing, inner card or polystyrene trays, pictorial stands, plastic protectors, transit card protection intended for removal by the retailer, instruction and information leaflets, catalogues, consumables (such as unopened packets of rockets, decals, etc). This particularly applies to some novelty and film/TV models, e.g. Nos 268, 277, 497, 511, 1123, 1139, 1144 and Gift Sets 3, 10, 20 and 21. A further example relates to the early 'Blue box' models each of which should contain a concertina catalogue leaflet plus a 'Join the Corgi Club' leaflet. If original items are missing, e.g. the plastic dome protector included with 511

Chipperfields Poodle Truck or card protectors with other models, it will affect the price that a model will achieve.

Boxes: July 1956 - Blue box, January 1959 - Yellow/Blue box (Two-tone cars were first to use them) December 1966 - Window box (2 square window ends) May 1973 - Angled window box (one square window end, coloured lines around box) 1980 - Yellow window box, 1987 New style Corgi logo box.

Whilst every effort has been made to describe models and, where known, their accompanying contents, any further information would be welcomed. The Corgi trademark is used by kind permission of Hornby Hobbies Ltd.

Market prices shown here are for guidance only. They refer ONLY to mint models in pristine boxes that are complete with all of their original contents. WW = WhizzWheels, MPR = Market Price Range.

Mettoy Diecast Toys – The 'Castoys' series

Castoys were produced by the Mettoy Company between 1948 and 1958 and were instigated by a request from Marks and Spencers for a robust, long lasting toy. The models were made of zinc alloy and were initially advertised as 'Heavy Cast Mechanical Toys'.

Generally, they had windows, a clockwork motor and brake, plus black rubber tyres on cast hubs. Of the original issues, only two models, No 840, the 'Eight Wheel Lorry' and No 870 'Delivery Van' remained in

production after 1951 and these were packaged in attractive Yellow/Red boxes which displayed a picture of the model inside. The later issues of the Delivery Van with their various attractive body designs are now rare and sought after items.

The following listing contains all the information available at present. The editor would welcome any additional information on body colours and variations.

Model and details	MPR	Model and details	MPR	Model and details	MPR

Large scale models 1:35

Presented in Yellow/Red endflap boxes each displaying an excellent picture of the model contained within.

Model and details	MPR
--- **Milk Handcart** 19?? With 'MILK' logo and Milkman	**£150-175**
718 **Luxury Observation Coach** 1956-58 Metallic Blue and Gold body with Silver raised roof section and base, Red door with Brown plastic male passenger. Destination board shows 'PRIVATE' and registration 'MTY 718'	**£250-350**
Metallic Brown and Pink body with Silver raised roof section and radiator, with Green female passenger........	**£200-300**
810 **Limousine** 1948-51 Cream, Red or Green body, Red interior, 'MTY 810', clockwork	**£100-200**
820 **Streamline Bus** 1948-51 Cream, Green or Red body, clockwork mechanism, Red pressed tin seating, solid rubber wheels, unpainted chassis. Registration No 'MTY 820'.............	**£100-200**
As previous model but with opening door, registration No. 'MTY 720'........	**£100-200**

Model and details	MPR
830 **Racing Car** 1948-51 Light Green, 6" long approx, 'METTOY' cast in base, tinplate hollow printed wheels with motor and brake........	**£100-200**
840 **8 Wheel Lorry** 1948-58 Metallic Blue cab with Grey rear body, Silver radiator and hubs	**£100-200**
850 **Fire Engine** 1948-51 Red body, Silver ladder and crank	**£100-200**
Red body, Silver extending ladder, no crank	**£100-200**
860 **Tractor** 1948-51 No models seen but shown in 1951 catalogue with Yellow/Red body...	**NPP**
863 **Ferguson TE20 Tractor and Trailer** 19?? Red/Blue tractor, Yellow trailer, Red hubs, painted plastic driver ...	**£200-300**

Model and details	MPR
870 **Delivery Van** (plain, without advertising) 1948-51 Dark Blue, Cream, Green or Red...	**£200-300**
870 **Delivery Vans** (with advertising or logo) **'EXPRESS DELIVERY'** 1952-55 Yellow or Blue body with Red logo and design on sides, clockwork	**£600-800**
'POST OFFICE TELEPHONES' 1955-58 Green body, White logo, Royal crest in Gold, Silver two part extending ladder	**£300-500**
'ROYAL MAIL' 1955-58 Red body, Silver trim, Yellow logo and Royal crest, 'MTY 870'	**£300-500**
'AMBULANCE' 1955-58 Cream body, Blue logo on sides....	**£200-300**
'BOAC' 1956-58 Blue body, Silver trim, White 'Fly By BOAC' on roof	**£400-600**

Small scale models 1:45

			MPR
no ref.	1955-57	**Karrier Bantam Soft Drinks Van** Dark red body, number plate 'CWS 300', spun huns, logo on rear: 'CWS SOFT DRINKS - THIRST COME - THIRST SERVED'	**£1,500-2,000**

Special 1:18 scale issue for Marks and Spencer

			MPR
no ref.	1958	**'VANWALL' Racing Car** Diecast body, perspex screen, driver, 'VANWALL' transfers, 'push and go' motor in some. 'Vanwall the famous British Grand Prix Winner' cast in base.	
		Green body, racing number '7' or '18', no Mettoy logo on base	**£300-350**
		French Blue body, racing number '20', no Mettoy logo on base	**£350-450**
		Red body, racing number '7'	**£300-350**
		Cream body, racing number unknown	**£300-350**

'Miniature Numbers' series

A range of models (produced between 1951 and 1954) based on just two vehicles - the Standard Vanguard and a Rolls Royce. They came in attractive window boxes and featured a clockwork motor plus brake, adjustable steering (controlled by moving the central fog lamp) and moulded grey plastic wheels. Both diecast and plastic bodies have been observed. This listing has been taken from the 1951 Mettoy Catalogue and the editor would welcome any additional information.

502 1951 **Standard Vanguard Saloon**
Shown with Green body in

catalogue, (2 7/8" inches long)............... £60-90
505 1951 **Rolls-Royce Saloon**
Red or Blue body, 3"............................ £60-90
510 1951 **Standard Vanguard Police Car**
Black with White 'POLICE' logo
on doors; roof siren and bell £60-90
511 1951 **Standard Vanguard Taxi**
Shown in 1951 catalogue with
Yellow body and Red roof rack............. £60-90
512 1951 **Standard Vanguard Fire Chief**
Red, White 'FIRE CHIEF' on doors;
single Silver ladder on roof.................... £60-90

Larger versions:
602 1951 **Standard Vanguard Saloon**
Blue body shown in catalogue
(larger version of 502, 4¼") £60-90
603 1951 **Standard Vanguard Saloon**
As 602 but with automatic
'to and fro' bump feature £60-90
605 1951 **Rolls-Royce Saloon**
Yellow body shown in catalogue
(larger version of 505, 4½") £60-90
606 1951 **Rolls-Royce Saloon**
As 605 but with automatic
'to and fro' bump feature £60-90

Corgi Toys Cars, 1956–1983 *See also 'Emergency,' 'Novelty, Film and TV-related' sections.*

Model and details	MPR

Vanwall Racing Car

150 1957-61 **Vanwall Racing Car**
• Green body, Yellow seat, large or small 'Vanwall', flat hubs, RNs '1', '3' or '7', clear or Blue screen. 'Made in Gt Britain' or 'British Made' and large 'CORGI TOYS VANWALL' cast along base. Blue box with leaflet............................ **£80-100**
• Mid-Green body, Silver seat, small 'Vanwall', clear screen. 'Made in Great Britain' cast along base. 'CORGI TOYS VANWALL' small across base. Flat hubs. RN '3' **£80-100**
• Vermillion Red body, Silver or Yellow seat, small or large 'Vanwall', Blue or clear screen. RN '1', '3' or '7'. 'CORGI TOYS VANWALL' cast small across or large along base. Flat or spoked hubs. Blue/Yellow box **£125-175**
150S 1961-65 **Vanwall Racing Car**
(with 'suspension')
• Vermillion Red body, Blue/White bonnet design plus Black RN '25', White driver, Silver seat, small 'Vanwall', 'Made in Gt. Britain' cast along base. '150S CORGI TOYS VANWALL' across base............. **£80-100**
* same with 150S sticker on 150 box .... NGPP
• Same but with Crimson body........... **£125-175**
• Promotional:'Vandervell Products' finish.. NGPP
150 1972-74 **Surtees TS9 Formula 1**
• Metallic Purple or Metallic Blue body, 'BROOKE BOND OXO' logo, 8-spoke WhizzWheels **£40-50**
• Metallic Turquoise body, cast 8-stud WhizzWheels **£30-40**
• 1975-76 Blue/Yellow body, DUCKHAMS', (GS 29 only)........................ GSP
151 1958-61 **Lotus XI Le Mans Racing Car**
• Blue body, Red or Maroon seats, clear or Blue-tinted windscreen, RN '1', or '3'.. **£200-250**
• Silver body, Red seats, RN '3'. Blue tinted screen............................ **£120-150**
• Red body, Beige seats, RN '1'. Blue tinted screen.............................. **£200-250**
151A 1961-65 **Lotus XI Le Mans Racing Car**
• Blue body, Red seats, Red/White bonnet stripe, White driver, Black RN '7' **£100-125**
• Blue body, no bonnet stripe,

Model and details	MPR

Red seats, White driver,
Black racing number '7' **£100-125**
• Lemon body, RN '3', driver.............. **£130-160**
151 1974-76 **Yardley Mclaren M19A**
• White body, 'YARDLEY', RN '55', 8-spoke or stud WhizzWheels **£40-50**
• With Blue stripe on White body, WhizzWheels, (GS30 only) .... GSP
152 1958-61 **B.R.M. Racing Car**
• Light or Dark Green body, Yellow seat, no driver, RNs '1', '3' or '7'. Blue box with leaflet............................ **£90-110**
• 1961-65 Turquoise body, Union Jack on bonnet, RN's '1', '3' or '7'. Blue/Yellow box, no leaflet................. **£90-110**
152S 1961-65 **B.R.M. Racing Car**
(with 'suspension')
• Turquoise body, Union Jack on bonnet, White driver, RNs '1', '3' or '7', Blue/Yellow box, no leaflet................. **£140-160**
* same with 152S sticker on 152 box NGPP
152 1974-75 **Ferrari 312 B2**
• Red body, 'Ferrari/Shell' logo, RN '5', White driver, Orange/Blue helmet, 8-spoke or 8-stud cast hubs.................. **£30-35**
153 1960-61 **Bluebird Record Car**
• Blue body, UK and US flags on nose, metal hubs................................ **£100-130**
153A 1961-65 **Bluebird Record Car**
• Blue body, UK and US flags on nose, plastic hubs **£100-130**
• Blue body with two Union Jacks on nose, plastic hubs........................ **£100-130**
153 1972-74 **Team Surtees TS 9B**
• Red body, Blue or Blue/White driver (Rob Walker), RN '26', 8-spoke hubs **£40-50**
• Red body, 'NORRIS', (GS 30 only) .... GSP

Ferrari Formula 1

154 1963-72 **Ferrari Formula 1**
• Red body, Ferrari bonnet badge, White driver, RN'36'. Plain blue/yellow card box **£60-80**
shaped or cast wheels
Late issue in blue and yellow window box
154 1974-79 **'JOHN PLAYER SPECIAL' Lotus**
(Drivers Emerson Fittipaldi or Ronnie Petersen).
• Black body, Gold trim, RN '1' or '4', 'JPS' logo, Black/Red helmet,

Model and details	MPR

8-stud hubs, 'Fittipaldi' on box **£40-50**
• 'JPS' logo, Black or Blue helmet, 'Petersen' on box **£40-50**
• 'JPS TEXACO' logo, Red helmet............ **£40-50**
• 'JPS TEXACO', Black helmet, 12-spoke hubs, (GS32 only)....................... GSP
• 'JPS SHELL' logo, Black/Red helmet, (GS30 only) .... GSP
• Marks & Spencers issue: No 'Corgi' on base, 'TEXACO' logo, Orange (?) helmet...................................... GSP

Lotus Climax Racing Car

155 1964-69 **Lotus Climax Racing Car**
• British Racing Green body, Yellow stripe on bonnet, White driver, Blue helmet, RN '1'.............................. **£40-50**
155 1974-76 **'SHADOW' Formula 1**
• Black, 'UOP', driver (Jackie Collins) White/Maroon helmet, RN '17'............. **£40-50**

Cooper-Maserati

156 1967-68 **Cooper-Maserati**
• Dark Blue body, RN '7', Silver or bronze hubs, White driver, Blue helmet........... **£40-50**
156 1974-76 **Graham Hill's Shadow**
• White/Red, RN'12', 'EMBASSY RACING'............................. **£40-50**
• Special issue model: Presentation box has outer sleeve with 'Graham Hill OBE, Honoured Guest of the National Sporting Club Café Royal - Monday 24th November 1975', plus the menu for the day **£300-450**
158 1969-73 **Lotus Climax Racing Car**
• Orange and White body, Blue driver, White helmet, Black RN '8' and bonnet stripe.............................. **£40-50**
158 1975-78 **Elf Tyrrell Ford F1**
• Blue body, RN '1', 'ELF', Jackie Stewart driving........................... **£40-50**

159 1969-72 **Cooper-Maserati**
- Yellow and White body, Black bonnet stripe, Blue driver, White helmet, cast wheels, Yellow number '3' **£40-50**

159 1974-76 **Indianapolis Racing Car**
- Red, RN '20', Patrick Eagle driving **£30-35**

160 1975-78 **'HESKETH' 308 F1**
- White body, Black helmet, 4-spoke or 8-stud hubs.......................... **£30-35**
- Yellow body, 'CORGI TEAM' logo, Orange driver (James Hunt), Black helmet, Blue belts, (GS26 only)........ GSP
- Marks & Spencers issue: White body and driver, 'CORGI' on some, Orange helmet .... GSP

161 1971-73 **Santa Pod 'COMMUTER'**
- Red 'Dragster' body, Chrome engine, RN '2', WhizzWheels **£25-30**

161 1977-78 **'ELF-TYRRELL' P34**
- Blue and Yellow body, 'ELF' logo, Red or Blue helmet, 8-stud hubs, Yellow RN '4' **£25-30**

162 1978-79 **'ELF-TYRRELL' P34**
- Blue / White, 'FIRST NATIONAL BANK' logo, Red or Orange helmet **£25-30**
- Marks & Spencers issue: As previous model but no 'Corgi' on base, 8-stud hubs .... GSP

162 1971-72 **'QUARTERMASTER' Dragster**
- Green / White, driver, plastic hubs **£50-60**

163 1971-73 **Santa Pod Dragster 'GLOWORM'**
- White, Blue trim, Red chassis, driver **£30-35**

164 1972-73 **Ison Bros Dragster 'WILD HONEY'**
- Yellow/Black, Green glass, WW............ **£40-50**

165 1972-74 **Adams Brothers 'DRAG-STAR'**
- Red/Yellow, 4 x V-8 engines, WW.......... **£30-35**

166 1971-74 **Ford Mustang 'ORGAN GRINDER'**
- Yellow/Green body, RN '39', driver **£30-35**

167 1973-74 **USA Racing Buggy**
- White/Red, RN '7', driver, US flag **£40-50**

169 1974-77 **'STARFIGHTER' Dragster**
- Blue/Silver/Red body, 'FIRESTONE' **£30-35**

170 1974-77 **John Woolfe's Dragster**
- 'RADIO LUXEMBOURG', '208'.............. **£35-45**

190 1974-77 **'JOHN PLAYER' Lotus**
- 1:18 scale, Black/Gold, RN '1', driver, removable wheels, tools included in box.**£40-50**

191 1975-80 **'TEXACO MARLBORO'**
  F1 Mclaren, 1:18 scale
- White/Red, RN '5', removable wheels, tools included in box **£40-50**

200 1956-61 **Ford Consul**
  (This was the first 'Corgi Toys' model). Flat spun hubs, no suspension, leaflet with early issues.
- Cream body............................... **£125-150**
- Dark or Pale Green body.................. **£125-150**
- Tan or Dark Tan body...................... **£125-220**
- Blue body **£125-150**
- Light Greyish-Brown body................ **£125-150**
- Bright Green body **£125-150**

200M 1956-59 **Ford Consul**
  (with flywheel motor) Flat spun hubs, no suspension, leaflet with early issues.
- Blue body **£160-280**
- Dark Green................................. **£130-160**
- Bright Green............................... **£130-160**
- Two-tone Green............................. **£130-160**
- Green/Cream................................ **£130-160**
- Silver/Cream............................... **£130-160**
- Pale Grey over Green....................... **£130-160**

200 1976-78 **BLMC Mini 1000**
- Metallic Blue body, Silver roof, Red or White interior **£20-25**

200A 1978-83 **BLMC Mini 1000**
- Met. Blue or Silver body, White or Red interior, Union Jack stripe on roof, WhizzWheels **£25-35**

201 1956-61 **Austin Cambridge**
  Flat spun hubs, no suspension, leaflet with early issues.
- Pale Blue body **£125-150**
- Turquoise body **£125-150**
- Light Grey body **£125-150**
- Mid-Grey body **£125-150**
- Green/Cream **£125-150**
- Two-tone Green............................ **£125-150**
- Silver over Metallic Green................ **£150-175**

201M 1956-59 **Austin Cambridge**
  (with flywheel motor) Flat spun hubs, leaflet with early issues.
- Cream body................................ **£130-160**
- Red body **£130-160**
- Slate Grey body **£130-160**
- Medium Grey body **£130-160**
- Silver or Metallic Blue **£130-160**
- Burnt Orange body........................ **£250-300**

201 1970-72 **The Saint's Volvo**
  See 'Novelty, Film and TV-related' section.

201 1979-82 **BLMC Mini 1000**
- Silver, 'TEAM CORGI'/'8' on some **£15-25**
- Same model but with Orange body **£15-25**
- Dk. Blue, without 'TEAM CORGI'......... **£15-25**
- Dark Blue, 'ESSO' and 'MICHELIN' labels **£15-25**

202 1956-61 **Morris Cowley**
  Flat spun hubs, no suspension, leaflet with early issues.
- Bright Green body **£125-150**
- Grey body **£125-150**
- Blue body **£150-220**
- Grey/Blue body............................ **£125-150**
- Blue/Cream body.......................... **£125-150**
- Pale Green/Blue body **£150-240**
- White/Blue body **£125-150**

202M 1956-59 **Morris Cowley**
  (with flywheel motor) Flat spun hubs, leaflet with early issues.
- Pale Green body **£130-160**
- Mid-Green body **£130-160**
- Dark Green body **£130-160**
- Off-White body **£130-160**

202 1970-72 **Renault 16TS**
- Blue/Silver, Yellow interior, WW **£25-30**

203 1970-72 **De Tomaso Mangusta**
- Met. Dk. Green, Gold stripes, RN '1'..... **£25-35**

203 1956-61 **Vauxhall Velox**
  Flat spun hubs, leaflet with early issues.
- Red body **£125-150**
- Cream body **£125-150**
- Yellow body **£125-150**
- Yellow/Red body........................... **£125-150**
- Blue body.................................. **£350-400**

203M 1956-59 **Vauxhall Velox**
  (with flywheel motor) Flat spun hubs, leaflet with early issues.
- Red body **£175-200**
- Orange body............................... **£250-300**

203 1971-72 **De Tomaso Mangusta**
- Green/Gold, White interior, WW **£30-40**
- Green body, White interior, Silver base, WhizzWheels **£30-40**

204 1956-61 **Rover 90**
  Flat spun hubs, leaflet with early issues.
- Cream or Off-White body **£140-160**
- Light or Dark Grey body, flat hubs.... **£140-160**
- Mid or Dark Green body, flat hubs ... **£140-160**
- Metallic Green body, flat hubs........ **£140-160**
- Met. Red lower body, Cream upper.. **£140-160**
- Metallic Cerise over Grey body **£140-160**

204M 1956-59 **Rover 90** (with flywheel motor)
  Flat spun hubs, leaflet with early issues.
- Bright Mid-Green or Dark Green **£150-175**
- Grey body **£150-175**
- Metallic Green body **£175-225**

204 1972-73 **Morris Mini-Minor**
  All have WhizzWheels.
- Dark Blue body, Lemon interior **£75-85**
- Deep Blue body, Lemon interior **£200-250**
- Met. Blue body, Lemon interior **£100-125**

- All-Orange body, Lemon interior...... **£100-125**
- Orange body, Black roof **£120-150**

205 1956-62 **Riley Pathfinder**
  Flat spun hubs, leaflet with early issues.
- Red body **£130-160**
- Blue body **£130-160**

205M 1956-59 **Riley Pathfinder**
  (with flywheel motor) Flat spun hubs, leaflet with early issues.
- Red body **£200-250**
- Mid Blue body............................. **£200-250**
- Navy Blue body............................ **£200-250**

206 1956-59 **Hillman Husky Estate**
  Flat spun hubs, leaflet with early issues.
- Tan or Greyish Light-Brown body..... **£100-125**
- Metallic Blue and Silver body........... **£130-170**

206M 1956-59 **Hillman Husky Estate**
  (with flywheel motor) Flat spun hubs, leaflet with early issues.
- Cream body................................ **£150-175**
- Mid-Blue body............................. **£150-175**
- Dark Blue body............................ **£150-175**
- Grey body **£150-175**
- Turquoise body............................ **£250-300**

207 1957-62 **Standard Vanguard III**
  Flat spun hubs, leaflet with early issues.
- Off-White body (Red roof top) **£150-175**
- Grey body (Red roof) **£120-140**
- Red over Green body....................... **£120-140**

207M 1957-59 **Standard Vanguard III**
  (with flywheel motor) Flat spun hubs, leaflet with early issues.
- Primrose Yellow body **£190-230**
- Pale Green body, Red roof pillars **£145-175**

208 1957-60 **Jaguar 2.4 litre**
  Flat spun hubs, leaflet with early issues.
- White body................................. **£120-150**

208M 1957-60 **Jaguar 2.4 litre**
  (with flywheel motor) Flat spun hubs, leaflet with early issues.
- Metallic Dark Blue body **£150-175**

208S 1960-63 **Jaguar 2.4 litre**
  (with spring suspension)
- Flat spun hubs, Lemon body............. **£120-150**
- Flat spun hubs, Pale Lemon body..... **£120-150**

Citroën DS19

210 1957-60 **Citroën DS19**
  Flat spun hubs, leaflet with early issues.
- Yellow body, Red roof, Grey or Silver baseplate **£120-160**
- Met. Dark Green body, Black roof..... **£120-160**
- As previous but with bulge in base to take flywheel motor. Note that a '210M' was not produced **£120-160**

210S 1960-65 **Citroën DS19** (with suspension)
- Red body, Lemon interior, Grey base**£130-160**

211 1958-60 **Studebaker Golden Hawk**
  Flat spun hubs, leaflet with early issues.
- Blue body, Gold rear wing flashes **£120-150**
- White body, Gold rear wing flashes .. **£120-150**

211M 1958-59 **Studebaker Golden Hawk**
  (with flywheel motor) Flat spun hubs, leaflet with early issues.
- White/Gold body............................ **£140-170**

211S 1960-65 **Studebaker Golden Hawk**
  (with spring suspension)
- Gold ('plated') body, Red interior, White flash, shaped hubs............ **£100-125**
- Gold (painted) body, shaped hubs ... **£100-125**

212 1958 **Road Racer** Not released, one example known to exist .... NPP

214 1959-65 **Ford Thunderbird Hardtop**
  Flat spun hubs, leaflet with early issues.

- Pale Green (Cream hardtop),
  '1959' rear no. plate £100-120
- Same but blank rear plate £100-120
- Grey body (Red top), '1959' no. plate £100-120

214M 1959-60 Ford Thunderbird Hardtop
  (with flywheel motor)
  Flat spun hubs, leaflet with early issues.
- Pink (Black top), '1959' rear no. plate £200-250
- Pale Green body, Cream hardtop £170-200

214S 1962-64 Ford Thunderbird Hardtop
  (with spring suspension)
- Shaped spun hubs, Metallic
  Grey/Red body, Lemon interior £100-120
- Black/Red body, Lemon interior £100-120

215 1959-62 Thunderbird Open Sports
- Flat spun hubs, White body,
  Blue interior £100-120
- Blue body, Silver interior £100-120

215S 1962-64 Thunderbird Open Sports
  (with spring suspension)
- Red body, Yellow interior / driver £125-150

216 1959-62 Austin A40
  Flat spun hubs, leaflet with early issues.
- Two-tone Blue body £100-120
- Red body, Black roof £100-120

216M 1959-60 Austin A40 (with flywheel motor)
  Flat spun hubs, leaflet with early issues.
- Red body, Black roof £175-200
- All-Red body £130-160

217 1960-63 Fiat 1800 Saloon
- Light Blue (Lemon interior),
  smooth or shaped hubs £60-70
- Two-tone Blue (Lemon interior),
  smooth or shaped hubs £80-90
- Light Tan body, Lemon interior £60-70
- Mustard Yellow body,
  Bright Yellow interior £100-120

Aston Martin DB4

218 1960-62 Aston Martin DB4
- Red body (bonnet vent on some),
  flat or shaped hubs £80-100
- 1961-62 Red body, Red interior,
  cast 'spoked' hubs £80-100
- Primrose Yellow body with bonnet vent,
  Red interior, flat spun hubs £80-100
- Same model, but with cast
  'criss-cross' wheels £140-170

219 1959-63 Plymouth Suburban Sports
- Cream with Fawn roof, Red interior,
  smooth flat hubs £80-100

220 1960-65 Chevrolet Impala
  All have spun hubs.
- Metallic Red body, Red or
  Lemon interior, leaflet £70-80
- Same, but Powder Blue body £70-80
- Pink body, Lemon interior £150-175
- Sky Blue body, Red interior £80-90

221 1960-63 Chevrolet Impala Cab
- Yellow body, 'NEW YORK TAXI',
  Red interior, smooth/shaped spun
  hubs, roof box £90-110

221 1960-63 Chevrolet Impala State Patrol
  See 'Emergency Vehicles' section.

222 1959-65 Renault Floride
- Dark Red/ Maroon body; Red, White or
  Yellow interior, flat or shaped hubs £60-70
- Light Olive, Red interior, flat hubs £70-80

- Metallic Blue body, Red interior,
  flat or shaped hubs £60-70
  Harder to find version: metallic blue
  with lemon interior, shaped hubs

Bentley Continental

224 1961-65 Bentley Continental
  Opening boot with removable spare,
  special lights.
- Cream over Metallic Apple Green,
  Red interior £120-140
- Black over Silver body, Red int. £120-140
- Two-tone Green or Gold body £120-140
- Metallic Green and White body £120-140
- Cherry Red body, Lemon interior £120-140

Austin 7 (Mini) Saloon

225 1961-65 Austin 7 (Mini) Saloon
- Red body, Yellow interior, spun hubs £100-120
- Primrose-Yellow body,
  Red interior, flat hubs £500-600
- Mid-Blue body, Red interior,
  shaped hubs £400-500
- Danish promotional: 'JENSEN'S', Red body,
  Lemon interior, flat spun hubs £1,000-1,200

Morris Mini Minor

226 1960-68 Morris Mini Minor
- Pale Blue body, Red or Yellow
  interior, flat or shaped hubs £80-100
- Pale Blue, Red interior, spun hubs ... £200-300
- Red body, flat or shaped hubs £100-120
- Metallic Maroon, Lemon interior,
  detailed cast hubs £120-140
- Yellow body £200-250
- Danish promotional:
  'JENSEN'S', Pale Blue body,
  Red interior, flat spun hubs £1,200-1,400
- Deep Blue body, (only in Gift Set 11) .... GSP
  NB The Light Blue version of 226 was
  also used for a short time by a US
  games manufacturer in a table-top
  racing game. This model has a large
  drive-pin hole in the base and
  'EAST AFRICAN RALLY' stickers
  on the bonnet, RN '3'.
  Not separately boxed £200-300

227 1962-65 Mini Cooper Rally
- Bright Blue body, White roof and
  bonnet, Yellow interior, spun hubs,
  Union Jack and chequered bonnet
  flags, racing numbers '1', '3' or '7' £200-300
- Same but Bright Blue body and
  bonnet, White roof £200-300
- Primrose Yellow body, Red interior,
  White roof and bonnet with flags
  and RNs '1', '3' or '7' £300-400
- Primrose Yellow body and
  bonnet, flags, RN '1' £200-300

228 1962-65 Volvo P-1800
- Beige body, Red interior, spun hubs £65-75
- Red body, Lemon interior, spun hubs £80-100
- Pink or Dark Pink body, Lemon int. £55-65

229 1961-66 Chevrolet Corvair
- Mid-Blue body, Bright Yellow
  interior, spun hubs £60-70
- Pale Blue body, Lemon or Red
  interior, shaped hubs £60-70
- Gold body, (in 'Golden Guinea' set) .... GSP

Mercedes-Benz 220 SE

230 1962-64 Mercedes-Benz 220 SE
  Shaped spun hubs, spare wheel in boot.
- Cream (Red interior) £70-80
- Maroon body, Lemon interior £70-80
- Black body, Lemon interior £150-190
- Dark Blue body, Lemon interior £70-80

231 1961-65 Triumph Herald
- Gold top / bottom, White in centre,
  Red interior, smooth flat hubs £100-130
- Mid-Blue top / bottom, White centre,
  Red interior, shaped hubs £70-80

232 1961-63 Fiat 2100
- Pale Pink with Mauve roof,
  Lemon interior, spun hubs £60-70

233 1962-72 Heinkel Trojan
  Spun hubs or detailed cast hubs.
- Red body, Lemon interior £75-80
- Dark Blue body, Lemon interior £75-80
- Lilac body, Lemon interior £100-125
- Orange body, Lemon interior £100-125
- Pink body, Lemon interior £100-125
- Metallic Blue body, spun hubs £100-125
- Fawn body, spun hubs £100-125
- Turquoise body, spun hubs £100-125
  NB This was the first Corgi model to have
  'By Special Request' flash on the box.

234 1961-65 Ford Consul Classic
- Beige body, Pink roof, Lemon int. £70-80
- Beige/pink body including base,
  Pink roof, Lemon interior £80-160
- Gold body £70-80

235 1962-66 Oldsmobile Super 88
  All with spun hubs.
- Black body, White side flash £85-95
- Metallic Steel Blue, White side flash,
  Red interior £85-95
- Light Blue body, Red interior,
  White side flash £85-95

236 1964-68 **'CORGI' Motor School**
(Austin A60)
- Light Blue body, two figures,
'Highway Code' leaflet, r/h drive **£90-110**

Jaguar Mk10

238 1962-67 **Jaguar Mk10**
All issues have spun hubs, luggage in boot.
Blue/Yellow box with leaflet.
- Pale Blue body, Red interior **£100-120**
- Mid-Green body, Red interior **£100-120**
- Deep Blue body, Red interior **£150-175**
- Kingfisher Blue body, Lemon int. **£100-120**
- Sea-Green body, Red interior **£200-300**
- Metallic Blue-Grey body, Red int. **£125-150**
- Metallic Deep Blue body,
Red or Lemon interior....................... **£125-150**
- Metallic Sea-Green body, Red int. **£175-200**
- Metallic Cerise body, Lemon int. **£120-140**
- Metallic Silver body, Red interior **£175-200**
- Metallic Green body, Red interior **£115-135**

VW 1500 Karmann Ghia

239 1963-68 **VW 1500 Karmann Ghia**
Spare wheel/suitcase in boot, spun hubs.
- Cream body (Red interior) **£80-90**
- Gold body, Red or Yellow interior....... **£90-100**
- Red body, White or Yellow interior....... **£80-90**
- Plum body, Red interior...................... **£90-100**
- Orange body, Yellow interior............. **£130-160**
240 1963-64 **Fiat 600 Jolly**
Spun hubs, two figures.
- Metallic Light Blue, Silver/Red top,
Red interior.................................**£150-200**
- Met. Dark Blue body, Red interior **£120-140**
- Blue body, Red interior **£120-140**
- Yellow body, Red interior.................... **£140-170**
241 1963-69 **Chrysler Ghia L64**
All have shaped spun hubs or
detailed cast hubs and a Corgi dog
on the rear shelf.
- Met. Blue/White body, Cream int. **£70-80**
- Metallic Green body, Cream interior.... **£70-80**
- Metallic Gold body.............................. **£70-80**
- Metallic Silver Blue body, Red int. **£120-150**
- Metallic Copper **£70-80**
- Lime Green, Yellow interior.............. **£100-125**
242 1965-66 **Ghia Fiat 600**
- Orange-Yellow body, Red interior,
two figures in swim gear,
windscreen but no canopy **£250-350**
245 1964-68 **Buick Riviera**
Model has 'Trans-O-Lites' and towbar.
- Metallic Gold body, Red interior,
spoked hubs...................................... **£70-80**
- Same, but with cast hubs **£110-130**
- Metallic Steel Blue (Red interior)......... **£70-80**
- Metallic Greenish Blue body **£70-80**
- Pale Blue body, spun or cast hubs **£70-80**

Chrysler Imperial Convertible

246 1965-68 **Chrysler Imperial Convertible**
Shaped spun or detailed cast hubs.
All issues should include driver and
passenger, golf trolley in boot,
Blue/Yellow box with inner packing.
Red car, green car on box
- Red/Deep Red body, Pale Blue or
Green interior **£80-140**
- Metallic Turquoise body, Green int. ... **£80-100**
- Metallic Blue body, Pale Blue int. **£110-130**
- Met. Kingfisher Blue, Green int......... **£300-480**
247 1964-69 **Mercedes-Benz 600 Pullman**
- Metallic Maroon body, Cream interior,
windscreen wipers, instruction sheet... **£80-90**
- Metallic Red body, Cream interior,
spun hubs.. **£80-90**
248 1965-67 **Chevrolet Impala**
- Light brown body, Cream roof/interior,
shaped spun hubs **£90-140**
249 1965-69 **Morris Mini-Cooper DeLuxe**
- Black body, Red roof, Lemon interior,
'wicker' panels, spun or cast hubs **£160-190**
251 1963-66 **Hillman Imp**
Model has spun hubs and luggage.
- Metallic Blue body, Yellow interior....... **£85-95**
- Metallic Bronze body,
White side stripe and interior............ **£100-150**
- Danish promotional:
'JENSEN'S', Light Blue body,
Yellow interior, logo.....................**£1,000-1,200**

Rover 2000

252 1963-66 **Rover 2000**
Spun hubs; leaflet in box.
- Metallic Light Blue or Steel Blue
body, Red interior................................. **£90-110**
- Metallic Maroon body,
Red or Yellow interior **£230-280**
253 1964-68 **Mercedes-Benz 220 SE**
- Maroon body, luggage,
spare wheel **£80-100**
- Met. Blue, luggage, spare wheel **£80-100**
255 1964-68 **Motor School A60**
- Dark Blue body, l/h drive, 5 language
leaflet, (Export issue of 236) **£125-150**
256 1965-68 **Volkswagen 1200 Rally**
- Orange body, RN '18', 'EAST AFRICAN
RALLY', steering wheel on roof,
Red/Yellow cardboard roof fitting,
Rhinoceros figure **£250-300**
258 1965-70 **The Saint's Volvo P1800**
See 'Novelty, Film and TV-related' section.

Volkswagen 1200 Rally

259 1966-69 **Citroën 'Le Dandy'**
- Metallic Dark Red, Yellow interior,
wire wheels **£80-120**
- Met. Blue body, White roof / boot **£125-150**
260 1969-69 **Renault 16 TS**
- Metallic Red, Yellow int., cast hubs....... **£35-45**
261 1965-69 **James Bond's Aston-Martin**
See 'Novelty, Film and TV-related' section.
262 1967-69 **Lincoln Continental
Executive Limousine**
Box should also contain a picture strip
for use with the on-board 'TV set'.
- Metallic Gold/Black body.................... **£90-100**
- Light Blue/Tan body........................... **£125-150**
263 1966-69 **Rambler Marlin Sports**
- Red body, Black roof White interior,
spun or cast hubs................................. **£60-70**
- White body, Blue roof, (GS10 only) .... GSP
264 1966-69 **Oldsmobile Toronado**
- Met. Medium or Dark Blue body, smooth
or cast spoked hubs, Cream interior..... **£50-60**
269 1977-83 **James Bond Lotus Esprit**
270 1968-78 **James Bond Aston-Martin**
271 1978-92 **James Bond Aston-Martin**
See 'Novelty, Film and TV-related' section.
271 1969-69 **Ghia Mangusta De Tomaso**
- Blue/White body, Gold stripes............ **£80-100**
- Orange-Red body **£80-100**
272 1981-83 **James Bond Citroën 2cv**
See 'Novelty, Film and TV-related' section.
273 1970-71 **Rolls-Royce Silver Shadow**
With 'Golden Jacks', 'Take-Off wheels',
and a spare wheel.
- Metallic Silver/Blue............................. **£75-95**
- Pearlescent White over Grey, Blue int. . **£50-75**
273 1982-83 **Honda Ballade**
'BSM' Driving School Car
- Yellow body with Red side stripes......... **£25-35**
274 1970-72 **Bentley 'T' Series**
- Bright Pink body, Cream interior,
special lights, WhizzWheels **£40-50**
275 1968-70 **Rover 2000 TC**
With 'Golden Jacks', 'Take-Off wheels',
and a spare wheel.
- Metallic Olive Green body, Brown or
Red interior, Amber roof panel............. **£75-85**
- Same but with White interior **£90-120**
- White body, Maroon interior,
Amber roof panel............................... **£120-150**
- Metallic Maroon body........................ **£90-120**
- Gold plated version **£150-250**
275 1981-84 **Mini Metro**
- Blue, Purple or Red body, Yellow int. ... **£10-15**
- Gold body... **£45-50**
- 'Royal Wedding' Metro
Mauve body, Silver 'Charles & Diana'
crest, special Mauve box **£20-25**
276 1968-72 **Oldsmobile Toronado**
With 'Golden Jacks', 'Take-Off wheels'.
- Metallic Blue or Red body **£45-65**
- Metallic Gold body, Cream interior...... **£45-65**
- Metallic Green body, Cream interior **£45-65**
- Metallic Brown body, Cream interior ... **£45-65**
276 1982-83 **Triumph Acclaim**
- Metallic Blue, or Cream body,
steering control.....................................**£7-10**
277 1982-83 **Triumph Acclaim**
'BSM' Driving School Car
- Yellow body, Black 'wheel' steering
control on roof **£15-20**

278 1982- **Triumph Acclaim 'CORGI MOTOR SCHOOL' Car**
- Yellow body, with steering control....... **£25-35**

279 1980- **Rolls-Royce Corniche**
- Metallic Dark Red body, opening doors/bonnet/boot **£20-35**

280 1970-78 **Rolls-Royce Silver Shadow**
- Metallic Silver upper body, Blue lower body, Brown interior, WhizzWheels **£35-40**
- Met. Blue body, Brown interior, WW .. **£35-40**

281 1971-72 **Rover 2000 TC**
- Metallic Red body, Yellow interior, Amber or clear roof, WhizzWheels **£60-75**
- Purple body, Amber roof **£100-125**

281 1982- **'DATAPOST' Metro**
- Blue/White body, RN '77', adverts. **£9-12**

282 1971-74 **Mini Cooper Rally**
- White/Black/Yellow, number '177', special lights, WhizzWheels **£55-65**

283 1971-74 **DAF 'City' Car**
- Red/Black body, White interior, WW.... **£15-20**

284 1970-76 **Citroën SM**
- Green body, Pale Blue interior, spoked wheels.......................... **£40-45**
- Metallic Cerise, Pale Blue interior, spoked wheels.......................... **£40-45**

285 1975-81 **Mercedes-Benz 240 D**
- Silver, Blue, Bronze or Beige (all Metallic), WhizzWheels.................. **£25-35**

286 1975-79 **Jaguar XJC V-12**
- Blue/Black, Red/Black, Red, Pearl, Blue or Orange (all Metallic), WW **£25-35**

287 1975-78 **Citroën Dyane**
- Metallic Green, duck decal, WW **£25-35**
- Same but Metallic Yellow/Black............ **£25-35**
- Metallic Bronze, duck decal, WW **£25-35**

288 1975-79 **Minissima**
- Beige/Black/Yellow body........................ **£25-35**

289 1976-80 **VW Polo 'DBP'** (German issue)
- Yellow/White body, l/h drive, WW **£55-75**

289 1977-81 **Volkswagen Polo**
- Lime Green or Orange body **£25-35**

289 1977-81 **VW Polo 'ADAC'** (German issue)
- As previous model but Yellow body...... **£55-75**

290 1976-77 **Kojak Buick**
See 'Novelty, Film and TV-related' section.

290 1977-82 **Starsky & Hutch Ford Torino**
See 'Novelty, Film and TV-related' section.

291 1977-80 **AMC Pacer**
- Metallic Red, opening doors / hatch **£20-25**

291 1982- **Mercedes Benz 240 Rally**
- Muddy Cream body, RN '5', 'EAST AFRICAN RALLY' or 'E.A.R.' logos **£20-25**

293 1977-80 **Renault 5 TS**
- Orange, Silver or Silver/Blue, WW **£20-25**
- French issue: Light Blue body, Dark Blue roof, 'SOS MEDICINS' **£80-100**

294 1980-84 **Renault 5 TS Alpine**
- Black body with White stripe................ **£10-15**

298 1982-83 **Magnum P.I. Ferrari 308GTS**
See 'Novelty, Film and TV-related' section.

299 1982- **Ford Sierra 2.3 Ghia**
- Metallic Light Brown/Black stripe, Dark Brown or Grey interior, Brown or Dark Grey base. In special two-tone blue 'Ford' box **£20-25**
- Met. Lt. Brown, Met. Blue, Red or Yellow. Packed in White/Red 'Ford' box or normal Black/Yellow/Red box .. **£15-20**

300 1956-65 **Austin Healey 100-4**
Flat spun hubs, leaflet with early issues.
- Red with Cream interior **£175-200**
- Cream with Red interior **£175-200**
- Blue body with Cream interior **£175-200**

300 1970-70 **Chevrolet Corvette Stingray**
- With 'Golden Jacks' / 'Take-Off Wheels', and luggage. 'Plated' Bright Green, Dark Red or Green body **£85-95**
- Metallic Red body, Black bonnet **£65-75**
- Metallic Green body, Black bonnet **£65-75**

NB Models without box header cards contained instructions.

300 1979-82 **Ferrari 'DAYTONA'**
- Green, multicoloured flash, RN '5' **£20-25**

301 1956-61 **Triumph TR2**
All have flat spun hubs.
- Cream body, Red seats...................... **£150-200**
- Red body with Cream seats **£150-200**
- Deep Green body with Cream seats . **£150-200**

301 1970-73 **Iso Grifo 7 litre**
- Met. Blue body, Black bonnet, White interior, Silver or Black roll-bar, WW **£30-35**

301 1979-82 **Lotus Elite Racing Car**
- Yellow/Red, RN '7', 'FERODO' **£20-25**

302 1957-65 **MG 'MGA'**
- Red (shades exist), Cream seats, smooth or chrome spun hubs **£200-240**
- Cream with Red seats **£200-240**
- Mid or Dark Metallic Green body, Cream or Yellow seats, smooth or shaped spun hubs **£200-240**

302 1969-72 **Hillman Hunter Rally**
- Blue body, White roof, Matt-Black bonnet, RN '75', equipment, kangaroo, 'Golden Jacks', transfers, toolbox, leaflet, instructions **£110-140**

302 1979-82 **VW Polo**
- Met. Brown/Red, RN '4', adverts............ **£20-25**

303 1958-60 **Mercedes-Benz 300 SL** (Open Roadster)
- Off-White body, Blue seats, smooth hubs, Blue box **£125-150**
- Blue body, White seats, smooth hubs, Blue box **£100-125**
- Cream body, Blue seats, smooth hubs, Blue box **£100-125**
NB If in rare plain overprinted box, add..... **£20-30**

303S 1961-63 **Mercedes-Benz 300 SL** (Open Sports) (with Suspension)
- Off-White body, Yellow interior, Red bonnet stripe, flat spun hubs, RNs '1' to '12' **£100-125**
- Off-White body, Light Blue interior, Red bonnet stripe, flat spun hubs **£175-200**
- Mid-Blue body, Yellow interior, Red bonnet stripe, RNs '1' to '12' **£150-175**
- First version; blue with white interior or white with blue interior, smooth hubs.
- Second version; has shaped hubs. No decals.
NB 'Open Sports' models were housed in 303S 'Open Roadster' boxes.

303S2 Mercedes-Benz 300 SL
1963-64 (Open Sports with Driver) (with Suspension)
- With driver dressed in Grey suit, White shirt and Red bow-tie. White body, Yellow interior, Red bonnet stripe, RNs '1' to '12', shaped spun hubs **£100-130**
- Blue body, Yellow int., Red bonnet stripe, RNs '1' to '12', shaped spun hubs **£100-130**
- Chrome plated body, Lemon/Brown interior, Red bonnet stripe, spoked or cast hubs, RNs '1' to '12' **£175-200**

303 1970-72 **Roger Clark's Ford Capri**
- White body, Black bonnet, RN '73', decal sheet, WhizzWheels **£70-80**
- As previous model but with Red spot hubs. Yellow/Red box with: '9 transfers for you to apply!' **£110-170**

304 1959-61 **Mercedes-Benz 300 SL Hardtop**
- Yellow body, Red hardtop, spun hubs, no suspension **£100-125**
- Yellow body / top, flat spun hubs...... **£300-400**

304S 1961-63 **Mercedes-Benz 300 SL Hardtop** (with Suspension)
- Chrome body, Red hardtop, stripe, smooth or shaped hubs, '3' or '7' **£100-130**
- White body, Red hardtop, RN '7', shaped hubs...................... **£300-400**

304 1971-72 **Chevrolet Camaro SS350**
- Dk. Blue body, White bonnet band, interior and detachable roof, special lights **£40-50**

305 1960-63 **Triumph TR3**
- Metallic Olive Green or Cream body, Red seats, smooth or shaped hubs ... **£150-175**

305S 1962-63 **Triumph TR3** (with spring suspension)
- Light Green, shaped spun hubs **£175-225**
- Cream body, shaped spun hubs........ **£175-225**

305 1972-73 **Mini Marcos GT 850**
- White body, Blue/White stripes, Red interior, RN '7', WhizzWheels **£30-35**

306 1971-73 **Morris Marina 1.8 Coupé**
- Met. Red body, Cream interior, WW **£45-55**
- Met. Lime Green, Cream int., WW **£40-45**

306 1980-81 **Fiat X1/9S**
- Metallic Blue body with Red/Yellow bands, racing number '3' or '6'........................ **£15-20**

Jaguar 'E' type

307 1962-64 **Jaguar 'E' type**
- Metallic Grey body with Red removable hard-top, Brown interior, spun hubs, box has inner packing **£100-125**
- Plum to Red body and top, inner packing **£100-125**

307 1981-82 **Renault Turbo**
- Yellow/Red body, 'CIBIE', RN '8', adverts **£10-15**

308 1972-76 **Mini Cooper 'S' 'MONTE CARLO'**
- Yellow body, '177', two spare wheels on roof-rack, WW, (339 update).......... **£75-100**
- Gold-plated body. Only 144 thought to exist **£1,000-1,500**

308 1982-82 **BMW M1**
- Yellow / Black, '25', 'TEAM BMW' **£10-15**

Aston-Martin DB4 Competition

309 1962-65 **Aston-Martin DB4 Competition**
- Turquoise/White body, Lemon interior, UK flags on bonnet, spun hubs, RN '1', '3' or '7'.................................. **£125-150**
- Variation with spoked hubs.............. **£125-150**

309 1982- **VW 'TURBO'**
- White / Orange, RN '14', Red decals...... **£10-15**

310 1963-67 **Chevrolet Corvette Stingray**
- Met. Cerise, Lemon int., shaped hubs .. **£70-80**
- Metallic Silver body, Lemon interior, 'wire' wheels **£70-80**
- Metallic Bronze body, Lemon interior, 'wire' wheels........... **£100-125**

310 1982- **'PORSCHE' 924 Turbo**
- Black/Gold, 'GOODYEAR' **£10-15**

311 1970-72 **Ford Capri V6 3-litre**
- Orange body, Gold wheels with Red WW hubs, Black interior................ **£80-90**
- Fluorescent Orange, WhizzWheels....... **£50-60**
- Fluorescent Orange, Red WW hubs...... **£70-90**
- Red body / WW hubs, Black bonnet..... **£70-90**

312 1964-68 **'E' type Jaguar**
- Silver (vacuum plated) body, RN '2', driver, spoked hubs.................. **£80-100**

312 1971-74 **Marcos Mantis**
- Met. Red, White int., spoked hubs........ **£30-40**

312 1983- **Ford Capri 'S'**
- White, '6', hinged parcel shelf, ads. **£10-15**

313 1970-73 **Ford Cortina GXL**
- Metallic Blue body, Black roof, Black and White interior, Graham Hill figure, WW...................... **£80-100**
- Bronze body, Black roof, White int. **£80-100**
- Yellow body, Black roof.................... **£175-220**
- Metallic Pale Green body, Black roof, White interior.................. **£80-90**
- Promotional: Tan body, Black roof, Red interior, left-hand drive, 'CORTINA' number plate.................. **£250-350**

Ferrari Berlinetta 250 LM

314 1965-72 **Ferrari Berlinetta 250 LM**
- Red body, RN '4', wire wheels **£60-70**

314 1976-79 **Fiat X1-9**
- Metallic Lime Green/Black body **£25-35**
- Silver/Black body................................... **£25-35**

314 1982- **Supercat Jaguar XJS-HE**
- Black body, Red or Tan interior............ **£10-15**

315 1964-66 **Simca 1000 Sports**
- Plated Silver, Red interior, RN '8', Red/White/Blue racing stripes............. **£70-80**
- Metallic Blue body, RN '8', Red/White/Blue stripes **£120-140**

315 1976-79 **Lotus Elite**
- Red or Yellow with White seats **£20-25**

316 1963-66 **NSU Sport Prinz**
- Metallic Red body, Yellow seats, spun hubs.. **£50-60**

316 1971-73 **Ford GT 70**
- Metallic Lime Green body, Black engine cover, White interior, RN '32', (unapplied) decal sheet........... **£30-40**

Mini Cooper 'S'

317 1964-65 **Mini Cooper 'S'**
  'MONTE CARLO 1964'
- Red body, White roof, Yellow interior, RN '37', roof spotlight. (Paddy Hopkirk) **£200-250**
- Red body, Pink roof variation............ **£250-300**

318 1965-66 **Mini Cooper 'S'**
  'MONTE CARLO 1965'
- Red body, White roof, 'AJB 44B', racing number '52', no roof spotlight **£175-200**

Lotus Elan S2 Open Top

318 1965-67 **Lotus Elan S2 Open Top**
- Metallic Steel Blue, RN '6' or '8', driver, 'I'VE GOT A TIGER IN MY TANK', 'tiger' decal, logo on boot lid, Blue/Yellow box, unapplied decals... **£115-135**
- White body, Black interior, same 'tiger' decal, spun hubs, unapplied decal sheet (RN '7'), figure **£500-600**

318 1965-68 **Lotus Elan S2 Open Top**
- Dark Green body, Yellow stripe with Black or Red interior (Gift Set 37) .... GSP
- White body, Black interior (GS40), 'tiger' label, unapplied decals **£250-300**
- Met. Copper body, decals sheet........ **£200-250**
- Yellow body, Green stripe, Black interior, spun hubs **£150-200**

318 1981- **Jaguar XJS**
- Blue/Cream body with Red line............ **£15-20**
- 1983-? Black/Red/White body, RN '4', 'MOTUL', 'JAGUAR'...................... **£15-20**

Lotus Elan S2 Hardtop

319 1967-69 **Lotus Elan S2 Hardtop**
  (with racing numbers)
- Yellow body (Green top), shaped hubs **£100-125**
- Blue body (White top), shaped hubs...................................... **£100-125**
- Red body, White top, cast hubs.......... **£75-100**
- Red body, Red top, cast hubs **£75-85**
- Blue body, White top, cast hubs........ **£100-180**
- Green and Yellow lift-off body.............. **£75-85**
- Red body with White top, WW **£75-85**
  NB 1967-69 boxed issues should include a sheet of self-adhesive racing numbers '1' to '12'.

319 1973-74 **Lamborghini P400GT**
- Metallic Silver body, Purple/Yellow stripes, RN '7', WW........ **£25-30**

319 1978-81 **Jaguar XJS**
- Met. Red body, Black roof...................... **£15-20**

320 1965-67 **Ford Mustang Fastback 2+2**
- Opening bonnet, suspension, Corgi dog, sliding windows. Silver (Red interior), detailed cast hubs................................ **£90-130**
- Metallic Deep Blue (Cream interior), detailed cast hubs, spoked hubs.........**£90-110**
- Light Green body (Cream interior), spoked hubs...................................... **£90-110**
- Metallic Purple body, Cream interior, spoked hubs...................................... **£90-110**
- Metallic Deep Yellow body, Black

bonnet and interior, cast hubs **£500-750**

320 1978-81 **The Saint's Jaguar XJS**
  See 'Novelty, Film and TV-related' section.

321 1965-66 **Mini Cooper 'S'**
  'MONTE CARLO 1965'
- (Timo Makinen). Red body, White roof without spotlight, 'AJB 44B' on bonnet, RN '52' **£200-250**
- Same, but in 317 picture box with 'No. 321' and 'MONTE CARLO WINNER' flash **£350-450**
- Red body, White roof with spotlight, RN '52', in 321 regular box.................. **£200-250**

321 1966-67 **Mini Cooper 'S'**
  'MONTE CARLO 1966'
- Red body, White roof with RN '2' and 'TIMO MAKINEN' and 'PAUL EASTER' signatures, no spotlight. White sticker on box reads: '1966 MONTE CARLO RALLY AUTOGRAPHED MINI-COOPER 'S' in red lettering **£250-350**
- Same but in 321 pictorial box with 'RALLY' text printed in Red panel..... **£350-450**

321 1978-81 **Porsche 924 Saloon**
- Metallic Green body with hook............ **£40-45**
- Red body **£20-25**
- Met. Light Brown body, Red interior **£60-70**

Rover 2000 'MONTE CARLO'

322 1967-67 **Rover 2000 'MONTE CARLO'**
- Met. Maroon body, White roof, Red int., '136', rally plaques, leaflet.......... **£250-300**
- Same model but with Green interior ...... NGPP
- Model boxed in rare 252 box with '322' labels over the box ends........... **£300-350**
- 1967 'INTERNATIONAL RALLY FINISH' White body, Black bonnet, Red interior, White/Orange label on doors with Black RN '21', cast hubs. 322 box with Red 'ROVER 2000 INTERNATIONAL RALLY FINISH' and box flash. Paint shade differences are known ... **£300-400**

323 1965-66 **Citroën DS19**
  'MONTE CARLO 1965'
- Pale Blue with White roof, Lemon interior, rally plaques and no. '75', suspension **£225-275**

323 1974-78 **Ferrari Daytona 365 GTB/4**
- White/Red/Blue body, RN '81' **£10-15**

Marcos Volvo 1800 GT

324 1966-69 **Marcos Volvo 1800 GT**
- White, Green bonnet stripes, Red interior **£80-100**
- Blue body, White bonnet stripes, Blue interior....................................... **£100-125**
  NB Boxed models should include an unused decal sheet with RNs '4' and '8'.

324 1973-75 **Ferrari Daytona Le Mans**
• Yellow, RN '33', 'A. BAMFORD' **£25-35**
325 1965-69 **Ford Mustang Competition**
• White body, double Red stripe on bonnet, roof and boot. Blue interior, spun hubs or 'wire' wheels or cast 'alloy' wheels **£80-120**
• White body, double Red stripe on bonnet, roof and boot plus Red side stripe, cast 'alloy' wheels.................... **£200-300**
NB An unused sheet of four racing numbers should be enclosed with this model.
325 1981- **Chevrolet Caprice**
• Met. Light Green or Dark Green............ **£20-25**
• Metallic Silver over Dark Blue (US export).................................... **£70-80**

MGB GT

327 1967-69 **MGB GT**
• Dark Red body, Blue or Light Blue interior, spoked wheels, Black suitcase, leaflet **£125-150**
327 1980-81 **Chevrolet Caprice Taxi**
• Yellow, 'THINK TWA' **£15-20**
328 1966-67 **Hillman Imp**
'MONTE CARLO 1966'
• Metallic Dark Blue/White, 'FRW 306 C', rally plaques and no. '107', spun hubs **£175-200**
NB If 'HILLMAN IMP 328' Yellow/Red advertising card is with model, expect price to be 20% higher.
329 1973-76 **Ford Mustang Rally Car** (391 special)
• Metallic Green, White roof, RN '69' **£25-30**
329 1980-82 **Opel Senator**
• Dark Blue or Bronze, opening doors **£15-18**
• Silver body... **£25-30**

Porsche Carrera 6

330 1967-69 **Porsche Carrera 6**
• White body, Red bonnet and doors, RN '60', cast hubs, Blue engine cover.... **£60-80**
• Some with RN '1' **£80-100**
• White body, Dark Blue bonnet and doors, RN '60', cast hubs, Orange engine cover **£110-130**
331 1974-76 **Ford Capri GT Rally**
• White body, Black bonnet and interior, Red over stripe, Red/Black 'TEXACO' logo, RN '5' **£20-25**
332 1967-69 **Lancia Fulvia Zagato**
• Metallic Green, Metallic Blue, or Orange body, cast hubs.................... **£60-70**
• Yellow body, Black bonnet **£100-125**

333 1966 **Austin Mini Cooper 'S'**
'SUN - RAC Rally'
Leaflet in Blue/Yellow box.
• Red body, White (without spotlight), RN '21' and 'SUN RAC INTERNATIONAL RALLY' decals, 225 box with White label: '1966 RAC INTERNATIONAL RALLY' in Blue. (Tony Fall / Mike Wood) **£275-325**
• Same model but with Morris grille ... **£500-800**
334 1968-70 **Mini Cooper 'Magnifique'**
• Metallic Dark Blue or Green, jewelled lights, sunshine roof, Cream int. **£80-120**
334 1981- **Ford Escort 1.3 GL**
• Blue, Green or Yellow body **£12-15**
• Red body with 'AVIS' logo on roof......... **£25-35**
335 1968-70 **Jaguar 4.2 litre 'E' type**
• Met. Dark Red body, Black int., spoked wheels, wing flap bubble pack **£100-125**
• Metallic Blue, Black interior, wing flap bubble pack **£100-125**
• Orange body, Black roof, wing flap bubble pack .... NGPP
336 1967-69 **James Bond Toyota 2000GI**
See 'Novelty, Film and TV-related' section.
337 1967-69 **Chevrolet Stock Car 'STINGRAY'**
• Yellow body, Red interior, RN '13'........ **£45-60**
338 1968-71 **Chevrolet SS 350 Camaro**
• Metallic Lime Green/Black (Red interior), Gold/Black or Bronze/Black, 'Golden Jacks' **£45-60**
338 1980-83 **Rover 3500**
• Metallic Blue, Red/Black or Bronze/Brown ..**£20-35**
339 1967-71 **Mini Cooper 'S'**
'MONTE CARLO 1967'
(i) Red body, White roof, RN '177', 2 spare wheels on roof-rack, Austin grille, cast hubs, in 227 box with White flash label with: '1967 MONTE-CARLO WINNER B.M.C. MINI-COOPER 'S'' in Red lettering, Red '339' flash on box end **£250-350**
(ii) As (i) but shaped spun hubs, slight Silver detail **£250-350**
(iii) As (i) but with Morris grille **£250-350**
(iv) As (i) but in 339 picture box with 'winners' text in Red lettering on box front. Special leaflet **£125-150**
(v) As (i) but in 339 box with the 'winners' text in Red panel **£125-150**
(vi) as (i) but in blue and yellow window box
340 1967-69 **Sunbeam Imp**
'MONTE CARLO 1967'
(i) Metallic Blue, RN '77', spun or cast hubs, flashed 328 box with '1967 MONTE CARLO SUNBEAM IMP WINNER PRODUCTION CARS UP TO 1000cc' text in Blue capitals plus model no. '340' **£200-300**
(ii) As (i) but in 340 pictorial box with 'winner' text printed in Red on box front plus cast detailed hubs **£200-300**
(iii) As (i) but Metallic Dark Blue body, cast detailed hubs, 'winner' text in Red panel on box front..................... **£250-350**
(iv) As (i) but in plain box with no 'winner' flash **£60-80**
340 1981-84 **Rover 'TRIPLEX'**
• White/Red/Blue, RN '1' **£15-20**

Mini Marcos GT 850

341 1968-70 **Mini Marcos GT 850**
• Metallic Maroon body (Cream seats), 'Golden Jacks' and 'Take-off' wheels.... **£60-70**

341 1981-82 **Chevrolet Caprice**
• Red/White/Blue body, RN '43', 'STP', White tyres.................................... **£10-15**
342 1970-72 **Lamborghini P400 Miura**
• Red body, White interior, Black plastic fighting bull figure, WW. 1st type box: Blue/Yellow with 'Revised specification' label for 'Take-off' wheels..................... **£85-95**
• 2nd type box: Red/Yellow box with 'Revised specification' label **£50-60**
Lime Green, Red int., bull figure **£50-60**
342 1980-82 **'The Professionals' Ford Capri**
See 'Novelty, Film and TV-related' section.
343 1969-73 **Pontiac Firebird**
• Met. Silver/Black, Red seats, Gold/Red 'Take-Off wheels', 'Golden Jacks' **£35-45**
• With Red-hub WhizzWheels **£50-60**
343 1980-81 **Ford Capri 3 litre**
• Yellow or Silver body, Black designs..... **£30-35**
344 1969-73 **Ferrari Dino Sports**
• Yellow with Black doors ('23'), WW **£40-50**
• Red with White doors ('30'), WW **£40-50**
• With Red-hub WhizzWheels **£50-60**

MGC GT 'Competition'

345 1969-69 **MGC GT 'Competition'**
• Yellow body, Black bonnet/tailgate/interior, spoked wheels, Black suitcase. 'MGB GT' on box overprinted 'NEW MGC'. Self-adhesive numbers enclosed **£120-140**
• Orange body, Black interior, spoked wheels. In early Car Transporter Gift Sets 41 and 48 only .... GSP
345 1981-82 **Honda Prelude**
• Metallic Blue body, sunshine roof **£10-15**
• Cream/Green body, sunshine roof **£10-15**
• Metallic Yellow body, sunshine roof..... **£10-15**
346 1982-84 **Citroën 2cv**
• Yellow/Black body **£10-15**
• Burgundy/Black body **£10-15**
• Red/White body **£10-15**
• Grey/Red body...................................... **£10-15**
• German promotional: Yellow, Black roof, 'REISGOLD' **£100-120**
347 1969-74 **Chevrolet Astro Experimental**
• Met. Dark Blue body, Red-hub WW...... **£40-50**
• Metallic Green body, Red-hub WW **£40-50**
• As previous but with plain WW............. **£30-40**
348 1968-69 **Ford Mustang 'Pop Art'**
• Blue body and interior, Red/Orange 'Flower-Power' labels, RN '20'. Not shown in catalogues................... **£100-150**
• Light Blue body without labels............. **£60-70**
348 1980-81 **'Vegas' Ford Thunderbird**
See 'Novelty, Film and TV-related' section.
349 1967-67 **'POP ART' Morris Mini**
Red body, Lemon interior, 4 psychedelic labels, 'MOSTEST' logo, few only made **£2,250-2,750**
• Pre-production model: Blue body, Red int., cast hubs **£1,750-2,250**
370 1982- **Ford Cobra Mustang**
• White/Black/Red/Blue, 'MUSTANG', with or without tailgate stripe **£10-15**
• White, Red int., Blue/Red design **£10-15**
371 1970-73 **Porsche Carrera 6**
• White/Red, RN '60', plated blue engine cover, WWs, (330 update)......... **£30-40**
372 1970-72 **Lancia Fulvia Zagato**
• Orange body, Black bonnet, Black interior, WhizzWeels **£35-45**

373 1981-   **Peugeot 505**
- Red body, Silver or Black lining **£10-15**

374 1970-76   **Jaguar 'E' type 4.2 litre**
- Red or Yellow, WW, (335 update) **£55-65**

374 1973-   **Jaguar 'E' type 5.3 litre**
- Yellow or Metallic Yellow body,
  'New' on box label **£55-65**

375 1970-72   **Toyota 2000 GT**
- Metallic translucent 'candy' Blue body,
  White interior, WW,
  (modified 336), leaflet **£50-60**
- Met. Purple body, White int., WW **£45-55**

376 1970-72   **Chevrolet Corvette Stock Car**
- Silver body, racing number '13',
  'GO-GO-GO', WW, (337 update)........... **£40-50**
- Met. Blue body, Red int., '13', WW........ **£40-50**

377 1970-72   **Marcos 3 litre**
- Yellow body, Black bonnet stripe and
  interior, WW, (324 conversion) **£40-50**
- White body, Grey sunroof, WW............ **£50-60**
- Metallic Blue-Green body, Black
  interior, bonnet decal, WhizzWheels.... **£50-60**

378 1970-72   **MGC GT**
- Deep Orange body, Black bonnet, interior and
  suitcase, WhizzWheels, (345 update) ... **£80-90**
- Red, (in GS 20) .... GSP

378 1982-   **Ferrari 308 GTS**
- Red or Black, pop-up headlights........... **£20-30**

380 1970-74   Alfa Romeo P33
- White, Gold rollbar, Red seats, WW **£25-30**

380 1983-   **'BASF' BMW M1**
- Red/White, RN '80', aerofoil............**£7-10**

381 1970-76   **VW Beach Buggy**
- Met. Red/White, Blue/White,
  Orange/White or Red/White,
  2 Maroon surfboards, WW................... **£15-20**

381 1983-   **'ELF' Renault Turbo**
- Red/White/Blue, RN '5', 'FACOM' **£10-15**
- Blue/White, number '13', 'ELF'............ **£10-15**

382 1970-75   **Porsche Targa 911S**
- Metallic Silver-Blue body, Black roof
  with Gold stripe, Black interior, WW **£30-40**
- Same but with Red interior................... **£35-45**
- Metallic Olive-Green body, Black roof
  with or without Gold stripe, WW **£30-40**

382 1983-   **Lotus Elite 22**
- Metallic Blue body, 'Elite 22' **£10-15**

383 1970-76   **VW 1200 'Flower Power'**
- Red with psychedelic Grenadine and
  Green daisy labels on bonnet / doors... **£40-50**
- Red body, Green base,
  White interior, no flower decals **£25-35**

383 1970-73   **Volkswagen 1200 'ADAC'**
- See 'Emergency Vehicles' section
- Volkswagen 1200 'PTT'
  Yellow/Black body, Red int., Swiss........ **£70-90**

383 1977-78   **Volkswagen 1200 Rally**
- Blue, '5', chequered roof and sides........ **£10-15**

384 1978-   **Volkswagen 1200 Rally**
- Blue body, RN '5', chequered stripes..... **£35-45**
- Same model but with 'CALEDONIAN
  AUTOMINOLOGISTS' logo **£100-125**
- Blue body, Cream interior, WW,
  '40th Anniversary 1938 - 1978' **£120-165**

384 1970-73   **Adams Brothers Probe**
- Red body, Silver base, WhizzWheels **£30-40**
- Metallic Gold body, WhizzWheels......... **£30-40**
- Green body, White interior................... **£30-40**

384 1983-84   **Renault 11 GTL**
- Dark Cream body, (export issue) **£25-30**
- Maroon or Metallic Mauve body.......... **£25-30**

385 1970-76   **Porsche 917**
- Metallic Blue or Red body, RN '3',
  cast or WhizzWheels, with leaflet.......... **£30-40**

386 1971-74   **Bertone Barchetta**
- Yellow/Black 'RUNABOUT', WW **£20-25**

387 1970-73   **Corvette Stingray Coupé**
- Metallic Blue body, Black bonnet,
  roof emblem, WhizzWheels.................. **£35-45**
- Metallic Pink body, Black bonnet,
  Black interior.................................... **£35-45**

388 1970-74   **Mercedes-Benz C111**

- Orange/Black body, WhizzWheels **£20-25**

389 1971-74   **Reliant Bond 'BUG' 700 ES**
- Orange body, 'BUG' labels,
  Cream interior, WW........................... **£35-45**
- Lime Green body, WhizzWheels........... **£65-75**

391 1972-72   **James Bond Ford Mustang**
- See 'Novelty, Film and TV-related' section.

392 1973-76   **Bertone Shake Buggy**
- Pink and Green body, detailed engine,
  flag, WhizzWheels **£25-30**
- Yellow body, Black or Green interior **£25-30**

393 1972-79   **Mercedes-Benz 350 SL**
- White body, Pale Blue interior,
  chrome spoked wheels **£25-30**
- Metallic Blue or Dark Blue body,
  chrome disc wheels............................ **£25-30**
- Metallic Green body, Brown interior..... **£65-75**

394 1972-77   **Datsun 240 Z 'Safari Rally'**
- 'East African Safari Rally' finish:
  Red body, RN '11', 'CASTROL' and
  'JAPAN' logos **£30-35**

395 1972-73   **Fire Bug**
- Orange body, Whizzwheels, Red/Black
  or Pink/Black stripe, Yellow ladder
  (381 Beach Buggy)............................. **£20-25**

396 1973-76   **Datsun 240 Z 'US Rally'**
- 'US Rally' finish:
  Red/White body, RN '46', 'JOHN
  MORTON' and 'DATSUN' logos............ **£30-40**

397 1974-76   **Porsche-Audi 917-10**
- White/Red body, 'L&M', RN '6',
  'CORGI', driver **£25-30**

400 1974-75   **Volkswagen 1300**
  'CORGI MOTOR SCHOOL'
- Met. Red, roof steering wheel, cones .. **£80-100**
- Metallic Blue body.............................. **£40-50**
- Metallic Blue body,
  'CORGI FAHR SCHULE', (German)... **£100-120**

401 1975-77   **Volkswagen 1300**
- As C400 but with 24 'bollards' and
  diorama for driving practice................. **£45-55**

Land Rover '109 WB'

406 1957-62   **Land Rover '109 WB'**
- Yellow body, Black roof,
  smooth hubs, thin tyres **£160-200**
- Met. Dark Blue body, Cream roof,
  smooth or shaped hubs,
  thin or thick tyres.............................. **£80-120**
- Green body with Tan tinplate cover,
  smooth hubs, thin or thick tyres **£60-70**
- 'ETENDARD' variant:
  As previous issue but with 'ETENDARD'
  decals, plus Red/White/Green roundels
  on front wings .... NGPP

406s 1963   Land Rover '109 WB'
- Yellow body, Red seats,
  shaped hubs, suspension.................. **£250-300**

411 1976-79   **Mercedes Benz 240 D**
- Orange/Black or Cream,
  'TAXI' on roof.................................... **£10-15**
- German issue: Black body, Red
  'TAXI' roof sign, 'TAXI' on doors **£35-45**

415 1976-78   **Mazda Camper**
- Red body with drop-down tailboard,
  White caravan.................................... **£25-30**

418 1960-65   **Austin FX4 'TAXI'**
- Black, flat or shaped hubs, no driver **£50-60**
- Black, flat or shaped hubs,
  younger' driver figure.......................... **£40-50**
- Black body, flat or shaped hubs,

  'older' driver figure................................. **£35-45**
- Maroon body, Lemon interior, Grey
  base, Orange/Yellow window box....... **£80-110**

419 1978-79   **AMC Jeep CJ-5**
- Metallic Green body with White plastic
  top, or Metallic Dark Green body.......... **£25-35**

Austin FX4 'TAXI'

420 1962-66   **Ford Thames 'Airborne' Caravan**
- Two-tone Green, Brown interior....... **£100-140**
- Blue/Cream, Red interior **£175-200**
- Blue/Green, Brown interior.............. **£100-140**
- Two-tone Lilac, Beige interior.......... **£100-140**

421 1977-80   **Land Rover Safari**
- Orange body, Black roof rack with
  ladder, spare wheel............................ **£20-25**
- Red body, White roof rack with ladder,
  'FOREST FIRE WARDEN' logo **£20-25**
- Land Rover Workman's Bus
  Yellow/Red body, no rack or ladder .... NGPP

424 1961-65   **Ford Zephyr Estate**
- Pale Blue body, Dark Blue bonnet and
  side flash, Lemon interior, luggage,
  flat or shaped spun hubs **£80-100**

425 1978-   **London Taxi** (FX4)
- Black body, 'TAXI', WW **£10-15**
- Maroon body, Red interior, WW **£80-100**

430 1962-64   **Ford Bermuda 'TAXI'**
  (Ford Thunderbird)
- White body, Yellow / Red canopy **£100-130**
- White body,
  Lime Green / Red canopy **£100-130**
- White body, Blue and Red canopy.... **£100-130**
- Metallic Blue body, Red canopy........ **£200-300**

436 1963-65   **Citroën ID19 'SAFARI'**
- Yellow body, driver and passenger,
  detailed interior, roof luggage,
  'Wild Life Reservation' logo.............. **£100-125**

Land Rover 109 WB

438 1963-77   **Land Rover 109 WB**
  Model has plastic canopy.
  Earlier issues have metal towhooks
  (plastic later), suspension.
- Dark Green body Grey or Tan/Cream canopy,
  Lemon or red interior, shaped hubs **£100-125**
- Dark Green body Cream canopy,
  Lemon interior, spun hubs **£175-200**
- Dk. Brown body, Lt. Brown canopy,
  Red interior, shaped hubs **£100-125**
- Metallic Green body, Olive-Green
  canopy, Yellow interior, shaped hubs ... **£60-80**
- Metallic Green body, Olive-Green
  canopy, Chrome hubs......................... **£60-80**
- Metallic Green body, Olive-Green
  canopy, WhizzWheels **£60-70**
- Red body, Brown tilt, Red interior,
  shaped hubs...................................... **£60-70**
- 'LEPRA' variant:
  Metallic Green body, Cream or Olive
  Green canopy with 'LEPRA' logo,
  Yellow interior, shaped hubs, Silver
  steering wheel................................. **£500-750**

- Red body, Blue canopy, (in Gift Set 19) ..... GSP
- Promotional: with '10 MILLIONTH CORGI LAND ROVER' label .... NGPP

440 1966-69 **Ford Consul Cortina Super Estate**
- Metallic Dark Blue with Brown side panels, Cream interior, plastic golfer, caddie and trolley **£200-250**

440 1979- **Mazda Custom Pick-Up**
- Orange/Yellow/Red, US flag **£20-30**
- Metallic Blue and Silver **£20-30**

441 1979-83 **'GOLDEN EAGLE' Jeep**
- Brown/Tan or Gold/White, spare wheel on some **£15-20**

445 1963-66 **Plymouth Suburban**
Sports Station Wagon
- Pale Blue or Eggshell Blue body, Red roof, Lemon interior, Silver stripe, spun hubs **£90-130**
- Beige body, Tan roof **£55-65**

447 1983- **'RENEGADE' 4x4 Jeep**
- Yellow, RN '5' (As 448 but without hood). Gift Set 36 model .... GSP

448 1983- **'RENEGADE' 4x4 Jeep**
- Yellow body, Red hood, RN '5' **£8-10**

450 1983- **Peugeot Taxi** (French issue)
- Beige with Blue label, '739:33:33' **£30-35**

451 NDF **Ford Sierra Taxi**
- Cream body .... NGPP

457 1981-83 **Talbot Matra Rancho**
- Red/Black or Green/Black, tilt seats **£10-15**

457 1984- **Talbot Matra Rancho**
- Orange/Black or White/Blue body, Brown seats **£20-25**

475 1964-65 **'Olympic Winter Sport'**
- White/Yellow Citroën Safari, '1964',

roof-rack, skier, skis.
Diorama 'By Special Request' box **£90-110**

'Olympic Winter Sport'

475 1965-68 **'CORGI SKI CLUB'**
- Citroën Safari with Off-White body, Red roof-rack, 4 Yellow skis and 2 poles, bonnet transfer, Brown dashboard/rear seats, Green front seats **£110-130**
- White body, Yellow Roof-rack, 4 Red skis and 2 poles, Green dashboard/rear seats, Brown front seats **£110-130**

480 1965-66 **Chevrolet Impala Taxi**
- Yellow body, Red roof, spun hubs **£180-220**
- Same but detailed cast wheels **£100-125**

Mini Countryman with Surfer

485 1965-69 **Mini Countryman with Surfer**
- Sea-Green body, Lemon interior, 2 surfboards on roof-rack, male figure, special leaflet **£200-250**
- Same but with unpainted grille .... **£200-250** shaped or cast wheel hubs

491 1966-69 **Ford Consul Cortina Estate**
All have Brown/Cream side/rear panels.
- Metallic Red, Metallic Blue .... **£90-110** Metallic Dark Grey **£200-250**
NB No golf equipment issued with this model (see 440).

497 1966-69 **'The Man From UNCLE' Car**
See 'Novelty, Film and TV-related' section.

499 1967-69 **'1968 Winter Olympics'**
- White/Blue Citroën, 'Grenoble Olympiade', Red or Yellow roof rack, Yellow or Red skis/poles, male tobogganist, female skier. Blue/Yellow 'window' box, instruction sheet **£200-250**

507 1969 **Chrysler Bermuda Taxi**
Shown in catalogue but not issued .... NPP

510 1970-73 **Team Manager's Car**
- Red Citroën, 'Tour De France', figures, spare wheels, 'Paramount' **£70-100**

513 1970-72 **Citroën Safari 'Alpine Rescue'**
- White/Red car, Yellow roof-rack, St Bernard, sled, skis, male figure. Blue/Yellow 'window' box **£200-250**

2894 NDF **VW Polo 'Deutsche Bundespost'**
- No details **£40-50**

2895 NDF **VW Polo 'PTT'**
- No details **£40-50**

Corgi Toys 'Cars of the 1950s' Series

C801		**1957 Ford Thunderbird**
	82	White/Tan, Cream/Orange or Cream/Black **£10-20**
C802		**Mercedes 300 SL**
	82	Burgundy or Silver, suspension **£10-20**
	82	Red body, no suspension **£10-20**
C803		**1952 Jaguar XK120 Sports**
	83	Red body/Black hood **£10-20**
C803/1		**1952 Jaguar XK120 Rally**
	83	Cream body, RN '56' **£10-20**
	83	White body, rally number '56' .. **£10-20**
C804		**Jaguar 'Coupé des Alpes'**
	83	Cream/Grey, RN '56' or '414', some have rear wheel 'spats' **£10-20**
C805		**1956 Mercedes 300SC**
	83	Black body, Tan hood **£10-20**
	84	Maroon body **£10-20**
	86	Beige body and hood **£10-20**
	87	Grey, Black hood, (export) **£10-20**
C806		**1956 Mercedes 300SL**
	83	Black body, Grey/Black hood ... **£10-20**

	86	Black/Green body, Beige seats . **£10-20**
	86	Red, (Cream int.), (export) **£10-20**
	86	Blue body **£10-20**
C810		**1957 Ford Thunderbird**
	83	White body **£10-20**
	84	Pink body **£10-20**
	87	Red body **£10-20**
	?	Cream body, Orange roof **£10-20**
	?	Black/White, Red/White int. **£10-20**
C811		**1954 Mercedes SL**
	84	Silver body **£10-20**
	86	Red body **£10-20**
	87	Grey body, export model **£10-20**
C812		**1953 MG TF**
	85	Green/Tan seats **£10-20**
C813		**1955 MG TF**
	85	Red/Black **£10-20**
	87	Cream/Red, export model **£10-20**
C814		**1952 Rolls-Royce Silver Dawn**
	85	Red/Black **£10-20**
	86	White/Beige **£10-20**

	86	Silver/Black, export model **£10-20**
C815		**1954 Bentley 'R' type**
	85	Black or Cream body **£10-20**
	86	Dark Blue and Light Blue body **£10-20**
	86	Cream/Brown, export model **£10-20**
	?	White body, Black roof **£10-20**
C816		**1956 Jaguar XK120**
	85	Red body, Black tonneau, '56' .. **£10-20**
	?	Red body, Cream hardtop **£10-20**
C819		**1949 Jaguar XK120**
	85	White body, Black hood, '7' **£10-20**
C825		**1957 Chevrolet Bel Air**
	85	Red body, White roof and flash **£10-20**
	87	Black/White, export model **£10-20**
C869		**MG TF Racing Car**
	86	Royal Blue body, Beige seats, RN '113' **£10-20**
C870		**Jaguar XK120**
	86	Green body, Yellow seats, RN '6', export model **£10-20**

'Corgi Classics' Cars (original mid-1960s issues)

ORIGINAL ISSUES. A factory fire ended production in 1969 of this original series of 'Classics' cars. Boxes are of two types: one with separate lid with coloured line-drawings printed on it and containing a separate picture of the model; and type two which has the model attached to a sliding-drawer style base in an outer box with half-flaps (similar printing to 1st type). Early issues have reference numbers '901' onwards which were changed to '9001' etc just before release.

9001 1964-69 **1927 3-litre Bentley**
British Racing Green, RN '3', detachable hood, driver **£30-50**

9002 1964-68 **1927 3-litre Bentley**
Red body, civilian driver, no RN,

detachable hood **£30-50**

9004 1967-69 **'WORLD OF WOOSTER' Bentley**
As previous model but in Green or Red and with Jeeves and Wooster figures **£90-100**

9011 1964-68 **1915 Model 'T' Ford**
Black body, driver, passenger, brass radiator **£30-50**

9012 1965-68 **Model 'T' Ford**
Yellow/Black body, Black or Yellow wheels **£30-50**

9013 1964-69 **1915 Model 'T' Ford**
Blue/Black body, detachable hood, spare wheel, driver cranks **£30-50**

9014 1967 **1915 'LYONS TEA' Van**

Appeared in 1967/68 catalogue but was not issued .... NPP

9021 1964-69 **1910 38 hp Daimler**
Red body, driver and 3 passengers, folded hood **£30-50**

9022 1966 **1910 38 hp Daimler**
Appeared in the 1966 catalogue but not issued .... NPP

9031 1965-68 **1910 Renault 12/16**
Lavender/Black body with carriage lamps **£30-50**

9032 1965-69 **1910 Renault 12/16**
Same but in Primrose Yellow and Black body **£30-50**

9041 1966-70 **1912 Rolls-Royce Silver Ghost**

Silver and Black body, carriage lamps, spoked wheels............ **£30-50**
Maroon body, Silver roof and bonnet **£75-85**

RE-INTRODUCED ISSUES. Four of the 'Classics' were **re-introduced** in 1985 when original tools were discovered. They have new numbers, 'SPECIAL EDITION' on their baseplates and are packed in Grey/Red boxes which do not contain a picture of the model. 13,500 of each colour were made.

C860 (9041) 1912 Rolls-Royce Silver Ghost
Silver, Black or Ruby Red body **£20-25**
C861 (9002) 1927 3-litre Bentley open top

British Racing Green, Black or Ruby Red body................................ **£20-25**
C862 (9031) 1910 Renault 12/16
Yellow, Pale Blue, Cream or Brown body **£20-25**
C863 (9012) 1915 Model 'T' Ford
Black, Red or Blue body **£20-25**

Corgi Toys Duo Packs

These packs combine standard models with (mainly) similar 'Junior' models. Launched early in 1982 in France with the name 'Les Plus de Corgi', the packs later became available in the UK in Woolworths as 'Little and Large; the Little One Free'.

See also 'Novelty, Film and TV-related' section for additional details.

No.53 **Triple Pack (1982), 'Stunt Bikes':**
171 Street Bike, 172 Police Bike,
173 Café Racer .... NGPP

'Les Plus de Corgi' Duo Pack range:
1352 Renault 5 (307) Metro (C275) **£15-25**
1353 Austin Metro **£15-25**
1354 Texaco Lotus (C154) Junior 53 .... **£15-25**
1355 Talbot Matra Rancho (457) **£15-25**
1356 Fiat XI/9 (306) **£15-25**
1357 Golden Eagle Jeep (C441) **£15-25**

1358 Citroën 2cv **£15-25**
1359 Ford Escort (334), Junior 105 .... **£15-25**

F.W. Woolworth's 'Little & Large'
Promotional Duo Pack selection:
1352 Renault 5 (307) Metro (C275) **£15-25**
1353 Austin Metro **£15-25**
1355 Talbot Matra Rancho (457) **£15-25**
1356 Fiat XI/9 (306) **£15-25**
1359 Ford Escort (334), Junior 105 .... **£15-25**
1363 Buck Rogers (607) **£50-60**
1364 Space Shuttle 'NASA' (648) **£20-30**
1365 469 Routemaster Bus, E71 Taxi............. **£20-30**
1371 Volkswagen Turbo (309) **£15-25**

Other Duo Packs (most available in UK).

1364 Space Shuttle 'NASA' (648) **£20-30**
1365 469 Routemaster Bus, E71 Taxi............. **£20-30**
1372 Jaguar XJS (319) **£15-25**

1373 Ford Capri (312) Junior 61 .... **£15-25**
1378 Porsche 924, Yellow............................... **£15-25**
1380 Mercedes 240D, Metallic Grey **£15-25**
1381 Ferrari 308GTS, Red **£15-25**
1382 Ford Mustang (320) **£15-25**
1383 Mack Fire Pumper **£15-25**
1384 Ford Thunderbird, Cream/Orange **£15-25**
Ford Thunderbird, Cream/Black **£15-25**
1385 Austin Metro 'DATAPOST'..................... **£15-25**
1389 Ford Sierra (299) Junior 129.................. **£15-25**
1390 Porsche 924, Black................................. **£15-25**
1393 447 Jeep and E182 Jeep **£15-25**
1394 448 Jeep and E183 Jeep **£15-25**
1395 495 Mazda, E184 Range Rover **£15-25**
1396 Space Shuttle **£15-25**
1397 BMW M1 'BASF' (380)........................... **£15-25**
1401 Lotus Elite and E10 TR7......................... **£15-25**
1402 1133 Tipper plus E85 Skip Truck **£15-25**
1403 Mercedes Tanker, E185 Van **£15-25**
1405 Jaguar **£15-25**

Corgi Toys Commercial Vehicles, 1959–1983 *See also 'Novelty, Film and TV-related' section.*

Model and details	MPR
100 1957-65 **Dropside Trailer**	
• Cream/Red or Yellow body, Wire drawbar or fixed towing 'eye', Blue box	**£50-60**
• Yellow & Blue box	**£50-60**
101 1958-63 **Platform Trailer**	
• Grey/Yellow or Silver/Blue or Silver/Lemon body	**£60-70**

'PENNYBURN' Trailer

Model and details	MPR
109 1968-69 **'PENNYBURN' Trailer**	
• Blue body, Yellow chassis, Tools include: Shovel, Pick-Axe & Brush, Plastic towing 'eye', leaflet Yellow & Blue box	**£40-50**
403 1956-60 **Bedford 12 cwt Van 'DAILY EXPRESS'**	
• Dark Blue. Blue box with leaflet	**£150-175**
• Same model but Deep Blue body	**£150-175**
403M 1956-60 **Bedford 12 cwt Van 'KLG PLUGS'** (with flywheel motor)	
• Bright Red body, leaflet in box	**£150-175**
403 1974-79 **Thwaites Skip Dumper**	
• Yellow/Green tipping body, driver, WhizzWheels	**£30-40**
404 1956-62 **Bedford Dormobile**	
Smooth or ribbed roof, smooth or shaped hubs. Early issues have divided windscreen.	
• Cream (Blue roof on some)	**£120-140**
• Turquoise	**£120-140**
• Blue	**£120-140**
• Red or Metallic Red	**£120-140**
• Yellow body, Pale Blue roof	**£300-350**

Model and details	MPR
• Yellow lower half, Blue upper half	**£300-350**
• All-Yellow body, with suspension	**£100-150**
404M 1956-60 **Bedford Dormobile** (with flywheel motor) Blue box also contains leaflet.	
• Red or Metallic Red	**£130-160**
• Turquoise body	**£130-160**
• Blue body	**£130-160**
405 **Bedford Van 'AFS'** See 'Emergency Vehicles' section.	
405 1981 **Ford Transit Milk Float 'DAIRY CREST'**	
• 'MILK MARKETING BOARD' on each side and 'MILK' on rear	**£20-30**
405 1982 **Ford Transit Milk Float**	
• Blue/White, 'LOTTA BOTTLE'	**£10-15**
406 1971-75 **Mercedes-Benz Unimog**	
• Yellow/Green body, Blue interior	**£25-35**
• Yellow/Red body with Blue interior	**£25-35**
• Blue/Red body with Blue interior	**£25-35**
407 1957-62 **Smiths Karrier Bantam**	
• 'HOME SERVICES HYGIENIC MOBILE SHOP', Pale Blue body, Red logo, smooth hubs	**£100-125**
409 1959-65 **Forward Control Jeep**	
• Light Blue body, Red grille, smooth or shaped hubs	**£60-90**
409 1976-77 **Unimog Dumper**	
• White/Red or Blue/Yellow body, suspension, hook	**£20-30**
409 1981-? **'ALLIS CHALMERS' Forklift**	
• Yellow body, pallets/load/driver	**£15-20**
411 1958-62 **Karrier Bantam Van 'LUCOZADE'**	
• Yellow body, Grey shutter, smooth hubs, Blue box	**£130-160**
• Shaped hubs, Blue/Yellow box	**£120-140**
413 1960-64 **Smiths Karrier Bantam Mobile Butchers**	
• White/Blue van, spun hubs, 'FAMILY BUTCHERS', meaty decals. Blue box with leaflet	**£125-150**
• Same model but with suspension	**£125-150**
413 1976-78 **Mazda Motorway Maintenance**	

Model and details	MPR
• Yellow/Black body, figure, road signs, bollards, decal sheet enclosed, (modified 478/493)	**£25-35**
417 1960-62 **Land Rover 'BREAKDOWN SERVICE'**	
• Red body, Yellow tinplate canopy, spun hubs	**£90-110**

Land Rover 'BREAKDOWN SERVICE'

Model and details	MPR
417s 1963-65 **Land Rover 'BREAKDOWN SERVICE'** (with suspension)	
• Red body, Yellow tinplate canopy, Lemon interior, shaped hubs	**£160-190**
421 1960-63 **Bedford 12 cwt Van 'EVENING STANDARD'**	
• Black body, Silver ridged roof, smooth hubs, undivided windscreen	**£150-175**
• Black lower body, Silver upper and roof	**£110-130**
• Medium Blue body, 'AVRO BODE' logo	**£250-300**
422 1960-62 **Bedford 12 cwt Van 'CORGI TOYS'**	
• Yellow body, Blue roof, smooth or shaped hubs	**£300-400**
• reversed colours: Blue body, Yellow roof, smooth hubs	**£600-800**
• variation: Blue lower half with Yellow upper body and roof	**£600-800**
424 1977-79 **Security Van**	
• Black/Yellow/White, 'SECURITY'	**£10-15**

426 1978-81 **Chevrolet Booking Office Van 'PINDER'**
- Yellow/Red/Blue body, 'PINDER JEAN RICHARD', WW, two loudspeakers **£35-45**

NB The 'clown's face' poster may be at the front or the rear on the n/s of the model.

428 1963-66 **Karrier Ice-Cream Van 'MR SOFTEE'**
- Blue/White body, detailed chassis, salesman swivels **£200-300**

431 1964-66 **Volkswagen Pick-Up**
- Yellow body, Red or Olive-Green canopy, Red 'VW' emblem **£100-150**
- Met. Gold body, Red 'VW' emblem, Red canopy and int., spun hubs.....**£250-350**

431, 432, 433   Chevrolet Vans
('VANATIC', 'VANTASTIC' and 'VANISHING POINT').
See 'Novelty' section.

433 1962-64 **Volkswagen Delivery Van**
- Red/White body, Red or Yellow int..**£70-100**
- Dutch promotional issue: 'VROOM & DREESMANN', Grey body, spun hubs **£200-300**

434 1962 **Volkswagen Kombi**
- Metallic Pale Grey over Green body, Red interior, spun hubs......................**£65-80**
- 1963-66 Two-tone Green, Red or Yellow interior **£65-80**

435 1962-63 **Karrier Bantam Van**
- Blue/White/Yellow, 'DRIVE SAFELY ON MILK' **£100-120**

437 1979-80 **Chevrolet Van 'COCA-COLA'**
- Red body, White logo, tinted roof windows, crates **£20-25**

440 1979-80 **Mazda Custom Pick-up**
- Yellow body, Red roof **£15-20**

441 1963-67 **Volkswagen Van 'CHOCOLATE TOBLERONE'**
- Blue body, Lemon interior, 'Trans-o-lite' headlamps **£80-100**

443 1963-66 **Plymouth Suburban US Mail**
- Blue/White body, red interior 'ADDRESS YOUR MAIL CAREFULLY' **£100-125**

'Walls Ice Cream' Van

447 1965-66 **'WALLS ICE CREAM' Van**
- Blue/Cream Ford Thames van, salesman, boy, spare transfers. Blue/Yellow card box, inner base, correct folded leaflet, unapplied decal sheet....................**£350-500**

Austin Mini Van

450 1964-67 **Austin Mini Van**
- Green body with unpainted grille, Red interior **£130-160**
- Green body, painted grille, Red interior. **£130-160**
- Promotional: Metallic Green body, Grey base, Red interior, White 'FDR1.2009/17' logo. In original 450 box with club slip. Dutch promotional?........**£300-400**

452 1956-63 **Commer Dropside Lorry**
- Red and Cream body, (raised ridge on some cab roofs), smooth or shaped hubs **£80-100**
- Blue body, Cream back....................**£80-100**

453 1956-60 **Commer Refrigerated Van 'WALLS ICE CREAM'**
- Dark Blue cab, Cream back, smooth roof, flat spun hubs............**£250-300**
- Light Blue cab, Cream back, cast roof, flat spun hubs.................**£125-150**

454 1957-63 **Commer Platform Lorry**
- Met. Blue cab and chassis, Silver-Grey platform, flat hubs, leaflet..............**£120-170**
- Yellow cab / chassis, Silver platform **£120-170**

455 1957-60 **Karrier Bantam 2-ton**
- Blue, Red or Grey body, Red platform, smooth hubs...........**£120-140**

456 1960-63 **ERF 44G Dropside Lorry**
- Yellow cab and chassis, Metallic Blue back, smooth/shaped hubs .....**£70-100** shaped hubs in yellow and blue box

457 1957-65 **ERF 44G Platform Lorry**
- Two-tone Blue or Yellow/Blue body, smooth hubs.................................**£140-160**

458 1958-66 **E.R.F. Earth Dumper**
- Red / Yellow, 'ERF' cast-in, smooth or shaped hubs **£80-100**

459 1958-60 **ERF 44G Van 'MOORHOUSES LEMON CHEESE'**
- Yellow/Red **£150-200**

459 1973-78 **Raygu Rascal Roller**
- Yellow/Green body, 'Road Roller'......**£20-30**

460 1959-61 **E.R.F. Neville Cement Tipper 'TUNNEL CEMENT'**
- Lemon cab/chassis, Silver base, metal filler caps **£40-50**
- As previous version, but with Red plastic filler caps **£70-80**

462 1970-? **Commer Van 'CO-OP'**
- White/Blue body, Blue/Yellow box..**£80-100**

462 1971-? **Commer Van 'HAMMONDS'**
- Green/Blue/White promotional model, cast hubs. In un-numbered Corgi box with '462' handwritten **£200-300**

465 1963-66 **Commer Pick-Up Truck**
- Red/Yellow, Yellow/Red or Green/Grey, 'Trans-O-Lites' **£90-120**

466 19?? **Commer Milk Float**
- White cab, chassis and load; Blue rear roof and sides **£80-100**
- Promotional issue: As previous model but with 'CO-OP' labels. Plain card box **£100-140**

470 1965-72 **Forward Control Jeep**
- Blue/Grey, Mustard Yellow, Pale Green or Light Blue body, detachable canopy **£35-40**

471 1965-66 **Karrier Bantam Snack Bar**
- Blue/White, 'JOE'S DINER', figure, opening hatch **£140-170**
- Belgian issue: Blue/White, 'PATATES FRITES'......**£280-320**

474 1965-68 **Musical 'WALLS ICE CREAM' Van**
- Ford Thames van in Blue/Cream, musical movement (must function for top price), diorama but no figures. Blue/Yellow card box with correct folded leaflet, fresh decal sheet......**£350-500**

Land Rover Breakdown

477 1966-67 **Land Rover Breakdown**
- Red body, Yellow canopy with spotlight and 'BREAKDOWN SERVICE' logo, rubber (or later plastic) 'tyre' crank, shaped or cast hubs...........................**£45-55**
- Same, but with large or small Silver crank, WW **£40-50**

478 1965-68 **Jeep Tower Wagon** (Forward Control)
- Green, Yellow and Silver, Red interior, figure...............................**£40-50**
- Green, Yellow and Silver, Cream interior, figure.....................**£250-340**

Commer Mobile Camera Van

479 1968-71 **Commer Mobile Camera Van**
- Blue/White body, shaped hubs, 'SAMUELSON FILM COMPANY LTD', camera and operator, equipment case **£100-125**
- Same model but with cast hubs **£100-125**

483 1968-72 **Dodge Tipper Truck**
- White cab, Blue tipper, 'KEW FARGO', cast hubs **£60-70**

484 1967-69 **Dodge Livestock Transporter**
See 'Agricultural Models' section

486 1967-69 **'KENNEL CLUB' Truck**
- White/Orange Chevrolet Impala with 'Vari-View' dachshund picture, four dogs, cast hubs...........................**£80-100**

493 1975-78 **Mazda B 1600 Pick-Up**
- Blue/White or Silver/Blue body.........**£20-25**

494 1967-72 **Bedford Tipper**
- Red cab/chassis, Yellow tipper...........**£60-70**
- Red cab/chassis, Silver tipper **£90-110**
- Yellow cab/chassis, Blue tipper......**£110-130**
- Blue cab/chassis, Yellow tipper......**£130-150**
- Late issue. Red cab and chassis. Yellow tipper in blue and yellow window box

508 **Commer Minibus 'Holiday Camp Special'**
- White/Orange, Green luggage, spun hubs, leaflet **£100-125**

701 1974-80 **Inter-City Mini-Bus**
- Orange body, Yellow labels, WW **£10-15**

MAJOR PACKS

1100 1958-63 **Bedford 'S' Carrimore** (Low-loader)
- Yellow cab, Metallic Blue low-loader trailer, smooth or shaped hubs **£140-240**

- Red cab, Metallic Blue low-loader
  trailer, winch **£140-170**
1100 1971-73 **Mack Truck
'TRANS-CONTINENTAL'**
- Orange cab, Black/Orange/Silver
  trailer **£40-50**
- Orange/Metallic Lime Green **£70-80**
1101 1957-62 **Bedford 'S' Carrimore
Car Transporter**
- Blue cab, Yellow transporter body,
  'CORGI CAR TRANSPORTER'........**£140-170**
- Red cab, Blue transporter body,
  smooth hubs **£140-170**
- Cerise cab, Blue transporter body,
  smooth hubs **£300-350**
- Yellow cab and transporter body,
  Silver ramps **£300-400**

Bedford 'S' Carrimore Car Transporter

1101 1976-81 **Mobile Crane**
- Yellow/Blue, 'Warner & Swasey' **£25-30**
1102 1958-62 **'EUCLID' TC-12 Bulldozer**
- Yellow body, Pale Grey tracks.
  Box has inner lining **£120-140**
- Same model but with Black tracks.**£120-140**
- Pale Lime-Green body **£120-140**
1102 1974-76 **Crane Freuhauf**
  (Berliet Dumper)
- Yellow cab, Orange dumper body,
  'Road Maker Construction' logo **£30-35**
1103 1960-65 **'EUCLID' Crawler Tractor**
- Yellow or Pale Lime-Green body,
  Pale Grey tracks **£125-150**
- Same model but with Black tracks.**£125-150**
1104 1958-63 **Bedford 'S' Carrimore
Machinery Carrier**
- Red cab, Silver trailer, smooth hubs,
  operable winch **£140-170**
- Same but with Blue cab **£140-170**
1104 1974-77 **Bedford 'TK' type
Horse Transporter**
- Green or Metallic Green,
  'NEWMARKET', 4 horses and boy **£50-60**
1105 1962-66 **Bedford 'TK' type
'Corgi Car Transporter'**
- Red cab, Blue/White trailer,
  collapsible decks **£150-200**
1105 1976-80 **Berliet Racehorse Transporter**
- Brown/White, 'NATIONAL RACING
  STABLES', four horses.........................**£40-50**
1106 1972-77 **Mack Container Truck 'ACL'**
- Yellow/Black/White body,
  two Red containers............................**£40-50**
- Promotional issue
  for the '3M' company........................**£120-140**
1107 1963-66 **'EUCLID' with
Dozer with Driver**
- Yellow body, Black or Grey tracks..**£150-200**
- Red body **£150-200**
- Lime-Green body **£80-100**
1107 1978-79 **Berliet Container Lorry
'UNITED STATES LINES'**
- Blue cab, White chassis,
  two Grey containers **£30-40**
1108 1982 **Ford Truck 'MICHELIN'**
- Blue/White artic. body, 2 containers.**£40-50**
1109 1979 **Ford Truck 'MICHELIN'**
- Blue/Yellow body, 2 containers **£40-50**

1110 1959-64 **Bedford 'S' Tanker
'MOBILGAS'**
- Red/White articulated body,
  detachable cab, Lemon interior **£150-200**
- Same but with shaped spun hubs..**£150-200**
1110 1965-67 **Bedford 'S' Tanker
'SHELL BENZEN'**
- Blue/White articulated tanker,
  Dutch model **£1,800-2,200**
1110 1976-80 **'JCB' Crawler Loader**
- Yellow/White body, Red bucket,
  Black tracks, driver **£30-35**
1110 1976-80 **'JCB' Crawler**
- Yellow and White body, driver **£30-40**
- Light Blue/Orange with
  Light Blue chassis **£30-40**
- Yellow body, Light Blue cab,
  Red bucket **£30-40**
- Red body, Light Blue cab and bucket **£30-40**
- Orange body,
  'BLOCK CONSTRUCTION' **£30-40**
1113 1981-86 **'HYSTER' Handler**
- Yellow or Black/White main body,
  'US Lines', hoist **£100-125**
- 1986-87 Yellow or Black/White
  main body, 'SEALINK', container,
  export model...................................**£100-125**
- 1986-87 White/Dark Blue/Yellow,
  'MICHELIN', container....................**£100-125**
1116 1979-? **Refuse Lorry**
  (Shelvoke and Drewry Revopak)
- Orange/Silver or Red/Silver body......**£20-30**
- 1988 Blue cab, White tipper,
  'BOROUGH COUNCIL' **£5-10**
1117 1980-85 **'FAUN' Street-sweeper**
- Orange and Yellow or All-Yellow,
  with operator **£20-30**
1119 1983 **Mercedes Load Lugger**
- Yellow/Red body, 'CORGI' **£15-20**
1121 1983 **Ford Tipper (Corgimatic)**
- Orange/Beige body, 'CORGI' **£15-20**
1126 1961-65 **Racing Car Transporter
'ECURIE ECOSSE'**
- Metallic Dark Blue body,
  logo in Yellow lettering **£200-250**
- later version:
  logo in Orange lettering **£130-160**
- with logo in White lettering............**£130-160**
- with logo and raised ridges
  in Light Blue...................................**£130-160**
- Metallic Light Blue body with
  logo in Red lettering.......................**£250-360**
1128 1963-76 **'PRIESTMAN' Cub Shovel**
- Red/Yellow body, driver **£100-125**
1129 1962-65 **Bedford 'S' Tanker 'MILK'**
- Blue/White articulated body,
  detachable cab................................**£200-260**
1130 19??-?? **Euclid TC12**
  Twin Crawler Tractor
- Lime Green body, Black tracks.......**£100-125**
1131 1963-66 **Bedford 'TK' Carrimore
Machinery Low Loader**
- Blue cab, Silver trailer, Yellow detachable
  rear axle unit, spun hubs **£120-140**
- Same, but Black detachable
  rear axle unit **£80-100**
1132 1963-65 **Bedford 'TK' Carrimore**
- Yellow cab and ramp, Red low loader
  trailer, spare wheels, no winch **£200-250**
1137 1965-71 **Ford Articulated Truck
'EXPRESS SERVICES'**
- Blue/Silver/Red body, Lemon interior
  mechanic figure. 'H' series tilt-cab **£100-120**
1138 1966-69 **Ford Articulated Transporter
'CORGI CARS'**
- Red body, Silver tilt cab,
  two-tone Blue trailer **£150-200**
1140 1965-67 **Bedford 'TK' Petrol Tanker
'MOBILGAS'**
- Red/Silver/White artic. body, tilting cab,
  box includes inner packing, leaflet **£150-240**

1141 1965-67 **Bedford 'TK' Milk Tanker
'MILK'**
- Blue/White artic. body, tilting cab.**£175-225**
1142 1967-74 **'HOLMES WRECKER' Truck**
- Red White & Black body, Grey or Gold twin
  booms, ladder on tilt-cab, 2 spare wheels
  two mechanics, Blue window box...**£100-125**
- Blue & Yellow window box........**£100-125**
- Striped window style box..........**£100-175**
1144 19??-?? **Berliet Wrecker Truck**
- Red/White/Blue, Gold booms/hooks,
  striped window box...........................**£50-70**
1145 1969-76 **Unimog Goose Dumper**
- Yellow/Red body, '406' **£50-60**
1146 1970-73 **Scammell Carrimore Mk.V**
- Orange/White/Blue Tri-deck Transporter
  articulated transporter with
  three collapsible decks...................**£125-150**
1147 1969-72 **Scammell Truck**
- Yellow/White, 'FERRYMASTERS
  INTERNATIONAL HAULIERS' **£75-125**
1148 1969-72 **Scammell Carrimore Mk.IV**
- Red/White car transporter body
  with Yellow chucks **£90-110**
1150 1971-77 **Mercedes (Unimog 406)
Snowplough**
- Green/Black, 2 Red flags,
  Orange/Silver plough **£30-35**
- Yellow cab and back, Red chassis,
  Silver plough **£30-35**
1151 1970 **'Co-operative Society'**
  See 'Gift Sets'.
1151 19?? **Mack Tanker 'EXXON'**
- Red/White body, striped window box**£60-70**
1152 1971-76 **Mack Tanker 'ESSO'**
- White/Red/Blue, Gloster Saro Tanker**£40-50**
- Same model but 'EXXON' logo **£70-80**
1152 1983- **'BARRATT' Tipper**
- Green/White body, tipper section tips **£5-10**
1153 1973-74 **'PRIESTMAN' Crane**
- Red/Orange body, 'Higrab'................**£45-55**
1153 1983-84 **'WIMPEY' Tipper (Scania)**
- Green/Silver body (later Yellow)..........**£5-10**
1154 1974-76 **Priestman Crane Truck**
- Yellow/Red body, Silver boom, hook.**£45-55**
1154 1979 **Giant Tower Crane
'BLOCK CONSTRUCTION'**
- Orange/Yellow crane, White body **£55-65**
1155 1975-79 **'Skyscraper' Tower Crane**
- Yellow/Red body, Black tracks **£35-40**
1156 1977-79 **Volvo Concrete Mixer**
- Yellow/Red/Orange body, 'RAPIER' ..**£30-35**
- 1980 Orange/White body,
  'BLOCK CONSTRUCTION' **£30-35**
1157 1976-81 **Ford Tanker 'ESSO'**
- White/Red articulated body **£25-35**
1158 1976 **Ford Tanker 'EXXON'**
- White/Black artic. body, US issue **£50-60**
1159 1976-79 **Ford Car Transporter**
- Metallic Blue/White artic. body **£60-70**
- Metallic Green articulated body **£60-70**
1160 1976-78 **Ford Tanker 'GULF'**
- White/Orange articulated body **£30-40**
1161 1976-78 **Ford Tanker 'ARAL'**
- Blue/White/Black, German export **£60-80**
1169 1982 **Ford Tanker 'GUINNESS'**
- Red/Cream/Black articulated body ..**£60-80**
1170 1982 **Ford Car Transporter**
- Red/White/Yellow articulated body ..**£50-60**

Ford Articulated Truck 'EXPRESS SERVICE'

Corgi Emergency Vehicles   Police, Fire, Ambulance and Rescue Vehicles, etc

See also 'Corgi Commercial Vehicles' (for other breakdown recovery vehicles, etc), and the 'Corgi Gift Sets' section.

Model and details	MPR

Riley Pathfinder 'Police' Car

209 1958-61   **Riley Pathfinder 'Police' Car**
• Black and Silver body, bell **£100-150**

213 1959-61   **Jaguar Fire Chief's Car**
• Red body, bell, Grey aerial,
roof sign, smooth spun hubs **£150-200**

213s 1961-62   **Jaguar Fire Chief's Car**
(with suspension)
• As 213 model but shaped hubs **£150-200**
• Deep Cherry Red, Lemon interior,
spun hubs **£500-600**

223 1959-61   **Chevrolet Impala 'State Patrol'**
• Black body, Silver stripe, Lemon interior,
Grey aerial. Box also contains
internal packing **£120-140**

237 1962-66   **Oldsmobile Sheriff's Car**
• Black body, White roof, 'COUNTY
SHERIFF', clear or Blue light.
Box also contains internal packing **£80-90**

260 1979-81   **Buick 'POLICE' Car**
• Metallic Blue/White, 'CITY OF
METROPOLIS', two light bars **£30-40**

284 1982-83   **Mercedes-Benz 240 D**
• Red body, 'NOTRUF 112', flashing
lights, German export model **£20-25**

293 1977-80   **Renault 5 TS**
• Metallic Orange or
Two-tone Blue body, WW **£15-25**
1980-81
• French issue: Two-tone Blue,
roof light, 'S.O.S. MEDICINS' **£25-35**

295 1982-83   **Renault 5 TS Fire Chief**
• Red/White 'SAPEURS POMPIERS',
French export **£15-20**

297 1982-86   **Ford Escort 'Panda' Car**
• Light or Dark Blue, White doors,
Blue warning lights, 'POLICE' **£15-20**

326 1980-81   **Chevrolet Caprice
'Police' Car**
• Black/White body, suspension **£20-30**

332 1980-81   **Opel Doctors Car**
• German issue:
White/Red, 'NOTARTZ' **£30-40**

339 1980   **Rover 3500 'POLICE' Car**
• White and Red body **£20-25**

373 1970-76   **VW 1200 Police Car**
• Green and White body, Red interior,
'POLIZEI', Blue roof light, WW **£70-80**
• White body, Red interior, Silver base,
Blue roof light, 'POLIZEI' **£90-120**
• Black/White/Blue, 'POLITIE' **£90-120**
• White body, Red int., Blue roof light,
Black 'POLICE' on White decal **£40-50**
• Same, but White 'POLICE' lettering
on Blue decal **£40-50**
• White body, Black hatch/bonnet stripes,
Red interior, 2 figures, 'POLICE' **£40-50**

383 1970-73   **VW 1200 'ADAC'**
• Yellow body, Black roof with '1341',
'ADAC STRASSENWACHT' logos **£75-85**

386 1987   **Mercedes 'POLIZEI'**
• Green/White body, two Blue warning
lights, German export model **£30-40**

395 1972-73   **Fire Bug**
• Orange body, Whizzwheels, Red/Black

Model and details	MPR

or Pink/Black stripe, Yellow ladder
(381 Beach Buggy) **£20-30**

402 1972-77   **Ford Cortina GXL Police Car**
• White/Red body, 'POLICE' labels,
(updated 313) **£55-65**
• White/Red body, 'POLIZEI',
German issue **£75-85**

405 1956-60   **Bedford Fire Tender 'A.F.S.'**
• Bright or Dark Green 'Utilicon' body,
divided windscreen, Silver or Black
ladder, smooth or shaped hubs.
Blue box with leaflet **£150-200**

405M 1956-59   **Bedford (Utilicon) Fire Tender**
• Red body, divided windscreen, Silver or
Black ladder, 'FIRE DEPT', smooth or
shaped hubs, friction motor.
Blue box with leaflet **£150-250**

405 1978-80   **Chevrolet Ambulance**
• White/Orange, patient on stretcher
and two attendants **£20-25**

406 1980-81   **Mercedes Bonna
'Ambulance'**
• White body, Red/Black design, opening
doors, stretcher, ambulancemen **£15-20**
• German issue: Cream body,
'KRANKENWAGEN' **£30-40**
• Danish issue: Red/White, 'FALCK' **£30-40**
• Swedish issue:
White/Red/Black body, 'SDL 951' **£30-40**

407 1980   **Mercedes Bonna
'Ambulance'**
• White body, Red/Black design, opening
doors, stretcher, ambulancemen **£15-20**

408 1957-59   **Bedford 'AA' Service Van**
• Yellow/Black, divided windscreen,
smooth hubs, Blue box, leaflet **£100-125**
• 1958-59   Yellow/Black, undivided
windscreen, smooth or shaped hubs,
Blue box, leaflet **£100-125**
• 1959-63   Yellow/Black, undivided
windscreen, shaped hubs,
Blue/Yellow box, no leaflet **£120-140**
• late issue: Yellow/Black, single
windscreen, sloped roof, flat hubs ... **£100-125**

412 1957-60   **Bedford 'AMBULANCE'**
• Cream 'Utilicon' body, divided screen,
smooth hubs. Blue box with leaflet . **£110-150**
• As previous but with
one-piece windscreen **£160-190**
• Factory error: A few examples of
412 were issued with
'HOME SERVICES' front labels .... NGPP

412 1976-79   **Mercedes Police Car**
• White/Black body, 'POLICE' logo,
Blue roof lamp **£30-35**
• Green/White body, 'POLIZEI' logo,
Blue roof lamp, German issue **£35-45**

414 1975-77   **Jaguar XJ12-C**
• White/Blue body, 'COASTGUARD' **£10-15**

R.A.C. Land Rover

416 1959-61   **R.A.C. Land Rover**
• Blue body, 'RADIO RESCUE' on cab
roof sign, metal canopy,
smooth hubs, Blue/Yellow box **£150-175**

Model and details	MPR

• Blue body, no cab roof sign, 'RADIO
RESCUE' on canopy, shaped hubs .. **£200-320**
• Belgian issue:
Yellow body and metal canopy, 'TS'
decals on sides, 'RADIO' on roof .. **£1,000-1,250**

416s 1962-64   **RAC Land Rover**
(with suspension)
• Blue body, Lemon interior, suspension,
'RADIO RESCUE', plastic canopy **£75-110**
• Belgian issue:
Yellow body, Red interior, Grey plastic
canopy, 'TS' decals on doors,
'RADIO' on bonnet **£1,000-1,250**

416 1977-79   **Buick Police Car**
• Blue body or Metallic Blue body,
'POLICE', two policemen
Window style box **£25-30**

Ford Zephyr Motorway Car

419 1960-65   **Ford Zephyr Motorway Car**
• White or Cream, smooth or shaped
hubs, 'POLICE', large or small roof light,
Blue and Yellow box **£100-125**
• Export issues: with 'POLITIE' or
'RIJKS POLITIE' logo (Dutch) **£150-200**

421 1977-79   **Land Rover Station Wagon**
• Red body, White roof-rack,
'FOREST WARDEN' **£20-25**

422 1977-80   **'Riot Police' Wagon**
• Red/White body, water cannon,
White number '6' **£15-20**

423 1960-62   **Bedford 12cwt. Tender**
• Red body, Black ladder, undivided
windscreen, smooth or
shaped hubs, 'FIRE DEPT.' **£110-150**
• Red body, unpainted ladder,
undivided screen, shaped hubs **£125-150**

424 1976-79   **'SECURITY' Van**
• Black/Yellow/White body,
mesh windows, WW **£10-15**

428 1978-80   **Renault 'Police' Car**
• Black/White body, (export isssue) **£55-65**

429 1978-80   **'Police' Jaguar XJ12-C**
• White/Red/Blue body, aerial, lights **£25-35**

430 1978-80   **Porsche 924 'Police'**
• Black/White body, warning light **£15-20**

430 1978-80   **Porsche 924 Police Car**
• German issue:
White/Green 'POLIZEI' **£40-50**
• French issue:
White/Black, 'POLICE' **£40-50**

437 1962-65   **Cadillac Superior Ambulance**
• Cream over Red body, 'AMBULANCE'
on side windows, Amber roof light **£80-90**
• 1965-68   Light Blue over White body,
'AMBULANCE' on sides, Red cross
on bonnet, Red roof light **£100-125**
• Met. Red over Met. Silver body **£100-125**

439 1963-65   **Chevrolet Impala**
• Red body, 'FIRE CHIEF', White stripe,
Lemon interior, aerial, Yellow roof
light, firemen, with White painted
door labels with 'FIRE DEPT' **£140-170**
• White rectangular label on front
doors 'FIRE DEPT' **£140-170**

- with round Red label on front
doors 'FIRE DEPT' **£80-100**

448 1964-69 **Austin 'Police' Mini Van**
- Dark Blue body, Red interior, shaped
or cast hubs, aerial, policeman and
dog, White Police logo, pictorial stand
and internal support packaging.........**£200-250**

461 1972-79 **'Police' Vigilant Range Rover**
- White/Blue, warning lights,
policemen, 8 'POLICE' emergency
signs plus bollards **£25-35**
- White/Red, 'LANGZAAM', policemen,
emergency signs, Dutch model **£50-60**

463 1964-66 **Commer 'AMBULANCE'**
- Cream or White body, Red interior,
Blue tinted windows and roof light . **£120-140**

Commer 'AMBULANCE'

464 1967-68 **Commer 'POLICE' Van**
- Dark Blue body, 'COUNTY POLICE',
window bars, clear roof light, leaflet ... **£100-125**
- Same, but Metallic Light Blue,
with Blue roof light **£100-125**
- Dark Blue, window bars, Red roof
light, 'CITY POLICE', leaflet.............. **£175-200**
Dark Blue, 'open' windows, Blue
roof light, White 'POLICE' cast
into sides, with instructions................**£90-110**
- Deep Green body, 'POLICE', export
model, opaque rear/side windows.. **£400-500**
- German issue:
Metallic Green body, 'POLIZEI' **£150-175**
- French issue:
Metallic Blue body, 'SECOURS'....... **£150-175**
- Dutch issue:
Metallic Blue body, window bars,
'RIJKSPOLITIE' **£350-400**

481 1965-69 **Chevrolet Police Car**
- White/Black body, 'POLICE PATROL',
Red roof lights, two policemen........ **£100-125**

482 1966-69 **Chevrolet Impala**
- Red over White body, Chrome stripe,
bonnet logo, Blue light, Grey aerial,
rectangular 'FIRE CHIEF' label on
front doors, detailed cast or shaped
spun hubs **£75-95**
- With round label on front doors
'FIRE CHIEF' **£75-95**

482 1974-77 **Vigilant Range Rover**
- Red and White body with
'AMBULANCE' logo **£25-30**
- White body with Blue side stripe and
'AMBULANCE' logo, stretcher and
two ambulancemen..............................**£25-30**

483 1979 **Belgian Police Range Rover**
- White body, Red stripes, warning
lights, policemen, emergency signs **£75-85**

484 1978-80 **AMC Pacer 'RESCUE'**
- White/Orange/Black body, '35' **£10-15**
- Same but with 'SECOURS' logo **£40-50**

489 1980 **Volkswagen Polo**
- German issue:
White/Green, 'POLIZEI' **£50-55**
- German issue: 'ADAC' **£50-55**

490 1967-69 **Volkswagen Breakdown**
- Unpainted fittings, Chrome tools,
Red 'VW' emblem, Red/Yellow stripe
label, two spare wheels. Avocado body,
shaped hubs, 'BREAKDOWN SERVICE'
labels, spun or cast hubs **£90-130**
- Same, but in white, spun hubs in early gift
sets (GS37) 'RACING CLUB' labels
- Same, in white with cast hubs........ ....**GSP**

VW 1200 Car

492 1966-70 **VW 1200 Car**
- Green body, White roof, White
'POLIZEI' on bonnet, No '18' logo **£80-95**
- White body with Black 'POLIZEI'
on doors and bonnet, (Germany) ... **£200-250**

492 1966-69 **VW European Police Car**
- Dark Green body, White roof and
wings, Red 'POLIZEI', Blue lamp.
Box should contain 'True Scale
Steering' Red/Yellow cardboard
roof fitting **£90-110**
- Dutch model: All-White body, Light
Brown interior, driver,crest on doors,
'POLITIE', Blue lamp......................... **£175-225**
- Swiss model: All-White body, Light
Brown interior, driver, crest on doors,
'POLITZIE', Blue lamp **£175-225**

506 1968-69 **Sunbeam Imp 'Panda' Car**
- White body, Black bonnet and roof,
Blue roof light..**£80-90**
- White body, Black roof, 'luminous'
door panels, Blue roof light..................**£80-90**
- Light Blue body, White roof, 'luminous'
door panels, Blue roof light.................**£80-90**

509 1970-75 **Porsche 911s Targa
'Police' Car**
- White/Red body, Black roof.................**£55-65**
- White/Red body, 'POLIZEI', siren,
warning lights.....................................**£55-65**
- 'RIJKSPOLITIE' export issue **£110-130**

700 1974-79 **Motorway Ambulance**
- White/Red, 'ACCIDENT' **£10-15**

702 1975-79 **'ACCIDENT' Breakdown Truck**
- Red/Black, single bumper, hook **£10-15**

703 1976-78 **Hi-Speed Fire Engine**
- Red body, Yellow ladder......................**£10-15**

911 1976-80 **Air-Sea Rescue Helicopter**
- Blue/Yellow body,
Black 'flick-spin' rotor, 'N 428' **£15-20**

921 1975-81 **Hughes OH-6A Helicopter**

- White/Red, 'POLICE', 'RESCUE',
warning lights.......................................**£15-20**

921/1 1975-80 **'POLIZEI' Helicopter**
- White/Blue, 'POLIZEI', Black
'flick-spin' rotor, German issue.............**£25-30**

921/2 1975-80 **'POLITIE' Helicopter**
- White/Blue, 'POLITIE',
Black 'flick-spin' rotor, Dutch issue......**£25-30**

921/4 1975-80 **'ADAC' Helicopter**
- Yellow body, 'D-HFFM',
Black 'flick-spin' rotor..........................**£25-30**

921/6 1975-80 **Swiss Red Cross Helicopter**
- Red helicopter body, Black blades,
'flick-spin' rotor....................................**£25-30**

922 1975-78 **Casualty Helicopter**
- Sikorsky Skycrane in Red and White....**£25-30**

923 1975-78 **Casualty Helicopter**
- Army Sikorsky Skycrane with
Olive/Yellow body.................................**£25-30**

924 1977-81 **Air-Sea Rescue Helicopter**
- Orange/Yellow/Black, 'RESCUE' **£25-30**

927 1978-79 **Surf Rescue Helicopter**
- Blue/White body, 'SURF RESCUE' **£25-30**

931 1979-80 **Jet Ranger Helicopter**
- White/Red, 'POLICE RESCUE',
'flick-spin' rotor **£25-30**

1001 1980-82 **HCB Angus Firestreak**
- Red body, Yellow ladder,
2 firemen plus equipment...................**£60-70**

1103 1976-81 **Chubb Pathfinder**
- Red/Silver, 'AIRPORT CRASH
TRUCK', operable pump and siren,
orange logo **£60-70**
- Same model but non-working
siren, Brick-Red body **£50-60**
- Red/Silver, 'NEW YORK AIRPORT' logo .**£80-90**

1118 1981-83 **Chubb Pathfinder**
- Red body, 'AIRPORT FIRE SERVICE',
operable water pump **£60-70**

1126 1977-81 **Dennis Fire Engine
'SIMON SNORKEL'**
- Red/White/Yellow, turntable,
ladder, 6 firemen **£55-65**

1127 1964-74 **Bedford Fire Engine
'SIMON SNORKEL'**
- Red/Yellow/Silver, turntable,
ladder, 6 fireman **£100-125**

1140 1982 **Ford Transit Wrecker**
- White/Red, '24 Hour Service',
operable winch, hook, ...**£15-20**
- As previous model but logo
changed to 'RELAY' **£15-20**
- 1982 Export model: Red/Yellow,
'ABSCHLEPPDEENST'............................**£15-20**

1143 1968-80 **'AMERICAN LA FRANCE'**
- Articulated Fire Engine in
Red/White/Yellow, shaped spun or
detailed cast wheels, 4-part extending
ladder, 5 firemen, plain early box **£90-120**
- As previous model but in later
striped window box **£80-100**

1144 1975-78 **Berliet Wrecker Recovery**
- Red/White/Gold body,
with Gold or Grey hoists **£60-70**

2029 1980-83 **Mack Fire Engine**
- Red body, warning light, detachable
ladder, 'HAMMOND FIRE DEPT'........**£15-25**

Agricultural Models

Agricultural models also appear in the Gift Sets section.

Model and details	MPR
50 1959-66 **'Massey-Ferguson 65' Tractor**	

- Bright Red bonnet, seat and metal hubs,
Pale Grey chassis,
Black plastic steering wheel **£160-200**
- Bright Red bonnet, bare metal seat,
Red metal hubs,
Grey plastic steering wheel............... **£100-125**
- Dark Red bonnet, Silver metal
steering wheel and seat,
Fawn engine, Red plastic hubs **£140-160**

'Massey-Ferguson 65' Tractor with Tipper Trailer

Model and details	MPR

NB A variation with Copper metal
seat is known to exist ....**NGPP**

50 1974-77 **'Massey-Ferguson 50B' Tractor**
- Yellow/Black/Red body, windows **£60-80**

51 1959-64 **'Massey-Ferguson' Tipper Trailer**
- Red chassis, Yellow or Grey body,
Red metal or plastic wheels..................**£40-45**

53 1960-66 **'Massey-Ferguson 65'
Tractor with Shovel**
- Bright Red bonnet without decals, Grey

plastic steering wheel, Silver metal
seat/shovel, fawn engine, fawn rams
with Black decals, Red metal hubs.... **£120-150**
- As previous model, but Bright
Red bonnet has thin Black outline
decals, Red plastic hubs..................... **£100-125**
- Same but Bright Red bonnet has
thin Black outline decals, bare metal
rams / shovel, Red plastic hubs......... **£100-125**
- Red bonnet with White/Black decals,
Silver metal steering wheel, Fawn engine
and rams, Fawn bucket with Silver
interior, Red plastic hubs **£150-180**
54   1974-??   **'Massey-Ferguson 50B'**
Tractor with Shovel
- Yellow and Red body and shovel **£60-80**
54   1962-64   **'Fordson Power Major' Tractor**
(Roadless Half-Tracks)
- Blue body, Orange rollers and wheels,
Black rubber tracks, lights in
radiator grille. Plain 'early' box.......... **£250-350**
- Same but with Grey rubber tracks, lights
at sides of grille, in picture box.......... **£250-300**
First type casting has lights at side of grille.
Orange or pale orange plastic hubs with
grey tracks.
55   1961-63   **'Fordson Power Major' Tractor**
- Blue/Grey/Red body, Orange metal
hubs, Silver seat/steering wheel........ **£400-500**
- Blue/Grey/Red body, Dull Orange plastic
hubs, Silver seat/steering wheel........ **£150-200**
55   1977-??   **'David Brown 1412' Tractor**
- Black/Red/White body.......................... **£60-80**
56   1961-63   **Four-Furrow Plough**
- Red/Brown/Yellow body........................ **£30-35**
56   1977-??   **Farm Tipper Trailer**
- Red/Yellow or Red/White body
with drop-down tailboard **£10-15**
57   1963-66   **'Massey Ferguson 65'**
Tractor with Fork
- Red/Silver/Cream body, Red hubs,
driver, steering wheel **£160-180**
- Same model but with Orange hubs .. **£125-150**
58   1965-72   **Beast Carrier**
- Red/Cream/Blue body, four calves....... **£45-55**
60   1964-71   **'Fordson Power Major' Tractor**
- Blue body / steering wheel, bare metal
seat, driver, Red plastic hubs **£150-200**

61   1964-71   **Four-Furrow Plough**
- Blue/Silver body **£30-35**

Four-Furrow Plough

62   1965-72   **Ford Tipper Trailer**
- Red/Yellow body, two raves.................. **£20-25**

Forward Control Jeep

64   1965-69   **Forward Control Jeep**
- Red body, Yellow/White working
conveyor, farmhand figure.................. **£80-100**
66   1966-72   **'Massey-Ferguson 165' Tractor**
- Red/Blue/White, engine sound **£120-140**
67   1967-72   **'Ford Super Major' Tractor**
- Blue/White/Silver body,
'FORD 5000', instructions.................. **£100-150**
- Blue with Grey plastic hubs,
Pale Blue mudguards, driver **£100-150**
69   1967-72   **'Massey-Ferguson 165'**
Tractor and Shovel
- Red/Grey body, Silver shovel, driver **£300-350**
71   1967-72   **Fordson Disc Harrow**
- Yellow/Red/Silver body **£30-35**
72   1971-73   **'Ford 5000'**
Tractor and Towbar
- As Corgi 67 but with frame,
bucket and pipes **£200-250**
73   1970-73   **'Massey-Ferguson' Tractor and Saw**
- As Corgi 66 + Yellow rotating saw **£185-225**

74   1969-72   **'Ford 5000' Tractor and Scoop**
- As Corgi 67 + Yellow/Silver scoop..... **£250-300**
100   1957-65   **Dropside Trailer**
- Cream/Red or Yellow body, Wire tow bar
or later die-cast tow bar, Blue box **£50-60**
- Yellow & Blue box................................. **£50-60**
101   1958-63   **Platform Trailer**
- Grey/Yellow or Silver/Blue or
Silver/Lemon body............. .... **£60-70**
102   1958-59   **Rice's Pony Trailer**
- Red body, Brown chassis, wire
drawbar, smooth hubs, plastic pony..... **£70-80**
- Red body, Silver chassis, wire drawbar,
smooth hubs, plastic pony.................... **£60-70**
- 1959-65   Red body, Black chassis, wire or
cast drawbar, smooth or shaped hubs.. **£60-70**
- Red body, Silver chassis, wire or cast
drawbar, smooth or shaped hubs......... **£60-70**
- Cream body, Red chassis, wire or cast
drawbar, smooth or shaped hubs......... **£60-70**
- 1961-68   Tan/Cream body, Silver chassis,
cast drawbar, shaped hubs **£60-70**
112   1969-72   **Rice Beaufort Horse-Box**
- Blue/White horse-box with mare and foal **£25-50**
484   1967-69   **Dodge Livestock Transporter**
- Beige/Green/Graphite Grey body, spun
hubs, 'KEW FARGO', 5 pigs.
Blue/Yellow card box **£75-150**
- Later issue with cast hubs.
Blue/Yellow window box **£70-80**

MAJOR PACKS
(and large farming models)
1111 1959-60   **'Massey-Ferguson'**
Combine Harvester
- Red/Yellow, Yellow metal wheels, metal
tines, card box has internal packing . **£100-150**
1111 1960-61   **'Massey-Ferguson 780'**
Combine Harvester
- Red/Yellow, Yellow metal wheels, plastic
tines, card box has internal packing . **£100-150**
- 1961-64   Red/Yellow, Red plastic wheels,
Yellow plastic tines, card box has
internal packing................................. **£175-225**
1112 1977-78   **'David Brown' Tractor**
and Combine Harvester
- Corgi 55 Tractor with Red/White/Black
combine harvester............................. **£150-175**

Aircraft

*BOX TYPES: All these aircraft models were presented in rigid perspex cases. Helicopters
and Space Vehicles are also listed in the Emergency Vehicles, Novelty and Military Sections.*

Model and details	MPR
650	1973-80 **'BOAC' Concorde**
•	White/Blue with Gold tail design, all-card box with 'BRITISH AIRWAYS', box has inner packing **£70-80**
•	White/Blue with Red/White/Blue tail, display stand, 'G-BBDG' **£50-60**
•	Version with White stripes on tail **£15-25**
•	Version with crown design on tail ... **£15-25**
651	1973-81 **'AIR FRANCE' Concorde**
•	White/Blue with Gold tail design, all-card box........ **£70-80**
•	White body, Red/White/Blue tail, display stand **£100-150**
652	1973-81 **'JAPAN AIRLINES' Concorde**
•	White/Red/Blue/Black, all-card box, inner packing **£150-200**
653	1973-81 **'AIR CANADA' Concorde**
•	White/Red/Blue/Black, all-card box, inner packing **£150-200**
1119	1960-62 **HDL Hovercraft 'SR-N1'**
•	Blue/Grey/White body, Yellow rudders and wheels (Major Pack)........ **£80-100**
1301	1973-77 **Piper Cherokee Arrow**
•	Yellow/Black with White wings, or White/Blue, 'N 286 4 A' **£35-45**
1302	1973-77 **Piper Navajo**
•	Red/White,'N 9219 Y'......................... **£35-45**

Model and details	MPR
•	Yellow/White,'N 9219 Y' **£35-45**
1303	1973-77 **Lockheed F104A Starfighter**
•	Silver body **£60-70**
•	Camouflage with Black crosses **£70-90**
1304	1973-77 **Mig-21 PF**
•	Blue or Silver, number '57', Red stars, retractable undercarriage **£35-40**
1305	1973-?? **Grumman F-11a Tiger**
•	Blue 'NAVY', or Silver with US stars .. **£60-70**
•	Dark Metalic Blue, Yellow engine vents **£70-90**
1306	1973-77 **North American P51-D Mustang**
•	Silver or Camouflage, Black props, US stars, moveable controls............. **£35-40**
1307	1973-77 **Saab 35 X Draken**
•	Silver or Camouflage, retractable undercarriage, Swedish markings.... **£35-45**
1308	1973-77 **BAC (or SEPCAT) Jaguar**
•	Silver or Camouflage, retractable wheels, moveable control surfaces .. **£35-45**
1309	1973-77 **'BOAC' Concorde**
•	Dark Silver/White, retractable wheels **£45-55**
1310	1973-77 **'AIR FRANCE' 'BOEING 707B'**
•	White/Blue body, Silver wings, retractable wheels............................ **£55-65**

Model and details	MPR
1311	1973-77 **Messerschmitt ME410**
•	All Silver body, Black Iron Crosses on wings and fuselage **£35-45**
1312	1973-77 **Boeing 727 'TWA'**
•	White body, Silver wings, retractable wheels................................ **£35-45**
1313	1973-77 **Japanese Zero-Sen A6M5**
•	Green or Silver with Red circles, retractable wheels............................ **£35-45**
1315	1973-77 **'PAN-AM' Boeing 747**
•	White body, Silver wings, hinged nose, retractable wheels, 'AIR CANADA' ... **£35-45**
1315/1	**'BRITISH AIRWAYS' Jumbo Boeing 747**
•	White/Silver, Blue logo, hinged nose, retractable wheels........ **£55-65**
1316	1973-77 **McDonnell Douglas F-4c5**
•	Phantom II in Silver or Camouflage with retractable undercarriage....... **£35-45**
1320	1978-80 **'BRITISH AIRWAYS' VC-10**
•	White/Silver with Red tail, Blue logo, retractable wheels........... **£35-45**
1325	1978-80 **'SWISSAIR' DC-10**
•	White/Silver with Red stripe and tail, retractable wheels **£35-45**

Military and RAF Models

Unless described otherwise, all models in this listing are finished in Military-Green or Olive-Drab camouflage.

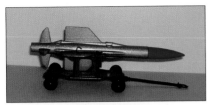

Thunderbird Missile

350 1958-62 **Thunderbird Missile**
- Blue, Green or Silver missile with Red tip, Air Force Blue loading trolley **£65-75**

RAF Land Rover

351 1958-62 **RAF Land Rover**
- Blue body, RAF roundel, spare wheel, windows, flat spun hubs **£90-110**
- Same model but with suspension, flat spun hubs **£90-110**

352 1958-62 **RAF Vanguard Staff Car**
- Blue body, Standard Vanguard with RAF roundel, Blue box.............. **£80-100**
- Blue & Yellow box **£80-100**

353 1959-61 **Decca Radar Scanner**
- Blue/Orange, scanner rotates.............. **£35-45**

354 1964-66 **Commer Military Ambulance**
- Military Green body, Red Interior, Red cross, driver, Blue glazing......... **£125-150**

355 1964-65 **Commer Van 'US MILITARY POLICE'**
- Red interior, driver, Blue roof light, leaflet in box **£125-150**

356 1964-66 **VW Personnel Carrier**
- Military Green, Red interior, driver, Blue roof light, 'US Personnel' **£125-150**

357 1964-66 **Land Rover**
- Military Green, Lemon interior, driver, White star, 'Weapons Carrier'.......... **£240-280**

358 1964-68 **Oldsmobile Staff Car**
- Red interior, White star, 'HQ STAFF', driver, 3 passengers, aerial.............. **£125-150**

359 1964-66 **Commer Army 'FIELD KITCHEN'**
- Blue interior, US star on roof, driver/attendant, 'US ARMY' **£125-150**

US Army Land Rover

414 1961-63 **Bedford Dormobile Military Ambulance**
- Olive drab body, Red crosses, smooth hubs **£100-125**
- Same model but with shaped hubs and suspension................................. **£100-125**

500 1963-64 **US Army Land Rover**

- Rare version of model 357 ....**£200-250**

900 1974-78 **German Tiger MkI Tank**
- Brown/Green, rubber tracks, fires shells (12 supplied) aerial, '144' **£30-40**

901 1974-78 **Centurion Mk.I Tank**
- Rubber tracks, fires shells (12 supplied), aerial, Union Jacks................................ **£30-40**

902 1974-80 **American M60 A1 Tank**
- Rubber tracks, fires shells (12 supplied) **£30-40**

903 1974-80 **British Chieftain Tank**
- Fires shells (12 supplied), rubber tracks... **£30-40**

904 1974-78 **German King-Tiger Tank**
- 'B 34', rubber tracks, fires shells, (12 supplied) Black crosses **£30-40**

905 1975-76 **Russian SU100 Tank Destroyer**
- Grey, Red Star, fires shells (12 supplied), rubber tracks **£30-40**

906 1975-76 **Saladin Armoured Car**
- Rubber tracks, fires shells (12 supplied), elevating gun **£30-40**

907 1976-80 **German Rocket Launcher**
- Steel Blue/Red, half-track, detachable limber, fires rockets (12)...................... **£30-40**

908 1977-80 **French AMX Recovery Tank**
- Crane, lifting dozer blade, equipment, 3 figures............................. **£40-50**

909 1977-80 **Tractor Gun and Trailer**
- Sand-coloured British gun and trailer, fires shells (12 supplied) **£40-50**

920 1975-78 **Bell Army Helicopter**
- Military-Green with Army markings, Black or Green rotor....................... **£15-20**

922 1975-78 **Casualty Helicopter**
- Red/White/Yellow Sikorsky helicopter, number '3', Red crosses **£15-20**

923 1975-78 **Sikorsky Sky Crane**
- Military-Green, Red cross, 'ARMY'...... **£15-20**

MAJOR PACKS (Military models)

1106 1959-61 **Karrier Decca Radar Van**
- Cream body, 4 Orange bands, rotating scanner, aerials, box has interior packing **£125-175**
- Same, but with 5 Orange bands **£100-125**

1108 1958-60 **Bristol Bloodhound Guided Missile and Launching Ramp**
- Green ramp, Yellow/Red/White Guided Missile, RAF markings...................... **£125-150** First type casting has four yellow metal side rocket boosters. Launching ramp has diecast locking piece at top of ramp to hold missile

1109 1959-61 **Bristol Bloodhound Guided Missile and Loading Trolley**
- Green ramp, Yellow/Red/White Guided Missile, RAF markings...................... **£125-150**

1112 1959-62 **Corporal Guided Missile on Launching Ramp**
- Military-Green mechanical base, White missile, Red rubber nose cone, instruction sheet in box **£200-250**
- 1960-62 Same but with separately boxed 1408 Percussion Head and instructions................................ **£200-250**

1113 1959-62 **Corporal Guided Missile Erector Vehicle**
- With lifting mechanism and Missile, spare wheel, leaflet **£250-350**

1115 1958-61 **Bristol Ferranti Bloodhound**
- Yellow/Red/White Guided Missile with RAF markings **£75-100**

1116 1959-61 **Bloodhound Launching Ramp**
- Launching ramp for 1115. Rotates, has lifting mechanism .... **£65-120** First type missile with yellow metal side rocket boosters.

Bloodhound Loading Trolley

1117 1959-61 **Bloodhound Loading Trolley**
- For use with 1115. Military-Green, spare wheel, drawbar pivots **£65-70**

International Tow Truck

1118 1959-64 **International Tow Truck**
- Military-Green with British markings (US markings on box picture)..........**£150-200**
- Dutch issue: Silver grille and sidelights **£125-150**
- US Army issues **£125-150**

1124 1960-61 **Launching Ramp for Corporal Guided Missile**
- Military-Green, operable mechanisms, in plain 'Temporary Pack' box.........**£100-125**

1133 1965-66 **Troop Transporter**
- International six wheeled truck, 'US 7811332', hook **£150-200**

'US ARMY' Fuel Tanker

1134 1965-66 **'US ARMY' Fuel Tanker**
- Olive Bedford 'S' Type Artic., US Army star, 'NO SMOKING'.........**£225-275**

1135 1965-?? **Heavy Equipment Transporter**
- Bedford Carrimore, Military Green, US Army star, driver, Red interior **£450-500**
- Military Green, Lemon interior **£450-560**

Novelty, Film and TV-related Models

Market Price Range: Please note that the prices shown refer to pristine models and boxes. Items failing to match this standard will sell for considerably less. Note also that boxes must contain all their original additional contents. See also Corgi model identification page.

Model and details	MPR

Dolphin Boat on Trailer

104 1965 **Dolphin Boat on Trailer**
- Blue/White boat, Red trailer,
Helmsman, Blue/yellow box **£50-75**

107 1967-70 **Batboat on Trailer**
- Black boat (tinplate fin cover) with
Batman and Robin figures,
gold trailer (suspension, cast wheels).
Blue/yellow pictorial box also contains
black accessory towing hook for
attachment to Batmobile **£125-160**
- 1974-81 Black boat (plastic fin),
Batman and Robin figures,
gold trailer (no suspension, WW),
striped window box **£90-100**

171 1982 **Street Bike**
Red, Silver and Black body,
multicoloured swirl **£5-10**

172 1982 **'POLICE' Bike**
White/Black/Silver body **£5-10**

173 1982 **Cafe Racer**
Silver and Black RN '26',
'750 cc Class' **£5-10**

201 1970-72 **The Saint's Volvo**
- White body, White 'Saint' logo on red
label, WhizzWheels, driver,
Red/Yellow 'window' box **£150-200**
- White body, Yellow interior,
Clear bonnet decal with black 'Saint'
outline figure, WhizzWheels, driver,
Red/Yellow 'window' box **£400-460**

258 1965-68 **The Saint's Volvo P1800**
- White body, Black 'Saint' logo (transfer),
Red interior, spun hubs,
Blue/Yellow card box **£200-250**
- 1968-70 White body, White 'Saint' logo
on Red label, Red interior, driver,
cast hubs, Blue/Yellow card box **£300-420**
1968-70 As previous version but
white 'Saint' logo on blue label .... **NGPP**
- 1970-71 White body, White logo on
Red label, Yellow interior, WW **£135-155**

259 1979-80 **Penguinmobile**
- White car with 'Penguin' and Red/Yellow
parasol, Black/Yellow 'window' box **£35-40**

260 1979-81 **Superman Police Car**
- Blue/White body,'CITY of METROPOLIS',
Black/Yellow pictorial window box **£60-70**

261 1965-69 **James Bond's Aston Martin**
(From the film 'Goldfinger')
- Bright Gold body (metal roof), Red interior,
wire wheels. With James Bond at the wheel,
passenger seat ejector (with bandit figure).
Accessories: envelope with 'secret
instructions', spare bandit figure,
self-adhesive '007' badge, (plus 'Model
Car Makers to James Bond' Corgi
Catalogue in earlier boxes).
Blue/Yellow picture box has
inner pictorial stand **£300-350**
- variant: Same model but the opening
roof component is made of plastic .... **NGPP**

261 1979-81 **Spiderbuggy**
- Red/Blue jeep body with crane,
Spiderman and Green Goblin figures.
Black/Yellow pictorial window box.... **£75-100**

James Bond's Aston Martin

262 1979-80 **Captain Marvel's Porsche**
- White with flames and stars, driver,
Black/Yellow 'window' box **£35-40**

263 1979-81 **Captain America's Jetmobile**
- White/Red/Blue body, Red wheels,
Black/Yellow 'window' box **£25-30**

264 1979-82 **Incredible Hulk Truck**
- Bronze Hulk in Red cage on Mazda
pick-up, Black/Yellow 'window' box.... **£60-70**
- Same model but Hulk in Grey cage...... **£70-80**
NB Dark Bronze Hulk is rare – add £10 to price.

265 1979-82 **Supermobile**
- Blue/Red/Silver body, Superman at the
controls, moving 'fists' . Black/Yellow
pictorial 'window' box has 10 spare
rockets and an instruction leaflet........ **£40-50**

Chitty Chitty Bang Bang

266 1968-72 **Chitty Chitty Bang Bang**
- Chrome, Brown and Red body, Red/Yellow
retractable 'wings', figures of Caractacus
Potts, Truly Scrumptious, a boy and a
girl. Pictorial Blue/Yellow 'window'
box comes in two sizes **£300-350**
- 1992 25th Anniversary replica:
model on 'mahogany' display stand.
Direct mail offer from Corgi.................. **£60-70**

266 1979-83 **Spider Bike**
- Red/Blue motorcycle, Spiderman rider,
Black wheels, Black or Red handlebars
forks, Black or Blue seat and fairing,
amber or clear windshield,
rocket launchers. Box also contains
10 spare rockets on sprue.
Box 1: Black/Yellow pictorial 'window'
box with header card **£100-125**
Box 2: Black/Yellow 'window' box
without header card **£100-125**
Box 3: Black/Red/Yellow striped
'window' box without header card .. **£100-125**

266 1980-82 **Spider Bike**
- Same model but White wheels **£100-125**

267 1966-67 **Batmobile**
- (i): Gloss Black body, Red 'Bat' logo
on doors and gold cast hubs, Batman

and Robin figures, 'pulsating exhaust
flame', sealed secret instructions
concealed in box base. 12 spare rockets
(Red or Yellow) attached to sprue,
self-adhesive 'Batman' badge. Pictorial
card box with diorama, earliest versions
had 'features' leaflet within **£400-500**

Batmobile

- (ii): As previous model but with
Matt Black body **£500-600**
- 1967-72 As (i) but with towing hook
cast into base. Blue/Yellow 'window'
box (some in earlier card boxes) **£225-275**
- 1967-72 (iv): As (i) but cast
Silver wheels. Black/Blue/Yellow
'window' box................................... **£225-275**
- 1973 (v): As (iv) but with Red
WhizzWheels (with Chrome hubs) and
without pulsating 'flame' effect.
Blue/Yellow 'window' box with
missiles and instructions **£300-400**
- 1974-77 (vi): As (v) but with Black
WhizzWheels and without pulsating
'flame' effect. Copyright information
cast in base, Dark Blue/Yellow
'window' box (header card on some),
spare rockets, no instruction sheet .. **£150-175**
- 1977-79 (vii): As (vi) casting but wider
WhizzWheels, no Robin figure.
Black/Red/Yellow 'window' box **£150-175**
- 1979-80 (viii): Gloss Black, Gold
slasher blade and tow hook, aerial,
Batman and Robin figures,
wide WW, striped 'window' box....... **£150-175**

268 1978-80 **Batman's Batbike**
- Black/Red rocket-firing motorcycle
with Red or Grey Batman figure.
Black and Yellow 'window' box (header
card on some), spare rockets **£80-100**
- 1980-83 As previous versions but
in Black/Red/Yellow striped
'window' box.................................... **£50-70**

268 1967-72 **The Green Hornet's**
'Black Beauty'
- Black body, Green interior, driver and
Green Hornet figures, transfer on roof,
spun hubs. Fires missiles from front,
radar spinners from rear. Four of each,
plus 'secret instructions' are in
Blue/Yellow pictorial card box which
should also include a greaseproof
paper roof decal protector
and inner pictorial card **£200-250**
- Same but with cast detailed hubs **£400-500**

269 1977-83 **James Bond Lotus Esprit**
(From film 'The Spy Who Loved Me')
- White body, Black windows, operable fins
and rocket mechanism. . Early Black/Yellow
pictorial 'window' box with plain base
must contain instruction sheet and
10 spare rockets attached to sprue... **£125-165**
- Later pictorial 'window' box has

instructions printed on base,
10 spare rockets **£80-100**
• 1977   10 gold-plated versions of 269
were presented to VIPs at the film's
launch. These models had special
mountings and boxes **£1,000-1,500**
• Pre-production model:
Demonstration model in a case.
Red/Yellow/Blue/Green............. **£1,000-1,400**

270 1968-76 **James Bond's Aston-Martin DB5**
• Silver body (slightly larger than 261).
Features as 261, plus revolving number
plates and extending tyre slashers. Box
must contain inner pictorial stand, James
Bond leaflet, sealed 'secret instructions'
packet, unused '007' lapel badge
(different from 261), set of unapplied
no. plates and bandit figure. Variations
include Gold or Silver coloured bumpers,
metal or plastic spoked rear wheels.
Box 1: Pictorial wing-flap box. Model sits
on card platform under vac-formed bubble
(fragile, few made).............................. **£300-400**
Box 2: Blue/Yellow 'window' box
(some with card 'upstand' till
1973, few made)................................ **£400-600**
Box 3: Black/Blue/Yellow striped
'window' box (1973-76)............... **£200-250**
• 1977-78 As previous version but with
fixed number plates, 'solid' chrome
WW, no tyre-slashers, Striped window
box (no 'secret instructions'), ejectable
passenger lodged in box inner **£100-130**

271 1978-81 **James Bond Aston-Martin**
• Silver body (1:36 scale), Red interior,
Gold radiator/bumpers, WhizzWheels
('spoked' detail or 'alloy racing'). Early
Black/Yellow boxes had '1:36' printed
on window tag, plus header card **£70-80**
• Later Black/Yellow boxes did not have
the window tag...................................... **£50-60**
• Final issues had Black/Red/Yellow striped
window boxes or Purple boxes............. **£50-60**
• 1990 'MODELAUTO' promotional:
Silver, Red interior, 2 figures, Blue logo
'National Motor Museum Holland'..**£180-220**
• 1991-92 Reissue of C271 in clear plastic
display box with plastic '007' badge..... **£20-30**
271/1 1992   Silver body (1:36 scale),
small 4-spoked wheels.......... **£70-90**
271/2 1993   Re-run of 271/1 .... **£70-90**

272 1981-83 **James Bond Citroën 2cv**
(From film 'For Your Eyes Only')
• Yellow body, opening bonnet, WW.
Box (1): Black/Red/Yellow 'window'
box with pictorial header card.............. **£30-40**
Box (2): Black/Red/Yellow 'compact'
box with pictorial top flap **£30-40**
• 1981 Gold plated version:
(12 only produced). 'Strada Jewellry'
Certificate should be present......**£2,000-3,000**

277 1968-72 **'MONKEES' Monkeemobile**
• Red body, White roof, Yellow logo, cast
detailed wheels. Figures of Mike,
Mickey, Davy and Pete plus red
plastic 'Monkees' guitar.
Blue/Yellow 'window' box **£200-250**
• Same, but no 'Monkees' guitar **£200-250**
• In Blue/Yellow 'window' box with
clip-in cardboard header as used for
shop display purposes...................... **£800-900**
NB Pre-production model with
plastic engine exists.

278 1981   **Dan Dare's Car**
• Red/Yellow space vehicle.
Planned but not produced........................**NPP**

290 1976-77 **Kojak's Buick**
• Bronze body (various shades), 4-spoke
or disc type wheel hubs, 'gunfire' sound,
self-adhesive 'Lieutenant' badge,
figures of Kojak (no hat) and Crocker
(blue jacket). Black/Yellow

pictorial 'window' box......................**£120-150**
• Same but disc type wheel hubs **£100-125**
• 1977-80 Same but Kojak figure has a
hat and Crocker has a Black jacket.
'New' tag on some boxes **£60-75**

292 1977-82 **Starsky & Hutch Ford Torino**
• Red/White body, figures of Starsky,
Hutch, and a suspect. Black/Yellow
pictorial 'window' box......................**£100-150**
• 1986 Reissued as export
model (20,000 units) **£10-15**

298 1982-83 **Magnum P.I. Ferrari 308GTS**
• Red Ferrari with 4-spoke or disc wheels.
Black/Red/Yellow pictorial
'window' box... **£20-30**

320 1978-81 **The Saint's Jaguar XJS**
• White body, standard or 'dished'
WhizzWheels. Black/Yellow 'window'
box (yellow or black inner) **£50-60**

336 1967-69 **James Bond's Toyota 2000 GI**
(From film 'You Only Live Twice')
• White body, Red aerial, 2 figures, rocket
launchers in boot. Diorama box must
have card reinforcements to protect aerial,
8 spare rockets on sprue, sealed envelope
marked 'Secret Instructions' which also
contains self-adhesive '007' badge...**£250-300**

342 1980-82 **'The Professionals' Ford Capri**
• Metallic Silver body, dished or disc hubs,
figures of Cowley, Bodie and Doyle.
Pictorial 'window' box....................... **£125-150**
• Same but with chrome wheel hubs.. **£150-175**
• Matt Silver body, Dk. Red interior.... **£125-150**

348 1980-81 **'Vegas' Thunderbird**
• Red body with Dan Tanner figure
Black/Yellow pictorial 'window' box.... **£60-80**

391 1972-72 **James Bond Mustang Mach I**
(From film 'Diamonds Are Forever')
• Red body, Black bonnet, White interior
and base, WW (2 types known).
• Red/Yellow 'window' box has
'007' Red sticker **£175-200**
• Same model but with 'CORGI
TOYS' shop display stand **£300-400**

CHEVROLET VANS
423 1978-78 **'ROUGH RIDER'**
• Yellow van, motorcycle labels.............. **£20-25**
431 1978-79 **'VANATIC'**
• White van, polychromatic side labels .. **£15-20**
432 1978-79 **'VANTASTIC'**
• Black van, Yellow/Red design............... **£15-20**
433 1978   **'VANISHING POINT'**
• Chevrolet van shown in 1978
catalogue but not issued ....**NPP**
434 1978-80 **'CHARLIE'S ANGELS' Van**
• Pink Chevrolet Custom van, Yellow or
Brown interior, 4-spoke wheels.
Black/Yellow pictorial 'window' box.... **£60-75**
• 2nd issue with solid disc wheels **£50-60**
435 1979-80 **'SUPERMAN' Van**
• Metallic Silver Chevrolet 'SuperVan'.
Black/Yellow pictorial 'window' box
(printing variations seen) **£35-45**
436 1979-80 **'SPIDERVAN'**
• Blue Chevrolet van, 'Spiderman' design,
4-spoke wheels.
Black/Yellow pictorial 'window' box.... **£80-90**
• 2nd issue with solid disc wheels **£50-60**
437 1979-80 **'COCA COLA'**
• Red Chevrolet van, White design,
tinted roof windows, crates.................. **£30-35**
NB Various other labels were designed for
the Chevrolet 'Van' series. Some prototype
labels were printed but not officially used.
Some of these may have found their way on
to repainted van castings - they are NOT
official Corgi issues. Logos include:
'Apache Patrol', 'Light Vantastic',
'Vanilla Treat', 'Cosmos', 'Columbia',
'Aquarius', 'Centaur', 'Colorama',
'Rocket Van', 'Centaur', plus four other
unlettered 'psychedelic' designs.

426 1962-64 **'CHIPPERFIELDS CIRCUS'**
Mobile Booking Office
• Karrier Bantam in red and blue, with
clown and circus posters, spun hubs.
Blue/yellow card box........................**£300-400**
• Same model but with shaped hubs.. **£250-300**

450 1968-71 **Lunar Bug**
• Red, White, Blue. Blue/Yellow window
box includes inner packing................... **£60-70**

472 1964-66 **'VOTE FOR CORGI'**
• Corgi 438 Land Rover in Green/Yellow,
Red interior, two figures,
Blue/Yellow card box......................**£100-120**

487 1965-69 **'CHIPPERFIELDS'**
Parade Vehicle
• 472 Land Rover in Red/Blue, 'CIRCUS
IS HERE' label, chimpanzee, clown,
Blue/yellow card box........................**£175-200**

497 1966-66 **'The Man From UNCLE's**
'Thrush Buster'
• Oldsmobile (235) with White body,
cast wheels, cast spotlights, 'UNCLE'
logo, gun sound, figures of Napoleon
Solo and Ilya Kuriakin. Blue/Yellow
pictorial card box (which must include
internal packaging, roof packing,
and 3-D 'Waverley' ring) **£500-600**
• Same but Metallic Purplish-Blue
body, cast or plastic spotlights **£175-250**

503 1964-70 **'CHIPPERFIELDS'**
Giraffe Transporter
• Red/Blue Bedford 'TK',
cast or spun wheels, 2 giraffes.
Blue/Yellow card box....................... **£85-125**
• 1970-71 As previous model but
larger 'stepped' front wheels............. **£130-170**
• Window box variation **£200-300**

511 1970-71 **'CHIPPERFIELDS'**
Poodle Truck
• Blue/Red Chevrolet Impala Pick-Up,
'PERFORMING POODLES' labels,
cast wheels, trainer (Mary Chipperfield),
4 White and 2 Black poodles. Blue
and Yellow 'window' box (should
include a plastic dome over dogs) ... **£250-300**

'Chipperfields' Elephant Cage

607 1963-68 **'CHIPPERFIELDS'**
Elephant Cage
• A Corgi Kit with Brown plastic cage
and elephant mouldings, instruction
leaflet. Blue/Yellow card box **£50-75**

647 1980-83 **Buck Rogers Starfighter**
• White/Blue, Yellow retractable wings,
Wilma Dearing and Tweaky figures,
Black/Yellow pictorial 'window' box,
10 spare rockets **£40-45**

648 1981-82 **NASA Space Shuttle**
• White/Black body, 'USA Satellite',
opening hatch **£20-25**

649 1979-82 **James Bond Space Shuttle**
(From the film 'Moonraker')
• White body (C468 casting), separate
satellite (early versions retained by
nylon strap). Larger pictorial
Black/Yellow box **£50-75**

681 1972   **Stunt Bike**
• Gold body, Blue and Yellow rider, Red
trolley, 'window' box, (19,000) **£125-170**

801 1969-69 **Noddy's Car**
- Yellow/Red car with dickey-seat, cast hubs, chrome bumpers. Figures of Noddy, Big-Ears, and black-faced Golly. Pictorial Blue/Yellow 'window' box **£1,000-1,500**
- As previous model but Golly has Light Tan face **£750-1,000**
- As previous model but Golly has Grey face **£300-400**
- 1969-73 As previous model but with Master Tubby (light or dark brown) instead of Golly.................... **£200-300**

802 1969-72 **Popeye's Paddle-Wagon**
- Yellow/White body, Red wings, Blue paddle covers, White or Yellow rear wheels, anchors, moving figures of Popeye, Olive Oyl, Swee'Pea, Bluto and Wimpey. Blue/Yellow pictorial 'window' box...................... **£260-310**

803 1969-72 **The Beatles Submarine**
- Yellow/White, psychedelic design, hatches (Yellow rear, White front) open to show John, Paul, George and Ringo, pictorial window box with Blue-Green inner lining........... **£250-300**
- 1970-71 With two Red hatch covers **£250-300**
- With one red hatch and one white hatch **£400-500**
- Pre-production issue: Gold plated, periscope attached to sprue. Only eight issued.................. **£600-750**

804 1975-78 **Noddy's Car**
- Red/Yellow car, no dickey-seat, no rear bumper. Figure of Noddy only. Dark Blue/Yellow pictorial 'window' box **£110-150**

805 1970-71 **Hardy Boys Rolls-Royce**
- 9041 Silver Ghost casting in Red, Blue and Yellow, plated wheels. Bubble-pack of five Hardy Boys figures also within the Blue/Yellow 'window' box **£150-175**

806 1970-72 **Lunar Bug**
- Red/White/Blue, 'Lunar Bug', windows, drop-down ramps................ **£65-75**

807 1971-73 **Dougal's Magic Roundabout Car** (based on 510 Citroën)
- Yellow/Red, with Brian, Dougal and Dylan. Yellow/Blue 'window' box with decal sheet **£175-225**
- 1973-74 Same but in Black/Yellow 'window' box, with decal sheet **£130-160**

808 1971-73 **Basil Brush's Car**
- Red/Yellow car with hand-painted Basil figure, 'Laugh tapes' and soundbox are in separate printed box within pictorial Blue/Yellow 'window' box..................................... **£175-200**

809 1973-73 **Dick Dastardly's Car**
- Blue/Red/Yellow racing car with

Dick and Muttley figures. Dark Blue/Yellow 'window' box **£150-175**

811 1972-74 **James Bond Moon Buggy**
- Blue/White body, Yellow WhizzWheels, Red scanner. Roof opening mechanism should be working. Blue/Yellow pictorial window box........................ **£200-250**

H851 1972-74 **Magic Roundabout Train**
- Red/Blue, Mr Rusty and Basil in the locomotive (engine sound), Rosalie and Paul in the carriage and Dougal in the van. Blue/Yellow pictorial 'window' box with Blue nylon tow-rope **£200-300**

H852 1972-74 **Magic Roundabout Carousel**
- Red/Yellow/Blue working roundabout with Swiss musical movement playing the TV theme. Dylan, Paul, Rosalie, Florence and Basil figures. Blue/Yellow pictorial card box **£350-400**

H853 1972-74 **Magic Roundabout Playground**
- Contains a modified H852, H851 (with the figures), plus Zebedee, Dylan, four kids, see-saw, park bench, 3 Blue and 3 Orange shrubs and 2 flowers. Operating carousel and track. Theme music plays when Dylan is wound up.....................**£1,000-1,250**

H859 1972-74 **Mr McHenry's Trike**
- Red/Yellow trike and trailer, Mr McHenry and pop-up Zebedee figures, Blue and Yellow pictorial 'window' box with blue towing cord and instruction sheet................ **£150-175**

H860-H868 1972-74 **Magic Roundabout figures** Packed in individual clear plastic tubs:
- 860 Dougal, • 861 Florence, • 862 Zebedee, • 863 Mr Rusty, • 864 Brian the Snail, • 865 Basil, • 866 Ermintrude the Cow, • 868 Dylan the Rabbit .... **Each: £25-35**

925 1976-81 **Batcopter**
- Black body, Red 'Bat' rotors, Batman figure, operable winch **£65-75**

926 1978-80 **Stromberg Helicopter** (From 'The Spy Who Loved Me')
- Black body/rotors, ten spare rockets. Black/Yellow 'window' box................... **£60-70**

927 1978-80 **Chopper Squad Helicopter**
- White/metallic Blue Jet Ranger helicopter, operating winch. Black/Yellow pictorial 'window' box.... **£35-45**

928 1981-82 **Spidercopter**
- Blue/Red body, 'spider legs'. Black/Yellow pictorial 'window' box.... **£40-50**

929 1979-80 **'DAILY PLANET' Jetcopter**
- Red/White body, rocket launchers, Black/Yellow pictorial 'window' box contains 10 spare rockets **£50-70**

930 1972-80 **'Drax' Helicopter** (From the film 'Moonraker')
- White body, 'Drax' logo, ten spare rockets. Black/Yellow 'window' box.................. **£60-70**

9004 1967-69 **'The World of Wooster' Bentley**
- Green 9002 Bentley with figures of Jeeves and Wooster, plated wheels. Bubble-packed in display base........... **£90-100**

MAJOR MODELS

1121 1960-62 **'CHIPPERFIELDS' Crane Truck**
- Red body, Raised Blue log and wheels, operable grey tinplate jib and hook, instruction leaflet. Blue/Yellow lidded box with packing............................... **£125-150**
- 1963-69 Red body, raised Blue logo and wheels, operable chrome tinplate jib / hook, leaflet. Blue/Yellow card box with end flaps............................ **£125-150**

1123 1961-62 **'CHIPPERFIELDS' Circus Cage**
- Red body, Yellow chassis, smooth hubs, red diecast and middle sliding doors, 2 plastic lions (in stapled bags), animal name decals, instructions. Blue/Yellow lidded box with packing................... **£100-110**
- 1963-68 Red body, Yellow chassis, smooth or spun hubs, Blue plastic end and middle sliding doors, 4 animals (lions, tigers or polar bears in stapled bags), animal name decals. Blue/Yellow card box with end flaps **£75-100**

1130 1962-70 **'CHIPPERFIELDS' Horse Transporter**
- Bedford TK truck, Red/Blue, Green or Red 'horse-head' design at rear, cast or spun hubs, 6 Brown or Grey horses, Blue/Yellow card box with card packing around horses...................... **£150-175**
- 1970-72 As previous model but with larger 'truck' wheels............... **£150-175**

1139 1968-72 **'CHIPPERFIELDS' Menagerie Transporter**
- Scammell Handyman MkIII, Blue/Red cab, Blue trailer with 3 plastic cages, 2 lions, 2 tigers and 2 bears. Blue and Yellow pictorial 'window' box with packing to hold animals, plus spare self-adhesive securing tape for animals **£250-300**

1144 1969-72 **'CHIPPERFIELDS' Crane and Cage with Rhino**
- Red/Blue Scammell Handyman MkIII, 'COME TO THE CIRCUS' on n/s, silver jib/hook, stepped 'truck' front wheels on some, Grey rhinoceros in plastic cage. Blue/Yellow 'window' box with pre-formed blister-pack around animals **£250-350**

1163 1978-82 **Human Cannon Truck**
- Red and Blue body, 'MARVO' figure.... **£30-40**

1164 1980-83 **Berliet 'DOLPHINARIUM'**
- Yellow cab, Blue trailer, Clear plastic tank, two dolphins, girl trainer. Black/Yellow 'window' box with header card on some........................... **£90-110**
- Yellow cab, Yellow trailer, 'window' box with header card on some **£100-150**

Marks & Spencer issues

In 1978 a special series of models and sets were produced for sale through selected M & S stores. They were packed in attractive non-standard boxes and had unique liveries. They were issued in small quantities.

SINGLE MODELS

8800 79 **Custom Van** No details................ **£25-35**

8801 79 **Spindrift Helicopter** Black body with Yellow chassis, floats and rotor blades **£25-35**

8802 79 **Massey Ferguson Tractor** Red/Black body with White arms and Red shovel..................... **£40-50**

8803 79 **Buick 'FIRE CHIEF' Car** Red body with 'City Fire Department' logo on bonnet **£50-75**

SMALL SETS

8000 78 **F1 Racing Set** 162 'ELF' Tyrrell (Dark Blue) and 160 Hesketh F1 (White)....... **£75-100**

8001 78 **Wings Flying Team** 301 Lotus Elite (Green), Nipper aircraft (White), Grey trailer **£100-150**

8002 78 **Motorway Police Patrol** C429 'POLICE' Jaguar (Green) and Blue Fiat X1-9......................... **£60-80**

8003 79 **Spindrift Power Boat Team** 301 Ferrari Daytona (Yellow) and Yellow power boat on trailer. **£60-80**

MEDIUM SETS

8100 78 **Racing Team** C421 Land Rover (White with 'FORMULA' logo), 338 Rover, and 301 Lotus on trailer........... **£150-200**

8101 78 **Wings Flying School** C421 Land Rover (Grey with 'WINGS' logo) Grey helicopter, Nipper aircraft on Grey trailer.. **£150-200**

8102 Motorway Breakdown Set.

8102 78 **Motorway Breakdown** C429 'POLICE' Jaguar, 293 Renault 5 (Yellow) plus Berliet Wrecker with 'RESCUE BREAKDOWN SERVICES' **£100-150**

8103 79 **Spindrift Power Boat Team**
Includes Spindrift 301 Ferrari,
Helicopter and Dinghy **£150-200**

LARGE SETS
8400 78 **GP 'FORMULA 1 RACING TEAM'**
160 Hesketh (White), 162 'ELF' Tyrrell
(Dark Blue), Fiat X1-9 (Blue)
and Land Rover (White) **£200-250**

8401 78 **Wings Flying Club**
Land Rover, Helicopter, Tipsy Nipper
aircraft on trailer, Lotus Elite.... **£200-250**

8402 78 **Motorway Rescue**
'POLICE' Jaguar, Berliet Wrecker,
Renault 5 and Fiat X1-9 ...... **£200-250**

8403 79 **Spindrift Power Boat Team**
Ferrari Daytona (Yellow), Yellow
power boat on trailer, Yellow/Black
helicopter, plus MF Tractor and
'RESCUE' dinghy....................... **£200-250**

Trophy Models
The models were specially produced in 1961 to
be sold by Marks & Spencer. The set consisted of
five vacuum-plated 'gold' models taken from the
existing Corgi product range, each mounted on a
detachable black moulded base with a gold name
label. The models were packaged in white boxes
with red/grey design plus 'St Michael Trophy
Models' in red. They did not sell well at the time
of issue but are keenly sought after by present day
collectors. All have Gold vacuum-plated body and
Red wheels and radiator grille.

150 S 61 Vanwall Racing Car **£100-200**
152 61 BRM Racing Car **£100-200**
300 61 Austin-Healey Sports Car **£100-200**
301 61 Triumph TR2 Sports Car........... **£100-200**
302 61 MG 'MGA' Sports Car................ **£100-200**

Duo Packs
(Film and TV-related models)
1360 82 **Batmobile**
267 plus a Corgi juniors version,
Black/Red/Yellow 'window' box.... **£125-150**
1361 7? **James Bond Aston-Martin**
271 plus a Corgi juniors version,
Black/Red/Yellow 'window' box.... **£100-125**
1362 7? **James Bond Lotus Esprit**
269 plus a Corgi juniors version,
Black/Red/Yellow 'window' box.... **£100-125**
1363 82 **Buck Rogers Set**
647 and a smaller version,

Black/Yellow pictorial 'window' box. **£40-50**
1376 82 **Starsky & Hutch Ford Torino**
292 plus a Corgi Juniors version **£50-70**
1372 ?? **'Magnum PI' Ferrari (298)** **£80-100**

The 'Exploration' Range
A range of fantasy toys introduced in 1980.
D2022 **'SCANOTRON',** Green/Black **£10-15**
D2023 **'ROCKETRON',** Blue/Yellow.............. **£10-15**
D2024 **'LASERTRON',** Orange/Black **£10-15**
D2025 **'MAGNETRON',** Red/Black **£10-15**

'The Muppets Show'
D2030 79 **Kermit's Car**
Yellow car with a famous Green
frog, bubble-packed **£40-45**
80 Same model but in Red/Yellow
pictorial 'window' box **£35-40**
D2031 79 **Fozzie Bear's Truck**
Red/Brown/White truck, Silver or
Black hooter, bubble-packed **£35-40**
80 Same model but in Red/Yellow
pictorial 'window' box **£30-35**
D2032 79 **Miss Piggy's Sport Coupé**
Pink sports car, Red or Pink dress,
bubble-packed **£40-45**
80 Same model but in Red/Yellow
pictorial 'window' box **£35-40**
D2033 79 **Animal's Percussionmobile**
Red traction-engine, Yellow or Red
wheels, Yellow or Black chimney,
Yellow or Silver cymbal.
Bubble-packed **£35-40**
80 Same model but in Red/Yellow
pictorial 'window' box **£30-35**

Qualitoys
A range of sturdy toys made up from the same basic
parts. First issued in 1969, they were aimed at the
pre-school age group. They were publicized as
being from the 'makers of Corgi Toys' and did not
form part of the Corgi range as such.
Though difficult to find, they have little collectable
value at the present time.

Q701 **Pick Up Truck** ....
Q702 **Side Tipper** ....
Q703 **Breakdown Truck** ....
Q704 **Tower Wagon** ....
Q705 **Horse Box** ....
Q706 **Giraffe Transporter** ....
Q707 **Fire Engine** ....

Q708 **Pick Up Trailer** ....

Corgitronics, Corgimatics
These models are generally of plastic construction
and feature a device called 'Battery-operated
Micro-Chip Action'.
1001 82 **HCB Angus Firestreak**
Red/Yellow/White, 'RESCUE',
electronic siren, on/off switch **£60-70**
1002 81 **Sonic Corgi Truck Set**
Yellow/White/Black/Red,
remote control,
SHELL SUPER OIL', 'BP OIL' **£25-30**
1002 81 **'YORKIE' Truck Set**
White/Yellow/Blue/Orange,
remote control,
'MILK CHOCOLATE YORKIE' **£25-30**
1003 81 **Ford Road Hog**
Black, Yellow/White twirls,
2-tone horn, press-down start **£15-20**
1004 81 **'Beep Beep Bus'**
Red, 'BTA WELCOME TO BRITAIN',
2-tone horn, press-down start ... **£20-25**
83 Red body with
'WELCOME TO HAMLEYS'.......... **£20-25**
1005 82 **Police Land Rover**
White/Red/Blue, 'POLICE',
electronic siren, press-down start **£15-20**
1006 82 **'RADIO WEST' Roadshow**
'Your Local Radio 605', AM radio,
advertised but not issued .... **NPP**
1006 82 **'RADIO LUXEMBOURG'**
Red/White, 'RTL 208',
AM radio, 3 loudspeakers............. **£25-30**
1007 82 **Road Repair Unit**
Land Rover and Trailer
Yellow/Red/Silver, 'ROADWORKS',
press start, road drill and sound .. **£25-35**
1008 82 **Fire Chief's Car**
Red/White/Yellow/Silver,
'FIRE DEPARTMENT',
press-down start, siren **£15-20**
1009 83 **MG Maestro 1600**
Yellow/Black, press start,
working front and rear lights........ **£15-20**
Red/Black body. Sold in
Austin-Rover Group box.............. **£20-25**
1024 83 **'Beep Beep Bus'**
Red, 'BTA', supplied exclusively
to Mothercare shops **£20-25**
1121 83 **Ford Transit Tipper Lorry**
Orange/Black, flashing light and
working tipper **£20-25**

Routemaster Buses
Only models thought to have been totally produced by Corgi have been included in these listings.

Identification of Routemaster Double-Decker Bus models

1ST CASTING, 1964 - 1975
MODEL No. 468 ONLY – CLOSED TOP MODEL
Length 114 mm, diecast body comprised two separate castings which make
up the lower and upper decks. The castings are separated by a white plastic joint.

The baseplate is diecast, painted grey and stamped 'Corgi Toys', 'LONDON
TRANSPORT', 'ROUTEMASTER', 'MADE IN ENGLAND' plus the Patent No
904525. The early issues had turned metal wheels with rubber tyres. These
lasted until 1973 when cast metal wheels were introduced with plastic tyres
and in 1974/75 WhizzWheels were seen.

Early issues also had jewelled headlights which were replaced in 1973 by
the cast-in type painted silver. The decals are of the transfer printed variety
and there is a board at the front only. The model has spring suspension,
windows, a metal platform handrail and a driver and clippie. The interior
seats are white or cream.

2ND CASTING, 1975 ONWARDS
CLOSED TOP AND OPEN TOP MODELS
MODEL Nos: C460, C463, C464, C467, C469, C470, C471, C473, C475, C476,
C477, C479, C480, 1004 and all the numbers allocated to the 'Specials'.
Length 123 mm, diecast body comprised two separate castings which make

up the lower and upper decks. The castings are separated by a cream plastic
joint for normal issues and very often by a coloured joint for 'Specials'. Until
Model No 480 was issued as an AEC Renown in 1983 the plastic baseplates
were stamped 'CORGI', 'LONDON TRANSPORT', 'ROUTEMASTER'
and 'MADE IN ENGLAND'. However 'LONDON TRANSPORT' and
'ROUTEMASTER' were removed from this time onwards.

The logos were originally stick-on labels followed by tampo printing in
the mid-1980s. The seats are normally white or cream but other colours
are used for the 'Specials' (eg. Red in the 'BRITISH DIE-CAST MODEL TOYS
CATALOGUE' Special). The model has silver painted cast-in headlights,
spring suspension, windows, a metal platform handrail but apart from the
very early issues does not have a driver or clippie.

The wheels are of the WhizzWheel type. The early issues were of a close
fitting type e.g. 'BTA', 'SWAN & EDGAR', 'DISNEYLAND'. However, by the
time the model was issued they had become protruding. The wheel hubs are
either chrome (earlier models) or painted with plastic tyres.

Routemaster Buses, 1964–1975 (1st casting)
468 64 **'NATURALLY CORGI',**
Red, London Transport, 'CORGI CLASSICS' adverts. **£60-70**
468 64 **'NATURALLY CORGI',** (Australian),
Green/Cream/Brown,
'NEW SOUTH WALES GOVERNMENT TRANSPORT',
'CORGI CLASSICS' adverts. **£1,000-1,250**

468	66	'RED ROSE COFFEE', (Canadian promotional), Red body, driver and clippie, 1st type box................**£1,000-1,250**
468	67	'OUTSPAN ORANGES', (Australian issue) 'NEW SOUTH WALES GOVERNMENT TRANSPORT', Green/Cream/Brown body **£1,000-1,250**

468	67	'OUTSPAN ORANGES', Red, London Transport, '10', (diecast or WhizzWheels)................................**£60-70**
468	68	'GAMAGES', Red, London Transport, '10' **£200-250**
468	69	'CHURCH'S SHOES', Red, London Transport, '10', Union Jacks.................................**£200-250**
468	70	'MADAME TUSSAUDS', Red, London Transport, '10' **£100-175**
468	75	'THE DESIGN CENTRE', Red, London Transport, '10' **£80-100**
468	?	'cokerchu', '2d', Red, London Transport, promo.............**£200-300**

Routemaster Buses, 1975 – 1983 (2nd casting)

C467	77	'SELFRIDGES', Red, London Transport, '12'. Box 1 – standard; Box 2 – 'SELFRIDGES' own **£20-25**
C469	75	'BTA WELCOME TO BRITAIN', Red, London Transport, '11', driver, clippie **£15-20**
C469	76	'THE DESIGN CENTRE', Red, LT, '11', driver, clippie, 'Visit The Design Centre' in black or red **£125-150**
C469	77	'CADBURYS DOUBLE DECKER', Orange, on-pack offer, special box **£12-18**
C469	77	'METTOY Welcomes Swiss Buyers to Swansea' **£300-400**
C469	79	'SELFRIDGES', Red, London Transport, '12'. Re-issue of C467 (see above)......................**£20-25**
C469	79	'LEEDS PERMANENT' BUILDING SOCIETY', 'LEEDS', '22' **£15-20**
C469	79	'SWAN & EDGAR', Red, London Transport, '11' **£25-35**
C469	79	'HAMLEYS', Red, London Transport, '11'..........................**£15-20**
C469	80	'HAMLEYS', Five clowns advert., '6' **£10-15**
C469	78	'BTA', Red, London Transport, ('7', '11' or '12').........**£10-15**
C469	82	'BLACKPOOL ILLUMINATIONS', Cream/Green, '21' **£30-40**
C469	83	'CORGI COLLECTORS VISIT'..............**£300-400**
C469	83	'GAMLEYS', Red, 'Toyshop Of The South' **£10-15**
C469	83	'EAGLE STAR', White/Black, '1 Threadneedle Street' **£10-15**
C469	83	'REDGATES', Cream/Brown (Red seats) '25' **£30-40**
C469	83	'L.T. GOLDEN JUBILEE', Red/White/Silver, 21, '1933-1983 `, (1,000) **£30-40**
C469	83	'BLACKPOOL PLEASURE BEACH', Cream/Green, Blackpool Transport, '23', 'Britain's No.1 Tourist Attraction' **£35-45**

C469	83	As previous model but open top......................**£50-55**
C469	83	'NORBROOK MOTORS', Dark Blue (White seats), '57' **£12-18**
C469	83	As previous model but Red version **£12-18**
C469	83	'DION DION', Dark Blue, 'Saves You More' **£10-15**
		S. African issue: incorrect label 'Saves You Money' **£15-20**
C469	83	'THORNTONS', Brown/Cream, route '14' **£10-15**
C469	83	'MANCHESTER LIONS', Cream, '105BN Manchester' **£15-20**
C469	84	'NEW CORGI COMPANY', Red, '29th March 84', 'South Wales - De Cymru, (2,000) **£15-20**
C469	84	'BRITISH MEAT', Red..........................**£10-15**
C469	?	'COBHAM BUS MUSEUM' **£25-35**
C470	77	'DISNEYLAND', Yellow open top...............**£10-15**
C471	77	'SEE MORE LONDON', Silver, '25', 'The Queen's Silver Jubilee London Celebrations 1977'......**£10-15**
C471	77	'WOOLWORTHS', Silver, '25', 'Woolworths Welcome The World', 'Queens Silver Jubilee 1977' **£20-30**
C523	86	'BRITISH DIECAST MODELTOYS CATALOGUE', Red........**£10-15**
C638	89	'Great Book of CORGI', Yellow/Blue, '1956-1983'. Originally only available with book **£25-35**
C469	83	'BLACKPOOL PLEASURE BEACH', Cream/Green, Blackpool Transport, '23', 'Britain's No.1 Tourist Attraction' **£35-45**
C469	83	As previous model but open top......................**£50-55**
C469	83	'NORBROOK MOTORS', Dark Blue (White seats), '57' **£12-18**
C469	83	As previous model but Red version **£12-18**
C469	83	'DION DION', Dark Blue, 'Saves You More'..........................**£10-15**
		S. African issue: incorrect label 'Saves You Money' **£15-20**
C469	83	'THORNTONS', Brown/Cream, route '14' **£10-15**
C469	83	'MANCHESTER LIONS', Cream, '105BN Manchester' **£15-20**
C469	84	'NEW CORGI COMPANY', Red, '29th March 84', 'South Wales - De Cymru, (2,000) **£15-20**
C469	84	'BRITISH MEAT', Red..........................**£10-15**
C469	?	'COBHAM BUS MUSEUM' **£25-35**
C470	77	'DISNEYLAND', Yellow open top...............**£10-15**
C471	77	'SEE MORE LONDON', Silver, '25', 'The Queen's Silver Jubilee London Celebrations 1977' **£10-15**
C471	77	'WOOLWORTHS', Silver, '25', 'Woolworths Welcome The World', 'Queens Silver Jubilee 1977' **£20-30**
C523	86	'BRITISH DIECAST MODEL TOYS CATALOGUE', Red **£10-15**
C638	89	'Great Book of CORGI', Yellow/Blue, '1956-1983'. Originally only available with book **£25-35**

Corgi Toys Accessories

Model and details	MPR

Corgi Kits

Batley 'Leofric' Garage

601	61-68	Batley 'LEOFRIC' Garage	**£20-25**
602	61-66	'A.A.' and 'RAC' Telephone Boxes	**£50-60**
603	61-66	Silverstone Pits	**£30-40**
604	61-66	Silverstone Press Box	**£50-60**
605	63-67	Silverstone Club House and Timekeepers Box.....................	**£60-70**
606	61-66	Lamp Standards (2)...........	**£5-10**
607	63-67	Circus Elephant and Cage.......	**£45-55**
608	63-66	'SHELL' Filling Station............	**£35-45**
609	63-66	'SHELL' Filling Station Forecourt Accessories	**£25-35**
610	63-66	Metropolitan Police Box and Public Telephone Kiosk	**£60-70**
611	63-66	Motel Chalet	**£25-35**

Self-adhesive accessories

1460	1959	'A' Pack (66 items) including Tax Discs, Number Plates, 'GB'	
		and 'Running-In' labels, etc......	**£10-15**
1461	1959	'B' Pack (36 items) including White-wall tyre trim, ' Styla Sportsdiscs', Number Plates, etc....................	**£10-15**
1462	1959	'C' Pack (69 items) including Number Plates, Commercial and Road Fund Licences (A, B and C), 20 and 30mph Speed Limit and Trailer Plates, etc	**£10-15**
1463	1959	'D' Pack (100 items) including Number Plates, 'Corps Diplomatique' and 'L' Plates, Touring Pennants, etc................	**£10-15**
1464	1961	'E' Pack (86 items) including Assorted Badges, 'Take-Off Wheels', Trade and Licence Plates, etc ...	**£10-15**

Spare wheels

for 'Take-off Wheels' models; bubble-packed on card.

1341	1970	for **344 Ferrari Dino Sport.** Shown in 1969 catalogue but model issued with WhizzWheels	**£10-15**
1342	1968	for **300 Chevrolet Corvette**	**£10-15**
1351	1968	for **275 Rover 2000 TC**	**£10-15**
1352	1968	for **276 Oldsmobile Toronado** . for **338 Chevrolet Camaro** .... for **343 Pontiac Firebird** Shown in 1969 catalogue but model issued without 'Take-off Wheels'	**£10-15** **£10-15**

1353	1970	for 342 Lamborghini P400......... for 302 Hillman Hunter Rally....	**£10-15** **£10-15**
1354	1970	273 Rolls Silver Shadow	**£10-15**
1361	1968	341 Mini Marcos GT 850. (The first 'Take-Off Wheels' model)..	**£10-15**

Figures

1501	63-69	**Racing Drivers and Pit Mechanics** (6)	**£10-15**
1502	63-69	**Silverstone Spectators** (6)	**£10-15**
1503	63-69	**Race Track Officials** (6)	**£10-15**
1504	63-69	**Press Officials** (6).....................	**£10-15**
1505	63-69	**Garage Attendants** (6)............	**£10-15**

Corgi 'Cargoes'

Bubble-packed on card.

1485	1960	**Lorry Load - Planks**	**£10-15**
1486	1960	**Lorry Load - Bricks**	**£10-15**
1487	1960	**Lorry Load - Milk Churns**	**£10-15**
1488	1960	**Lorry Load - Cement**	**£10-15**
1490	1960	**Skip and 3 Churns**	**£10-15**

Spare tyre packs

1449	70-71	New Standard 15 mm.............	**£10-15**
1450	58-70	Standard 15 mm....................	**£10-15**
1451	61-70	Utility Vehicles 17 mm...........	**£10-15**
1452	61-70	Major Models 19 mm	**£10-15**
1453	65-70	Mini Cars 13 mm	**£10-15**
1454	67-70	Tractor wheels (Rear) 33 mm ...	**£10-15**
1455	67-70	Tractor wheels (Front) 19 mm..	**£10-15**
1456	67-70	Racing wheels (Rear) 16 mm ...	**£10-15**
1457	67-70	Racing wheels (Front) 14 mm ...	**£10-15**

1458 67-70 Commercial (Large) 24 mm...... **£10-15**
1459 67-70 Commercial (Medium) 19 mm **£10-15**

Miscellaneous
1401 58-60 Service Ramp (operable).......... **£15-20**
1445 1962 Red bulb for 437 Ambulance **£2-3**
1441 1963 Blue bulb for 464 Police Van **£2-3**
1443 1967 Red flashing bulb, 437 Amb. **£2-3**
1444 1967 Blue flashing bulb, 464 Police.......**£2-3**
1445 1967 Bulb for 'TV' in 262 Lincoln........**£2-3**
1446 1970 Tyres for 1150 Snowplough........**£2-3**
1480 1959 Nose cone, Corporal Missile.........**£2-3**
1497 1967 James Bond Spares
2 Bandits + lapel badge (261) ... **£15-25**

Corgi Club Badge

1498 1967 James Bond Spares
Missiles for 336 Toyota **£10-15**
1499 1967 Green Hornet Spares
Missiles & scanners (268)......... **£10-15**

? 1960s Corgi Club Badge
Gold Corgi dog, Red backing.... **£20-25**
? 62-64 'SHELL' Filling Station and
Garage. Blue/Red/White, single
floor, plastic 'SHELL' logo **£300-400**
? 62-64 'CENTRAL PARK GARAGE'
Blue/Yellow/Red/White, three
floors, 'SKYPARK' logo **£300-400**
24205 1967 Batmobile Accessory Pack
(sprue of missiles).................... **£25-35**

Gift Sets

Original internal packaging for securing models and accessories must all be present before sets can be considered complete and therefore achieve the best price. See Corgi Toys model identification page.

Ref	Year(s)	Set details	MPR

1 1957-62 **Transporter and 4 Cars**
• 1101 Blue/Yellow Bedford Carrimore Transporter plus 201 Austin Cambridge, 208 Jaguar 24, 301 Triumph TR2 (or 300 Austin-Healey) and 302 MGA, plus two Yellow/Black 'Corgi Toys' dummy boxes.................................... **£700-900**
1a 1957-62 **Transporter and 4 Cars**
• 1101 Red/Two-tone Blue Transporter, 200 Ford Consul, 201 Austin Cambridge, 204 Rover 90, 205 Riley, 2 Yellow 'Corgi Toys' dummy boxes................. **£400-500**
1b 1959-62 **Transporter and 4 Cars**
• 1101 Red/Two-tone Blue Transporter, 214 Thunderbird Hardtop, 215 Thunderbird Convertible, 219 Plymouth Suburban, 220 Chevrolet Impala. (US set).......... **£500-750**
• 1101 Yellow/Blue Transporter **£750-1000**
1c 1961-62 **Transporter and 4 Cars**
• 1101 Red/Two-tone Blue Transporter, 210s Citroën (or 217 Fiat 1800), 219 Plymouth Suburban, 226 Mini, 305 Triumph TR3. (US issue set)....... **£400-500**
1 1966-72 **Farm Set**
• Ford 5000 Tractor + 58 Beast Carrier, pictorial stand **£100-120**
1 1983 **Ford Sierra**
• Ford Sierra 299 with Blue body, Blue/Cream Caravan.............................. **£20-30**
2 1958-68 **Land Rover and Pony Trailer**
• 438 Land Rover (Green, Beige tin tilt) and 102 Rice Pony Trailer (Red/Black) **£175-225**
• Same but All Red Land Rover **£175-225**
• Lt. Brown Land Rover (Apricot plastic tilt), Lt. Brown/Cream trailer............. **£175-225**
2 1971-73 **Unimog Dumper and Shovel**
• 1128 Mercedes Tipper and 1145 Unimog Goose. Yellow/Blue 'window' box **£60-70**
2 1980-81 **Construction Set**
• 54 Tractor, 440 Mazda, tool-box and cement mixer................................... **£30-35**
1980-80 French export:
• 1110 and 1156 plus cement mixer......... **£30-40**

Thunderbird Missile Set

3 1959-63 **Thunderbird Missile Set**
• 350 Thunderbird Missile and 351 Land Rover. Blue/Yellow card box **£175-220**
3 1967-69 **Batmobile and Batboat**
• 1st issue: 267 Batmobile with 'Bat' wheels, plus 107 Batboat, in plain Blue 1st issue 'window' box with inner tray and 4 figures, instruction sheet **£500-700**

• 2nd issue: 267 Batmobile with Red wheels (without 'Bat' design), plus 107 Batboat. Yellow/Blue 'window' box should also have unopened instruction pack ...**£900-1,100**
1980
• 3rd issue: 267 Batmobile (plain cast wheels), and 107 Batboat (WW), two figures. Striped 'window' box should also contain instructions in unopened packet **£200-300**
4 1958-60 **Bristol Ferranti Bloodhound Guided Missile Set**
• Contains: 351, 1115, 1116, 1117. Blue/Yellow card box **£250-350**
4 1974-75 **Country Farm Set**
• Models 50 and 62 plus hay load, boy and girl. Yellow/Blue 'window' box ...**£100-125**
5 1959-60 **Racing Car Set**
• 150 (Red), 151 (Blue), 152 (Green). Smooth wheels. Yellow/Blue lift-off lid box, vac-formed inner.......................**£200-300**
1960-61
• 150 (Red), 151 (Blue with Red bonnet stripe), 152 (Green). Flat or cast spoked wheels. Yellow/Blue box, polystyrene tray.....**£300-350**

Bristol Ferranti Bloodhound Guided Missile Set

5s 1962-63 **Racing Car Set**
• 150s (Red), 151a (Blue), 152s (Turquoise). Yellow/Blue box with 'Gift Set 5s' stickers, inner polystyrene tray.........**£400-500**
5 1967-72 **Agricultural Set**
• 484 Livestock Transporter and pigs, 438 Land Rover (no hood) 62, 69, 71, accessories 1490 skip and churns, 4 calves, farmhand and dog, 6 sacks. Box has inner pictorial stand............**£500-750**
5 1976-77 **Country Farm Set**
• As Farm Set 4, but minus boy, girl and hay load **£100-150**
6 1959-60 **'Rocket Age' Set**
• Contains: 350, 351, 352, 353, 1106, 1108, 1117 ....**£3,000-4,000**
6 1967-69 **Cooper-Maserati Set**
• Contains 490 VW Breakdown Truck plus 156 Maserati on trailer. 'Window'/flap box **£150-180**

7 1959-64 **Tractor and Trailer Set**
• 50 Massey-Ferguson 65 Tractor and 51 Trailer. Yellow/Blue card box........ **£300-400**
7 1968-76 **'DAKTARI' Set**
• 438 Land Rover in Green with Black Zebra stripes, spun or cast hubs. 5 figures: Paula, Dr Marsh Tracy with chimp Judy on his lap, a Tiger on the bonnet, and Clarence The Short-Sighted Lion (with spectacles!). Yellow/Blue 'window' box **£175-225**
• With WhizzWheels. Striped box **£100-125**
8 1959-62 **Combine Harvester, Tractor and Trailer Set**
• Contains 1111, 50 and 51. Tractor has Copper seat, Red metal hubs......**£250-300**
8 1968-74 **'Lions of Longleat' Set**
• Land Rover with shaped hubs, keeper, 3 lions, plastic den, 3 joints of meat. Yellow/Blue 'window' box with header card and inner packing **£175-225**
• Same but WW. Striped 'window' box**£100-125**
9 1959-62 **Corporal Guided Missile Set**
• Contains: 1112, 1113, 1118 ....**£300-400**
9 1968-72 **Tractor, Trailer and Shovel Set**
• Contains 66 Ferguson 165 Tractor with 69 Shovel and 62 Tipper with detachable raves. Yellow/Blue all-card box with inner pictorial stand **£200-250**
9 1979-82 **'RNLI' Rescue Set**
• Land Rover and Dinghy on trailer. White, Blue, Red, Black. Striped 'window' box **£75-95**
9 19?? **3 Racing Minis Set**
• Yellow, White and Blue, numbers/stripes and adverts, special 'Hamleys' box.....**£90-110**
10 1968-69 **Marlin Rambler Set**
• Blue/White 319 with Trailer, 2 canoes (1 with figure). Yellow/Blue box, inner packing, pictorial tray **£200-250**
10 1973-78 **Tank Transporter Set**
• Contains 901 Centurion Mk.I Tank and 1100 Mack articulated transporter. Picture card box.................................**£100-120**
10 1982 **Jeep Set**
• Red 441 Jeep motorcycle on trailer **£20-25**
10 1985 **Sierra and Caravan Set**
• C299 Sierra + Pale Brown caravan **£25-35**
11 1960-64 **ERF Dropside and Trailer**
• 456 and 101 with cement and planks load. Yellow/Blue picture box, inner card stand.................................**£125-175**
• As above but WhizzWheels **£90-110**
11 1971-72 **London Transport Set**
• Contains 418 Taxi, 468 'OUTSPAN' Bus, 226 Mini (Deep Blue), policeman on stand, Striped 'window' box with inner tray.................................**£140-160**
• 1980-82. C425 Taxi with C469 Bus 'B.T.A.' and policeman figure.........**£35-45**
12 1961-64 **'Chipperfields Circus' Set**
• 1121 Crane Truck 'CHIPPERFIELDS'

and 1123 Circus Cage, plus instructions.
Yellow/Blue all-card picture box....... **£250-350**

12 1968-71 **Grand Prix Racing Set**
- 155, 156 and 330 with 490 VW tender,
3 mechanics, 16 bollards and hay bales.
Yellow/Blue 'window' box also contains
cones in bag, instructions, 'Mr Retailer'
card and inner polystyrene tray **£350-450**
- 1971-72. 158, 159 and 330 (or 371) with
490 Volkswagen tender, 3 mechanics,
16 bollards and hay bales. The artwork
on the box and the vac-formed base
are different from previous issue **£250-350**

12 1981- **Glider and Trailer Set**
- 345 with Trailer and Glider.................... **£50-60**

13 1964-66 **Fordson Tractor and Plough Set**
- Contains 60 Fordson Power Major Tractor
and 61 Four Furrow Plough in Blue,
Orange plastic front and rear hubs.
Yellow/Blue box with inner tray........ **£250-350**

13 1968-72 **Renault 16 Film Unit**
- White/Black, 'TOUR DE FRANCE' ,
'PARAMOUNT', cameraman, cyclist.
Yellow/Blue box with inner tray plus
plain orange card backdrop.............. **£250-300**

13 1981-82 **Tour de France**
'RALEIGH' Team Car
- 373 Peugeot, White body, Red/Yellow
'RALEIGH' / 'TOTAL' logos, racing
cycles, Manager with loudhailer **£150-175**

14 1961-64 **Tower Wagon Set**
- 409 Jeep, Yellow cradle, lamp standard,
electrician. Yellow/Blue card box **£100-120**

14 1969-73 **Giant 'DAKTARI' Set**
- Gift Set and items plus 503 and 484
transporters (spun hubs), large and small
elephants. Blue/Yellow window box with
pictorial header card, inner tray **£250-350**
- Version with WhizzWheels. Striped
'window' box with pictorial header
card and inner tray **£150-200**

15 1963-64 **Silverstone Set**
- 150s, 151a, 152s, 215s, 304s,
309, 417s, 3 buildings,
plain box (no picture) **£1,500-2,500**
1964-66
- 150s, 154, 152s, 215s, 304s, 309, 417s,
3 buildings, layout on box............ **£1,500-2,500**

15 1968-77 **Land Rover and Horsebox Set**
- Contains 438, 112, spun hubs, mare and
foal. Yellow/Blue box contains inner
polystyrene tray **£100-150**
- Version with WhizzWheels. Striped
'window' box has inner tray packing ... **£55-75**

15 1986 **'TARMAC' Motorway Set**
- 'Motorway Maintenance' Green/Black
1128 Mercedes Tipper, Mazda Pickup
and a compressor **£20-30**

16 1961-65 **'ECURIE ECOSSE' Set**
- 1126 Transporter with 3 individually boxed
racing cars in all-card lift-off lid box with
instruction leaflet and internal packing.
Metallic Dark Blue 1126 Transporter (with
Orange lettering), 150 Vanwall (Red, '25'),
151 Lotus XI (Blue, RN '3'), 152 BRM
(Turquoise, RN '3') **£400-500**
- Met. Dk. Blue 1126 Transporter (with
Yellow lettering), 150s Vanwall, 151a
Lotus XI (Blue, '7'), 152s BRM........... **£400-500**
- 1965. Met. Light Blue 1126 Transporter
(with Red Lettering), 150s Vanwall,
152s BRM, 154 Ferrari (RN '36')........ **£380-480**
- Met. Dk. Blue 1126 Transporter (with
Light Blue lettering and ridges), 150s
Vanwall, 152s BRM, 154 Ferrari......... **£300-350**

17 1963-67 **Ferrari Racing Set**
- 438 Land Rover in Red with Green top,
Red 154 Ferrari F1 on Yellow trailer.
Yellow/Blue box has inner tray **£225-275**

17 1977-80 **Military Set**
- Contains 904, 906, 920 .... **£40-50**

18 1961-63 **Ford Tractor and Plough Set**
- 55 Fordson Power Major Tractor and
56 Four Furrow Plough in Blue/Red/Yellow.
Drab Orange hubs. Yellow/Blue box
with inner tray..................................... **£200-250**

Ferrari Racing Set

18 1975-80 **Emergency Gift Set**
- Contains 402, 481, C921 .... **£60-70**

18/1 19?? **3 Mini Racers Set**
- CHELSEA, 'PARK LANE' and
'PICADILLY' logos **£20-30**

18/2 19?? **Mini Special Editions Set**
- with 'RED HOT', 'RITZ' and
'JET BLACK' logos **£20-30**

NB C18/1 and C18/2 were sold (in long
'window' boxes) exclusively by Woolworths.

'Chipperfields' Cage Set

19 1962-68 **'CHIPPERFIELDS' Cage Set**
- 1st issue: 438 Land Rover (metal tilt) and
607 Elephant and cage on trailer.
Blue/Yellow picture box has inner
card tray + additional packing........... **£250-300**
- 2nd issue: As before but 438 Land
Rover has a plastic tilt **£175-225**

19 19?? **'RNLI' Set**
- 438 Land Rover plus Orange dinghy on
trailer with 'Mumbles Lifeboat' logo **£60-70**

19 1972-77 **Land Rover and Nipper Aircraft**
- 438 Land-Rover (Blue/Orange, tinplate tilt)
+ trailer. Blue/Orange/Yellow plane '23' or
Blue/Orange/White plane '23'.
Yellow/Blue 'window' box **£60-70**

19 1973-77 **'CORGI FLYING CLUB'**
- As previous set but Land-Rover
has a plastic tilt **£45-60**

19 1979-82 **Emergency Gift Set**
- C339 and C921. Striped 'window' box.. **£40-60**

19 1980-82 **Emergency Gift Set**
- C339 and C931 in Red/White.
Striped 'window' box **£40-60**

20 1961-64 **'Golden Guinea' Set**
- Gold-plated 224 Bentley Continental,
234 Ford Consul, 229 Chevrolet Corvair,
Catalogue, 2 Accessory Packs. Inner
card tray with lower card packing, outer
Dark Green sleeve with window **£400-500**

20 1970-73 **Tri-Deck Transporter Set**
(Scammell Handyman Mk.III)
- 1st issue contains 1146 Transporter with six
'WhizzWheels' cars: 210 'Saint's' Volvo,
311 Ford Capri, 343 Pontiac, 372 Lancia,
377 Marcos, 378 MGC GT (Red body).
Instruction sheet, 'Mr Retailer' transit
card protector **£600-700**

NB GS 20 may be found with widely
differing contents as Corgi used up excess
stock in this Set.
- Harrods set: Late issue set with:
1146 Transporter, 382 Porsche Targa

(Silver Blue), 313 Ford Cortina GXL
(Bronze/Black), 201 Volvo (Orange 'Saint'
label), 334 Mini (Orange) and
377 Marcos (Silver Green).
Box also has instruction sheet and
'Mr Retailer' transit card protector ... **£600-700**

20 1978-80 **Emergency Gift Set**
- C429, C482, C921. Box has inner tray ... **£35-45**

21 1962-66 **ERF Dropside and Trailer**
- 456 and 101 with milk churns and
self-adhesive accessories. Yellow/Blue
box with inner card stand **£225-275**

21 1969-71 **'Chipperfields' Circus Set**
- Contains 1144 Crane and Cage, and
1139 Menagerie Transporter.
Yellow/Blue window box with
internal packaging and
'Mr Dealer' box protector card....**£1,400-1,600**

21 1980-82 **Superman Set**
- Contains 260, 265 and 925, plus inner
tray and plastic rockets on sprue **£100-125**

22 1962-65 **Farming Set**
- Contains 1111 M-F Combine Harvester,
406 Land-Rover and Trailer,
51 Tipping Trailer, 101 Platform Trailer,
53 M-F 65 Tractor with Shovel,
1487 Milk Churns, 1490 Skip and
3 churns, plus models in Gift Set 18.
Lift-off lid all-card picture box
with inner polystyrene tray.........**£1,500-2,000**

22 1980-82 **James Bond Set**
- 269 Lotus Esprit, 271 Aston-Martin DB5
and 649 Space Shuttle + rockets, 2 spare
bandit figures. Box has inner tray **£350-450**

23 1962-66 **'CHIPPERFIELDS' Set**
- 1st issue: 1121 Crane Truck, 2 x 1123
Animal Cages (2 lions, 2 polar bears),
plus Gift Set 19 and 426 Booking Office.
All-card lift-off lid picture box with
inner polystyrene tray **£400-500**
1964
- 2nd issue: as 1st issue but 503 'TK Giraffe
Truck' replaces 426 Booking Office,
inner polystyrene tray **£300-400**

23 1980-82 **Spiderman Set**
- 261 Spiderbuggy, 266 Spiderbike,
928 Spidercopter with figures, missiles
on sprue. In striped 'window' box **£150-200**

24 1963-68 **Commer Constructor Set**
- 2 cab/chassis units, 4 interchangeable
bodies plus milkman and accessories.
Yellow/Blue picture box with lift-off
lid and inner polystyrene tray **£100-130**

24 1976-78 **Mercedes and Caravan**
- 285 in Metallic Blue plus 490 Caravan
in White. Striped 'window' box **£30-40**
- 1979. 285 in Met. Brown plus 490 Caravan
in Bronze. Striped 'window' box **£30-40**

25 1963-66 **BP or Shell Garage Set**
- 224, 225, 229, 234 and 419 all in Blue/
Yellow boxes plus: 601 Batley Garage,
602 'AA' and 'RAC' Boxes, 606 Lamp
Standards (2), 608 Filling Station, 609
accessories, 1505 Figures. Plain card box
with or without layout picture.....**£1,000-1,500**
Contains No224 Bentley Continental,
No225 Austin Seven, No229 Chevrolet
Corvair, No234 Ford Consul, No419 Ford
Zephyr, Motorway Patrol, No601 Bentley
Garage x 3, No606 Lamp Standards x 2,
No608 Shell filling station, No609 Shell
filling station accessories, No1505
Garage Attendants.

25 1969-71 **Racing Car and Tender**
- 159 and VW Tender, 2 sets of decals in
stapled bags. Blue/Yellow window
box, inner plastic tray......................... **£120-150**

25 1980-81 **Talbot Rancho Set**
- 457 plus two motorcycles on trailer **£25-30**

26 1971-76 **Beach Buggy Set**
- 381 plus Red Sailing Boat with Blue
sail. Orange/Yellow 'window' box......... **£40-50**

26 1981-83 **Corgi Racing Set**
- 457 Talbot Matra Rancho, 160 Hesketh (Yellow), 'Corgi Racing Team' trailer **£35-45**

27 1963-72 **Priestman Shovel on Machinery Carrier**
- 1128 and 1131 (Bedford). Blue/Yellow box with inner tray........ **£175-225**

28 1963-65 **Transporter and 4 Cars**
- 1105 Bedford TK Transporter with 222 Renault Floride, 230 Mercedes-Benz, 232 Fiat, 234 Ford Classic, 2 dummy 'Corgi Toys' boxes, instructions. Pictorial box, internal card packing.. **£400-500**

28 1975-78 **Mazda B1600 Dinghy Set**
- 493 Mazda + dinghy and trailer. Striped 'window' box **£35-40**

Massey-Ferguson Set

29 1963-65 **Massey-Ferguson Set**
- Contains 50 Massey-Ferguson Tractor with driver and 51 Tipper Trailer - Cream/Yellow, Red plastic rear hubs. Yellow/Blue all-card box with inner tray **£250-300**

29 1981-82 **'CORGI' Pony Club**
- Contains 441 Jeep, 112 trailer, girl on pony, 3 jumps, 3 hay bales. Striped 'window' box **£55-65**

29 1975-76 **'DUCKHAMS' F1 Racing Set**
- Surtees Racing Set with 323 Ferrari Daytona and 150 Ferrari in Blue/Yellow 'DUCKHAMS RACING TEAM' livery. Striped 'window' box **£35-40**

30 1973-73 **Grand Prix Gift Set**
- 'Kit' versions of 151 Yardley (1501), 154 JPS (1504), 152 Surtees (1502) plus 153 Surtees (1503)? in unique Norris livery. Picture 'window' box. Mail order only **£100-120**

30 1979-80 **Circus Gift Set**
- Land Rover and Trailer **£60-75**

31 1964-68 **Buick Riviera Boat Set**
- 245 Buick, Red boat trailer, and Dolphin Cabin Cruiser towing lady water-skier. Pictorial sleeve box with internal packing display tray around models. **£250-350**

31 1976-80 **Safari Land Rover Set**
- C341 Land Rover with animal trailer, Warden and Lion. Box has inner polystyrene tray **£35-45**

The 'RIVIERA' Gift Set

Buick Riviera Boat Set

32 1965-68 **Tractor, Shovel and Trailer Set**
- 54 Massey-Ferguson 65 Tractor, 69 Shovel, 62 Tipping Trailer with detachable raves - Red/Cream/Yellow. Yellow/Blue picture box with inner pictorial stand **£250-300**

32 1976-79 **Lotus Racing Set**
- C301 Lotus Elite, and C154 JPS Lotus on trailer **£100-125**
- 1979-83. C301 Lotus Elite, and C154 Texaco Lotus on trailer **£35-45**

33 1965-68 **Tractor and Beast Carrier**
- Contains 55 and 58 .... **£200-250**
- 1968-72. Contains 67 and 58 .... **£80-100**

33 1980-82 **'DLRG' Rescue Set**
- White/Red 421 Land Rover and boat on trailer **£50-70**

34 1976-79 **Tractor & Tipping Trailer**
- Contains 55 and 56 .... **£55-65**

35 1964-68 **London Traffic Set**
- 418 Taxi with 468 'Corgi Toys' or 'Outspan' Bus, policeman on stand. Yellow/Blue box, inner tray **£200-300**

35 1978-79 **'CHOPPER SQUAD' Surf Boat**
- Contains 927, 419, trailer, rescue boat .. **£30-40**

36 1967-70 **Marlin Rambler Set**
- Contains 263 and Boat **£45-65**

36 1967-71 **Oldsmobile Toronado Set**
- 276 (Greenish-Blue), Chrome trailer, Yellow/Blue 'SWORDFISH' boat, 3 figures. Yellow/Blue box **£200-300**

36 1983 **Off-Road Set**
- 447 (Dark Blue/Cream, RN '5') plus power-boat on trailer **£25-35**

36 1976-78 **Tarzan Set**
- Light Green 421 Land Rover and trailer, paler Green 'zebra' stripes, Tarzan, Jane, Cheetah (chimp), boy, dinghy with hunter, elephant, snake, vines, etc. Yellow/Blue 'window' box with inner pictorial backing display......... **£250-350**

37 1966-69 **'Lotus Racing Team'**
- 490 VW Breakdown Truck, Red trailer with cars 318, 319, 155, plus 2 sets of spare racing numbers ('5' and '9' or '4' and '8'), a 1966 illustrated checklist, a sealed pack of cones, set of bollards and a spare Lotus chassis unit. Yellow/Blue 'window' box has inner polystyrene tray **£400-500**

37 1979-80 **Fiat X-19 Set**
- Fiat X-19 and Boat 'Carlsberg' **£30-40**

38 1977-78 **Mini 1000 Camping Set**
- Cream Mini with 2 figures, tent, barbecue, in inner display stand....... **£100-130**

38 1965-67 **'1965 Monte Carlo Rally'**
- 318 Mini Cooper 'S', 322 Rover 2000, and 326 Citroën DS19. Monte Carlo Rally emblem on each bonnet. Yellow/Blue all-card box contains pictorial stand and inner card packing **£1,000-1,250**

38 1980- **Jaguar XJS Set**
- 319 with Powerboat on Trailer **£20-30**

40 1966-69 **'The Avengers' Set**
- John Steed's Bentley (Green body, Red wire wheels), Emma Peel's Lotus Elan (Black/White body), Steed and Emma Peel figures, 3 Black umbrellas. Yellow/Blue picture box with inner pictorial stand **£500-600**
- With Red/Black Bentley with Silver wire wheels **£350-450**

40 1976-82 **'Batman' Gift Set**
- Contains modified 107 Trailer plus 267 Batmobile (WW) and 925 Helicopter. 12 missiles on a sprue. Striped box also has inner tray with card packing....... **£500-600**

41 1966-68 **Carrimore Car Transporter with Ford Tilt Cab**
- 1138 Transporter (Red/Two-tone Blue), 252 Rover 2000 (Metallic Plum), 251 Hillman Imp (Metallic Bronze), 440 Ford Cortina Estate (Metallic Blue), 226 Morris Mini-Minor (Light Blue), 321 Austin Mini Cooper 'S' (Red, RN '2', '1966 Monte Carlo Rally', with roof signatures), 249 Morris Mini Cooper DeLuxe (Black/Red, 'wickerwork' panels). Pictorial lift-off lid box with inner polystyrene tray. Only sold by mail order...................... **£750-850**

41 1969-69 **Carrimore Car Transporter with Scammell Cab**
- 1148 Transporter (Red/Two-tone Blue), 226 Morris Mini-Minor (Metallic Maroon), 345 MGC GT (Orange in earliest sets, Yellow/Black later), 340 Sunbeam Imp (1967 Monte Carlo, Metallic Blue, RN '77'), 258 Saint's Volvo P1800 (White with Orange label), 249 Morris Mini Cooper DeLuxe (Black/Red with 'wickerwork' panels), 339 Mini Cooper 'S' ('1967 Monte Carlo Rally', RN '177'), plus sealed bag of cones and leaflet. Pictorial lift-off lid box with inner polystyrene tray. Only sold by mail order **£750-850**

41 1977-81 **Silver Jubilee Set**
- The State Landau, HRH Queen Elizabeth and Prince Phillip (+ a Corgi!) **£15-20**

42 1978-79 **Agricultural Set**
- Contains 55 David Brown Tractor plus 56 Trailer, Silo and Elevator............... **£100-125**

43 1979-80 **Silo and Conveyor Set**
- 'CORGI HARVESTING COMPANY Ltd' **£40-50**

44 1978-80 **Metropolitan Police Set**
- 421 Land Rover, 112 Horsebox, Policeman on horse. Striped 'window' box............. **£40-50**

44 1978-80 **Mounted Police Set**
- French issue, Policeman on horse **£50-75**

45 1966 **'All Winners' Set**
- 261 James Bond's Aston-Martin, 310 Chevrolet Stingray, 324 Marcos Volvo, 325 Ford Mustang Competition, 314 Ferrari Berlinetta. Yellow/Blue 'window' box **£350-450**

45 1978-79 **Royal Canadian Police Set**
- Land Rover (421), Trailer (102), 'Mountie' on horse **£125-150**

46 1966-69 **'All Winners' Set**
- 264 Oldsmobile Toronado (Metallic Blue), 307 Jaguar 'E'-type (Chrome finish, RN '2', driver), 314 Ferrari Berlinette (Red, RN '4'), 337 Chevrolet Stingray (Yellow, RN '13'), 327 MGB GT (Red/Black, suitcase). Box should contain unopened bag of cones and decal sheets **£500-660**

46 1982 **Super Karts Set**
- Red Kart, Purple Kart, with Silver/Red driver in each ....NGPP

47 1966-71 **Ford 5000 Tractor and Conveyor Set**
- Contains 67, trailer with conveyor belt, figure and accessories. Box has inner display card................. **£200-250**

47 1978-80 **Pony Club Set**
- 421 Land Rover and Horsebox in Metallic Bronze, girl on pony figure...... **£35-40**

48 1967-68 **Carrimore Car Transporter with Ford Tilt Cab**
- 1138 Transporter (Orange/Silver/Two-tone Blue) with 252 Rover 2000 (Metallic Plum), 251 Hillman Imp (Metallic Maroon), 440 Ford Cortina Estate (Metallic Blue), 249 Morris Mini Cooper DeLuxe (with 'wickerwork' panels), 226 Morris Mini-Minor (Metallic Maroon), 321 Mini Cooper 'S' ('1966 Monte Carlo Rally', Red/White, RN '2'. Blue/Yellow 'window' box with inner polystyrene packing......... **£600-800**
- 1968 'SUN/RAC' variation: As previous set but 321 Mini Cooper is replaced by 333 SUN/RAC Rally Mini. 251 Hillman Imp is changed to Metallic Gold with White stripe and the 226 Austin 7 Mini is now Metallic Blue with RN '21'...................................... **£700-900**

48 1969 **Carrimore Car Transporter with Scammell Cab**
- 1148 Transporter (Red/White) with 345 MGB (Orange), 340 Sunbeam Imp (1967 Monte Carlo, Metallic Blue, RN '77'), 258 Saint's Volvo P1800 (White with Orange label), 249 Morris Mini Cooper

DeLuxe (with 'wickerwork' panels), 339 Mini Cooper 'S' ('1967 Monte Carlo Rally', RN '177'), 226 Morris Mini-Minor (Metallic Maroon), plus sealed bag of cones and leaflet. Blue/Yellow 'window' box, inner polystyrene packing **£500-750**

48 1978-80 **'PINDER' Circus Set**
- Contains C426, C1163, C30, ringmaster, artistes, animals, seating, and cardboard cut-out 'Jean Richard Pinder' 'Big-Top' circus tent. Striped 'window' box...... **£100-110**

49 1978-80 **'CORGI FLYING CLUB'**
- Metallic Green/White Jeep (419) with Blue/White Tipsy Nipper Aircraft **£50-60**

51 19?? **'100 Years of the Car' Set**
- 3 Mercedes: C805 (White), C806 (Black), C811 (Red), Originally for Germany **£20-25**

? 1978-80 **'The Jaguar Collection'**
- C804 (Cream), C816 (Red), C318 (Mobil Green/White). ('UNIPART' stores) **£30-35**

53 19??-?? **Land Rover and Thunderbirds Missile Set**
- Models as listed **£500-750**

54 1978-80 **Swiss Rega Set**
- Bonna Ambulance and Helicopter **£30-35**

55 1978-80 **Norway Emergency Set**
- Police Car, Breakdown Truck, Ford Transit Ambulance, 'UTRYKKNINGUSSETT' **£20-30**

56 1978-80 **Swedish Set**
- Ford 'POLIS', Bonna Ambulance **£12-18**

57 1978-80 **Swedish Set**
- Contains Volvo and Caravan **£12-18**

57 1978-80 **Volvo 740 and Caravan**
- Red Volvo, White/Red/Blue Caravan. Swedish export **£15-20**

61 1978-80 **Swiss 'FEUERWEHR' Set**
- 1120 Dennis Fire Engine, Sierra 'POLITZEI', Escort Van 'NOTRUF'......... **£30-35**

64 1965-69 **FC Jeep 150 and Conveyor Belt**
- Jeep (409) Yellow/White Conveyor ... **£100-130**

65 1978-80 **Norway Set**
- Ford Transit Ambulance plus Helicopter **£20-30**

67 1978-80 **Cyclists Sets**
- Sold in France, 2 Cars, 2 Bicycles. Three sets: 67/1, 67/2, 67/3 ... Each set: **£20-30**

70 1978-80 **Danish 'FALCK' Set**
- Bonna Ambulance and Ford Breakdown Truck **£20-30**

72 1978-80 **Norway Set**
- With C542 plus Helicopter 'LN OSH'.... **£20-30**

1151 1970 **Scammell 'Co-op' Set**
- Blue/White 1147, 466 and 462. Promo in brown box.......................... **£500-580**

? 1967 **Monte Carlo Game** (Scandinavian set)
- Fernel Developments game with two Lavender 226 Minis, '1967 Rallye Monte Carlo' bonnet labels, RNs '1' and '4',

plastic/paper winding roads, cards, dice shakers, Blue/White/Red box............ **£350-450**

? 1980 **Construction Site Set**
- Contains 54 with 440 (Mazda Pick-Up) £30-35

US EXPORT SETS — made exclusively for FAO Schwarz of America.

FAO-012
c1966 **'BEST IN SHOW' Animal Gift Set**
- Contains: GS2 Land-Rover with Rice's Pony Trailer, 484 Dodge Kew Fargo and 486 Chevrolet Impala 'Kennel Club'. Blue/Yellow individual card boxes, Blue/Yellow presentation box **£1,500-2,000**

FAO-804
c1968 **'CIRCUS' Set**
- Contains: GS7 'Daktari' Set, 470 Forward Control Jeep, 1123 'Chipperfields' Circus Animal Cage and GS19 'Chipperfields Circus' Land-Rover and Elephant Cage on Trailer. Blue/Yellow individual boxes, Blue/Yellow presentation box **£1,750-2,250**

? 1995 **'The Italian Job'**
- Produced by TMC Marketing for Rover MG to celebrate shipment of real Minis. Finished in Red, White and Blue with 'Longbridge Channel Tunnel Crossing 1965' decal on roof. 1:36 scale, on wooden plinth and in presentation box. Only100 sets issued **£200-300**

'Husky' Models and 'Corgi Juniors'

Husky models were introduced by Mettoy Playcraft in 1965 to compete with the Matchbox 1-75 range. These small-scale models have plenty of detail and action features and the range includes cars, commercials, military and film/TV specials.

The models have either a plastic or diecast chassis together with various types of regular wheels and WhizzWheels. Models could only be obtained from Woolworths stores and were only sold in blister packs. Production under the 'Husky' trade name ceased in 1969 and the range was reissued in 1970 as 'Corgi Juniors'. To facilitate this change, 'HUSKY' was removed from the baseplates which were then re-engraved 'CORGI JUNIORS'.

The models were mostly fitted with WhizzWheels to enable them to be used on the 'Rocket Track' and to compete against the new Matchbox 'Superfast' range. Corgi Juniors were blister packed on blue/white card for the 'regular' issues and red/white card for the 'specials'. Each pack incorporated a 'Collectors' Card' picture of the real vehicle and these could be cut out and pasted into a special collectors' album.

The Market Price Range shown for 'Husky' and 'Corgi Juniors' refers only to mint condition models in unopened blister packs (and later in pristine boxes).

'Husky' models 1965–1969

Model and details			MPR
1	65-69	**Jaguar Mk.10**	
		All have Yellow interior.	
1-a1	65-66	(small), Met. Blue, GPW........	**£20-25**
1-a2	1966	(small), Red body, GPW........	**£50-60**
1-b1	1967	Light Metallic Blue, GPW	**£20-25**
1-b2	1967	Blue body, GPW.....................	**£25-30**
1-b3	1968	Light Met. Blue body, tyres	**£25-30**
1-b4	1968	Cream body, tyres..................	**£45-55**
1-b5	1969	Dark Blue body, tyres............	**£25-30**
1-b6	1969	Dark Maroon body, tyres.......	**£30-35**
2	65-69	**Citroën Safari with Boat**	
2-a1	65-66	(small casting) Pale Yellow body, Tan green, GPW............	**£20-25**
2-b1	1967	Metallic Green body, Brown boat, GPW	**£50-60**
2-b2	1967	Metallic Gold body, Blue boat, GPW......................	**£40-45**
2-b3	68-69	Met. Gold, Blue boat, tyres.....	**£20-25**
3-a1	65-67	**Mercedes 220** Pale Blue, GPW	**£15-20**
3-bt	67-68	**Volkswagen Police Car** White/Black doors, smooth hubs with tyres......	**£25-30**
3-b2	1969	With detailed hubs / tyres......	**£25-30**

Mercedes 220

Model and details			MPR
4	65-69	**Jaguar Fire Chief**	
4-a1	65-66	(small casting), Red body, chrome siren, 'Fire', GPW	**£25-30**
4-bl	1967	as previous model..................	**£25-30**
4-b2	68-69	Same but with tyres	**£30-35**

Jaguar Fire Chief

Model and details			MPR
5-a1	1965	Lancia Flaminia, Red, GPW ...	**£45-55**
5-a2	65-66	Blue, GPW..............................	**£15-20**
5-b1	67-69	**Willys Jeep,** Metallic Green, Grey windshield	**£15-20**
5-b2	67-69	With Yellow windshield..........	**£25-30**
6-a1	65-67	**Citroën Safari Ambulance,** White, Red cross, GPW	**£20-25**

Ferrari Berlinetta

6-b1	68-69	**Ferrari Berlinetta** Red body, tyres........................	**£25-30**
6-b2	68-69	Maroon body, tyres................	**£25-30**
7-a1	65-66	**Buick Electra** Orange-Red, GPW..................	**£15-20**

7-b1	1967	**Duple Vista 25 Coach**	
		Green/White, GPW	£30-35
7-b2	68-69	Same but with tyres	£20-25

Guy Warrior Coal Truck

8-a1	65-66	**Ford Thunderbird** (open)	
		Pink, Black open body, GPW .	£30-35
8-b1	1967	**Ford Thunderbird Hardtop**	
		Yellow, Blue top, GPW	£45-55
8-c1	67-69	**Tipping Farm Trailer**	
		Yellow, Red back, GPW	£10-15
9-a1	65-67	**Buick 'Police' Patrol**	
		Dark Blue, GPW	£20-25
9-b1	68-69	**Cadillac Eldorado**	
		Light Blue, tyres	£20-25
10-a1	65-67	**Guy Warrior Coal Truck**	
		Red, GPW	£15-20
10-a2	68-69	Same model	£15-20

Forward Control Land Rover

11-a1	65-67	**Forward Control Land Rover**	
		Green body (shades), metal or plastic base, rear corner windows, GPW	£15-20
11-a2	68-69	Same, but Metallic Green, no corner windows, GPW	£15-20
12-a1	65-66	**Volkswagen Tower Wagon**	
		Yellow/Red, GPW	£20-25
12-b1	1967	**Ford Tower Wagon**	
		Yellow, Red tower, GPW	£30-35
12-b2	1967	White, Red tower, GPW	£30-35
12-b3	68-69	White, Red tower, tyres	£20-25

Guy Warrior Sand Truck

13-a1	65-66	**Guy Warrior Sand Truck**	
		Yellow, GPW	£15-20
13-a2	67-68	Blue, GPW	£15-20
13-a3	1969	Blue, tyres	£20-25
14-a1	65-66	**Guy Warrior Tanker 'Shell'**	
		Yellow, round tank, GPW	£20-25
14-b1	1967	Same, square tank	£20-25
14-b2	1967	**Guy Warrior Tanker 'Esso'**	
		White, square tank, GPW	£20-25
14-b3	68-69	Same, but with tyres	£20-25

VW Pick Up

15-a1	65-66	**VW Pick Up,** Turquoise, GPW	£15-20
15-b1	67-68	**Studebaker Wagonaire TV Car**	
		Yellow body, GPW	£20-25
15-b2	1968	Metallic Blue body, GPW	£25-30
15-b3	1969	Metallic Blue body, tyres	£25-30
16-a1	65-66	**Dump Truck/Dozer**	
		Yellow, Red back, GPW	£15-20
16-a2	1966	**Dump Truck/Dozer**	
		Red, Grey back, GPW	£20-25
17	65-69	**Guy Warrior 'Milk' Tanker**	
17-a1	65-66	White, round tank, GPW	£20-25
17-b1	1967	White, square tank, GPW	£20-25
17-b2	1968	Cream, round tank, GPW	£20-25
17-b3	1969	Cream, round tank, tyres	£20-25
18-a1	65-66	**Plated Jaguar** (small casting)	
		Chrome, GPW	£20-25
18-bi	67-68	Same, but larger casting	£20-25
18-b2	1969	Larger casting, tyres	£30-35
19-a1	1966	**Commer Walk Thro' Van**	
		Red body, GPW	£40-45
19-a2	66-67	Green body, GPW	£25-30
19-b1	68-69	**Speedboat on Trailer**	
		Gold trailer, Red, White and Blue boat, tyres	£15-20
20-a1	65-66	**Ford Thames Van**	
		Red, Yellow ladder, GPW	£20-25
20-b1	1967	**VW 1300 with Luggage**	
		Tan body, tyres	£35-45
20-b2	67-69	With Blue body	£20-25
21-a1	66-67	**Forward Control Military Land Rover,** GPW	£15-20
21-b1	68-69	**Jaguar 'E'-type** 2+2	
		Maroon body, tyres	£20-25
22-a1	65-66	**Citroën Safari Military Ambulance,** GPW	£20-25
22-b1	67-68	**Aston-Martin DB6**	
		Metallic Gold body, GPW	£20-25
22-b2	68-69	**Aston-Martin DB6**	
		Purple body, tyres	£30-35
23-a1	66-67	**Guy Army Tanker,** GPW	£15-20
23-b1	1968	**Loadmaster Shovel**	
		Orange body, BPW	£25-30
23-b2	68-69	Yellow body, BPW	£15-20
24-a1	66-67	**Ford Zephyr Estate**	
		Blue body, GPW	£20-25
24-a2	68-69	**Ford Zephyr Estate**	
		Red, GPW	£25-30
25-a1	66-67	**SD Refuse Van,** Blue, GPW	£15-20
25-a2	1968	Red body, GPW	£40-50
25-a3	68-69	Red body, tyres	£40-45

Sunbeam Alpine

26-a1	66-67	**Sunbeam Alpine**	
		Metallic Bronze body, Blue hard top, GPW	£25-30

26-a2	1967	Same, but Red body, GPW	£45-55
26-a3	68-69	Red body, Blue top, tyres	£50-55
27-a1	66-67	**Bedford Skip Lorry**	
		Maroon body, GPW	£20-25
27-a2	1967	**Bedford Skip Lorry**	
		Dark Green body, GPW	£50-60
27-a3	1967	Orange body, GPW	£20-25
27-a4	68-69	Orange body, tyres	£20-25
28-a1	66-67	**Ford Breakdown Truck**	
		Blue, metal jib, GPW	£15-20
28-a2	68-69	Blue, Gold jib, tyres	£20-25
29-a1	66-67	**ERF Cement Mixer,**	
		Yellow, Red barrel, GPW	£15-20
29-a2	68-69	Yellow, Red barrel, tyres	£20-25
30-a1	66-67	**Studebaker Wagonaire Ambulance,** White, Red Cross, stretcher, GPW	£25-30
30-a2	68-69	Same, but with tyres	£25-30
30-a3	1969	**Studebaker Wagonaire**	
		Pale Green body, tyres	£35-40
31-a1	66-67	**Oldsmobile Starfire Coupé**	
		Olive Green body, GPW	£15-20
31-a2	68-69	Same but with tyres	£20-25
32-a1	66-67	**Volkswagen Luggage Elevator**	
		White body, Yellow conveyor, GPW	£25-30
32-a2	1967	With Blue conveyor, GPW	£35-45
32-a3	68-69	Red, Blue conveyor, GPW	£35-40
33-a1	1967	**Farm Trailer and Calves**	
		Olive Green, tyres	£10-15
33-a2	68-69	Turquoise, tyres	£10-15
34-a1	1967	**Tractor**	
		Red, Red exhaust, tyres	£30-40
34-a2	68-69	Red, Black exhaust, tyres	£20-25
35-a1	1967	**Ford Camper**	
		Yellow, GPW	£20-25
35-a2	1967	Metallic Blue, GPW	£30-40
35-a3	68-69	Metallic Blue, tyres	£25-30
36-a1	1967	**Simon Snorkel Fire Engine**	
		Red, GPW	£20-25
36-a2	68-69	Red, with tyres	£20-25
37-a1	68-69	**NSU Ro80**	
		Metallic Blue, tyres	£25-30
38-a1	1968	**Rices Beaufort Single Horse Box**	
		Turquoise, tyres	£10-15
38-a2	1969	Metallic Green body, tyres	£20-25
39-a1	1969	**Jaguar XJ6 4.2**	
		Yellow, Red interior, tyres	£45-55
40-a1	1969	**Ford Transit Caravan**	
		Red body, tyres	£25-35
40-a2	1969	Lime green body, tyres	£25-35
41-a1	?	**Porsche Carrera 6**	
		In catalogue but not issued	NPP
42-a	1969	**Euclid Truck**	
		Yellow body, Red dumper	£40-45
43-a	?	**Massey-Ferguson 3003**	£40-45

See also following section and 'Corgi Rockets'

Husky models: No 32 VW Luggage Elevator, No 8 Ford Thunderbird, No 1 Jaguar Mk10 and No 14 Guy Warrior Tanker 'Esso'

Husky Film and TV-related Models, 1967–1969

James Bond Aston Martin DB6

James Bond Aston Martin DB5

1001-a1 1967 **James Bond Aston Martin DB6**
Silver, Red or brown interior,
2 ejector figures, GPW **£180-200**

1001-a2 68-69 **James Bond Aston Martin DB6**
Same but with tyres **£180-200**
1002-a1 67-69 **Batmobile**

Black, Batman and Robin
figures, tow hook, GPW **£150-160**
1003-a1 67-69 **Batboat**
Black boat, Red fin, Batman
and Robin figures, GPW **£150-160**
1004-a1 68-69 **Monkeemobile**
Red, White roof, 4 figures,
'Monkees' on doors, tyres **£160-180**
1005-a1 68-69 **Man From UNCLE Car**
Blue, 3 Missiles on sprue,
2 figures, tyres..................... **£160-175**
1006-a1 1969 **Chitty Chitty Bang Bang**
Chrome, Dark Grey base, Red wings,
Yellow fins, 4 figures, tyres.......... **£140-180**

Husky and Corgi Juniors Gift Sets 1968–1970

3001 68-69 **4 Garage Set**,
Contains 23, 27, 29, or 9, 30 or 36 ...... **£75-130**
3002 68-69 **Batmobile Set**
1002 Batmobile and 1003 Batboat
on trailer............................. **£250-320**
3002 1970 **'Club Racing' Set**
Juniors set of 8 racing cars including
Mini Cooper 'S' in Metallic Mauve,
Ford Capri, Morgan, etc.................. **£150-250**
3003 68-69 **Car Transporter Set**
2002 Husky Car Transporter plus

16, 26, 6-2, 21-2, 22-2, 26 .... **£260-360**
3004 68-69 **4 Garage Set**,
Contains 23-2, 29.............................. **£80-160**
3004 19?? **James Bond 'OHMSS' Set**
Contains 1004, 1001, 1011, 1012 plus
un-numbered VW Beetle in Red with
Black No'5' on White circle on
sides. (Film 'On Her Majesty's
Secret Service')..........................**£5,000-6,000**
3005 68-69 **Holiday Time / Leisure Time**
Contains 2-2, 5-2, 7-2, 15-2, 19-2,

20-2, 21-2, 35-1 .... **£200-260**
3006 68-69 **Service Station,**
Contains 14-c, 22-2, 28 .... **£60-80**
3007 68-69 **'HUSKY MULTIPARK'**
In 1968 catalogue but not issued ....**NPP**
3008 68-69 **Crime Busters Set** (Husky set)
Contains 1001, 1002, 1003, 1005 ...... **£400-600**
1970 Corgi Juniors 3008 set **£400-600**
3011 19?? **Road Construction Set**
Gift Set containing seven models **£120-140**

Corgi Juniors 1970–1972

The models in this list were each accompanied by a colourful Picture Card

Model and details			MPR
1-a1	1970	**Reliant TW9 Pick Up**	
		Beige body, Black WW...........	**£20-25**
1-a2	70-72	Orange body, Black WW	**£15-20**
2-a1	1970	**Citroën Safari with** (white) **Boat**	
		Blue body, tyres.....................	**£30-40**
2-a2	1970	With Black WhizzWheels	**£20-25**
2-a3	71-72	Yellow body, BWW.................	**£20-25**
2-a4	71-72	Purple body, CWW.................	**£20-25**
3-a1	1970	**Volkswagen 1300 Police Car**	
		White body, tyres	**£30-35**
3-a2	1970	With Black WhizzWheels	**£20-25**
3-a3/4	71-72	With chrome WhizzWheels ..	**£20-25**
4-a1	70-72	**Zeteor 5511 Tractor**	
		Orange, Red base, BPW.........	**£10-15**
5-a1	1970	**Willys Jeep**	
		Tan body, Brown int., tyres ..	**£15-20**
5-a2	1970	With Black WhizzWheels	**£10-15**
5-a3	1971	With chrome WhizzWheels ...	**£10-15**
5-a4	1970	Orange, Brown int., BWW	**£10-15**
5-a5	1971	Same, chrome Whizzwheels.	**£10-15**
5-a6	71-72	Red body, Yellow int., CWW.	**£10-15**
6-a1	1970	**De Tomaso Mangusta**	
		Lime Green, BWW	**£10-15**
6-a2	1970	Metallic Purple, Black WW ..	**£10-15**
6-a3	71-72	Metallic Purple, CWW..........	**£10-15**
7-a1	1970	**Duple Vista 25 Coach**	
		Red body/White roof, tyres..	**£20-25**
7-a2	1970	Yellow/White, Black WW......	**£12-15**
7-a3	71-72	Purple/White, chrome WW ..	**£12-15**
7-a4	71-72	Orange/White, chrome WW .	**£12-15**
8-a1	1970	**Tipping Farm Trailer**	
		Blue, Orange back, tyres........	**£10-15**
9-a1	1970	**Cadillac Eldorado**	
		Met. Green, Red int., tyres.....	**£25-30**
9-a2	1970	With Black WhizzWheels	**£15-20**
9-a3	1970	White/Black, BWW	**£15-20**
9-a4	1971	White/Black, chrome WW ...	**£15-20**
9-b1	71-72	**Vigilant Range Rover**	
		White body, chrome WW	**£12-15**
10-a1	1970	**Guy Warrior Coal Truck**	
		Orange body, tyres................	**£15-20**
10-b1	71-72	**Ford GT7O**, Orange, CWW....	**£20-25**

Model and details			MPR
11-af	1970	**Austin Healey Sprite Le Mans**	
		Red body, Blue interior, Grey base, '50', sticker pack, Black WW ..	**£30-35**
11-a2	1971	Yellow int., chrome WW........	**£30-35**
11-a3	71-72	Red body, Yellow interior, Black base, CWW	**£30-35**
12-a1	1970	**Reliant-Ogle Scimitar GTE**	
		White body, Black WW..........	**£20-25**
12-a2	1970	Metallic Blue, chrome WW ...	**£20-25**
12-a3	71-72	Matt Blue, chrome WW	**£20-25**
13-a1	1970	**Guy Warrior Sand Truck**	
		Blue body, tyres.....................	**£20-30**
13-a2	71-72	Red body, chrome WW	**£12-15**
14-a1	1970	**Guy Warrior Tanker 'ESSO'**	
		(square tank), White, tyres..	**£25-35**
14-a2	71-72	White, chrome WW................	**£15-20**
15-a1	1970	**Studebaker Wagonaire TV Car**	
		Metallic Turquoise , tyres....	**£35-40**
15-a2	1970	Yellow body, Black WW.........	**£25-30**
15-a3	1970	Met. Lime Green, BWW.........	**£25-30**
15-a4	71-72	Met. Lime Green, CWW	**£25-30**
16-a	70-72	**Land Rover Pick Up**	
		Metallic Green, CWW	**£20-25**
17-af	1970	**Volkswagen 1300 Beetle**	
		Met. Blue, 'flower' decals	**£45-50**
17-a2	70-72	Metallic Green body	**£20-25**
19-a1	1970	**Speedboat on Trailer**	
		Blue trailer, Red, White and Blue body, tyres.....................	**£20-30**
19-a2	1970	With Black WhizzWheels	**£20-30**
19-a3	71-72	With chrome WhizzWheels ..	**£10-15**
20-a1	1967	**Volkswagen 1300 with Luggage**	
		Mustard Yellow body, tyres ..	**£30-40**
20-a2	67-69	Red body, Black WW	**£20-25**
21-a1	71-72	**BVRT Vita-Min Mini Cooper S**	
		Metallic Purple, CWW	**£30-40**
22-a1	1970	**Aston-Martin DB6**	
		Purple body, tyres	**£50-60**
22-a2	1970	Metallic Olive body, tyres....	**£45-50**
22-b1	71-72	**Formula 1 GP Racing Car**	
		Yellow body, WW	**£15-20**
23-a1	70-72	**Loadmaster Shovel**	

Model and details			MPR
		Yellow body, BPW.................	**£10-12**
24-a1	71-72	**Aston-Martin DBS**	
		Green body, chrome WW....	**£30-40**
25-a1	70-72	**SD Refuse Van**	
		Orange / chrome, tyres.........	**£15-20**
26-a1	71-72	**ERF Fire Engine Water Tender**	
		Red body, chrome WW	**£12-15**
27-a1	1970	**Bedford Skip Lorry**	
		Orange, Silver skip, tyres	**£20-25**
28-a1	1970	**Ford Breakdown Truck**	
		Blue body, tyres.....................	**£20-25**
28-a2/3	1970	Blue or Turquoise, BWW.......	**£15-20**
29-a1	71-72	**Simon Snorkel Fire Engine**	
		Red body, chrome WW	**£12-15**
30-a1	1970	**Studebaker Wagonaire**	
		Ambulance, White body, removable stretcher, tyres	**£25-30**
30-a2	1970	With Black WhizzWheels	**£20-25**
30-a3	1970	With non-removable stretcher, Black WhizzWheels	**£15-20**
30-a4/5	71-72	Fixed stretcher, small CWW ...	**£15-20**
31-a1	70-71	**Land Rover Breakdown**	
		Purple body.........................	**£15-20**
31-a2	1972	Red body..............................	**£12-15**
32-a1	70-71	**Lotus Europa,**	
		Met. Green, CWW	**£20-30**
32-a2	1972	Green body, CWW	**£15-20**
33-a1	1970	**Farm Trailer and Calves**	
		Orange, tyres.......................	**£10-15**
33-b1	70-72	**Jaguar 'E'-type Series 2**	
		Yellow, CWW.......................	**£20-30**
34-a1	70-72	**B.M. Volvo 400 Tractor**	
		Red, Yellow wheels, tyres	**£15-20**
35-a1	1970	**Ford Camper**	
		Turquoise, tyres...................	**£30-35**
35-a2	70-2	Same, but Black WW	**£25-30**
35-a3	70-2	Red, Cream back, BWW	**£20-25**
36-a1	1970	**Simon Snorkel Fire Engine**	
		Red body, tyres.....................	**£20-25**
37-a1	1970	**NSU Ro80**	
		Metallic Blue, tyres.......	**£25-30**
37-a2	1970	Metallic Mauve body,	

		Black WhizzWheels **£15-20**	
37-a3	1970	Purple body, Black WW **£15-20**	
37-a4	71-72	Purple body, CWW **£15-20**	
37-a5	71-72	Metallic Copper body, CWW **£15-20**	
38-a1	1970	**Rices Beaufort Single Horse Box**	
		Metallic Green body, tyres **£20-30**	
38-a2	1970	Red body, tyres...................... **£20-30**	
38-a3	1970	Red body, Black WW **£20-25**	
38-a4	71-72	Metallic Copper, CWW **£20-25**	
39-a1	1970	**Jaguar XJ6 4.2**	
		Yellow, Red interior, tyres...... **£35-40**	
39-a2	1970	Silver, Red interior, BWW **£25-35**	
39-a3	71-72	Silver, Red interior, CWW **£25-30**	
39-a4	71-72	Met. Red, Yellow int., CWW .. **£25-30**	
39-a5	71-72	Red body, Yellow int., CWW . **£25-30**	
40-a1	1970	**Ford Transit Caravan**	
		Yellow body, Blue interior,	
		Silver rear door, tyres............ **£25-30**	
40-a2	1970	Yellow, Cream int., BWW **£20-25**	
40-a3	1970	Blue body, Cream int., BWW **£20-25**	
40-a4	71-72	Blue body, Cream int., CWW **£20-25**	
40-a5	71-72	Metallic Pale Blue body,	
		Cream interior, CWW **£15-20**	
40-a6	1972	Metallic Pale Blue body, Cream	
		int., Black plastic base, CWW **£15-20**	
41-a1	1970	**Porsche Carrera 6**	
		White body, clear canopy,	
		RN '19', tyres **£25-35**	
41-a2	1970	Blue tinted canopy, BWW **£20-25**	
41-a3	71-72	Blue tinted canopy, CWW **£15-20**	
42-a1	1970	**Euclid Dumper**	
		Yellow cab, Red back, Dark	
		Grey base, Black wheels **£15-20**	
42-a2	1970	Red cab, Yellow back,	
		unpainted base, CWW........... **£10-15**	
42-a3	71-72	Yellow cab, Red back,	
		Dark Grey base, BWW **£10-15**	
42-a4	71-72	Blue cab, Silver back,	
		Dark Grey base, CWW **£10-15**	
42-a5	71-72	Blue Cab, Yellow back,	
		Dark Grey base, CWW **£10-15**	
43-a1	1970	**Massey Ferguson Tractor Shovel**	
		Yellow body, Red int., BPW .. **£12-15**	
43-a2	71-72	Yellow body, Red shovel	
		and interior, BPW.................. **£10-15**	

44-a1	70-72	**Raygo Rascal Road Roller**	
		Blue / Orange, BPW.............. **£10-12**	
45-a1	1970	**Mercedes 280SL**	
		Met. Silver, Red int., tyres...... **£30-35**	
45-a2	1970	Metallic Blue body,	
		Red interior, Black WW **£20-25**	
45-a3	1970	Yellow body, Red interior,	
		unpainted base, BWW **£15-20**	
45-a4	1970	Yellow body, Red interior,	
		White base, BWW **£15-20**	
45-a5	1970	Red body, Cream int., BWW . **£25-30**	
45-a6	71-72	Red body, Cream int., CWW . **£25-30**	
45-a7	71-72	Blue body, Cream interior,	
		unpainted base, CWW.......... **£20-25**	
46-a1	1970	**Jensen Interceptor**	
		Maroon body, Yellow interior,	
		unpainted base, tyres **£35-40**	
46-a2	1970	Maroon body, Black WW **£25-30**	
46-a3	1971	Orange body, CWW **£25-30**	
46-a4	1972	Metallic Green body, CWW .. **£25-30**	
47-a1	71-72	**Scammell Concrete Mixer**	
		White / Red, CWW................ **£10-15**	
48-a1	71-72	**ERF Tipper Truck**	
		Red cab, Silver back, unpainted	
		or Grey base, CWW............... **£15-20**	
48-a1	71-72	Blue cab, Orange back........... **£15-20**	
48-a1	71-72	Blue cab, Yellow back **£15-20**	
49-a1	71-72	**Pininfarina Modulo**	
		Yellow, Red stripe, CWW....... **£15-20**	
50-a1	71-72	**Ferrari 512s**	
		Metallic Red, CWW................ **£15-20**	
51-a1	71-72	**Porsche 917**	
		Gold, RN '23', CWW **£15-20**	
52-a1	71-72	**Adams Probe 16**	
		Metallic Pink, CWW............... **£15-20**	
54-a1	71-72	**Ford Container Wagon**	
		Red, Yellow skip, CWW.......... **£15-20**	
55-a1	70-72	**Daimler Fleetline Bus**	
		Red, 'Uniflo', CWW **£15-20**	
56-a1	70-72	Ford Capri Fire Chief	
		Red/White, 'Fire' decal	
		on door, White int., CWW **£25-30**	
56-a2	70-72	With 'Fire Chief' decal............ **£25-30**	

56-a3	70-72	All-Red, 'Fire Chief' on door,	
		Yellow interior, CWW **£25-30**	
57-a1	70-72	**Caddy Hot Rodder**	
		Metallic Blue, 'Caddy Hot Roddy'	
		on doors, sticker pack, CWW **£12-15**	
57-a2	70-72	Metallic Pink body, CWW **£12-15**	
58-a1	71-72	**G.P. Beach Buggy**	
		Met. Red, Cream int., CWW .. **£10-12**	
58-a2	71-72	Same, but Yellow interior **£10-12**	
59-a1	71-72	**The Futura,** Orange, Black	
		base, sheet of stickers, CWW **£15-20**	
60-a1	71-72	**VW Double Trouble Hot Rod**	
		Metallic Pink, CWW............... **£15-20**	
61-a1	70-72	**Mercury Cougar Police Car £15-20**	
62-a1	1970	**Volvo P1800**	
		Red, Yellow int., CWW........... **£35-40**	
62-a2	71-72	Red, Blue interior, CWW **£25-30**	
62-a3	1972	Red, Cream interior, CWW..... **£45-50**	
63-a1	70-72	**Ford Escort Monte Carlo**	
		Rally Car, Met. Blue, RN '32',	
		Red int., stickers sheet, CWW **£40-50**	
63-a2	1972	With Yellow interior, CWW ... **£50-60**	
63-a3	1972	With Cream interior, CWW ... **£50-60**	
64-a1	71-72	**Morgan Plus 8**	
		Yellow, CWW......................... **£25-35**	
64-a2	71-72	Red, RN '20', CWW **£25-35**	
65-a1	71-72	**Bertone Carabo**	
		Met. Purple, White int, CWW **£12-15**	
65-a2	71-72	Orange interior, CWW **£10-12**	
67-a1	71-72	**Ford Capri 'Hot Pants' Dragster**	
		Yellow body, CWW **£35-40**	
70-a1	71-72	**US Racing Buggy,** Blue... **£15-20**	
71-a1	71-72	**Marcos XP, Orange,** CWW ... **£15-20**	
72-a1	71-72	**Mercedes-Benz C111,** Red... **£15-20**	
73-a1	71-72	**Pininfarina Alfa Romeo P33**	
		Blue body, chrome WW **£15-20**	
74-a1	71-72	**Bertone Barchetta,** Orange . **£15-20**	
75-a1	71-72	**Superstock Car**	
		Silver, Union Jack, stickers **£20-25**	
76-a1	71-72	**Chevrolet Astro,** Met. Red.... **£15-20**	
77-a1	71-72	**Bizzarrini Manta,** Pink......... **£15-20**	
78-a1	71-72	**Old MacDonald's Truck**....... **£30-40**	
1017	71-72	**Holmes Wrecker and**	
		Towing Cradle, Yellow cab,	
		Red back, 'Auto Rescue' **£100-120**	

Husky/Juniors Major Models

2001	68-69	**'HUSKY' Multi Garage**	
		A set of four garages (no cars),	
		'Husky' on base **£20-30**	
	70-75	Corgi Juniors issue as previous	
		model but with 'CORGI' logo,	
		'Juniors' on base.................... **£10-15**	
2002	67-69	**'HUSKY' Car Transporter**	
		Hoynor MkII, White/Blue/Orange,	
		cab, 'Husky' on base **£30-40**	
	70-72	Corgi Juniors issue as previous	

		model but with 'CORGI' logo,	
		'Juniors' on base..................... **£25-35**	
2003a	68-69	**Machinery Low-Loader**	
		Red/Blue/Yellow, cab, drop-down	
		ramp, 'Husky' base **£25-35**	
2003b	70-73	Corgi Juniors issue as previous	
		model with metal wheels or	
		WW, 'Juniors' on base **£25-35**	
2004a	68-69	**Removals Delivery Van**	
		Red or Blue cab, plated box,	

		'HUSKY REMOVALS', metal	
		wheels, 'Husky' on base **£45-55**	
2004b	70-72	Corgi Juniors issue:	
		'CORGI REMOVALS',	
		WW, 'Juniors' base **£30-35**	
2006	70-79	**Mack 'ESSO' Tanker**	
		White body and tank,	
		WW, 'Juniors' on base **£30-35**	

Husky Accessories

1561/2	68-69	Traffic Signs	£20-30
1571	68-69	Pedestrians	£10-15
1572	68-69	Workmen	£10-15
1573	68-69	Garage Personnel	£10-15
1574	68-69	Public Servants	£10-15
1580	68-69	Husky Collector Case storage for 48 models	£15-25

1585	68-69	Husky Traveller Case, opens to form Service Station (this item never seen)	NPP
2001	68-69	'HUSKY' Multi Garage, A set of four garages, (no cars), 'Husky' on base	£25-35
	70-75	As previous but with 'CORGI'	

logo, 'Juniors' on base **£10-15**

--- 1970s USA Dealer Display Unit. A wooden revolving unit with lighting, brown/black, 'Collect Husky Models' **£200-300**

Corgi Juniors Film and TV-related models, 1970–1972

1001-a1 1970 **James Bond Aston-Martin DB6** Silver, Red interior, 2 ejector figures, Grey plastic wheels **£150-175**

1001-a2 1970 **James Bond Aston-Martin DB6** Silver, Red interior, 2 ejector figures, Black WhizzWheels **£150-175**

1001-a3 71-72 **James Bond Aston-Martin DB6** Silver, Red interior, 2 ejector figures, chrome WhizzWheels **£150-175**

1002-a1 1970 **Batmobile** Black, Batman and Robin figures, tow hook, GPW, 'Corgi Junior' base ... **£125-150**

1002-a2 1970 **Batmobile** Black, Batman and Robin figures, tow hook, Black WhizzWheels **£125-150**

1002-a3 71-72 **Batmobile** Black, Batman and Robin figures, tow hook, chrome WhizzWheels. **£125-150**

1003-a1 1970 **Batboat** Black boat, Red fin, Batman and Robin figures, GPW, 'Junior' base **£125-150**

1003-a2 1970 **Batboat**

Black boat, Red fin, Batman and Robin figures, Black WhizzWheels **£125-150**

1003-a3 71-72 **Batboat** Black boat, Red fin, Batman and Robin figures, chrome WhizzWheels **£125-150**

1004-a1 1970 **Monkeemobile** Red, White roof, 4 figures, 'Monkees' on doors, tyres, 'Junior' base **£125-150**

1004-a2 1970 **Monkeemobile** Red, White roof, 4 figures, 'Monkees' on doors, tyres, 'Junior' base **£125-150**

1004-a3 1971 **Monkeemobile** Red, White roof, 4 figures, 'Monkees' on doors, tyres, Black WW **£125-150**

1005-a1 1970 **Man From U.N.C.L.E. Car** Blue, 3 missiles on sprue, 2 figures, tyres, 'Junior' label on base **£125-150**

1006-a1 1970 **Chitty Chitty Bang Bang** Chrome body, 4 figures, tyres **£100-125**

1006-a2 1971 **Chitty Chitty Bang Bang** Chrome body, 4 figures, BWW **£100-125**

1007-a1 71-72 **Ironsides Police Van** Blue, 'San Francisco' logo, Ironside in back, chrome WhizzWheels **£100-125**

1008-a1 71-72 **Popeye's Paddle Wagon** Yellow, Blue, Popeye with Olive and Swee' Pea, chrome WW **£100-130**

1010-a1 1970 **James Bond Volkswagen** Orange, Green stripe / 'Corgi Toys' on roof, RN '5', Yellow interior, chrome WhizzWheels **£700-900**

1011-a1 71-72 **James Bond Bobsleigh** Yellow, '007' decal, Grey plastic bumper, George Lazenby figure, BWW **£400-600**

1012-a1 71-72 **S.P.E.C.T.R.E. Bobsleigh** Orange, 'Boars Head' decal, Grey plastic bumper, Blofleld figure, Black WhizzWheels **£700-900**

1013-a1 71-72 **Tom's Go Cart** Yellow, Tom figure, chrome WW **£50-60**

1014-a1 71-72 **Jerry's Banger** Red, Jerry figure, CWW **£50-60**

Husky and Corgi Juniors Catalogues and Listings

HUSKY CATALOGUES

Leaflet (single fold) Mettoy Playcraft (Sales) Ltd 1966. Red, illustrating No.1 Jaguar Mk.10 on cover and Nos.1-29 inside. '1/9 each' **£20-25**

Leaflet (Belgian issue) Mettoy Playcraft (Sales) Ltd 1966. As previous leaflet but Nos.1-32 shown, printed in French **£20-25**

Booklet (10 pages) Mettoy Playcraft (Sales) Ltd 1966. Front/rear covers feature a row of garages and

cars. 1002 Batmobile and 1001 JB's Aston-Martin featured, plus Nos.1-36 ..... **NGPP**

Catalogue (24 pages) no ref. 1967. Cover shows boy with Husky vehicles and sets. Good pictures of all the rare models and Gift Sets plus accessories and models 1-41 ..... **£30-40**

CORGI JUNIORS CATALOGUES

Catalogue (16 pages) Mettoy Playcraft 1970. Blue cover with 10 models featured. Fine

pictures of all the rare early models including GS 3004 Bond 'O.H.M.S.S.' Set etc. **£30-40**

Corgi Juniors Collectors Album no ref. 1970. 28 pages. To hold cards cut from Corgi Junior bubble packs. Has details of featured models below space for card. Centre two pages have 'Corgi Toys' adverts plus articles, etc. **£10-15**

Corgi Juniors 1975–1983

Market Price Range - scarcer items as shown, otherwise under £15. These models are fitted with WhizzWheels.

Model and details			MPR
E2	80-81	Blake's Seven Liberator	£75-100
E3	77-81	Stromberg's Helicopter	£25-35
E6	79-80	'Daily Planet' Helicopter	£15-20
E11	79-85	Supermobile	£20-30
E17-2	79-81	Metropolis 'POLICE' Car	£25-35
E19	80-82	Pink Panther Motorcycle	£15-20
E20-2	79-81	Penguinmobile	£20-30
E21	77-80	Charlie's Angels Van	£15-20
E23	79-81	Batbike	£75-100
E24	79-80	'SHAZAM' Thunderbolt	£40-50
E25	79-80	'Capt. America' Porsche	£40-50
E32	70-74	The Saint's Jaguar XJS	£65-85
E33	79-80	'Wonderwoman's Car	£30-40
E38	80-83	Jerry's Banger	£15-20
E40-2	79-81	J. Bond's Aston-Martin	£100-125
E41	79-81	J. Bond Space Shuttle	£15-20
E44-2	79-80	Starship Liberator	£50-75
E45	77-81	Starsky & Hutch Ford Torino	£15-20
E49-2	81-83	Woody Woodpecker's Car	£15-20
E50	79-80	'Daily Planet' (Leyland) Van, Red or Silver	£15-20
E52-2	82-83	Scooby Doo's Vehicle	£20-25
E56	79-80	Chevrolet 'SPIDERVAN'	£20-25
E57-2	79-80	Spiderbike	£20-25
E59-1	80-83	Tom's Cart	£15-20
E60	77-79	James Bond Lotus Esprit 1: with side & rear wings ... £100-125 2: without wings; some have 'TURBO' side design £100-125

'James Bond' Lotus Esprit taken from the film The Spy Who Loved Me.

E64	80-82	'The Professionals' Ford Capri	£15-20
E67-2	80-83	Popeye's Tugboat	£15-20
E68	77-79	Kojak's Buick Regal	£20-25
E69	76-80	Batmobile	£75-100
E72-2	79-83	Jaguar XJS, Blue or Red	NGPP
		Jaguar XJS, Red with White 'MOTOR SHOW' logo	£20-30
E73	80	'DRAX' Helicopter	£20-25
E75	77-80	Spidercopter	£20-30
E78	76-81	Batcopter	£60-70
E79-2	80-83	Olive Oyl's Aeroplane	£15-20
E80	79-80	'MARVEL COMICS' Van	£20-25
E82-2	81-82	Yogi Bear's Jeep	£20-30

Model and details			MPR
E84-2	80-83	Bugs Bunny Vehicle	£15-20
99	79-81	Jokermobile	£30-40
100	81-83	Hulk Cycle	£30-40
E115	81-83	James Bond 2cv Citroën	£40-50
128	82-83	Fred's Flyer	£25-35
131	82-83	Ferrari 308, 'Magnum PI'	£25-35
133	82-83	Buick Regal 'POLICE' Car, 'Magnum PI'	£25-35
134	82-83	Barney's Buggy, Red/Orange, (The Flintstones')	£25-35
E148	83-84	USS Enterprise	£15-20
E149	83	Klingon Warship	£15-20
E151	83	Wilma's Coupé	£25-35
198	83	James Bond Citroën 2cv	£50-75
E2009	?	James Bond 'Aerocar' ('The Man With the Golden Gun'). **NB:** Not a licensed product	£160-190

GERMAN ISSUES:

E119	83	'FLUGHAFEN-FEURWEHR' Fire Engine	£15-20
120	?	Leyland Van, 'Eiszeit'	£15-20
120	83	Ice Cream Van, 'FRESHLICHE'	£15-20
121	83	Chevrolet Van, 'TECHNISCHER'	£15-20
126	82-83	Ford Transit Breakdown, 'ABSCHIEPPDIENST'	£15-20
127	82-83	'ADAC' Car	£20-25

Corgi Juniors Sets

2601	**Batman Triple-Pack**	£150-200
E2001	**Multi Garage Complex.** 4-garages	£30-35
E3001	**Multi Garage and three cars**	£45-55
E3005	**Leisure Time Set**	£100-125
E3009	**Service Station and three cars**	£80-100
E3013	**Emergency Rescue Set** Rescue Station + 3 models	£70-85
E3109	**Agricultural Set.** 2 Tractors, Land-Rover, 3 Trailers, 2 Huts	£90-110
3019/1	**James Bond 'Octopussy' Set,** 1983-84	£100-125
E3021	**Crimefighters Gift Set** (E45, E60, E68, E69, E75, E78)	£400-600
E3023	**Mercedes Transporter plus 4 cars**	£75-100
E3024	**Construction Gift Set** (6 vehicles)	£75-100
E3026	**Emergency Gift Set** (6 vehicles)	£75-100

E3030	**James Bond 'The Spy Who Loved Me' Gift Set,** 76-77. (E3, E60, 'Jaws' Van, Mercedes, Speedboat)	£250-350
E3040	**Superman 'Metropolis' Set**	£75-100
E3071	**'Growlers' Speed Set.** Ford GT70, Ferrari 312s, Marcos XP, CanAm, Jaguar 'E'-type, Porsche 917	£100-150
E3080	**Batman Gift Set,** 1980-82 (E20, E23, E69, E78, E99)	£300-400
E3081	**Superman Gift Set** (E6, E11, E17, E47, E50)	£125-150
E3082	**James Bond 'Goldfinger' Gift Set,** 1980-82, (E40, E41, E60, E73, + 'Jaws' van)	£400-500
E3084	**Cartoon Characters Set** (E19, E38, E58, E67, E79)	£100-125

E3100	**Construction Gift Set** (7 items)	£75-100
E3101	**Fire Gift Set** (6 items)	£75-100
E3103	**Emergency Gift Set** (6 items)	£75-100
E3105	**Transporter Gift Set** (Mercedes Transporter + 4 cars)	£75-100
3107	**'Sports Cars.'** Five pieces in set	£30-40
E3108	**'Scoobie & His Friends' Set,** 5 items	£75-100
E3114	**'Superheroes' Gift Set** (Batman / Superman vehicles)	£100-125
E3116	**'Crimefighters' Gift Set** (Starsky & Hutch, James Bond and Buck Rogers vehicles)	£125-150
E3184	**'Data Post' Set** Contains 6 items	£40-50

Corgi Super Juniors and Superhaulers

FORD D SERIES TRUCK (1970-75)

2002	**Car Transporter,** White cab, Blue lower, Red deck	£20-25
	Red cab, White deck	£40-50
2003	**Low Loader,** Blue	£20-25
2004	**'CORGI' Removals Van,** Red cab	£40-50
	Light Blue cab	£40-50
2007	**Low Loader,** Red cab, Blue trailer with Orange Junior digger load	£25-35
2012	**Military Low Loader + US vehicle**	NGPP

FORD D SERIES SETS (1970-76)

3003	**Car Transporter Set,** White or Red cab, 5 Juniors	£40-50
3011	**Low Loader Set,** Red cab, 6 Juniors	£50-60
3024	**Low Loader Set,** Red cab, Yellow trailer (1976), 6 Juniors	£50-60
3025	**Car Transporter Set,** Yellow cab, Orange deck (1976), 5 Juniors	£30-35

MACK TRUCKS (issued 1971-75)

2006	**'ESSO' Tanker,** White	£10-15
2010	**'EXXON' Tanker,** White	£20-25
2011	**'US' Army Tanker,** Military Green	£20-25
2027	**'RYDER RENTALS',** Yellow cab + box trailer	£10-15

MERCEDES TRACTOR UNITS, CAR TRANSPORTER (issued 1976)

2014/15	White cab and deck, Blue chassis	£20-25
2015	White cab, Yellow deck, Red chassis	£20-25
	NB. Transporter Sets 3023, 3015, 3105	£30-35

MERCEDES TANKERS (1983-84)

1130	**'CORGI CHEMCO',** Red or White	£10-15
1130	**'SHELL'** Yellow or White cab	£10-15
1166	**'GUINNESS'**	£10-15
1167	**'DUCKHAMS'**	£10-15
1167	**'7 UP'**	£20-30

MERCEDES BOX TRAILERS (1978-85)

1111	**'SAFEWAY'**	£15-20
1129	**'ASG SPEDITION'**	£10-15
1129	**'CORGI'** Black or White cab	£10-15
1131	**'CHRISTIAN SALVESON'**	£10-15
1137	**'SOUKS SUPERMARKET'** (Saudi issue)	£25-30
1139	**'HALLS FOOD'**	£10-15
1144	**'ROYAL MAIL PARCELS'**	£10-15
1145	**'YORKIE'**	£10-15
1146	**'DUNLOP'**	£10-15
1166	**'ARIA DAIRY'**	£10-15
1175	**'INTERNATIONAL'**	£60-70
1175	**'TI RALEIGH'**	£10-15
1176	**'ZANUSSI'**	£10-15
1177	**'WEETABIX'**	£10-15
1178	**'MAYNARDS'**	£10-15
1202	**'PICKFORDS HOMESPEED'**	£60-70
2028	**'GERVALS DANONE'**	£10-15
2020	**'BIRDS EYE'**	£10-15
---	**'B. H. S.'**	£20-30
---	**'CARTERS Lemonade'**	£25-35

MERCEDES SETS

1200	**'DUCKHAMS' & 'GUINNESS'** Tanker plus 3 Scammells	£40-50
1403	**'CORGI CHEMCO',** plus Junior Van	£25-30
3128	**'DUCKHAMS' & 'YORKIE',** plus 10 Juniors	£40-50

RECOMMENDED READING
'CORGI SUPER JUNIOR and SUPERHAULER GUIDE'. Full details plus pictures compiled by Andy and Pat Browning, 3 Waterside Terrace, Ninn Lane, Great Chart, Ashford, Kent, TN23 3DD. The lack of which could adversely affect the model's potential price

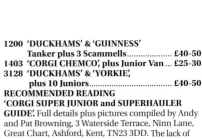

'Transporter' Gift Set – six-piece set comprising Volkswagen Beetle, Mini, Lotus, Ford Escort, Ford GT and Articulated Car Transporter (not listed).

Corgi Juniors Twin-Packs

Corgi Juniors bubble-packed in pairs from 1977 (approx)

'Batman' two-piece Gift Set comprising Batmobile and Batboat on Trailer.

2501	London Bus and Taxi	£20-30
2502	Land Rover Breakdown / Jaguar XJS	£30-40
2503	Land Rover and Horse Box	£20-30
2504	Land Rover Breakdown plus AMC Pace Car	£30-40
2505	'DAILY PLANET' Van + Helicopter	£20-30
2506	Supermobile and Superman Van	£50-60
2507	Tom's Cart and Jerry's Banger	£20-30

2508	Popeye's Tugboat plus Olive Oyl's Aeroplane	£20-30
2510	F1 and F5000 Racing Cars	£30-40
2511	Sting Helicopter and Scout Car	£20-30
2512	Space Shuttle + Star Ship 'Liberator'	£40-50
2513	Fire Tender and Ambulance	£20-30
2514	Building Set	£25-35
2515	Citroën and Speedboat	£25-35
2516	Tractor and Tipping Trailer	£25-35
2518	Mercedes and Caravan	£25-35
2519	Batmobile and Batboat	£150-200
2520	Rescue Set	£30-40
2521	James Bond Lotus plus Aston-Martin DB5	£150-200
2522	Army Attack Set	£30-40
2523	Police Car and Helicopter	£25-35
2524	Custom Van Twin	£25-35
2525	Triumph TR7 + Dinghy on Trailer	£40-50
2526	Dumper Truck + Shovel Loader	£25-35
2527	'Kojak' and Police Helicopter	£50-60
2528	Starsky and Hutch Twin Pack	£50-60
2529	James Bond Lotus and Helicopter	£100-150

2530	Rescue Range Rover and Helicopter	£30-40
2506	AMF 'Ski-daddler' Snowmobile and trailer	£100-150
2538	Buck Rogers Starfighter and NASA Columbia Shuttle	£40-50

'Commando' Military Gift Set comprising three vehicles and plastic buildings.

Corgi Rockets

This model range was issued between 1970 and 1972 to compete against Mattel 'Hot Wheels' and similar products. The models had WhizzWheels and featured a special 'Tune-Up' system which increased the play value and speed

D 901	1970-72	**Aston-Martin DB-6**	
	Met. Deep Gold, Green interior		£60-70
D 902	1970-72	**Jaguar XJ-6**	
	Metallic Green, Cream interior		£80-90
D 903	1970-72	**Mercedes-Benz 280 SL**	
	Met. Orange body, White interior		£60-70

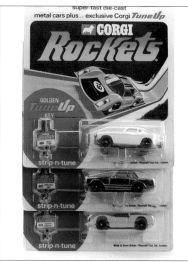

No 904 Porsche Carrera 6 - yellow, blue, racing number 19, No 903 Mercedes 280SL - metallic blue and No 905 'The Saint's' Volvo - white, blue interior and bonnet label.

D 904	1970-72	**Porsche Carrera 6**	
	Orange-Yellow body, Black '19'		£60-70
D 905	1970-72	**'The Saint's Volvo P1800**	
	White body, Blue/White 'Saint' label on bonnet		£80-90
D 906	1970-72	**Jensen Interceptor**	
	Metallic Red, Yellow interior		£60-70
	Pink / Cream body		£80-90
D 907	1970-72	**Cadillac Eldorado**	
	Metallic Copper, White interior		£60-70
D 908	1970-72	**Chevrolet Astro**	
	Metallic Red/Black body		£40-50
D 909	1970-72	**Mercedes-Benz C111**	
	Red or Blue, White interior		£40-50
D 910	1970-72	**Beach Buggy**	
	Orange body, Black interior		£30-40

of the virtually frictionless wheels. They were very robust, being advertised as 'four times stronger' than most other diecast racers. To begin with, seven Corgi Juniors were adapted as Rockets and five of those received a vacuum metallised finish. A range

D 911	1970-72	**Marcos XP**	
	Gold body, Chrome interior		£30-40
?	1970-72	**Ford Capri**	
	Purple body		£40-50
D 913	1970-72	**Aston-Martin DBS**	
	Metallic Blue, Yellow interior		£70-90
D 916	1970-72	**Carabo Bertone**	
	Met. Green/Blue, Orange interior		£20-30
D 917	1970-72	**Pininfarina Alfa-Romeo**	
	Metallic Purple/White		£20-30
D 918	1970-72	**Bitzzarini Manta**	
	Metallic Dark Blue, White interior		£20-30
D 919	1970-72	**'Todd Sweeney' Stock Car**	
	Red/Purple/Yellow/Black, '531'		£75-100
D 920	1970-72	**'Derek Fiske' Stock Car**	
	White/Red, Silver bonnet, Red logo, RN '304'		£75-100
D 921	1970-72	**Morgan Open Sports**	
	Metallic Red body, Black seats		£60-75
D 922	1970-72	**Rally Ford Capri**	
	Yellow, Orange/Black stripe, '8'		£75-100
	Green, Black bonnet, (GS 2 model)		£60-75
D 923	1970-72	**'James Bond' Ford Escort**	
	White, Pale Blue stripes, '7', 'JAMES BOND', White '007' and 'SPECIAL AGENT' logos (from film 'On Her Majesty's Secret Service')		£500-700
D 924	1970-72	**Mercury Cougar XR7**	
	Red body, Black roof, Yellow int.		£30-40
D 924		**'James Bond' issue:** Red/Black with Yellow side flash, interior and skis on roof rack (from film 'On Her Majesty's Secret Service')		£500-700
D 925	1970-72	**'James Bond' Ford Capri**	
	White body, Black/White check design, 2 bonnet stripes, RN '6', (film'On Her Majesty's Secret Service')		£500-700
D 926	1970-72	**Jaguar 'Control Car'**	
	Metallic Brown body, Red roof blade, Blue/White figures		£200-250
D 927	1970-72	**Ford Escort Rally**	
	White, Red '18', 'DAILY MIRROR' labels on doors, '1970 Mexico World Cup Rally Winner'		£250-300
D 928	1970-72	**Mercedes 280 SL 'SPECTRE'**	
	Black body with Red 'SPECTRE' logo, plus boar's head design		£250-300
D 930	1970-72	**Bertone Barchetta**	
	Met. Green over White, Red int.		£40-50
D 931	1970-72	**'Old MacDonald's Truck'**	
	Yellow cab, Brown rear		£75-100
D 933	1970-72	**'Holmes Wrecker'**	
	White or Blue cab, White back,		

of accessories was also issued in the form of 'Speed Circuits' etc, and each car was provided with a special 'Golden Tune-Up Key' which released the base. The bubble-packed models are difficult to find in top condition and prices reflect their scarcity.

	'AUTO RESCUE'		£125-150
D 937	1970-72	**Mercury Cougar**	
	Met. Dark Green body, Yellow int.		£20-30

Rockets Gift Sets

D 975	1970	**Super Stock Gift Set 1,** D 905, D 919, Trailer, 3 figures	£250-350
D 976	1970	**Super Stock Gift Set 2,** D 922, D 920, Trailer, 3 figures	£250-350
D 977	1970	**Super Stock Gift Set 3,** D 926, D 919, D 920, 5 figures	£300-400
D 978		**'OHMSS' Gift Set,** Models of cars in the James Bond film 'On Her Majesty's Secret Service': D 923 and D 925 (as driven in the ice-racing scene), D 924 (as driven by 'Tracey'), D 928 (as driven by the Chief of 'SPECTRE')	£5,000-6,800

NB Male skier has red metal base, red/yellow skis, yellow poles.

Rockets Catalogues

1969	**8-page booklet,** listing the first 7 issues, Green model on cover		£20-25
1970	**16-page booklet,** most issues, good pictures of rare models, sets, etc.		£30-35

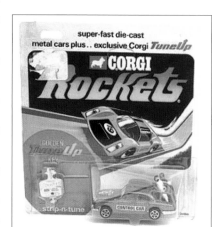

Jaguar S-type Control Car, comes with figures and key in blister pack.

Rockets Accessories (Introduced in 1970. All NGPP)

D 2051 Action Speedset, One car,
'Autostart', 12 ft of track ....

D 2052 Super Autobatics Speedset,
One car, 'Autostart', 16 ft
of track plus 'leaps' etc.......................

D 2053 Clover Leaf Special
Speedset, A car, 'Autostart',
track,'clover-leaf leaps' etc ....

D 2058 Race-Abatic Speedset,
2 cars, 'Autostart', 32' of track plus 'leaps' etc

D 2071 Jetspeed Circuit, One car,

'Superbooster', 16 ft of track + 'leaps' etc......

D 2074 Triple-Leap Speed Circuit,
One car, 19 ft, 6 in of track ....

D 2075 Grand Canyon Circuit,
One car, 12 ft of track ....

D 2079 World Champion Speedset,
Two cars, 2 x 16 ft of track,two Boosters.......

D 1928 Rocketlube Tune-up Kit

D 1931 Superleap ....

D 1934 Autofinish..

D 1935 Connections (3) ....

D 1936 Space Leap ....

D 1937 Autostart...

D 1938 Super Crossover ....

D 1945 Adaptors (3) ....

D 1963 Track (16ft).....................................

D 1970 Super Booster ....

D 1971 Hairpin Tunnel ....

D 1976 Quickfire Start ....

D 1977 Lap Counter ....

D 1978 Pitstop...

D 1979 Spacehanger Bend ....

Catalogues (UK Editions)

Information taken from the Cecil Gibson Archives and previous compiler's own collection of reference material. Note: 'Concertina' leaflets were issued with models sold in the early Blue boxes.

Year	Publication details	MPR
1956	**Concertina leaflet** No ref. Blue cover with, famous Corgi dog, shows first 14 models, no prices	£25-30
1956	**Concertina leaflet** No ref. Blue cover with Red/Gold Corgi dog. Depicts first 14 models; shows prices of both normal and mechanical models	£25-30
1957	**Concertina leaflet 50/157/K1.** Blue cover with Red/Gold Corgi dog. Depicts ten models and lists mechanical models in red	£25-30
1957	**Concertina leaflet 40/257/K1.** As previous item, but no mechanical models	£25-30
1957	**Concertina leaflet 40/257/K2.** As previous leaflet but with the addition of 208	£25-30
1957	**Concertina leaflet 50/557/K3.** As 40/257/K2 plus 100,150, 408, 454, 'WOW! CORGI TOYS' logo	£25-30
1957	**Catalogue Leaflet 20/657/C2.** Unfolded size (11" x 8 3/4"). Cover shows 1st type blue box for 208 Jaguar	£25-30
1957	**Concertina leaflet 100/1057/K3.** Blue cover showing 100, 150, 207, 208, 302, 405, 408, 453, 455	£25-30
1957	**Concertina leaflet 50/1057/K4.** Blue cover, 'WOW! CORGI TOYS' logo. First 'MAJOR' toy (1101) within	£25-30
1957	**Concertina leaflet 50/1157/K4.** Cover shows 102, 210, 406, 407, 412, 1101, 'WOW! CORGI TOYS' logo	£25-30
1957	**Four-fold leaflet 25/257/C1/UK.** 'Blue box' 208 Jaguar on cover, 15 model pictures inside	£25-35
1957	**Four-fold leaflet 25/257/C2/UK.** As previous item but 24 model pictures	£25-35
1957	**Four-fold leaflet 50/1057/C3/UK.** Shows GS 1 Bedford Transporter and six cars on Blue/Yellow cover	£25-35
1957	**Four-fold leaflet 25/1157/C4/UK.** As previous leaflet plus 101 and 102	£25-35
1958	**Catalogue Leaflet 15/158/C4.** Unfolded size (1' x 11"). 1101 Transporter on cover	£20-25
1958	**Catalogue Leaflet 10/258/C5.** Unfolded size (1' x 11"). 1101 Transporter on cover	£20-25
1958	**Catalogue Leaflet 40/258/C5.** Same	£20-25
1958	**Concertina leaflet 52/258/K5.** Cover shows GS 1 and 2, 101, 211, 302, 457, 459, 1100, 1401, 1450	£20-25
1958	**Box Insert 52/258/K5.** 1401 Corgi Service Ramp on cover	£15-20
1958	**Box Insert 52/258/K6.** 350 'Thunderbird' Missile on cover	£15-20
1958	**Concertina leaflet 52/258/K6.** Cover has GS 1 and 2, 101, 211, 302, 457, 459, 1100, 1401, 1450, + 350, 351	£20-25
1958	**Concertina leaflet 300/658/K7.** Shows GS 3, 151, 209, 458, 'NEW CORGI TOYS' logo + prices	£20-25
1958	**Box Insert 3.350/658/K7.** 1401 Corgi Service Ramp on cover	£15-20
1958	**Four-fold leaflet** No ref. Shows GS 1 Bedford Transporter and 6 cars on Blue/Yellow cover, plus 211. No prices or car listing	£25-35
1958	**Box Insert 5/658/K7.** 458 E.R.F. Truck and 209 Police Car on cover	£15-20
1958	**Catalogue 650/858/C8.** First 'book' catalogue. Cover depicts boy playing with Bloodhound Missile + other vehicles	£40-50
1958	**Box Insert 10/658/K7.** 458 E.R.F. Truck and 209 Police Car on cover	£15-20
1958	**16 page Catalogue 40/1058/C8.** Boy and large collection on cover	£20-25
1958	**Box Insert 120/1058/K8.** 458 E.R.F Truck and 209 Police Car on cover	£15-20
1959	**Four-fold leaflet** No ref. Blue cover with 'THE ROCKET AGE WITH CORGI TOYS' (issued with Rocket Age models)	£20-30
1959	**Interim leaflet** No ref. September 1959. Lists 152, 50 Tractor, 350 Thunderbird, new Ford TT van and accessories	£20-30
1959	**16 page Catalogue UK 9/59.** M-F Tractor No. 50 and BRM No. 152 on cover. Farming + 'MAJOR' issues	£35-45
1959	**20 page Catalogue** No ref. Racing Car and Tractor design on cover	£30-35
1959	**Single page leaflet** No ref. Features Renault Floride plus 'STRAIGHT FROM THE MOTOR SHOW' logo	£20-30
1959	**Two fold leaflet** No ref. 'AUTHENTIC ROCKET AGE MODELS' models	£20-30
1960	**Interim leaflet** No ref. Depicts M1 Motorway scene	£20-30
1960	**20 page Catalogue** No reference number, otherwise as next item	£25-35
1960	**20 page Catalogue UK 9/60.** Cover has motorway bridge scene and Corgi models. First 'CHIPPERFIELDS' issues	£30-40
1960	**Interim Leaflet** No ref. 1119 Hovercraft, etc. on cover	£20-25
1961	**24 page Catalogue** No reference number, otherwise as next item	£30-40
1961	**24 page Catalogue UK 9/61.** Racetrack scene on cover. Listings/pictures include new Sports Cars, Express Coach and Kits	£30-40
1961	**Price List** No ref. Single double-sided sheet (size as catalogue), 'Revised price list as from August 1961.' 'UK' on back	£1-2
1961	**Interim Leaflet** No ref. 231 Triumph Herald, etc. on cover	£20-25
1962	**Two-fold Checklist** No ref. Front depicts Blue/Yellow 'CORGI TOYS' + 7 models. Red/Grey interior plus first check list	£20-30
1962	**Interim Leaflet** No ref. 224 Bentley plus 304s Mercedes on cover	£20-25
1963	**32 page Catalogue C/100/62.** Cover depicts schoolboy (in red cap and blazer) crossing road with Corgi dog. No date shown	£40-50
1963	**32 page Catalogue** No ref. Same cover as C/100/62 but boy's cap and blazer are Blue. '1963-64' shown on cover	£30-40
1963	**40 page Catalogue** As previous item, but expanded to 40 pages	£30-40
1964	**Interim Leaflet - Playcraft Toys Ltd 1964.** 251 Hillman Imp, etc. on cover	NGPP
1964	**40 page Catalogue - Playcraft Toys Ltd 1964.** '1965', 'CORGI TOYS', 'CORGI CLASSICS'. First Routemaster listed	£25-35
1964	**Two-fold Checklist - Playcraft Toys Ltd 1964.** Leaflet featuring 241 Ghia	£25-35
1965	**Interim Leaflet - Playcraft Toys Ltd 1965.** 155 Lotus Climax Racing Car, etc.	£20-25
1965	**40 page Catalogue** No reference number or text, otherwise as next item	£25-35
1965	**40 page Catalogue - Playcraft Toys Ltd 1965.** 261 JB's Aston Martin DB5 on cover. Rallye Monte Carlo issues. 'Price 3d'	£25-35
1965	**Two-fold Checklist - Mettoy Playcraft (Sales) Ltd 1965.** Leaflet with 6 model cars from 6 nations on cover	£20-25
1966	**48 page Catalogue C2017/9/66.** Features 'BATMAN' and 'THE AVENGERS' etc. Includes price list. 190 x 78mm.,'4d'	£25-35
1966	**Leaflet C2038/66.** 'MODEL CAR MAKERS TO JAMES BOND'	£20-25
1966	**Four-fold Checklist C2039/4/66.** Leaflet similar to previous with 'MODEL CAR MAKERS TO JAMES BOND'. 1127 Simon Snorkel featured	£20-25
1967	**Three-fold Checklist - Mettoy Playcraft (Sales) 1967.** Front shows 'NEW' in five languages + 1142 Holmes Wrecker	£20-25
1967	**48 page Catalogue C/2017/7/67.** Lincoln Continental (262) on both covers. 'Price 6d'. Unissued 9022 Daimler and 9014 'Lyons Tea' shown	£30-35
1967	**Interim Leaflet** No ref. 1142 'Holmes' Wrecker on cover	£20-25
1968	**48 page Catalogue C2017/9/68.** Cover has 268 'Chitty Chitty Bang Bang'. 'Take-off Wheels' issues listed	£30-35
1969	**Seven-fold Checklist - Mettoy Playcraft (Sales) Ltd 1969.** Unfolds to 2'6" x 8 3/4". 'Concorde' model on cover + 302 Hillman Hunter. Listings include 'Corgi Comics', 'CHIPPERFIELDS' and Set No.48	£30-35
1970	**48 page Catalogue - The Mettoy Co Ltd 1970.** 388 Mercedes-Benz C111 on cover, first 'WhizzWheels' models listed	£30-35
1971	**Two-fold Checklist - 1970 Mettoy Co Ltd.** 6 WhizzWheels models on the cover. The final 'Take-Off Wheels' issues listed	£15-20
1972	**48 page Catalogue C2017 Petty 7/71/LOI7b.** Cover shows 1972 Car models. 'CORGI COMICS' inside	£20-25
1972	**48 page Catalogue** C2017 Petty 7/71/LOI7B (2nd). Cars across both covers	£20-25
1972	**4-page Brochure (A4)** No ref. 'Corgi Juniors with WhizzWheels' 'Juniors Extra' section of TV models	£10-15
1973	**40 page Catalogue 1973 Mettoy Co Ltd.** F1 Racing Cars featured on the cover	£10-15
1974	**40 page Catalogue C2107.**	

'Corgi '74' on cover.............................. **£10-15**
1974 **40 page Catalogue C2111.** Same........ **£10-15**
1974 **40 page Catalogue 1974 Mettoy Co Ltd.**
'John Player' Lotus on cover.............. **£10-15**
1975 **Catalogue Leaflet** No ref. Unfolded size
2' x 8½". 'Corgi 75' on cover **£10-15**
1975 **Three-fold leaflet - 1975 Mettoy Co Ltd.**
Helicopters, Noddy's Car, etc on the
cover. Numbers given 'C' prefix.......... **£10-15**
1976 **Three-fold leaflet - 1976 Mettoy Co Ltd.**
'KOJAK' on first page. Roadmaking
and Public Services listings **£10-15**
1977 **48 page Catalogue C2210.**
Silver Jubilee Coach on cover.
Large section listing Corgi 'Juniors' **£10-15**
1977 **48 page Catalogue C2211.**
'Corgi 77' on cover............................... **£10-15**
1977 **32 page Catalogue C2222.**
'Corgi 77' on cover............................... **£10-15**
1978 **48 page Catalogue The Mettoy Co Ltd.**
James Bond's Lotus on cover, 'JEAN
RICHARD PINDER' models within..... **£10-15**
1979 **48 page Catalogue C2250.** James Bond's
Space Shuttle on the cover. 'SUPERMAN'
and 'THE MUPPETS' listed inside **£10-15**
1980 **48 page Catalogue C2270.** C339 Rover

'Police' and C1001 HCB ANGUS on cover.
Foreign 'POLICE' issues listed............. **£10-15**
1980 **48 page Catalogue C2275.** 'RESCUE'
Vehicle plus '1980/81' on cover........... **£10-15**
1980 **32 page Catalogue C2282.**
As previous, but no Juniors included.. **£10-15**
1980 **32 page Catalogue C2283.** Same........ **£10-15**
1981 **32 page Catalogue C2285.**
'CORGI' container on cover................. **£10-15**
1981 **32 page Catalogue C2290.** Same........ **£10-15**
1981 **32 page Catalogue C2292.** Same........ **£10-15**
1982 **32 page Catalogue C2337.** C802 Mercedes
on cover, 'Corgitronics' within............. **£10-15**
1983 **36 page Catalogue - Mettoy Co PLC.**
Boxed models on cover, new Mercedes
and Scania trucks inside **£10-15**
1984 **32 page Catalogue** No ref. 'CORGI '84'
and boxed models on cover. The last
catalogue with the Corgi Dog emblem..**£5-10**
1985 **48 page Catalogue** No ref. Cover shows
new 'CORGI' trade name logo. The new
'CLASSICS' Commercials listed **£5-10**

Trade catalogues

Catalogues for trade purposes have been produced for some years and occasionally are offered for sale to collectors. No information is available on catalogues issued before 1980 but those from the 1980-90 decade tend to be in the **£5** to **£15** range.

Newsletters and club magazines

Mettoy Corgi Newsletters................................ **£5-6**   **Corgi Club Magazines**   1950s .... **£20-25**   **Corgi Club Magazines**   1960s **£15-18**

Corgi Triumph Herald Coupé

Corgi Batmobile and Batboat on Trailer

Catalogues, Leaflets and Box Inserts (Overseas Editions)

IDENTIFICATION of OVERSEAS CATALOGUES

The overseas editions comprised specially amended UK editions and there are many versions. They may be identified by:

- All the text being in the relevant language.
- A special reference number (but not always), e.g. 52/258/K5 AUSTRALIA.
- An adapted checklist/pricelist in the language/currency of the country concerned.
- The name of the country either on the cover, on page two, or on the checklist.
- Some complete catalogues were issued with all the text being in the language concerned, e.g. French, German, etc.
- Normally overseas editions, unlike UK editions, do not display the catalogue price on the cover. The exception to this rule being those issued with all the text in the language concerned.

As stated above, the overseas editions are basically the same as the UK editions. Similarly the catalogues, leaflets and box inserts issued in any one particular year were the same for all overseas countries. The only differences being the reference numbers, the type of language and currency shown. The following listing of overseas editions correspond with the country by country listings and will assist collectors identify the various editions. The reference codes shown, e.g. '52/258/K5' are common to all countries with a country reference being added as required, e.g. '52/258/K5 EAST AFRICA.' The '258' part refers to the

month and year of issue, i.e. Feb 1958.

TYPES of CATALOGUES LISTED

Box Inserts - These were inserted in the early blue box issues circa 1957-1959. They have a single fold and contain a checklist with prices in the local currency, plus a few pictures of the latest models.

Catalogue Leaflets - These are large, full colour leaflets, usually listing the full range available, together with pictures plus a checklist with prices.

Catalogues - These may contain 16, 20, 32, 40 or 48 pages and are full colour booklets containing the complete current range.

Interim Leaflets - Usually a double folded leaflet issued to supplement the main catalogues. These contain six pages, plus a checklist of the latest issues.

The information contained in these listings has been obtained from Corgi archive material. Whilst many issues have been listed, we believe others exist and we would welcome any such information.

Overseas catalogues were produced in much smaller numbers than the UK editions. Consequently as they seldom appear for sale, it is not possible to give their individual market prices. For guidance purposes, however, some have been known to sell for prices in excess of £100. As a result, the extremely rare issues, such as British East Africa, West Africa, Malta, Hong Kong, etc, may be expected to attract a premium.

African issues

English text - local currency

BRITISH EAST AFRICA

1959	16 page Catalogue '8/59'. 'British East Africa 8/59' on cover, along with a tractor and racing car ...	£70-80
1960	20 page Catalogue '9/60'. 'British East Africa 9/60' on cover.....	£50-60
62/63	Interim Leaflet (no ref.). 'British East Africa' on checklist.......	£25-35
61/62	Interim Leaflet (no ref.). 'British East Africa' on top of page 2.	£25-35

EAST AFRICA

1958	Box Insert '52/258/K5 East Africa'. 'East Africa' on checklist....................	£25-35
1965	Interim Leaflet (no ref.). 'East Africa' plus 'Mettoy 1965' on checklist.	£20-25
64/65	40 page Catalogue (no ref.). 'East Africa 8/64' on checklist..........	£35-45

KENYA, UGANDA & TANGANYIKA

1958	Catalogue Leaflet '15/158/C3 KUT'. 'Kenya, Uganda and Tanganyika'......	£30-35
1958	Box Insert '3.350/658/K7/KEN.-UG.-TAN'.......	£30-35

RHODESIA

Early Distributors: Coombe & Dewar Pty Ltd. P.O. Box 1572, Bulawayo and P.O. Box 663, Salisbury.

61/62	Interim Leaflet (no ref.). 'Rhodesia' top of page two	£25-35
62/3	Interim Leaflet (no ref.). 'Rhodesia' on checklist	£25-35
1962	32 page Catalogue 'C/100/62'. 'Rhodesia 1/63' on checklist. Red suited boy on cover	£50-60
1964	Interim Leaflet (no ref.). 'Rhodesia' plus 'Playcraft 1964' on checklist......	£20-30
1965	Interim Leaflet (no ref.). 'Rhodesia' + 'Mettoy 1965' on checklist	£20-30

RHODESIA, ZAMBIA & MALAWI

65/66	40 page Catalogue (no ref.). 'Rhodesia/Zambia/Malawi 8/65' on checklist, + '1965' on cover...............	£50-60

SOUTH AFRICA & RHODESIA

1958	Box Insert '52/258/K5 South	

Africa/Rhodesia' on checklist £25-35

1958	Box Insert '52/258/K6 South Africa/Rhodesia'. 'South Africa/Rhodesia' on checklist	£25-35

SOUTH AFRICA

1958	Box Insert '10/658/K7/S. Africa'. 'S. Africa' on checklist page	£25-35
58/59	16 page Catalogue '40/1058/C8/S. Africa'. 'S. Africa' on back	£50-60
61/62	Interim Leaflet (no ref.). 'South Africa' on page two................	£25-35
62/63	Interim Leaflet (no ref.). 'South Africa' on checklist	£25-35
1964	Interim Leaflet (no ref.). 'S. Africa' and 'Playcraft Toys Ltd. 1964' checklist	£25-35
1965	Interim Leaflet (no ref.). 'South Africa' plus 'Mettoy 1965' on checklist........	£25-35
1966	48 page Catalogue 'C/2017/9/66'. 'South Africa' on checklist and cover	£30-40
1967	Interim Leaflet (no ref.). 'South Africa' on cover, plus 'Mettoy, etc. 1967' on last page	£25-35
1971	2-fold checklist '© 1970 Mettoy Co Ltd'. 'Corgi Toys with WhizzWheels' plus 'Australia', 'S.Africa' and 'USA' on cover. Checklist prices in all 3 currencies ...	£15-20

NB As listed under CANADA, a catalogue was issued in 1970 with a combined CANADA and SOUTH AFRICAN checklist.

Australia

Address of Corgi Club in 1959: The Secretary, Corgi Model Club (Australian Section), P.O. Box 1607, M. Melbourne C1.

1957	Catalogue Leaflet '20/657/C2/AUS'. Checklist dated 1.6.57. Cover shows early 'Blue Box' with model 208........	£25-35
1958	Box Insert '52/258/K5/Australia'. Cover shows model 350	£25-35
1958	Box Insert '52/258/K6/Australia'. 1401 Service Ramp on cover	£25-35
1958	Box Insert '10/658/K7/Aus'. Cover shows models 209 & 458........	£25-35
1959	16 page Catalogue (no ref.).	

'Australia 8/59' on cover £70-80

61/62	Leaflet (no ref.). 'Australia' on top of page two	£25-35
62/63	Leaflet (no ref.). 'Australia' checklist	£25-35
1967	Leaflet (no ref.). 'Australia' on cover	£20-25
1971	2-fold Checklist '© 1970 Mettoy Co Ltd'. 'Corgi Toys with WhizzWheels' plus 'Australia', 'S.Africa' and 'USA' on cover. Checklist prices in all 3 currencies ...	£10-15

Austria

German Text. 'Kontrolliste fur den sammler'

1957	Leaflet '20/657/C2/A'. 'Austria' on checklist	£30-35
61/62	Interim Leaflet (no ref.). 'Austria' on top of page two	£20-25
1964	Interim Leaflet (no ref.). 'Austria' on checklist	£20-25
64/65	40 page Catalogue (no ref.). 'Austria 9/64' on checklist.................	£35-45
1965	Interim Leaflet (no ref.). 'Austria' on checklist	£20-25

Belgium

Early distribution:

Joets Eisenmann, S.A.,
111/113 Rui Masui, Bruxelles, Teleph: (02) 15.48.50.

1958 Belgian Corgi Club:

M. Le Secretaire du Club Corgi,
Jouets Eisenmann,
20 BD M. Lemonnier, Bruxelles.

English Text - French Checklist:

'Liste de Contrôle pour le Collectionneur'

1958	Box Insert '52/258/K6/Belgium'. 'Belgium' on checklist......................	£30-35
1958	Box Insert '5/658/K7/Belg'. 'Belg' on checklist	£30-35
1967	Leaflet (no ref.). 'Belgium' on cover.	£20-25

English Text - Flemish Checklist:

'Kontroleer zo de Verzameling'

1966	48 page Catalogue 'C/2017/9/66'. 'Belgium' on cover and on checklist.	£35-45
1967	Leaflet (no ref.). 'Belgium (Flemish)' on cover............	£20-25

English Text - separate French and Flemish checklists:

61/62 Interim Leaflet (no ref.). 'Belgium' on top of page two........... £20-25
62/63 Interim Leaflet (no ref.). 'Belgium' on checklist...................... £20-25
63/64 40 page Catalogue (no ref.). 'Belgium 8/63' on checklist............ £40-50
64 Interim Leaflet (no ref.). 'Belgium' and 'Playcraft 1964' on checklist £20-25
65 Interim Leaflet (no ref.). 'Belgium' and 'Mettoy 1965' on checklist........ £20-25
1967 Leaflet (no ref.). 'Belgium' on cover. £20-25
67/68 48 page Catalogue 'C/2017/7/67'. 'Belgium (French) 1967' on checklist£35-45
67/68 48 page Catalogue 'C2017/7/67'. 'Belgium 8/67' on Flemish checklist and 'Belgium (French) 8/67' on French checklist £35-45
1974 40 page Catalogue (no ref.). 'C2103 Belgium' on Flemish checklist plus '2107' on French checklist......... £15-25

English Text - French/Flemish combined checklist:

1957 Catalogue Leaflet '20/657/C2/B'. 'Belgium' on checklist....................... £25-35
1958 Catalogue Leaflet '20/258/C5/B'. 'Belgium' on checklist..................... £25-35

French Text - French checklist :

1958 Box Insert '120/1058/K8/Belg'. No. 458 E.R.F. on cover....................... £25-35
1960 20 page Catalogue (no ref.). 'Belgium 9/60' and 'Frs.3.' on cover.. £40-50
1961 24 page Catalogue (no ref.). 'Belgium 9/61' and 'Frs.3.' on cover.. £40-50
65/66 40 page Catalogue (no ref.). 'Belgium 8/65' on checklist £30-40

Canada

English text - local currency

1958 Catalogue Leaflet '40/258/C5/CA'. 'Canada' on checklist £30-35
1958 Box Insert '52/258/K5/Canada'. 'Canada' on checklist £30-35
1958 Box Insert '52/258/K6/Canada'. 'Canada' on checklist £30-35
1958 Box Insert '5/658/K7/CAN'. 'CAN' on checklist £30-35
1960 20 page Catalogue 'Canada 9/60'. 'Canada 9/60' on cover £40-50
60/61 Interim Leaflet 'Canada'. 'Canada' on checklist £30-35
61/62 24 page Catalogue 'Canada 9/61'. 'Canada 9/61' on cover £60-70
61/62 Interim Leaflet 'Canada'. 'Canada' on checklist £30-35
1963 32 page Catalogue 'C/100/62'. 'Canada 1/63' on checklist £50-60
1964 Interim Leaflet 'Canada'. 'Canada' and 'Playcraft Toys Ltd. 1964' checklist ... £30-35
1965 Interim Leaflet 'Canada'. 'Canada' and 'Mettoy etc. 1965' on checklist £30-35
64/65 40 page Catalogue 'Canada 9/64'. 'Canada 9/64' on checklist plus '1965' on cover £40-50
65/66 40 page Catalogue 'Canada 8/65'. 'Canada 8/65' on checklist plus '1966' on cover £40-50
1966 48 page Catalogue 'C2017/9/60'. 'Canada' on cover and checklist £40-50
1967 Interim Leaflet 'Canada'. 'Canada' on cover plus 'Mettoy 1967' on last page£25-35
1969 7-fold Leaflet 'Canada'. Concorde featured on cover; '8/69' on checklist.£50-60

French Text Issue

1966 48 page Catalogue 'C/2017/9/66'. 'Canadian (French)' on cover £50-60
Combined Canadian and South African checklist
1970 48 page Catalogue (no ref.). 'Canada, South Africa' on checklist. 'The Mettoy Co. Ltd. 1970' on rear cover .. £50-60

Denmark

All the text in Danish

1960 20 page Catalogue (no ref.). 'Denmark 9/60' and '25 re' on cover £40-50
1961/62 24 page Catalogue (no ref.). 'Denmark 9/61' and '25 re' on cover £40-50
1977 48 page Catalogue 'C2214'. 'Katalog' and 'Corgi '77' on cover £10-15

English text - Danish checklist.
'Samlerers Kontrolliste'

60/61 Interim Leaflet (no ref.). 'Denmark' £20-25
61/62 Interim Leaflet (no ref.). 'Denmark' on page two £20-25
63/64 40 page Catalogue (no ref.). '1963-64' on cover, 'Denmark 8/63' on checklist .. £50-60
1964 Interim Leaflet (no ref.). 'Denmark' and 'Playcraft 1964' on checklist....... £20-25
64/65 40 page Catalogue (no ref.). '1965' on cover, 'Denmark 9/64' on checklist .. £40-50
65/66 40 page Catalogue (no ref.). 'Denmark 8/65' on checklist plus '1966' on cover........ £30-40
1966 48 page Catalogue 'C2017/9/66'. 'Denmark' on cover and checklist £30-40
1974 40 page Catalogue 'C2105 1974'. Danish checklist, 'Corgi 74' on cover £10-15
80/81 48 page Catalogue 'C2271'. Checklist + '1980/81' on cover £10-15
81/82 30 page Catalogue 'C2292'. Checklist + '1981-82' on cover £10-15

Eire

1958 Box Insert '52/258/K6/EIRE'. 'Eire' on checklist £20-25
1958 Box Insert '5/658/K7/EIRE'. 'Eire' on checklist £20-25
60/61 Interim Leaflet (no ref.) 'Eire' on checklist £20-25
62/63 Interim Leaflet (no ref.) 'Eire' on checklist £15-20
64/65 Interim Leaflet (no ref.). 'Eire' plus 'Playcraft 1964' on checklist £15-20

Finland

English Text - local currency

63/64 40 page Catalogue (no ref.). 'Finland 8/63' on checklist plus '1963-64' on cover. £30-40
1965 Interim Leaflet (no ref.). 'Finland 6/65' and 'Mettoy 1965' on checklist......... £15-20

France

English Text - French checklist

61/62 Interim Leaflet (no ref.). 'France' on page two £30-40
62/63 Interim Leaflet (no ref.). 'France' on checklist £30-40
63/64 40 page Catalogue (no ref.). 'France 8/63' on checklist plus '1963-64' on cover £60-70
64/65 Interim Leaflet (no ref.). 'France' and 'Playcraft 1964' on checklist £30-40
1965 Interim Leaflet (no ref.). 'France' and 'Mettoy 1965' on checklist £30-40

French Text and checklist .
'Liste de Controle pour le Collectioneur'.

1965 40 page Catalogue (no ref.). 'France 8/65' on checklist plus 'Playcraft Toys Ltd. 1965' on rear cover £50-60
1968 48 page Catalogue 'C2017/8/67'. French text - '1968' on cover £30-40
1969 48 page Catalogue 'C2017/9/68'. French text - '1969' on cover............ £20-30
1973 40 page Catalogue (no ref.). French text - '1973' on cover........... £15-20
1974 40 page Catalogue 'C2107 1974'. French text - '1974' on cover £15-20
1975 Catalogue Leaflet (no ref.). French text - 'Corgi '75' on cover £10-15
1977 16 page Catalogue 'C2222'. French text plus 'Corgi '77' on cover £20-30
80/81 48 page Catalogue 'C2275'. French text plus '1980/81' on cover

(includes Juniors)................................ £20-25
80/81 32 page Catalogue 'C2282'. French text plus '1980/81' on cover.. £15-20
81/82 32 page Catalogue 'C2290'. French text plus '1981 Mettoy' on rear cover £15-20

Holland

Agent for Holland:
N.V.S/O, Herengracht 25, Amsterdam.
Dutch Text throughout
1959 20 page Catalogue (no ref.). 'Holland 8/59' plus 'FL.O.10' on cover plus Dutch text £70-80
1961 24 page Catalogue (no ref.). 'Holland 9/61' plus 'F.O.10' on cover plus Dutch text £50-60
French Text - Dutch checklist.
'Kontroleer zo de Verzameling'.
80/81 48 page Catalogue 'C2281'. '1980 Mettoy' on rear cover £20-30
81/82 30 page Catalogue 'C2291'. French text, Dutch checklist, plus '1981 Mettoy' on rear cover £20-30
English Text with French and Dutch checklists
1974 40 page Catalogue (no ref.). 'C2107 1974' on French checklist. 'C2103 1974' on Dutch checklist £20-30
English text - Dutch checklist
1957 Catalogue Leaflet '20/657C2/NL'. 'Holland' on checklist £20-30
1958 Catalogue Leaflet '15/158/C4/H'. 'Holland' on checklist £25-30
1958 Box Insert '52/258/K5/HOLLAND'. 'Holland' on checklist....................... £25-30
1958 Box Insert '52/258/K6/HOLLAND'. 'Holland' on checklist....................... £25-30
1958 Box Insert '5/658/K7/HOL'. 'HOL' on checklist £25-30
60/61 Interim Leaflet (no ref.). 'Holland' on checklist £25-30
61/62 Interim Leaflet (no ref.). 'Holland' top of page two £25-30
62/63 Interim Leaflet (no ref.). 'Holland' on checklist £25-30
63/64 40 page Catalogue (no ref.). 'Holland 8/63' on checklist £60-80
1964 Interim Leaflet (no ref.). 'Holland' on checklist £25-30
64/65 40 page Catalogue (no ref.). 'Holland 9/64' on checklist £25-30
1965 Interim Leaflet (no ref.). 'Holland' on checklist £25-30
1966 48 page Catalogue 'C2017/9/66'. 'Holland' on cover and checklist .. £40-50
1967 Interim Leaflet (no ref.). 'Holland' on cover........................ £20-25
67/68 48 page Catalogue 'C2017/7/67'. 'Holland 8/67' on checklist £50-60
1969 48 page Catalogue 'C2017/9/68'. 'Holland 10/68' on checklist £30-40
1974 40 page Catalogue 'C2211 1974'. Dutch text in checklist £20-25
1974 40 page Catalogue (no ref.). C2107 on French checklist plus C2103 on Dutch checklist................... £20-25

Hong Kong

1961 Catalogue (no ref.). 24 pages, 'Hong Kong 9/61' on cover £70-80
61/62 Interim Leaflet (no ref.). 'Hong Kong' on page two £20-25
1963 Catalogue 'C/100/62'. 24 pages, 'Hong Kong 3/63' on checklist £60-80
1963 Interim Leaflet (no ref.). 'Hong Kong' on checklist................... £20-25
1964 Interim Leaflet (no ref.). 'Hong Kong' on checklist................... £20-25
65/66 40 pages (no ref.). 'Hong Kong 8/65' on checklist £60-80
1966 Catalogue 'C2017/9/66'. 48 pages, 'Hong Kong' on cover and checklist. £60-80

Italy

1963 Concessionaria per l'Italia: Ditta 'Guimar' via Disciplini 7, Milano (303). 'Distinta di Controllo per i Collezzionisti'.

1958	**Box Insert '52/258/K5 ITALY'.** 'Italy' on checklist	£25-35
1958	**Box Insert '52/258/K6 ITALY'.** 'Italy' on checklist	£25-35
1958	**Box Insert '5/658/K7 ITALY'.** 'Italy' on checklist	£25-35
1959	**Catalogue** (no ref.). 20 pages, 'Italy 8/59' on cover	£50-75
60/61	**Interim Leaflet** (no ref.). 'Italy' on checklist	£20-25
1961	**Catalogue** (no ref.). 24 pages, 'Italy 9/61' on cover	£40-50
61/62	**Interim Leaflet** (no ref.). 'Italy' on page two	£20-25
62/63	**Interim Leaflet** (no ref.). 'Italy' on checklist	£20-25
63/64	**Interim Leaflet** (no ref.). 40 pages, 'Italy 8/63' on checklist	£70-80
1964	**Interim Leaflet** (no ref.). 'Italy' on checklist	£20-25
64/65	**Catalogue** (no ref.). 40 pages, 'Italy 9/64' on checklist	£30-40
1965	**Interim Leaflet** (no ref.). 'Italy' on checklist	£20-25
1967	**Interim Leaflet** (no ref.). 'Italy' on cover. 'ATTENDETE OGNIMESE LE NOVITA 'CORGI'	£20-25

1974 Concessionaria per l'Italia:
Toyuro s.n.c., Via S. Vittore 45, Milano (20123).

1974	**Catalogue 'C2112 1974'.** 40 pages, 'Italia' reference on checklist	£15-20
80/81	**Catalogue 'C2278'.** 48 pages, Italian text throughout	£10-15
81/82	**Catalogue 'C2293'.** 32 pages, Italian text throuhout	£10-15

Japan

1968	**Folded Leaflet**	£40-50
1973	**Catalogue** (no ref.). 40 pages, Japanese text throughout	£20-30

Malta

1964	**Leaflet** (no ref.). 'Malta' on checklist	£25-35
64/65	**Catalogue** (no ref.). 40 pages, 'Malta 8/64' on checklist	£50-60
1965	**Leaflet** (no ref.). 'Malta' on checklist	£25-35

New Zealand

64/65	**Catalogue** (no ref.). 40 pages, 'New Zealand 8/64' on checklist	£50-60
1965	**Leaflet** (no ref.). 'New Zealand' on checklist	£25-30
65/66	**Catalogue** (no ref.). 40 pages, 'New Zealand 8/65' on checklist	£50-60

Norway

'Se dem alle 1 den nye Katalogen, Samlers Liste'.
English Text - Norwegian checklist

61/62	**Leaflet** (no ref.). 'Norway' on page 2	£25-35
62/63	**Leaflet** (no ref.). 'Norway' checklist	£25-35
1964	**Leaflet** (no ref.). 'Norway' checklist	£20-25
64/65	**Catalogue** (no ref.). 40 pages, 'Norway 9/64' on checklist	£30-40
1965	**Leaflet** (no ref.). 'Norway' checklist	£20-25
1966	**Catalogue** (no ref.). 40 pages, 'Norway 8/65' on checklist	£30-40
1966	**Catalogue 'C2017/9/66'.** 48 pages, 'Norway' on cover and checklist	£35-45
67/68	**Catalogue 'C2017/7/67'.** 48 pages, 'Norway 8/67' on checklist	£35-45
1970	**Catalogue** (no ref.). 48 pages, 'Norway' on checklist	£25-30
1974	**Catalogue 'C2113'.** 40 pages, Norwegian checklist	£15-20
80/81	**Catalogue 'C2272'.** 48 pages, Norwegian checklist	£10-15

1975	**Catalogue Leaflet** (no ref.). Norwegian text throughout, plus '1975 Mettoy'	£10-15

Portugal

'Lista de controle para o colecionador'.
English Text - Portuguese checklist.

1957	**Catalogue Leaflet '25/257/C2/P'.** 'Portugal' on checklist	£25-35
1960	**Leaflet** (no ref.). 'Portugal' checklist	£20-25
61/62	**Leaflet** (no ref.). 'Portugal' on page 2	£20-25
62/63	**Leaflet** (no ref.). 'Portugal' checklist	£20-25
63/64	**Catalogue** (no ref.). 40 pages, 'Portugal 8/63' on checklist	£35-45
1964	**Leaflet** (no ref.). 'Portugal' checklist	£20-25
67/68	**Catalogue 'C2017/7/67'.** 48 pages, 'Portugal 8/67' on checklist	£35-45

Singapore / Malaya

1958	**Box Insert '52/258/K5 SINGAPORE/MALAYA'.** 'Singapore/Malaya' on checklist	£25-35
1958	**Catalogue Leaflet '10/258/C5/SM'.** 'Singapore/Malaya' on checklist	£25-35
1958	**Box Insert '3.350/658/K7 SING.-MAL'.** 'Sing.-Mal' on checklist	£25-35
1960	**Catalogue** (no ref.). 20 pages, 'Singapore Malaya 9/60' on cover	£70-80
1960	**Leaflet** (no ref.). 'Singapore/Malaya' on checklist	£25-35
1961	**Catalogue** (no ref.). 24 pages, 'Singapore/Malaya 9/61' on checklist	£60-70
62/63	**Leaflet** (no ref.). 'Singapore/Malaya' on checklist	£25-30
62/63	**Catalogue 'C/100/62'.** 32 pages, 'Singapore/Malaya 2/63' on checklist	£50-60
1965	**Leaflet** (no ref.). 'Singapore/Malaya' on checklist	£20-25

Spain

Spanish Text and checklist. 'Lista de Coleccionistas'.

1961	**Checklist.** 24 pages, 'Spanish 9/61' on cover	£30-40

English Text - Spanish checklist. 'Lista de Precios para Coleccionistas'

1962	**Checklist 'C/100/62'.** 'Spanish' on checklist	£25-30
80/81	**Checklist 'C2273'.** Spanish text in checklist	£10-15

Sweden

'Kontrollista för Samlaren'.
English text - Swedish checklist

1958	**Box Insert '52/258/K5/SWEDEN'.** 'Sweden' on checklist	£25-35
1958	**Box Insert '52/258/K6/SWEDEN'.** 'Sweden' on checklist	£25-35
1958	**Box Insert '5/658/K7/SWEDEN'.** 'Sweden' on checklist	£25-35
1959	**Catalogue** (no ref.). 16 pages, 'Sweden 8/59' on cover	£40-50
60/61	**Leaflet** (no ref.). 'Sweden' checklist	£20-25
1961	**Catalogue** (no ref.). 24 pages, 'Sweden 9/61' on cover	£40-50
61/62	**Leaflet** (no ref.). 'Sweden' on page 2	£20-25
62/63	**Leaflet** (no ref.). 'Sweden' checklist	£20-25
63/64	**Catalogue** (no ref.). 40 pages, 'Sweden 8/63' on checklist	£50-60
64/65	**Catalogue** (no ref.). 40 pages, 'Sweden 9/64' on checklist	£40-50
1965	**Leaflet** (no ref.). 'Sweden' checklist	£20-25
1966	**Catalogue** (no ref.). 40 pages, 'Sweden 6/65' on checklist	£35-45
1966	**Catalogue 'C2017/9/66'.** 48 pages, 'Sweden' on cover and checklist	£35-45
1967	**Leaflet** (no ref.). 'Sweden' on cover	£20-25
1974	**Catalogue 'C2106 1974'.** 40 pages, Swedish text on checklist	£15-20
1975	**Leaflet** (no ref.). All Swedish text	£10-15
80/81	**Catalogue 'C2277'.** 48 pages, Swedish text throughout	£10-15

Swedish text - Norwegian checklist

81/82	**Catalogue 'C2287'.** 32 pages, Swedish text + Norwegian checklist	£10-15

Switzerland

English Text - English/Swiss checklist

1957	**Catalogue Leaflet '20/657/C2/CH'.** 'Switzerland' on checklist	£70-80
1958	**Box Insert '52/258/K5/Switzerland'.** Reference on checklist	£25-35
1958	**Box Insert '52/258/K6/Switzerland'.** Reference on checklist	£25-35
1958	**Box Insert '5/658/K7/SWITZ'.** Reference on checklist	£25-35
1958	**Catalogue '25/1058/C8/SWITZ'.** 16 pages, 'Switz' on checklist. New issues in French	£70-80
1958	**Catalogue Leaflet '5/658/C5/CH'.** 'Switzerland' on checklist	£25-35
1960/61	**Leaflet** (no ref.). 'Switzerland' on checklist	£25-30
1961	**Catalogue** (no ref.). 24 pages, 'Switzerland 9/61' on cover	£40-50
61/62	**Leaflet** (no ref.). 'Switzerland' on p.2	£20-25
62/63	**Catalogue 'C100/62'.** 32 pages, 'Switzerland 1/63' on checklist	£40-50
62/63	**Leaflet** (no ref.). 'Switzerland' on checklist	£20-25
1964	**Leaflet** (no ref.). 'Switzerland' on checklist	£20-25
64/65	**Catalogue** (no ref.). 40 pages, 'Switzerland' on checklist	£25-35
1965	**Leaflet** (no ref.). 'Switzerland' on checklist	£20-25
1966	**Catalogue** (no ref.). 40 pages, 'Switzerland 8/65' on checklist	£30-40
1966	**Catalogue 'C/2017/9/66'.** 48 pages, 'Switzerland' on cover and checklist	£30-40
1967	**Leaflet** (no ref.). 'Switzerland' on cover	£20-25
1969	**Catalogue 'C2017/9/68'.** 48 pages, 'Switzerland 10/68' on checklist	£30-40

USA

1958 Sole Distributor for U.S.A.: Reeves International Incorp., 1107 Broadway, New York 10, N.Y.

1958	**Catalogue Leaflet '20/458/C5/U.S.A'.** 'U.S.A.' on checklist	£30-40
1958	**Box Insert '20/658/K7/U.S.A'.** 'U.S.A.' on checklist	£30-40
1959	**Catalogue 'USA 8/59'.** 16 pages, pictures of tractor and racing car on cover	£70-80
1961	**Catalogue 'USA 9/61'.** 24 pages, 'U.S.A. 9/61' on cover	£50-60
1961/62	**Leaflet.** 'U.S.A.' on page two	£25-30
1962/63	**Catalogue 'C/100/62'.** 32 pages, Cover shows boy in red with corgi dog. 'U.S.A. 5/63' on checklist	£70-80
1962/63	**Catalogue 'USA 8/65'.** 'USA' on checklist	£25-30
1964	**2-fold Checklist** (no ref.). Ghia L 6.4 featured on cover. 'USA' and '© Playcraft Toys 1964'	£25-35
1964/65	**Catalogue** (no ref.). 40 pages, Green 9001 Bentley and Ghia L6.4 on cover. 'USA 8/64' on checklist	£55-65
1965/66	**Catalogue** (no ref.). 40 pages, 'U.S.A. 8/65' on checklist	£55-65
1967	**Leaflet** (no ref.). 'U.S.A.' on cover	£20-25
1968/69	**Catalogue 'C2017/9/68'.** 48 pages, Chitty-Chitty-Bang-Bang on cover. 'USA 10/68' on checklist	£30-40
1971	**2-fold Checklist '© 1970 Mettoy Co Ltd'.** 'Corgi Toys with WhizzWheels' plus 'Australia', 'S.Africa' and 'USA' on cover. Checklist prices in all three currencies	£25-30

International issues 1981–1985

The catalogue listings are printed in English, French and German.

Catalogue 'C2293' was issued as a miniature booklet.

Shop Display and 'Point-of-Sale' Items

Year	Item details	MPR
1950s	**Carded 3-D display stand** Red, yellow, blue black 'CORGI TOYS' plus 'NEW' in various languages ..	**£250-300**
57-59	**Display stand**, wooden. Ten cream 'corrugated' hardboard shelves, pale blue display background with yellow and blue plastic 'CORGI TOYS' sign screwed to top of display, (30 x 29 x 12 inches)	**£200-300**
57-59	**Display card/sign.** Tin/cardboard, yellow/blue with gold 'dog' logo, 'Wow! Corgi Toys-The Ones with Windows'	**£100-150**
57-59	**Display card/sign** As previous item but with 'New Corgi Major Toys - The Ones With Windows'	**£100-150**
57-59	**Wooden display unit.** Two shelf stand with Blue backing logo 'CORGI TOYS', 'THE ONES WITH WINDOWS', 'MODEL PERFECTION' and 'NEW' plus the early gold Corgi dog on red background	**£200-300**
57-59	**Counter display unit.** Cardboard, single model display card with Dark Blue inner display area, 'new - CORGI TOYS' ..	**£75-125**
57-59	**Counter display unit** Cardboard, 2 tiers with 'New - CORGI MAJOR TOYS' in yellow/blue	**£200-300**
57-59	**Counter display unit.** Cardboard, 2 tier unit, 'COLLECT CORGI TOYS' and 'New MODELS EVERY MONTH' logos in yellow/blue	**£200-300**
57-59	**Counter display unit** Cardboard, Renault Floride (222) pictorial display card with '1959 MOTOR SHOW' and 'EARLS COURT' logos	**£300-400**
57-59	**Counter display unit** (cardboard) Citroën (475) pictorial display card with 'new - THE CITROEN' and 'OLYMPIC WINTER SPORTS' logos	**£200-300**
1959	**Display unit** Shows picture of GS8 'Combine Harvester Set'. 'At work in the field' logo	**£150-200**
57-67	**Metal display stand** Tiered stand 75cm x 30cm x 45cm high, three 'CORGI TOYS' and Black logos, + 3 early gold Corgi dog emblems ..	**£175-225**
1960	**Counter display box.** Stand for GS1 Bedford Carrimore (1101) and 4 cars	**£300-400**
1960	**Window display sign** Yellow background with 'Naturally Corgi Toys' in Red and Blue, illuminated. 27" long x 8" high. (Belgian market?)..	**£500-700**
60-61	**Window sticker** 'NEW MODELS EVERY MONTH'	**£30-40**
1960s	**Metal display stand** has 'Corgi Display C2034' on the back	**£100-150**
66-69	**Window sticker** Advertising new releases	**£20-30**
60-69	**Oblong window sign.** Glass or plastic	

Year	Item details	MPR
	with 'CORGI TOYS' and 'PRECISION DIE-CAST SCALE MODELS' logos plus gold Corgi 'dog' logo in blue/yellow/red design	**£200-300**
1960s	**Tinplate stand.** 5 Grey tiers topped by 'CORGI TOYS'/Gold dog header	**£200-300**
60-69	**Glass display sign** Square sign, gold corgi dog on Red panel within Blue lined glass surround ..	**£150-200**
1961	**Moulded Corgi Dog.** on hind feet holding a 'CORGI CHRISTMAS CARD'	**£200-300**
68-83	**Metal display stand.** Tiered stand 75 cm x 45 cm high, with three 'CORGI TOYS' Black/Yellow logos, plus 3 White/Red late Corgi dog emblems	**£150-200**
71-73	**Oblong sign.** Plastic, with 'CORGI' and 'TESTED BY THE CORGI TECHNOCRATS' plus white Corgi 'dog' logo on red square, yellow background plus three 'Technocrats' faces	**£100-150**
63-65	**Display stand**, rotary, C2001/2 For self-selection, 7 tray unit, large 'CORGI TOYS' header sign	**£200-300**
63-65	**Display stand**, rotary, C2003. Self-selection, 4 columns, 4 compartments (45 x 30 in.), large 'CORGI TOYS' header boards	**£200-300**
63-65	**Display stand**, rotary, C2004 Self-selection, 4 column, 72 compartments (72 x 30 in.)	**£200-300**
63-65	**Display stand**, rotary, C2005 Self-selection, 2 column, 36 compartments (72 x 30 in.)	**£150-200**
63-65	**Display stand**, rotary, C2006 Self-selection, 2 column, 36 compartments (55 x 30 in.)	**£100-150**
63-65	**Display stand**, plastic, C2007 Large moulded plastic counter display to house up to 50 models, large black header display board with 'NATURALLY CORGI TOYS' on yellow/blue background, and 'JOIN THE CORGI MODEL CLUB' on display front	**£200-300**
1960s	**Electric Display stand**, revolving, C2008 Glass fronted, to house 100-120 models with light and dark simulated wood panels with four 'CORGI' logos, (38 x 24 x 24 in.)	**£400-600**
57-66	**Showcase**, glass, C2009 3 glass shelves, 3 'CORGI TOYS' logos (black/blue) plus gold Corgi 'dog' logo on red background, (20x15x9 in.)	**£200-300**
1970s	**Corgi Juniors unit**, E9051. Yellow plastic (21.75 x 21.75 in.), for 48 models, 'LOOK FOR WHIZZWHEELS MODELS'	**£100-150**
1970	**Retailers Shop Display Cabinet**, Illuminated 'Corgi Toys', 172cms high,	

Year	Item details	MPR
	121cms wide, 50cms deep, 3 drawers, Upper glass fronted display cabinet, 8 glass shelves	**£900-1000**
1975	**Army diorama,** Plastic vacuum formed To hold various models from Corgi Military Range Green, Grey and Brown	**£300-380**
1976	**Kojak's Buick.** Card counter-top..	**£100-125**
1979	**'Corgi Toys' display unit.** Metal, approx. 3' x 2' with 4 shelves / racks	**£250-300**
?	**Shop display card.** 'Mr SOFTEE Ice Cream free with this Corgi Toy'	**£300-400**
?	**Shop display stand** 'New! Chrysler Imperial'	**£150-200**
?	**Shop Display Stand** with 'New! The Bentley Continental'. Brown and Cream fold out cardboard counter display unit	**£400-500**
?	**'Corgi Toys' Hanging Tin Sign.** 'Corgi Dog and 'Corgi Kits' (52cm x 20cm)	**£400-500**
1979	**'CORGI TOYS' Metal Stand.** Approx. 3ft x 2ft with 4 shelves/racks	**£250-300**
	Magic Roundabout display stand. Cardboard	**£400-500**

Corgi Shop display sign

CORGI TOYS WINDOW POSTERS
485 Mini Countryman with Surfer.
 'New This Month', 245mm x 200mm **£100-150**
428 Karrier Bantam Ice Cream Van.
 'Mister Softee' 'New This Month', 245mm x 200mm **£100-150**
Citroën Safari 'Wildlife Preservation'.
 'New This Month' 245mm x 200mm **£100-150**
428 Karrier Bantam Ice Cream Van. 'Mister Softee'. 'Each box end worth 6d For any Mister Softee Van', 270mm x 140mm **£100-150**
270 Aston-Martin DB5. 'James Bond' - 'Now with Revolving Number Plates and Tyre Slashers', 400mm x 120mm **£200-250**
261 Aston-Martin DB5. 'James Bond' and 'Goldfinger', 300mm x 200mm **£200-250**

Corgi Comics No 802 Popeye Paddle Wagon

Corgi No 258 The Saints Car Volvo P.1800

Corgi No 336 James Bond Toyota GT2000GT from 'You Only Live Twice'

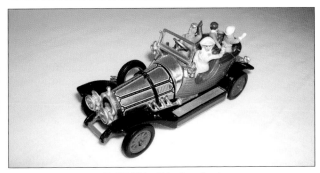

No 266 'Chitty Chitty Bang Bang'

Buick Riviera Boat Set

'US ARMY' Fuel Tanker

'Massey-Ferguson 65' Tractor with Tipper Trailer

VW 1200 Police Car

Corgi Point of Sale items consisting of Corgi plastic and cardboard hanging display signs and Corgi Juniors tinplate header from a display rack.

ABOVE Corgi Toys Counter Display signs and stands.

RIGHT Large Counter Display Stand for Corgi Military Range, made in plastic, finished in camouflage colours & pictorial header card - showing models No 900, 901, 902, 904, 905, 906, 907, CGS10.

Crescent Toys

The Crescent Toy Company was founded in July 1922 by Henry G. Eagles and Arthur A. Schneider in a workshop 30 feet square at the rear of a private house at 67 De Beauvoir Crescent, Kingsland Road, London N1.

They manufactured model soldiers, cowboys, kitchen sets, etc. from lead alloy. These were hollow castings, hand painted, packed one dozen to a box, and sold to wholesalers at six shillings per dozen boxes. The small firm prospered and eventually opened up a factory in Tottenham. With the second World War came a ban on metal toys and production was changed to munitions. After the War the firm resumed making metal hollow-cast toys and in addition marketed the diecast products of a firm called DCMT (Die Casting Machine Tools Ltd).

As a consequence early post-war models had 'DCMT' cast into the underside of the body. In 1948 the firm opened a modern factory on a four-acre site at Cymcarn, a Welsh mining village near Newport, Monmouth (now Gwent) and two years later transferred all production there, maintaining only an office in London. From this time Crescent toys made their own diecast products without 'DCMT' on them. Hence it is possible to find the same models with or without 'DCMT' cast in. Die Casting Machine Tools went their own way and from 1950 produced models under the name of 'Lone Star'.

Crescent Toys will be best remembered for their excellent ranges of military models and farm equipment but probably most of all for their superb reproductions of the racing cars of the 1950s.

The post-war model listings printed here were extracted from a unique collection of original trade catalogues (1947-80) most kindly provided by Mr. J. D. Schneider, the former Managing Director of Crescent Toys Ltd. All of the original research and actual compiling of the lists was undertaken by Ray Strutt.

The editor would also like to thank Les Perry of Rochdale for additional information.

Model and details			MPR

Early Post-war Models (various colours)

223	1948	Racing Car	£40-60
422	1949	Sports Car	£40-60
423	1949	Oil Lorry	£40-60
424	1949	Truck Lorry	£40-60
425	1949	Saloon Car	£40-60
800	47-49	Jaguar	£40-60
802	47-49	Locomotive	£40-60
803	47-48	Locomotive, Silver	£40-60
804	48-49	Police Car, Black	£40-60
	48-50	Deep Sea Diver, in diving suit, with equipment, boxed	£250-325
1221	1949	Fire Engine, Red body	£40-60
1225	1949	Dog Display Set	£200-250
---	---	Garages, retailing at 1/-, 1/6, 2/6 and 4/-. Complete with Modern Pumps, Motor Cars and Garage Attendants, 'CRESCENT GARAGES' logo	£200-300
FC330	---	Domestic Iron and Stand	£20-30
---	---	Zulu-drawn Rickshaw. Red/Green rickshaw, 'Zulu' with wheel attached to foot, colonial couple in tropical dress and pith helmets in rickshaw	£125-175
---	---	Milk Bar Set	£300-400
---	---	Barber Shop Set	£300-400

Farm Equipment
(various colours)

1802	49-60	Tractor and Hayrake	£300-400
1803	67-74	Dexta Tractor and Trailer	£300-400
1804	50-59	Tractor and Disc Harrow	£300-400
1805	50-61	Tractor	£200-300
1806	50-60	Hayrake	£10-15
1807	1950	Disc Harrow	£10-15
1808	50-56	Platform Trailer	£10-15
1809	50-60	Ricklift Trailer	£10-15
1809	62-80	Dexta Tractor	£150-200
1810	50-80	Box Trailer / Farm Trailer, (No.148 1968-74)	£15-20
1811	50-67	Animal Trailer / Cattle Trailer, (No.148 1968-71)	£10-15
1811	75-81	Dexta Tractor and Trailer	£150-200

1813	1950	Timber Wagon (Horse Drawn)	£75-95
1814	50-60	Plough Trailer, (No.150 1968-71)	£20-30
1815	1950	Hayloader	£20-30
1816	1950	Roller Harrow	£20-30
1817	50-56	Timber Trailer	£20-30
1818	54-60	Tipping Farm Wagon	£20-30
1819	54-55	Large Farm Wagon	£30-40

Diecast Action Toys
(various colours)

1219	54-59	'Milking Time' Set. 2 Milkmaids, 2 cows, calf. Card box, picture on lid	£125-175
1222	54-59	Builders & Decorators Truck Red handcart, unpainted ladder and bucket, beige figure on green base. Grey card box with drawing of set	£125-175
1268	54-59	Mobile Space Rocket	NGPP
1269	54-59	Mobile Crane	£80-100
1272	54-59	Scammell Scarab and Box Trailer	£100-150
1274	54-59	Scammell Scarab and Low Loader	£100-150
1276	55-59	Scammell Scarab and Oil Tanker 'ESSO'	£150-200
2700	56-60	Western Stage Coach	£80-90
2705	1955	Western Stage Coach	£80-90
-		Scammell Scarab Set, Mechanical Horse, Box Trailer and Low Loader	£100-150

Military Models
(All in military colours)

155	60-68	'Long Tom' Artillery Gun	£20-35
235	1946	Cannon, operable	£20-25
F 355	1938	Tank and Cannon Set	£100-125
650	54-59	Military Set: two 696 British Tanks, one 698 Scout Car, one 699 Russian Tank	£150-200
NN656/2	38-40	Field Gun and Gunner	£40-50
NN692	38-40	Deep Sea Diver, with equipment	£300-350
NN693	38-40	A.R.P. Searchlight Unit, 3 personnel, boxed	£150-175

NN694	38-40	A.R.P. Rangefinder Unit, 2 personnel, boxed	£150-175
695	38-40	A.R.P. First Aid Post: a tent, two stretcher bearers and patient, Red Cross nurse	£150-175
F 695	1946	Howitzer, unpainted, with spring and plunger, 'CRESCENT' cast-in	£10-20
696	54-59	British Tank	£40-50
698	54-56	Scout Car	£30-40
699	54-56	Russian Tank	£40-50
NN700	38-40	Royal Engineers Field Set: Engineers (2 standing, 2 kneeling), telegraph pole, transmitter, aerial. Box has colour picture of set on lid	£150-200
701	-	GPO Telephone Engineers Set: 4 men, telegraph pole, hut, cart, accessories. Box has colour picture of set on lid	£150-200
702	-	Sound Locator Unit, operator figure, boxed	£60-80
K 703	38-40	Field Wireless Unit with two Soldiers	£120-150
K 704	38-40	R.A.M.C. Stretcher Party, 2 Soldiers and Patient	£125-150
1248	1957	Field Gun	£5-10
1249	58-79	18-lb Quick-Firing Gun	£10-15
1250	58-80	25-pdr Light Artillery Gun	£10-15
1251	58-80	5.5" Medium Heavy Howitzer	£10-15
1260	76-79	Supply Truck	£40-60
1263	62-80	Saladin Armoured Car	£50-60
1264	75-80	Scorpion Tank	£12-16
1265	77-80	M109 Self-Propelled Gun	£12-15
1266	78-79	Recovery Vehicle	£12-15
1267	58-63	'Corporal' Rocket and Lorry	£125-150
1270	58-60	Heavy Rescue Crane	£50-60
1271	58-60	Long Range Mobile Gun	£100-125
1271	76-80	Artillery Force	£20-30
2154	62-74	Saladin Armoured Patrol (No.1270 1975-80)	£60-75

Historical Models
(in regal colours)

1300	75-76	Royal State Coach	£20-30
1301	77-79	Royal State Coach, (Commemorative box)	£20-30

State Coach - finished in gold plate effect.

1302	77	**Royal State Coach / Figures**	£20-30
1450	56-60	**Medieval Catapult**	£20-30
1953	54-60	**Coronation State Coach**	£100-125

Miniature 'wild west' transport (various colours)

| 906 | 1956 | **Stage Coach** | £30-40 |
| 907 | 1956 | **Covered Wagon** | £30-40 |

G.P. Racing and Sports Cars

| 1284 | 56-60 | **Mercedes-Benz,** all-enveloping silver body, racing number '12' | £90-120 |

GP racing cars: 1285 BRM MkII green RN7, 1286 Ferrari red RN5, 1287 Connaught green RN8, 1288 Cooper-Bristol blue RN2, 1289 Gordini light blue RN14, 1290 Maserati red RN3.

1285	56-60	**B.R.M. Mk.II,** mid green, '7'	£90-120
1286	56-60	**Ferrari,** orange-red	£90-120
1287	56-60	**Connaught,** dark green, racing number '8'	£90-120
1288	56-60	**Cooper-Bristol,** light blue, racing number '2'	£90-120
1289	56-60	**Gordini,** French blue, racing number '14'	£90-120
1290	56-60	**Maserati,** cherry red, racing number '3'	£90-120
1291	57-60	**Aston-Martin DB3s,** white/light blue	£100-150
1292	57-60	**Jaguar 'D' type,** dk. green	£100-150
1293	58-60	**Vanwall,** dark green, racing number '10'	£150-200
6300	1957	**Racing Cars Set,** 1284 - 1289 in display box	NGPP
	58-60	Same, but 1290 replaces 1284	NGPP

Long Vehicles
(various colours)

1350	75-80	**Container Truck**	£20-25
1351	75-80	**Petrol Tanker**	£20-25
1352	75-80	**Girder Carrying Truck**	£20-25
1353	75-80	**Flat Platform Truck**	£20-25

'Trukkers' (various colours)

1360	76-81	**Cement Mixer**	£5-20
1361	76-81	**Covered Truck**	£5-20
1362	76-81	**Tipper Truck**	£5-20
1363	76-81	**Recovery Vehicle**	£5-20
1364	76-81	**Super Karrier**	£5-20

Crescent Ships

SHIP MODEL IDENTIFICATION. Crescent Ships are of rather crude manufacture and have virtually no identifying features. Only the HMS 'Vanguard' and the 'H' or 'I' Class Destroyer are known to have 'CRESCENT' cast in. A few of the early models had a little paper 'Crescent' half-moon label. Ship models were packed in cream cardboard boxes of varying quality.

Battleships

HMS 'King George V'. Grey hollow-cast, with main armament only, boxed ... £20-30
Same but additional separately cast secondary armament ... £20-30
HMS 'Vanguard'. Grey / black / white, solid, 'CRESCENT' cast-in ... £10-15

Q 3	1940	**Battleship Set.** Battleship plus four Sailors	£80-100
S 3	1940	**Warships Set.** Battleship and Destroyer, eight Sailors	£100-200
NN691		**HMS 'Malaya'.** Grey hollow-cast, black funnels, boxed	£90-120

Aircraft carriers

| - | | **HMS 'Victorious'** (boxed). Grey hollow cast body, separate unpainted aircraft | £20-35 |
| NN 667 | | **HMS 'Eagle'.** Grey hollow-cast, Union Jack sticker on box, unpainted planes | £20-35 |

Other warships

'H' or 'I' Class Destroyer. Unpainted solid cast body, CRESCENT cast into bow ... £20-30
'H' or 'I' Class Destroyer. Same model plus three lead figures of naval personnel ... £40-60
'V' and 'W' Class Destroyer.
Grey hollow-cast body ... £5-8

A 34		**Gunboat.** Grey hollow cast	£5-8
234		**Submarine.** Unpainted, conning tower and deck gun, 4"	£20-30
C 310		**'County' Class Cruiser, 'Cumberland',** Grey hollow-cast	£10-20
K 664		**'County' Class Cruiser,** Grey hollow-cast	£10-20
K 665		**War Transport Ship,** Grey hollow-cast, boxed	£20-30

Passenger ships

---		**'Queen Mary'.** Black / white / red, hollow-cast body, boxed	£50-75
---		**'Dunnottar Castle'.** Mauve / white / red, hollow-cast, boxed	£50-75
---		**'Athlone Castle'.** Mauve / white / red, hollow-cast, boxed	£50-75

'Dunnottar Castle' and 'Athlone Castle' were part of the 'Union Castle' fleet and the models were sold in souvenir boxes, probably on board.

Crescent aircraft

O 2	1940	**Spitfire Set.** Two Spitfires with two Pilots and two Mechanics.	£100-200
Q 2	1940	**Spitfire Set.** As O 2 but new ref. no.	£100-200
U 2	1940	**Aircraft Set.** Five Aircraft plus three Pilots and six Groundcrew	£200-300
FC38	1946	**Aeroplane,** Spitfire	£25-35
FC89	1946	**Aeroplane,** Mosquito	£25-35
FC90	1946	**Aeroplane,** Lightning, 3" x 2", US markings	£25-35
FC179	1946	**Khaki Bomber**	£15-20
FC372	1946	**Aeroplane,** Lightning, 4.75" x 3", US markings	£25-35
FC663	1946	**North Sea Patrol.** Aeroplane with pilot and one other crew member	£80-100

Miscellaneous Models and Sets

'Dodgem' Car, Blue version seen, other colours possible ... £100-200
'Tower Bridge', various colours ... £20-30
'Dial 999' Police and Robbers Set. Contains black police car with loudhailer on roof and four semi-flat action figures (policeman running, policeman and dog, two fleeing villains, (one with swag). In card box with b/w label ... £200-300
Road and Car Set. Racing Car, Mechanic, Garage sign, Petrol Pump etc. ... £100-125

'Dan Dare' Set. With figures of Dan Dare, Miss Peabody, Dan Dare in spacesuit, 2 Treens (1 silver, 1 gold), rocket and launcher. Packed in card box ... £400-500
Trade Box   for 6 x No.363 'Shell-BP' clip-on signs. Green/red/blue box with lid ... £30-40
Gas Cooker. White, boxed ... £100-125
1225 'My Doggies' Set. With printed card wall backdrop and instructions. Green/Red kennel, three dogs, two bones, 'Beware of the Dog' sign ... £200-300
1201 Petrol Station. With two 'Power' and one 'Fina' petrol pumps, air pump. Box folds out to reveal forecourt scene ... £175-225
1823 Model Bridge. Green bridge/ 2 flights of steps and 'Esso' adverts. ... £50-75
1236 Bridge Signal. White gantry with 4 mechanically operated signals ... £45-55
Miniature Train Set. Blue locomotive with 4 open wagons ... £60-80
Miniature Train Set. Red locomotive with 3 green passenger coaches ... £60-80
Station Set. Station Master, Porter and trolley, 2 lady passengers, negro porter and waiter, mechanic ... £125-175
521 Cowboy Set. Comprising 5 cowboys on foot in various poses ... £80-100
? Indian Set. One mounted Indian and four on foot, various poses ... £80-100
2214 Wild Animals Set. Kangaroo, Lion, Polar Bear, Giraffe, Zebra, Gorilla, Horse, baby Elephant, baby Giraffe ... £120-160
Farm Set. Cow, Goat, Sheep, Dog, Farmhand with Pitchfork ... £140-170
Farm Display Set. Red Tractor and Trailer, Cow, Goose, Donkey, Pony, Plough Horse, Calf, Bullock, Pig, Goat, Farmhand with Pitchfork, Girl, Driver ... £350-450
Hen Coop Set. Green hen house, girl/bucket, two hens, cockerel, dish ... £130-160
Stage Coach Set. Yellow Coach with red wheels, driver, 2 horses ... £100-150
Tricky Tractor. Yellow tractor, green/black driver, clockwork action ... £200-260
1450 Medieval Catapult. Green metal catapult, brown plastic wheels ... £90-110
The Crescent Fortress. Tinplate Castle with internal fold out section ... £240-280
160/1 Tank Set. Three camouflaged miniature tanks and an armoured car ... £250-300
Naval Set. Warship with officer, rating with flags, rating with telescope ... £60-75
Deep Sea Diver Set. Diver in Grey diving suit, helmet, compressor and pump, bollards, three tools ... £125-150
North Sea Patrol. Two Aeroplanes, one brown and one green with pilots ... £100-140
Royal Horse Artillery Set. 6 Horse team, 3 field drivers with whips, limber with 2 seated gunners, field gun with sprung breech ... £200-250
RAF Set. Two Officers, Pilot, Mechanic and two small aircraft ... £100-150
2107 Farm Animals. 12 Farm animals in pictorial box ... £100-130

Meccano
Dinky Toys

HISTORY OF DINKY TOYS

In 1931, Meccano Ltd introduced a series of railway station and trackside accessories to accompany their famous 'HORNBY' train sets. These 'Modelled Miniatures' were in sets numbered 1 - 22 and included railwaymen, station staff, passengers and trains. Set number 22 was comprised of six vehicles which were representative rather than replicas of actual vehicles. It was first advertised in the Meccano Magazine of December 1933.

At about this time 'Tootsie Toys' of America were introducing model vehicles into the United Kingdom and they were proving to be very popular. Consequently Meccano Ltd decided to widen their range of products and issue a comprehensive series of models to include vehicles, ships and aircraft.

'Modelled Miniatures' therefore became 'Meccano Dinky Toys' and set number 22 the first set of 'Dinky Cars'. The first 'Dinky Toys' advertisement appeared in the April 1934 edition of the Meccano Magazine. The first Dinky car produced after the change of name was 23a in April 1934. It was probably based on an early MG but was again generally representative rather than an accurate model. Set 22 cost 4/- and consisted of: 22a Sports Car, 22b Sports Coupé, 22c Motor Truck, 22d Delivery Van, 22e Tractor and 22f Tank and is today highly sought after.

The range of models produced grew quickly so that the Meccano Magazine of December 1935 was claiming that there were 200 varieties to choose from! Although the phrase 'Dinky Toys' became a household name, the actual range was of course far greater and was not limited to cars; it even included dolls house furniture. Indeed, by the time the famous Binns Road factory in Liverpool finally closed its doors in November 1979 over 1,000 different designs had been produced. Pre-war models are rare today and fetch high prices, which reflects how difficult it is to find a model in really good condition. This is because so many 1930s models were made from an unstable alloy which has tended to crystallise and disintegrate. Fortunately the post-war models do not suffer from the same problem and much of today's collecting interest is centred around the delightful models produced in the fifties and sixties with Gift Sets being particularly sought after. Most Dinky Toys boxes were made by McCorquodale in Northern Ireland.

In 1987 the Dinky trade name was bought by Matchbox who were at the time part of the Universal International Co. of Hong Kong. They introduced the 'Dinky Collection' in 1988 with some very fine models in a constant scale of 1:43. On the 7th May 1992 it was announced in the 'New York Times' that 'Tyco Toys Inc.' had acquired by merger the 'Universal Matchbox Group' and with it the famous 'Dinky Toys' brand name.

In 1998, Mattel bought the Matchbox brand and in 1999 disclosed that all new car models will be classified as 'Dinky Toys', including those previously included in their Matchbox Models of Yesteryear range. At the beginning of 2001, however, both of those famous names have been all but buried in favour of Mattel's 'Hot Wheels' brand since most of their products have been aimed at the US toy market.

Thank you to Phil Silvester for completely revising and updating the Car and Farm sections in this issue. Further comprehensive updates of remaining models will be available in the next edition.

Dinky Toys Model Identification

Common Features. There are several features common to various groups of models and to avoid unnecessary repetition in the listings they are shown below. Exceptions to these general indications are noted in the listings.

'Dinky Toys', 'Meccano Ltd', or 'Meccano Dinky Toys'.
These wordings are to be found cast or stamped on the base-plate or chassis or in the case of early models without a base they are cast into the model itself. Some very early models have 'HORNBY SERIES' cast-in (e.g, those in the 22 series).

Wheel hubs. Solid one-piece wheel/tyre castings were fitted to the 'Modelled Miniatures' and first pre-war 'Dinky Toys'. They had 'Hornby' or 'Meccano' cast onto their rims and were covered in a thin colour wash or silver-plated. This casting was soon replaced with more realistic cast hubs (having a smooth convex face) fitted with white (sometimes coloured) rubber tyres. Pre-war hubs may be black, coloured or sometimes silver-plated. Post-war hubs were of the 'ridged' type having a discernible ridge simulating a hub cap. They were painted and usually fitted with black rubber tyres.

Supertoys hubs and tyres. When Supertoys were introduced in 1947 the ridged type of hub was used on the Fodens with black 'herringbone pattern' tyres, and on the Guys with smooth black tyres. Fodens graduated to the use of 'fine radial-tread' tyres first in black, later in grey, then to black again but with a more chunky 'block' tread. Supertoys later acquired plastic hubs and plastic tyres.

Hub materials. Lead was used originally for a short time, the majority of models from the mid-1930s to the early 1960s having diecast mazak hubs. Small models like motor-cycles or the 35b Racer were fitted with solid one-piece wheel/tyre moulding (white or black rubber pre-war, black post-war). In 1958/9 aluminium hubs were introduced and some models (such as 131, 178, 179,

Market Price Range

Please note that the prices shown refer to pristine models and boxes.
Items failing to match this standard will sell for less.
Note also that boxes must still contain all their original packing pieces and additional contents where appropriate.

180, 181, 182 and 290 Bus) appeared fitted with either type. Plastic hubs replaced the diecast versions on racing cars numbered 230-235 while the Austin A30 and Fiat 600 were given solid one-piece wheel/tyre plastic injection mouldings. **Speedwheels** were introduced in the 1970s and some model can be found fitted with metal wheels or Speedwheels. The former are more collectable.

Baseplates are tinplate or diecast unless described otherwise. Plastic moulded baseplates are generally restricted to a few models made after 1970. **Model Numbers** appear on many Dinky Toys baseplates but not all. The Model Name however appears on virtually every post-war Dinky Toy. Pre-war models usually had neither (the 38 and 39 series are exceptions having the model name on their baseplates).

Construction Materials. All models assumed to be constructed at least in part of a diecast alloy. Some pre-war models were made of a lead alloy like the 22 and 28 series plus the few odd models such as 23 a Racing Car and 23m Thunderbolt. The Blaw-Knox Bulldozer was one of the very few produced (right at the end of its production) in plastic.

Windows. Pre-war and early post-war models had tinplate or celluloid windscreens. Moulded plastic windscreens appeared in the 1950s on open car models. The first Dinky to be fitted with all-round plastic window glazing was the Austin A105 Saloon. Some models in production at the time were fitted with glazing later and may therefore be found with or without it.

Hooks were not fitted to the first Supertoys Foden models (1947). Small hooks were fitted in early 1948, the usual (larger) hook appearing in mid-1948.

Axles were all 'crimped' pre-war and on these series of models post-war: 23, 25, 29, 30, 34, 35, 36, 37, 38, 39, 40 and 280. Otherwise models had rivet-ended axles until the advent of Speedwheels. Early Guy models had tinplate clips to retain the front axles. Pre-war axles are generally thinner than post-war at 0.062mm diameter while post-war axles are 0.078mm in diameter.

Size of models (where shown) is in millimetres and refers to the longest overall measurement (usually the length). In the case of pre-war models slight inaccuracies may occur from expansion of the casting as it ages in the course of time.

The Scale of Dinky Toys was originally 1:43 (with a few exceptions). Supertoys Foden and Guy vehicles (introduced in 1947) were in a scale of 1:48 while military models issued from 1953 were smaller at 1:60. Most aircraft models before 1965 were around 1:200 and ships 1:1800. In the late 1960s and early 1970s the 1:36 scale was introduced, mostly for cars.

Dinky Numbering System. The dual/triple reference numbers used on some Dinky Toys and Supertoys (for example 409 / 521 / 921 Bedford Articulated Lorry) refers to the basic model type and casting and not to model colours. The renumbering by Meccano was an administration process to re-catalogue production of existing lines and introduce new models. New colours on existing castings which arise at about the time of renumbering are therefore coincidental with it rather than a consequence of it.

Identification of early post-war Dinky Toys cars.
Note that pre-war wheel hubs may be smooth diecast or the rare chrome ('Tootsie-Toy' type) hubs which attract a premium.

Post-war 30 Series

Circa 1946	Open chassis with smooth black wheel hubs.
Circa 1948	Plain chassis with ridged black wheel hubs.

36 Series

Circa 1946	Moulded chassis; smooth black wheel hubs.
Circa 1948	Moulded chassis; ridged black wheel hubs.

38 Series

Circa 1946	With pre-war lacquered tinplate base secured by spread spigots (not rivets), silvered sidelights, smooth black hubs.
Circa 1946	Solid steering wheels, smooth black hubs, silvered sidelights, black painted baseplate.
Circa 1947	As above but with silver-edged windscreen.
Circa 1948-49	Open or solid steering wheel, ridged hubs, black painted baseplate.
Circa 1950	As above but with coloured wheel hubs.

39 Series

Circa 1946	'Gold' pre-war baseplate, smooth black wheel hubs, silver door handles and radiator cap.
Circa 1948	Black painted baseplate, ridged black hubs.
Circa 1950	As above but with coloured wheel hubs.

40 Series

See page 86 for identification and illustrations.

Dinky Toys Cars – Box Types

Box Types Introduction

A mint condition model car without its correct box is worth but a fraction of its mint boxed equivalent. Furthermore, as model boxes made from card do not survive as well as their die-cast contents, pristine box examples are scarce and becoming scarcer. The condition of a box is of paramount importance and attention is drawn to the section in the catalogue introduction, namely: 'Classifying the Condition of Models and Boxes'.

The following listing provides collectors with a working knowledge of the range of box types issued. In addition details are given of their dates of issue, their design and of the models which used them. See also the colour sections for examples of many types of boxes.

Whilst every care has been taken in preparing the listing, other variations may exist and information on them is welcomed. Similarly, with no 'dates of birth' available the dates of issues shown are approximate and again any further information is welcomed.

Box Identification

Model colour identification marks - colour spots

These are shown on the box lid end flap and take the form of a circular colour spot. This may be either a single colour or, in the case of the later two-tone car issues, a two-tone colour spot. Colour spots were used until the early 1960s.

NB The dual numbered 234/23H box displays the Ferrari model name against a blue panel which matches the main body colour.

Dual numbered boxes 1953 - 1954

A new numbering system was introduced which resulted in models being issued displaying both the old and new reference numbers. The information was shown on the box end flaps as follows:

Old model number shown in red letters on either side of a larger white number set on a black oval background, e.g. 40J 161 40J. Dual numbered boxes were only issued for a short period and may attract a premium. The numbers may be large or small.

Pre-war issues

Apart from special issues such as 23m Thunderbolt Speed Car and 23p Gardner's M.G. Record Car, individual models were sold unboxed. They were usually packaged in half-dozen retailers trade packs (see the section on Trade Packs). Models were also sold in boxed sets (see the Gift Set Section).

Post-war After the second world war models continued to be sold unboxed from trade boxes until 1953/54 when the first individual boxes were introduced. The boxes have been catalogued into three types as follows:

Type 1: Card boxes with tuck-in flaps
Type 2: Display boxes -Blister packs, rigid plastic packs, vacuform packs and card window boxes.
Type 3: Export Issue boxes.

Type 1 1953 – 1975 All card box with tuck-in end flaps

(i) 1953- 1954 Deep yellow box with 'DINKY TOYS' in red plus the model's name and type in black. A white reference number on a black oval background is on the box end flaps but no reference number is shown on the box face. The model is pictured on the box sides but without a white shaded background. Colour spots shown on box-end flaps as applicable. Foreign language information is shown on one of the end flaps of the early issue boxes. Box in general use during the model renumbering period. Consequently, dual numbered boxes will be found. It would appear that only models 23f, g, h, j, k and n, and 40j were housed in individual boxes prior to renumbering. Please supply details of any other models housed in boxes displaying just their old reference number.

(ii) 1955 - 1956 Same as (i) but a white reference number on a black oval background is shown on the face of the box to the left of the model picture. Also as (i) but with a white reference number on a red oval background and placed either to the left or the right of the model picture. Box in general use for all issues.

(iii) 1956 - 1960 Same as (ii) but model pictures are displayed against a white shadow background. In some instances only one picture. had a shadow, e.g. 171 Hudson Commodore and in others both pictures were given a shadow; e.g. 152 Austin Devon. Box in general use for all issues. Later issues display 'WITH WINDOWS', caption in a red line features box.

(iv) c1960 Deep yellow plain box with no model picture, 'DINKY TOYS' and text in red; rarely used. Colour spots shown as applicable. We believe these boxes may have been used for mail-order or possibly export purposes. The Editor would welcome any new information. Known examples: 103, 108, l09, 163, 178 and 191.

(v) 1959–1961 Plain lighter yellow box with no model picture. It has two yellow and two red sides. 'DINKY TOYS' is shown in yellow on red sides. Colour spots shown as applicable. Models recorded: 105, 109, 131, 150, 157, 165, 169, 173. 174, 176, 178, 187, 189, 191, 192 and 230 to 235. The special issue 189 Triumph Heralds used this box.

(vi) 1960 - 1966 Yellow box with a separate red line features box placed to the right of the model picture. Colour spots still in use on early 1960s issues. Foreign language text on one box end flap and 'WITH WINDOWS' captions on box face. Models recorded: 105, 112, 113, 131, 144, 148, 155, 157, 164–167, 176–178, 181/2, 184, 186, 191-195, 197, 199, 230-235, 237, 239 and 449. Later issues without colour spots. Boxes used for some South African issues display both English and Afrikaans text.

(vii) c.1962 – 1963 Lighter yellow box similar to (v) but colour spots not in use. A scarce issue box which may attract a premium. Model recorded: 166.

(viii) 1962 – 1963 Yellow box with a red end features panel around the left side of the box. Recorded models: 113, 147 and 198.

(ix) 1962 – 1963 (?) Yellow/red box similar to previous items, but has yellow ends, yellow top and bottom panels and red side panels, the latter virtually filled with the text: 'DINKY TOYS'. Colour spots not seen. See page vii of the colour section for an illustration of this box (containing 178 Plymouth Plaza).

(x) 1963 – 1970 Yellow box with a red end features panel around the right side. The panel is bisected by the model picture and is with or without a large or small white arrow design. Models recorded: 112-114. 120, 127-130, 133-139, 140-148, 198, 240-243, 268, 273 and 274. Some South African issues used this box, e.g. 141 Vauxhall Victor Estate Car. They display both English and Afrikaans text. The rare Triumph 2000 Saloon promotional issues will be found in this box. Some have an applied white label on the box face showing the colour of the model, e.g. Olive-Cactus.

(xi) 1966 – 1969 Detailed full colour picture box with pictorial scene on two sides with 'DINKY TOYS' in red letters. Recorded issues: 133, 136, 183, 212, 214, 225 plus Hong Kong issues 57/001-57/006.

(xii) 1968 – 1974 White-fronted box with a thin yellow band across the box face. A yellow laurel leaf design on a black background is a main box feature. The white face of the box may contain features information such as '1st AGAIN' and 'SPEEDWHEELS'. Variation exists with a semi-pictorial box face (probably an export special) e.g. 176 NSU R80. Models recorded: 157, 159 165/6, 169, 174/5, 179, 183, 192, 205 and 212. NB. A variation of this box exists with a large red 'DINKY TOYS' and number to the left of the picture and no yellow band across the face, e.g. 138 Hillman Imp.

Type 2 1962 – 1980 Display boxes, Blister packs, Rigid plastic and Vacuform packs, Window boxes

(i) 1962 – 1964 Blister Card Packs used for racing cars nos. 205210. Red/yellow display card with chequered flag design.

(ii) 1967 – 1971 Rigid plastic 'see-through' case with lift-off lid. models displayed on a card base with a black 'roadway' surface. The base sides are yellow with 'DINKY TOYS' in red. Recorded issues: 110, 116, 127, 129, 131/2, 142, 152-154, 158, 161, 163/4, 168,

175, 187-189, 190, 208, 210, 213, 215, 216, 220/1 and 223/4.

(iii) 1972 – 1976 Vacuform Packs. Models displayed on a black base with a blue surface with 'DINKY TOYS' in red/white letters. The model is covered by a close fitting plastic cover. Known issues: 129, 131, 149, 168, 178 and 192 plus 1:25 issues 2214, 3162 and 2253.

(iv) 1976 – 1979 Window Box with 'see-through' cellophane front and blue and red header card with a 'DINKY DIECAST TOYS' in yellow letters. Variations exist with a model picture on the header card e.g. 112 'Purdey's TR7'. Known issues: 113, 120, 122/3/4, 128, 180, 192, 207/8, 211, 221/2/3 and 226/7.

(v) 1968 – 1969 Plastic see-through red box made in a garage shape to house 'Mini Dinky' issues.

(vi) 1979 Bubble Pack 219 'Big Cat' Jaguar.

Type 3 1966 – 1980 Export issue boxes

(i) 1966 – 1980 An all yellow card and cellophane 'see-through' display box with outward-folding ends. 'DINKY TOYS' and four diagonal stripes plus 'A MECCANO PRODUCT MADE IN ENGLAND' are in red on the box face. The box display base may be either yellow or have a black 'roadway' design.
Whilst generally used for export issues it was specifically used for

the U.S. export series 'MARVELS IN MINIATURE - which appeared in red letters on the box front. Later issues listed the models on the base of the box.

A box variation exists with just 'DINKY' and 'A MECCANO PRODUCT' on the face of the box plus the model name and number. The base of the box is yellow. The box was issued with a card protection strip which stated: 'Mr DEALER PLEASE REMOVE THIS STRIP'. Models known to have been issued in this box include: 110-115, 120, 127/8, 133-138, l41/2. 151, 161, 170-172, 190, 192, 196, 215, 237, 240-243, 257/8, 57/006. NB We believe this box was probably used in the UK but would be grateful for confirmation.

(ii) 1966 – 1968 All gold card and cellophane 'see-through' display box with just 'DINKY' in gold letters set in a red panel on the box front plus red and black diagonal stripes. 'A MECCANO PRODUCT MADE IN ENGLAND' in black is also on the front of the box. Only used for a short time so models in these boxes often sell at a premium. The known issues are: 112, 113, 148, 193, 215, 238, 240-243, 340 and 448.

(iii) 1979 – 1980 A flat yellow box with blue end flaps. Used to house the Swiss promotional issue No. 223 Hesketh F1 Racing Car 'OLYMPUS CAMERAS'.
Export issue: 449 has been observed in an 'all gold' box.

40 Series issues distribution, renumbering and packing

Models in the 40 Series were initially sold unboxed from retailers' trade boxes of 6 models as follows:

i)	1947-50	Plain Brown card box with lift-off lid. On the end of the lid was a Yellow label displaying the quantity, the model's name and its reference number, e.g., '6 RILEY SALOON 40a'.
ii)	1950-54	All Yellow card box with lift-off lid. The contents were printed in Black on the end of the box lid.
iii)	1954	Models renumbered. When the 40 Series models were renumbered, the final all-Yellow card boxes for six displayed both the original number and its new number, for example: '158 RILEY SALOON 40a'.
iv)	1954-60	The renumbered models were individually boxed in the first type of Yellow end-flap boxes as follows: a) Displaying the dual numbers for a short time, e.g., '40a 158 40a' on the end flap. b) Displaying just the model's new number, e.g., '158' plus the correct colour spot for the model.

Dinky Toys Cars – Identification of casting types

Chassis types, 1934 – 1950

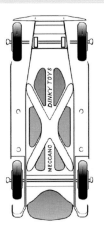 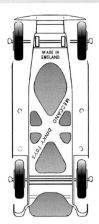 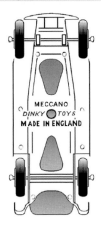 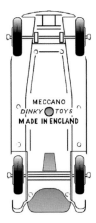 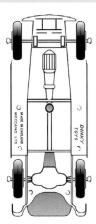

| **1934 - 1935**
'Criss-cross' chassis
1st type
with or without
slot for spare wheel | **1935 - 1936**
'Criss-cross' chassis
2nd type
with or without
slot for spare wheel | **1936 - 1940**
Open chassis
with or without
slots for figures | **1946 - 1947**
Plain chassis, no
slots for figures,
hole for caravan
drawbar | **1948 - 1950**
'Moulded'
(detailed) chassis,
hole for caravan
drawbar |

24 Series radiator grille types, 1934 – 1940

**1st type
1934 - 1938**
With diamond shape
in centre of bumper
No radiator badge
No over-riders

**2nd type
1934 - 1938**
No diamond shape in
centre of bumper
No radiator badge
No over-riders

**3rd type
1938 - 1940**
'Bentley' style
with radiator badge
and over-riders

The first and second type grilles will be found on the both the first and second type chassis.
The later third type grille will be found with the second type chassis.

Dinky 110 Aston Martin Competition. Shows scarce Connaught (light) green and very unusual dark green shade, see page 96.

Dinky Toys Cars - Identification of wheel types

These drawings are provided for general guidance only. They are not all strictly to the same scale.

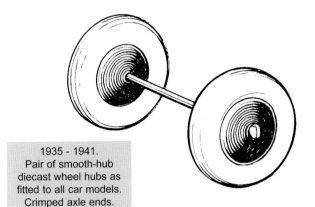

1935 - 1941.
Pair of smooth-hub diecast wheel hubs as fitted to all car models. Crimped axle ends.

1935 - 1941.
Smooth-hub diecast wheel hubs as fitted to 23a Racing Car. Note the 'arrow-head' or 'herring-bone' tyre treads.

1947 onwards.
Ridged-hub diecast wheel as on all early post-war issues. Rounded axle ends. Smooth tyres. French versions are often referred to as 'convex' and are sometimes plated.

1958
Treaded plastic wheel fitted to 160 Austin A30. Smooth (non-treaded) wheels were also fitted to this model.

c1958.
Treaded tyre design as fitted to 111 Triumph TR2.

c1959.
Spun aluminium hubs as fitted to many car models.

c1967.
16-spoke cast wheel as on 281 Fiat Pathé News car.

c1970.
No. 100 Lady Penelope's 'FAB 1' 2nd type wheel shown. 1st type has six raised studs in a 'starfish' pattern.

c1968.
Cast wheel used on No. 13 Ferrari in the 'Mini-Dinky' series.

c1972.
Detailed cast wheel as fitted to 252 Pontiac Parisienne Police Car.

40 Series cars identification

See also the 'Dinky Toys Cars - Box Types' and 'Model Identification' information pages.
Please note that the illustrations on this page are not all to the same scale.

40b and 151 Triumph 1800 Saloon
Casting with rear axle pillars — 1948 - 50
Small lettering on baseplate, as illustrated — 1948 - 53
Large lettering on baseplate (not illustrated) — 1954 - 60
Two raised rails on baseplate, as illustrated — 1948 - 53
No raised rails on baseplate (not illustrated) — 1954 - 60

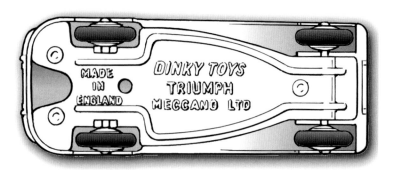

40e and 153 Standard Vanguard
Tinplate clip secures rear axle — 1948 - 49
Small lettering on baseplate — 1948 - 53
Baseplate has raised rails — 1948 - 53

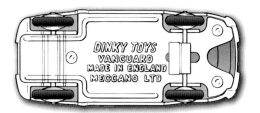

Casting with open wheel arches
(no spats) — 1948 - 50

Baseplate tabs secure rear axle — 1949 - 60
Large lettering on baseplate — 1954 - 60
No raised rails on baseplate — 1954 - 60
Body casting includes rear wheel spats — 1951 - 60

40f and 154 Hillman Minx
1951 - 54 — Small lettering on baseplate, two raised rails on baseplate, rear axle secured by baseplate tabs.
1954 - 59 — Large lettering on baseplate, no raised rails on baseplate, rear axle secured by baseplate tabs.

Dinky Toys Commercial Vehicles Identification

The 25 Series Lorries 1934 - 1950

Type 1: **(1934-36)**, 'open' chassis (usually black), tinplate radiator, no headlamps,
no front bumper, 'smooth' cast hubs (various colours) with large white tyres. 105 mm.

Type 2: **(1936-46)**, 'open' chassis (usually black), diecast radiator with headlamps but
no front bumper, 'smooth' cast hubs (various colours), with large white tyres. 105 mm.

Type 3: **(1947-48)**, 'closed' chassis (only in black), diecast radiator with headlamps but
no front bumper, 'smooth' or 'ridged' wheel hubs (only in black) ,with black tyres. 105 mm.

Type 4: **(1948-50)**, detailed moulded chassis (only in black), diecast radiator with headlamps and
with bumper, 'ridged' coloured wheel hubs with black tyres. 110 mm.

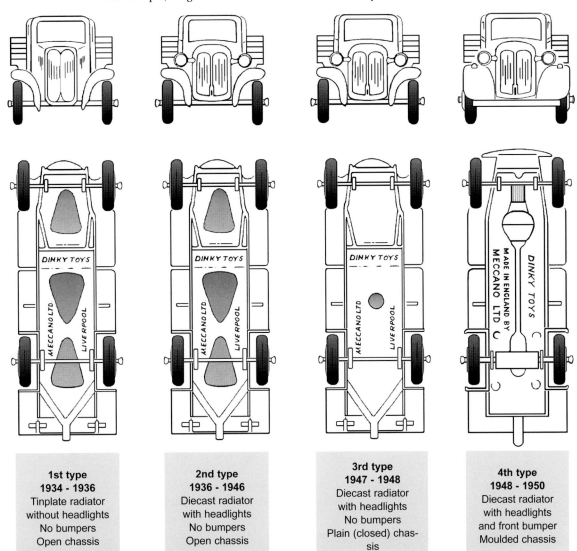

| **1st type**
1934 - 1936
Tinplate radiator
without headlights
No bumpers
Open chassis | **2nd type**
1936 - 1946
Diecast radiator
with headlights
No bumpers
Open chassis | **3rd type**
1947 - 1948
Diecast radiator
with headlights
No bumpers
Plain (closed) chassis | **4th type**
1948 - 1950
Diecast radiator
with headlights
and front bumper
Moulded chassis |

25 Series Trucks 1934-50 Wheel types The first pre-war issues have cast metal wheels followed by chrome (rare) or diecast hubs with large white tyres. The early post-war issues c.1946 have smooth hubs and large black tyres. **1947-48** issues have ridged black hubs with large black tyres. The last issues **c.1949-50** have coloured ridged hubs and attract a premium. Similarly early cast or chrome hubs also attract a premium.

Guy cab types

Guy 1st type cab 1947 - 1954
Exposed radiator
No gusset at either
side of number plate

Guy 2nd type cab 1954 - 1958
Exposed radiator
With gusset at each
side of number plate

Guy Warrior cab 1958 - 1964
Radiator behind grille
Restyled front with
sidelights in wings

Foden cab types

1947 - 1952
Foden 'DG'
(1st type) cab
Exposed radiator
Colour flashes on sides

1952 - 1964
Foden 'FG'
(2nd type) cab
Radiator behind grille
No colour flashes on sides

Identification of Ford Transit Van castings (not illustrated)

Type 1: (1966-74), has sliding driver's door, opening hinged side door, and twin rear doors. **Type 2: (1974-78)**, non-sliding driver's door, one side-hinged door, one top-hinged rear door. **Type 3: (1978-80)**, as Type 2 but with a slightly longer bonnet (18 mm.)

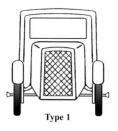 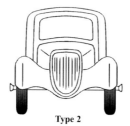 

Type 1   Type 2   Type 3

28/280 Series Delivery Van Identification

Type 1: **(1933-35)**, two-piece lead body with *'HORNBY SERIES'* (early issues) or *'DINKY TOYS'* cast-in under cab roof, tinplate radiator, no headlamps, thinly-painted coloured solid wheel/tyre castings (some bright plated), 84 mm. (Coloured wheels tend to attract a premium to the price of the model.)

Type 2: **(1935-39)**, one-piece diecast body, cast-in shield-shaped radiator, rear wheel spats, cast smooth wheel hubs with rubber tyres (usually white), 81 mm. All carried advertising.

Type 3: **(1939-41)**, one-piece diecast body with rear wheel spats, cast smooth wheel hubs (various colours) with black tyres, open rear windows, 83 mm. All carried advertising.

Type 3: **(1947-54)**, one-piece diecast body with rear wheel spats, cast ridged wheel hubs (usually black) with black tyres, filled-in rear windows, cast boss under roof, 83 mm. No advertising.

29c Double Decker Bus identification

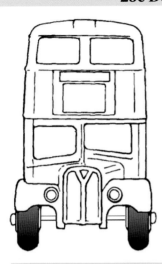 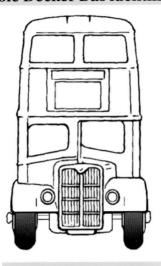 

1st Type 1938-47
AEC/STL grille, large 'V' shape. Cutaway wings, smooth hubs.
No model number on base.

2nd Type 1949-53 and 1957-59
AEC/Regent grille, small 'V' shape. Straight across wings, ridged hubs. '29c' cast into base of <u>some</u> issues.

3rd Type 1948-49 and 1954-63
Leyland grille, undivided shape. Straight across wings, ridged hubs.
'29c', '290' or '291' on base.

Dinky 340 Land Rover.

Dinky 38e Armstrong Siddeley versions, see page 93.

ABOVE Dinky 182 Porsche 356A. This picture emphasises the different red and pink shades of the model.

RIGHT Dinky 100 series Tourers with spun wheels.

Dinky Toys Cars

Market Price Range (MPR) for pre-1954 unboxed car models. Prior to 1954, virtually all the cars were sold unboxed from retailer's trade boxes of either 6, 4 or 3 models. Consequently, all pre-1954 issues (except for 23m and 23s) have been priced as being unboxed. Post-1954 models were all boxed and have been priced accordingly. As a consequence, models which have been renumbered will often be found to have two differing prices – one for the pre-1954 unboxed version and another for its boxed and renumbered successor. See also the Trade Box section for details of individual boxes and packs that were used to supply shops.

Model and details	MPR

22a 1933-35 **Open Sports Car**
'Modelled Miniature' with 'HORNBY SERIES' cast into lead body, solid metal wheel/tyre castings (thinly painted in metallic blue, purple, green, yellow or red, or not painted at all) lead windscreen surround, tinplate radiator (grille may be same colour as body, or overpainted with the colour of the mudguards).
- Blue body, Yellow seats and mudguards **£400-600**
- Blue body, Red seats / mudguards .. **£400-600**
- Cream body, Red seats / mudguards **£400-600**
- Cream body, Green seats and mudguards **£400-600**
- Cream body, Blue seats and mudguards **£400-600**
- Red body, Cream or Blue seats and mudguards **£400-600**
- Yellow body, Green seats and mudguards **£400-600**
- Orange-Brown body, Cream seats and mudguards **£400-600**
- Green body, Yellow seats and mudguards **£400-600**

22b 1933-35 **Closed Sports Coupé**
'Modelled Miniature' with 'HORNBY SERIES' cast into lead body, solid metal wheel/tyre castings (coloured or plain, as 22a), tinplate radiator (painted in main body colour).
- Cream body, Red roof and mudguards **£1,500-2,000**
- Cream, Green roof and mudguards **£1,500-2,000**
- Red body, Blue roof/mudguards **£1,500-2,000**
- Red body, Cream roof and mudguards.........................**£1,500-2,000**
- Blue body, Red roof/mudguards **£1,500-2,000**
- Blue body, Yellow roof and mudguards........................**£1,500-2,000**
- Yellow body, Green roof and mudguards........................**£1,500-2,000**
- Orange body, Green roof and mudguards, Gold wash wheels ..**£1,500-2,000**

22g 1935-41 **Streamline Tourer**
Model has cast steering wheel and windscreen, smooth diecast hubs which may be painted as body colour or a contrasting colour. Some have chrome hubs.
Body colours:
- Green, Maroon, Red, Light or Dark Blue, Cream, Buff or Black....... **£300-400**
- Turquoise body, Blue hubs, White tyres **£750-1,000**
South African issues:
Leaf Green with plated hubs **£250-350**

22h 1935-41 **Streamlined Saloon**
A saloon version of 22g (no steering wheel). Wheels may be painted as body colour or a contrasting colour.
- Red, Maroon, Blue or Cream **£300-400**

23 1934-35 **Racing Car** (1st casting)
Lead body, no racing number, no driver, 0, 2, 3 or 4 exhausts stubs (without pipe), coloured tyres on some.
- Cream or White body with either Blue, Cream, Green, Orange or Red top and nose flash...................... **£200-300**
- Yellow body with Blue upper body flash, 3 exhaust stubs **£200-300**

Model and details	MPR

23a 1935-41 **Racing Car** (23 re-issued)
As 1st casting but diecast body, no driver, no number, Black or White tyres, 4 exhausts.
- White body and hubs, Blue top flash and circle on nose **£200-300**
- Cream body and hubs, Red top flash and circle on nose **£200-300**
- Blue body, White top flash and circle on nose **£200-300**
- Orange body, Green top flash and circle on nose **£200-300**
- Yellow body, Dark Blue flash and circle on nose **£200-300**
- Brown body, Cream top flash........... **£200-300**
- Silver body, Green number '8'.......... **£200-300**

23a **Racing Car** (2nd casting)
With driver plus raised circles for racing numbers, 6 exhausts in fishtail.
Colour type 1:
With minor colour sidestripes and perhaps coloured tyres.
(Sometimes known as 'humbug' version).
Colour type 2:
Broad nose flash, even width top rear flash. (Also known as 'humbug' version).
Colour type 3:
Broad flash at cockpit and pointed ends top flash, cast circle on nose.
Variations:
- Type 1, Cream body, Red stripes, number '9'...................................**£1,000-1,500**
- Type 2, Blue with White stripes / driver, RN '11'.....................................**£1,000-1,500**
- Type 2, Yellow body, Dark Blue top flash, racing number '7' or '1'.................... **£200-300**
- Type 2, Blue body, White top flash, racing number '11', '4' or '5'.......... **£200-300**
- Type 2, Yellow with Blue stripes, racing number '7', silvered 'Tootsie Toy' type hubs **£1,000-1,500**
- Type 2, Orange with Green stripes, racing number '10', silvered 'Tootsie Toy' type hubs **£1,000-1,500**
- Type 3, White body, Blue nose/circle and top flash, racing number '2' **£200-300**
- Type 3, Cream body, Red nose/circle and top flash, racing number '3' **£200-300**
- Type 3, Red body, Cream nose and flash, no number, no transverse ribs **£200-300**
- Type 3, White body, Green nose/circle and top flash, racing number '6' **£200-300**
- Type 3, Orange body, Green nose/circle and top flash, racing number '4' **£200-300**
- Casting variation with driver, raised racing number circle on nearside only, no detailed exhaust, Orange body, Green nose circle, Green RN '4' **£150-175**
- Orange body, long Green upper body flash, 3 exhaust stubs, Green racing number '4' or '10' **£150-175**
- Yellow body, long Dark Blue upper body flash, plated hubs **£200-250**

23a 1946-52 **Racing Car** (3rd casting)
With transverse body ribs, no raised circle for racing numbers, and only issued in colour type 3, with or without racing numbers. (Re-introduced in 1954 as 220).

Model and details	MPR

- Red or Red/Green body, Silver nose circle, top flash and side circle (Red RN '4'), Red hubs.......................... **£50-75**
- Silver body, Red nose circle, top flash and side circle (Silver RN '4'), Red hubs..... **£50-75**
- Red body, Cream flashes, Black hubs.. **£50-75**

23b 1935-41 **Hotchkiss Racing Car**
- Blue body with Dark Blue, Red or Silver flash and number '2', '5' or '8'..... **£300-400**
- Cream body, Red flash and RN '1' ... **£300-400**
- Yellow body, Blue flash and RN '3' .. **£300-400**
- Orange body, Green flash / RN '6' ... **£300-400**
- Green body, Yellow flash / RN '5' ... **£300-400**
- Turquoise body, Red flash / RN '4' ... **£300-400**
- Turquoise body, Blue flash/RN '4' ... **£300-400** 1946-48
- Red with Silver flash and RN '5' **£50-75**
- Silver with Red flash and RN '5' **£50-75**

23c 1936-38 **Mercedes-Benz Racing Car**
- Red, Light Blue, Silver, Yellow or Light Green body with contrasting body flashes, with or without racing numbers '3', '4' or '5', driver cast-in, Black hubs, treaded tyres................. **£200-250**
- 1938-40 As previous model but with rivetted baseplate bearing information........ **£150-200**
- 1946-50 ('Large Open Racing Car'). Re-issued 23c in Blue or Silver, with various racing numbers............... **£40-50**

23d 1936-38 **Auto-Union Racing Car**
Early pre-war issues without driver:
- Red, Turquoise, Pale Green, Yellow or Silver body, racing numbers on some, clipped-in tinplate base **£300-500**
- Bottle-Green body......................**£750-1,000**
- 1938-41 Later pre-war issue with driver, rivetted baseplate **£250-350**
- 1946-50 Early post-war issue with driver: Red or Silver body, with or without racing number, Black or White tyres.. **£80-100**
- Later post-war issue without driver ... **£80-100**

23e 1936-38 **'Speed Of The Wind' Racing Car**
- Red, Blue, Light Blue, Green, Yellow or Silver body, plain clipped-in tinplate base, driver, with or without racing numbers '3' or '6', Black hubs and herringbone tyres. Lead fakes exist............................ **£50-75**
- 1938-41 With rivetted baseplate bearing information **£50-75**
- 1946-49 Red or Silver, rivetted informative baseplate, Red hubs, Grey tyres **£35-45**
- 1950-54 (Renumbered to 221) Silver body and hubs, plain base **£35-45**

23f 1952-54 **Alfa-Romeo Racing Car**
- Red body, White racing number '8', Red diecast hubs, not boxed............. **£100-110** Items sold individually from a trade box.
- Later models sold from individual dual no box marked 23f or 23f/232 .... **£130-150** 1954 (Renumbered to 232)

23g 1952-54 **Cooper-Bristol Racing Car**
- Green body, White RN '6', Green ridged hubs, ... **£90-110**
Note boxes both 23g & Dual 23g/233

1954   (Renumbered to 233)

23h 1953-54 **Ferrari Racing Car**
- Blue body, Yellow nose, RN '5'
  and ridged hubs,.............................. **£130-150**
  Note boxes both 23h & Dual 23h/234
  1954   (Renumbered to 234)

23j 1953-54 **H.W.M. Racing Car**
- Light Green body, Yellow '7',
  Green ridged hubs,........................... **£120-140**
  Note boxes both 23j & Dual 23j/235
  1954   (Renumbered to 235)

23k 1953-54 **Talbot-Lago Racing Car**
- Blue body, Yellow RN '4',
  Blue diecast hubs,............................. **£120-140**
  Note boxes both 23k & Dual 23k/230
  1954   (Renumbered to 230)

23m 1938-41 **'Thunderbolt' Speed Car**
- Silver body, Black detailing, Union Jacks
  on tail, Silver baseplate. In original Blue
  box dated '2-38', code: 'A2247' **£125-150**
- Red body, Silver detailing **£300-400**

23n 1953-54 **Maserati Racing Car**
- Red, White flash and RN '9',
  Red diecast hubs, not boxed................ **£85-95**
  1954   (Renumbered to 231)

23p 1939-40 **Gardner's MG Record Car**
- Dark Green, White flash and 'MG' logo,
  Union Jacks, 'MG Magnette' on lacquered
  unpainted tinplate baseplate,
  Yellow box, dated '9-39' **£300-400**
- 1946-47   Dark Green body,
  Union Jacks, no flash, 'MG Record Car'
  on base, not boxed **£80-100**

23s 1938-40 **Streamlined Racing Car**
- Light Green body, Dark Green
  detailing, lead **£100-125**
- Light Blue body, Dark Blue or
  Silver detailing, lead **£100-125**
- Orange body, lead **£100-125**
- Light Green, Light Blue, Red or
  Orange body, mazak diecasting **£75-100**
- 1948-54   Light, Mid or Dark Green
  body, Silver or Green flashes............... **£50-65**
- Navy Blue body with Silver or
  Green flashes **£50-65**
- Silver body with Red, Green or
  Blue flashes **£50-65**
- Red body with Silver or Black flashes,
  Black base... **£50-65**
  1954   (Renumbered to 222)

24a 1934-40 **Ambulance**
  See 'Emergency Vehicles' Section.

24b 1934-38 **Limousine**
  Types 1 or 2: criss-cross chassis.
  Types 1, 2 or 3: grille, no sidelights,
  no spare wheel, 3 side windows,
  3 'stacked' parallel horizontal bonnet
  louvres. Blue, Black or plated
  'Tootsie-Toy' type hubs.
- Body/chassis colours:
  Maroon/Dark Maroon, Maroon/Grey,
  Maroon/Black, Blue/Yellow,
  Dark Blue/Black, Yellow/Brown **£300-500**
  1937-40   casting change:
- Same colours but no spare wheel slot,
  3 parallel bonnet louvres, open chassis,
  'Bentley' grille and bumper.............. **£200-400**

24c 1934-38 **Town Sedan**
  Types 1 or 2: criss-cross chassis.
  Types 1, 2 or 3: grille, spare wheel,
  no sidelights, separate windscreen/steering
  wheel casting, smooth Blue, Black or
  plated 'Tootsie-Toy'type hubs.
- Body/chassis colours:
  Green/Black, Green/Yellow,
  Pale Green/Red, Dark Blue/Dark Blue,
  Cream/Dark Blue, Cream/Black,
  Dark Blue/Black.................................. **£300-500**
  1937-40   casting change:
- Same colours but open chassis,
  no spare wheel slot, narrower
  boot, shorter door handles **£200-400**

24d 1934-38 **Vogue Saloon**
  Types 1 or 2: criss-cross chassis.
  Types 1, 2 or 3: grille, with nearside spare
  wheel, no sidelights. Smooth Blue,
  Black or plated hubs with White tyres.
- Body/chassis colours:
  Blue/Dark Blue, Blue/Black, Blue/Maroon,
  Cream/Blue, Brown/Green, Pink/Green,
  Red/Grey, Green/Blue, Green/Black,
  Maroon/Black **£400-60**0
  1937-40   casting change:
- Same colours but open chassis, higher
  'domed' roofline, no spare wheel..... **£300-500**

24e 1934-38 **Super Streamlined Saloon**
  Types 1 or 2: criss-cross chassis.
  Types 1, 2 or 3: grille, no spare or sidelights,
  12 bonnet louvres. Smooth Blue, Black or
  plated 'Tootsie-Toy' type hubs.
- Body/chassis colours:
  Maroon/Black, Red/Maroon, Green/Maroon,
  Red/Black, Green/Blue, Red/Brown,
  All Maroon **£400-600**
  1937-40   casting change:
- As previous model but with
  13 bonnet louvres **£400-600**

24f 1934-38   Sportsmans Coupé
  Criss-cross chassis, with spare wheel,
  no sidelights, smooth hubs.
- Blue/Blue, Blue/Black, Yellow/Brown,
  Cream/Dark Blue, Tan/Brown **£200-400**
- 1937-40   casting change:
  Open chassis, higher 'domed'
  roofline, no spare wheel.................... **£200-400**

24g 1934-38 **Sports Tourer Four-seater**
  Types 1 or 2: criss-cross chassis.
  Types 1, 2 or 3: grille, spare wheel hub
  cast-in, no sidelights, open tinplate
  windscreen, separate dashboard/steering
  wheel casting. Blue or Black smooth hubs
  or plated 'Tootsie-Toy'type hubs.
- Body/chassis colours:
  Yellow/Black, Yellow/Blue, Yellow/Brown,
  Blue/Brown, Cream/Green, Cream/Brown,
  Black/Cream, Blue/Maroon **£300-500**
- 1937-40   casting change:
  Open chassis, filled-in windscreen,
  cast impression of spare wheel **£300-500**

24h 1934-38 **Sports Tourer Two-seater**
  Types 1 or 2: criss-cross chassis.
  Types 1, 2 or 3: grille, spare wheel hub
  cast-in, no sidelights, open tinplate
  windscreen, separate dashboard/steering
  wheel casting. Plated, Blue or
  Black smooth hubs.
- Body/chassis colours:
  Red/Red, Green/Dark Green, Yellow/Green,
  Yellow/Blue, Yellow/Black, Yellow/Brown,
  Black/Cream, Cream/Green, Red/Green,
  Blue/Brown, Yellow/Purple.............. **£400-600**
- 1937-40   casting change:
  Open chassis, filled-in windscreen,
  cast impression of spare wheel **£400-600**

25j 1947-48   **Jeep**
- Red body, Blue hubs **£140-170**
- Red body, Black hubs   **£180-200**
- Light Green body, Red hubs............. **£120-150**
- Light Green body, Black hubs **£100-120**
- Aqua or Sky Blue body, Yellow hubs **£150-180**
- Aqua or Sky Blue body, Black hubs **£100-120**

25y 1952-54   **Universal Jeep**
- Red body, Blue hubs **£130-150**
- Red body, Red hubs **£80-100**
- Dark Green body, Mid-Green hubs **£80-120**
- Dark Green body, Maroon hubs **£120-140**
  Individually sold from a Trade Box of 4.
  1954   (Renumbered to 405)

27d 1950-54   **Land Rover.**
  See 'Farm and Garden Models'.

27f 1950-54   **Estate Car.**
  See 'Farm and Garden Models'
  Note all 30 series cars were sold from Trade
  Boxes of 6.

30a 1935-40   **Chrysler 'Airflow' Saloon**
    (renumbered to 32)
  No chassis, separate bumper units, lead
  versions exist, smooth plain or silvered hubs.
- Turquoise, Maroon, Cream, Green,
  Purplish Blue, Red,
  (hubs may be any colour)................ **£500-750**
- With 'Tootsie-Toy' type plated
  chrome hubs **£300-400**
- 1946 Cream or Green body,
  Black smooth hubs, White tyres....... **£250-300**
- 1946-48   Cream or Green body,
  ridged hubs usually Black................ **£200-250**
- Blue body & Black hubs. **£300-350**
  South African issue:
- Turquoise body, Dark Blue hubs,
  White tyres **£300-500**
- Dark Blue body, Dark Blue hubs,
  White tyres **£300-500**

30b 1935-40   **Rolls-Royce**
  Open chassis, no sidelights, authentic radiator,
  smooth Black hubs or coloured hubs.
  NB: Models with coloured hubs
  attract a premium.
- 1935-40   Cream/Black, Red and Maroon,
  Blue/Black, Dark Blue/Black,
  Fawn/Black, Tan/Dark Brown,
  Red/Black, All Black **£500-600**
- Yellow/Brown, Red/Red, Grey/Grey,
  Green/Light Green,
  Pale Green/Black.............................. **£250-350**
- Turquoise/Dark Blue, Silvered hubs **£500-750**
- Light Blue body,
  smooth Black wheel hubs................. **£250-350**
- Fawn body, Black hubs,
  Black open chassis............................ **£250-350**
- 1946 Fawn body, Black open
  chassis and smooth hubs **£150-200**
- Fawn, Black open chassis,
  ridged Silver hubs............................ **£200-250**
- 1946-50 Plain (closed) chassis,
  ridged hubs, Mid-Blue/Black,
  Violet-Blue/Black, Greyish-Brown/Black,
  Dark Blue/Black, Light Blue/Black,
  Fawn/Black **£150-200**

Dinky 30c Daimler in rare blue with black chassis.

30c 1935-40   **Daimler**
  Open chassis, no sidelights, authentic
  radiator, smooth hubs.
- 1935-40   Cream/Black, Blue/Black,
  Dark Blue/Black, Yellow/Black,
  Fawn/Black **£300-400**
- Turquoise/Black, Fawn/Black,
  Light Green/Black **£200-300**
- Pink/Maroon, Red/Red.................... **£175-250**
- Two-tone Grey or two-tone Green... **£300-500**
- 1940-41 Pale Tan body,
  Black chassis and hubs **£200-250**
- 1945-46
  Beige body, smooth black hubs **£400-500**
- Green or Fawn body,
  smooth or ridged hubs...................... **£90-120**
- 1946-50 Plain (closed) chassis, ridged hubs.
  Dark Green/Black, Cream/Black, ... **£200-300**
- Fawn/Black,Grey/Black,Grn/Black
  Dk Blueish Grn/Black **£100-150**
- Mid-Green body, Pale Green hubs .. **£400-500**

30d 1935-38   **Vauxhall**
  Open chassis, no sidelights, spare wheel
  in wing, 'egg box' or 'shield' grille.
- Green/Black, Blue/Black, Grey/Black,
  Yellow/Black, Brown/Black **£200-300**

- Yellow/Brown, Cream/Brown,
  Tan/Brown **£200-300**
- Two-tone Grey or two-tone Green...**£300-400**
- 1938-40   Radiator change:
  As previous model but with 'shield'
  grille, Black or coloured chassis **£200-300**
- 1946   Dark Olive Green, open chassis,
  smooth Black hubs, White tyres **£100-125**
- 1946-50   Plain (closed) chassis, no spare
  wheel, Green/Black, Dark Brown/Black,
- Olive-Green/Black,...........................**£100-125**
- Grey/Black, ...**£140-170**
- Maroon/Black,.................................**£180-220**
- Brown/Black silver hubs. **£200-250**
- Hub variation:
  Dark Olive Green body, Black chassis,
  Silver ridged hubs, thick axles **£200-250**

30e 1935-48   **Breakdown Car**
  See 'Commercial Vehicles' section.
30f 1936-41   **Ambulance**
  See 'Emergency Vehicles' section.
30g 1936-50   **Caravan**
  See 'Accessories (Pre-War)' section.
32 1934-35   **Chrysler 'Airflow' Saloon**
  (renumbered from 30a)
- Maroon (lead) body, no chassis,
  separate bumpers.............................**£200-250**
- Same model, but diecast body **£200-250**
34a 1935-40   **'Royal Air Mail' Service Car**
  See 'Commercial Vehicles and Vans' section.
35a 1936-40   **Saloon Car**
  Some versions may have spare wheel cover
  in a darker shade of the main colour.
- Mid-Blue, Dark Blue, Maroon, Grey,
  Yellow, Red, Turquoise, Black or
  White solid rubber wheels...................**£65-75**
- 1946-48   Grey or Light Blue body
  (spare wheel cover not enhanced),
  Black rubber wheels.............................**£50-60**
35az 1939-40   **Fiat 2-seater Saloon**
- Red, Blue or Green, White rubber wheels,
  'Simca 5' cast inside. French issue **£80-100**
35b 1936-39   **Racer**
- Red, Silver, Yellow or Blue body, with or
  without driver, White solid rubber wheels,
  Red grille and steering wheel **£65-75**
35b 1939-54   **Midget Racer**
- Silver body, Red grille, Brown driver,
  solid Black rubber wheels only **£65-75**
- Same, but with Silver driver.................**£65-75**
- Green body, Black tyres **£150-175**
  1954   (Renumbered to 200)
35c 1936-40   **MG Sports Car**
- Red, Pale or Dark Green, Turquoise, Yellow,
  Dark Blue or Maroon, Silver detailing,
  White solid rubber wheels
  (Black later)..**£75-100**
- 1946-48   Red or Green body, Silver on
  grille only, Black rubber wheels only....**£40-50**
35d 1938-40   **Austin 7 Car** (open tourer)
  Wire windscreen frame, Black or White
  rubber wheels, Silver radiator and steering
  wheel, hole for driver.
- Light Blue, Dark Blue, Turquoise, Grey,
  Lime Green, Maroon or Yellow, (Yellow
  may have Orange spare wheel cover)..**£50-60**
  1946-48   No wire windscreen frame,
  no hole for driver.
- Light Blue, Grey or Yellow body, Silver on
  grille only, Black rubber wheels only...**£35-45**
- As previous model, but Fawn body......**£45-55**
  Note all 36 series cars were sold from Trade
  Boxes of 6.
36a 1937-41   **Armstrong-Siddeley Limousine**
  with Driver and Footman
  Detailed chassis with slots, tinplate figures,
  sidelights, Black smooth hubs.
- Red/Dark Red, Grey/Dark Grey,
  Maroon/Dark Maroon,
  all-Maroon...............................**£1,000-1,500**
- 1946   Grey body, Black smooth
  wheel hubs, moulded chassis with

or without slots, no figures **£100-130**
36a 1947-50   **Armstrong-Siddeley**
  (no slots or figures), moulded chassis,
  Black ridged hubs plated radiator.
- Mid-Blue/Black, Grey/Black.   **£100-130**
- Maroon/Black,Powder Blue/Black,
- Saxe Blue/Black **£140-170**
36b 1937-41   **Bentley 2 seat Sports Coupé**
  with Driver and Footman
  Detailed chassis with slots, tinplate figures,
  sidelights, smooth black hubs.
- Cream/Black, Yellow/Maroon,
  Grey/Grey...................................**£1,000-1,500**
- 1946 Blue/Black, L Grey/Black & black
  ridged hubs Light Green or Saxe Blue body,
  smooth black hubs, moulded chassis
  (slots on some), no figures...............**£200-300**
36b 1947-50   **Bentley**
  Moulded chassis (no slots/figures),
  ridged hubs, plated radiator.
- Mid Blue/Black ,Mid Green/Black,..**£120-140**
- Dark Green/Black, ...**£150-180**
- Light Brown/Black, ...**£180-200**
- Saxe Blue/Black, ...**£220-250**
- Light Green/Black, ...**£120-140**
- Burgundy/Black,.............................**£350-400**

*Dinky 36c grey, 30c blue (rare), 25d red, 25f orange, 30b
tan/brown pre-war, 25a Wagon blue.*

36c 1937-41   **Humber Vogue Saloon**
  with Driver and Footman
  Detailed chassis with slots, tinplate figures,
  sidelights, plated radiator.
- Green/Dark Green, Blue/Dark Blue, all
  Royal Blue, Black smooth hubs..**£1,100-1,400**
- 1946   Early post war issues with
  smooth Black hubs, moulded chassis
  with or without slots, no figures **£150-200**
36c 1947-50   **Humber Vogue**
- Grey/Black, Dark Brown/Black,
  Brown/Black, ...**£130-150**
- Mid Blue/Black,..............................**£150-200**
36d 1937-41   **Rover Streamlined Saloon**
  with Driver and Footman
  Detailed cast chassis with slots, tinplate
  driver and passenger, sidelights,
  Black smooth hubs.
- Light Green body,
  mid-Green wings, White tyres....**£1,000-1,500**
- Red Green body, Maroon wings,
  White tyres **£400-600**
- 1946   Early post war issues with
  smooth Black hubs and moulded
  chassis with or without slots............**£150-200**
36d 1947-50   **Rover**
  No slots or figures, ridged hubs.
- Dark, Saxe, Mid or Bright Blue/Black,
  Light or Mid-Green/Black **£130-170**
- Green body with Light Green hubs..**£300-350**
- Dark Blue body, Black wings,
  Light Blue hubs...............................**£300-350**
- Navy Blue body, Black wings/hubs..**£300-350**
36e 1937-41   **British Salmson Two-seater**
  Sports Car with Driver
  Detailed chassis, hole in seat for driver,
  cast Red or Green body, Black hubs,
  solid windscreen, sidelights, spare
  wheel on some.
- Royal Blue, Blue/Dark Blue,
  Black/Red, Grey/Dark Grey,
  Silver/Black, Red/Maroon **£1,000-1,500**
- 1946 Early post war issues with smooth
  Black hubs, moulded chassis, no driver
  ....**£125-175**
- Rare Brown issues **£400-600**

36e 1947-50   **British Salmson Two-seater**
  Sports Car
  Moulded chassis, no hole in seat,
  tinplate windscreen, ridged hubs.
- Light Blue/Black, Fawn/Black, Powder Blue/
  Black, Sky-Blue/Black or Saxe-Blue/Black........
  ....**£90-150**
- Dark Green/Black, ...**£250-300**
- Red/Black **£130-160**
- Brown/Black **£300-400**
36f 1937-41   **British Salmson Four-seater**
  Sports Car with Driver
  Detailed chassis, hole in seat for driver,
  cast driver, sidelights, Black smooth hubs
  and solid windscreen, cast-in spare wheel
  at rear.
- Red/Maroon, Green/Dark Green,
  Grey/mid-Grey, Deep Blue/Black **£1,000-1,500**

36f 1947-50   **British Salmson Four-seater**
  Sports Car
  No hole or driver, tinplate windscreen,
  ridged hubs. Black moulded chassis.
- Light or Mid-Green, Fawn,
  Greenish-Grey, Light Grey...............**£100-140**
  NB Early Post War Issues 38 and 39 Series:
  see the Model Identification section for details.
  Note all 38 series cars were sold
  from Trade Boxes of 6.

38a 1940-41   **Frazer Nash BMW Sports**
  Early versions have smooth wheel hubs and
  solid steering wheels.
- Red body, smooth Black hubs,
  Red or Maroon seats **£500-600**
- Light Green with Dark Green seats ..**£500-600**
- Dark Blue body and smooth hubs,
  Fawn seats **£300-350**
- Light Grey body, Brown seats...........**£300-350**
- 1946 Special issue:
  This version can be found with black or
  laquered blue.
  Dark Blue body, Light Blue seats,
  'Hornby Series' tinplate sheet base..**£150-250**
  1947-50 Regular issue:
  Black base, Black ridged hubs,
  celluloid windscreen: Body colours can vary
  from gloss to matt and many slight variations.
- Dark Grey, Putty seats. **£100-120**
- Blue, grey seats................................**£100-120**
- Light Grey, Blue seats......................**£100-120**
- Blue & Grey seats, Blue hubs. **£200-230**
- Light Grey, Red seats & hubs. **£200-230**
- Violet Blue, Grey seats and mid blue hubs.
  ....**£300-400**
- 1950-55 As previous models but
  made for export only................. Prices similar
  1955   (Renumbered 100)
38b 1940-41   **Sunbeam Talbot Sports**
  NB All 38b issues may be found with or
  without silver edging to the windscreen
  though this is normally on the early versions.
  Early versions have smooth wheel hubs and
  solid steering wheels
  1946
- Red (Maroon tonneau), and Red
  smooth hubs, lacquered metal base **£350-400**
- Green with Dark Green tonneau,
  Black smooth hubs **£300-400**
  1947-49
  From 1947, most have Black
  ridged hubs and Black tinplate baseplate.
  and spoked steering wheel.
- Green, Dark Green tonneau **£300-400**
- Maroon, Grey tonneau.....................**£220-250**
- Grey body, Dark Grey tonneau.........**£220-250**
- Red, Maroon tonneau.. ....**£140-160**
- Yellow, Fawn tonneau......................**£140-160**
- Brown, Blue tonneau. **£170-200**
- Blue, Grey tonneau..........................**£220-250**
- Light Blue, Grey tonneau..................**£220-250**
- Dk. Blue body, Light Grey tonneau..**£220-250**

1950-55 Late post war issues with coloured hubs made for Export only..
- Yellow body, Dark Green tonneau, Yellow hubs **£230-260**
- Red body, Maroon tonneau, & Red hubs **£230-260**
- Yellow body, Fawn tonneau, yellow hubs **£350-400**

38c 1946 Lagonda Sports Coupé
Early post war issues with smooth Black hubs & solid steering wheels and silver edged screen.
- Green body, Dark Green seats.........**£150-180**
- Light Grey, Mid Grey seats...............**£150-180**
1947-50
From 1947, most have ridged Black hubs.
- Green body, Dark Green seats **£100-120**
- Maroon body, Dark Blue seats **£220-250**
- Light Grey body Dark Grey seats......**£120-140**
- 1950-55 As previous models but made for export only.
Late post war issues with coloured hubs.
- Green body, dark Green seats, Light Green hubs **£150-170**
- Grey body, dark Grey seats, grey hubs. **£250-280**
- Grey body, Maroon seats grey hubs. **£220-250**
1955 (Renumbered 102)

38d Alvis Sports Tourer
Early Pre-War Prototype.
- Blue body, tan seats, grey tonneau **£500-600**
Early Post War issues with smooth black hubs and solid steering wheel.
1940-41
- Green body, Brown seats and hubs, Khaki base **£320-350**
- Maroon body, Red seats, Khaki coloured base..........................**£320-350**
1946
- Early post war issues with smooth hubs. **£160-200**
From 1947, all had a Black painted baseplate. and ridged hubs.
1947-50:
- Green body, Black seats **£100-120**
- Maroon body, Grey seats **£100-120**
- Very Dark Maroon body, Grey seats **£150-180**
- 1950-55 As previous models but made for export only
- Green body, Black seats, green hubs **£140-170**
- Maroon body, Grey seats, Red hubs **£140-170**
1955 (Renumbered 103)

38e 1940 ? Triumph Dolomite
Planned and catalogued but not issued ... NPP

Dinky 38e Armstrong Siddeley versions, see page 89.

38e Armstrong Siddeley Coupé
Pre War Prototype.
- Mid Blue body,Green seats, Black ridged hubs, Brown dashboard with no steering wheel. Khaki base. **£500-600**
- Green body , Dark Green seats, Black ridged hubs, Brown dashboard with no steering wheel.
- Khaki Base...**£500-600**
1947-50
From 1947, all have a Black painted baseplate. and black ridged hubs.Earlier models usually with silver edged windscreen.:
- Red body, Maroon seats, Silver

edged Screen......................................**£300-350**
- Deeper Mid green body, Dark Green seats, Silver Edged Screen...........................**£250-300**
- Dark Grey body, Deep Blue seats.....**£130-150**
- Light Grey body, Deep Blue seats. ...**£130-150**
- Paler Light Green body, Grey seat....**£130-150**
- 1950-55 Models with coloured hubs made for the export market.
- Bright Green body, Grey seats with Bright Green hubs. **£300-350**
- Light Green body, Grey interior, Mid-Green hubs **£250-280**
- Light Grey body, Deep Green seats with Light Grey hubs./Blue **£250-280**
- Light Grey body, Deep Blue seats with Blue hubs ....**£250-280.**
- Light Grey body, Deep Blue seats with Grey hubs ....**£280-320.**
1955 (Renumbered 104)

38f Jaguar (SS100) Sports Car
Pre War Prototype.
Dark Green body, Black seats and smooth hubs with white tyres Solid steering wheel. **£600-800**
1940-41
Early post war issues with smooth black hubs & solid steering wheel. 2 celluloid windscreens, clear lacquered baseplate. Some windscreen edges have silver detailing.
1947-50 From 1947, all have a Black painted baseplate and black ridged hubs.
- Putty body, Black interior **£375-425**
- Red body, Maroon interior **£170-200**
- Light Blue body, Light Grey or Mid Grey interior. **£140-170**
- Brown body, Dark Blue interior **£250-280**
- Dark Blue body, Grey interior **£180-220**
1950-55 Models made for export with coloured hubs.
- Red body, Maroon interior, red hubs .**£200-220**
- Light Blue body, Light Grey or Mid Grey interior with Blue hubs. **£200-220**
- Light Grey body, Red interior & hubs. .**£300-350**
- Light Blue body, Red interior with Blue hubs. **£250-280**
- Red body, Dark Blue interior & red hubs **£300-350**
1955 (Renumbered 105)

39a 1939-41 Packard Super 8 Tourer
- Smooth hubs, Silver or lacquered baseplate. Light Green, Grey, Black, Yellow, Blue. **£300-400**
- 1946 Early post-war issues with Black smooth hubs
- Brown body...................................**£140-170**
- Olive Green body............................**£140-170**
- 1947-50 All have a Black painted baseplate, ridged hubs.
- Dark Brown body............................**£170-200**
- Brown body.....................................**£110-140**
- Olive Green body.............................**£110-140**

39b 1939-41 Oldsmobile 6 Sedan
- Smooth hubs, Silver or lacquered baseplate. (open at rear), Black, Maroon, Violet Blue, Light or Mid Grey, Green, Yellow. **£300-400**
1946 Early post-war issues with Black smooth hubs
1947-50 All have Black baseplate (open at rear), black ridged hubs.
- Grey, ...**£110-130**
- Violet-Blue **£130-170**
- Brown, ...**£250-280**
- Light Blue body, Black hubs **£800-1,100**

39bu 1950-52 Oldsmobile Sedan (US issue)
- Light Blue body, Dark Blue wings, Light Blue hubs. Black baseplate Open at rear,...............................**£1,500-2000**
- Cream body, Tan wings, Black hubs. Black baseplate open at rear, ...**£1,500-2000**
- Cream body, Tan wings, Cream hubs. Black baseplate closed at rear,....**£1,800-2,300**

- Light Blue body, Dark Blue wings, Light Blue hubs. Black baseplate closed at rear, ...**£1,700-2200**
- Cream body, Tan wings, Black hubs. Black baseplate closed at rear,.....**£1,700-2200**
- Tan body and hubs, black baseplate closed at rear.............................**£1000-1250**

39c 1939-41 Lincoln Zephyr Coupé
- Lacquered baseplate, smooth Black hubs. Grey/Black, Yellow, Red or Green....**£300-400**
1946 Early post-war issues with smooth Black hubs
- Light Grey..**£300-400**
- 1947-50 Black painted baseplate, ridged hubs.
- Light Grey body...............................**£100-130**
- Brown body.....................................**£150-180**

39cu 1950-52 Lincoln Zephyr Coupé
(US issues). All have Black painted baseplate and ridged hubs.
- Tan with Brown wings, Black hubs.................................**£1,800-2,000**
- Red body, Maroon wings, black hubs,.................................**£3,000-3,500**
- Tan body & Brown wings, Tan hubs **£2,000-2,500**
- Red body, Maroon wings and Red hubs,........... ....**£2,500-3,000**
- Yellow body and green hubs **£1,800-2,000**
- Red body and hubs.....................**£1,500-2,000**

39d 1939-41 Buick Viceroy Saloon
Lacquered baseplate, smooth Black hubs.
- Grey, Green, Maroon, Cream, Blue..**£300-400**
- 1946 Early post-war issues with Black smooth hubs..........................**£250-300**
- Olive body, smooth hubs.................**£300-350**
1947-50 All have Black painted baseplates & ridged hubs.
- Beige body....................................**£120-150**
- Grey body......................................**£120-150**
- Maroon body..................................**£160-190**
- Sand body......................................**£220-250**
1950 Late post-war issues with coloured ridged hubs,
- Beige body, Tan hubs. **£250-280**
- Beige body, yellow hubs..................**£330-360**
- Beige body, Green hubs. **£380-400**
- (Riley) Green body & hubs............**£380-400**
- (Triumph) Blue body & hubs..........**£500-600**

39e 1939-41 Chrysler Royal Sedan
Lacquered baseplate, smooth black hubs.
- Yellow body, Black hubs **£800-1,100**
- Violet Blue body. **£200-300**
- Green body. **£200-300**
- Powder Blue. **£280-350**
- 1946 Early post-war issues with black baseplate & smooth Black hubs. **£200-300**
1947-50 All have black ridged hubs.
- Green body (Various shades) **£100-120**
- Dark Grey body. **£120-150**
- Dark Blue body. **£120-150**
1950 Late post-war issues with coloured ridged hubs,
- Light (Triumph 1800) Blue & Blue hubs **£800-1,100**
- Cream body, Green hubs. **£1,000-1,500**

39eu 1950-52 Chrysler Royal Sedan
(US issues). Black baseplate, can have Blued axles.
- Yellow body, Red wings, Black or Yellow hubs **£3,000-3,500**
- Two-tone Green body, Light Green hubs **£1,500-2,000**

39f 1939-41 Studebaker State Commander
- Lacquered baseplate, smooth Black wheel hubs. Yellow, Black, Maroon, Green or Dark Grey body **£300-400**
1946 Early post-war issues with smooth Black hubs, Brown inner baseplates.
- Various colours include; Olive or Dark Green, Grey **£180-250**

- 1946 Yellow, smooth Black hubs. **£800-1,100**
  1947-50 From 1947, all have Black
  baseplate, ridged hubs.
- Dk. or Lt. Grey body, ...**£120-140**
- Olive Green, body............................**£120-140**
- Green body,.......................................**£130-160**
- Dark Blue body, ...**£120-140**
- Midnight Blue body,.........................**£170-200**

40a and 158   RILEY SALOON
1947-53   40a Riley Saloon
1st baseplate: Tinplate baseplate '40A' has small
lettering. Ridged hubs. Not individually boxed
but sold from a trade box of six.
- Dark Grey, black hubs. **£100-120**
- Dark Green, black hubs. **£100-120**
- Dark Blue, black hubs. **£140-160**
- Mid Blue, black hubs. **£300-400**
- Peppermint Green, green hubs. **£120-150**
- Light Green, green hubs...................**£100-120**
- Mid Green body and hubs. **£300-400**
- Light Grey body and hubs. **£220-250**
- Mid Blue (darker than wheels),
  Blue hubs..**£500-750**
  1954 - 40a was renumbered to 158

158 1954-55   **Riley Saloon**
(renumbered from 40a)
158 baseplate has large lettering, retains
40a on baseplate.
Boxes.
Type1 Dual Picture box 158/40a.
Type 2 Picture box no 158.
- Cream body, Mid-Green hubs **£150-175**
- Lemon, Mid Green hubs..................**£250-300**
- Green body, Mid-Green hubs **£150-175**
  Late models with M Tyres.

40b and 151   TRIUMPH 1800 SALOON
1948-49
1st baseplate: Tinplate baseplate
'40b' has small lettering. Ridged hubs. Not
individually boxed but sold from
a trade box of six.

40b 1948-49   **Triumph 1800 Saloon**
Rear axles held by cast pillars.
- Black body, Black hubs **£400-600**
- Mid Grey body, grey hubs................**£120-140**
- Blue body and hubs **£120-140**
- Fawn (Taupe) body and hubs **£160-200**
  1949-54
  2nd baseplate: Tinplate baseplate
  40b' has small lettering. No cast pillars.
  Ridged hubs. Not individually boxed but
  sold from a trade box of six.
- Blue body and hubs...........................**£120-140**
- Blue body and Fawn hubs **£140-170**
- Seablue body and Fawn hubs..........**£220-250**
  1954 - 40b was renumbered to 151
  Boxes.
  Type1 Dual Picture box 151/40b.
  Type 2 Picture Box no 151 shows small
  black ovals & white nos on box side.
  Type 3 Box shows large red ovals
  and white nos on box side.

151 1954-60 **Triumph 1800 Saloon**
(renumbered from 40b)
2nd baseplate
- Light Blue body and hubs. **£130-160**
- Light Blue body, Light grey hubs......**£260-280**
- Fawn body, Green hubs **£130-160**
- Blue body, Fawn hubs.......................**£160-180**
- Dark Blue body, Blue hubs **£300-330**
  Note box is 151 & shows large printed
  dark blue spot.
  Late models with M tyres. Also note some late
  models with chequered pattern on underside ..
  of roof.

40c 1940   **Jowett Javelin. Factory drawing**
exists but model not issued ....NPP
40d and 152   AUSTIN (A40) DEVON
1st baseplate: Tinplate baseplate '40d' has
small lettering. Ridged hubs.
Not individually boxed but sold from
a trade box of six.

40d 1949-54   **Austin (A40) Devon**
Rear axle held by the baseplate.
- Maroon body and hubs................... **£100-125**
- Dark-Blue body, Blue hubs **£100-125**
- Red body, Maroon hubs.................. **£600-700**
- Light Grey-Green body and hubs **£100-125**
- Suede-Green body, Beige hubs........**£100-125**
  Boxes.
  Type1 Dual Picture box 152/40d.
  shows no box side no ovals.
  Type 2 Box shows large red ovals
  and white no's on box side.
  Type 3 Box show 2 Tone colour models.
  1954 - 40d was renumbered to 152

152 1954-59   **Austin (A40) Devon**
(renumbered from 40d)
Type 1 Box.
Large baseplate lettering sold individually
boxed.
(see example diagrams).
Some small lettering models will have been
boxed in Type 1 boxes during transition.
- Tan body, Suede Green hubs............**£600-800**
- Suede Green body and hubs **£230-250**
- Dark Blue body, Mid-Blue hubs......**£200-225**
  Type 2 Box
  Later models have 'DEVON' cast into
  underside of roof.
- Suede Green body with Fawn hubs .**£230-250**
- Suede Green body, Maroon hubs ...**£600-800**
- Dark Blue body, Mid-Blue hubs......**£200-225**
- Dark Green body with Fawn hubs ...**£230-250**
- Dark Green body with Cream hubs .**£230-250**
- Light Blue body and hubs................**£500-600**
  1956-59 Two-tone issues:
  Type 3 Box
- Blue upper body and hubs,
  Yellow lower body **£350-400**
- Cerise lower body, Lime Green upper
  body, Cream hubs **£350-400**

40e and 153 STANDARD VANGUARD
40e 1948-49   **Standard Vanguard**
1st casting: Open rear wheel arches,
small baseplate lettering and rear axle secured
by tinplate clip. Ridged hubs.
Not individually boxed but sold from
a trade box of six.
- Fawn body, Red hubs **£350-400**
- Fawn body and hubs **£125-150**
- Cream body, Green hubs ....NGPP
  Boxes.
  Type1 Dual Picture box 153/40e.
  shows no box side no ovals.
  Type 2 Box shows large red ovals
  and white no's 153 on box side.
  1949-54 2nd casting baseplate change:
  Closed rear wheel arches, large base lettering,
  rear axle held by baseplate tabs.
  Type1 Dual Picture box
- Fawn body and hubs **£125-150**
- Mid-Blue body and hubs **£125-150**
- Maroon body and hubs.................**£2000-2500**
- Maroon body, Fawn hubs.............**£1000-1500**
- Dark Blue body, Fawn hubs.............**£500-600**
  1954 - 40e was renumbered to 153

153 1954-60   **3rd casting**
'VANGUARD' cast into underside of roof,
large baseplate lettering.
Type 2 Box shows large red ovals
- Fawn body, Fawn hubs **£125-150**
- Mid-Blue body, Fawn hubs,............**£220-250**
- Mid-Blue body, Blue hubs, ...**£250-300**
- Mid-Blue body, Cream hubs, ...**£200-250**
- Cream body, Cream hubs,
  Tan spot box....................................**£250-275**
  Late models with M tyres & painted rear lights.
  NB The ridge which appears on the boot
  of some Vanguard models is the result
  of worn die replacement.

40f and 154   HILLMAN MINX
40f 1951-54   **Hillman Minx**
1st baseplate: Small baseplate lettering

(see diagram). Ridged hubs.
Not individually boxed but sold through
a trade box
1st casting no name on underside roof.
- Dark Green body, Mid-Green hubs .**£180-220**
- Mid-Green body, Light Green hubs.**£130-160**
- Butterscotch body, Siege Green hubs**£300-350**
- Butterscotch body, Blue hubs **£250-280**
  Boxes.
  Type1 Dual Picture box 154/40f.
  shows no box side number ovals. Coloured
  spot may be applied.
  Type 2 Box shows large red ovals
  and white no's 154 on box side.
  Type 3 Box show 2 Tone colour models.
  2nd casting shows Hillman Minx name on
  underside roof.
  Small lettering to base.
  This was a transition time. Some models sold
  from trade box, others from Type1 Dual
  Picture box normally with a coloured spot
  attached.
- Pale Green body, Cream hubs..........**£250-280**
- Pale Green body, Various shades,
  Green hubs.......................................**£175-225**
- Light Tan body, Blue hubs **£250-280**
- Butterscotch body, Green hubs........**£275-325**
- Butterscotch body, Dark Tan hubs ..**£225-250**
- Butterscotch body, Tan hubs...........**£225-250**
  1955 - 40f was renumbered to 154
  3rd casting shows Hillman Minx name on
  underside roof.
  Large lettering to base.
  Type 2 Box shows large red ovals
  and white no's 154 on box side.
- Pale Green body, Various shades,
  Green hubs.......................................**£175-225**
- Light Tan body, Cream hubs **£250-280**
- Butterscotch body, Cream hubs.......**£225-250**
- Mid-Green body, Light Green hubs .**£160-180**
- Peppermint Green, Green hubs........**£180-220**
- Dark Tan body, Green hubs..............**£275-325**
- Dark Tan body, Blue hubs **£275-325**
- Dark Tan body, Cream hubs.............**£150-180**
- Dark Tan body, Green hubs..............**£180-220**
  Type 3 Box show 2 Tone colour models.
  Two-tone issues:
- Pale Blue lower body and hubs,
  Cerise upper body **£300-350**
- Lime Green lower body,
  Cream upper body and hubs............**£300-350**
  Note;
  Point 1 Some Type 3 Boxes used for late
  single colours showing coloured spots
  Point 2 Some 2 tone models packed in
  Type 2 Boxes showing coloured spot.

*Dinky 40g Morris Oxford, Blue with Grey wheels and
all-Tan version (rare items).*

40g and 159 MORRIS OXFORD
1950-54
1st baseplate: Small baseplate lettering.
Ridged hubs.
Not individually boxed but sold through
a trade box
1st casting no name on underside roof.
- Blue body, Grey hubs....................**£2000-2500**
- Sand body and hubs........................**£800-1000**
- Stone body, Light Grey hubs **£90-110**
- Green body, Light Green hubs **£90-110**
- Dark Green body and hubs **£200-230**
  Boxes.
  Type1 Dual Picture box 159/40g.
  shows no box side number ovals. Coloured

spot may be applied.
Type 2 Box shows large red ovals
and white no's 159 on box side.
Type 3 Box show 2 Tone colour models.
2nd casting shows Morris Oxford name on
underside roof.
Small lettering to base.
This was a transition time. Some models sold
from trade box, others from Type1 Dual Picture
box normally with a coloured spot attached.
- Green body, Light Green hubs **£150-175**
- Fawn body, Grey hubs...................... **£150-175**
- Fawn body, Fawn hubs **£80-100**
1954 - 40g was renumbered to 159
1st casting no name on underside roof. Type 2
Box
- Very Dark Green body and hubs In a 159 box,
showing printed dark green spot. **£300-400**
2nd casting shows Morris Oxford name on
underside roof.
Type 2 Box shows large red ovals
and white no's 159 on box side.
- Green body, Light Green hubs **£150-175**
- Stone body, Fawn hubs.................... **£150-175**
Type 3 Box show 2 Tone colour models and
No 159.
Two-tone issues:
- Cream upper body, Cerise lower body,
Beige hubs. **£240-300**
- Green upper body and hubs,
Cream lower body **£250-300**
- Turquoise upper body, Cream lower
body, Green hubs **£600-800**

40h and 254   AUSTIN (FX3) TAXI
40h   1952-54   **Austin (FX3) Taxi**
1st baseplate shows 40H on large lettering
Ridged hubs. Not individually boxed
but sold from a box of six.
- All-Yellow body and hubs,
Brown chassis, interior and driver ... **£120-150**
- Dark Blue body, Light Blue hubs,
Black chassis, interior and driver **£150-180**
Boxes.
Type1 Dual Picture box 254/40h shows
yellow/brown & dark blue model on box.
shows no box side number ovals. Coloured
spot may be applied.
Type 2 Box shows large red ovals and
white no's 254 on box side. shows same
Colour models.
Type 3 Box show 2 Tone colour model
254 on large red ovals& white Nos..
Type 4 Box is Light yellow showing last
black model. Shows large red ovals and
white no's 254 on box side.
1954 - 40h was renumbered to 254
This was a transition time. Some models sold
from trade box, others in Type1 Dual
Picture box.
- Dark Blue body, Light Blue hubs,
Black chassis, interior and driver **£200-230**
- All-Yellow body and hubs,
Brown chassis, interior and driver ... **£180-300**
- All-Yellow body and hubs,
Black chassis, interior and driver **£170-200**

254   1956-59   **Austin (FX3) Taxi**
(renumbered from 40h)
2nd baseplate shows no 40H.
- All-Yellow body and hubs,
Black chassis, interior and driver **£170-200**
- Dark Blue body, Light Blue hubs,
Black chassis, interior and driver **£250-280**
- Bright Blue body and blue hubs,
Black chassis, interior and driver **£500-700**
- Violet Blue body and blue hubs,
Black chassis, interior and driver **£400-500**
Two-tone issue:
- Yellow upper body and hubs,
Dark Green lower body,
Black ('254'),
Black interior and driver.................. **£150-180**
- Black body, spun hubs, Grey chassis ('254'),

Grey interior and driver **£200-230**
- Black body, spun hubs, Navy Blue chassis
('254'), Navy Blue interior and driver . **£300-350**

40j and 161   AUSTIN (A40) SOMERSET
40j   1953-54   **Austin (A40) Somerset**
Large lettering on baseplate shows 40j. .
Not individually boxed but sold from a
trade box of six.
- Dark Blue body, Blue hubs **£170-200**
- Red body and hubs........................... **£100-125**
- Pale Blue body and blue hubs.......... **£100-125**
1954 - 40j was renumbered to 161
Boxes.
Type1 Dual Picture box 161/40j.
shows no box side number ovals.
Coloured spot may be applied.
Type 2 Box shows large red ovals
and white no's 161 on box side.
Type 3 Box show 2 Tone colour models.

161   1954   **Austin (A40) Somerset**
(renumbered from 40j)
Large baseplate lettering, 'AUSTIN SOMERSET'
cast into underside of roof. Type 2 Box
- Pale Blue body, Blue hubs **£130-150**
- Red body and hubs........................... **£150-180**
- Pale Blue body, Cream hubs **£450-550**
1956-59   Two-tone issues:
Type 3 Box.
- Red lower body and hubs,
Yellow upper body........................... **£375-475**
- Cream lower body and hubs,
Black lower body **£350-425**
Note 1 Some 2 tone models packed in
Type 2 Boxes showing coloured spot.
Note 2. Late models of the Two tones have
M Tyres and rear lights highlighted.
Late gloss black base with M tyres & rear lights.
- Cream lower body and hubs,
Black lower body £400-600
Sports Tourer set from 101-105 no number on
base. Box type yellow picture box.

*Dinky 101 Sunbeam Alpine with late rare
spun wheels.*

101   1957-60   **Sunbeam Alpine** (touring finish)
- Cerise (Deep Pink), Cream interior,
Cream diecast hubs, Grey driver...... **£225-250**
- Light Blue body, Dark Blue interior,
Blue diecast hubs............................. **£200-230**
- Very Light Blue body, Dark Blue interior,
diecast hubs **£200-230**
- Turquoise Blue body, Dark Blue interior,
Blue diecast hubs............................. **£200-230**
Later models came with a black gloss base
highlighted tail lights, M tyres. These models
could fetch higher prices.
- Turquoise Blue body, Cream diecast
hubs **£500-700**
- Cerise (Deep Pink), Cream interior,
Spun hubs, Grey driver **£750-1,000**
- Turquoise Blue body, Spun hubs **£750-1,000**
102   1957-60   **MG Midget** (touring finish)
Box type yellow picture box.
- Deep Yellow body, Red interior,
Red diecast hubs, Grey driver.......... **£250-325**
- Pale Green body, Cream interior,
Cream diecast hubs, Grey driver...... **£250-350**
- Pale Green body, Cream interior,

Red diecast hubs, Grey driver
.... **£500-750**
Later models came with a black gloss base
highlighted tail lights, M tyres, spun hubs
- Deep Yellow body, Red interior,
spun hubs, Grey driver................. **£750-1,000**
- Pale Green body, Cream interior,
spun hubs, Grey driver................. **£750-1,000**

Dinky 102 M G Midget, scarce spun wheel variant.

103   1957-60   **Austin Healey 100** (touring finish)
Box type 1 yellow non picture box. (Scarce.)
NB; Possible premium if with Type 1 box.
Box type 2 yellow picture box.
- Red body, Grey interior,
diecast hubs and driver.................... **£250-300**
- Cream body, Red interior and hubs,
Grey driver **£250-300**
Later models came with a black gloss base
highlighted tail lights, M tyres.
- Red body, Grey interior,
diecast hubs and driver.................... **£300-400**
- Cream body, Red interior and hubs,
Grey driver **£300-400**
As above models with the addition of spun hubs.
- Red body, Grey interior,
spun hubs and driver
Guide only **£1000-2000**
- Dull Reddish Pink body, Grey interior,
spun hubs and driver
Guide only **£1500-2500**
- Cream body, Red interior and spun hubs,
Grey driver
Guide only **£1000-2000**

*Dinky 103 Austin Healey. Rare late spun wheels showing
unusual Dark Cherry Red version. Very rare.*

104   1957-60   **Aston-Martin DB3S** (touring finish)
Box type yellow picture box.

Dinky 104 Aston Martin with spun wheels - rare.

- Light Blue body, Dark Blue interior,
Mid-Blue hubs, Grey driver **£150-200**
- Salmon-Pink body, Red interior
and hubs, Grey driver,
Matt or Gloss baseplate....................**£150-200**
Later models came with a black gloss base
highlighted tail lights, M tyres.
- Red body, Grey interior,
diecast hubs and driver....................**£300-400**
- Cream body, Red interior and hubs,
Grey driver **£300-400**
As above models with the addition of spun hubs.
- Light Blue body, Dark Blue interior,
Mid-Blue hubs, Grey driver
Guide only   £1000-2000. .... NGPP.
- Salmon-Pink body, Red interior
and diecast hubs, Grey driver,
Guide only   £1000-2000. .... NGPP.

Dinky 105 Triumph TR2 Scarce spun wheel variants.
Easiest to find with spun wheels but still scarce.

105 1957-60   **Triumph TR2** (touring finish)
Box type 1 yellow picture box.
Box type 2 Lighter yellow picture box.
Box type 3 Red/Yellow panel Non Picture Box.
- Grey body, Red interior and hubs,
Grey driver **£250-300**
- Lemon Yellow body, Pale Green interior,
Mid-Green hubs, Grey driver **£275-350**
Box type 2 Lighter yellow picture box.
Box type 3 Red/Yellow panel Non Picture Box.
- Grey body, Red interior, Spun hubs
Grey driver **£400-500**
- Lemon Yellow body, Pale Green interior,
Spun hubs, Grey driver **£450-600**
Box type 2 Lighter yellow picture box.
Box type 3 Red/Yellow panel Non Picture Box.
106 1954-58   **Austin A90 Atlantic**
             (Renumbered from 140a)
Boxes.
Type1 Dual Picture box 106 Shows Black
Model & Black hubs. Blue model Red
Int and Cream hubs. No ovals on side of box.
Type 2 Box shows small black ovals. No 106.
Model colours as Box 1.
Type 3 Box shows large red ovals No 106
and model colours as box 1.
Type 4 Box No 106. late Box as Box 3
but models Black, Red interior & hubs,
Blue model red interior and hubs.
- Light Blue body, Red interior,
Cream hubs....................................**£200-250**
- Light Blue body,
Red interior and hubs. **£170-200**
- Black body, Red interior and hubs,
White tyres **£150-180**
NB Interiors may have a gloss or matt finish.
Sports Tourer Competition series from 107-111
models found with no number on base.
Note; Occasionally a model is found with a
different transfer no applied or a transfer with
no white background to the black racing no, this
may attract a premium.There are some genuine
examples of no transfer applied at all.(Be Careful)
107 1955-59   **Sunbeam Alpine Sports**
             (competition finish)
- Pale Blue, Cream interior,
Cream hubs, '26', white racing driver **£125-150**

- Deep Pink body, Grey interior,Cream hubs,
RN '34', white racing driver **£125-150**
Model no 107 usually on base.
Box type yellow picture box.
108 1955-59   **MG Midget** (competition finish)
- Red body, Tan interior, Red hubs,
RN '24', white racing driver **£250-350**
- Cream body, Red interior, Red hubs,
RN '28', white racing driver **£200-275**
- Cream body, Maroon interior, Yellow hubs,
RN '28', white racing driver **£600-750**
Model no 108 usually on base.
Box type 1 early Yellow Non picture.
Box type 2 yellow picture box.
NB Above Type 2 box shows rare white version
with yellow hubs. See Note on 129 entry.
NB The version of 108 issued in the
US is numbered 129. It retains 108 on base.
109 1955-59   **Austin-Healey 100** (competition
             finish)
- Cream body, Red interior and hubs,
white racing driver and no '23'........**£200-275**
- Yellow body, Blue interior and hubs,
white racing driver and no. '21" **£175-250**
Model no 109 usually on base.
- Cream body, Red interior and hubs,
white racing driver and no '22'
M tyres Rear lights highlighted.
No number on base. **£400-500**
- Yellow body, Blue interior and hubs,
white racing driver and no. '28" with
no white background. M tyres
and no number on base. **£400-500**
Box type 1 early Yellow Non picture.
Box type 2 yellow picture box.

Dinky 110 Aston Martin Competition. Shows scarce
Connaught (light) green and very unusual
dark green shade, see page 84.

110 1956-59   **Aston-Martin DB3S**
             (competition finish)
- Grey body, Blue interior and hubs,
white racing driver and number '20'**£175-250**
- Mid-Green body, Red interior & hubs,
white racing driver,& number '22' ...**£175-250**
- Light Green body, Red interior & hubs,
white racing driver, RN '22' **£350-450**
- Deep Blue-Green body, Red interior & hubs,
white racing driver,& number '22' ...**£500-600**
Box type 1 early Yellow Non picture
Model no 110 usually on base.
This model not part of Competition series.
110 1966-67   **Aston-Martin DB5**
- Metallic Red, Cream or Black interior,
'110' on base, spoked wheels **£80-100**
- 1967-71   Metallic Red or Blue,
Cream or Black interior, plain base,
spoked wheels.....................................**£80-100**
111 1956-59   **Triumph TR2 Sports Car**
             (competition finish)
- Salmon-Pink body, Blue interior & hubs,
white racing driver and no. '29'........**£175-250**
- Turquoise body, Red interior and hubs,
white racing driver and racing no '25'**£175-250**
- Light Blue body, Red interior and hubs,
white racing driver and racing no.'25' **£225-325**
- Turquoise body, Red interior, Blue hubs,
white racing driver and racing no. '25'**£600-750**
Box type yellow picture box.
Model no 111 usually on base.

112 1961-66   **Austin-Healey Sprite Mk.II**
- Red body, Cream int., spun hubs and
black gloss base. **£120-150**
South African issues:
(English / Afrikaans on box,
all have spun hubs)
- Turquoise body, Cream interior.**£1,200-1,800**
- Dark Blue body, Cream interior.**£1,200-1,800**
- Lilac body, Cream interior..........**£1,200-1,800**
Box type yellow picture box
113 1962-69   **MG 'MGB' Sports Car**
- Cream body, Red interior, Grey plastic driver,
spun hubs, black gloss or matt base. .**£80-110**
South African issues:
(English / Afrikaans on box,
all have spun hubs and black gloss base.)
- Mid-Blue body, Red interior.......**£1,200-1,800**
- Red body, Cream interior..........**£1,500-2,500**
Box type yellow picture box
114 1963-71   **Triumph Spitfire**
Sports car with Blue lady driver (plastic),
spun hubs, jewelled headlamps.
1963-66
- Red body, Cream interior Grey base.**£130-160**
- Met. Silver-Grey body, Red interior.
Matt black base. **£100-120**
Only version with colour spot on box.
1966-70
- Metallic Gold body, without bootlid logo,
Red interior, silver base.....................**£120-140**
- Metallic Gold body, Red
interior, 'Tiger In Tank' on bootlid,
Black shiny base. **£120-140**
1970-71
- Metallic Purple body, Gold interior,
Base may be silver,black or grey.......**£150-200**
Purple model only has label applied to box
saying "Colour of model may differ from
illustration" Box type yellow picture box
115 1965-69   **Plymouth Fury Sports**
- White open body, Red interior, cast wheels,
driver and passenger, ...**£50-70**
Box type yellow window box
116 1966-71   **Volvo P 1800 S**
- Red body, White interior, wire wheels. **£50-70**
- Metallic Red, Light Blue interior,
wire wheels **£70-90**
Box type Hard Plastic case
120 1962-67   **Jaguar 'E' type**
- Red body, detachable Black hardtop plus
optional Cream folded soft-top,spun hubs.
                         ....**£120-140**
- Red body, detachable Grey hardtop plus
optional Cream folded soft-top, spun hubs
                         ....**£200-250**
- Metallic Light Blue body, Black hardtop plus
optional Cream folded soft-top,spun hubs
Dark blue spot to box. **£1,250-1,750**
Box type yellow picture box
122 1977-78   **Volvo 265 DL Estate**
(Some made in Italy by Polistil under license)
- Metallic Blue (Brown interior), or Cream
with '265DL' wing badges, cast hubs ...**£25-30**
- 1979-80   Orange version without
'265 DL', Brown box...............................**£35-40**
Box type Blue/Red window box.
123 1977-80   **Princess 2200 HL**
- Metallic Bronze with black roof side
panels, plastic wheels..........................**£30-35**
- All White body **£30-35**
- White body, with Blue roof OR Blue
side panels **£30-35**
Box type Blue/Red window box
124 1977-79   **Rolls-Royce Phantom V**
- Metallic Light Blue, boot opens -
bonnet does not (see 152) **£35-45**
Box type Blue/Red window box.
127 1964-66   **Rolls-Royce Silver Cloud Mk.3**
- Metallic Blue or Metallic Green body,
White interior, spun hubs **£65-75**
- 1966-69   Metallic Gold body,
White interior, cast hubs **£55-65**

- 1969-72   Metallic Red body,
  White interior, cast hubs **£55-65**
  Box type1 yellow window box
  Box type 2 Hard Plastic case
128 1964-67   Mercedes-Benz 600
- Metallic Maroon body, White interior,
  spun hubs, three figures/luggage......... **£45-55**
- 1967-75   Metallic Maroon body, White
  interior, Blue base, spun hubs or
  Speedwheels, driver only **£30-40**
- 1975-79   Metallic Blue, White
  interior, driver, Speedwheels **£30-35**
  Box type1 yellow windowe box
  Box type 2 Hard Plastic case
  Box type 3 Bubble Pack
129 1954?   MG Midget (US issue)
- Ivory body, Maroon and tonneau, Red hubs,
  no driver or RN. (see 108).
  '129' on Yellow box.........................**£900-1,100**
- Red body, Tan interior and tonneau,
  Red hubs, no driver or RN (see 108),
  Yellow box with '129'.....................**£900-1,100**
  NB Yellow Picture box shows usual white
  version with red hubs. See Note on 108
  entry.
129 1965 -72   Volkswagen 1300 Sedan
- Met. Blue body, White interior, spun
  hubs, registration plate 'K.HK 454' **£45-55**
- 1972-76   Metallic Bright Blue,
  White interior, Speedwheels................. **£30-35**
  Box type3 Hard Plastic case
130 1964-66   Ford Consul Corsair
- Red or Metallic Wine Red body,
  Off-White interior, spun hubs............... **£70-85**
- 1966-69   Pale Blue, Metallic Dark Grey
  base, Off-White interior, spun hubs... **£80-100**
- Red body, Off-White interior,Mat Black
  base, spun hubs with Chauffer   **£600-800**
  Box type yellow picture box
  NB Baseplates may have rounded or
  dimpled rivets.
131 1956-61   Cadillac Eldorado
  Models with the normal mottled base.
- Yellow body, Cerise interior, Grey driver,
  Cream hubs,.. **£130-160**
- Salmon-Pink body, Grey interior, Grey
  driver, Beige hubs, ... **£130-160**
  Models with Black Gloss base.
- Cream body, Grey interior, Grey driver,
  Beige hubs.. **£300-350**
  Box type 1 yellow picture box
  1962-63
- As previous models but with spun hubs
  & Black Gloss base............................ **£250-300**
  Box type 1 Lighter yellow picture box
  Box type 3 Red/Yellow panel Non picture Box.
131 1968-70   Jaguar 'E'-type 2+2
- White body, Light Blue or Red interior,
  Gold base, cast spoked wheels........... **£90-110**
- 1970-75   Metallic Copper body,
  Blue interior, Gold base, cast spoked
  wheels or plastic wheels **£70-80**
- 1975-76   Metallic Purple body, Light
  Blue interior, cast spoked wheels....... **£80-100**
- 1976-77   Bronze body, Speedwheels
  .... **£70-90**
- 1977-77   Metallic Red or Post Office
  Red body, Blue int., Speedwheels **£80-100**
  Box type1 Hard Plastic case
  Box type2 Bubble pack wondow box.
132 1955-61   Packard Convertible
  Models with the normal mottled base.
- Light Green body, Red interior and
  hubs, Grey driver.............................**£110-140**
- Tan body, Red interior and
  hubs, Grey driver **£110-140**
  1962-63
- As previous models but with spun hubs.
  Black gloss base M tyres. **£170-200**
132 1967-74   Ford 40 RV
- Metallic Silver body, Red interior,
  spoked wheels....................................... **£30-40**

- Fluorescent Pink body, Yellow engine
  cover, White interior, spoked wheels ... **£35-45**
- Metallic Light Blue body,
  Red or Yellow interior **£30-40**
  NB Early models have red headlight recesses.
  Box type Hard Plastic case.
133 1955-60   Cunningham C5R Road Racer
- White body, Dark Blue stripes,
  Brown interior, RN '31', Blue hubs,
  Light Blue driver. Mottled base. **£80-110**
- Off-White body, Blue interior and
  driver. Black Gloss base. M tyres. **£170-200**
- Off-White body, Dark Blue stripes, Brown
  interior, RN '31', Blue hubs,Black gloss base,
  Spun hubs, M tyres, Blue driver........ **£200-250**
  Box type 1 early Yellow Non picture.
  Box type 2 yellow picture box.
  Box type 3 Red/Yellow panel non picture Box.
133 1964-66   Ford Cortina
  (issued to replace 139)
- Metallic Gold/White body,
  Red interior, spun hubs........................ **£70-85**
  Window box.
- 1966-68   Pale Lime body,
  Red interior, spun hubs........................ **£75-90**
  Box Type 1.Window box.
  Box Type 2 Picture Box showing background.
134 1964-68   Triumph Vitesse
- Metallic Aqua Blue body, White side
  stripe, Red interior, spun hubs **£80-110**
- Metallic Aqua Blue body, White side
  stripe, Grey interior, spun hubs **£150-180**
  Box Type. Red/Yellow Picture Box.
  Indian issues:
  Manufactured in India and fully licensed by
  Meccano. Sold as 'Dinky Toys' and not the
  later 'Nicky Toys'. Box marked 'Licenced
  Manufacturer & Registered User in India,
  S. Kumar & Co., Registered Proprietors of
  Trade Mark Meccano Ltd.' Model base also
  marked 'Licensee in India S. Kumar & Co.'.
  Variations:
- Green body, Red or White flash,
  cast hubs, rubber tyres **£300-400**
- Light Blue body, dark Red flash,
  cast hubs, rubber tyres **£300-400**
- Red body, cast hubs, rubber tyres.... **£300-400**
  NB These models are also found with plastic
  wheels.
135 1963-69   Triumph 2000 Saloon
  Red interior, Grey base, spun hubs,
  wipers, luggage.
- Normal colours:
  Metallic Green with White roof.
  Spun hubs.1 or 2 suitcases. Base usually light
  grey but also found In dark graphite grey. ....
  .... **£70-90**
- Gift Set 118 colour:
  White body, Blue roof, Red interior,
  spun hubs, Usually light grey base,
  individually boxed **£120-150**
  Box Type. Red/Yellow Picture Box.
  Promotional colours:
  Each promotional issue was packed in a
  standard Yellow/Red card picture box.
  Had a promotional sticker attached
  stating the colour of the model inside.
- Black body, Cactus-Green or
  White roof...................................... **£750-900**
- Blue Grey body, Black roof **£750-900**
- Light Green body with Lilac roof **£750-900**
- Metallic Green with White roof........ **£750-900**
- Olive Green body & Cactus roof....... **£750-900**
- British Racing Green, White roof **£750-900**
- White body, Black roof, Blue int....... **£750-900**
- White body, Light Green roof,
  Blue interior **£750-900**
- White body, Light Grey roof,
  Blue interior **£750-900**
- Conifer Green body, Cactus-Green roof**£750-900**
- Gunmetal body, Black roof,
  with 'Gunmetal/WD' label on box ... **£750-900**

- Dark Grey body, Sky-Blue roof......... **£750-900**
- White body, Wedgewood Blue roof,
  Blue interior **£800-950**
- Red or Cherry Red body,
  White roof, Blue interior **£800-1100**
- Chrome Plated. Red Interior .... NGPP
136 1964-65   Vauxhall Viva
- White-Grey body, Red int., spun hubs **£60-90**
- 1965-68   Metallic Bright Blue body,
  Red interior, spun hubs...................... **£60-90**
- 1969-73   Pale Metallic Blue body,
  Red interior, spun hubs...................... **£60-90**
- Dark Metallic Blue body,
  Red interior, spun hubs.,................... **£90-120**
- Pale Metallic Blue body,
  No interior, spun hubs .... NGPP
  Red/Yellow Picture Box
137 1963-66   Plymouth Fury Convertible
  All issues have spun hubs.
- Metallic Light Green body, Cream
  or Dark Green plastic hood. **£70-100**
- Pink body, Red interior, Cream
  plastic hood..................................... **£100-130**
- Dark Metallic Blue,Red interior,
  white plastic hood. **£100-130**
  Red/Yellow Picture Box
138 1963-66   Hillman Imp
  All issues have spun hubs and 'luggage'.
- Metallic Silver-Green body, White
  interior, cast headlamps................... **£100-130**
- Metallic Silver-Green body, Red interior,
  cast headlamps **£60-80**
  1966-68
- Metallic Red body, Blue interior,
  jewelled or plastic headlamps............. **£60-80**
  1968-73
- Metallic mid-Blue body,
  Red interior, jewelled headlamps **£120-140**
- Metallic mid-Blue body, Blue interior, **£175-200**
  Box Type 1. Red/Yellow Picture Box
  Box Type 2. Red/Yellow Picture Box, white
  background.
  Box Type 3. Yellow Window Box.
139 1963-64   Ford Consul Cortina
- Pale Blue body, Off-White interior,
  spun hubs, cast headlamps **£75-85**
- 1964-65   Metallic Blue body,
  Fawn interior, spun hubs **£65-75**
  Box Type. Red/Yellow Picture Box
  South African issues:
  (English / Afrikaans on box, spun hubs).
- Bright Green body, Fawn interior**£1,500-2,000**
  Red/Yellow Picture Box
139a 1949-54   Ford Fordor Sedan
  1st baseplate small writing. Ridged hubs.
  Not individually boxed but sold through
  a trade box
  All have small lettering on the black
  baseplates which may be gloss or matt.
- Yellow body and hubs....................... **£130-160**
- Green body and hubs........................ **£150-200**
- Tan body, Red hubs.......................... **£100-130**
- Red body, Maroon hubs.................... **£100-130**
- Red body, Red hubs **£100-130**
  NB Later issues have 'Ford Sedan' cast
  into underside of roof.
- Tan body, Red hubs.......................... **£100-130**
- Red body, Maroon hubs.................... **£100-130**
- Red body, Red hubs.......................... **£100-130**
  1954   (Renumbered to 170)
139am 1950-54   US Army Staff Car
  See 'Military Vehicles' section.
139b 1950-54   Hudson Commodore
  1st baseplate small writing. Ridged hubs.
  Not individually boxed but sold through
  a trade box No writing on underside of roof.
- Deep Blue body, Stone roof / hubs .. **£300-400**
- Deep Blue body, Tan roof and hubs **£150-180**
- Deep Cream body,
  Maroon roof and hubs **£140-170**
  1954   (Renumbered to 171)

140a 1951-53 **Austin A90 Atlantic**
Not individually boxed but sold from
a trade box of six.
- Pink body, Cream interior and hubs **£225-275**
- Light Blue body, Red interior and
Cream hubs. **£150-175**
- Light Blue body, Dark Blue interior
and Cream hubs **£150-175**
- Red body,
Maroon interior and hubs **£1,500-2,000**
- Mid-Blue body and hubs,
Dark Blue interior **£1,500-2,000**
- Deep Blue body,
Red interior and hubs **£1,400-1,700**
- Mid-Blue body, Purple
interior, Cream hubs **£1,500-2,000**
- Mid-Blue body, Red interior,
Cream hubs **£1,400-1,700**
NB Interiors may have a gloss or matt finish.
1954   (Renumbered to 106)
140 1963-69 **Morris 1100**
- Light Blue body,Red Interior spun hubs £60-70
Box Type. Red/Yellow Picture Box
South African issues:
(English / Afrikaans on box, spun hubs).
- Caramel (Cream)body, Red interior **£1,000-1,500**
- Sky Blue body, Red interior **£1,000-1,500**

*Dinky 140b Rare Red Rover version with
Maroon wheels.*

140b 1951-54 **Rover 75 Saloon**
Not individually boxed but sold from
a trade box of six.
Same base large writing throughout its life.
No writing on underside of roof.
- Red body, Maroon hubs................**£800-1,200**
- Cream body and hubs.....................**£100-140**
- Maroon body and hubs....................**£100-140**
1954   (Renumbered to 156)
141 1963-67 **Vauxhall Victor Estate Car**
- Yellow body, Blue interior, Gloss or
Matt black base. Spun hubs.................. **£60-70**
Box Type. Red/Yellow Picture Box
1963   South African issues:
(English / Afrikaans on box, spun hubs).
- Pink body, Blue interior **£1,000-1,500**
- Ivory body, Blue interior **£1,000-1,500**
- Pale Yellow body, Blue interior ..**£1,000-1,500**
- US promotional: Maroon Red body, Blue
interior, spun hubs.
Paper labels with Yellow wording:
'LIGHTNING FASTENERS LTD',
'TECHNICAL SERVICES' **£800-1,000**
142 1962-68 **Jaguar Mk.10**
All have M tyres on spun hubs, suitcase in the
boot and Red/Yellow picture box.
- Light Metallic Blue, Red interior, ... **£50-70**
- Mid Metallic Blue, Red interior, ... **£70-90**
1963   South African issues:
(English / Afrikaans on box, spun hubs).
- Ivory body, Red interior, ...**£1,000-1,500**
- Avocado Green body & red Interior ....
......................................**£1,000-1,500**
- Pale Blue body, Red interior, ...**£1,000-1,500**
NB Gold, US export issue 'see-through'
window boxes. Model nos. 134, 138 and
142 housed in these boxes may attract a
premium of 50%.
See 'Cars - Box Types' for a complete listing.
143 1962-67 **Ford Capri**
Red/Yellow Picture Box

All models Spun hubs & M Tyres.
- Turquoise body, White roof,
Red interior, spun hubs........................**£70-90**
144 1963-67 **Volkswagen 1500**
All have M tyres on spun hubs, suitcase in the
boot and Red/Yellow picture box.
- Off-White body, Red interior,
luggage, Black gloss or Matt Base.......**£70-100**
- Bronze body, Red Interior.
Matt Black base................................**£100-130**
- Bronze body, Blue Interior.
Matt Black base................................**£175-225**
1963 South African issues:
(English / Afrikaans on box, spun hubs).
- Sage Green body, Red Interior....**£1,000-1,500**
- Caramel body, Red Interior. **£1,000-1,500**
- Pale Blue body, Red Interior. **£1,000-1,500**
145 1962-67 **Singer Vogue**
Red/Yellow Picture Box
All models Spun hubs Red interior.M Tyres
- Metallic Light Green body **£75-100**
- Yellow body................................**£1,500-2,000**
146 1963-67 **Daimler 2.5 litre V8**
Red/Yellow Picture Box
All models Spun hubs. M Tyres...
- Metallic Pale Green body, Red interior **£100-120**
147 1962-69 **Cadillac '62**
Red/Yellow Picture Box
All models Spun hubs M Tyres..
- Metallic Green body, Red interior, ... **£70-90**
- Metallic Green body, White interior, . **£80-110**
148 1962-65 **Ford Fairlane**
Red/Yellow Picture Box
All models Spun hubs. M tyres
- (Non-metallic) Pea Green body, Cream
interior, open or closed windows, ... **£80-100**
- Same model but with Red interior...**£150-200**
1965-69
- Light Metallic Green body, Off-White interior,
open windows. Standard card box...**£140-170**
- US issue:
- Bright (Emerald) Metallic Green body,
Off-White interior, open windows.   **£500-700**
1963 South African issues:
(English / Afrikaans on box,)
Spun hubs, Light Grey Interiors.
- Bright Blue body,(As 113 MGB) ..**£1,000-1,500**
- Dark Blue body,(As 112 Sprite.) .**£1,000-1,500**
- Heather Grey body, ...,**£1,000-1,500**
149 1971-75 **Citroën Dyane**
- Light Grey body,Dark Grey or Black roof £30-50
- Metallic Bronze body, Black roof & interior,
Speedwheels **£30-50**
150 1959-64 **Rolls-Royce Silver Wraith**
Boxes.
Type1 Yellow non Picture box.
Type2 Yellow picture box.
Type 3 Lighter yellow picture box.
Type 4 Red & Yellow panel non picture box.
- Two-tone Grey body, suspension,
spun hubs, Chromed metal bumpers **£80-110**
- Later issues with plastic bumpers.....**£80-110**
NB The French version of 150 (French
reference 551) was cast from English-made
dies, was assembled in France, and has
'Made in France' on the baseplate.
151 1954-59 **Triumph 1800 Saloon**
(renumbered from 40b). See '40 Series' pages.
151 1965-69 **Vauxhall Victor 101**
Box Type1. Red/Yellow picture box
All models Spun hubs. M Tyres
- Pale Yellow body, Red interior **£80-120**
Type 2 Yellow window box.
- Pale Yellow body, Red interior **£70-90**
- Metallic Red body, White interior........ **£50-70**
152 1954-59 **Austin (A40) Devon**
(renumbered from 40d). See '40 Series' pages.
152 1965-67 **Rolls-Royce Phantom V**
Box type1 Hard Plastic case
- Navy Blue body, Beige interior,
chauffeur and two passengers,
spun hubs or cast hubs **£90-120**

1967-77   Design change:
- Very Dark Blue body, White interior
with Chauffeur but no passengers,
Blue base, cast hubs **£50-60**
Box type2 Bubble pack wondow box.
- Light Blue body , White Interior,
cast wheels. **£80-100**
153 1954-59 **Standard Vanguard**
(renumbered from 40e). See '40e' listing.
153 1967-71 **Aston-Martin DB6**
Box type Hard Plastic case
All issues have spoked wheels.
- Metallic Silver Blue body, Red interior.**£60-70**
- Metallic Turquoise body, White interior   .....
....**£80-100**
154 1955   **Hillman Minx**
(renumbered from 40f). See '40f' listing.
154 1966-69 **Ford Taunus 17M**
Box type Hard Plastic case
- Yellow body, White roof, Red interior,
rounded spun hubs or cast wheels **£40-50**
155 1961-66 **Ford Anglia 105E**
Box Type. Yellow picture box
All models Spun hubs. M Tyres
- Turquoise, Red interior. **£80-100**
- Turquoise body, Pale Blue interior ..**£150-175**
- Very Pale Green body, Red interior.
In mail-order box with correct spot.**£450-600**
NB Meccano issued a batch to Ford to
mark the first Ford made on Merseyside
on 8th March 1963. Some were fixed
on plinths and given as souvenirs.
1963   South African issues:
(English and Afrikaans on box, spun hubs).
- Caramel body, Red interior **£1,000-1500**
- Off-White body, Red interior **£1,000-1500**
- Light Blue body, Red interior **£1,000-1500**
- Light grey-Blue body, Red interior.**£1,000-1500**

*Dinky 156 Rover 75 Rare version, Maroon body,
Cream hubs.*

156 1954-56 **Rover 75** (renumbered from 140b)
Model name on underside of roof.
Box Type 1 Yellow Picture Box Dual no 156/140b.
Colour stick on spot to identify model colour
- Red body, Maroon hubs................**£800-1,200**
- Cream body and hubs.....................**£175-225**
- Maroon body and hubs....................**£175-225**
- Maroon body, Red hubs...................**£275-350**
- Cream body, Red hubs....................**£350-450**
Type 2 Box shows large red ovals
and white no's on box side.
- Maroon body and hubs....................**£275-350**
- Maroon body, Cream hubs..........**£1,000-1,500**
1956-59   Two-tone issues:
2 Tone but came in Type 2 box with colour spot
applied.
No 156 on base, some without.
- Violet-Blue upper body,
Cream lower body and hubs **£600-750**
Type 3 Box show 2 Tone colour models.
- Light Green upper body, Green lower
body and hubs **£200-250**
- Dull two-tone Green body, Green hubs
....**£500-600**
- Light Green upper body, Turquoise
lower body, Green hubs..................**£750-1,000**
- Mid-Blue upper body, Cream lower
body and Beige hubs. **£200-250**
Note; Late models with M tyres & highlighted
rear tail lights.
156 1968-71 **Saab 96**
Box Type. Yellow picture box with background.

All models Spun hubs. M Tyres
- Metallic Red body, spun hubs **£70-90**

157 1954-57 **Jaguar XK120**
One casting with name on roof underside.
Boxes.
Type 1 Yellow Picture Box shows Red & Yellow model shows number box side no ovals.
- Yellow body, Light Yellow hubs........ **£225-275**
- Red (Various shades) Red hubs...... **£150-175**
- White body, Fawn hubs White Box spot. ......
.... **£250-350**
Type 2 Yellow Picture Box shows Red &Dk Green model. shows Red ovals on box side .
- Red body, Red hubs **£150-175**
- White body, Fawn hubs White Box spot. ....
.... **£250-350**
- White body, Cream hubs White Box spot. ......
.... **£350-450**
- White body, Yellow hubs White Box spot. ....
.... **£500-700**
- Dark Sage Green body, Fawn hubs ..**£150-225**
Following models can be found with late black gloss base, M tyres and tail lights.
- Red (Various shades)body, Red and
red hubs **£250-325**
- Dark Sage Green body, Beige hubs..**£250-325**
Type 3 Yellow Picture Box shows 2 Tone models. shows Red ovals on box side .
1957-59 Two-tone issues:
Type 4 Lighter Yellow Picture Box shows Red & Dark Green models with spun wheels. Red number ovals.
- Yellow lower body, Light Grey
upper body and hubs **£275-350**
- Turquoise lower body, Cerise upper
body and hubs. **£275-350**
- Sky-Blue lower body, Cerise upper
body and hubs. **£275-350**
1959-62 Singles colours.
Type 4 Lighter Yellow Picture Box shows Red & Dark Green models with spun wheels. Red number ovals.
Type 5 Red and Yellow Panel Non Picture box.
Following models can be found with late black gloss base, M tyres and tail lights.
- Bright Red body, spun hubs **£300-400**
- Dark Sage Green body, spun hubs... **£300-400**

157 1968-73 **BMW 2000 Tilux**
Box Type. Yellow picture box with white background Box has inner pictorial stand.
Flashing Lights
- Blue/White, Red interior, cast hubs **£60-80**

158 1954-55 **Riley Saloon**
See '40' Series information.

158 1967-70 **Rolls-Royce Silver Shadow**
Box type Hard Plastic case
All issues have cast hubs.
- Metallic Red, White interior **£40-60**
- 1970-73 Metallic Bright Blue,
White interior....................................... **£40-60**

159 1954 **Morris Oxford**
See '40' Series information.

160 1958-62 **Austin A30**
Smooth or treaded solid grey plastic wheels.
- Turquoise body.................................. **£90-120**
- Pale Beige body................................. **£90-120**
NB A version of the Austin A30 has been reported with spun hubs, but is not confirmed.

160 1967-74 **Mercedes-Benz 250 SE**
Box Type.1 Yellow picture box with white background. Box has inner pictorial stand.
Flashing Lights
- Met. Blue body, working stop-lights **£30-40**
Box Type 2 Bubble Pack. Cast hubs.
- 1974 Metallic Blue body, White interior, bare metal baseplate, spun hubs, ... **£60-80**

161 1954 **Austin (A40) Somerset**
See the '40j' listing.

161 1965-69 **Ford Mustang Fastback**
Box type1 Export Yellow window Box.
Box type 2 Hard Plastic case
- White (Red seats), 'MUSTANG' decal

badge on wings,chrome cast hubs....... **£70-90**
1969-73
- Yellow body, Blue seats, cast-in logo
replaces decal **£60-70**
- Orange body (no decal), Speedwheels **£40-50**

162 1956-60 **Ford Zephyr Mk.I**
Box Type. Yellow picture box
Mottled Base, Usually smooth tyres.
- Cream upper body, Dark Green lower
body, Cream hubs **£100-125**
- Cream upper body, Lime Green lower
body, Cream hubs **£140-170**
- Two-tone Blue body, Grey hubs....... **£100-125**
Late model with Gloss Black base, M Tyres
- Two-tone Blue body, Grey hubs....... **£150-180**
NB Rear no. plate may be plain or Silver.

162 1966-70 **Triumph 1300**
Box Type. Yellow picture box with background.
All models Spun hubs. M Tyres
- Light Blue body, Red interior, spun hubs **£65-75**

163 1956-60 **Bristol 450 Coupé**
Box type 1 yellow non picture box. (Scarce.)
Box type 2 yellow picture box.
- British Racing Green body, Green hubs,
racing number '27' **£120-140**

163 1966-70 **Volkswagen 1600 TL**
Box type Hard Plastic case
- Red or Dark Metallic Red,
cast detailed hubs................................. **£40-50**
- Metallic Blue body, Speedwheels **£60-70**

164 1957-60 **Vauxhall Cresta**
Box Type. Yellow picture box
- Maroon lower body, Cream (Light Beige)
upper body, Same hubs **£110-140**
- Green lower body,
Grey upper body, Grey hubs **£110-140**
NB Rear no. plate may be plain, black or Silver. Known example to exist with base plate reversed.

164 1966-71 **Ford Zodiac Mk.IV**
- Metallic Silver body, Red interior,
Yellow or Black chassis, cast wheels **£50-60**
- Light Met. Blue body, Red Interior.
Yellow chassis, cast wheels **£80-100**
- Metallic Copper body, Red interior,
Yellow chassis, cast wheels,
rigid plastic case **£80-100**
- Light Metallic Copper body, Red interior,
Yellow chassis, cast wheels,
rigid plastic case **£100-150**

165 1959-60 **Humber Hawk**
All models Spun hubs and M tyres.
Box Type1. Yellow picture box
Box Type 2. Lighter Yellow picture box
Box Type 3 Yellow& Red panel Non picture box
- Black and Green lower body,
Black roof, ... **£130-160**
- Maroon lower body and roof,
Cream (Light Beige)upper body,..... **£100-130**
- Black & Blue-Green lower body,
Black roof, ... NGPP
NB. Similar shade as occasionally found on the 156 Rover and 159 Morris Oxford.
NB Both versions have been observed with or without a front number plate casting.
Type 2 or 3 Box.
- 1959-63 Black lower body, all Green
upper body, with front number
plate casting, ... **£200-250**

165 1969-76 **Ford Capri**
Box Type. Yellow picture box with white background
- Metallic Purple body, Orange interior,
Cast or Speedwheels **£50-60**
- Met. Turquoise body, Yellow interior,
Cast or Speedwheels **£60-70**

166 1958-63 **Sunbeam Rapier**
Box Type. Yellow picture box
- Yellow lower body, Deep Cream
upper body, Beige hubs................... **£100-120**
- Same but with spun hubs **£120-140**
- Blue lower body, Turquoise upper

body, Blue hubs **£100-120**
- Same but with spun hubs **£120-140**
Box Type. Lighter Yellow picture box
- Either model with Type 2 Box. **£140-160**

166 1967-70 **Renault R16**
Box Type. Yellow picture box with white background
- Metallic Blue, Red seats. spun hubs **£60-80**

Dinky 167 A C Aceca. Rare all-cream version is the hard one to find.

167 1958-63 **A.C. Aceca Sports Coupé**
Box Type1. Yellow picture box
Box Type2. Yellow & Red panel Non picture box
Mottled Base .Coloured hubs.
- Grey body, Red roof, Red hubs........... **£90-110**
- Cream body, Dark Brown roof,
Beige hubs.. **£90-110**
Black gloss base. Coloured hubs
- Grey body, Red roof, Red hubs........ **£170-200**
- Cream body, Dark Brown roof,
Beige hubs... **£170-200**
Black Gloss base. Spun hubs.
- Grey body, Red roof, Red hubs........ **£140-170**
- Cream body, Dark Brown roof,
Beige hubs... **£140-170**
Box Type 3. Lighter Yellow picture box.
Clear colour spot.
- Cream body, Reddish-Maroon roof. **£250-300**
- All Cream body. **£600-800**
Black Gloss base. Silver painted hubs.
- Cream body,Reddish-Maroon roof, **£275-325**

168 1959-63 **Singer Gazelle Saloon**
Box Type 1. Yellow picture box
Box Type 2. Lighter Yellow picture box
- Deep Brown lower, Cream upper
body, spun hubs **£100-120**
- Dark Green lower, Grey upper
body, spun hubs **£100-120**
Box Type 2. Lighter Yellow picture box
- As above with Type 2 boxes. **£120-140**
- Black body, spun hubs .... NGPP

168 1968-70 **Ford Escort**
Box Type1. Yellow picture box with white background
- Pale Blue, Red interior. Cast hubs **£50-65**
- White body, red interior. Cast hubs. **£50-65**
Box Type2. Bubble pack box
1970-74
- Met.Red body, White interior cast hubs, **£70-90**
1974-75
- Met. Blue, White or Black interior.
Speedwheel... **£60-80**

169 1958-63 **Studebaker Golden Hawk**
All models white M tyres
Box Type1. Yellow Non picture box
Box Type2. Lighter Yellow picture box
- Tan body, Red rear side panel and hubs,
mottled base. **£100-130**
- Light Green body, Cream rear side
panel and hubs, Mottled base. **£100-130**
Box Type2. Yellow picture box
Box Type3. Yellow & Red panel Non picture box
- Tan body, Red rear side panel and hubs
but spun hubs, Gloss base. **£140-180**
- Light Green body, Cream rear side
panel, spun hubs. Gloss base. **£140-180**

169 1967-69 **Ford Corsair 2000 E**
Box Type Yellow picture box with white background

- Silver body, Black textured roof.
  Red Interior **£70-85**
  (renumbered from 139a)

170   1954-56   **Ford Fordor Sedan**
  Transition period from old base to new
  large writing on base showing No 170..Ridged
  hubs.
- Tan body, Red hubs.......................... **£200-250**
- Red body, Maroon hubs.................... **£200-250**
- Red body, Red hubs **£200-250**
  Box Type 1 Yellow Picture Box Dual no 170/139a.
  Colour stick on spot identifies colour.
  Models as above similar values. with large
  lettering, 2nd casting with name on
  underside of roof.
  Box Type 2 No 170 has black ovals on box sides
  1956-58 'Highline' versions: Type 2 Casting
  as above.
- Red lower body, Cream upper body,
  Red hubs **£350-450**
- Blue lower body, Pink upper body,
  Blue ridged hubs **£350-450**
  1958-59 'Lowline' versions:
- Red lower body, Cream upper body,
  Red ridged hubs................................ **£250-330**
- Blue lower body, Pink upper body,
  Blue ridged hubs **£250-330**
  Box Type 2 showing single colour model
  with spot colour indentificaion.
  Box Type 3 yellow Picture box showing
  two tone highline model.
  Late model produced with 3rd casting
  chequered pattern on underside of roof
  and highlighted rear lights.
- Either lowline versions..................... **£300-375**
  Very late model as above with Black gloss base
  and M tyres.
- Blue lower body, Pink upper body,
  Blue ridged hubs **£400-500**
  Box Type 3 yellow Picture box showing
  two tone highline model.

170m 1954-54 **Ford US Army Staff Car**
  See 'Military Vehicles' section.

170   1964-70   **Lincoln Continental**
  Box type1 Export Yellow window Box.
  Box type 2 Hard Plastic case
- Metallic Bronze body, White roof,
  Blue interior, cast wheels **£60-80**
- Light Blue body, White roof,
  Mid-Blue interior, cast wheels............. **£60-80**

170   1979   **Ford Granada Ghia**
  Not issued, but a Metallic Silver factory
  publicity sample was sold by Vectis Auctions
  in 1999 for £470.

171   1954-56   **Hudson Commodore Sedan**
  (renumbered from 139b)
  Transition period from old base to new
  large writing on base showing No 170.Ridged
  hubs.
  Box Type 1 Yellow Picture Box Dual no 171/139b
  Colour stick on spot identifies colour.
  Box Type 2 showing single colour model no
  170 with spot colour indentificaion.
- Deep Blue body, Tan roof and hubs **£175-250**
- Cream body, Maroon roof and hubs **£175-250**
- Light Blue body,
  Pale Tan upper body, Fawn hubs **£500-700**
- Cream body, Maroon roof and Red
  hubs **£175-250**
  Box Type 3 yellow Picture box showing
  two tone highline model.
  1956-58 'Highline' versions:
  Roof colour continues over bonnet and boot.
- Turquoise lower body,
  Red upper body, Red hubs **£275-350**
- Pale Blue lower body,
  Red upper body, Red hubs **£275-350**
- Blue lower body,
  Maroon upper body and hubs **£500-700**
- Light Grey lower body with
  Mid-Blue upper body, Blue hubs..... **£275-350**
  1958-59 'Lowline' versions:

Models top body colour flows in line midway
along side of body.
- Turquoise lower body,
  Red upper body and hubs. **£275-350**
- Pale Blue lower body,
  Red upper body, Red hubs **£275-350**
- Light Grey lower body with
  Mid-Blue upper body, Blue hubs..... **£275-350**
- Light Grey lower body with
  Mid-Blue upper body, Cream hubs . **£500-600**
  Note; Late models with M tyres and
  highlighted rear tail lights.

171   1965-68   **Austin 1800**
  Box type 1 Picture Box with background..
  Box type 2 Export Yellow window box.
- Met. Blue body, Red int., spun hubs.... **£30-50**
- Light Blue body, Red int., spun hubs.**£150-200**

172   1954-56   **Studebaker Land Cruiser**
  Box Type 1. Yellow picture box
- Light Green body, Mid-Green hubs.**£100-120**
- Light Green body, Mid-Blue hubs...**£300-400**
- Blue body, Fawn hubs....................**£100-120**
- Blue body, Beige hubs.....................**£170-220**
- Light Beige body, Cream hubs **£400-500**
  1956-58 'Highline' versions:
- Cream lower body, Maroon upper
  body, Beige hubs **£250-300**
- Beige lower body, Tan upper body,
  Beige hubs **£275-350**
  1958-59 'Lowline' versions:
- Cream lower body and Beige body,
  Maroon upper body **£140-180**
- Beige lower body and hubs,
  Light Tan upper body **£120-140**

172   1965-69   **Fiat 2300 Station Wagon**
  Box type 1 Picture Box with background..
  Box type 2 Export Yellow window Box.
- Pale Grey body, Dark Blue roof,
  Red interior, hubs **£75-100**

173   1958-62   **Nash Rambler Station Wagon**
  Box Type1. Yellow Non picture box
  Box Type2. Yellow picture box
  Box Type3. Yellow and Red panel non-picture box
  Following models with number on baseplate
  and mottled bases.
- Turquoise body with Red flash, Grey hubs .....
  ....**£90-120**
- Pink body, Blue flash, Beige hubs...... **£90-120**
- Flesh body, Blue flash, Beige hubs...**£150-180**
  Following models with number on baseplate
  and black gloss base. With coloured hubs.
- Turquoise body with Red flash, Grey hubs ......
  ....**£100-120**
- Pink body with Blue flash, Beige hubs**£100-120**
- Flesh body with Blue flash, Beige hubs**£150-180**
  Following models with no number on
  baseplate. Black gloss base & Spun hubs.
  Usually Type 3 Box.
- Turquoise body with Red flash.........**£120-150**
- Pink body with Blue flash..................**£120-150**
- Flesh body with Blue flash **£200-230**

173   1969-72   **Pontiac Parisienne**
  Box Type Yellow picture box with white
  background
- Metallic Maroon body, Lemon interior,
  retractable aerials, cast hubs **£50-75**
- Metallic Bronze Body Lemon interior,
  retractable aerials, cast hubs. Possibly
  pre production................................**£150-200**

174   1958-63   **Hudson Hornet**
  All models with windows, M tyres and 174 on
  base.
  Box Type 1. Yellow picture box
  Box Type 2. Yellow & Red panel Non picture
  box First models with mottled bases &
  coloured hubs.
- Red lower body, Cream roof & side flash,
  Beige hubs, White tyres....................**£100-130**
- Yellow lower body, Dark Grey roof
  and flash, Grey hubs, White tyres.....**£100-130**
  Later issues with spun hubs & black gloss base.
- Red lower body, Cream roof & side flash,

White tyres **£130-160**
- Yellow lower body, Dark Grey roof
  and flash, White tyres........................**£130-160**
- Cerise lower body, Cream roof
  and side flash, White tyres...............**£200-250**
  All models have 174 on base.

174   1969-72   **Ford Mercury Cougar**
  Box Type Yellow picture box with white
  background
- Metallic Blue body and cast hubs,
  Yellow Interior. **£35-50**
- Dark Metallic Blue body and cast hubs,
  Yellow Interior..................................... **£50-80**

175   1958-61   **Hillman Minx**
  All models with windows, M tyres and 175 on
  base. Box Type 1. Yellow picture box
- Grey lower body, Mid-Blue upper
  body and hubs.................................**£100-130**
- Flesh body, Green roof and boot,
  Beige hubs **£100-130**
  Later issues with spun hubs and black gloss base.
- Grey lower body, Mid-Blue upper
  body. **£250-300**
- Flesh body, Green roof & boot,
  Beige hubs...**£250-300**

175   1969-73   **Cadillac Eldorado**
  Box type Hard Plastic case
- Metallic Purple body, Black roof,
  Yellow interior, cast hubs. **£30-50**
- Metallic Blue body, Black roof,
  Yellow interior, cast hubs. **£60-90**

176   1958-63   **Austin A105 Saloon**
  First dinky model to be issued with windows.
  All models with windows, White M tyres, 176
  on base.
  Box Type 1. Yellow picture box shows models
  same colour roof as model.
  Box Type 2. Yellow picture box shows models
  colour roof different to body.
  Box Type 3. .Lighter Yellow picture box
  then as Type 2.
  Box Type 4. Yellow & Red panel Non picture
  box Body sides have a contrasting panel line.
  1958-59
- Cream body, Violet Blue panel line,
  Cream hubs.......................................**£110-140**
- Pale Grey body, Red line, Red hubs .**£110-140**
  1959-63
  The following later models had Black gloss bases.
- Cream body Mid-Blue roof and panel line,
  Cream hubs.......................................**£200-250**
- Pale Grey body, Red roof and panel
  line, Light Grey hubs **£200-250**
- Cream body Mid-Blue roof and panel line,
  Spun hubs **£200-250**
- Pale Grey body, Red roof & panel
  line, Spun hubs **£200-250**
- Pale Grey body, Red line, Spun hubs**£225-275**

176   1969-74   **N.S.U. Ro80**
  Box type Picture Box with background..
- Metallic Red body, spun hubs,
  luminous seats, working lights **£40-60**

177   1961-66   **Opel Kapitan**
  Box Type. Light Yellow picture box
  All models windows , M tyres, spun hubs.
- Light Greyish-Blue body, Red interior, **£60-100**
- Light Blue body, Red interior,............. **£60-100**
  1963   South African issues:
    (English and Afrikaans on box).
- Bright Blue body with Red interior **£1,000-1,500**
- Caramel body, Red interior **£1,000-1,500**
- Pale Yellow body, Red interior ...**£1,000-1,500**

178   1959-63   **Plymouth Plaza**
  Box Type 1. Yellow Non picture box
  Box Type 2. Yellow picture box
  Box Type 3. Lighter Yellow picture box
  Box Type 4. Yellow & Red panel Non picture box
  All models with windows, M tyres, no
  interior, spun hubs, No 178 on base.
- Light Blue body, Dark Blue roof and
  side flash, mottled base **£120-160**
- Light Pink body, Light Green

roof and side flash, mottled base.... **£120-160**
- Salmon Pink body, Light Green
roof and side flash, mottled base.... **£200-250**
Late Issues
- Beige body, Light Green
roof and side flash. Matt Black base **£175-225**
- Light Blue body, White roof and flash,
Gloss Black base with no number
Usually Type 3 Box........................... **£250-325**
- Light Blue body, White roof and flash,
Matt Black base with no number
Usually Type 3 Box........................... **£300-400**

178 1975-79 **Mini Clubman**
Box Type 1 Red & Yellow window Box.
Box Type 2 Bubble pack.
- Bronze body, opening doors, jewelled
headlights on some, Speedwheels.......**£40-50**
- Red body, Speedwheels.................... **£100-125**

179 1958-63 **Studebaker President**
Box Type 1. Yellow picture box
Box Type 2. Lighter Yellow picture box
All models with window, White M tyres,
179 on base.
- Light Blue body, Dark Blue flash,
Fawn hubs, mottled base....................**£90-140**
- Yellow body, Blue flash and hubs,
mottled base.......................................**£90-140**
- Late issues of both colours with spun hubs,
Black gloss base.
Usually Type 2 Box........................... **£120-160**

179 1971-75 **Opel Commodore**
Box Type Yellow picture box with white
background
- Metallic Blue body, Black roof,
Speedwheels.....................................**£55-75**

180 1958-63 **Packard Clipper**
Box Type . Yellow picture box
All models with windows, White M tyres,
180 on base
- Cerise upper body, Cream lower body
and hubs, mottled base **£100-140**
- Orange lower body, Light Grey upper
body and hubs, mottled base.......... **£110-150**
- Late issues with spun hubs and Gloss black
bases.
- Cerise upper body, Cream lower ... **£130-160**
- Orange lower body, Light Grey upper body
. ... **£140-170**

180 1979-80 **Rover 3500**
Box Type Red & Yellow window Box.
- White body, plastic chassis and wheels.
Made in Hong Kong, scale 1:35............**£25-35**

181 1956-70 **Volkswagen Saloon**
Box Type 1. Yellow picture box
Box Type 2. Lighter Yellow picture box
Box Type 3. Yellow & Red panel Non picture
box. Early models with 181 on mottled base,
smooth tyres, usually Type 1 box, coloured
hubs.
Cast coloured hubs issues:
- Light Grey body, Mid-Blue hubs........**£80-110**
- Lime Green body, Mid-Green hubs **£120-140**
- Greyish Blue body, Mid-Blue hubs. **£120-140**
- RAF Blue body (darker shade to above)
Mid-Blue hubs **£120-140**
- Very Dark Blue body, Mid-Blue
hubs **£200-250**
- Dark Blue body, Mid-Blue hubs **£180-230**
- Light Grey body, Green hubs
....**£400+**
- Light Blue body, Blue hubs
....**£400+**
Following models usually no number on
base, M tyres, spun hubs. Various bases.
- Light Grey body, Black gloss base... **£110-140**
- Greyish Blue body , Black gloss base.**£90-130**
- RAF Blue body , Black gloss base.....**£90-130**
- Light Blue body, unpainted base **£80-120**
- Light Blue body, Matt Black base.......**£80-120**
Plastic hubs issue:
- Pale Blue body, Mid-Blue plastic
hubs, Matt Black base **£400-500**

South African issues:
(English and Afrikaans text on box, spun
hubs).
- Pale Green body.......................... **£1200-1500**
- Pale Lemon body **£1200-1500**
- Pale Blue body............................. **£1200-1500**
- Dark Green body......................... **£1200-1500**
- Bright Green body....................... **£1200-1500**
- Mid Grey body............................ **£1200-1500**
- Metallic Blue body **£1200-1500**

Dinky 182 Porsche 356A showing the wheel variation.
The red paint on this and other models is notorious for
chipping and it can be difficult to find perfect models
without small paint chips.

182 1958-66 **Porsche 356a Coupé**
Box Type 1. Yellow picture box
Box Type 2. Lighter Yellow picture box
Box Type 3. Yellow & Red panel Non picture
box
All models with windows, M tyres, 182
on early mottled base
- Cream body, Blue hubs **£120-140**
- Pale Blue body, Cream hubs **£120-140**
- Light Grey-Blue body,
Blue hubs...................................... **£150-200**
- Cream, body, Beige hubs.....................**£500+**
- Cream, body, Red hubs.......................**£600+**
- Pale Blue body, Red hubs...................**£600+**
- Pale Blue body, Blue hubs ....**£500+**
- Red body, Blue hubs...........................**£600+**
Following models came with later
Black gloss base. Type 2 Box.
- Cream body, Blue hubs **£160-200**
- Cream body, spun hubs **£120-140**
- Pale Blue body, spun hubs **£250-350**
- Deep Pink body, spun hubs. **£250-300**
- Cerise body, spun hubs **£275-350**
- Red body, Silver painted hubs &
Gloss black base.............................. **£325-400**
Last issue with Matt black base.
- Red body, spun hubs,
Matt black base. **£275-350**

183 1958-60 **Fiat 600**
Box Type. Yellow picture box
- Red body, smooth or treaded solid
Grey plastic wheels **£80-100**
- Pale Green body, smooth or treaded
solid Grey plastic wheels **£80-100**

183 1966-74 **Morris Mini Minor** (Automatic)
Box Type 1 Yellow picture box with white
background
Box Type 2 Yellow picture box with
background
Box Type 3 Bubble pack
- Red body, Gloss Black roof,
White interior, spun hubs....................**£70-90**
- Metallic Red body, matt Black
roof, White interior, spun hubs **£70-90**
- Metallic Bright Blue body,
White interior, spun hubs...................**£80-110**
- Box should contain 'Meccano Automatic
Transmission' leaflet
- Metallic Red body, Black roof,
White interior, Speedwheels **£70-90**
- NB Late issues with 'Austin Cooper S'
cast on boot (250 casting) exist............ NGPP
Various registration numbers will also
be found, e.g., 'UVR 576D',
'MTB 21G', 'HTB 21H'.

Dinky 184 Volvo. Missing darker red version. Green and
blue versions are the South Afican colours. Note the SA
box shows a red roof not cream.

184 1961-65 **Volvo 122 S**
Box Type 1. Yellow picture box
All models windows, M tyres, spun hubs,
White interior.
- Red body. Black gloss base. **£80-120**
- Darker Red body. Black gloss base ..**£120-150**
- Deep Red body. Black gloss base **£150-200**
- Off-White body, Matt Black Base.
White spot on box............................ **£300-400**
1962 South African issues:
(English and Afrikaans on box).
- Bright Blue body, White interior **£1,000-1,500**
- Sage Green, White interior **£1,000-1,500**
- Lilac body, White interior **£1,000-1,500**

185 1961-63 **Alfa Romeo 1900 Sprint**
Box Type. Yellow picture box
All models windows ,M tyres, spun hubs
- Yellow body, Red interior,................. **£80-120**
- Red body, Off-White interior **£80-120**

186 1961-67 **Mercedes-Benz 220 SE**
Box Type . Light Yellow picture box
All models windows, M tyres, spun hubs
- RAF Blue body, Off White interior
Black Gloss Base. **£50-80**
- Lt. Blue body, Off White interior
Black Gloss Base **£80-120**
- Light Blue body, Yellow interior.
Matt Black base.................................**£150-180**
- Light Blue body, Red interior.
Matt Black base.................................**£170-200**
1963 South African issue:
(English and Afrikaans text on box).
- Sky Blue body, Off White Int.......**£1,000-1,500**
- Smoke Grey body, Off White Int........**£1,000-1,500**

Dinky 187 Volkswagen Kharmann Ghia Shows the very
rare picture box. One of the rarest post war boxes.
Also rare blue-green shade model.

187 1959-64 **VW Karmann Ghia Coupé**
All models windows, M tyres, spun hubs
Box Type 1. Light Yellow picture box
(The above box is one of the rarest post war
Dinky boxes.)

- Green body, Cream roof .... **£600+**
- Dull Darker Green body, Cream roof,
.... **£700+**
Box Type 2. Yellow & Red panel Non picture box
- Red body, Black roof, ...**£100-140**
- Green body, Cream roof, ...**£100-140**
- Dark Green body, Cream roof, ...**£250-300**

187 1968-77 **De Tomaso Mangusta 5000**
Box type 1 Hard Plastic case
Box Type 2 Bubble pack
- Fluorescent Pink body, White panels
front/rear, Black interior, cast wheels,
racing number '7' **£20-30**

188 1968-74 **Jensen FF**
Box type 1 Hard Plastic case
Box Type 2 Bubble pack
• Yellow body, Black interior, cast wheels
or Speedwheels. **£30-50**

189 1959-64 **Triumph Herald Saloon**
Box Type 1 Yellow picture box
Box Type 2. Light Yellow picture box
Box Type 3. Yellow & Red panel Non picture box
All models windows, M tyres, spun hubs
• Pale or Light Blue roof and sides
with White centre **£70-100**
• Green roof / sides with White centre . **£70-100**
Special issues:
All box types are available. Coloured spot to
denote colour.
• Red body **£900-1,500**
• Alpine Mauve body **£900-1,500**
• Black body **£900-1,500**
• Monaco Blue body **£900-1,500**
• Lichfield (dark)Green body **£900-1,500**
• White body, ... **£900-1,500**
• Red roof and sides, white centre. .. **£700-1,200**
• Monaco Blue roof and sides, white centre
.... **£700-1,200**
• Dark Greyish-Green roof and sides, white
centre **£700-1,200**
• Pinkish-Brown roof and sides, white centre
.... **£700-1,200**
• Dark Grey roof and sides, white centre
.... **£700-1,200**
• Pale Lilac roof and sides, white centre
.... **£700-1,200**
• Powder Blue roof and sides, white centre
.... **£700-1,200**

189 1969-76 **Lamborghini Marzal**
Box Type 1 Hard Plastic case
Box Type 2 Red and Yellow window Box.
Box Type 3 Bubble pack
• White/Orange body, cast detailed hubs **£70-100**
• Yellow/White body, cast detailed hubs ...**£25-35**
• Green/White body, cast detailed hubs....**£30-50**
• 1976-78
Met Blue/White body, Speedwheels **£30-50**
• Dark Met Green/White body, Speedwheels **£30-50**

190 1970-74 **Monteverdi 375 L**
Box Type Hard Plastic case
• Metallic Maroon body, White interior,
Cast or Speedwheels. **£50-70**

191 1959-64 **Dodge Royal Sedan**
Box Type 1. Yellow Non picture box
Box Type 2. Yellow picture box
Box Type 3. Lighter Yellow picture box
Box Type 4. Yellow & Red panel Non picture box
All models windows, M tyres, spun hubs
Mottled 191 base.
• Pale Green body with Black flash..... **£120-160**
• Cream body with Tan rear flash **£120-160**
Black Gloss 191 base. Most likely Type 3 or 4 Box.
• Pale Green body with Black flash..... **£120-160**
• Cream body with Tan rear flash **£120-160**
• Cream body, Blue rear flash, ... **£180-250**
Late Issue Matt black base with no number 191.
Type 3 or 4 Box.
• Cream body, Blue rear flash **£180-250**
NB Casting used for 258 'USA Police Car'.

192 1959-64 **De Soto Fireflite**
Box Type 1. Yellow Non picture box
Box Type 2. Yellow picture box
Box Type 3. Lighter Yellow picture box
Box Type 4. Yellow & Red panel Non picture box
All models windows, M tyres, spun hubs
mottled 192 base.
• Grey body, Red roof and side flash .. **£120-160**
• Turquoise body, Lt. Tan roof / flash. **£120-160**
Same models as above with black gloss base
without number.
• Grey body, Red roof and side flash .. **£120-160**
• Turquoise body, Lt. Tan roof / flash. **£120-160**

192 1970-80 **Range Rover**
Box Type1 Yellow picture box with white
background

Box Type 2 Red and Yellow window box.
Cast detailed hubs or Speedwheels.
• Met. Bronze body, Pale Blue,
white or Red interior **£25-40**
• Yellow body, Red interior.................... **£40-60**
• Black body, Red interior **£40-60**

193 1961-69 **Rambler Station Wagon**
Box Type 1. Yellow picture box showing yellow
model.
Box Type 2. Yellow picture box showing Blue
model
Box Type 3 Gold 'US export window-box
All models with Black gloss 193 base,
White M tyres, spun hubs.
• Pale Yellow body, White roof,
Red interior, Black plastic roof-rack,
Type 1 Box.. **£70-80**
• Same model but with White interior. **£150-175**
Type 2 or 3 Box may attract a premium.
1962 South African issues:
(English / Afrikaans on box, spun hubs).
• Sage Green body, Red interior ...**£1,000-1,500**
• All-Lilac body, Red interior **£700-1,200**
• Lilac body, Cream roof, Red interior**£700-1,200**
• Pale Smokey Blue body, Cream roof,
Red interior **£1,000-1,500**
• Dark Blue body, White roof,
Red interior **£1,000-1,500**

194 1961-67 **Bentley 'S' Coupé**
Box Type. Light Yellow picture box
All models with window, M tyres, spun hubs
and 194 on base
• Grey body, Maroon interior, Tan hood,
Grey male driver, Black gloss base..... **£70-110**
• Grey body, Red interior, Tan hood,
Grey male driver, Black gloss base ... **£100-150**
• Metallic Bronze body, Cream interior,
Dark Blue hood, Grey male driver &
Matt Black Base **£170-220**
NB Late issues of 194 have plated plastic parts.
1962 South African issues:
(English / Afrikaans on box, spun hubs).
• Lime Green body, Red interior,
Black hood **£1,000-1,200**
• Cream body, Red interior,
Dark Cream hood **£1,000-1,200**

195 1961-71 **Jaguar 3.4 Mk.II**
Box Type . Light Yellow picture box
All models with window, M tyres, 195 Black
Gloss base.
• Cream body, Red interior **£80-120**
• Grey body, Red interior...................... **£100-130**
• Maroon body, White interior............. **£110-140**
1962 South African issues:
(English and Afrikaans on box,
Spun hubs, Black Gloss base).
• Off-White body, Red interior **£1,000-1,500**
• Red body, Off-White interior **£1,000-1,500**
• Sky Blue body,Off-White int **£1,000-1,500**
• Smokey Blue body, Off- White
interior **£1,000-1,500**

196 1963-70 **Holden Special Sedan**
Box Type 1. Yellow picture box
Box Type 2 Export Red & Yellow window Box.
All models with window, M tyres, spun hubs.
(First Dinky to have jewelled headlights).
• Metallic Copper body, White roof,
Red Interior, Black Gloss Base, ... **£90-120**
• Turquoise body, White roof,
Pale Blue interior **£80-130**
• Turquoise body, White roof,
Red interior **£80-130**

197 1961-71 **Morris Mini Traveller**
Box Type . Yellow picture box
All models with window, M tyres, spun hubs.
• Cream body, Red interior, Black Gloss base.   .
.... **£90-120**
Following models with Black Matt base.
• Cream body, Red interior,................. **£150-200**
• Cream body, Lemon interior............ **£400-600**
• Cream body, Pale Blue interior **£500-700**
• Dark Green body, Pale Blue interior **£400-600**

• Dark Green body, Yellow interior **£300-400**
• Dark Green body, Red interior...... **£800-1,200**
• Fluorescent Green body, Red interior, front
number plate on some, no 'colour change'
label on box...................................... **£220-280**

198 1962-69 **Rolls-Royce Phantom V**
Box Type. Red/Yellow picture box
All models with window, White M tyres,
spun hubs.
Blue Chauffer driver, Black Gloss base.
(First Dinky Toys model with metallic
paint and opening windows).
• Metallic Light Green upper body,
Cream lower body, Red interior, ... **£75-100**
• Metallic Light Green upper body,
Cream lower body, Light Blue int **£85-110**
• White Body, Light Grey sides, red interior
.... **£75-100**
1963 South African issues:
(English / Afrikaans on box, spun hubs).
Note box shows different shade model to the
UK box.
• Sage Green body, Red Interior....**£1,200-1,800**
• Dark Grey body, Red Interior......**£1,200-1,800**
• Dark Grey body, Cream sides.
Red interior **£1,000-1,500**
• Grey body, Cream sides.
(Darker than the UK version) Red interior
....**£1,000-1,500**

199 1961-71 **Austin 7 Countryman**
Box Type. Yellow picture box
All models with window, M Tyres & Spun hubs
• Light Blue body, Red interior, Black Gloss
Base. **£80-110**
• Grey Blue body, Red interior, Black Gloss Base.
.... **£80-110**
• Blue body, Yellow interior, Black Gloss base...
.... **£200-250**
• Blue body, Pale Blue interior, Gloss Black
base .... **£600+**
Following have later Matt Black base.
• Blue body, Yellow interior,.............. **£150-200**
• Fluorescent Orange/Pink body, Red interior,
Matt Black base. Box must bear a small oblong
label stating: 'COLOUR OF MODEL MAY
DIFFER FROM ILLUSTRATION' **£220-280**

200 1954-57 **Midget Racer**
Sold from a Trade Box of six.
(renumbered from 35b)
• Silver body, Red grille, Brown driver,
solid Black rubber wheels **£65-75**

200 1971-78 **Matra 630 Le Mans**
Box Type Yellow picture box with white
background
• Blue body, RN '36', Speedwheels......... **£25-30**

201 1979-80 **Plymouth Stock Car**
Box Type Coloured picture box with background
• Blue body, racing number '34',
wide plastic wheels............................. **£35-45**

202 1971-75 **Fiat Abarth 2000**
Box Type 1 Yellow picture box with white
background
Box Type 2 Bubble pack
• Fluorescent Red/White, Speedwheels. **£20-30**

202/2 1979-80 **Customised Land Rover**
Box Type window Box.
• Yellow body, White crash guard. White
or Black rails/aerials (344 casting)....... **£25-35**

203 1979-80 **Customised Range Rover**
Box Type window Box.
• Black body, Yellow/Red design,
White plastic chassis/crash guard **£25-30**

204 1971-74 **Ferrari 312 P**
Box Type 1 Yellow picture box with white
background
Box Type 2 Bubble pack
• Metallic Red body and doors,
Speedwheels, RN '60' **£30-35**
• Same, but with White doors **£30-35**

205 1962-64 **Talbot Lago Racing Car**
Box Type Blister pack.
Model never had 205 on base but only 230 on

a black gloss base.
(renumbered from 230)
- Blue, body Red plastic hubs. RN '4', . **£400-500**
- Blue, body Yellow plastic hubs RN '4', **£400-500**

205 1968-73 **Lotus Cortina Rally**
Box Type Yellow picture box with white
background
- White body, Blue interior, Red bonnet
and side stripe, 'Monte Carlo' logo,
RN '7', 2 aerials, cast hubs **£70-80**

206 1962-64 **Maserati Racing Car**
Box Type Blister pack.
Model never had 206 on base but only 231 on
a black gloss base.
(renumbered from 231)
- Red/White body, Yellow plastic hubs **£400-500**

206 1978-80 **Customised Corvette**
Box Type Red and Blue window box.
- Red/Yellow or White/Black, plastic
chassis, speedwheels........................... **£20-30**

207 1962-64 **Alfa-Romeo Racing Car**
Box Type Blister pack.
Model never had 207 on base but only 232 on
a black gloss base.
(renumbered from 232)
- Red body, Red plastic hubs **£400-500**

207 1977-80 **Triumph TR7 Rally**
Box Type Red & Yellow window Box.
- White/Red/Blue, RN '8',
plastic chassis and wheels, 'Leyland' .. **£25-35**

208 1962-64 **Cooper-Bristol Racing Car**
Box Type Blister pack.
Model never had 208 on base but only 233 on
a black gloss base.
(renumbered from 233)
- Dark Green, White flash, RN '6',
Red plastic hubs,................................ **£350-425**

208 1971-75 **VW Porsche 914**
Box Type 1 Hard Plastic case
- Yellow body, Black interior,
cast detailed hubs................................ **£25-30**
Box Type 2 Yellow Promotional Box
- Yellow body, Black interior,
cast detailed hubs................................ **£50-70**
Box Type 1 Red and Yellow window box.
- 1976-80 Metallic Blue/Black body,
Speedwheels **£25-30**

209 1962-64 **Ferrari Racing Car**
Box Type Blister pack.
Model never had 209 on base but only 234 on
a black gloss base.
(renumbered from 234)
- Blue, Yellow triangle, RN '5',
Yellow plastic hubs, ... **£500-550**

210 1962-65 **Vanwall Racing Car**
Box Type Blister pack.
Model never had 210 on base but only 239 on
a black gloss base.
(renumbered from 239)
- Green, Yellow plastic hubs,.............. **£400-500**

210 1971-73 **Alfa-Romeo 33 Tipo**
Box Type Hard Plastic case
- Fluorescent Red body, Black doors, White
interior,
RN '36', cast wheels, leaflet in box **£30-40**
- Metallic Blue body, Black bonnet, Red interior,
RN '36', cast wheels, leaflet in box **£60-70**

211 1975 **Triumph TR7 Sports Car**
Box Type Red and Yellow window box.
- Yellow, Black bumpers and interior..... **£60-70**
- Red body, Black bumpers and interior **£25-30**
- Red body, Grey bumpers and interior . **£25-30**
- White body, Black base and interior.
Red/Blue decals RN 8. Speedwheels ... **£40-50**
- White body, Black base and interior.
Saudi trial decals. Speedwheels. **£80-100**

212 1965-70 **Ford Cortina Rally**
Box Type Yellow picture box with background
- White body, Black bonnet, 'EAST
AFRICAN SAFARI' and 'CASTROL'
logos, Black or Red RN '8', spotlight,
Red interior, spun hubs...................... **£80-100**

213 1970-73 **Ford Capri Rally**
Box Type 1 Hard Plastic case
Box Type 2 Bubble pack
- Metallic Blue body, Black bonnet, Yellow
interior, RN '20', cast or Speedwheels. . **£55-70**
- 1973-75 Bronze body, Black bonnet,
RN 20, cast or Speedwheels, ... **£80-100**

214 1966-69 **Hillman Imp Rally**
Box Type Yellow picture box with
background
- Dark Blue body, Red interior,
'MONTE CARLO RALLY' logo, RN '35',
spun hubs, picture box.......................... **£70-80**

215 1965-66 **Ford GT Racing Car**
Box Type 1 Hard Plastic case
Box Type 2 Yellow Export window Box
- White body, Red interior,
RN '7', spun hubs **£55-65**
- 1966-70
Same, but with Silver spoked wheels... **£40-50**
- 1970-74 Metallic Green body, Gold
engine, Orange/Black stripe, Yellow
interior, RN '7', Silver spoked wheels ... **£50-60**
- Metallic Green body, Silver engine,
Red interior Silver Spoked wheels **£70-90**

216 1967-69 **Dino Ferrari**
Box Type 1 Hard Plastic case
Box Type 2 Bubble pack
- Red body, Light Blue interior,
Gold spoked wheels. RN 20 .... **£30-40**
- 1969-75 Metallic Blue/Black, Silver
spoked wheels. RN '20'....................... **£25-30**

217 1968-70 **Alfa Romeo Scarabeo OSI**
Box Type Yellow picture box with white
background
- Fluorescent Pink body, Yellow interior
cast spoked wheels **£30-40**

218 1969-73 **Lotus Europa**
Box Type Yellow picture box with white
background
- Yellow body, Blue panels/roof, chequered
flags, Gold engine Speedwheels.......... **£35-45**
- 1973-75 Yellow/Black or Metallic Blue
body, Silver engine, Speedwheels........ **£30-35**

219 1977-79 **Leyland Jaguar XJ-5.3**
Box Type Blister pack with back card.
- White body, 'Leyland' decal.
(Made in Hong Kong)........................... **£35-45**

219 1978-79 **'Big Cat' Jaguar**
- White/Red, Black 'Big Cat' decal,
sold unboxed **£35-45**
- Boxed version with 'Big Cat' logo **£50-75**

220 1954-56 **Small Open Racing Car**
Sold from a trade box of six only.
(renumbered from 23a)
- Silver with Red hubs, RN '4' **£40-50**

220 1970-73 **Ferrari P5**
Box Type 1 Yellow picture box with white
background
Box Type 2 Hard Plastic case
- Metallic Red body,
Yellow interior, cast hubs **£25-30**
- 1973-75 Metallic Red body,
Yellow interior, Speedwheels................ **£25-30**

221 1954-56 **'Speed Of The Wind'
Racing Car**
Sold from a trade box of six only.
(renumbered from 23e)
Individually valued
- Silver body with plain baseplate **£40-45**

221 1969-76 **Corvette Stingray**
Box Type 1 Hard Plastic case
Box Type 2 Red and Yellow window box.
- Metallic Gold body, Black interior
Silver or Gold spoked wheels **£25-35**
- 1976-78 Red or White body,
Black bonnet, Speedwheels.................. **£25-35**

222 1954-56 **Streamlined Racing Car**
Sold from a trade box of six only.
(renumbered from 22s)
- Silver body; Red, Blue or Green trim
with Fawn hubs..................................... **£60-70**

222 1978-80 **Hesketh 308 E**
Box Type Red & Yellow window Box
- Dark Blue or Bronze, RN '2',
cast-detailed or Speedwheels.............. **£20-30**
- Swiss promotional issue: Same but
in 'OLYMPUS CAMERAS' box **£50-75**

223 1970-75 **McLaren M8A Can-Am**
Box Type1 Yellow picture box with white
background
Box Type 2 Red & Yellow window Box.
- White body, Metallic Blue engine
cover, cast detailed wheels **£25-35**
- 1976-78 Metallic Green body,
Black engine cover, White interior,
Speedwheels.. **£25-35**

224 1970-74 **Mercedes-Benz C111**
Box Type Hard Plastic case
- White body, Blue interior, cast hubs.... **£25-35**
- Metallic Dark Red body,
White interior, cast hubs **£25-35**

225 1971-76 **Lotus F1 Racing Car**
Box Type1 Yellow picture box with Inner stand.
Box Type 2 Hard Plastic case
Box Type 3 Red & Yellow window Box.
Box Type 4 Bubble pack
- Metallic Red body with number '7',
inner pictorial box and stand **£25-35**
- 1976-77 Lime-Green or Metallic
Blue body with RN '7'........................... **£25-35**

226 1972-75 **Ferrari 312 B2**
Box Type 1 Red & Yellow window Box.
Box Type 2 Bubble pack
- Red body with racing number '5'........ **£25-35**
- 1976-80 Bronze or Gold body, Black,
White or Yellow rear wing, RN '5' **£25-35**

227 1975-77 **Beach Buggy**
Box Type 1 Bubble pack
- Yellow/Grey or Yellow/White body...... **£25-35**
- Green/Grey or Pink/Black body.......... **£25-35**

228 1970-72 **Super Sprinter**
Box Type Yellow picture box with white
background
- Blue/Silver or Blue/Orange body,
Speedwheels **£25-35**
For Racing Cars models 230/231/232/233/234
the following box types apply.
Box Type 1 Early ref no e.g. 23k
Box Type 2 Dual Picture box e.g. 230/23k.
Box Type 3. Yellow picture box
Box Type 4. Lighter Yellow picture box
Box Type 5. Yellow & Red panel Non picture box

230 1954-60 **Talbot Lago Racing Car**
(renumbered from 23k) (renumbered to 205)
- Blue body, Yellow RN '4', Blue cast hubs,
mottled base, '23k' or '230' base.......**£140-160**
- As above in Box Type 1. .... **£170-200**
- 1960-62 Blue body, Yellow RN 4,
Blue hubs, Black gloss '230' base **£180-250**
- 1960-62 Blue body, Yellow RN '4',
Spun hubs, Black gloss '230' base ...**£200-300**
- Blue body, Yellow RN '4', Yellow plastic
hubs,Black gloss '230' base **£280-350**
- Blue body, Yellow RN '4', Red plastic
hubs,Black gloss '230' base **£280-350**
Note a model sold with spun hubs in a Vectis
auction July 2004 for £580 + commission.

231 1954-60 **Maserati Racing Car**
(renumbered from 23n) (renumbered to 206)
- Red body, White flash, RN '9', Red cast hubs,
mottled base, '23n' or '231' on base.**£140-160**
- As above in Box Type 1 .... **£170-200**
- 1960-62 Red body, RN '9', Red hubs,
Black gloss '231' base **£180-250**
- 1960-62 Red body, white flash, RN '9',
Spun hubs, Black gloss '231' base ...**£160-220**
- Red body, white flash, RN '9', Red plastic
hubs, Black gloss '231' base.
.... **£450-550**
- Red body, white flash, RN '9', Yellow plastic
hubs, Black gloss '231' base **£200-300**
Note a model sold with spun hubs in a Vectis
auction July 2004 for £440 + commission.

232 1954-60 **Alfa-Romeo Racing Car**
(renumbered from 23f) (renumbered to 207)
Note; Only racing car of this series that was
first introduced from through a trade box of
six.
- Red body, RN '8', Red cast hubs,
mottled base, '23f' or '232' on base .. **£150-180**
- As above in Box Type 1 .... **£180-230**
- 1960-62   Red body, RN '8', Red hubs,
Black gloss '232' base **£180-250**
- Red body, RN '8', spun hubs,
Black gloss '232' base **£200-300**
- Red body, RN '8', Red plastic
hubs, Black gloss '232' base. **£250-350**
Note a model sold with spun hubs in a Vectis
auction July 2004 for £700 + commission.

233 1954-60 **Cooper-Bristol Racing Car**
(renumbered from 23g) (renumbered to 208)
- Green body, White flash, RN '6' Green cast
hubs, mottled base, '23g' or '233' ... **£100-130**
- As above in Box Type 1. .... **£120-150**
- 1960-62   Green body, White RN '6',
Green hubs, Black gloss '233' base ...**£180-250**
- 1960-62   Green body, White flash, RN '6',
Spun hubs, Black gloss '233' base **£180-230**
- Green body, RN '8', Red plastic hubs,
Black gloss '233' base **£200-300**
- Green body, RN '8', Primrose Yellow plastic
hubs, Black gloss '233' base,
.... **£500-600**
Note a model sold with spun hubs in a Vectis
auction July 2004 for £380 + commission.

*Dinky Toys Racing Cars: 233 Cooper-Bristol with
yellow wheels, 234 Ferrari with blue ridge hubs and 206
Maserati with red plastic hubs.*

234 1954-60 **Ferrari Racing Car**
(renumbered from 23h) (renumbered to 209)
- Blue body, Yellow nose-cone & cast hubs
Yellow RN '5', mottled base
23h or 234 .... **£150-180**
- As above in Box Type 1 .... **£180-230**
- Blue body, Yellow nose-cone and cast hubs
Yellow RN '5', Black gloss '234' base **£210-260**
- 1960-62   Blue body, Yellow nose-cone,
RN '5', spun hubs, Black gloss base ..**£275-375**
- 1962-62   Blue body, Yellow triangle nose cone
RN '5', spun hubs, Black gloss base ..**£275-375**
- Blue body, Yellow triangle nose-cone and
Blue cast hubs Yellow RN '5', mottled
'234' base **£500-600**
- Blue body, Yellow triangle on nose, RN '5',
Yellow plastic hubs, Black gloss base
.... **£400-450**
- Blue body, Yellow triangle on nose, RN '5',
Blue plastic hubs, Black gloss base . **£400-500**
Note a model sold with spun hubs in a Vectis
auction July 2004 for £950 + commission.
A further model in March 2008 sold for £600 +
commission.

235 1954-60 **H.W.M. Racing Car**
(renumbered from 23j)
Box Type 1 Early ref no e.g. 23j
Box Type 2 Dual Picture box e.g. 235/23j.
Box Type 3. Yellow picture box
- Pale Green body, Yellow RN '7',
Green cast hubs. **£120-160**
- As above Type 1 Box. **£140-180**

236 1956-59 **Connaught Racing Car**
Box Type 1. Yellow Non picture box
Box Type 2. Yellow picture box

- Pale Green body, Red interior, Mid-Green
hubs, RN '32', White driver................ **£120-160**

237 1957-60 **Mercedes-Benz Racing Car**
Box Type 1. Yellow picture box
Box Type 2 Lighter Yellow picture box
Box Type 3. Yellow & Red panel Non picture box
Box Type 4 Red & Yellow window box.
Box Type 5 Gold Export Window Box.
- Gloss White or Off White body, Red interior,
Blue driver, Red cast hubs, RN '30',
mottled base, M tyres. **£100-130**
- 1960-62 Gloss or Matt White body, Red interior,
Blue driver, spun hubs, RN '30',
Black gloss base, M tyres................. **£150-200**
- 1962-64   White or Off-White body, Red
interior, Blue driver, Red plastic hubs.
RN '30' Matt Black base, M tyres....... **£110-150**
- White or Off-White body, Red interior, Yellow
Driver, Red plastic hubs, RN '30',
Matt Black base, M tyres **£130-170**
- Late issue:
- White body, Red interior, Blue driver, Red
plastic hubs, paper labelled RN '36'
Semi Matt black base & M Tyres. **£225-275**
Late models in Gold Export Box may attract a
premium.

238 1957-60 **Jaguar 'D' type**
Box Type 1. Yellow Non picture box
Box Type 2. Yellow picture box
Box Type 3 Lighter Yellow picture box
Box Type 4 Yellow and Red panel Non picture box
Box Type 5 Red and Yellow window Box.
Box Type 6 Gold Export Window Box.
- Turquoise body, Blue interior, White driver,
Blue cast hubs, M tyres, mottled base
Black Metal Steering wheel **£100-140**
- Turquoise body and interior, Yellow driver,
Blue cast hubs, M tyres, Black gloss base,
plastic steering wheel **£140-175**
- 1960-62 Turquoise body, Blue interior, White
driver, spun hubs, M tyres, Black gloss base,
Black metal steering wheel **£160-200**
- Turquoise body and interior, White driver,
spun hubs, M tyres, Black gloss base,
Black plastic steering wheel **£200-250**
- 1962-65   Turquoise body and interior, White
or Yellow driver, Yellow plastic hubs, M tyres,
Black gloss base, Black plastic steering wheel
.... **£280-350**
- Turquoise body and interior, White or Yellow
driver, Blue plastic hubs, M tyres, Black gloss
base, Black plastic steering wheel....**£280-350**
Late models in Gold export box may attract a
premium.
NB Boxes for 238 that have a descriptive
adhesive label stating 'Le Mans 1955/56/57'
may attract a premium.

239 1958-60 **Vanwall Racing Car**
Box Type 1. Yellow picture box
Box Type 2. Lighter Yellow picture box
Box Type 3. Yellow and Red panel Non picture box
All models have M tyres and RN '35' unless
stated and Vanwall logo. Metal steering wheel.
- Green body, Green hubs, White or
Yellow driver, mottled base.............. **£120-140**
- Green body, Green hubs, White or
Yellow driver, RN '25' or '26'
mottled base. **£140-170**
- 1960-62   Green body, White driver, spun
hubs, Black gloss base, RN '25', 26', '35'
.... **£130-180**
Following models had plastic steering wheel.
- 1962-65   Green body, Yellow driver,
Yellow plastic hubs, Black gloss base..**£180-220**
- Green body, Yellow Driver, Green plastic
hubs, Matt Black base. **£180-220**
- Green body, Green hubs, Yellow driver,
Black matt base.................................**£130-180**
Following box types refer to
Racing Cars 240, 241, 242, & 243
Box Type1 Red & Yellow picture Box.
Box Type 2 Red & Yellow window Export Box

Box Type 3 Gold window Export Box

240 1963-70 **Cooper Racing Car**
All models with M tyres, spun hubs.
- Blue body, White racing stripe, RN '20',
White driver (Silver or Yellow helmet) **£60-75**
- As above with Red helmet. **£75-100**
- As above with Green helmet.............. **£90-120**
South African issue: with Afrikaans box.
- Blue body, White racing stripe, RN '20',
White driver (Yellow helmet)
.... **£1,000+**
Note there may be other helmet colours.

241 1963-70 **Lotus Racing Car**
All models with M tyres, spun hubs.
- Green body RN '7' or '24' White
driver (Silver helmet) **£60-75**
- Green body, RN '24' White
driver (Red or Yellow helmet) **£60-75**
- South African issue: : with Africaan box.
- Green body with RN '24', White driver
with Red helmet
.... **£1,000+**
Note there may be other helmet colours.

242 1963-71 **Ferrari Racing Car**
All models with M tyres, spun hubs.
- Red body, with RN '36',
White driver, Green or Silver helmet ... **£60-75**
- Red body, with RN '36',
White driver, Red helmet **£75-100**
- South African issue: with Afrikaans box.
- Red body with RN '36', White driver,
Green or Silver helmet.
.... **£1,000+**
Note there may be other helmet colours.

243 1963-71 **B.R.M. Racing Car**
All models with M tyres, spun hubs, Matt
Black base.
- Dark Green body, Yellow cowl, RN '7',
Red helmet **£80-100**
- 1963-71 Metallic Green body (shades exist),
Yellow cowl, RN '7' Silver or Red helmet. **£60-75**
- South African issue: with Afrikaans box.
- Green body with RN '24', White driver
with Red helmet
.... **£1,000+**
Note there may be other helmet colours.

254 1956-59 **Austin Taxi** (FX3)
See '40h' listing.

260 1971-72 **VW 'Deutsche Bundespost'**
- Yellow body (129 casting, 100mm),
German export model.......................**£100-150**

262 1959-60 **Volkswagen 'PTT' Car**
All are Swiss Post export models.
Box Type 1 Yellow Non picture box
Box Type 2 Hard Plastic case
Box Type 3 Bubble pack
(181 casting, 90mm, fixed doors),
No windows or Interior. Fixed doors.
Type 1 Box only.
- Yellow/Black, Yellow cast hubs **£500-750**
- 1960-62 Yellow/Black, Yellow plastic
hubs **£600-750**
- 1962-66 As previous issue but with
spun hubs...................................... **£500-750**
NOTE: 262 models listed above should
be in the correct French / German box
with 'Auto Suisse VW' and 'Schweizer
Postauto VW' on the end flap.
Type 2 or 3 Box only. Following models with
windows and interior.
- 1966-68   129 casting (100mm):
Yellow/Black, opening doors,
spun hubs, hard plastic case **£100-140**
- 1968-72   Yellow/Black, opening
doors, plastic hubs **£60-100**
- 1972-76   Yellow/Black, opening
doors, Speedwheels............................ **£60-100**

268 **Renault Dauphine Mini-cab**
See 'Public Transport' section.

281 **'PATHE NEWS' Camera Car**
See 'Novelty, Film and TV' section.

295 1963-69 **Atlas Kenebrake Bus**

- Light Blue/Grey body, windows, Red interior **£40-70**
- All Blue Body, Red interior **£80-120**
- Blue Body, Lemon Interior **£250-350**

340 1954-66 Land Rover
(renumbered from 27d)
See 'Farm and Garden Models'

341 1954-66 Land-Rover Trailer
(renumbered from 27m)
See 'Farm and Garden Models'

342 1966-72 Austin Mini-Moke
Box Type 1 Yellow picture box with white background
Box Type 2 Yellow picture box with background
Box Type 3 Bubble pack
- Metallic Green, Grey or Buff canopy with 1 or 2 windows, spun hubs. **£50-75**
- 1972-75
Metallic Greenish-Blue, 1 canopy window, Speedwheels............................ **£50-75**

344 1954-61 Estate Car
See 'Farm and Garden Models'.

344 1970-72 Land Rover Pick-Up
See 'Farm and Garden Models'.

370 1969-76 Dragster Set
Box Type 1 Yellow picture box with background
Box Type 2 Bubble pack
- Yellow/Red, driver, 'FIREBALL', 'INCH-PINCHER', starter unit............... **£40-50**

405 1954-60 Universal Jeep
(renumbered from 25y)
Box Type 1. Yellow dual No picture box
(Shows red model with blue hubs)

Box Type 2. Yellow picture box shows red model with Red hubs
Box Type 3. Lighter Yellow picture box
Box Type 4. Yellow and Red panel Non picture box
- Red body and cast hubs with smooth or ribbed tyres. Mottled base........... **£110-140**
- Green body and cast hubs with smooth or ribbed tyres. Mottled base........... **£120-160**
1960-67
- Red body and plastic hubs with ribbed tyres. Black gloss base **£140-180**
- Orange body and Red plastic hubs with ribbed tyres. Black gloss base **£400-600**
- Red body and plastic hubs with ribbed tyres. Black Matt base.................................. **£150-200**
- Red body and Spun hubs with ribbed tyres. .... **£600+**
1963 South African issue: with Afrikaans box.
- Green body with Red hubs **£1500-2500**
- Off-White body with Red hubs.....**£1500-2500**

448 / 449 Chevrolet El Camino Pick-up
See 'Commercial Vehicles' section

475 1964-66 Model 'T' Ford
Box Type Red & Yellow window box.
- Blue body, Yellow panels and wheels, driver/female passenger **£45-60**
- Blue body, Yellow panels and Brown wheels, driver/female passenger **£25-40**

476 1967-69 Morris Oxford ('Bullnose')
Box Type Red & Yellow window Box.
- Yellow body, Blue chassis, Red wheels Fawn hood, driver **£25-40**

---

675 1954-59 Ford US Army Staff Car
See 'Military Vehicles' section
Models 2162, 2214 and 2253 are in a scale of 1:25. They were mounted on a printed card base with a vacuform display cover which is photo-sensitive and vulnerable to yellowing.

2162 1973-76 **Ford Capri**
- Metallic Blue, Black roof, Black or Blue interior **£100-125**

2214 1974-76 **Ford Capri Rally Car**
- Red, Black roof and bonnet, RN '12', Black or Blue interior **£100-125**

2253 1974-76 **Ford Capri 'Police' Car**
- White/Orange, Blue light **£100-125**

Dinky 405 Universal Jeep. The models shown here are the very rare South African versions. Note the green model has red wheels not maroon like the UK version.

Dinky Toys cars made by Meccano, Paris, France and sold in Britain (see French Dinky Toys listings)

Models 57-001 to 57-006 all have spun hubs, detailed end-flap picture boxes, and are in a scale of 1:42. Hong Kong made models were issued in tab-ended alternative pictorial card boxes or rare yellow 'see-through' cellophane window boxes. See the French Dinky Toys section for prices.

24kz	1939-40	**Peugeot Car**, Red or Blue, (rubber tyres for UK)	
516		**Mercedes-Benz 230sl**, Bronze body, Cream interior..............	
518	1962-65	**Renault 4L**, Brown or Grey body, steering, windows	
524	1965-67	**Panhard 24c** Dark Metallic Grey body	
532		**Lincoln Premiere**, Metallic Light Green body, Dk. Green roof	
530	1965-66	**Citroën DS19**, Light Green body, Light Grey roof	
535	1962-65	**Citroën 2cv**, Blue body, steering, windows...............................	
550	1962-65	**Chrysler Saratoga**, Pink/White body, windows.......................	
551	1959-64	**Rolls-Royce Silver Wraith** Same as UK issue 150 'Made in France'	
553	1962-65	**Peugeot 404**, Green or White, windows...................................	
555	1962-65	**Ford Thunderbird**, White, driver, steering	

Dinky Toys cars made in Hong Kong

57-001	1965-67	**Buick Riviera**	Light Blue body with Cream roof and Red interior, cast wheels	**£140-180**
57-002	1965-67	**Chevrolet Corvair Monza**	Red body, Black roof, White interior, cast wheels	**£140-180**
57-003	1965-67	**Chevrolet Impala**	Yellow body with White roof and Red interior, cast wheels	**£140-180**
		US / Canadian issue:	Yellow body with Yellow roof, cast wheels	**£140-180**
57-004	1965-67	**Oldsmobile Dynamic '88'**	White body, Blue roof, Red interior, cast wheels	**£180-220**
57-005	1965-67	**Ford Thunderbird**	Blue body with Ivory roof, Red interior, cast wheels	**£180-220**
57-006	1965-67	**Nash Rambler Classic**	Light Green body with Silver roof trim, Cream interior, cast wheels	**£180-220**

'Mini-Dinky' models

Models 10 – 61 inclusive were made in a scale of 1:65.
Models 94 – 99 inclusive were made in a scale of 1:130.

Mini-Dinky models were issued in 1968 and were made in Hong Kong and Holland. Each model was sold with a free red plastic garage. The cars are fitted with Flexomatic Independent Suspension. Racing cars 60 and 61 were made by Best Box of Holland (now EFSI). The models listed are illustrated in the 1968 US issued 3-page fold-out leaflet which advertised them as 'Swinging Value' at 59 cents and 69 cents. Models 94-99 Construction Vehicles are illustrated in a US issued 'Mini-Dinky' fold-out launch leaflet '1'.

10	**Ford Corsair**, Yellow or Metallic Gold ... **£40-50**	**20**	**Cadillac Coupé de Ville**, Silver or White **£50-60**	**32**	**Vauxhall Cresta**, Silver or Dark Green... **£40-50**
11	**Jaguar 'E' type**, Red or Met. Maroon...... **£50-75**	**21**	**Fiat 2300 Station Wagon**, Blue or Yellow/White................................ **£40-50**	**33**	**Jaguar**, Red **£50-75**
12	**Corvette Stingray**, Blue or Metallic Dark Blue **£50-60**	**22**	**Oldsmobile Toronado**, Met. Pale Blue .. **£40-50**	**57**	**Chevrolet Corvair Monza**, Red/Black ... **£40-50**
13	**Ferrari 250 LM**, Red or Met. Maroon **£40-50**	**23**	**Rover 2000**, Blue **£40-50**	**60**	**Cooper**, Blue '10' **£50-75**
14	**Chevrolet Chevy II**, Yellow or Metallic Maroon **£40-50**	**24**	**Ferrari Superfast**, Red **£40-50**	**61**	**Lotus Racing Car**, Green, '4' **£50-75**
15	**Rolls-Royce Silver Shadow**, Blue.......... **£60-80**	**25**	**Ford Zephyr 6**, Silver **£40-50**	**94**	**International Bulldozer**, Yellow **£70-90**
16	**Ford Mustang**, White, Cream or Metallic Blue **£40-50**	**26**	**Mercedes 250 SE**, White or Bronze........ **£40-50**	**95**	**International Skid Shovel**, Yellow...... **£100-150**
17	**Aston Martin DB6**, White...................... **£50-75**	**27**	**Buick Riviera**, Blue **£40-50**	**96**	**Payloader Shovel**, White **£70-90**
18	**Mercedes Benz 230 SL**, White/Black.... **£40-50**	**28**	**Ferrari F 1**, Red, '7' **£40-50**	**97**	**Euclid R40**, Yellow, 10 wheels **£70-90**
19	**MGB Roadster**, Blue **£50-75**	**29**	**Ford F 1**, White **£40-50**	**98**	**Michigan Scraper**, Yellow **£100-125**
		30	**Volvo 1800s**, Blue **£40-50**	**99**	**Caterpillar Grader**, Orange **£70-90**
		31	**VW 1600TC**, Blue or Metallic Green **£40-50**	**-**	**'Mini-Dinky' 12-Car Collector Case**, with models... **£500-750**

'Dinky Toys' issued by Airfix Products Ltd

Issued by Airfix as 'DINKY TOYS'; made in France to 1:43 scale. Supplied in the last design of Red/Yellow/Blue 'Dinky Toys' window box with header card. They were all issued circa 1980 and all are in the Market Price Range of £10-15.

500	**Citroën 2cv** ....Red/Orange or Green body, 'duck' motif, open roof
500	**Citroën 2cv** ....Red/Orange or Green body, 'duck' motif, closed roof
501	**Fiat Strada** ....Blue or Metallic Bronze body, no decals..................
502	**BMW 530**...........Purple body with 'flame' decal on doors ....
502	**BMW 530**...........Metallic Green with Black 'cougar' decal................
503	**Alfetta GTV** ....Red or Yellow body, Green 'clover leaf' on bonnet ..
504	**Citroën Visa**.......Red body, no decals ....
505	**Peugeot 504**.......Blue body with 'flame' decal on doors ....
505	**Peugeot 504**.......Greenish-Gold with Black 'cougar' decal on doors..
506	**Alfa-Sud** ....Not seen ....NPP
507	**Renault 14** ....Not seen ....NPP
508	**Ford Fiesta**.........Not seen ....NPP

Cougar Model Toys

Many of the 'Airfix Dinky Toys' appeared erratically in the early 1980s (in France, then in the UK), under the name 'Cougar Model Toys'. For information on this small range of 'budget' toys, please see the 'French Meccano Dinky Toys' chapter where they are listed at the end of the 'Cars' section.

Airfix – matchbox sized miniatures made in Hong Kong

Although announced in 1980, only a few seem to have appeared in the UK. Market Price Range £10-15.

101	**'56 Corvette**	White body with Red flash, bubble-packed ....
103	**Chevette**	Yellow, 'Turbo' decal, Silver base, bubble-packed ..
104	**Honda Accord**	Lilac body, Orange flash, Silver base, bubble-pack.
105	**Toyota Celica**	Red body, '3', Silver base, Orange bubble-pack ....
106	**Datsun 280Z**	Brown body, bubble-packed ....
107	**BMW Turbo**	Orange body, Black/Yellow flash, bubble-packed...
108	**Alfa Romeo**	Purple body with Yellow flash, bubble-packed ....
110	**Stepside Pick-up**	Blue and Brown body, bubble-packed ....
110	**Camper**	Yellow and Two-tone Brown body........................
113	**Pick-up**	Red and Black body, '4 x 4' decal ....
114	**Firebird**	Black body..
115	**Camaro**	Red body with racing-number 'Z28' ....
116	**'63 Corvette**	Metallic Blue body...
117	**'71 Corvette**	Yellow body with 'Vette' decal............................
119	**Ford Van**	Blue body with Orange flash...............................
120	**Renegade Jeep**	Yellow/Green body, Silver base, Green packaging..
121	**Chevy Blazer**	Red body ....
122	**Sun Van**	Orange body with 'Sun Van' decal, Blue packaging
123	**Yamaha 250 MX**	Blue body with 'Yamaha' decal ....
124	**Honda MT 250**	Orange body with 'Honda' decal ....
125	**Kawasaki Fll 250**	Red body with 'Kawasaki' decal...........................
126	**Suzuki TM 400**	Yellow/Black body with 'CCI' and 'Suzuki' decals..
129	**T-Bird Convertible**	Red and White body...
130	**Chevy Convertible**	Metallic Blue and White body ....

Wooden prototypes, first castings and factory colour samples

These are unique items, produced as samples within the factory to aid the design and development process. Some were made for publicity and catalogue illustration purposes prior to actual volume production. Price guidance is usually not possible since they so rarely come to market in significant quantities. However, the sale in 2001 by Christie's of the Remy-Meeus Collection has enabled us to list the following:

Pre-war items

38a Frazer-Nash BMW, Blue with Grey interior, Turquoise hubs..... £400-500
38a Frazer-Nash BMW, (first casting) Green with Dark Green seats, fabricated, painted tinplate baseplate £300-400
38d Alvis, (first casting), Blue with Tan seats, 'ALVIS' in Indian ink on base £300-400
38e Armstrong-Siddeley Coupé, (colour sample), plain Brown dashboard, production baseplate painted Khaki £200-300
38f Jaguar Sports Car, (wooden prototype), Dark Green body, 'JAGUAR' in Indian ink on base £1,200-1,500
38f Jaguar Sports Car, (1st casting), Green body, Grey seats.........£800-1,000
39a Packard Sedan, (wooden prototype), Dark Blue with Silver windows, 'PACKARD' on base £600-800
39b Oldsmobile Six Sedan, (wooden prototype), Dark Green with Silver windows, 'Oldsmobile Six Sedan' in Indian ink on base £500-800
39c Lincoln Zephyr, (wooden prototype of saloon version, not coupé), unpainted, with 'Lincoln Zephyr' in pencil on base £500-600
39d Buick Viceroy, (wooden prototype), Maroon with Silver windows, 'BUICK' in pencil on base £600-800
39e Chrysler Royal Sedan, (wooden prototype), Red with Silver windows, 'CHRYSLER' in Indian ink on base £1,400-1,700
39f Studebaker State Commander Coupé, (wooden prototype), Yellow Ochre with Silver windows, 'STUDEBAKER' in Indian ink on base..£1,500-1,750
39 Series Hupmobile, (wooden prototype), Green with Silver windows, 'HUPMOBILE' in Indian ink on base. Not issued as a production model £1,200-1,500
39 Series Luxicab, (wooden prototype), Dark Green and Pale Yellow with Silver windows, 'LUXICAB' in pencil on rear spare wheel cover and '1st sample not approved' in pencil on base. Not issued as a production model £1,100-1,400
39 Series Luxicab, (wooden prototype), Black and Canary Yellow with Silver windows, 'LUXICAB' in pencil on rear spare wheel cover. Not issued as a production model £1,100-1,400

Post-war paint colour samples

38b Sunbeam-Talbot, Red body, hubs and tonneau. Tie-on label stating: 'Approved 22 Oct 1948', plus paint code details £200-300
38e Armstrong-Siddeley Coupé, Green body, Light Grey interior, Green hubs. Tie-on label stating: 'Approved 22 Oct 1948', plus paint code details £200-300
39b Oldsmobile Sedan, Beige body, Fawn hubs. Tie-on label stating: '1 Oct 1948', plus paint code details £300-500

39e Chrysler Royal Sedan, Cream body, Light Green hubs. Tie-on label stating: '1 Oct 1948', plus paint code details £300-500
40b Triumph 1800, Black body, Silver hubs, rear window pillars. Two tie-on labels stating: '30/9/48', + paint code details £500-600
40d Austin Devon, Red body, Maroon hubs. Tie-on label stamped: '6 Jan 1950', plus paint code details................................£400-600
40e Standard Vanguard, Fawn body, Fawn hubs, axle clip, open rear wheel arches. Tie-on label stating: '18 Oct 1948', plus paint code details................£400-600

Other prototypes and designs

We are also aware of the following (these were not in Christie's sale)
107 Sunbeam Alpine in Maroon with Grey interior (unfinished casting) NPP
107 Sunbeam Alpine in Light Blue with Cream interior (unfinished casting)
110 Aston-Martin in Grey with Blue interior (unfinished casting)............NPP
111 Triumph TR2 in Pink with Blue interior ....NPP
122 Volvo 256DL Estate in White..NPP
122 Volvo 256DL Estate in Red...NPP
122 Volvo 256DL Estate in Green...NPP
170 Ford Granada Ghia in Metallic Silver ....NPP
181 Volkswagen Saloon in Pale Blue (with baseplate, 1970s) ....NPP
181 Volkswagen Saloon in Pale Blue (with spun hubs, 1970s) ....NPP
181 Volkswagen Saloon in Metallic Blue ....NPP
181 Volkswagen Saloon in Turquoise..NPP
190 Monteverdi 375L Metallic Gold (Copper), White interior, cast wheels...NPP
190 Monteverdi 375L in Metallic Black, Red interior, cast wheels........NPP
211 Triumph TR7. Metallic Green body, Red, Grey or Green interior ......NPP
227 Beach Buggy. Copper body, Grey hood, 'fire' design ....NPP
507 Albion Tanker. Green, 'MILK MARKETING BOARD' £2,000-2,500
57-001 Buick Riviera with Slate Grey body (Hong Kong made model)....NPP

All wooden prototypes

found in Liverpool Charity Shop and sold by Bonhams in 2004:

29h Duple Roadmaster Coach, light blue/grey £680
25y Universal Jeep, dark green, tin windscreen £650
30w Hindle Smart Helecs, maroon 'BR' logo on front..............................£600
40g Morris Oxford, cream/blue, '17/64 Morris' on base £2,000
132 Packard Convertible, cream, red interior £880
472 Austin Van, green, light green hubs £720
480 series Bedford Van, cream, green hubs £850
Unreleased Austin Wagon prototype, red cab, blue back £1,500
522 Big Bedford Lorry, orange cab, green back £1,500
Unreleased Leyland Fire Engine prototype...£600

641 Army 1 ton Lorry, military green, grey windows £600	**Motorised Tram 'LYNDAS COMPOUND'**, Blue, Cream, Grey roof,
673 Army Scout Car, military green £360	2" long, complete with photos of model on layout £240
674 Army Champ, military green..£300	**Wooden mock-up Tram** with plastic wheels, Cream and Red with
	roof pole £280

Dinky Toys Commercial Vehicles Box Types

Commercial Vehicles Box Types Introduction

A mint condition commercial vehicle without its correct box is worth a fraction of the value of its boxed equivalent. Furthermore, as model boxes made from card do not survive as well as their die-cast contents, pristine box examples are scarce and becoming scarcer. The condition of a box is of paramount importance and attention is drawn to the section in the main catalogue introduction, namely: 'Classifying the Condition of Models and Boxes'.

The following listing provides collectors with a working knowledge of the range of box types issued. In addition details are given of their dates of issue, their design and of the models which used them. See also the colour sections for examples of many types of boxes.

Whilst every care has been taken in preparing the listing other variations no doubt exist and information on these is welcomed.

Similarly with no 'dates of birth' available the dates of issue shown are approximate and again any further information is welcomed.

Commercial Vehicles Box Identification

(See also 'Dinky Toys Trade Boxes' section).

Model Colour Identification Marks

These are shown on the box lid and label and take the form of either a circular colour spot or a capital letter, e.g. 'R' for red. A colour spot may be a single colour or in the case of the later two-tone colours models a two-tone colour spot.

'Lead-free' labels 'LF'

In the l950s the government introduced new regulations concerning the lead content of die-cast models. Consequently, to indicate that a model complied with the new regulations, a round white label with 'LF' in blue was added to box end labels for a short time. Alternatively, an 'LF' coloured ink stamp was used. (See example in the colour section.)

Model Reference Numbers

These are always shown on the box lid and label.

Dual numbered boxes c. l953 – 1954

A new numbering system was introduced which resulted in models being issued displaying both the old and new reference numbers. The information was shown in one of two ways:
(a) A black new number stamped alongside the old number
(b) A small old model number shown in red on either side of a larger black new number, e.g. 511 911 511'. (See examples in the colour section). Dual numbered boxes (issued for a relatively short period) may attract a premium.

Quality Control Box Markings. 1947 – 1957
    (a) Factory Checkers' Marks

A quality control mark may be found on the base of the buff coloured boxes. This takes the form of a coloured ink stamp of a reference number within a circle, e.g. 'M42' or 'M19'. Stamped on the underside of the blue covered box lid may be found a similar ink stamp e.g. 'ZQ Z8'.
    (b) Date Stamps

Ink stamped on the base of boxes or box lids may be found a purple date stamp relating to the date of the model's issue. Recorded examples include: 'GR950' on a (25x) orange coloured box; '10 KR 55' on a (933) blue/white stripe box; 'H656' on a (902) blue/white stripe box; 'KB956' on a (433) yellow covered box lid; '01057' on a (689) military blue/white box.
The Editor would welcome any further information on this subject.

Pre-war issues 1933 – 1939

Apart from sets (see the Gift Sets listing) commercial vehicles were sold unboxed. They were usually packaged in half-dozen retailers trade packs such as Nos. 28/1, 28/2 and 28/3 Delivery Vans.

Post-war Issues 1947 – 1979

In 1947 the first individual boxes were introduced to house the exciting new range of 'Supertoys' models. However, the small commercial vehicles continued to be sold unboxed from trade packs until 1953/54.
The boxes have been catalogued into four types as follows:
    Type 1 1947-75 - Boxes with lift-off lids
    Type 2 1953-75 - All card boxes with tuck-in end flaps
    Type 3 1963-79 - Display boxes
    Type 4 l964-64 - Export only boxes

TYPE I	**1947 - 69**	**BOXES WITH LIFT-OFF LIDS**

A 1947-49

(A-a) Brown card box with wrap around all-white label with red lettering 'DINKY SUPERTOYS' and model number shown in black. Model shown as a black/white photographic illustration, e.g., 563 Heavy Tractor.

(A-b) Brown card box with separate labels on the box top and one box end. The half red and white box labels show 'DINKY SUPERTOYS' in red. Model number is white on a black oval background. In addition the main label displays an illustration of the model and whilst the main design of the label remains constant, the position of the model does vary as follows:

(i) Facing inwards on the right side of the label.
Models recorded using this box: 25x, 501 (1st type), 521 and 563.

(ii) Facing outwards on the left side of the label.
Models recorded using this box: 502, 503, 511, 512, 513 (all 1st types). The small separate label attached to the right side of the box lid is white with red model information text. Some labels include a line drawing of the model eg. 503 and 513.
(iii) Buff plain card box with a single 'wrap round' red and white label which covers the box lid from end to end with 'DINKY SUPERTOYS' in red on the larger Foden type box, one of the end of the label contains information about the model in German, French and Spanish. In addition, the model number on the top and ends is now white on a circular black background. The model picture is facing inwards from the right and the models recorded in this box to date are: 504 Tanker 1st type and 531.

(iv) As previous issue but the model picture is facing outwards from the left. Models recorded: 511, 512, 521 and 533.

B c.1950

(i) Green covered box with red and white wrap-around label. Models recorded in this box: 25x, 501, 502, 503, 504 (1st and 2nd types), 504 'MOBILGAS', 511, 512, 513 and 521. Model picture facing inwards from the right. 'DINKY SUPERTOYS' in red letters.
(ii) Orange card box with black printing, e.g., 25x Breakdown Lorry.
(iii) Orange card box with orange/white label, e.g., 25x Breakdown Lorry.

C c.1951

(i) Pale or dark blue covered box with wrap-around red and white label. Model picture facing inwards from the right with 'DINKY SUPERTOYS' logo. Models recorded: 25x, 501, 502, 503, 504 (1st and 2nd types), 505, 511, 512, 513, 514 (all issues except 'Spratts'), 521, 531/931, 532/932 and 533/933.

(ii) Pale or dark blue box with wrap-around orange and white label with 'DINKY SUPERTOYS'. Model picture facing inwards from the right front. Beneath the model picture is a black factory code, e.g. on the 522 Big Bedford lorry issue the code is '50522'. Models recorded: 25x, 504 (1st / 2nd), 511, 514 'LYONS' and 'SLUMBERLAND', 531 and 571.

(iii) Same as C(ii) but with model picture facing outwards from the left. Models recorded: 502(1st), 503 (2nd) and 512.

(iv) Same as C(ii) but with model picture facing inwards from the right front but with 'DINKY TOYS'. Models recorded: 501(1st type), 504 Tanker (1st and 2nd types), 504 'MOBILGAS', 514 'WEETABIX', 514 'SLUMBERLAND', 514'SPRATTS', 521, 522, 564, 591/991, and 917.

(v) Same as C (iv) but with model picture facing outwards from the left front. Models recorded: 502, 503 (1st types), 512, 513 (1st types).

(vi) Same as C (iv) but with model picture facing inwards from the left front. Models 505 (1st type), 532 and 581 US issue.

D c1953

(i) Blue and white striped box lid with dark blue bottom section. Box lid is white with dark blue parallel stripes. 'DINKY TOYS' logo is shown in red plus a colour picture of the model facing inwards from the right. The model number is on the left of the picture. Colour identification spots shown as appropriate on box ends. Models recorded:

409, 418, 430, 582, 511, 511/911, 512, 512/912, 513, 513/913, 521/921, 901/2/3 (2nd type), 911/12/13. 917, 921, 923 ('ketchup bottle)', 923 ('baked beans can'), 930, 931, 932/33, 941/42, 963, 980, 982, 991.

NB The 417 Leyland Comet Lorry yellow/green issue was housed in a box with a blue/yellow picture.

(ii) As D (i), but with 'DINKY SUPERTOYS' logo and with the model picture facing inwards from the right. Models recorded:
901/2/3, 905, 913, 918/9, 923, 930, 934/5/6, 942/3, 948, 954, 958, 960, 963/4, 966/7/8/9, 973, 977, 982/3/4, 986, 991, 994.
On the box side is a note stating the colour of the model which may vary from the one illustrated on the box front. This only happened when a model was issued for a short time and hence some of the rarest models were issued in this manner (e.g. 902 Foden Flat Truck in yellow/green livery was issued in box with red/green model picture; 913 Guy Flat Truck with tailboard in yellow/green livery issued in box with all-green model picture; 934 Leyland Octopus Wagon in blue and yellow livery was issued on the standard box with a yellow/green model picture but displaying a dark blue colour spot). The Editor would welcome any further examples.

(iii) As D (ii), but with model picture facing outwards from the left. 'DINKY SUPERTOYS' logo. Model recorded No.982.

(iv) As D (ii), but with model picture facing inwards from the left. 'DINKY SUPERTOYS' logo. Model recorded No. 979.

(v) Plain blue and white striped box with no model picture on lid. A white end label 'DINKY SUPERTOYS' and the model details in blue letters. Models recorded: 920 and 923.

E Yellow covered box lid with blue bottom section.
(i) c.1956 - 1959
On two of the box sides is a picture of the model set against a white shadow background. The top of the box lid has a 'DINKY TOYS' logo in red. Colour spots shown as appropriate. In addition white circular 'LF' (lead free) labels may be found. Models recorded: 408/9, 417, 419, 430/1/2/3, 437.
NB. The rare 408 Big Bedford Lorry in pink and cream livery was issued in this box but with the standard maroon and fawn model box picture.

(ii) Yellow covered box lid but with red side panels with pictorial scene with 'DINKY TOYS' logo in red. The box lid shows the model picture facing inwards from the right with a pictorial scene in an end panel on the left. Models recorded: 401, 408, 417, 419, 425, 430, 434, 448, 450, 925, 960, 964, 972 and 978.

(iii) Same as previous issue but with 'DINKY SUPERTOYS' logo. Models recorded: 908, 934, 935, 944, 958/9, 962, 964, 972 and 978.
NB. No. 935 Leyland Octopus with chains in the rare dark blue and grey livery was issued in the standard box with the green and grey version illustrated but with a dark blue spot displayed.

(iv) All yellow covered lid with a pictorial scene in the middle of the box lid top. 'DINKY SUPERTOYS' in red. Models recorded: 959, 987/8/9.

F 'One off' box issues with lift-off lids.

(i) Plain dark blue covered box with no picture. White label on box lid end with dark blue text. Model recorded: 982 Pullman Car Transporter in rare mid-blue livery with brownish-grey decks.

(ii) Orange covered box (c.1950) with white/orange wrap-around lid label. Models recorded: 25x Breakdown Truck and 14c Coventry Climax Fork Lift Truck.

TYPE 2   1953 - 1975
ALL CARD BOXES WITH TUCK-IN END FLAPS

A l953 - 1964
(i) Deep yellow box with 'DINKY TOYS' in red plus the model's name and type in black. A white reference number on a black or red oval background is on the box end flaps but no reference is shown on the box face. The model is pictured on the box sides with or without a white shadow background. Colour spots shown as applicable. Foreign language information is shown on one of the box end flaps. Box used for small and medium size models, e.g., 431/432. Box in general use during the model renumbering period. Consequently dual numbered boxes will be found.
Very few boxes were issued displaying just the old type of reference number. Recorded models to date: 25d, e, f, g and 30e. In addition, 29c Bus and 29e Coach have been identified. Please send details if you have any other examples. Later issues display 'WITH WINDOWS' captions.

(ii) Plain light yellow box with two red sides and no model picture. The

'DINKY TOYS' logo, the model type and its reference number are shown in yellow and white. Colour spots are shown as appropriate. Models recorded: 252, 413, 414 and 428 plus 070 and 071 Dublo Dinky.

(iii) 1963 - 1970
Yellow box with red end features panel around the front right side, with or without an upward pointing white arrow. Models recorded: 273, 274, 435.

(iv) 1966 - 1969
A detailed full colour picture box with 'DINKY TOYS' in red plus a pictorial scene on two sides. A yellow laurel leaf design on a black background incorporates the model number Models recorded: 280, 402, 407 'KENWOOD', 914, 923, 944/5, 959/60, 965, 970, 972 and 978.

(v) 1968 - 1974
White fronted box with a narrow yellow band across the face. The box front displays 'DINKY TOYS' in red plus the model number and type in black and white letters. A colour picture of the model is shown on two sides. Models recorded: 407, 438/9/40, 91, 917, 974, 978 and 980.

(vi) 1966 - 1970
Picture box used for large commercials with two full pictorial sides with 'DINKY TOYS' in red. The other sides are yellow and red. Models recorded: 434 'AUTO SERVICES', 914 and 945.

(vii) 1970 - 1975
Heavy card box used for heavy models e.g. 924 Centaur Dump Truck. Box has white face with a colour picture of model combined with a black band across the face and sides.

(viii) Promotional Box Types
(a) No. 274 'JOSEPH MASON PAINTS' Minivan. Dark red box with white letters plus an enclosed leaflet.
(b) No. 491 Plain yellow box with red letters. 'JOBS DAIRY'.
(c) No. 917 Mercedes-Benz LP1920 Truck with 'HENRY JOHNSON' logo. Plain white card box with no lettering.
(d) No. 940 Mercedes-Benz, 'FISONS', plain white box

TYPE 3   l963 - 1979   DISPLAY BOXES

A l970 - 1976 Vacuform packs
Models displayed on a black card plinth with a blue surface with 'DINKY TOYS' in red and white. The model is covered by a close-fitting see-through protective plastic cover. Known examples include: 407,416, 438/9, 915, 944, 945 'ESSO' and 'LUCAS' issues.

B 1976 - 1979 Window boxes
Cellophane fronted window boxes with a dark blue and red header card giving the model's name and 'DINKY DIECAST TOYS' in yellow and white letters. Known examples include: 275, 432, 440, 451, 940, 950 and 980.
C 1963 - 1966 Fold-back lid display box
224 Commer Convertible Truck and 975 Ruston Bucyrus Excavator which also had a coloured outer box display wrapper issued for a while.

TYPE 4   1964 - 1966   EXPORT ONLY BOXES

A l964 - 1966
An all-yellow card and cellophane 'see-through' display box.
'DINKY' plus the model type and number is shown across the box front in red letters plus 'A MECCANO PRODUCT MADE IN ENGLAND'. Box issued with a card protection strip. Known models include: 275, 434, 492, 914. A version of this box was used for the 944 'SHELL BP' tanker - see picture in the colour section, Also used for the U.S. Export Series: 'MARVELS IN MINIATURE' which is shown on the sides of the box front in red capital letters, e.g. 275, 434, 437, 448 and 965. Later issues display the range on the base of the box.

B c.1965
Same as previous issue but all-gold box with two black and red diagonal stripes. A rare box type. Known issues include 434 and 989.

INNER BOX LININGS and MODEL SUPPORTS

To be complete a box should contain all its original model supports. The following issues all had supports or linings. In some instances top and bottom linings were included (2).
14c, 400, 561, 581, 908(2), 924, 930(3), 958, 964, 965, 967, 968, 969(2), 972, 974, 976, 977(2), 979(2), 980, 982, 983(2), 984(2), 985(2), 986, 989(2).

Dinky Toys Commercial Vehicles

Market Price Range (MPR) for pre-1954 unboxed commercial vehicle models: Prior to 1954, virtually all smaller, non-Supertoy commercial vehicle models were sold unboxed from retailer's trade boxes of either 6, 4 or 3 models. Consequently, all pre-1954 issues have been priced as being unboxed.

Post-1954 models were all boxed and have been priced accordingly. As a consequence, models which have been renumbered will be found to have two differing prices – one for the pre-1954 unboxed version and another for its boxed and renumbered successor. See also the Trade Box section for details of individual boxes and packs that were used to supply shops.

Model and details	MPR
14a B.E.V. Truck	
1948-54 (renumbered in 1954 to 400)	
• Mid-Blue body with Blue hubs, Fawn driver, hook	**£30-35**
• Grey body (with Blue, Grey or Red hubs), Fawn driver, hook	**£30-35**
14c Coventry Climax Fork Lift	
1949-54 (renumbered in 1954 to 401)	
• Orange, Brown or Dark Red body, Green forks, Fawn driver, 1 PP	**£25-30**
14z Three-wheel Delivery Van	
• 1938-40 'Triporteur' with Green, Red, Grey, Blue or Yellow body, Black hubs, White tyres, driver is always a different colour from van, imported French model	NGPP

22 Series

Model and details	MPR
22c Motor Truck	
1933-35 Two-piece lead body with 'HORNBY SERIES' cast-in, tinplate radiator, diecast wheels that may be plain or may have an applied colour wash.	
• Blue cab, Red truck body	**£1,250-1,500**
• Blue cab, Cream or Yellow truck body, Blue wash wheels	**£1,250-1,500**
• Red cab, Green truck body	**£1,250-1,500**
• Red cab, Blue truck body	**£1,250-1,500**
• Red cab, Cream truck body	**£1,250-1,500**
• Yellow cab, Blue truck body	**£1,250-1,500**
22c Motor Truck	
1935-40 Diecast one-piece body, open rear window.	
• Orange-Red, Maroon, Green or Blue coloured diecast hubs	**£125-150**
• Dark Blue body, chrome hubs	**£125-150**
• Off-white body, Mid-Blue hubs 1945-47	**£125-150**
• Red, Green or Brown body, open rear window, Black diecast hubs 1948-50	**£60-70**
• Red, Green or Brown body, closed rear window, Black diecast hubs	**£60-70**
22d Delivery Van (no advertising)	
1933-33 Type 1, lead body, tinplate radiator, 'HORNBY SERIES' cast-in.	
• Green cab, Blue van body, Blue wash wheels 1933-34	**£2,500-3,000**
• Orange/Blue body, plain metal wheels (no colour wash)	**£2,500-3,000**
• Blue/Yellow body, Red wheels	**£2,500-3,000**
• As previous models but with 'DINKY TOYS' cast-in	**£400-500**
22d Delivery Van 'MECCANO'	
• 1934 Type 1, Orange cab and chassis, Blue van with Red/Black 'Meccano Engineering For Boys'	**£3,000-5,000**
• 1934-35 Type 1 Yellow body (lead), 'Meccano Engineering For Boys' in Red and Black. Model number was 22d until April 1935, then it was renumbered **28n**	**£900-1,200**

25 Series

Model and details	MPR
25a Wagon	
1934-36 Type 1, Black chassis.	
• Maroon body	**£300-400**

Model and details	MPR
• Green body	**£300-400**
• Red body	**£300-400**
• Blue body	**£300-400**
1936-40 Type 2, Black or Red chassis.	
• Maroon body	**£125-150**
• Green body	**£125-150**
• Red body	**£125-150**
• Blue body	**£125-150**
1936-40 Type 2	
• Blue body with Orange chassis	**£150-200**
1947-48 Black chassis, Type 3	
• Grey, Green, Red, Orange, Stone or Blue body	**£70-80**
1948-50 Black chassis, Type 4	
• Grey, Green, Light Blue, Orange, Cream or Red body	**£70-80**

25a Open Wagon - scarce colour variation, cream, with black type 4 chassis, red ridged hubs.

Model and details	MPR
25b Covered Wagon	
1934-36 (plain, no advertising) Type 1, Black chassis.	
• Blue body, Cream tilt	**£300-400**
1936-40 Type 2, Black chassis.	
• Green body, Green, Cream or Yellow tilt	**£140-180**
• Cream body, Yellow tilt	**£140-180**
• Fawn body, Cream tilt	**£140-180**
1936-40 Type 2, Green chassis.	
• Orange body, Cream tilt	**£150-200**
25b Covered Wagon 'CARTER PATERSON'	
1936-40 Type 2, Black chassis.	
• Green body, Blue hubs, Green or Cream tilt, 'Express Carriers London'	**£500-750**
• Green body, Blue hubs, 'Special Service To The Seaside'	**£500-750**
• Variation with silvered hubs	**£500-750**
25b Covered Wagon 'MECCANO'	
1936-40 Type 2, Black chassis.	
• Green body, Cream tilt, 'Engineering For Boys'	**£300-400**
• Variation with silvered hubs	**£500-600**
• Orange body, Cream tilt, Green chassis, Blue hubs	**£2,000-2,500**
25b Covered Wagon 'HORNBY TRAINS'	
1936-40 Type 2, Black chassis.	
• Fawn body, Cream tilt, Gold lettering	**£300-400**
25b Covered Wagon	
1945-47 Type 3, Black chassis,	
• Green/Green, Grey/Light or Dark Grey, Blue/Grey	**£100-140**
1947-50 Type 4, Black chassis,	
• Green/Green, Grey/Grey, Cream/Red or Cream/Blue	**£100-140**
• Yellow body, Blue tilt, Black ridged hubs	**£300-400**

Model and details	MPR
25c Flat Truck	
1934-36 Type 1, Black chassis,	
• Dark Blue body	**£150-200**
1936-40 Type 2, Black chassis,	
• Green or Stone body	**£125-150**
1946 Type 2, Black chassis,	
• Fawn, Green or Grey body, smooth hubs	**£70-80**
1947-48 Type 3, Black chassis,	
• Green, Blue, Stone or Grey body	**£70-80**
1948-50 Type 4, Black chassis,	
• Green, Blue, Orange or Stone body	**£70-80**
NB Some pre-war (1934-40) Truck issues will be found with a '20 mph' disc on the rear.	

25d Petrol Tanker 'Pool' - scarce 1946 example has a dark grey body with black smooth hubs and thick axles.

Model and details	MPR
25d Petrol Tank Wagon	
1934-35 Same chassis casting as other 25 series lorries but with hook removed. Type 1 with Black chassis.	
• **(plain, unlettered)** Red body, no advertising, open windows to back of cab	**£500-750**
• 'SHELL BP' Red body	**£500-750**
• 'SHELL' Red body, Blue hubs, 'SHELL LUBRICATING OIL' in Gold serif lettering	**£500-750**
• 'ESSO' Green body	**£500-750**
• 'POWER' Green body	**£500-750**
• 'PRATTS' Green body	**£500-750**
• 'CASTROL' Green body, Blue hubs	**£500-750**
• 'TEXACO' Red body, Black hubs, White logo: 'PETROLEUM & PRODUCTS'	**£500-750**
25d Petrol Tank Wagon	
1936-46 Type 2 with Black chassis.	
• 'PETROL' Red body, Black or White lettering	**£500-750**
• 'SHELL BP' Red body, Blue or chrome hubs	**£500-750**
• 'MOBILOIL' Red body	**£500-750**
• 'TEXACO' Red body	**£500-750**
• 'PETROL' Green body	**£500-750**
• 'ESSO' Green body, Black or Blue hubs	**£500-750**
• 'POWER' Green body	**£500-750**
• 'CASTROL' Green body, Black or Blue hubs	**£500-750**
• 'REDLINE GLICO' Blue body, Red panel, Gold lettering	**£500-750**
1945 **'POOL' (Wartime)**	
• Type 2, White chassis. Grey body, Black hubs, Black lettering	**£300-400**
1945-46 **'POOL' (Wartime)** Type 2.	

- Grey or Khaki body, Black chassis ... **£300-400**
- Dark Green body, Black chassis, Blue hubs, Gold logo **£300-400**
  1946-47 **'PETROL'**
  Type 3, Black chassis,
- Red body **£200-250**
- Orange body....................................... **£200-250**
- Mid-Green body **£200-250**
- Dark Green body **£200-250**
  1947-48 **'PETROL'**
  Type 4, Black chassis,
- Mid-Green body **£200-250**
- Dark Green body **£200-250**
- Orange body....................................... **£300-400**
  1948-50 **'PETROL'**
  Type 4, Black chassis,
- Red body **£150-200**
- Light Green body **£150-200**
- Mid-Green body **£150-200**
  1948-? **'PETROL'**
  Type 4, Black chassis,
- Yellow body.. **£200-300**

25e Tipping Wagon
  1934-35 Type 1, Black chassis,
- Maroon/Yellow body.......................... **£150-200**
  1936-40   Type 2, Black chassis,
- Maroon/Yellow **£100-125**
- Brown/Turquoise **£100-125**
- Fawn/Fawn.. **£100-125**
  1946-46   Type 2, Black chassis,
- Grey, Green or Fawn **£70-80**
  1947-48   Type 3, Black chassis,
- Grey, Stone, Green or Yellow body **£70-80**
  1948-50   Type 4, Black chassis,
- Grey, Stone or Brown body.................. **£70-80**
- Blue/Pink body **£70-80**
  NB Some early post-war 25 series Trucks exist with smooth hubs.

25f Market Gardener's Lorry - scarce colour variation is yellow, with yellow ridged hubs, black type 4 chassis.

25f Market Gardeners Lorry
  1934-35   Type 1
- Green body, Black chassis **£150-200**
- Yellow body, Green chassis **£150-200**
  1936-40   Type 2
- Green body, Black chassis **£70-80**
- Yellow body, Black chassis................. **£70-80**
- Green body, Yellow chassis **£150-200**
  1945-47   Type 3, Black chassis and hubs,
- Green, Grey, Stone or Yellow body **£70-80**
  1947-50   Type 4, Black chassis and hubs,
- Green, Grey, Yellow or Red body **£70-80**
- Orange body, Black hubs.................. **£140-160**
- Orange body, Green hubs................. **£300-400**
- Green body, Black chassis, Yellow hubs.. **£70-80**
- Yellow body and hubs, Black chassis.... **£70-80**

25g Trailer   (renumbered in 1954 to 429)
  1935-40
  Cast-in hook, tinplate drawbar,
- Dark Blue body **£35-40**
- Green body.. **£35-40**
  1946-47   Cast-in hook, tinplate drawbar,
- Green, Grey, Stone, Pale Blue or Orange.............................. **£15-20**
  1947-48   Cast-in hook, wire drawbar,
- Green, Stone, Pale Blue or Orange body. **£15-20**
  1948-49   Tinplate hook, wire drawbar,

- Green, Stone, Pale Blue or Orange body.......................... **£15-20**
  1950-54   Tinplate hook, wire drawbar,
- Green or Red body **£15-20**
  NB Most 25g Trailers have a white 'T' on a square black background, located at the rear.

25m Bedford End Tipper
  (renumbered in 1954 to 410).
  All 25m models were sold from trade packs of six.
- 1948-52 Dark Green cab and truck body, Black hubs, crank-handle operates tipper.................................. **£100-120**
  1948-54
- Orange cab and truck body, Black hubs.. **£100-120**
- Orange cab and truck body, Light Green hubs................................ **£500-750**
- Cream cab / truck body, Red hubs ... **£500-750**
- Dark Green cab and truck body, Light Green hubs................................ **£300-400**
- Red cab, Cream back, Red hubs....... **£100-120**
- Yellow cab / hubs, Mid-Blue back..... **£100-120**

25p Aveling Barford Road Roller
  1948-54   (renumbered in 1954 to 251)
- Mid or Pale Green body with driver and hook, Red wheels **£30-40**
- All-Orange body, Tan driver **£150-200**

25r Forward Control Lorry
  1948-54   (renumbered in 1954 to 420)
- Orange body, Black hubs.................. **£100-150**
- Orange body, Green hubs................. **£100-150**
- Cream body, Black hubs **£100-150**
- Cream body, Blue hubs **£100-150**
- Cream body, Black hubs **£100-150**
- Dark Brown body, Green hubs........... **£100-150**
- Green body, Cream hubs.................. **£100-150**
- Green body, Red hubs **£100-150**
- Grey body, Red hubs **£100-150**

25s Six-wheeled Wagon
  1937-40
- Reddish-Brown body, Cream, Brown or Grey tilt, holes in seat (but no figures) **£100-125**
- Royal Blue body **£200-250**
  1945-48
- Brown (various shades), Green or Dark Blue body, Grey or Light Blue tilt, with or without holes for figures (but no figures) **£100-125**
- Brick Red body, Grey tilt, Black hubs... **£125-150**

25t Flat Truck and Trailer
  (25c Flat Truck, and matching 25g Trailer).
  1945-47   Type 3.
- Green, Blue, Orange or Stone........... **£140-160**
  1947-50
- Type 4. Green or Orange................... **£120-140**

25v Bedford Refuse Wagon
  (renumbered in 1954 to 252).
  1948-54   (Trade box contains 4)
- Fawn body, Green opening shutters and rear door **£90-110**

25w Bedford Truck   (renumbered in 1954 to 411)
  1948-54
- Light Green cab, truck body and hubs. (Shades of Pale Green exist) **£90-110**
- As previous model, but with 'straight across' Black front mudguards **£250-350**
- Dark Green cab, Light Green truck body, Light Green hubs..................... **£300-400**
- Light Green cab / body, Red hubs **£500-750**

25x Commer Breakdown Lorry
  (renumbered in 1954 to 430)
  1949-54   'DINKY SERVICE' logo.
  First issues in Trade Boxes of 4, then individually in Orange card boxes.
- Tan cab and chassis (various shades), Light Green back, Red hubs, Black logo **£125-150**
- Dark Grey cab, Violet Blue back, Red hubs, White logo **£150-175**

- Dark Grey cab, Royal Blue back, Red hubs, White logo **£135-165**

28 Series

28 Series Delivery Vans
  NB   After reaching '28y' in Meccano's numbering system, further issues in this series were numbered '280'.

28a Delivery Van 'HORNBY TRAINS'
  1934-34
- Type 1. Orange body, 'Hornby Trains' logo **£3,000-5,000**
  1934-35
- Type 1. Yellow body, 'Hornby Trains British & Guaranteed' in Gold. Blue wash wheels...........**£3,000-4,000**
  1935-36
- Type 2. With smooth cast hubs **£400-500**

28a Delivery Van 'GOLDEN SHRED'
  Cream body, 'Golden Shred Marmalade' on right hand side, 'Silver Shred Marmalade' on left hand side.
- 1936-39 Type 2 ....**£3,000-4,000**
- 1939-41 Type 3 .... **£750-1,000**

28b Delivery Van 'PICKFORDS'
  Royal Blue, 'Pickfords Removals & Storage, Over 100 Branches' in Gold.
  1934-35
- Type 1, Purple wash wheels.........**£4,000-5,000**
  1935-39
  Dark Blue. Diecast hubs, White tyres
- Type 1 ....**£4,000-5,000**
- Type 2 .... **£750-1,000**

28b Delivery Van 'SECCOTINE'
  Blue body, 'Seccotine Sticks Everything' in Gold.
- 1935-39 Type 2 .... **£750-1,000**
- 1939-41 Type 3 .... **£300-400**

28c Delivery Van 'MANCHESTER GUARDIAN'
  'The Manchester Guardian' in Gold.
  1934-35 Type 1.
- Black/Red body, Yellow wash wheels....................**£4,000-5,000**
  1935-39 Type 2.
- Red body, smooth cast hubs............. **£400-500**
  1939-41 Type 3
- Red body **£400-500**

28d Delivery Van 'OXO'
  Blue body, 'Beef In Brief' and 'Beef At Its Best' in Gold.
  1934-35 Type 1.
- Green wash wheels.....................**£4,000-5,000**
  1935-39 Type 2.
- Smooth cast hubs **£750-1,000**
- 1939-41 Type 3 .... **£700-900**

28e Delivery Van 'ENSIGN CAMERAS'
  Orange body, 'ENSIGN CAMERAS' (on n/s) and 'ENSIGN LUKOS FILMS' (on o/s) in Gold.
  1934-35
- Type 1, Blue wash wheels **£4,000-5,000**

28e Delivery Van 'FIRESTONE TYRES'
  'Firestone Tyres' in Gold.
  1934-35
- Type 1, White body......................**£4,000-5,000**
  1935-39
- Type 2, Blue or White body **£750-1,000**
  1939-41
- Type 3, Blue or White body **£400-500**

28f   Delivery Van 'PALETHORPES'
  Pale Grey-Blue body, Pink sausage decal, 'Palethorpes Royal Cambridge' on van sides, 'Palethorpes Model Factory' on rear (Red and Navy Blue transfers).
  1934-35
- Type 1, Blue wash wheels **£4,000-5,000**
  1935-38
- Type 2, smooth cast hubs **£750-1,000**

28f   Delivery Van 'VIROL'
  Yellow body, 'Give Your Child A Virol

Constitution' in Black.
1938-39
- Type 2, Blue wash wheels **£750-1,000**
1939-41
- Type 3, smooth cast hubs **£400-500**

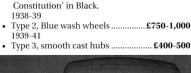

2nd type Kodak van

28g Delivery Van 'KODAK'
Yellow body,
'Use Kodak Film To Be Sure' in Red.
1934-35
- Type 1, Blue wash wheels **£4,000-5,000**
1935-39
- Type 2, smooth cast hubs **£750-1,000**
1939-41
- Type 3 .... **£400-500**
28h Delivery Van 'SHARPS TOFFEES'
'Sharps Toffee, Maidstone' in Gold.
1934-35
- Type 1, Black/Red body,
Yellow wash wheels **£1,500-2,000**
1935-35
- Type 2, Red body, smooth cast hubs **£500-700**
28h Delivery Van 'DUNLOP'
Red body, 'Dunlop Tyres' in Gold.
- 1935-39 Type 2 .... **£750-1,000**
- 1939-41 Type 3 .... **£400-500**
28k Delivery Van 'MARSH & BAXTER'
Dark Green body,
'Marsh's Sausages' and pig logo in Gold.
1934-35
- Type 1, Purple wash wheels.........**£4,000-5,000**
- Type 1, Green wash wheels **£4,000-5,000**
1935-39
- Type 2, smooth cast hubs **£750-1,000**
1939-41
- Type 3 .... **£500-700**
28L Delivery Van 'CRAWFORDS'
Red body, 'Crawfords Biscuits' in Gold.
1934-35
- Type 1, Yellow wash wheels.........**£2,500-3,500**
- Type 1, Green wash wheels **£2,500-3,500**
28m Delivery Van 'WAKEFIELD'S CASTROL'
Green body, 'Wakefield Castrol
Motor Oil' in Red.
1934-35
- Type 1, Yellow wash wheels.........**£4,000-5,000**
1935-39
- Type 2, smooth cast hubs **£400-500**
1939-41
- Type 3 ....**£1,500-2,000**
28n Delivery Van 'MECCANO'
Lemon Yellow body, 'Meccano Engineering
For Boys' in Red and Black.
1934-35
- Type 1. Renumbered from 22d....**£4,000-5,000**
1935-39
- Type 2, smooth cast hubs **£400-500**
28n Delivery Van 'ATCO'
Green body, 'Atco Lawn Mowers Sales and
Service' in Gold/Red.
- 1935-39 Type 2 .... **£750-1,000**
- 1939-41 Type 3 .... **£500-700**
28p Delivery Van 'CRAWFORDS'
Red body, 'Crawfords Biscuits' in Gold.
- 1935-39 Type 2 .... **£750-1,000**
- 1939-41 Type 3 .... **£750-1,000**
28r Delivery Van 'SWAN'
Black body, 'Swan Pens' and logo in Gold.
- 1936-39 Type 2 .... **£750-1,000**

- 1939-41 Type 3 .... **£750-1,000**
28s Delivery Van 'FRYS'
Brown or Cream body,
'Frys Chocolate' in Gold.
- 1936-39 Type 2 .... **£750-1,000**
- 1939-41 Type 3 .... **£300-400**
28t Delivery Van 'OVALTINE'
Red body,
'Drink Ovaltine For Health' in Gold/Black.
- 1936-39 Type 2 ....**£2,000-3,000**
- 1939-41 Type 3 .... **£400-500**
28w Delivery Van 'OSRAM'
Yellow body, 'Osram Lamps - a G.E.C.
Product' in Gold/Black.
- 1936-39 Type 2 .... **£750-1,000**
- 1940-41 Type 3 .... **£500-700**
28x Delivery Van 'HOVIS'
White body, 'Hovis For Tea' in Gold/Black.
- 1936-39 Type 2 .... **£750-1,000**
- 1939-41 Type 3 .... **£400-500**
28y Delivery Van 'EXIDE'
Red body, 'Exide Batteries' and
'Drydex Batteries' in Gold/Black.
- 1936-39 Type 2 .... **£400-500**
- 1939-41 Type 3 .... **£400-500**
**NB Further issues in this series were numbered
'280', as follows:**
280 Delivery Van (plain, no advertising)
1945-47
- Red or Blue, Type 3, open windows...... **£50-60**
1948-54
- As previous model, but with
filled-in rear windows **£50-60**
- Green body, Type 3,
filled-in rear windows **£400-500**
- Olive ('Military') Green body, Type 3,
filled-in rear windows **£80-95**
NB The 280 casting provided the basis
for 34c Loudspeaker Van.
280a Delivery Van 'VIYELLA'
Blue body,'Viyella Regd. for the Nursery'
in White and Black.
- 1937-39 Type 2 ....**£2,000-2,500**
- 1939-41 Type 3 .... **£700-950**
280b Delivery Van 'LYONS TEA'
1937-39
- Dark Blue body, 'Lyons Tea Always
the Best' in Red and White.
Only issued as Type 2......................**£750-1,000**

280b Delivery Van 'HARTLEYS JAM'
Cream body, 'Hartleys is Real Jam'
in Red/Green.
- 1939-39 Type 2 .... **£800-1,000**
- 1939-41 Type 3 .... **£400-500**
280c Delivery Van 'SHREDDED WHEAT'
Cream body, Red stripe,
'Welwyn Garden City, Herts' in Black.
- 1937-39 Type 2 .... **£750-1,000**
- 1939-40 Type 3 .... **£400-500**
280d Delivery Van 'BISTO'
1937-40
- Yellow body, 'Ah! Bisto' with logo,
Type 2 .... **£350-500**
1938-39
- Type 2, with large
'Bisto Kids' transfer **£750-1,000**
- Type 2, small Bisto Kids transfer,
with pie on table **£600-800**
1939-40
- Type 3, small Bisto Kids transfer
with pie on table **£400-500**
1940
- Yellow body, wording altered to
'Bisto' with logo **£400-500**
280e Delivery Van 'ECKO'
1937-39
- Type 2, Dark Green body,
'ECKO Radio' in Gold........................ **£500-750**
**280e Delivery Van
'YORKSHIRE EVENING POST'**
Cream body, 'Yorkshire Evening Post -

The Original Buff'.
- 1938-39 Type 2 .... **£750-1,000**
- 1939-39 Type 3 .... **£600-800**
280f Delivery Van 'MACKINTOSHS'
Red body, Gold logo: 'Mackintosh's Toffee
- A Smile in Every Piece'.
- 1937-39 Type 2 .... **£750-1,000**
- 1939-40 Type 3 .... **£400-500**
**NB Nos. 280g – 280m Delivery Vans were
made as promotional models.** All are Type 2.
280g 1939 'BENTALLS'
- Green body, Yellow upper side panels,
White roof, 'Bentalls Kingston on Thames'
and 'Phone Kin: 1001' in Yellow.
Two examples known..............**£10,000-12,500**
280h 1939 'MAISON de BONNETERIE'
- Dark Red, 'Maison de Bonneterie,
Leverancier' **£10,000-12,500**
280i 1939 'LIVERPOOL ECHO'
- Type 2, no details available......**£10,000-12,500**
280j 1939 'FENWICK'
- Apple Green body, White roof,
'Newcastle on Tyne'.
Two examples known..............**£10,000-12,500**
280k 1939 'H. G. LOOSE'
- Dark Green body, 'H. G. LOOSE' on
Cream panel, 'Looe' and 'Phone 123'.
One example known **£10,000-12,500**
280L 1939 'DE BIJENKORF'
- 'Amsterdam DenHaag Rotterdam'**£10,000-12,500**
280m 1939 'LAND'S FOR BAGS'
- Green, 'Land's for Bags' in Gold.
One example known (in very
poor condition)....................................... NGPP

*28 Series Delivery Van 'Hovis' - type 2 body, white with
gold lettering to sides, smooth black cast hubs, white
tyres.*

*28a pre-war Delivery Van 'Hornby Trains' - type 1, 'Dinky
Toys' impressed to underside of cab roof, yellow, 'Hornby
Trains - British & Guaranteed' logos to each side, very
light gold wash solid metal wheels.*

*28 pre-war Series Van - type 1, 'Palethorpes' grey, with
blue effect to wheels, 'Hornby Series' cast into underside,
fitted with tinplate radiator grille.*

30 Series

30e post-war Breakdown Lorry - grey, including jib, complete with wire hook and searchlight, black ridged hubs.

30e Breakdown Car (Crane Lorry)
1935-40
- Red, Yellow, Green, Brown or Grey body, Black wings, Black or Blue smooth hubs, open rear window **£100-120**
- Blue body, Dark Blue wings, Blue hubs, open rear window **£100-120**
1946-46
- Red or Grey body, Black wings, open rear window, ridged hubs **£60-70**
1947-48
- Red, Grey or Green body and wings, no rear window, ridged hubs **£40-50**

30j Austin Wagon (renumbered in 1954 to 412)
1950-54
- Blue body with hook, Mid-Blue hubs **£100-120**
- Light, Medium or Dark Maroon body, Maroon or Red hubs **£100-150**
- Brown body, Tan hubs **£400-500**
- Dark Blue body, Mid-Blue hubs .... NGPP
- Red body, Red hubs .... NGPP

30m Rear Tipping Wagon
1950-54 (renumbered in 1954 to 414)
- Maroon cab, Pale Green tipper and hubs, 'Dodge' on baseplate **£500-750**
- Orange cab, Pale Green tipper and hubs, 'Dodge' on baseplate **£500-750**
- Blue or Dark Blue cab, Grey rear **£60-70**

30n Farm Produce Wagon (1950-54)
See 'Farm and Garden Models'.

30p Petrol Tanker
- 1950-51 **'PETROL'**, Red or Green, cast in aluminium **£80-90**
- 1951-52 **'PETROL'**, Red or Green, cast in mazak **£80-90**
- 1952-54 (renumbered in 1954 to 440) **'MOBILGAS'**, Red body, Blue lettering on White background **£80-90**

30pa Petrol Tanker (renumbered in 1954 to 441)
- 1952-54 **'CASTROL'**, Green body and hubs, some aluminium, most mazak ... **£80-90**

30pb Petrol Tanker (renumbered in 1954 to 442)
- 1952-54 **'ESSO'**, Red body and hubs, 'MOTOR OIL - ESSO - PETROL' **£80-90**

30r Fordson Thames Flat Truck
1951-54 (renumbered in 1954 to 422)
- Red or Green body with hook **£60-70**
- Brown body, Brown hubs **£60-70**
- Brown body, Maroon hubs .... NGPP

30s Austin Covered Wagon
1950-54 (renumbered in 1954 to 413)
- Maroon body, Cream cover, Cream hubs, sold unboxed **£100-150**
- Dark Blue body, Light Blue cover, Light Blue hubs, sold unboxed **£300-400**
- Mid-Blue body, Light Blue cover, Light Blue hubs, sold unboxed **£100-150**

30v Electric Dairy Van 'EXPRESS DAIRY'
1949-54 (renumbered in 1954 to 490)
- Cream body, Red chassis, hubs and logo **£75-90**
- Grey body, Blue chassis, hubs and logo **£90-120**

30v Electric Dairy Van 'NCB' - light grey, with mid blue platform and ridged hubs.

30v Electric Dairy Van 'N.C.B.'
1949-54 (renumbered in 1954 to 491)
- Cream body, Red chassis, hubs and logo **£75-90**
- Grey body, Blue chassis, hubs and logo **£75-90**

30w Hindle-Smart Helecs
1952-54 (renumbered in 1954 to 421)
- Maroon body, Maroon or Red hubs, 'British Railways', hook, trailer uncouples **£60-70**

31 Series

31 Holland Coachcraft Van
1935-35
- Red, Green, Blue or Orange, 'Holland Coachcraft Registered Design', lead body **£2,000-3,000**
1935-35
- Mid-Green body, Gold stripe, Silver advert., Chrome hubs **£2,000-3,000**
- Cream body, Red coachline **£2,000-3,000**
1935-36
- Red, Blue or Orange, 'Holland Coachcraft Registered Design', diecast body **£2,000-3,000**
  NB A Red variant from 1935/6 was sold by Christie's in 2001 for £2,350.
- Light and Dark Blue with Silver coachlines, Silver grille and Yellow headlights. .... NGPP

31a Trojan 15 cwt Van 'ESSO'
1951-54 (renumbered in 1954 to 450)
- Red body, Maroon or Red hubs **£80-100**

31b Trojan 15 cwt Van 'DUNLOP'
1952-54 (renumbered in 1954 to 451)
- Red body, Maroon or Red hubs, 'The Worlds Master Tyre' **£80-100**

31c Trojan 15 cwt Van 'CHIVERS'
1953-54 (renumbered in 1954 to 452)
- Green body and hubs, 'CHIVERS JELLIES' and design **£80-100**

31d Trojan 15 cwt Van 'OXO'
1953-54 (renumbered in 1954 to 453)
- Mid-Blue or Violet-Blue body, Mid-Blue hubs, 'BEEFY OXO' **£300-400**

33 Series

33a Mechanical Horse
1935-36
NB 1st type have long slot and chrome hubs.
- Red, Green, Blue or Yellow body, 2.5 mm. trailer step **£150-175**
1936-40
- Same but 9.5 mm. trailer step **£125-150**
1946-?
- As previous model but also in Brown, Grey or Khaki **£125-150**

33b Flat Truck Trailer
1935-40
- Red, Green, Blue or Yellow body, no sides **£45-55**

33c Open Truck Trailer
1935-40

- Red, Green, Blue or Yellow body with sides **£45-55**

33d Box Van Trailer
1935-40
- Green tinplate body on cast chassis, no advertising **£100-125**
- **'HORNBY TRAINS'**, Dark Blue body, 'Hornby Trains British and Guaranteed' in Gold.. **£300-400**
- **'HORNBY TRAINS'**, Green body, 'Hornby Trains British and Guaranteed' in Gold.. **£300-400**
- **'MECCANO'**, Green body, 'Meccano Engineering For Boys' in Red and Black................................. **£300-400**
  NB Models 33a and 33d combined and given Ref No 33r - see below.

33e Dust Wagon Trailer
1935-40
- Blue, Yellow Grey or Green 33c (Open Trailer) Blue, Yellow, Grey or Green tinplate top **£70-90**
1946-47
- Grey body with Blue or Yellow tinplate top.. **£70-90**
- Red body with Blue or Yellow tinplate top.. **£70-90**

33f Petrol Tank Trailer
1935-40
- Green (33b) chassis/Red tank, or Red chassis/Green tank, no logo...... **£70-90**
- **'ESSO'** Green chassis/Red tank with 'ESSO' in Gold............................ **£80-120**
- **'CASTROL'** Red chassis/Green tank, 'Wakefield Castrol' **£80-120**

33r Railway Mechanical Horse and Trailer Van
1935-40 33a Mechanical Horse and 33d Box Van Trailer in railway liveries. These were also available separately as 33ra and 33rd (see below).
- **'L.N.E.R.'** Blue and Black, 'L.N.E.R. Express Parcels Traffic' **£250-350**
- **'L.M.S.'** Maroon and Black, 'L.M.S. Express Parcels Traffic' **£250-350**
- **'G.W.R'** Brown and Cream, 'G.W.R. Express Cartage Services'..... **£250-350**
- **'S.R.'** Green (Cream cab roof) and Black, 'Southern Railway'.......... **£500-750**

33ra Mechanical Horse
1935-40
'L.N.E.R.' Blue and Black, 'L.N.E.R. 901' **£250-350**
- **'L.M.S.'** Maroon and Black, 'L.M.S. 2246' **£250-350**
- **'G.W.R.'** Brown and Cream, 'G.W.R. 2742' **£250-350**
- **'S.R.'** Green (Cream roof) and Black, '3016 M' **£250-350**

33rd Railway Trailer
1935-40
- **'L.N.E.R.'** Blue and Black, 'L.N.E.R. Express Parcels Traffic' **£250-350**
- **'L.M.S.'** Maroon and Black, 'L.M.S. Express Parcels Traffic' **£250-350**
- **'G.W.R.'** Brown and Cream, 'G.W.R. Express Cartage Services'..... **£250-350**
- **'S.R.'** Green and Black, 'Southern Railway' **£350-500**

33w Mechanical Horse and Open Wagon - scarce colour variation comprising olive green prime mover, black ridged hubs with maroon trailer.

33w Mechanical Horse and Open Wagon
1947-54 (renumbered in 1954 to 415)
- Cab colours: Grey, Fawn, Dark or
Mid-Green, Olive, Red, Brown, Blue or
Yellow. Trailer colours:
Grey, Fawn, Maroon, Brown,
Dark or Mid-Green, Olive or Cream **£75-95**

34 Series

34a 'ROYAL AIR MAIL SERVICE'
1935-40
- Blue car, Silver lettering,
Gold crest **£400-500**

*34b post-war Royal Mail Van - red, with black roof,
bonnet and ridged hubs,*

34b 'ROYAL MAIL' Van
1938-47
- Red body, open rear windows,
Black bonnet/wings/roof/hubs **£150-175**
1948-51
- Red body, Black bonnet/wings/roof,
Black or Red hubs,
filled rear windows.......................... **£100-125**
1952-52
- Red body/roof/hubs, Black bonnet/front
wings, filled-in rear windows **£125-150**
34c Loudspeaker Van (280 casting)
1948-54 (renumbered in 1954 to 492)
- Fawn, Grey, Green, Brown or
Blue body Black loudspeakers **£70-80**
- Brown, Blue or Green body,
Silver loudspeakers **£70-80**
60y Thompson Aircraft Tender
1938-40
- Red with 'Shell Aviation Services' in Gold;
Black or White solid rubber wheels.. **£300-400**
151b 6-wheel Covered Wagon
1937-40 (renumbered in 1940 to 25s)
- Gloss Green body, tinplate canopy,
seat holes, spare wheel **£125-150**
1947-54 (export only from 1950)
(renumbered in 1954 to 620)
- Matt-Green or Greenish-Brown body .. **£60-70**
251 Aveling Barford Road Roller
1954-63 (renumbered from 25p in 1954)
- Mid or Dark Green body, Red rollers ... **£45-55**
- Lime Green body, Red rollers **£70-90**
- Apple Green body, Red rollers **£70-90**
252 Bedford Refuse Wagon
1954-60 (renumbered from 25v in 1954)
- Tan body, Green tinplate shutters,
Red hubs, window glazing in some .. **£100-125**
1960-63
- Lime Green body, Black tinplate
shutters, Cream hubs, window
glazing in some................................. **£125-150**
1963-63
- Orange cab, Light Grey back, Green
tinplate shutters and diecast hubs,
window glazing, Black grille............. **£300-350**
1964-64
- Orange cab, Light Grey back and
diecast hubs, Green plastic shutters,
window glazing................................. **£250-350**
1964-65
- Bright Orange cab, Light Grey back,
Green plastic shutters, Red plastic

hubs, window glazing **£250-350**
- As previous but matt-Black base....... **£250-350**
260 'ROYAL MAIL' Van (Morris 'J')
1955-61
- Red body, Black roof,
Gold 'E II R' crest.............................. **£125-150**
260 VW 'DEUTSCHE BUNDESPOST'
1971-72
- Yellow body (129 casting, 100mm),
made for German Market.................. **£100-150**

261 Telephone Service Van.

261 Telephone Service Van (Morris 'Z')
1955-61
- Olive-Green/Black, 'POST OFFICE
TELEPHONES', ladder....................... **£100-125**
273 Mini Minor Van 'R.A.C.'
1965-70
- Blue body, White roof, Black base,
Red interior, 'ROAD SERVICE'
on sides **£175-200**
- Same model but with Blue interior .. **£175-200**
- With Red interior, Silver baseplate
and redesigned rear doors **£150-175**
NB Factory errors have resulted in
some rear door logos reading
'ROAD ROAD' instead of
'ROAD SERVICE' as normal .... NGPP
274 Mini Minor Van 'A.A.'
1964-73
- Yellow body, White roof,
'PATROL SERVICE', original
'entwined' logo **£125-150**
- Same, but Yellow roof, Blue int. **£125-150**
- Yellow body, White roof, Red interior,
'AA SERVICE', modern 'simple'
logo, Silver or Black base **£90-120**
- Same model but with Blue interior **£90-120**
- With Yellow roof and Blue interior **£90-120**
Note: 'AA' logo designs:
a) Embossed logo 'AA',
b) Waterslide transfer in square recess
c) Waterslide transfer on raised panel
Rear door casting variations:
a) Rear door hinge pins extend directly
into chassis holes
b) Rear door hinge pins located into slots.
Central base colour variations:
a) Red, b) Blue, c) White

*274 Mini Van 'Joseph Mason Paints' - note the included
leaflet and the essential protector for the roof sign.*

274 Mini Minor Van
'JOSEPH MASON PAINTS'
1969-70
- Promotional in special Red box with
advert card. 650 issued. Maroon
body, Red seats and rear van
body base, roof sign, 'PAINTS'
labels, spun hubs, special box........**£800-1,000**

275 Brinks Armoured Car
1964-66
- Grey/Blue, 'Brinks Security Since 1859',
2 figures, 2 crates, plastic hubs.......... **£300-400**
1966-70
- Same as previous model but no driver
or crates, US packaging...................... **£150-200**
- Grey body White roof, Blue base,
metal hubs, assembled in USA .... NGPP
- Mexican issue:
Blue body with Grey doors and
Red/White/Blue crests,
plastic hubs.................................. **£750-1,000**
279 Aveling Barford Diesel Roller
1965-71
- Orange body, Grey engine covers,
Blue or Green rollers, Blue driver **£75-95**
1971-80
- Yellow cab, Black roof, Silver rollers **£35-45**
- Yellow cab, Black roof, Black rollers **£35-45**
- Yellow cab, Blue roof, Yellow square
engine covers, Silver rollers.................. **£35-45**
- Yellow cab, Black roof, Yellow
square engine covers, Silver rollers **£35-45**
- Yellow cab, Grey Roof, Yellow
square engine covers, Silver rollers **£35-45**
280 Series Delivery Vans
See '28 Series Delivery Vans' listing.
280 Mobile 'MIDLAND BANK'
1966-68
- White/Silver, Blue stripe, Gold
crest, opening doors, figure **£120-140**
343 Farm Produce Wagon
See 'Farm and Garden Models'.

'Convoy' Series (380-387)

380 Skip Truck
- 1977-79 Yellow and Orange body **£10-20**
381 Farm Wagon
- 1977-80 Yellow and Brown body.......... **£10-20**
382 Dumper Truck
- 1978-80 Red body/Grey back,
Red body/Black back or Yellow
body/Grey back **£10-20**
383 'N.C.L.' Truck
- 1978-80, Yellow,
'NATIONAL CARRIERS Ltd' **£10-20**
384 Fire Rescue Wagon
- 1977-79 Red body, White fire escape... **£10-20**
385 'ROYAL MAIL' Truck
- 1977-79 Red body.............................. **£10-20**
386 'AVIS' Truck
- 1979 Red body. Catalogued
but not issued .... NPP
387 'PICKFORDS' Truck
- 1979 Red / Blue. Catalogued
but not issued .... NPP
? 'HARRODS' Truck
- 1979 Khaki body .... NGPP
? 'POST OFFICE TELEPHONES'
- 1979 Khaki body .... NGPP
? 'A.A.' Truck
- 1979 Yellow body.................................. NGPP
? 'AMERICAN FIRE BRIGADE'
- 1979 No details .... NGPP
NB See also 687 Convoy Army Truck
in the Military Vehicles section.
390 Customised Transit Van
- 1978 Type 3 Metallic Blue body with
'VAMPIRE' and 'flame' design .... NGPP
400 B.E.V. Truck
1954-60 (renumbered in 1954 from 14a)
- Dark Blue or Mid-Blue or Grey with
Blue, Grey or Red hubs, 1 PP **£30-35**
401 Coventry Climax Fork Lift
1954-64 (renumbered in 1954 from 14c)
- Orange body, Green forks, Tan driver .. **£30-35**
- Red body, Green forks **£300-400**
402 Bedford 'COCA-COLA' Truck
1966-69
- Red cab and back, White roof,
Blue interior, six trays of crates,

Red plastic hubs **£130-160**

404 Climax Fork Lift
1967-72
- Red/Yellow with 'CG4' rear logo **£25-35**
- Red/Yellow front with all Red rear,
  plus stick-on 'CG4' label **£20-25**
  1978
- Yellow body with 'Climax' on fork
  guide and 'TC4' on engine cover **£20-25**

406 Commer Articulated Truck
1963-66 (424 without accessories,
Supertoy)
- Yellow/Grey, Blue plastic hubs **£110-140**

407 Ford Transit Vans
See 'Commercial Vehicles Identification'
pages for an explanation of casting
Types 1, 2 and 3.
- 1966-69 **'KENWOOD'**
  Blue/White, promotional. Type 1 ..... **£100-125**
- 1970-71 **'TELEFUSION'**
  White body, 'Colour TV, Telefusion'.
  Intended promotional not issued .... NPP
  1970-75 **'HERTZ TRUCK RENTALS'**
  Promotionals. Type 1.
- Yellow body, Red interior,
  Blue baseplate **£80-100**
- Yellow body, Grey interior,
  Black baseplate **£80-100**
- 1970-73 **'AVIS TRUCK RENTALS'**
  Red body. Kit only but not issued .... NPP
- **'PELTZ BADKEREI'** (promotional)
  Blue lower, Yellow upper **£50-60**

408 Big Bedford Lorry
1956-63 (renumbered from 522 / 922)
- Maroon cab, Light Tan back,
  Fawn or Cream hubs,
  (with window glazing from 1961) **£125-150**
- Dark Blue cab, Yellow back,
  Yellow or Cream hubs **£175-225**
- Pink cab, Cream back,
  Cream hubs **£1,500-2,000**

409 Bedford Articulated Lorry
1956-63 (renumbered from 521 / 921)
All have Black knobbly tyres.
- Deep Yellow cab and back, Black
  wings, Red hubs, Yellow box **£175-225**
- As previous model but with window
  glazing. Lighter Yellow box................ **£150-200**

410 Bedford End Tipper - yellow cab and chassis, with ridged hubs, mid blue tipping body.

410 Bedford End Tipper Truck
1954-61 (renumbered in 1954 from 25m)
- Red cab, chassis and diecast hubs,
  Cream back **£175-200**
- Yellow cab, chassis and diecast hubs,
  Mid-Blue back, window glazing........ **£150-175**
  1962-63
- Red cab, chassis and plastic hubs,
  Cream back, window glazing **£175-200**
- Yellow cab, chassis and plastic hubs,
  Dark or Mid-Blue back, glazing **£300-350**

410 Bedford CF Vans
- 1972-72 **'SIMPSONS'**
  Canadian promotional.
  Red/Black, 'Simpsons' and logos........ **£75-100**
- 1974 **'DANISH POST'**
  Danish promotional.
  Yellow body, 'Danish Post' emblem ... **£75-100**
- 1974-75 **'JOHN MENZIES'**
  Promotional, Dark Blue body,
  'John Menzies' logo............................ **£100-125**

- 1974-74 **'BELACO'**
  Promotional, Brown/Black,
  'Brake and Clutch Parts' **£75-100**
- 1975-76 **'M.J. HIRE'** promotional.
  White body, 'M.J. Hire Service' **£25-30**
- 1975-77 **'MODELLERS WORLD'**
  White body, 'Modellers World'.
  This is a Code 2 model........................... **£25-30**
- 1975-75 **'MARLEY TILES'**
  Red body with 'Marley Building' logo .. **£25-30**
- 1979 **'COLLECTORS GAZETTE'**
  White body. A Code 2 model................ **£25-30**
- 1972-74 **'ROYAL MAIL'**
  Red body with 'ROYAL MAIL' and
  'E II R' crest **£15-20**
- 1974-80 **'ROYAL MAIL'**
  As previous model but with raised
  rectangle on roof **£15-20**
NB Many Code-2 issues exist (produced
by John Gay) and include the following
liveries: 'MOBIL', 'BN',
'HERTZ TRUCK RENTAL',
'JIMMY CARTER', 'MATRA',
'ELF', 'SILVER JUBILLEE 1952-1977',
'KLG', 'PORTAKABIN', 'WIMPEY'.

411 Bedford Truck
1954-59 (renumbered in 1954 from 25w)
- Mid-Green cab, chassis,
  back and hubs **£100-125**
  1959-60
- Mid-Green cab and body, Pale Green
  hubs, gloss base, block-tread tyres ... **£100-125**

412 Austin Wagon
1954-60 (renumbered in 1954 from 30j)
- Powder Blue body, Lemon or
  Dark Blue hubs **£350-450**
- Maroon body, Red hubs **£120-140**
- Dark Blue body, Mid-Blue hubs **£140-160**
- Lemon Yellow body,
  Mid-Green hubs **£750-1,000**
- Lemon Yellow body, Blue hubs...... **£750-1,000**

412 Bedford CF Van 'AA'
1974-80
- Yellow or Lemon-Yellow body, headboard,
  'AA SERVICE', plastic hubs.................... **£15-20**

413 Austin Covered Wagon - scarce example with dark blue body, mid blue tinplate tilt and ridged hubs.

413 Austin Covered Wagon
1954-60 (renumbered in 1954 from 30s)
- Maroon body,
  Cream tinplate tilt / hubs **£100-150**
- Maroon body and hubs,
  Tan tinplate tilt **£100-150**
- Dark Blue body, Mid-Blue tinplate
  tilt, Light Blue hubs **£150-200**
- Mid-Blue body, Mid-Blue tinplate
  tilt, Light Blue hubs **£150-200**
- Red body, Light Grey tinplate tilt,
  Cream or Grey hubs **£300-400**
- Red body, Beige tinplate
  tilt, Red hubs **£300-400**
- Light or Mid-Blue body, Cream
  tinplate tilt, Cream hubs. Plain box .. **£400-500**
- Red body, Grey or Beige tinplate
  tilt, Grey hubs **£400-500**
- Maroon body, Beige tilt, Red hubs ... **£300-400**
- Olive-drab body,
  (Royal Army Volunteer Reserve)............ NGPP

414 Dodge Tipper late model with light yellow box and rare spun aluminium hubs.

414 Dodge Rear Tipping Wagon
1954-64 (renumbered in 1954 from 30m)
- Red cab and hubs, Green back.......... **£160-190**
- Orange cab and hubs, Green back.... **£160-190**
- Orange cab,
  Mid-Green back and hubs................. **£160-190**
- Greyish-Blue cab, Grey back,
  Mid-Blue hubs.................................... **£160-190**
- Mid-Blue cab and hubs, Grey back .. **£160-190**
- Mid-Blue cab, Cream hubs, Grey back.
  In late issue lighter Yellow box.......... **£160-190**
- Violet-Blue cab, Grey back / hubs **£250-300**
- Royal Blue cab, Grey back / hubs **£250-300**
NB Early issues with or
  without bonnet louvres.

415 Mechanical Horse and Wagon (33a + 33c)
1954-59 (renumbered in 1954 from 33w)
- Blue horse, Cream trailer................... **£125-175**
- Red horse, Brown trailer **£125-175**
Ford Transit Vans.
See 'Commercial Vehicles Identification'
pages for an explanation of
casting Types 1, 2 and 3.

416 Ford Transit Van, 'FORD' promotional.
1975-78
- Orange-Yellow body, cast hubs,
  '1,000,000 TRANSITS', Type 2 .... NGPP

416 Ford Transit 'MOTORWAY SERVICES'
- 1975-78
  Yellow body, special lights, Type 2,
  with two warning boards and cones..... **£45-55**

417 Ford Transit 'MOTORWAY'
- 1978-79 As model 416 but Type 3 .... **£30-40**

417 Leyland Comet Lorry with Stake Body
1956-58 (renumbered in 1956 from 931)
(Stake body secured by a rivet. Yellow box).
- Violet Blue cab and chassis, Dark Yellow
  back, Mid-Blue hubs, Yellow box...... **£185-225**
- Dark Blue cab and chassis,
  Brown back, Red hubs **£300-350**
  1958-59
- Yellow cab and chassis, Pale Green
  back, Mid-Green hubs, Grey tyres **£350-400**

418 Comet Wagon with hinged tailboard - dark green cab and chassis, orange rear body, this is a scarce colour variation with cream Supertoy hubs.

418 Leyland Comet with Hinged Tailboard
1956-59 (renumbered in 1956 from 932)
Back of model secured by a rivet. Yellow box.

- Dark Green cab and chassis, Orange back, Mid-Green hubs **£175-225**
- Dark Blue cab and chassis, Mid-Blue back, Blue, Cream or Red hubs **£175-225**

419 Leyland Comet Cement Lorry
1956-59 (renumbered in 1954 from 933)
- Yellow body and hubs, 1 packing piece. 'Portland Blue-Circle Cement' **£145-175**

420 Forward Control Lorry
1954-61 (renumbered in 1954 from 25r)
- Cream body, Mid-Blue hubs **£100-125**
- Red body, Cream hubs **£100-125**
- Red body, Mid-Green hubs **£160-190**
- Mid-Green body, Cream hubs **£190-230**
- Mid-Green body, Red hubs **£140-170**
- Blue body, Cream hubs **£140-170**

421 Hindle Smart Helecs 'British Railways'
1955-59 (renumbered in 1955 from 30w)
- Maroon body, Red hubs, hook **£90-110**

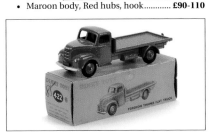

No 422 Fordson Thames Flat Truck - orangey red including ridged hubs.

422 Fordson Thames Flat Truck
1954-60 (renumbered in 1954 from 30r)
- Red body and hubs **£125-150**
- Bright Green body and hubs **£125-150**
- Dark Green body, Mid-Green hubs. In dual-numbered box **£125-150**

424 Commer Convertible Articulated Vehicle
1963-66
- Primrose-Yellow cab, Silver-Grey back, Blue plastic tilt, Blue plastic hubs, plus detachable White plastic 'stake' body **£200-300**
424 lift-up lid box types:
1 - Lemon, Green and Orange,
2 - Grey, Red and Yellow.

425 Bedford TK Coal Wagon 'HALL & Co.'
1964-69
- Red body, interior and plastic hubs, clear windows, 6 bags, scales **£160-190**
- Red body and plastic hubs, Blue windows and interior, 6 bags, scales **£175-225**

428 Large Trailer (all with hook)
1956-66 (renumbered in 1956 from 951)
- Grey body, Red hubs, Grey tyres **£75-100**
- Grey body, Mid-Blue hubs, Grey tyres **£75-100**
- Grey body, Light Green hubs, Grey tyres **£75-100**
- Grey body, grooved Yellow hubs, Black tyres, late issue lighter Yellow box ... **£100-150**
- Grey body, grooved Red hubs, Black tyres, late issue lighter Yellow box **£75-100**
- Yellow body, Red hubs, Black tyres, late issue lighter Yellow box **£75-100**
1967-71
- Grey body, Red plastic hubs, Black tyres **£100-150**
- Red body, Silver 'button' hubs, Black tyres **£100-150**

429 Trailer
1954-64 (renumbered in 1954 from 25g)
- Dark Green body, Light Green hubs, wire drawbar, Black treaded tyres, hook, axle pivot is part of main casting **£80-100**
- As previous model, but with Red body, Black or Red hubs................................. **£80-100**

430 Commer Breakdown Truck
1954-64 (renumbered in 1954 from 25x)
- 'DINKY SERVICE' logo, operable crane, late issues have window glazing.
- Tan cab, Mid-Green back with Black logo, Red hubs. Yellow or Blue/White striped box **£125-150**
- Cream cab, Mid-Blue back with Black logo, Red hubs. Yellow box **£450-550**
- Dark Stone cab, Blue back with Black logo, Red hubs. Yellow box **£450-550**
- Red cab, Light Grey back with Blue logo, Mid-Blue or Red metal hubs. Yellow box **£450-550**
- Red cab (glazed), Light Grey back, Blue logo, Blue plastic hubs. Yellow box... **£450-550**
- Red cab (glazed), Light Grey back with Blue logo, Red plastic hubs. Yellow box **£500-750**

430 Commer Breakdown Lorry - scarce later version with windows and pink/red cab and chassis, blue plastic hubs, light grey body and jib.

430 Johnson 2 ton Dumper
1977-80
- Orange/Red or Orange/Yellow body, Blue and Red driver, Black or Orange engine **£20-25**

431 Guy 4 ton Lorry (2nd type)
1956-58 (renumbered in 1956 from 911)
- Red cab/chassis, Fawn back, Red hubs, unpainted hook **£200-250**
- Violet Blue cab/chassis, Mid-Blue back, Mid-Blue hubs **£200-250**
- Mid-Blue cab, chassis and back, Supertoys hubs. Later yellow/blue card box with lift-off lid................**£1,000-1,400**

431 Guy Warrior 4-ton Lorry. The red and green version is possibly the scarcer of the two.

431 Guy Warrior 4 ton Lorry
1958-60
- Light Tan cab (no window glazing), Dark Green back, Mid-Green hubs .. **£300-400**
- Light Tan cab (with window glazing), Dark Green back, Mid-Green hubs .. **£300-400**
1960-64
- Red cab (with window glazing), Red chassis and back, Dark Green back.. **£300-400**

432 Guy Flat Truck (2nd type)
1956-57 (renumbered in 1956 from 912)

- Mid-Blue cab/chassis/hook, Red flatbed, Mid-Blue hubs **£200-250**
- Red cab/chassis/hook, Mid-Blue flatbed and hubs................ **£375-425**
- Dark Blue cab, Mid-Blue hubs, Red flatbed, in a lift-off lid box with 'H. Hudson Dobson' label **£1,750-2,000**

432 Guy Warrior Flat Truck - tan cab and chassis, windows, dark green flat back, mid green Supertoy hubs, riveted back.

432 Guy Warrior Flat Truck
1958-60
- Green cab (no window glazing), Red flatbed, Red hubs **£200-300**
1960-64
- Green cab (with window glazing), Red flatbed, Red hubs **£200-300**

432 Foden Tipping Lorry
1976-79 (Same casting as 668).
- White cab, Red chassis, Yellow back..... **£35-45**

433 Guy Flat Truck with Tailboard (2nd type)
1956-57 (renumbered in 1956 from 913)
- Dark Green cab/chassis/hook, Mid-Green flatbed and hubs............. **£200-250**
- Violet Blue cab/chassis/hook, Orange flatbed, Mid-Blue hubs, one packing piece in box **£200-250**

433 Guy Warrior Flat Truck with Tailboard
1958 Listed in catalogue but not issued ... NPP

434 Bedford TK Crash Truck
1964-66 'TOP RANK Motorway Services'
- White body with Green flash, Dark Green hubs, Red interior **£140-160**
1966-70 'AUTO SERVICES'
- Red or Metallic Red cab, Pale Grey back, Red metal or plastic hubs **£90-120**
NB Add 15% to price if in detailed picture box or with Green hubs.

435 Bedford TK Tipper
1964-66
- Grey cab, Blue roof, Orange back........ **£90-120**
1966-68
- Yellow cab with Yellow or Black roof, Silver back, Yellow sides, Red hubs .. **£175-225**
1968-71
- White cab / roof, Silver back, Blue sides, Blue hubs **£175-220**
- Blue cab, Orange and Grey back....... **£150-175**
- Red cab / sides, Black roof, Silver back.. **£150-175**

436 'ATLAS COPCO' Lorry
1963-69
- Yellow, Pale Grey interior, matt baseplate **£50-60**
- Yellow, Dark Blue interior, gloss baseplate **£50-60**
- Yellow body, Black roof, Red interior, Silver/Yellow back, Blue plastic hubs **£80-100**

437 Muir Hill 2WL Loader
1962-70
- Red body with hook, no grille detail..... **£20-25**
- Yellow body with Red or Silver hubs **£20-25**
1970-78
- Yellow with Red arms with hook, with or without grille detail **£20-25**
- Orange body, Orange or Black arms..... **£30-40**

438 Ford D800 Tipper Truck
(with opening doors)
1970-77
- Metallic Red cab, Yellow tipper,
  Yellow or Silver hubs.............................. **£55-65**
- Metallic Red cab, Metallic Blue tipper,
  Yellow plastic hubs, White interior... **£100-125**
- Orange cab, Orange or Yellow
  tipper, Silver hubs.............................. **£125-150**
- Bright Red cab, Orange tipper,
  Silver hubs **£50-60**
- Bright Red cab and tipper, Silver hubs . **£50-60**
- Promotional: White cab, Blue back,
  Silver chassis, with cardboard load
  'POLCARB'. In plain White box
  with folded leaflet.............................. **£200-250**

439 Ford Snowplough and Tipper Truck - scarce colour variation with light metallic blue cab, pale blue tipping body, cast hubs, silver chassis, yellow plough attachment with white cab interior.

439 Ford D800 Snow Plough
1970-76
- Dark Metallic Blue cab, Orange
  tipper, Yellow plough, White hubs.... **£100-120**
  1976-78
- Dark Metallic Blue cab, Pale Blue
  tipper, Yellow plough, Silver hubs..... **£125-145**
- Light Metallic Blue cab, Orange tipper,
  Dark Yellow plough, Silver hubs **£50-70**
- Light Metallic Blue cab,
  Pale Blue tipper, Red plough **£100-125**
- Medium Blue cab, Yellow plough,
  Powder Blue tipper, Silver hubs **£50-70**
- Medium Blue cab, Yellow plough,
  Powder Blue tipper, Lemon hubs **£50-60**
- Orange cab and tipper,
  Dark Yellow plough, Silver hubs **£50-60**
- Orange cab, Dark Yellow tipper and
  plough, Silver hubs.............................. **£50-60**
- All-Orange body, cast Silver hubs......... **£50-60**

440 Ford D800 Tipper Truck
(non-opening doors)
1977-78
- Orange cab, Yellow tipper,
  Silver or Black chassis **£35-40**
- Orange cab, Orange tipper **£35-40**
- Orange cab, Light Blue tipper **£35-40**
- Red cab, Red Tipper, Silver hubs.......... **£35-40**
- Red cab, Orange Tipper, Silver hubs..... **£35-40**
- Red cab, Light Blue Tipper,
  Silver hubs **£35-40**
- Red cab, Black roof,
  Red tipper and hubs.............................. **£35-40**

440 Petrol Tanker 'MOBILGAS'
1954-58 (renumbered in 1954 from 30p)
- Red body and hubs, 'MOBILGAS' in
  White letters with Blue borders **£135-150**
  1958-61
- Red body and hubs, 'MOBILGAS' in
  Blue letters on White background **£135-150**

441 Petrol Tanker 'CASTROL'
1954-60 (renumbered in 1954 from 30pa)
- Mid-Green body and hubs **£135-150**

442 Petrol Tanker 'ESSO'
1954-60 (renumbered in 1954 from 30pb)
- Red body and hubs, Dark Blue decal:
  'ESSO MOTOR OIL - PETROL' **£135-150**
- As previous model but with
  Pale Blue outline decal **£125-150**

443 Petrol Tanker 'NATIONAL'
1957-58
- Yellow body and hubs, 'NATIONAL
  BENZOLE MIXTURE'........................ **£200-250**

448 Chevrolet El Camino Pick-Up with Trailers
1963-68
- Turquoise and Ivory with Yellow interior,
  Red 'ACME HIRE', spun hubs,
  open trailer, Red box trailer **£275-325**

449 Chevrolet El Camino Pick-up
1961-69 (All have spun hubs)
- Off-White lower body, Turquoise
  upper body and roof, Red interior **£100-125**
- Off-White lower body, Turquoise upper
  body and roof, Yellow interior........... **£175-225**
- Off-White lower body, Turquoise upper
  body and roof, Turquoise interior..... **£175-225**
  NB Various shades of Turquoise are
  known to exist.
  South African issues (all with Red interior):
- All-Turquoise body......................**£1,000-1,200**

- Cream top, Caramel lower...........**£1,000-1,200**
- Turquoise top, Cream lower........**£1,000-1,200**
- All-Cream body **£1,000-1,200**

449 Johnston Road Sweeper
1977-79 Later version of model 451 but
with cast-in (non-opening) cab doors.
- Yellow or Lime-Green body **£30-35**
- All Yellow promotional with
  'JOHNSTON' stickers, normal box........ **£40-50**
- All Yellow promotional with
  'JOHNSTON' stickers, special box **£70-80**
- Orange or Metallic Red cab,
  Metallic Green rear **£40-50**

450 Esso Trojan Van - red, with maroon ridged hubs.

450 Trojan Van 'ESSO'
1954-57 (renumbered in 1954 from 31a)
- Red body, White stripe,
  Red or Maroon hubs, 'Esso' logo **£150-175**
- Maroon hub version issued in
  U.S.A. trade packs.................................... NGPP

450 Bedford TK Van 'CASTROL'
1965-70
- Metallic Green body, 'CASTROL' in
  thick lettering, gloss chassis, Red
  interior and plastic hubs,
  'The Masterpiece In Oils'................. **£135-155**
- Same, but 'CASTROL' in thin
  lettering, and with matt chassis **£135-155**

451 Trojan Van 'DUNLOP'
1954-57 (renumbered in 1954 from 31b)
- Red body and hubs,
  'Dunlop The Worlds Master Tyre'..... **£160-200**

451 Johnston Road Sweeper
1971-77
- Orange cab (opening doors),
  White interior, Metallic Green tank **£40-50**
- Yellow cab and tank, White interior . **£125-150**
- Light Metallic Blue cab, White
  interior, Metallic Green tank **£110-130**
- Metallic Green cab, White interior,
  Orange tank **£40-50**

452 Trojan Van 'CHIVERS'
1954-57 (renumbered in 1954 from 31c)
- Dark Green body, Mid-Green hubs,
  'CHIVERS JELLIES' logo **£250-300**

453 Trojan Van 'OXO' (not boxed)
1954-54 (renumbered in 1954 from 31c)
- Mid-Blue or Violet-Blue body, Mid-
  lue hubs, White 'BEEFY OXO' **£300-400**

454 Trojan Van 'CYDRAX'
1957-59
- Light Green body and hubs,
  'DRINK CYDRAX' logo **£160-190**

455 Trojan Van 'BROOKE BOND TEA'
1957-60
- Dark Red or Cherry-Red body,
  Red hubs **£160-190**
- Promotional issue: As previous issue with
  white label on roof. The red logo states:
  'Since 1924 more than 5,700 Trojan 'Little
  Red Vans' supplied. Replaced on a long life
  basis'. A similar label is attached to
  its (normal) box **£400-600**

465 Morris 10 cwt Van 'CAPSTAN'
1959-59
- Light Blue and Dark Blue body, Mid-
  Blue hubs, 'Have A CAPSTAN' **£160-190**

470 Austin A40 Van 'SHELL-BP'
- Red and Green body with 'SHELL'
  and 'BP' decals **£120-140**

470 Austin A40 Van 'OMNISPORT'
1954 Factory drawing exists
but not issued .... NPP

471 Austin A40 Van 'NESTLES'
1955-60
- Dark Red body, Yellow hubs **£120-140**
- Dark Red body, Beige hubs **£120-140**

*472 Raleigh Cycles Austin Van - dark green,
yellow ridged hubs.*

472 Austin A40 Van 'RALEIGH'
1956-60
- Dark Green body, Yellow hubs.......... **£120-140**

480 Bedford CA Van 'KODAK'
1954-56
- Yellow body, 'Kodak CAMERAS
  & FILMS' in Red and Black................ **£120-140**

481 Bedford CA Van 'OVALTINE'
1955-60
- Blue body with 'Ovaltine' and
  'Ovaltine Biscuits' logo on Cream
  panel and sides................................. **£120-140**

482 Bedford Van 'DINKY TOYS'
1956-60
- Orange-Yellow lower body,
  Lemon upper body and hubs,
  'Dinky Toys' in Red........................... **£160-180**
- Deep Yellow lower body,
  Pale Yellow upper body and hubs **£160-180**

490 Electric Dairy Van 'EXPRESS DAIRY'
1954-60 (renumbered in 1965 from 30v)
- Cream body, Red chassis,
  hubs and logo **£135-150**
- Light Grey body,
  Blue chassis/hubs/logo **£135-150**

491 Electric Dairy Van 'N.C.B.'
1954-60 (renumbered in 1954 from 30v)
- Cream body with Red chassis,
  hubs and logo, export model **£135-150**
- Grey body, Blue chassis,
  hubs and logo, export model **£135-150**
- Trade Pack of Six **£1,200-1,400**

491 Electric Dairy Van 'JOB'S DAIRY'
- 1960 Cream/Red. 1,176 Code-2 models
  made for promotional purposes **£200-250**
- Trade pack of six models **£800-900**

492 Loudspeaker Van (280 casting, Type 3)
1954-57 (renumbered in 1954 from 34c)
- Violet-Blue, Fawn or Green body,
  Silver, Mid-Blue or Black hubs,
  Silver or Black loudspeakers **£125-150**

- Violet-Blue body.................................**£175-200**

492 Election Mini-Van 'Vote for Somebody'
1964-64
- White body, Red interior, Orange
loudspeakers, figure, microphone and
cable. Yellow 'see-through' box.........**£160-190**

501 1st cab Foden 8-wheeled Wagon - fawn cab and rear body, red ridged hubs and chassis, with small hook to rear and herringbone tyres.

501 Foden Diesel 8-Wheel Wagon
1947-48
1st type cab with flash, spare wheel,
hook on some, no tank slits in chassis,
no chain-post bosses, Black
'herringbone' tyres, Supertoy.
- Pale Grey cab and back, Red flash
and hubs, Black chassis, no hook **£650-750**
- Dark Blue cab, Mid-Blue back
and hubs, Silver flash,
Black chassis, no hook **£400-500**
- Chocolate Brown cab and back,
Silver flash, Brown hubs,
Black chassis, no hook **£400-500**
- (US only issue)
Red cab and back, Silver flash, Red
hubs, Black chassis, no hook.......**£2,000-3,000**
- Dark Grey cab and back, Red flash,
chassis and hubs, small unpainted
hook on some **£400-600**
1948-52
- Hook and tank-slits in chassis
(introduced in 1948), Black 'radial
tread' tyres. Violet-Blue cab/chassis,
Mid-Blue flash, back and hubs,
small unpainted hook.................**£1,000-1,250**
- Red cab/chassis/hubs, Silver flash,
Fawn back, unpainted hook,
slits on some **£300-400**
1952-54 (renumbered in 1954 to 901)
2nd cab, no flash, large painted hook,
Supertoy hubs.
- Violet-Blue cab/chassis, Mid-Blue
back and hubs, Grey tyres **£500-700**
- Red cab/chassis, Fawn back,
Red hubs, Grey tyres **£250-350**

502 Foden Flat Truck
1947-48
1st type cab with flash, spare wheel,
hook on some, no tank slits in chassis,
no chain-post bosses, Black 'herringbone'
tyres, Supertoy.
- Dark Green cab and back, Silver flash,
Black chassis, Dark Green hubs,
no hook **£500-750**
- Mid-Blue cab and back, Dark Blue
flash/chassis/hubs, no hook **£1,500-1,750**
1948-52
Hook and tank-slits in chassis introduced
in 1948, Black 'radial' tyres.
- Dark Blue cab/wings/chassis,
Red flash and back, Mid-Blue hubs,
slits on some, small hook **£1,000-1,250**
- Burnt Orange cab/chassis,
Mid-Green flash and back, Green hubs,
slits on some. Dark Blue box
showing 2nd cab model.....................**£500-600**
1952-52
2nd cab, no flash, large painted hook,

Supertoy hubs.
- Dark Blue cab/chassis, Red back,
Mid-Blue hubs,
chain-post bosses.........................**£1,000-1,500**
1952-54 (renumbered 902)
- Dull Orange cab/chassis, Mid-Green
back and hubs, chain-post bosses **£300-400**
- Red cab/chassis,
Green back and hubs **£300-400**
- Yellow cab/chassis,
Green back/hubs.............................**£900-1,100**

503 1st cab Foden Flat Truck with tailboard - scarce example has a light grey cab and rear body, dark blue cabside flash, chassis and ridged hubs, black ridged tyres with small hook to rear.

503 Foden Flat Truck with Tailboard
1947-48
1st type cab with flash, spare wheel,
hook on some, no tank slits in chassis,
no chain-post bosses,
Black 'herringbone' tyres, Supertoy.
- Red cab and flatbed,
Black flash and chassis,
Red hubs, no hook **£1,200-1,500**
- Pale Grey cab and flatbed,
Dark Blue flash and chassis,
Blue hubs, no hook **£1,000-1,250**
- Mid-Green cab and flatbed, Mid-
Blue flash, chassis and hubs........**£1,000-1,250**
1948-52
Hook and tank-slits in chassis
introduced in 1948, Black 'radial' tyres.
- Dark Green cab/chassis,
Mid-Green flash/flatbed/hubs,
small hook.................................**£1,000-1,500**
- Deep Blue cab/chassis,
Dull Orange flatbed,
Light Blue hubs, hook, slits **£1,000-1,500**
- Violet-Blue cab/chassis,
Orange back and flash,
Mid-Blue hubs, hook, slits...........**£1,000-1,500**
1952-52
2nd cab, no flash, large painted hook,
Supertoy hubs.
- Dark Green cab/chassis,
Light Green flatbed and hubs,
Grey tyres, bosses **£1,500-2,000**
- Dark Green cab/chassis, Orange flatbed,
Mid-Green hubs. 1st type picture
box (blue, lift-off lid) **£1,500-2,000**
1952-56 (renumbered 903)
- Violet-Blue cab/chassis,
Orange flatbed, Mid-Blue hubs,
chain-post bosses **£500-700**
1952-53
- Burnt Orange cab/chassis,
Yellow flatbed and hubs,
Grey tyres, bosses **£3,000-4,000**
1953-54 (renumbered 903)
- Violet-Blue cab/chassis,
Yellow flatbed, Mid-Blue hubs,
chain-post bosses **£500-700**

504 Foden 14 ton Tanker
1948-52
1st type cab with flash, spare wheel,
tinplate tank, small hook, no advertising,
Black 'fine radial tread' tyres, Supertoy.
- Dark Blue cab/chassis, Silver flash,
Light Blue tank and hubs..................**£300-400**

- Violet Blue cab/chassis,
Mid-Blue flash, tank and hubs **£300-400**
1948-52
- Red cab/chassis, Silver flash,
Fawn tank, Red hubs..........................**£450-550**
1952-57
2nd cab, no flash, large painted hook, Supertoy.
1952-52
- Violet-Blue cab/chassis, Mid-Blue
tank and hubs, Grey tyres.
In 2nd type picture box................**£1,500-2,000**
1952-53
- Red cab/chassis, Fawn tank,
Red hubs, Grey tyres **£450-550**

504 Foden 14 ton Tanker 'MOBILGAS'
1953-54 (renumbered in 1954 to 941)
- Red cab/chassis/tank/filler caps/hubs,
Grey tyres. With Red 'Pegasus' logo
at cab end of tank facing the cab **£400-500**
- Same, but with Red 'Pegasus'
logo at rear of tank facing
away from cab..............................**£1,500-2,000**

505 Foden Flat Truck with Chains
1952-52
1st type cab with flash, spare wheel,
large hook, slits in chassis, 'dimpled' post
bosses, Black 'fine radial tread' tyres,
Supertoy. Blue covered box
showing 1st type cab.
- Dark Green cab/chassis/flatbed,
Mid-Green flash and hubs............**£3,500-4,500**
- Maroon cab/chassis, Silver flash,
Maroon flatbed and hubs **£7,500-10,000**
1952-54
2nd cab, no flash, large painted hook,
Supertoys hubs. Early Blue box with
Orange/White label.
- Dark Green cab/chassis/flatbed,
Mid-Green hubs,
'dimpled' chain-post bosses.............**£300-400**
- Maroon cab/chassis/flatbed/hubs,
'dimpled' chain-post bosses.............**£500-600**
1954-56 (renumbered in 1954 to 905)
- Green cab/chassis/body,
Mid-Green hubs, 'rounded' bosses,
Blue/White box..................................**£250-350**
- Maroon cab/chassis/body/hubs,
'rounded' bosses, Blue/White box....**£250-350**

511 Guy 4 ton Lorry
1947-48
1st type cab casting, Supertoy, spare wheel,
small unpainted hook.
- Green cab, back and hubs,
Black chassis and wings....................**£350-450**
- Brown cab, back and hubs,
Black chassis and wings....................**£350-450**
- Fawn cab and back, Red chassis,
wings and hubs..................................**£350-450**
- Maroon cab and back,
Black chassis and wings....................**£350-450**
- Grey cab, back and hubs,
Red chassis and wings **£350-450**
1948-52
1st type cab casting, Supertoy,
large painted or unpainted hook.
- Red cab/chassis/wings/ 'ridged' hubs,
Fawn back **£300-350**
- Violet-Blue cab/chassis/wings,
Mid-Blue back and 'ridged' hubs **£300-350**
1952-54 (renumbered in 1954 to 911)
- Red cab/chassis/wings/'grooved'
hubs, Fawn back **£300-350**
- Violet-Blue cab/chassis/wings,
Mid-Blue back and 'grooved' hubs ...**£300-350**
1954 **2nd type cab** casting.
- Violet-Blue cab and chassis,
Mid-Blue back and hubs **£300-350**

512 Guy Flat Truck
1947-48 **1st type cab** casting, Supertoy,
spare wheel, small unpainted hook.
- Maroon cab, flatbed and hubs,
Black chassis and wings....................**£400-600**

- Dark Brown cab, Mid-Green flatbed and hubs, Black chassis and wings... **£400-600**
- Yellow cab and flatbed, Black chassis and wings, Red hubs **£600-800**
- Khaki cab and flatbed, Black chassis and wings, Green hubs **£400-600**
- Grey cab and flatbed, Red chassis and wings, Red hubs **£400-600**
- Grey cab and flatbed, Black chassis, Black hubs............................. **£400-600**
- Red cab and flatbed, Black chassis, Black hubs............................. **£400-600**
  1948-48
- Brown cab/chassis/wings, Green flatbed, Mid-Green 'ridged' hubs **£400-600**
  1948-54 (renumbered in 1954 to 912)
  1st type cab casting, Supertoy, small or large unpainted hook.
- Dark Blue cab/chassis/wings, Red flatbed, Mid-Blue 'ridged' hubs **£300-350**
  1949-54
- Orange cab/chassis/wings, Green flatbed, Green 'ridged' hubs.............. **£300-400**
  1952-54
- Dark Blue cab/chassis/wings, Red flatbed, Mid-Blue 'grooved' hubs...... **£300-350**
  1954 **2nd type cab** casting.
- Red cab and chassis, Mid-Blue back and hubs **£300-350**
- Mid-Blue cab / chassis / hubs, Red back.. **£300-350**

513 Guy Flat Truck with Tailboard
1947-48
1st type cab casting, Supertoy, spare wheel, small unpainted hook.
- Green cab and flatbed, Black chassis, wings and hubs **£200-250**
- Dark Yellow cab and flatbed, Black chassis, wings and hubs **£300-400**
- Dark Yellow cab and flatbed, Dark Blue chassis, wings and hubs... **£300-400**
- Grey cab and flatbed, Black chassis, wings and hubs **£300-400**
- Grey cab and flatbed, Dark Blue chassis, wings and hubs ... **£500-750**
  1948-52
  1st type cab, 'ridged' hubs, Supertoy, small or large unpainted hook.
- Dark Green cab/chassis/wings, Mid-Green back and hubs, small hook **£200-250**
- Violet-Blue cab/chassis/wings, Orange back, Mid-Blue hubs, large hook **£200-250**
  1952-54 (renumbered in 1954 to 913)
  1st type cab, Supertoy, 'grooved' hubs, large unpainted hook.
- Dark Green cab/chassis/wings, Mid-Green body and hubs **£250-350**
- Deep Blue cab/chassis/wings, Orange body, Mid-Blue hubs........... **£200-250**
- Yellow cab/chassis/wings, Green hubs **£750-950**
  1954
- **2nd type cab**.Violet-Blue cab and chassis, Orange back, Mid-Blue hubs **£200-250**

514 Guy Vans

Dinky 514 Guy Slumberland lorry. Note the rare version with late ST grooved wheels. At its sale in May 2009, Vectis Auctions sold a rare version with black ridged wheels.

514 1950-52
Guy Van 'SLUMBERLAND'
- Red **1st type cab**/chassis/body/'ridged' hubs. 'Slumberland Spring Interior Mattresses', spare wheel, Supertoy.... **£300-400**

514 Guy Lyons Van - dark blue, with mid blue ridged hubs.

514 1952-52
- **Guy Van 'LYONS'**
  Dark Blue **1st type cab**/body, Mid-Blue 'ridged' hubs, 'Lyons Swiss Rolls', spare wheel, Supertoy....................... **£700-900**
- Same model but rear axle in cast mounts.. **£700-900**

514 1952-52
- **Guy Van 'WEETABIX'**
  Yellow **1st type cab**/body, Yellow 'ridged' hubs, 'More Than a Breakfast Food', spare wheel, Supertoy................. **£2,000-3,000**
  1952-54
- As previous model but with Yellow 'grooved' hubs **£2,000-3,000**

514 1953-54
- **Guy Van 'SPRATTS'**
  (renumbered 917 in 1954)
  Red/Cream **1st type cab**/body, Red 'grooved' hubs, 'Bonio Ovals & Dog Cakes', spare wheel, Supertoy.... **£300-400**

521 Bedford Articulated Lorry
1948-48
- Red body, Black wings, Black or Red hubs, '20' transfer, 'Supertoys' on base, Brown box........................... **£250-350**
  1949-50
- Yellow body, Black wings, Black hubs, '20' transfer, 'Supertoys' on base. Brown box with Red/White label...... **£250-350**
  1950-54 .... (renumbered in 1954 to 921)
- Yellow or Yellowish-Orange body, Black wings, Red hubs, '20' transfer, 'Supertoys' or 'Dinky Toys' on base. Blue box, Orange or White label **£150-200**

522 Big Bedford Lorry
(renumbered in 1954 to 922)
1952-54
- Maroon cab, Fawn truck body, Fawn hubs, Supertoy........................ **£130-160**
  Dark Blue cab, Yellow truck body, Yellow hubs, Supertoy........................ **£175-200**

531 Leyland Comet Lorry with Stake Body
1949-54 (renumbered in 1954 to 931)
- Red cab and chassis, Yellow back and hubs, Blue box........................... **£350-400**
- Dark Blue cab and chassis, Brown back, Red or Blue hubs, Blue box **£350-400**
- Violet-Blue cab and chassis, Red hubs, Orange-Yellow back, Blue box........... **£150-200**
- Yellow cab and chassis, Pale Green back, Mid-Green hubs, Grey tyres **£300-400**
NB Odd colours: Be wary of colour combinations not listed. The screw fitting makes it easy to interchange the chassis and body components.

532 Leyland Comet Lorry with Hinged Tailboard
1952-54 (renumbered in 1954 to 932)
- Dark Green cab and chassis, Orange

back, Cream hubs, Blue box.............. **£200-250**
- Dark Green cab and chassis, Orange back, Green hubs, Blue box.............. **£150-175**
- Mid-Green cab and chassis, Cherry-Red back, Cream hubs, Blue box.......... **£200-250**
- Dark Blue cab and chassis, Mid-Blue back, Cream hubs, Blue box.......... **£350-400**
- Dark Blue cab and chassis, Mid-Blue back, Red hubs, Blue/White box....... **£150-175**
NB Odd colours: Be wary of colour combinations not listed. The screw fitting makes it easy to interchange the chassis and body components.

533 Leyland Comet Cement Wagon
1953-54 (renumbered in 1954 to 933)
- Yellow body and hubs, 'PORTLAND BLUE-CIRCLE CEMENT', Supertoy .. **£175-200**

551 Trailer (renumbered in 1954 to 951)
1948-54
- Grey body, Black hubs, hook, Supertoy...................................... **£30-40**
- Yellow body, Black hubs, hook, Supertoy...................................... **£90-110**
- Green body, Black hubs, hook, Supertoy...................................... **£90-110**
  1969-73
- Gift Set issue: Red body, Grey front chassis, protruding chromed hubs. Only in Set 399............................ GSP

561 Blaw Knox Bulldozer - red, very dark green tracks.

561 Blaw Knox Bulldozer
1949-54 (renumbered in 1954 to 961)
- Red body, Green or Black rubber tracks, driver, lifting blade, Supertoy. Blue box with Orange/White label, or 'natural' card box with Red/White label, 1 packing piece **£125-150**

561 Citroën Delivery Van
1962-64
- Light Blue body, Red/Yellow 'CIBIE' logo, sliding door. French issue............ **£60-70**

562 Muir Hill Dump Truck
1948-54 (renumbered in 1954 to 962)
- Yellow, metal wheels/tyres, hook **£15-20**

563 Blaw Knox Heavy Tractor
1948-54 (renumbered in 1954 to 963)
- Red, Orange or Blue 561 without the dozer blade. Buff cardboard box has Red/White label, 1 packing piece **£70-90**
- Dark Blue body, Mid-Blue rollers, Green rubber tracks, Beige driver. Buff box with Red/White picture label **£200-250**

564 Elevator Loader
1952-54. Renumbered 964 – see that entry for details.

571 Coles Mobile Crane
1949-54 (renumbered in 1954 to 971)
- Yellow and Black, operable crane, 1 driver, Supertoy, 3 packing pieces + instructions............. **£30-40**

579 Simca Glazier's Lorry
1961-63
- Yellow and Green body, mirror/glass load, 'MIROITIER'. French-made model for issue in the UK **£90-110**

581 Horsebox 'BRITISH RAILWAYS'
1953-54 (renumbered in 1954 to 981)
- Maroon body (aluminium), 2 PP **£80-100**

581 Horsebox 'EXPRESS HORSE VAN'
1953-54 (renumbered in 1954 to 980)
- US issue: Maroon, 'Hire Service'.
Blue box has Orange/White labels
with picture of US model, 2 PP **£500-700**

581 Berliet Flat Truck
1962-64
- Red and Grey body, 6 wheels plus
a spare, hook. French issue **£70-80**
NB The French issues listed above have been
included because they were sold in the U.K.

582 Pullmore Car Transporter
1953-54 (renumbered in 1954 to 982)
Bedford cab/chassis, aluminium trailer with
'DINKY TOYS DELIVERY SERVICE'
logo on sides. Same logo on rear ramp
plus '20' sign. No window glazing,
'DINKY TOYS' on baseplate,
Black grille/bumper, Silver trim.
1953-53
- Light Blue cab, trailer and hubs,
Fawn decks, six lower deck retaining
rivets. Model only issued for a
very short period **£400-600**
1953-54
- As previous model but decks may
be Fawn or Grey.
Four lower deck retaining rivets **£110-140**
1954-54
- Dark Blue cab, trailer and hubs, Fawn
decks, four lower deck retaining rivets.
Model supplied in 582/982 all Dark
Blue box with White end label **£500-750**
- In 582/982 Blue/White striped box... **£200-300**

591 A.E.C. Tanker
'SHELL CHEMICALS LIMITED'
1952-54 (renumbered in 1954 to 991)
- Red/Yellow, Supertoy........................ **£140-175**

620 6-wheel Covered Wagon
1950-54 (renumbered in 1950 from 151b)
- Matt-Green or Greenish-Brown body,
'Export only' (to USA) **£60-70**

752 Goods Yard Crane
1953-54 (renumbered in 1954 to 973)
- Yellow operable crane on mid- or Dark Blue
base (steps in some). Dark Blue box **£50-75**

893 Unic Pipe Line Transporter
1962-64
- Beige articulated body, spare wheel, 6 pipes.
Made in France for issue in the UK **£90-110**

894 Unic Boilot Car Transporter
1962-64
- Grey body, 'Dinky Toys Service Livraison'.
Made in France for issue in the UK .. **£100-120**

901 Foden 8-wheel Diesel Wagon
1954-57 (renumbered in 1954 from 501)
2nd type cab, Supertoy with
spare wheel and large hook.
- Red cab/chassis/hubs,
Fawn truck body **£300-350**
- Red cab/chassis/hubs,
Grey truck body **£300-350**
- Violet-Blue cab and chassis,
Mid-Blue truck body and hubs **£700-850**
- Dark Green cab and chassis, Light Green
truck body and hubs. 'LF' sticker on
Blue/White striped box lid, '1956'
stamped inside bottom of box **£5,000-7,500**

902 Foden Flat Truck
1954-56 (renumbered in 1954 from 502)
2nd type cab, Supertoy with
spare wheel and large hook.
- Yellow cab and chassis, Mid-Green
flatbed body, Green hubs **£1,250-1,500**
1954-57
- Burnt-Orange cab and chassis,
Mid-Green flatbed body and hubs ... **£300-400**
1957-59
- Dark Red cab and chassis, Green flatbed,
Green hubs (NB Red similar to
colour of 919 Guy
'GOLDEN SHRED' van)...............**£1,000-1,500**

- Cherry-Red cab, wings and chassis,
Green flatbed body and hubs........... **£500-600**
- Orange cab and chassis, Fawn flatbed
body, Mid-Green hubs...................... **£300-400**

903 Foden Flat Truck with Tailboard
1954-55 (renumbered in 1954 from 503)
2nd type cab, Supertoy with
spare wheel and large hook.
- Violet-Blue cab and chassis,
Yellow flatbed, Mid-Blue hubs.......... **£350-450**
- Orange cab, chassis and flatbed,
Green hubs with Grey tyres **£1,250-1,500**
- Yellow cab, chassis and flatbed,
Mid-Green hubs. In box with
correct colour spot **£2,000-2,500**
1954-57
- Violet-Blue cab and chassis,
Orange flatbed, Mid-Blue hubs.......... **£300-350**
1957-60
- Mid-Blue cab and chassis,
Fawn flatbed, Mid-Blue hubs,
rivetted spare wheel **£800-1,000**

905 Foden Flat Truck with chains.

905 Foden Flat Truck with Chains
1954-64 (renumbered in 1954 from 505)
2nd type cab, Supertoy with
spare wheel and large hook.
1954-57
- Maroon cab, chassis, flatbed and
hubs, 'rounded' chain-post bosses.... **£300-350**
1954-58
- Dark Green cab/chassis/flatbed,
Mid-Green hubs,
'rounded' chain-post bosses **£300-350**
1956-57
- Maroon cab/chassis/flatbed, Red
hubs, 'rounded' chain-post bosses.... **£350-450**
1957-64
- Red cab and chassis, Grey flatbed,
Red metal hubs, 'rounded' bosses.... **£300-350**
19??-64
- Red cab and chassis, Grey flatbed,
Red plastic hubs **£400-500**
NB A version of 905 with Light Blue
cab/chassis and hubs, and Grey flatbed
sold for **$3,700** on eBay in 2004.

*Dinky 908 Mighty Antar with Transformer. Scarce yellow
wheel variant in foreground.*

908 Mighty Antar and Transformer
1962-66
- Yellow tractor unit, Light Grey trailer,
Red ramp and hubs, transformer,
3 packing pieces **£500-600**

911 Guy 4 ton Lorry
1954-56 (was 511, renumbered in 1956 to 431)
2nd type cab casting, Supertoy,

'grooved' hubs, large hook.
- Red cab/chassis/hubs, Fawn back.... **£250-350**
- Violet-Blue cab and chassis,
Mid-Blue back and hubs **£200-250**
- Mid-Blue cab/chassis/back and
hubs. (Factory trial model)..........**£1,250-1,500**

912 Guy Flat Truck
1954-56 (was 512, renumbered in 1956 to 432)
2nd type cab casting, Supertoy,
'grooved' hubs, large hook.
- Orange cab and chassis,
Green flatbed body and hubs............ **£400-500**
- Mid-Blue cab and chassis,
Red flatbed body, Mid-Blue hubs **£400-500**
- Dark Green cab and chassis,
Light Green flatbed body and hubs .. **£400-500**

913 Guy Flat Truck with Tailboard
1954-56 (was 513, renumbered in 1956 to 433)
2nd type cab casting, Supertoy,
'grooved' hubs, large hook.
- (1954 only) Yellow cab and
chassis, Green body, Green hubs...... **£750-950**
1954-56
- Dark Green cab and chassis,
Mid-Green flatbed body and
hubs.. **£250-300**
- Violet-Blue cab and chassis, Orange
flatbed body, Light Blue hubs.
Usually in Blue/White striped box
with picture of Green lorry **£200-250**
- Deep Blue/Orange model in box
with correct colours **£750-950**

914 A.E.C. Articulated Lorry
1965-70
- Red cab ('CIA 7392' on doors),
White interior, Light Grey trailer,
Red plastic hubs, Green
tilt 'BRITISH ROAD SERVICES'......... **£140-160**
- With chromed domed hubs,
pictorial box..................................... **£200-250**

915 A.E.C. with Flat Trailer
1973-74
- Orange cab, White trailer,
'Truck Hire Co Liverpool' **£55-65**
- Orange cab, White trailer,
'Thames Board Paper Mills',
bubble-packed. Truck carries load
of four Brown card tubes with
'UNILINER' logos in Black **£2,000-2,500**
- Bright Metallic Blue cab,
White interior, Orange chassis,
Yellow trailer **£140-160**

917 Guy Spratts Van - red type 1 cab.

917 Guy Van 'SPRATTS'
1954-56 (renumbered in 1954 from 514)
- Red **2nd type cab**, chassis and Supertoy
hubs, Cream/Red van body with
'Bonio Ovals & Dog Cakes' **£400-500**

917 Mercedes Truck and Trailer
1968-74
- Blue cab/chassis (White roof),
Yellow trailers, White tilts,
pictorial stand and tray...................... **£85-115**
- Blue cab/chassis (White roof),
Yellow trailers, Yellow tilts,
pictorial stand and tray...................... **£85-115**

- Dark Blue cab/chassis,
Yellow trailers, Dark Blue tilts,
pictorial stand and tray.....................**£300-350**
- 'MUNSTERLAND' promotional.
Dark Green cab and trailers, White tilts,
Green logo, pictorial stand and tray . **£350-450**
- 'HENRY JOHNSON' promotional.
Dark Green body, White tilts,
plain White box **£350-450**

918 Guy Van 'EVER READY'
1955-58
- Blue **1st type cab** with small square
sides to front number plate **£400-500**
- Blue **2nd type cab**/body, Red
'grooved' hubs, 'Ever Ready Batteries
For Life', spare wheel, Supertoy **£300-400**

919 Guy Van 'GOLDEN SHRED'
1957-58
- All Red **2nd type cab** and body,
Yellow Supertoy hubs,
'Robertsons Golden Shred'
and 'golly' design, spare wheel **£700-900**

920 Guy Warrior Van 'HEINZ'
1960-61
- Red cab and chassis, window glazing,
Yellow van body and Supertoy hubs,
spare wheel, 'HEINZ 57 VARIETIES'
and 'Tomato Ketchup' design.
NB The correct box for this model has
Blue/White stripes but no model
illustrations (see Box Type 1D (v) on
'Commercial Vehicles
Box Types' page)..........................**£2,500-3,500**

921 Bedford Articulated Vehicle
1954-56 (was 521, renumbered in 1956 to 409)
- Yellowish-Orange body, Black wings,
Red hubs, Supertoy **£120-140**

922 Big Bedford Lorry
1954-56 (was 522, renumbered in 1956 to 408)
- Maroon cab, Fawn back,
Fawn hubs, Supertoy.......................... **£110-130**
- Dark Blue cab,
Yellow back and hubs **£200-250**

923 Big Bedford Van 'HEINZ'
1955-58
- Red cab and chassis, Yellow back
and hubs, 'HEINZ 57 VARIETIES'
plus '**Baked Beans can**' picture.
Supertoy in Blue/White striped box
with correct model picture **£350-450**
1958-59
- As previous model but with
'**Tomato Ketchup bottle**' advertising.
Supertoy in Blue/White striped box
with correct model picture **£2,500-3,500**

924 Aveling Barford 'CENTAUR'
1972-76
- Red/Yellow body, tipping dump truck . **£30-40**

*925 Leyland Dump Truck – off-white cab and chassis,
mid blue roof and plastic hubs, orange tipping body.*

925 Leyland Dump Truck
1965-69
- 8-wheeled Supertoy with 'SAND
BALLAST GRAVEL' on tailgate.
White (tilting) cab and chassis, Blue
cab roof, Orange diecast
tipper, Mid-Blue plastic hubs............ **£175-200**
- As previous model but with tinplate
tipper in Orange, Pale Grey or Red
.... **£175-200**

930 Bedford Pallet-Jekta Van
1960-64

- Orange and Yellow body, 'Dinky Toys'
and 'Meccano', 3 pallets,
1 packing piece, Supertoy.................. **£350-450**

931 Leyland Comet Lorry with Stake Body
1954-56 (was 531, renumbered in 1956 to 417)
- Violet-Blue cab and chassis, Orange-
Yellow back, Red hubs, Supertoy **£175-225**

932 Leyland Comet with Hinged Tailboard
1954-56 (was 532, renumbered in 1956 to 418)
- Dark Green cab and chassis,
Orange back, Mid-Green hubs.......... **£130-160**
- Dark Green cab and chassis,
Red back, Cream hubs **£130-160**
- Dark Blue cab and chassis,
Mid-Blue back and hubs **£130-160**
- Dark Blue cab, chassis and
truck body, Red hubs **£130-160**
- Dark Blue cab and chassis, Light
(Powder) Blue back, Cream hubs **£250-350**
- Red cab and chassis,
Mid-Blue back and hubs **£500-750**
NB Odd colours: Be wary of colour
combinations not listed. The screw fitting
makes it easy to interchange the chassis
and body components.

933 Leyland Comet Cement Wagon
1954-56 (was 533, renumbered in 1956 to 419)
- Yellow body and hubs, 'Portland
Blue-Circle Cement', Supertoy **£110-130**

934 Leyland Octopus Wagon
1956-58
- Yellow cab and chassis, Green truck
body secured to chassis by a screw,
Green band around cab (but without
Yellow band above radiator), Red
diecast Supertoy hubs, 1 PP **£150-175**
1958-59
- As previous model but with Green
diecast hubs. Body held by rivet **£150-175**
1958-63
- As previous model but with Yellow
band immediately above radiator, Red
diecast hubs, body held by rivet **£250-300**
1963-64
- Dark Blue cab/chassis, Pale Yellow
cab band and rivetted back, Red
diecast hubs. In picture box **£2,500-3,500**
1964-64
- Dark Blue cab/chassis, Pale Yellow
cab band and rivetted back, Grey
plastic hubs. In picture box **£2,500-3,500**
1964-64
- Dark Blue cab/chassis, Pale Yellow
cab band and rivetted back, Red
plastic hubs. In picture box **£2,500-3,500**

935 Leyland Octopus Flat Truck with Chains
1964-66
- 6 chain-posts, 8 wheels, flatbed held
by rivet, Supertoy, 1 packing piece,
picture box.
- Mid-Green cab/chassis,
Pale Grey cab band and flatbed,
Red plastic hubs **£1,500-1,750**
- Mid-Green cab/chassis,
Pale Grey cab band and flatbed,
Grey plastic hubs..........................**£1,500-1,750**
- Blue cab/chassis, Yellow cab flash,
Pale Grey flatbed and hubs **£4,000-5,000**

936 Leyland 8-wheel Chassis
1964-69
- Red/Silver, 'Another Leyland on Test',
three '5-ton' weights **£120-140**

940 Mercedes-Benz LP.1920 Truck
1977-80
- White cab, Pale Grey cover,
Red chassis, hubs and interior **£35-45**
- Same, but Black interior, White hubs ... **£40-50**
- 'HALB UND HALB' Promotional
with 'MAMPE' & 'BOSCH' on
Blue cab, Elephant design **£300-400**
- 'FISON'S' Promotional. White body,
Red interior, chassis and hubs, Grey
plastic cover, 'FISON'S THE GARDEN

PEOPLE' labels, 2 peat samples **£300-400**
- 'HENRY JOHNSON' Promotional.
Green body, White cover **£400-500**

941 Foden 14 ton Tanker 'MOBILGAS'
1956-56 (renumbered in 1956 from 504)
- 2nd type cab. Red body and hubs,
Black filler caps, Black tyres,
Supertoy **£450-550**

942 2nd cab Foden Regent Tanker.

942 Foden 14 ton Tanker 'REGENT'
1955-57
- 2nd type cab. Dark Blue cab/chassis,
Red/White/Blue tank, Black tyres,
Supertoy... **£400-500**

943 Leyland Octopus Tanker 'ESSO'
1958-64
- Dark Red body and diecast hubs, Red
tinplate tank with waterslide transfers,
'ESSO PETROLEUM', spare wheel,
hook, Supertoy, 1 packing piece **£300-400**

- As before but Red plastic hubs.......... **£300-400**
- With Red plastic hubs,
logos on self-adhesive labels............. **£350-450**

944 Leyland Octopus Tanker 'SHELL-BP'
1963-70
- White/Yellow cab and body,
Grey chassis and plastic hubs **£225-275**
- White/Yellow cab and body,
Grey chassis, Black plastic hubs....... **£300-400**
- White/Yellow cab and body,
Grey chassis, Red plastic hubs **£300-400**
- White/Yellow cab and body, White
chassis, Grey or Black plastic
hubs.. **£225-275**
- Export issue: Yellow cab, White
chassis, White plastic tank, Red plastic
hubs. 'See-through' export box .... NGPP
NB Each issue has 'SHELL' and 'BP' sticky
labels on the front half of the plastic tank.

**944 Leyland Octopus Tanker
'CORN PRODUCTS'**
1963-64
Only 500 of these promotionals issued.
- White body and plastic tank,
'Sweeteners For Industry' in White on
Black labels. In 944 'ESSO' box with
'CORN PRODUCTS' sticker,
wrapped in Green/Grey
striped gift paper **£7,500-10,000**

945 A.E.C. Fuel Tanker 'ESSO'
1966-75
- White cab/chassis, White tank, 'ESSO
PETROLUEUM', 'Tiger in Your Tank'
logo on rear, 1 packing piece.............. **£90-110**
1975-77
- As previous model but without logo at
rear, card boxed or bubble-packed....... **£75-95**
- Metallic Blue cab, White tank,
Black filler caps................................. **£100-125**

945 A.E.C. Tanker 'LUCAS OIL'
1977-77 Promotional.
- Green cab and tank, White design
on labels, bubble-packed **£100-125**

948 Tractor-Trailer 'McLEAN'
1961-67
- (i): Red cab, Light Grey trailer, Red
plastic hubs, Supertoy, 2 PP **£200-250**

- (ii): As previous model but with
  Black plastic hubs............................. **£200-250**
- 19?? **'ROADWAY DOVER'**
- (iii): As model (i) but with extra graphics
  on the front of the trailer and on the rear of
  the cab: 'Roadway Dover Del Express Inc'.
  Black plastic hubs............................ **£300-500**
  1964 ? **'BROWN SHOE Co.'**
- (iv): As 'McLean' model but with
  'Brown Shoe Co.' adhesive labels.
  US Promotional (75 only made) .... NGPP

NB The trailer moulding is light-sensitive
and varies in shade from Pale Grey to
Light Grey with a Greenish tinge, through
to very Pale Brown. The 'McLean'
logo can be Red or Light Orange.

950 Foden S20 Tanker 'BURMAH'
1978-79
- Red cab, Red/White trailer, Black or
  Grey hatches, Red or Cream hubs **£50-75**
950 Foden Tanker 'SHELL'
1978-78
- Red cab, Red/White trailer,
  Cream hubs... **£75-100**
951 Trailer
1954-56 (was 551, renumbered in 1956 to 428)
- Grey body with hook, Red hubs............ **£30-40**
- Dark Grey body, hook, Lemon hubs..... **£50-75**
958 Guy Warrior Snow Plough
1961-66
- Yellow/Black body and plough blade,
  spare wheel, 1 PP, Supertoy.............. **£145-165**
- Yellow/Black body, Silver blade........ **£200-250**
- Silver blade version in box with
  picture showing Silver blade **£250-300**
959 Foden Dump Truck & Bulldozer
1961-68
- Red or Deep Red body,
  Silver chassis and blade,
  Red hubs (plastic front; metal rear).. **£350-500**
- Same, but with Pale Yellow plastic
  front hubs, Yellow metal rear hubs ... **£150-175**
- All-Red body version.......................... **£150-175**

*960 Lorry Mounted Concrete Mixer - orange Albion cab
and chassis, blue barrel with yellow panel, black hubs.*

960 Albion Lorry Concrete Mixer
1960-68
- Orange body, Blue rotating drum with
  two Yellow triangles, Black plastic
  hubs, Grey tyres. Supertoy................ **£125-150**
- Orange body, Grey drum, Black
  plastic hubs, Grey tyres. Supertoy..... **£150-200**
961 Blaw-Knox Bulldozer
1954-62 (renumbered in 1954 from 561)
- Red or Yellow body, rubber tracks,
  Tan driver, Supertoy **£45-55**
  1962-64
- Blue body, rubber tracks, Tan driver **£45-55**
  1963-64
- Red or Yellow body, rubber tracks,
  Blue driver **£45-55**
  1964-64
- Orange plastic body with Silver engine
  detail, Black diecast lifting gear,
  Green plastic blade and exhaust pipe,
  Blue driver, Light Green or

Olive-Green roller wheels.................. **£400-600**
962 Muir Hill Dumper
1954-66 (renumbered in 1954 from 562)
- Yellow body, hook, Supertoy, 1 PP **£15-20**
963 Blaw Knox Heavy Tractor
1954-58 (renumbered in 1954 from 563)
- Red or Orange body, Green or Black
  tracks. Blue/White striped box, 1 PP **£50-60**
  1958-59
- Yellow body, Green or Black tracks.
  Blue/White striped box, 1 PP **£60-75**
963 Road Grader
1973-75
- Yellow/Red articulated body,
  Silver blade, Red lower arm.................. **£20-30**
- White or Yellow lower arm. **£30-40**

*964 Elevator Loader - scarce colour variation with mid
blue body and plastic hubs, removable rear tailgate,
yellow fittings.*

964 Elevator Loader
1954-68 (renumbered in 1954 from 564)
- Yellow with Mid-Blue or Dark Blue
  chutes, Blue or Yellow hubs, 1 PP **£45-55**
  Boxes: Early Blue boxes were replaced
  by Blue/White boxes, then by Yellow
  'Supertoys' boxes.
- Late issue:
  Mid-Blue with Yellow chutes, as
  shown on late picture box design **£100-150**
965 'EUCLID' Dump Truck
1955-61
- Pale Yellow body ('EUCLID' cast under
  cab), Yellow hubs, no windows,
  'STONE - ORE - EARTH',
  operable tipper, 1 packing piece **£150-175**
  NB 1955-56 Grey backed logo;
  1959-61 Red backed logo.
  1961-69
- Same model but with glazing............ **£150-175**
- Pale Yellow body, Red or
  Dark Green hubs, window glazing.
  In detailed picture box....................... **£200-250**
965 'TEREX' Rear Dump Truck
1969-70
- Yellow body and hubs, 'TEREX' in red
  on doors, 'EUCLID' cast under cab.
  In 'EUCLID' picture box, one PP **£300-350**
- Same model but 'TEREX' cast
  under cab. 'TEREX' picture box **£200-250**
966 Marrel Multi-Bucket Unit
1960-64
- Pale Yellow body, Grey skip and tyres,
  Black hubs, Supertoy, one PP........... **£140-160**
967 BBC TV Control Room
1959-64
- Dark Green, 'BBC Television Service',
  Supertoy, drawing on box lid, 1 PP ... **£125-150**
967 Muir-Hill Loader/Trencher
1973-78
- Yellow/Red body, with driver................ **£25-35**
- Orange/Black body, with driver............ **£25-35**
968 BBC TV Roving-Eye Vehicle
1959-64
- Dark Green body, BBC crest, camera,
  Supertoy, drawing on box lid, 1 PP ... **£125-150**
969 BBC TV Extending Mast
1959-64
- Dark Green body, BBC crest,

dish aerial, mast, Supertoy, drawing
on box lid, 2 packing pieces **£125-150**
970 Jones Fleetmaster Crane
1967-71
- (Bedford TK) Red cab, White roof,
  Red interior, Red plastic hubs,
  White jib, two packing pieces.............. **£80-100**
  1971-77
- Metallic Red cab, White interior and
  jib, chrome domed hubs, two PP........ **£80-100**
  1971-77
- Pale Yellow cab, White interior and
  jib, chrome domed hubs, two PP........ **£80-100**
971 Coles Mobile Crane
1954-62 (renumbered in 1954 from 571)
- Yellow and Black, operable crane,
  one driver, Supertoy........................... **£30-40**
972 Coles 20 ton Lorry-Mounted Crane
1955-62
- Yellow/Orange (no 'Long Vehicle' signs),
  two drivers, Supertoy, one PP **£40-50**
  1962-69
- Yellow/Orange (with 'Long Vehicle'
  signs), two drivers, Supertoy **£40-50**
  1967-69
- Yellow/Black, Blue metal driver in lorry
  cab only, Yellow plastic hubs, Black tyres,
  Black/White diagonal stripes around jib,
  Yellow 'COLES CRANE" at rear......... **£100-150**
- Variation with Black hubs.
  (In end-flap box) **£100-150**
- Regular issue model in promotional
  'Coles Crane' box given away at the 16th
  Commercial Motor Show. Box has three
  labels on lid for '16th International
  Commercial Motor Transport Exhibition',
  'Commercial Motor Show at Earls Court
  London September 26 - October 4' and
  'See our Exhibit, Stand No. 137
  Avenue U 1st Floor',
  blue striped box................................ **£400-500**
973 Goods Yard Crane
1954-59 (renumbered in 1954 from 752)
- Yellow operable crane on Blue base.
  Blue/White striped box, one PP........... **£30-40**
973 Eaton 'YALE' Tractor Shovel
1971-75
- Red/Yellow body with Yellow or
  Silver bucket exterior, cast hubs........... **£20-30**
- Yellow/Red body, Silver wheels,
  no engine covers, cast hubs.................. **£25-35**
- All Yellow body, Blue wheels,
  engine covers, cast hubs **£25-35**
- Factory special:
  Window in cab roof, yellow plastic
  hubs, 'Trojan 6000' tampo prints,
  'Eaton' underneath. This unique model
  was presented to the man
  who designed the actual vehicle............ NGPP
974 A.E.C. Hoynor Car Transporter
1968-75
- Bright Metallic Blue cab, White interior,
  Pale Orange/Dark Orange back,
  Grey plastic hubs, three PP................. **£90-110**
- Dark Metallic Blue cab,
  Pale Orange/Dark Orange back,
  Grey plastic hubs, three PP................. **£90-110**
- Dark Metallic Blue cab,
  Yellow and Bright Orange back,
  chrome domed hubs, three PP **£90-110**
975 'RUSTON-BUCYRUS' Excavator
1963-67
- Pale Yellow plastic body, Red jib and
  bucket, Black rubber tracks,
  with instructions **£300-350**
976 'MICHIGAN' Tractor Dozer
1968-76
- Yellow/Red body, driver, engine covers,
  Red hubs, one packing piece................. **£30-35**
- Promotional: All Yellow with Blue hubs.
  (100 / 200 made for Michigan Co.) ... **£100-150**
977 Servicing Platform Vehicle

1960-64
- Red and Cream body, operable platform, spare wheel, two packing pieces....... **£140-160**
  NB Version seen using 667 Missile Servicing Platform Vehicle chassis in the Red/Cream 977 livery .... NGPP

977 Shovel Dozer
1973-78
- Yellow/Red/Silver, Black or Silver plastic tracks, bubble-packed................ **£20-25**

978 Bedford TK Refuse Wagon
1964-72
Diecast cab, plastic tipping body, two plastic dustbins.
- Green cab, Grey body, Red hubs, White (later Grey) plastic roof rack....... **£50-60**
  1973-74
- Dark Metallic Green cab, Grey body, Red plastic hubs, White (later Grey) plastic roof rack **£70-85**
  1975-77
- Lime-Green cab, White interior, Black or Brown chassis, plastic or cast roof rack.. **£70-85**
  1978-80
- Yellow cab, Brown chassis, cast rack **£35-45**
  NB Over its 16-year production run, 978 came in five different types of packaging: lidded box, pictorial and non-pictorial end-flap boxes, bubble-pack, and window box.

979 Racehorse Transport
1961-64
- Grey lower body and roof, Lemon-Yellow upper body sides, two horses, 'Newmarket Racehorse Transport Service Ltd', Supertoy, two packing pieces........... **£350-450**

980 Horsebox (US issue)
1954-60 (renumbered in 1954 from 581)
- Maroon body (cast in aluminium), 'Hire Service', 'Express Horse Van', 'Express'. In Blue/White striped box with picture of model and 'Hudson Dobson' mark, two packing pieces... **£500-600**

980 Coles Hydra Truck 150T
1972-79
- Lemon-Yellow body, triple extension crane, handle at side and rear.............. **£30-40**

- Yellow or Orange body, two side handles, no rear handle........................ **£50-60**
- **'SPARROWS CRANE HIRE'** Promotional model, Red body **£200-300**

981 Horsebox
1954-60 (renumbered in 1954 from 581)
- Maroon body (cast in aluminium), 'British Railways', two PP **£100-125**

982 Pullmore Car Transporter with ramp - mid blue prime mover and hubs, with light blue trailer with tinplate ramp No 994.

982 Pullmore Car Transporter
1955-63 (renumbered in 1955 from 582)
Bedford 'O' series cab and chassis plus aluminium trailer with 'DINKY TOYS DELIVERY SERVICE' on sides. Same logo on rear ramp but without '20' sign. Black grille/bumper, Silver trim, one packing piece.
1955-61
- Blue cab and back, Mid-Blue hubs, Fawn decks... **£400-500**
- Dark Blue cab, Mid-Blue hubs, Light Blue back and decks, no window glazing. Blue/White striped box has picture of 994 Loading Ramp introduced in 1955 .... **£125-150**
  1961-63
- Same, but with cab window glazing . **£140-170**

983 Car Carrier and Trailer
(Supertoys 984 and 985)
1958-63
- Red/Grey, 'Dinky Auto Service', five packing pieces **£225-275**

984 Car Carrier
1958-63
- Red/Grey body, Grey hubs, 'Dinky

Auto Service', two PP, Supertoy **£250-350**

984 Atlas Digger
1974-79
- Red/Yellow body, Yellow arm/cylinders, Silver or Yellow bucket........................... **£30-40**
- Red/Yellow body, Black plastic arm, Black or Yellow cylinders, Silver bucket **£30-40**

985 Trailer for Car Carrier
1958-63
- Red/Grey body, 'Dinky Auto Service', two packing pieces, Supertoy................ **£50-60**

986 Mighty Antar with Propeller
1959-61
- Red cab (window glazing on some), Grey low-loader, Bronze propeller, three packing pieces **£300-350**

987 'ABC TV' Control Room
1962-69
- Blue/Grey/Red, 'ABC TELEVISION', camera/operator/cable **£175-225**

988 TV Transmitter Van 'ABC-TV'
1962-69
- Blue/Grey body, Red stripe, revolving aerial dish, Supertoy.......... **£175-225**

989 Car Transporter 'AUTO TRANSPORTERS'
1963-65
- Lemon Yellow cab, Pale Grey back, Metallic Light Blue ramps, Red plastic hubs, Supertoy boxed in all-card picture box or export-only Gold 'see through' window box, two packing pieces **£2,500-3,000**

990 Pullmore Car transporter with Four Cars
See Gift Sets section.

991 Large Trailer
1954-70 Renumbered in 1954 from 551 – see that entry for details.

991 A.E.C. Tanker
1954-55 (renumbered in 1954 from 591)
- Red/Yellow, Supertoy, 'SHELL CHEMICALS LIMITED' **£130-160**
  1955-58
- Red/Yellow, Supertoy, 'SHELL CHEMICALS' **£120-140**

Dinky Toys Emergency Vehicles

Ford Transit casting types:

Type 1: **(1966-74)**, has sliding driver's door, opening hinged side door, and twin rear doors.
Type 2: **(1974-78)**, non-sliding driver's door, one side-hinged door, one top-hinged rear door.
Type 3: **(1978-80)**, as Type 2 but with a slightly longer bonnet (18 mm.)

24a Ambulance
1934-38
Types 1 or 2 criss-cross chassis, types 1, 2 or 3 grille, plated chrome or Black hubs, open windows.
- Cream body, Red chassis.................. **£250-350**
- Cream body, Grey chassis................. **£250-350**
- Grey body, Dark Grey chassis........... **£200-250**
- Grey body, Maroon chassis **£200-250**
  1938-40
  Type 2 criss-cross chassis, open windows, type 3 grille. See 30f.
- Cream body, Red chassis.................. **£200-250**
- Cream body, Grey chassis................. **£200-250**
- Grey body, Dark Grey chassis........... **£250-300**
- Grey body, Maroon chassis **£250-300**
- Black body, Black chassis (thought to be for export only).......... **£500-750**

25h Streamlined Fire Engine
(renumbered in 1954 to 250)
1936-37
- Red body, no tinplate baseplate, tinplate ladder and bell, White tyres. **£175-225**
  1937-40

- Red body, tinplate baseplate, ladder and bell, Black or White tyres............ **£125-150**
  1948-54
- Red body and ladder, tinplate baseplate, brass bell, Black tyres......... **£80-100**

25h Streamlined Fire Engine - red body, ladder, ridged hubs, black tinplate base, smooth tyres.

25k Streamline Fire Engine
1937-39
- Red body, tinplate base, 6 firemen, ladder, bell, White tyres **£400-500**

30f Ambulance
1935-38
- Grey body, Red wings/criss-cross chassis, plain radiator, open windows............ **£150-200**
  1938-40
- Grey body, Black moulded chassis, radiator badge, open windows............ **£90-110**
  1938-40 South-African issue:
- Grey body, Red cross, 'Bentley type' radiator **£750-950**
  1946-47
- Grey body, Black moulded chassis, open windows......................... **£80-100**
  1947-48
- Cream body, Black moulded chassis, filled-in or open windows................... **£80-100**

30h Daimler Ambulance
1950-54 (renumbered in 1954 to 253)
- Cream body, Red crosses and wheels, no window glazing.................... **£80-90**

30hm Daimler Military Ambulance
1950-54 (renumbered in 1954 to 624)
- Military-Green body, Red crosses on White backgrounds, (US issue) **£200-300**

123-P Austin Princess 'POLICE' Car
1977
- White body, Black roof and interior, plastic wheels......................................**£300-350**
NB This model was not officially released. A prototype (?) was sold by Vectis Auctions for £360.

195 Fire-Chief's Range Rover
1971-78
- Red or Metallic Red, 'Fire Service', Speedwheels, bubble-packed................**£35-40**

243 Volvo 'POLICE' Car
(Some made in Italy by Polistil under license)
1979-81
- White body, plastic chassis...................**£35-40**

244 Plymouth Fury Police Car
1977-81
- Black/White, 'POLICE', warning lights, plastic chassis and wheels..........**£25-30**

250 Streamline Fire Engine
1954-62 (renumbered in 1954 from 25h)
- Red body and hubs, Silver tinplate ladder, bell and trim...........................**£100-120**
- Red body, hubs and tinplate ladder....**£80-100**

250 Police Mini Cooper 'S'
1967-71
- White body, Austin Cooper 'S' boot lid transfer, roof sign and aerial, 'POLICE' on doors.................................**£55-65**
1971-73
- As previous model but cast boot detail, no aerial.......................................**£45-55**
1973-75
- Same model but with Speedwheels......**£35-45**
NB Boot casting variations:
(1) 'Morris Mini-Minor' cast-in,
(2) 'Austin Mini-Cooper S' cast-in.

251 U.S.A. 'POLICE' Car (Pontiac Parisienne)
1971-72
- White body, Black textured roof, Off-White interior, twin aerials, siren, rooflight.......................................**£60-75**

252 R.C.M.P. Police Car (Pontiac Parisienne)
1969-74
- Dark Blue body, White door panels and interior, driver, twin aerials, Red light...**£60-75**

253 Daimler Ambulance
1954-58 (renumbered in 1954 from 30h)
- Cream body, Red crosses and cast hubs, no window glazing......................**£75-85**
1958-60
- White body, Red crosses and cast hubs, no window glazing...................**£100-125**
1960-62
- White body, Red crosses and cast hubs, with window glazing.................**£80-100**
1962-64
- White body, Red plastic hubs, with window glazing.............................**£90-110**

254 'POLICE' Range Rover
1971-81
- White body, Orange side stripes, twin aerials on some, Speedwheels......**£30-35**

255 Mersey Tunnel Police Van (Land Rover)
1955-61
- Gloss or Matt Red body, smooth or treaded Black tyres, hook, 'POLICE' and 'MERSEY TUNNEL'.....................**£125-150**

255 Ford Zodiac 'POLICE' Car
1967-71
- White body, driver, 'POLICE' on doors and roof sign, aerial.....................**£55-65**
- As previous model but with paper labels on door and blue base................**£45-55**

255 Police Mini Clubman
1977-79
- Blue/White body, 'POLICE', opening doors and bonnet, plastic wheels.........**£30-35**

256 Humber Hawk 'POLICE' Car
1960-64
- Black body, Cream interior, White 'POLICE' sign on roof,

'PC 49' licence plates, driver and observer, spun hubs..........**£80-100**

257 Nash Rambler 'Fire Chief' car.

257 Canadian 'FIRE CHIEF' Car
(Nash Rambler)
1960-69
- Flashing light, suspension, window glazing.......................................**£55-65**

258 U.S.A. 'POLICE' CAR (De Soto Fireflite)
1960-61 (192 casting)
- Black body, White front doors, 'POLICE' on doors, roof and bonnet, Red roof-light.......................**£100-125**
- Same, but with Red interior..............**£100-125**

258 U.S.A. 'POLICE' CAR (Dodge Royal)
1961-62 (191 casting)
- Black body, White front doors, 'POLICE' on doors, roof and bonnet, Red roof-light.......................**£100-125**

258 U.S.A. 'POLICE' CAR (Ford Fairlane)
1962-66 (149 casting)
- Black body, White front doors, 'POLICE' on doors, roof and bonnet, Red light, open window.........................**£80-90**
- Same but Dark Blue/White, with closed windows............................**£80-90**

258 U.S.A. 'POLICE' CAR (Cadillac 62)
1966-68 (147 casting)
- Black/White, suspension/steering....**£100-125**

259 Fire Engine (Bedford Miles)
1961-69
- Red body and hubs, 'FIRE BRIGADE' and crest, Red tinplate ladder and bell, Yellow box...................................**£125-150**
- Same model but with 'AIRPORT FIRE TENDER' (from 276).................**£125-150**
- Red body, spun aluminium hubs......**£125-150**

261 Ford Taunus 'POLIZEI'
1967-77 (German issue)
- White and Green body, box has card packing ring and label: 'Special contract run for Meccano Agent in W. Germany'.......**£200-300**

263 Superior Criterion Ambulance
1962-68
Bright or Dull White body, Red side stripes, cab siren and roof beacon. 'AMBULANCE' in Red/White on rear windows, cast hubs. Two attendants + patient on stretcher. Versions:
- Bright White body, Turquoise int........**£80-100**
- Dull (dirty) White body, Red interior....**£70-80**
- Same but with Yellow interior...............**£60-70**
- Same but with Pale Turquoise interior....**£50-60**
- Same but with White interior...............**£70-80**

263 Airport Fire Rescue Tender - yellow body and plastic hubs.

263 E.R.F. Fire Tender 'Airport Rescue'
1978-81
- Yellow body, flashing light.....................**£40-50**

264 R.C.M.P. Ford Fairlane
1962-65
- Dark Blue body, White doors, aerial, red beacon, two Mounties......**£100-125**

264 R.C.M.P. Cadillac
1965-68
- Dark Blue body, White doors, aerial, red beacon, two Mounties........**£90-110**

264 Rover 3500 Police Car
1978-80
- White body, Yellow stripe with 'POLICE' and crest (some made in Hong Kong)..**£20-30**

266 E.R.F. Fire Tender
1976-79
- Red body, 'Fire Service', White wheeled escape ladder................**£50-60**
1979-80
- Same but with Metallic Red body.........**£50-60**
1976-79
- Danish issue: Red body, 'FALCK'..........**£70-85**

267 Superior Cadillac Ambulance
1967-71
- Cream and Red, 'AMBULANCE' on roof, flashing light, stretcher, patient....**£50-65**

267 Paramedic Truck
1978-79
- Red, Yellow cylinders, two figures, lapel badge, (TV Series 'Emergency')...**£20-30**

268 Range Rover 'AMBULANCE'
1973-77
- White body, stretcher, bubble-packed..**£20-30**

269 Jaguar Motorway 'POLICE' Car
1962-66
- White body, Red interior, two figures, spun hubs, Grey plastic aerial, Blue roof-light....**£120-140**
- Same but with White interior.............**£80-120**
- Same but with Cream interior.............**£80-120**
- Matt White body, Light Grey int.......**£125-150**

269 Ford Transit 'POLICE' Van
1978-79
- White/Red/Blue, with figures, lights, signs and cones. Type 3 casting...........**£35-45**

270 Ford 'POLICE' Panda Car
1969-72
- Turquoise body, White doors, Blue/White roof sign, cast hubs............**£45-55**
1972-77
- Same model but with Speedwheels......**£40-50**

271 Ford Transit 'FIRE'
1975-76
- Red body, with hose/axe/bells/plastic ladder, bubble-packed, Type 2..............**£55-65**
- Danish issue: Same model but with 'FALCK' logo......**£65-75**

272 'POLICE' Accident Unit
1975-78
- White body, with radar gun, beacon, aerial, cones and signs, Type 2 casting.**£35-45**

274 Ford Transit Ambulance
1978-79
- White, 'AMBULANCE', Red crosses, beacon, Type 3 casting..........................**£35-45**

276 Airport Fire Tender
1962-69
- Red body, 'AIRPORT FIRE CONTROL', bell, packing ring in box......................**£75-100**
- Same but in yellow/red Export box ..**£200-250**
- Same model but 'FIRE BRIGADE' logo (from 259), no crest...................**£75-100**

276 Ford Transit Ambulance
1976-78
- White body, 'AMBULANCE', Type 2 casting, packing ring in box.......**£30-40**

277 Superior Criterion Ambulance
1962-69
- Metallic Blue, White roof and tyres, flashing light, box has lift-off lid and

one packing piece.................................. **£75-85**
- As previous model but in Gold
'see-through' box **£80-90**

277 'POLICE' Land Rover
1977-80
- Black body, White tilt, Blue beacon **£20-30**

278 Vauxhall Victor 'AMBULANCE'
1964-69
White body, Red Cross on doors, Blue roof
beacon, driver, opening tailgate, Red/White
stretcher with patient. Versions:
- With Pale Brown interior **£70-85**
- With Blue interior **£70-85**
- With Sea Green interior **£60-75**
NB Baseplates: Examples of 278 will be
found with either 'VAUXHALL VICTOR'
or just 'VICTOR' imprinted on their baseplates.

282 Land Rover Fire Appliance
1973-79
- Red, 'Fire Service', metal ladder,
bubble-packed.. **£30-40**
1974-78
- Danish issue:
Same model but with 'FALCK' logo **£35-45**

285 Merryweather Marquis
1969-79
- Metallic Dark Red body, escape ladder,
working pump, 'FIRE SERVICE' **£55-65**
- With non-Metallic Red body **£55-65**
- Danish issue: Same model but Red or
Metallic Dark Red body, 'FALCK'.......... **£85-95**

286 Ford Transit 'FIRE'
1968-74
- Red, 'Fire Service', hose,
Type 1 casting, bubble-packed............. **£75-90**
- Same but with Metallic Red body **£75-90**
- Danish issue: Same model but with
'FALCK ZONEN' logo **£85-95**

*287 Police Accident Unit - orange, cream, with 3 plastic
cones and 2 accident signs.*

287 Police Accident Unit
1967-71
- White body, Orange panels,
roof rack and sign, radar gun,
aerial, Type 1 casting......................... **£100-125**

1971-74
- White body, Red panels, Type 1 casting,
roof rack and sign, radar gun, traffic
cones, two 'POLICE' warning boards ... **£65-75**

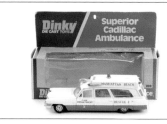

*288 Superior Cadillac Ambulance - unusual variation
has red lower, white upper, with stretcher accessory inside.*

288 Superior Cadillac
1971-79
- White body with Red lower panels,
'AMBULANCE', stretcher and
patient, no flashing light **£40-45**
- Danish issue: Black body/White roof,
Blue interior and roof bar, 'FALCK'
on roof bar and tailgate....................... **£100-125**

442 Land Rover Breakdown Crane
1973-79
- White and Red body, 'Motorway
Rescue', operable winch **£25-30**
1975-78
- White body, Red bonnet and door panels,
Blue interior, 2 Orange rooflights,
Black jib, 'FALCK' **£40-50**
- All Red body, Blue interior, Light Blue
header board, Black jib, Speedwheels,
'FALCK' **£50-60**
- All Red body, Black interior, deeper
Blue header board, Black jib,
Speedwheels, 'FALCK' **£50-60**

*555 Fire Engine with extending ladder, scarce variation
with brown ladder.*

555 Fire Engine (Commer)
1952-54 (renumbered in 1954 to 955)
- Red body with Silver trim and ladder,
no windows... **£75-85**

624 Daimler Military Ambulance
1954-? (renumbered in 1954 from 30hm)
- Military-Green body, Red crosses on
White backgrounds, (US issue) **£200-300**

954 Fire Station
1961-64
- Red, Yellow and 'brick' plastic,
base 252 mm. x 203 mm.................... **£200-250**

955 Fire Engine (Commer)
1954-64 (renumbered in 1954 from 555)
- Red body and diecast Supertoy hubs,
no window glazing **£90-110**
1964-70
- Red body, Red diecast or plastic hubs,
window glazing, Black or Grey tyres,
housed in Yellow box with drawing
or scene, card packing....................... **£150-175**

*956 Turntable Fire Escape with windows - scarce later
version with plastic hubs.*

956 Turntable Fire Escape Lorry (Bedford cab)
1958-60
- Red body and diecast hubs,
no windows, Silver deck and ladder ... **£80-100**
1960-70
- Red body, diecast then plastic hubs,
window glazing, instructions,
'Tested' label, card packing **£80-100**
NB A version of 956 has been discovered
(in Norway) that has 3 ladders instead of 2.

956 Turntable Fire Escape Lorry (Berliet cab)
1970-74
- Metallic Red body and hubs, windows,
'ECHELLE INCENDIE',
Black platform.................................... **£150-200**
- Same but with Silver platform........... **£175-225**
1974-?
- Danish issue: Metallic Red body
and hubs, windows, 'FALCK'............. **£175-225**

2253 Ford Capri Police Car
1974-76
- White/Orange, 'POLICE', Blue light,
suspension. (1:25 scale) **£80-100**

Dinky Toys Farm and Garden Models

Model and details	MPR

22e Farm Tractor
1933-40
- 'Modelled Miniature' with
'HORNBY SERIES' cast-in, no hook,
Yellow/Dark Blue (lead) body,
Red or Yellow (lead) wheels **£300-400**

22e 'DINKY TOYS' cast-in, with hook,
Red or Yellow wheels are lead, diecast
or both, body colours:
- Green/Yellow **£300-400**
- Yellow/Blue/Red................................ **£300-400**
- Red/Blue £300-400
- Red/Red £300-400
- Cream/Blue.. **£300-400**
- Cream/Red... **£300-400**
- Blue/Cream/Red **£300-400**

Model and details	MPR

27a 'MASSEY-HARRIS' Tractor
1948-54 (renumbered in 1954 to 300)
Sold through a trade box x3.
Individually sold as below;
Black mottled base.
- Red body, Yellow cast wheels,
driver, hook **£80-100**
Box Type 1.Rare Dual Yellow picture box
- Red body, Yellow cast wheels,
driver, hook **£200-300**

27ak Tractor and Hay Rake
1952-54 (renumbered in 1954 to 310)
Box Type Blue & White Stripped Dual No
Picture Box
- 27a Tractor and 27k Hay Rake.......... **£300-350**

27b Halesowen Harvest Trailer
1949-54 (renumbered in 1954 to 320)

Model and details	MPR

Sold through a trade box x3.
Individually sold as below;
- Brown & Red body, Red racks, drawbar, hook
Yellow cast wheels **£40-50**

27c M.H. Manure Spreader
1949-54 (renumbered in 1954 to 321)
Sold through a trade box x 3
Individually sold as below;
- Red body with drawbar, hook,
working shredders................................. **£40-50**
Box Type 1.Rare Dual No Yellow picture box
- As above but in individual box............. **£70-90**

27d Land Rover
1950-54 (renumbered in 1954 to 340)
Sold through a trade box x 4.
Individually sold as below;
Black mottled base. Tan cast Driver.

- Dark Blue body, Cream interior,
  Dark Blue hubs
  Guide Only £1500-2000 .... NGPP
- Orange body, Dark Brown interior,
  Tan cast driver, Red hubs **£120-170**
- Orange body, Dark Green interior,
  Tan cast driver, Red hubs **£90-110**
- Mid-Green body, Light Brown
  interior, Tan cast driver, Green hubs .. **£90-110**
- Gift Set model: Dark Brown body,
  Beige driver. Only issued in
  Commercial Vehicles Gift Set No.2.
  If sold individually (unboxed) **£800-1,100**
  Box Type 1. Rare Dual No Yellow picture box
- Orange body, Dark Green interior,
  Tan cast driver, Red hubs **£110-170**
- Mid-Green body, Light Brown
  interior, Tan cast driver, Green hubs **£110-170**

27f Estate Car
1950-54 (renumbered in 1954 to 344)
Sold through a trade box x 4.
Individually sold as below;
- Pale Brown body with Dark Brown panels,
  rear axle pillars, Fawn hubs, small
  lettering on mottled base. Tan hubs ... **£60-100**
  Box Type 1. Rare Dual No Yellow picture box
- As above but individually boxed   .**£150-200**

27g Moto-Cart
1949-54 (renumbered in 1954 to 342)
Sold through a trade box x 3
Individually sold as below;
- Dark Green with Tan back and
  driver, Red cast wheels, hook **£150-200**
- Brown and Green body, driver,
  Red cast wheels, hook **£40-60**
  Box Type 1. Rare Dual No Yellow picture box
- Brown and Green body, driver,
  Red cast wheels, hook **£80-120**

27h Disc Harrow
1951-54 (renumbered in 1954 to 322)
Sold through a trade box x 4
Individually sold as below;
- Red/Yellow body, Silver disc blades,
  tinplate hook **£30-40**

27j Triple Gang Mower
1952-54 (renumbered in 1954 to 323)
Sold through a trade box x 3
Individually sold as below;
- Red frame, Yellow tines,
  Green wheels, cast-in hook **£50-80**

27K/No 324 Hay Rake - red, yellow.

27k Hay Rake
1953-54 (renumbered in 1954 to 324)
Sold through a trade box type but for only 1
model.
- Red frame, Yellow wheels, wire tines,
  operating lever **£30-50**

27m Land Rover Trailer
1952-54 (renumbered in 1954 to 341)
Sold through a trade box x 4
Individually sold as below;
- Mid Blue body and Blue hubs **£180-250**
- Burnt Orange body, Cream hubs **£50-70**
- Green body and hubs............................. **£30-50**
- Orange body & Red hubs **£40-60**
- Militarised version:
  see 'Military Vehicles' section.

27n 'FIELD MARSHALL' Tractor
1953-54 (renumbered in 1954 to 301)
Box Type 1. Dual No Yellow picture box
& Inner packing piece.
Black mottled base.
- Burnt Orange body and exhaust, Silver
  Cast wheels, Tan driver, hook............ **£170-220**
- As previous model but with
  Green cast wheels, hook **£170-220**

30n Farm Produce Wagon
1950-54 (renumbered in 1954 to 343)
Sold through a trade box x 6
Individually sold as below;
Model has stake sides to rear body;
Black mottled base and hook;
hubs same colour as rear body.
- Yellow cab with Green back.............. **£100-130**
- Green cab with Yellow back................. **£80-100**
- Cherry Red cab with Blue back **£80-100**
  Box Type 1. Dual No Yellow picture box
- Yellow cab with Green back.............. **£150-180**
- Green cab with Yellow back.............. **£120-150**
- Cherry (Red) cab with Blue back **£120-150**
Note; following models listed from 105a - 107a
All came in trade boxes of 6.
If individualy sold:

105a Garden Roller
1948-54 (renumbered in 1954 to 381)
- Green handle and Red roller sides........ **£25-40**

105b Wheelbarrow
1948-54 (renumbered in 1954 to 382)
- Brown or Tan and Red body,
  single metal wheel................................. **£25-40**

105c 4 wheeled Hand Truck
1948-54 (renumbered in 1954 to 383)
- Green/Yellow or Blue/Yellow **£25-40**

105e Grass Cutter
1948-54 (renumbered in 1954 to 384)
- Yellow handle, Green metal wheels,
  Red blades.. **£25-40**
- Yellow handle, unpainted metal
  wheels, Green blades **£50-75**

107a Sack Truck
1948-54 (renumbered in 1954 to 385)
- Blue or Pale Green body,
  two Black metal wheels......................... **£20-30**

192 Range Rover
1970-74
Box Type1 Yellow picture box with white
background
Box Type 2 Red & Blue window Box.
- Bronze body, various interior colours,
  cast detailed or Speedwheels **£25-35**
1973-79
- Black or Yellow body, Speedwheels...... **£25-35**

300 'MASSEY-HARRIS' Tractor
1954-62 (renumbered in 1954 from 27a)
Box Type 1. Yellow picture box
Box Type 2. Lighter Yellow picture box
Box Type 3. Yellow & Red panel Non picture box
Box Type 4 Yellow picture box with white
background
- Red body, cast wheels (Green centre,
  unpainted 'tyres'), Tan cast driver .... NGPP
- Red body, cast wheels (Yellow centre,
  unpainted 'tyres'), Tan cast driver.
  Mottled base. Metal S/W. **£145-175**
1962-64
- Red body & Yellow cast wheels & Tan cast
  driver. Mottled base. Black .Metal S/W.**£130-180**
1964-66
- Red body & Yellow cast Rear wheels Yellow
  plastic front wheels & Brown driver.
  Mottled base.Black Metal S/W. **£180-220**
1963   South African issue:
(English and Afrikaans text on box)
Box Type 3. Lighter Yellow picture box
- Red body, Yellow hubs (cast rear,
  plastic front, rubber tyres), Blue plastic driver
  Massey Harris logo in yellow.
  Black Metal S/W.Black gloss base. **£1500-2000**

300 'MASSEY-FERGUSON' Tractor
1966-71
Box Type 2. Lighter Yellow picture box
Box Type 3. Yellow & Red panel Non picture box
Box Type 4 Yellow picture box with white
background
Black gloss base & Blue plastic driver.
Models have either Black or Silver S/W
and black or yellow exhaust stack.
- Cherry Red body, Yellow hubs (cast rear,
  plastic front, rubber tyres),
  no decals Black Metal S/W **£225-300**
- Cherry Red body, Yellow hubs (cast rear,
  plastic front, rubber tyres),
  no decals Black Metal S/W **£170-250**

*Dinky 300 Field Marshall Tractor. The late version with
blue plastic driver is scarce.*

301 'FIELD MARSHALL' Tractor
1954-64 (renumbered in 1954 from 27n)
Box Type 2. Yellow picture box
Box Type 3. Lighter Yellow picture box
Box Type 4. Yellow & Red panel Non picture box
Mottled base. Internal packing piece all options.
- Orange or Burnt Orange body, cast wheels
  (Green or Silver centres, unpainted 'tyres'),
  Tan driver, hook **£175-225**
- Same but with Type 4 box.................. **£200-250**
1964-66
  Black gloss base. Type 3 or 4 box.
- Orange or Burnt Orange body, cast Green
  rear wheels & plastic front wheels with tyres.
  Blue plastic driver, hook **£350-450**

305 'DAVID BROWN' 990 Tractor
1964-67
Box Type 1 showing red & yellow model,
Box Type 2 Yellow picture box with
white background showing white model.
Box Type 3 Yellow window Box.
Box Type 4 Bubble pack
- Yellow cab and hubs, Red cowl, Black
  engine, stickers: 'David Brown 990'.
  Detailed picture box........................... **£150-200**
1967-73
- White cab/hubs/cowl,
  Brown engine, stickers:
  'David Brown Selectamatic 990'........ **£100-130**
- Promotional issue: In Red box with
  'IT WAS MADE BY MECCANO
  DINKY TOYS' logo. Brown engine,
  Black engine stickers: 'David Brown
  990 Selectamatic Tractor',
  Red exhaust....................................... **£150-200**
1974-75
- White cab and cowl, Red hubs and engine,
  stickers: 'Case David Brown 995'.
  Bubble-packed................................... **£130-160**

308 'LEYLAND' 384 Tractor
1971-72
Box Type 1 White Panel Picure box, showing
Blue model.
Box Type 2 Blue & Red picture hanging box.
Box Type 3 Bubble pack
All models white cast rear and plastic front hubs.
- Metallic Red body,, Blue Plastic driver,
  Type 1,2 or 3 box. **£100-130**
1973-79
- Blue or Dark body, with Blue Plastic driver,
  Type 1,2 or 3 box **£100-130**
1978-79

- Orange body, Blue plastic driver,
  Type 2 and 3 Box. **£100-130**
- Factory error: Blue body and plastic
  driver, Red hubs, White exhaust
  stack. Bubble-packed **£200-250**

310 Tractor and Hay Rake
1954-60 (renumbered in 1954 from 27ak)
Box Type 2 Blue & White Stripped Picture Box
Box Type 3 Large Yellow Picture Box.
Single packing piece.
- 300 Massey Harris Tractor and
  324 Hay Rake Either above box type. **£280-350**
- 300 Massey Ferguson Cherry Red body,
  Yellow hubs (cast rear, plastic front, rubber
  tyres), Metal S/W. 324 Hay Rake. Type 3 box
  only. with single packing piece **£320-400**

319 Weeks Tipping Trailer
1961-71
Box Type 1. Yellow picture box
Box Type 2 Yellow window Box.
Box Type 3 Gold window Box.
- Red/Yellow body, Red ST hubs,
  One packing piece **£40-60**
- Red/Yellow body, Yellow ST hubs,
  One packing piece **£40-60**
- Red/Yellow body, Yellow Plastic hubs,
  One packing piece **£50-80**

320 Harvest Trailer with removable racks.

320 Halesowen Harvest Trailer
1954-60 (renumbered in 1954 from 27b)
Box Type 1. Yellow picture box
Box Type 2. Lighter Yellow picture box
- Brown & Red body, Red racks, drawbar, hook,
  Yellow cast wheels **£60-80**
- Red body, Yellow racks,
  drawbar, hook, Yellow plastic wheels ... **£60-80**

321 M.H. Manure Spreader
1954-62 (renumbered in 1954 from 27c)
Box Type 2. Yellow picture box
Box Type 3 Yellow picture box with white
background
Box Type 4. Yellow & Red panel Non picture box
Box Type 5 Yellow window Box.
- Red body, Yellow cast wheels,,Silver spreader
  'MASSEY-HARRIS' **£30-50**
  1962-73
- Red body, Red ST hubs Slver Spreader
  'MASSEY-HARRIS' **£150-200**
  Note Model sold at Vectis Auction Dec2007
  with plain red yellow panel box £280 +
  Commission.
- Red body, Yellow plastic hubs ,Silver spreader
  No Decals or wirh decals. **£30-50**
- Red body, Red plastic hubs ,Silver spreader
  No Decals or wirh decals **£40-70**

322 Disc Harrow
1954-67 (renumbered in 1954 from 27h)
Box Type 1. Yellow picture box
Box Type 2 Picture Box showing white & Red
model.
- Red/Yellow body, Silver disc blades,
  tinplate hook **£25-35**
  1967-73
- White/Red, Silver blades, no hook........ **£25-35**
- All White version **£40-50**

323 Triple Gang Mower
1954-63 (renumbered in 1954 from 27j)
Box Type. Yellow picture box
- Red frame, Yellow tines,
  Green wheels, cast-in hook **£60-80**

324 Hayrake
1954-64 (renumbered in 1954 from 27k)
Box Type 1. Yellow picture box
Box Type 2. Yellow & Red panel Non picture box
- Red frame, Yellow wheels,
  Black or Silver lever **£40-60**

**325 'DAVID BROWN' Tractor and
Disc Harrow**
1967-73
Box Type 1 White panel picture box shows
white model.
Box Type 2 Picture Box shows white model in
field scene.
- 305 and 322 in White and Red.
  Box has inner packing piece **£250-330**
- 305 and 322 in Yellow and Red.
  Box has inner packing piece **£250-330**

*Dinky Toys 340 Land Rover in Ministry of Food livery.
This is a promotional model with extra silver detailing.
Very few were produced.*

340 1954-66   Land Rover
(renumbered from 27d)
Early mottled base.
- 1954 Promotional:
  Box Type1 Yellow dual No picture box
  Issued to MOF Sales Representatives to give to
  farmers to promote the products of the MOF.
  Very Dark Green body & hubs,
  Tan cast driver., Extra Silver detailing
  (Ministry of Food promotional) **£2000-2500**
  Box Type 1.Dual Yellow picture box
  Box Type 2. Yellow picture box
- Orange body, Dark Green interior,
  Tan cast driver, Red hubs **£125-175**
- Mid-Green body, Light Brown
  interior, Tan cast driver, Green hubs **£125-175**
  1966-69
  Box Type.2 Yellow picture box
  Box Type 3. Lighter Yellow picture box with no
  spot.
  Black Gloss Base. Blue Plastic Driver.
- Orange body, Dark Green interior,
  Red Plastic hubs **£140-180**
- Red body, Red interior,
  Red plastic hubs **£225-300**
  1969-71
- Dark Red body, Yellow Interior, Red
  plastic hubs, ... **£225-300**
- Orange body, Dark Green interior,
  Green plastic hubs **£350-450**
  Note: Green wheel version can be found in
  Type 6 Box.
  1971
  Box Type 3. Lighter Yellow picture box No spot.
  Box Type 4. Lighter Yellow picture box Clear
  spot.
  Box Type 5. Red & Yellow panel Non picture box
  Box Type 6 Red & Yellow window Box
  Matt Black Base. Blue Plastic Driver.
- Red body, Red interior,
  Red plastic hubs **£275-350**
- Red body, Yellow interior,
  Yellow plastic hubs **£250-325**
- Orange body, Black interior,
  Red plastic hubs **£350-450**

341 1954-66   Land-Rover Trailer
(renumbered from 27m)
Box Type 1. Dual No Yellow picture box
Box Type 2. Yellow picture box
Box Type 3. Lighter Yellow picture box
Box Type 4. Red & Yellow and Red panel non
picture box
- Green body, Green cast hubs **£50-70**
- Orange body, Red cast hubs **£50-70**
- Orange body, Red plastic hubs **£50-70**
- Red body, Red plastic hubs **£50-70**
- Red body, Black plastic hubs............ **£150-250**
- Red body, Yellow plastic hubs.......... **£150-250**
- Orange body, Green Plastic hubs...... **£150-250**
  Note later models have no hook.
- Militarised version:
  see 'Military Vehicles' section.
- Olive-Drab body **£300-500**

342 Moto-Cart
1954-61 (renumbered in 1954 from 27g)
Box Type 1. Yellow picture box
- Light Green with Tan back and
  driver, Red hubs.................................. **£80-140**
- Dark Olive Green with Tan back and
  driver, Red cast wheels, hook **£220-300**

*343 Farm Produce Wagon - deep red cab, chassis, mid
blue rear body and ridged hubs, black knobbly tyres.*

343 Farm Produce Wagon
1954-64 (renumbered in 1954 from 30n)
Box Type 1. Yellow picture box
Box Type 2. Lighter Yellow picture box
Box Type 3.Red & Yellow panel Non picture box
Mottled base.
- Mid-Green cab and chassis,
  Yellow back and hubs........................ **£140-170**
- Cherry Red cab,
  Mid-Blue back / hubs........................ **£160-200**
  Late models Black Gloss Base & M tyres.
- Mid-Green cab and chassis,
  Yellow back and hubs........................ **£200-250**
- Cherry Red cab,
  Mid-Blue back / hubs........................ **£200-250**
- Mid-Green cab and chassis,
  Yellow back and plastic hubs........... **£175-225**

344 Estate Car
1954-61 (renumbered in 1954 from 27f)
Box Type 1.Dual Yellow picture box
Box Type 2. Yellow picture box
Box Type 3. Rare Yellow picture box showing
Red panels not Brown.
Box Type 4. Red & Yellow panel Non picture box
Mottled base Smooth Tyres.
- Brown & Dark Brown side panels, Tan hubs,
  Small base writing, Type 1 or 2 Box. **£125-175**
- Brown & Dark Brown side panels, Cream hubs,
  Large base writing, Type 2 or 3 Box. . **£125-175**
- Brown & Dark Brown side panels,
  spun hubs, M Tyres Type 2 or 4 Box. **£350-450**
  Black Gloss Base M Tyres.
- Brown & Dark Brown side panels,
  spun hubs Type 4 Box. **£300-400**

344 Land Rover Pick-Up
1970-72
Box Type 1 Yellow picture box with white
background
Box Type 2 Hanging Red & Yellow window Box.
Box Type 3 Soft plastic case window box.
- Metallic Blue body, White back,Yellow
  Interior & cast hubs, Box Type 1. .... **£20-35**
- Metallic or Dark Blue body, White back,Yellow
  Interior & cast hubs, or speedwheels

Box Type 2 or 3. .... **£20-35**
1973-78
- Metallic Red body, White back,
  Speedwheels. Type 3 Box. **£20-35**

381 Garden Roller
1954-58 (renumbered in 1954 from 105a)
Sold from a trade box of six.
- Green and Red **£25-35**

381 Convoy Farm Truck
1977-80
Box Type 1 Hanging Red & Yellow window Box.
- Yellow cab, Brown plastic high-sided
  truck body, Black plastic hubs. **£15-25**
- Pre production all-Orange version .... NGPP

382 Wheelbarrow
1954-58 (renumbered in 1954 from 105b)
Sold from a trade box of six.
- Brown and Red body, metal wheel **£30-40**

383 4 wheeled Hand Truck
1954-58 (renumbered in 1954 from 105c)
Sold from a trade box of six.
- Green body, Yellow cast hubs **£30-40**
- Blue body, Yellow cast hubs **£30-40**

384 Grass Cutter
1954-58 (renumbered in 1954 from 105e)
Sold from a trade box of six.
- Yellow handle, Green metal wheels,
  Red blades. **£30-40**
- Yellow handle, unpainted
  metal wheels, Green blades. **£50-75**

385 Sack Truck
1954-58 (renumbered in 1954 from 107a)
Sold from a trade box of six.
- Blue with black metal wheels. **£15-25**

386 Lawn Mower
1954-58 (renumbered in 1954 from 751)
Solid Yellow Picture Box.
- Green/Red, separate grassbox,
  'Dinky Toys' cast-in **£120-160**

399 Tractor and Trailer
1969-75
Box Type Window.
Model 300 combined with 428.
- Red Massey Ferguson Tractor with Yellow
  front plastic wheels & yellow metal rear wheels
- Blue Plastic Driver, Trailer Red body with
  crome cast wheels. **£250-300**

428 Large Trailer
1955-71
See 'Commercial Vehicles' section

561 Blaw Knox Bulldozer
1949-54 (renumbered in 1954 to 961)
Box Type 1 Brown box with Red label & white
background.Picture Box.
Box Type 2 Brown box with Orange label &
white background. Picture Box.
Box Type 3 Blue Box , Orange label & white
background. Picture Box.
- Red body, Green or Black rubber tracks,
  Cast Tan driver, black, lifting blade,
  one packing piece. **£60-80**

563 Blaw Knox Heavy Tractor
1948-54 (renumbered in 1954 to 963)
Box Type 1 Brown box with Red label & white
background.Picture Box.
Box Type 2 Brown box with Orange label &
white background. Picture Box.
Box Type 3 Blue Box , Orange label & white
background. Picture Box.
All models includee packing piece.
- Dark Blue body, Mid-Blue rollers,
  Green rubber tracks, Tan cast driver. **£300-400**
- Red, body & black rollers & green
  rubber tracks. Tan cast driver. **£60-100**
- Orange, body & green rollers & green
  rubber tracks. Tan cast driver. **£60-100**

564 Elevator Loader
1952-54 (renumbered in 1954 to 964)
Box Type 1 Blue Box , Orange label & white
background. Picture Box.
Box Type 2 Blue & White striped picture box.
- Yellow with Mid-Blue chutes, Yellow hubs,
  one packing piece. **£60-70**

751 Lawn Mower
1949-54 (renumbered in 1954 to 386)
Box Type1 Blue Box , Orange label & white
background. Picture Box.
- Green/Red, 'Dinky Supertoys' cast-in **£80-110**

961 Blaw-Knox Bulldozer
1954-62 (renumbered in 1954 from 561)
Box Type. 1 Blue & White striped picture
box showing Red model. Box base blue.
Packing piece in box.
Box Type. 2 as Type 1 box but showing
Primrose model

Packing piece in box.
Mottled base.
- Red body & blade, Black or green rubber
  tracks, Tan cast driver, Black rollers **£50-80**
- Primrose Yellow body and Grey blade,
  Black or green rubber tracks, Tan cast driver,
  Black rollers. **£60-100**
1962-64
Following models Black gloss base
- Primrose Yellow body and Grey blade,
  Black or green rubber tracks, Blue Plastic driver,
  Black rollers, ... **£90-130**
1964-64
- Orange plastic body, Silver engine detail,
  Black diecast lifting gear, Green plastic blade
  and exhaust, Blue Plastic driver, Light Green or
  Olive-Green roller wheels. **£500-600**

963 Blaw Knox Heavy Tractor
1954-58 (renumbered in 1954 from 563)
Mottled base.
Box Type 1 Blue & White striped picture
box showing Red model.Box base blue.
Box Type 2 as Type 1 box but showing
Primrose model
Packing piece in box.
- Red body, Black or green rubber
  tracks, Tan cast driver, Black rollers
  .... **£90-120**
- Orange body, Black or green rubber
  tracks, Tan cast driver, Black rollers.... **£90-120**
1958-59
- Primrose Yellow, Green rubber tracks,
  Tan cast driver, Black rollers,. **£120-150**

964 Elevator Loader
1954-68 (renumbered in 1954 from 564)
Box Type 1 Blue & White striped picture box.
Box Type 2 Yellow Supertoys Lift off Picture
box showing yellow model.
Box Type 3 Late Picture Box with fold in
end tabs showing Blue model.
- Yellow with Mid-Blue chutes,
  Yellow ST hubs. **£70-90**
- Mid-Blue with Yellow chutes,
  Yellow ST hubs. **£90-130**
  Late issue: Type 3 Box.
- Mid-Blue with Yellow chutes, Blue
  plastic hubs **£150-200**

Dinky Toys Motor Cycles   *See also Military, Accessories and Gift Sets sections.*

Model and details	MPR
041 Police Motor Cyclist	
1952-54	
• Post-war reissue for US market of 37a .... NGPP	
042 Civilian Motor Cyclist	
1952-54	
• Post-war reissue for US market of 37b .... NGPP	
043 Police Motorcycle Patrol	
1952-54	
• Post-war reissue for US market of 42b .... NGPP	
044 'R.A.C.' Motorcycle Patrol	
1952-54	
• Post-war reissue for US market of 43b .... NGPP	
045 'A.A.' Motorcycle Patrol	
1952-54	
• Post-war reissue for US market of 44b .... NGPP	
14z 'Triporteur'	
1938-40	

- Three-wheel delivery van with Green,
  Red, Grey, Blue or Yellow body,
  Black hubs, White tyres, rider is always
  a different colour from van.
  French model, imported into
  England in very small numbers **£200-300**

37a Civilian Motor Cyclist
(renumbered in 1954 to 041)
1937-40

Model and details	MPR

- Black motor cycle, Silver engine/exhaust
  detail; Blue, Maroon, Green or Black
  rider, SWRW or thick SBRW **£40-50**
  1946-49
- Black motor cycle without Silver detail,
  Green or Grey rider, thin SBRW **£40-50**
  1950-54
- As previous version, but export only **£40-50**

37a Civilian Motorcyclist - scarce colour variation with grey rider, black bike and white rubber tyres.

Model and details	MPR
37b Police Motor Cyclist	
(renumbered in 1954 to 042)	
1937-40	

- Black motor cycle with Silver
  engine/exhaust detail, Dark Blue
  rider, SWRW or thick SBRW **£75-85**
  1946-49
- Black motor cycle without Silver
  engine/exhaust detail,
  Dark Blue rider, thick SBRW **£40-50**
  1950-54
- As previous model, but export only **£40-50**

37c Royal Signals Dispatch Rider
1937-41
- Green body, Khaki rider,
  White or Black rubber wheels.
  Sold unboxed **£150-175**
- Boxed version:
  It is believed that only 1,000 were
  sold boxed. Blue box/lid with
  insert, 'A2237' .... NGPP

42b Police Motorcycle Patrol
(renumbered in 1955 to 043)
1935-40
- Black motor cycle, Silver engine
  and exhaust detail, Dark Green and

Black sid ecar, Dark Blue figures,
SWRW or thick SBRW............................. **£75-95**
1946-49
- As previous model but without Silver
detailing and with thin SBRW **£45-55**
1950-55
- Blue/Green, Blue figures, little
detailing, SBRW, export only **£40-50**

43b 'R.A.C.' Motorcycle Patrol
1935-40
- Blue/Black motor cycle/sidecar,
Silver engine/exhaust detail,
Blue/Black rider with
Red sash, SWRW or thick SBRW **£75-95**
1946-49
- As previous model but no Silver

detailing, thin SBRW.
NB - two shades of Blue used post-war **£45-55**

44b 'A.A.' Motorcycle Patrol
1935-40
- Black/Yellow, Brown rider, more
detailing, 5mm 'AA' badge,
solid white rubber wheels.................. **£100-125**
1946-50
- Black/Yellow, Tan rider, little detailing,
7mm 'AA' badge, SBRW........................ **£50-60**
NB   This version remained in the catalogue,
was renumbered in 1954 to 270 but was
not re-introduced until 1959 - see 270 below.
1950-55
- As previous model but export only
(renumbered in 1955 to 045) **£50-60**

270 'A.A.' Motorcycle Patrol
1959-62   (renumbered in 1954 from 44b)
- Black/Yellow, Tan rider,
'AA' sign, SGPW...................................... **£40-50**
- Black/Yellow, Tan rider, 'AA' sign,
solid knobbly Black plastic wheels ... **£100-150**

271 'T.S.' Motorcycle Patrol
1959-62
- Yellow motorcycle combination,
Belgian equivalent of the A.A............ **£150-200**

272 'A.N.W.B.' Motorcycle Patrol
1959-62
- Yellow motorcycle combination,
Dutch equivalent of the A.A **£250-300**

Dinky Toys Military Vehicles
See also Action Kits, Aircraft, Ships, Gift Sets and Factory Samples sections.

Colour finish of Dinky Toys Military models.
Military colours tend to be described by collectors, dealers and observers variously as 'Olive Drab' or 'Military Green' or 'Khaki' or 'Matt Green'.

This is a less than satisfactory method of describing the colour finish of these models, especially when there are also shades of colour and depth of gloss (or lack of it).

We are of the opinion that they fundamentally relate to the same finish anyway, so for the sake of simplicity, this listing contains colour information ONLY where it is clearly specific (sand, camouflage or German grey, for example). Assume that all the

models in this listing are finished in one form or another of this 'Military Green' unless specifically stated otherwise. For all other descriptions of single colour finishes, the following **general** comments may be noted:

Pre-war issues have variations in shade, depth and degrees of gloss or matt surface. Some have a distinct brownish bias. None of these variations affect the price.

1950's Military Vehicles finish is generally regarded as Khaki. Mike and Sue Richardson prefer to regard

pre-war military finish as Matt Green and post-war as Olive Drab.

US issues are generally considered to be Olive Drab (a term that seems to have originated in a 1950's US Army recruitment poster referring to uniforms).

Late Lines Bros issues are in various green shades, often quite light green.

French issues are said to be more Olive Drab than British Khaki but all generally appear consistent in their groups.

Model and details	MPR
1 **Military Vehicles (1) Set**	
1954-55 See 'Gift Sets' section.	
22f **Army Tank**	
1933-34	
- 'Modelled Miniature' with 'HORNBY SERIES' cast-in. Green lead body, Orange revolving turret, Red, White or Green rubber tracks.	**£250-350**
1934-39	
- Green/Orange lead body, 'DINKY TOYS' cast-in, Red or Green tracks	**£250-300**
- Khaki lead body, 'DINKY TOYS' cast-in, Red or Green tracks	**£250-300**
- Grey lead body, 'DINKY TOYS' cast-in, Red or Green tracks	**£250-300**
22s **Searchlight Lorry**	
1939-41	
- Green body, (22c casting, open cab rear window), smooth hubs. Not boxed	**£100-150**
- Same, but in yellow lidded box marked 'A2309'	NGPP
25b **Army Covered Wagon**	
1948-50	
- Military-Green body and hubs. South-African issue	**£750-1,000**
25wm Bedford Military Truck	
1952-54 (renumbered in 1954 to 640)	
- With tow hook. USA export only	**£200-250**
27m **Land Rover Trailer**	
1952-54 (renumbered in 1954 to 341)	
- Made to accompany 669, unpainted hook and drawbar clip	**£300-400**
28 **Army Delivery Van**	
1948-56	
- South-African issue: Type 3 with Military-Green body and hubs	**£750-1,000**
30hm Daimler Military Ambulance	
1952-54 (renumbered in 1954 to 624)	
- Red crosses on White backgrounds. (US export issue)	**£200-250**
30sm Austin Covered Wagon	
1952-54 (renumbered in 1954 to 625)	
- Made for export to USA only	**£100-125**

Model and details	MPR
37c **Royal Signals Dispatch Rider**	
1937-41	
- Green body, Khaki rider, White or Black rubber wheels. Sold unboxed	**£150-175**
- Boxed version: It is believed that only 1,000 were sold boxed. Blue box/lid with insert, 'A2237'	NGPP
139am US Army Staff Car	
1952-54 (renumbered in 1954 to 170m)	
- Ford Fordor with White stars on roof and doors	**£175-250**
- Canadian issue: As previous model but without stars	NGPP
150 **Royal Tank Corps Set**	
1937-41 See Gift Sets section.	
1952-55 See Gift Sets section.	
150a Royal Tank Corps Officer	
1937-41	
- Khaki uniform, Black beret, binoculars in hand	**£25-30**
1952-54	
- Khaki figure. In box of 12	**£100-120**
1954 (renumbered to 600)	
150b Royal Tank Corps Private	
1938-41	
- Black overalls, seated	**£25-30**
1952-54	
- Khaki, seated. In box of 12	**£100-120**
1954 (renumbered to 604)	
150c Royal Tank Corps Private (standing)	
1937-41	
- Diecast figure in Black overalls	**£25-30**
1953-54	
- Mid-Brown overalls, Black base	**£100-150**
150d Royal Tank Corps Driver (sitting)	
1937-41	
- Die-cast figure in Black overalls	**£25-30**
150e Royal Tank Corps NCO (walking)	
1937-41	
- Die-cast figure in Black uniform	**£10-15**
151 **Medium Tank Set**	
1937-41 See Gift Sets section.	

Model and details	MPR
151a Medium Tank	
1937-41	
- White markings, bright chain tracks, aerial, round jockey wheels locating tracks	**£75-90**
- Version with 'flatted' jockey wheels	**£75-90**
- Version with 'spray hole' cast in	**£75-90**
- With Black rubber wheels instead of tracks	NGPP
1947-49	
- USA export version, no markings, bright tracks	**£150-200**
- USA export version, no markings, black tracks	**£150-200**
151b 6-wheel Covered Wagon	
1937-41	
- Lead body, tinplate canopy, seat holes but no figures	**£150-200**
1937-41	
- Diecast body, tinplate canopy, seat holes but no figures	**£150-200**
1946	
- With smooth hubs and early tyres	**£150-200**
1947-54	
- With ridged hubs, no seat holes	**£150-200**
1954-55	
- USA export model with fixed driver, no other seat holes. (Renumbered to 620)	**£200-250**
151c Cooker Trailer	
1937-48	
- Wire stand, hole in seat but no figure	**£50-70**
NB Two styles of baseplate lettering are known for 151c.	
151d Water Tank Trailer	
1937-48	
- Gloss Green, sold unboxed	**£50-70**
152 **Light Tank Set**	
1937-41 See Gift Sets section.	
152a Light Tank	
1937-41	
- White markings, chain tracks, aerial	**£75-100**
- Black rubber wheels instead of tracks	**£100-125**
1947-50	

- No markings, chain tracks, aerial
  .... £125-150
  1954-55
- US export model, no markings, bright or
  black tracks, (renumbered to 650)
  .... £150-200
- Mid (Chocolate) Brown variation... £150-200

152a Light Tank - scarce US export version is dark green in colour, with black tracks.

152b Reconnaissance Car
  1937-41
- Six wheels (smooth hubs).
  Earliest versions had additional front
  axle support from baseplate............ £100-150
- Later pre-war versions
  with normal base £100-150
  1946
- With smooth hubs, early tyres £100-150
  1947-49
- With ridged hubs............................. £100-150
  1953-54
- USA export model
  (renumbered to 671)....................... £125-175

152c Austin Seven
  1937-41
- Wire windscreen frame,
  hole in seat, no baseplate............... £100-150
  1940-41
- Same, but cast in lead,
  hole in seat, no baseplate............... £100-150

153a Military Jeep - brownish green including ridged hubs, with white markings and black ridged tyres, scarce variation.

153a Jeep
  1946-47
- US White star on flat bonnet and left
  rear side, smooth hubs, solid steering
  wheel, no round hole in base.......... £100-125
  1947
- With open spoked steering wheel £60-75
- Brown body, open steering wheel
  .... £100-125
  1948-52
- With raised 'domed' bonnet,
  round hole in base £60-75
  1952-54
- US export model, some have rounded
  axle ends, (renumbered to 672) £100-125

160 Royal Artillery Personnel Set
  1939-41

See Gift Sets section.

160a Royal Artillery NCO
  1939-41
- Khaki uniform; part of 160 Set........... £20-30

160b Royal Artillery Gunner
  1939-54
- Khaki, seated, hands on knees;
  part of 160 Set...................................... £20-30
  1952-55
- US export issue: Same, but in green
  box of 12, (renumbered to 608) £150-200

160c Royal Artillery Gunlayer
  1939-41
- Khaki, seated, hands held out;
  part of 160 Set...................................... £20-30
  1952-55
- US export issue:
  Same, but in green box of 12.......... £150-200

160d Royal Artillery Gunner
  1939-41
- Khaki uniform, standing; part of 160 Set. £20-30
  1952-55
- US export issue:
  Same, but in green box of 12.......... £150-200

161 Mobile Anti-Aircraft Set
  1939-41

See Gift Sets section.

161a Searchlight on Lorry
  1939-41
- 151b casting plus diecast or
  lead searchlight.................................. £200-250

161b Anti-Aircraft Gun on Trailer
  1939-41
- Gloss Green, gun elevates, holes for
  figures, cast drawbar and hook....... £200-250
  1946-50
- Matt Green or Dark Brown................ £80-100
  1950-54
- US export issue
  (renumbered to 690)....................... £125-175

162 18-pounder Field Gun Set
  1939-41

See Gift Sets section.

162a Light Dragon Tractor
  1939-41
- Gloss Green, holes in seats,
  chain tracks £100-125
- Black rubber wheels
  instead of tracks £250-350
  1946-55
- Matt Green, holes in some,
  chain tracks £100-150

162b Ammunition Trailer
  1939-41
- Gloss Green body, baseplate,
  drawbar and hook.............................. £20-25
  1946-55
- Matt Green body, Black baseplate...... £20-25
  1948-55
- US export issue:
  Matt Green body, Black baseplate...... £20-25

162c 18 pounder Gun
  1939-41
- Gloss Green, drawbar cast-in,
  tinplate shield..................................... £20-25
  1946-55
- Matt Green body and shield £20-25

170m Ford US Army Staff Car
  1954-54 (renumbered in 1954 from 139am)
- Ford Fordor Sedan in Matt Olive,
  US export issue
  (renumbered to 675)....................... £200-250

281 Military Hovercraft 'ARMY'
  1973-76
- Olive-Drab body, Gunner, aerial £25-35

341 Land Rover Trailer
  1960 (renumbered in 1954 from 27m)
- Olive-Drab body, drawbar, hook
  .... £300-400

600 Royal Tank Corps Officer
  1952-55
- US only re-issue

  (renumbered from 150)..........................£8-12

601 Austin Paramoke
  1966-76
- Khaki, Grey top, spun hubs, parachute,
  in flap-end box, instructions............... £50-60
  1976-78
- Dark Grey, Grey top, Speedwheels,
  parachute, in bubble-pack with
  card base, instructions £40-50

602 Armoured Command Car
  1976-77
  See 'Novelty', section.

603 Army Private (seated)
  1957-68
- Diecast, Khaki, Black beret,
  seated, box of 12................................ £40-50
  1968-71
- Plastic, Khaki, Black beret,
  seated, box of 12................................ £40-50

603a Army Personnel Set
  1957-68
- Six diecast figures
  (Khaki, Black berets, seated)............... £20-30
  1968-71
- Same 6 figures, but in plastic £20-30

604 Royal Tank Corps Private
  1954-60 (renumbered in 1954 from 150b)
- Diecast, Khaki uniform, seated,
  export only (to USA), box of 12........... £50-70

604 Army Personnel
  1960-72
- Six driver figures
  (Khaki uniforms)................................ £20-30

604 Land Rover Bomb Disposal
  1976-77
- Olive-Drab/Orange, 'Explosive Disposal',
  Speedwheels, robot de-fuser kit on
  sprue. In 'hanging' box...................... £55-65

608 Royal Artillery Gunner
  1954-55
- Khaki uniform, seated, hands on knees.
  US export issue
  (renumbered from 160b)..................... £10-15

609 105 mm. Howitzer and Crew
  1974-77
- Olive-Drab body, three soldiers,
  Green metal wheels or Grey plastic
  wheels, bubble-packed........................ £30-40

612 Commando Jeep
  1973-80
- Driver (green helmet), solid axles,
  plastic gearstick, two guns, jerricans,
  aerial. In 'hanging' box...................... £25-35
- Driver (brown helmet), split axles,
  metal gearstick. In bubble-pack
  with card base £25-35

615 US Jeep and 105 mm. Howitzer
  1968-77
- Based on 612, US Army markings,
  driver (brown helmet),
  display box with pull-out tray £80-90

616 AEC with Chieftain Tank
  1968-77
- AEC articulated Transporter 'ARMY'
  with 683 Tank. Instructions printed
  on pictorial box £90-110

617 VW KDF and 50 mm. Gun
  1967-77
- Grey body, German markings,
  Green metal or Grey plastic wheels,
  long display box or bubble-pack £75-85

618 AEC with Helicopter
  1976-80
- AEC articulated Transporter 'RESCUE',
  724 Helicopter + net. Flap-end box
  .... £90-110

619 Bren Gun Carrier and Anti-Tank Gun
  1976-77
- Khaki, plastic tracks, 2 figures, gun,
  2 sprues each with 6 shells, White '57'
  on red shield. Bubble-pack £35-40
  NB Two variations of markings exist:

(i) '2035703 4', (ii) 'T2272616' plus star.

620 6-wheel Covered Wagon
1954-55 (renumbered in 1954 from 151b)
- US export model, blued axles **£200-250**

620 Berliet Missile Launcher
1971-73
- UK issue of French 816. 'NORD R20' missile. Yellow flap-end box **£120-150**

621 3 ton Army Wagon (Bedford 'RL')
1954-60
- Tin tilt, no windows, driver in some. In yellow flap-end box **£60-70**
1960-63
- Same but with window glazing.......... **£60-70**

622 10 ton Army Truck
1954-64
- (Foden) driver, tin tilt, Supertoys box. **£70-80**
1954-64
- Same, but in Dinky Toys striped box **£70-80**
- Late issue:
In yellow lidded picture box **£200-300**
NB Two types of casting have been observed:
1 - Smooth cab roof, less cab/chassis strengthening.
2 - Ridge across cab roof, thicker strengthening.

622 Bren Gun Carrier
1975-78
- White star, driver, passenger, plastic tracks. Bubble-pack also has decal sheet **£25-35**

623 Army Covered Wagon (Bedford 'QL')
1954-63
- Driver in some, no window glazing, flap-end box **£35-45**

624 Daimler Military Ambulance
1954-? (renumbered in 1954 from 30hm)
- Red crosses, White backgrounds, US export issue................................. **£400-500**

625 Austin Covered Wagon
1952-54 (renumbered in 1954 from 30sm)
- US export issue................................. **£400-500**

625 Six-pounder Gun
1975-77
- Anti-tank gun, 2 plastic sprues each with 6 shells, bubble-pack with flat card base **£15-20**

626 Military Ambulance (Fordson)
1956-61
- Red crosses cast-in, no windows, deep yellow non-picture end-flap box **£60-75**
1961-62
- Same, but with window glazing, pictorial end-flap box **£80-100**
1962-62
- In non-pictorial end-flap export box with red side **£100-125**

630 Ferret Armoured Car
1973-78
- Plastic wheels, spare wheel **£15-20**

640 Bedford Military Truck
1954-? (renumbered in 1954 from 25wm)
- US export issue................................. **£250-350**

641 Army 1-ton Cargo Truck - military green body, tin tilt and ridged hubs, windows.

641 Army 1 ton Cargo Truck
1954-61
- Tin tilt, driver in some, no windows, flap-end box **£35-40**

1961-62
- Same, but with window glazing.......... **£40-50**

642 R.A.F. Pressure Refueller
1957-62
- RAF Blue, 'French' roundel, with or without driver, blue/white striped Supertoys box **£100-130**
1957-62
- Same, but in Dinky Toys box.......... **£110-140**

643 Army Water Tanker
1958-61
- No window glazing, driver in some, yellow box.............................. **£30-35**
1961-64
- With window glazing, yellow box with red side **£30-35**

650 Light Tank
1954-55
(renumbered in 1954 from 152a)
- US issue. Black base, no markings **£100-125**

651 Centurion Tank
1954-70
- Matt or Gloss Olive-Drab body, metal rollers, rubber tracks, Supertoys Blue/White box, packing piece.......... **£80-90**
- US export issue:
In U.S. Gold 'see through' box......... **£150-175**
- US export issue:
In Yellow/Blue Dinky Toys lidded box with packing piece and 'H.Hudson Dobson' sticker............. **£150-175**
- In Blue/White Dinky Toys lidded box with packing piece **£90-120**
- Late issue:
Plastic rollers, screws (not rivets), in Yellow/Blue lidded box or Yellow end-flap picture box, one PP **£130-160**

654 155 mm. Mobile Gun
1973-79
- Operable gun, 4 plastic shells, bubble-packed **£15-20**

656 88 mm. Gun
1975-79
- German Grey, 6 plastic shells. Bubble-packed **£15-20**

660 Tank Transporter - military green body and Supertoy hubs, windows.

660 Tank Transporter
(Thornycroft Mighty Antar)
- 1956 (May only, 1st issue)
'Dinky Toys' cast under the trailer, Yellow lid 'DINKY TOYS' box.......... **£120-150**
- 1956 (June to November, 2nd issue)
'Dinky Supertoys' casting under the trailer, Yellow lidded 'DINKY TOYS' box **£90-100**
- 1956 (November) - 1957 (September)
2nd issue in blue/white striped box, 'DINKY SUPERTOYS' in block lettering **£90-100**
- 1957 (October) - 1961 (November)
2nd issue in a blue/white striped box, 'DINKY SUPERTOYS' in italic printing **£90-100**
- 1961 (November) - 1963 (December)
3rd issue with windows, blue/white striped box, 'DINKY SUPERTOYS' in italic printing **£120-140**

- 1964 (January - July)
4th issue, with windows, detachable trailer, blue/white striped box, 'DINKY SUPERTOYS' in italic printing.............................. **£140-160**

660a Anti-Aircraft Gun with Crew
1978-80
- With three soldiers. Bubble-packed **£15-20**

661 Recovery Tractor
1957-65
- Six wheels, driver, operable crane, with windows from 1960, Blue/White Supertoys box, one packing piece **£80-100**
- With plastic wheels, in Yellow 'picture' box **£150-200**

662 88 mm. Gun with Crew
1975-77
- German Grey (656 without wheels), 3 crew, bubble-packed **£15-20**

665 Honest John Missile Launcher
1964-75
- Green platform, White missile. Yellow Dinky Toys end-flap box...... **£120-140**
- Black platform, White missile. Yellow Dinky Toys end-flap box...... **£140-160**
- Green platform, Grey missile. Yellow scenic Supertoys lidded box **£90-120**
- Green platform, White missile. Bubble-packed **£70-90**

666 Missile Erector Vehicle and Corporal Missile Launcher
1959-64
- Metal erector gears, White missile with Black fins, Blue/White Supertoys box with one packing piece............. **£200-250**
- Black plastic erector gears, all-White missile, Blue/White Supertoys box with one packing piece............. **£175-200**

667 Missile Servicing Platform Vehicle - military green body, extending platform and Supertoy hubs.

667 Missile Servicing Platform
1960-64
- With windows, Blue/White Supertoys box, one packing piece .. **£175-200**

667 Armoured Patrol Car
1976-78
- 680 body with 676 turret, in 'hanging' box **£15-20**

668 Foden Army Truck
1976-79
- With windows, plastic tilt and wheels, in 'hanging' box..................... **£25-35**

669 U.S.A. Army Jeep
1955-57
- White star, (US issue in 'plain' box)................... **£200-300**

670 Armoured Car
1954-64
- Olive-Drab body, diecast hubs, yellow flap-end box............................. **£20-25**
1964-70
- Olive-Drab body, plastic hubs, yellow flap-end box............................. **£20-25**
- Late issue in red-sided yellow flap-end box **£25-35**

671 Reconnaissance Car
1954-55 (renumbered in 1954 from 152b)
- (Matt) Green body, for export only **£75-95**

672 US Army Jeep
1954-55 (renumbered in 1954 from 153a)

- US export issue.
  Some have rounded axle-ends **£75-95**

673 Scout Car (Daimler)
1953-61
- Driver fixed in position,
  passenger seat hole in some **£20-30**

674 Austin Champ
1954-66
- Cast driver fixed in position, cast steering
  wheel and risged hubs, seat holes for
  personnel, deep yellow end-flap box. **£75-85**
- No driver, plastic steering wheel,
  cast hubs, yellow end-flap box........... **£75-85**
  1966-71
- Plastic driver, plastic steering wheel,
  plastic hubs, yellow end-flap box **£65-75**

674 'U.N.' Austin Champ
1958-70
- White body, no holes for personnel,
  yellow end-flap box.
  Made for export only **£300-400**

Dinky 674 UN Austin Champ. A hard one to find.
came in a standard box.

675 Ford US Army Staff Car
1954-59 (renumbered in 1954 from 170m)
- Matt Olive body with cross-hatching
  cast inside roof, sheer-cut star transfers
  on doors, White circled star on roof.
  US issue in 'plain' printed box........ **£250-300**

676 Armoured Personnel Carrier
1955-62
- 6 wheels, revolving turret,
  yellow end-flap box............................. **£25-30**
- Late issue in red-sided yellow
  end-flap box **£30-35**

676a Daimler Armoured Car
1973-76
- Speedwheels, (new version of 670) **£15-20**
  1973-74

- French made version: With camouflage
  net, ('Made in England' on base) .... NGPP

677 Armoured Command Vehicle
1957-62
- 6 wheels, yellow end-flap box............. **£60-70**

680 Ferret Armoured Car
1972-78
- Sand or Khaki, Speedwheels,
  bubble-pack.. **£10-15**

681 DUKW Amphibious Vehicle
1972-78
- RAF Blue or Army-Green body,
  Speedwheels, bubble-packed **£10-15**

682 Stalwart Load Carrier
1972-78
- 6 Speedwheels, bubble-packed **£10-15**

683 Chieftain Tank
1972-80
- Black plastic tracks, fires shells.
  End-flap 'window' box with
  polystyrene inner or bubble-packed .. **£25-35**

686 25-pounder Field Gun
1957-71
- Cast drawbar, cast hubs (1957-68),
  plastic hubs (1968-71) **£10-15**

687 25-pounder Trailer
1957-67
- Cast hubs, plastic from 1968.
  Not individually boxed **£10-15**

687 Convoy Army Truck
1978-79
- Khaki tilt 'ARMY'. In 'hanging' box **£10-15**

688 Field Artillery Tractor
1957-61
- Driver in some, no windows,
  cast hubs, end-flap box........................ **£30-40**
  1961-70
- Driver in some, windows,
  (plastic hubs from 1968).................... **£30-40**

689 Medium Artillery Tractor
1957-65
- Driver in some, holes, 6 wheels,
  tin tilt, in Blue/White Supertoys box
  with lift-off lid **£80-100**
- In Yellow picture box,
  plastic driver, windows **£150-200**

690 Anti-Aircraft Gun on Trailer
1954-55 (renumbered in 1954 from 161b)
- Matt Green, made for export only **£80-100**

690 Scorpion Tank
1974-80
- Brown or Green camouflage net.
  Decal sheet, spare shells. End-flap
  'hanging' box or bubble-packed......... **£15-20**

691 Striker Anti-Tank
1974-80
- Plastic tracks, 6 spare missiles.
  Bubble-packed **£15-20**

692 5.5 Medium Gun
1955-62
- Twin cast drawbar, elevating barrel.
  In yellow end-flap box or later
  red-sided yellow end-flap box **£15-20**

692 Leopard Tank
1974-80
- Grey with German markings, plastic
  tracks, 6 shells on sprue, decal sheet,
  bubble-pack.. **£40-50**

693 7.2 inch Howitzer Gun
1958-67
- Cast drawbar, yellow end-flap box,
  packing piece...................................... **£30-40**

694 Hanomag Tank Destroyer
1975-80
- Grey, German markings,
  plastic tracks/wheels, bubble-packed **£40-50**

696 Leopard Anti-Aircraft Tank
1975-80
- Grey-Green, German markings,
  plastic tracks, 2 plastic sprues each
  with 6 shells, bubble-packed **£40-50**

697 25 pounder Field Gun Set
1957-71 See Gift Sets section.

698 Tank Transporter Set
1957-64 See Gift Sets section.

699 Military Vehicles (1) Set
1955-58 See Gift Sets section.

699 Leopard Recovery Tank
1975-77
- Grey-Green, German markings,
  dozer blade/jib, aerial, tow-rope,
  bubble-packed **£40-50**

815 Panhard Armoured Tank
1962-64
- Olive Drab body, French flag,
  French issue **£75-100**

816 Berliet Missile Launcher
1969-71
- Olive Drab, French issue **£150-200**

817 AMX 13-ton Tank
1962-64
- Olive Drab body, French flag,
  French issue **£75-100**

822 Half-Track M3
1962-64
- Olive Drab body, rubber tracks,
  French issue **£75-100**

884 Brockway Bridge Truck
1962-64
- Olive Drab, 10 wheels, bridge parts,
  inflatables. French issue **£200-250**

Dinky Toys Aircraft *See also Gift Sets section.*

Model and details	MPR
60a Imperial Airways Liner (Armstrong-Whitworth Atalanta) 1934-36	

- Cast body, tinplate wings,
  4 x 2-blade propellers.
  Various colours, in three different patterns:
  1: 'Sunray' main colour with contrasting
     radial stripes on wings: Silver/Blue,
     Gold/Blue, Yellow/Blue, Blue/Yellow,
     Red/Cream, Cream/Red, Cream/Green,
     White/Blue, White/Blue/Green.
  2: 'Two-tone' main colour with
     contrasting tail and wingtips:
     Gold/Blue, Yellow/Blue,
     Cream/Green, Gold/Blue, Yellow/Blue,
     Cream/Green, Cream/Red.

Model and details	MPR

3: 'Striped' main colour with contrasting
   chordwise stripes and tail:
   Cream/Green, White/Blue.
   Other variations on these themes
   may exist, all without registration
   marks. Each **£500-600**
   1936-39
- Blue, Pale Blue, Cream, Gold, Red,
  Silver or White; all with
  Black 'G-ABTI' marking.................... **£500-600**
  1939-41
- Gold, Green or Silver, 'G-ABTI',
  'Imperial Airways Liner' under
  wing, (reissued as 66a) **£500-600**

Model and details	MPR
60b De Havilland 'Leopard Moth' 1934-36	

- Cast fuselage, tinplate wings, single
  2-blade propeller. Green with Yellow
  tail and wingtips or Dark Blue/Orange,
  Silver/Green, Blue/Yellow, Blue/Red,
  Gold/Red, no markings,
  open windows **£500-600**
  1936-39
- All-over Light Green, Dark Green,
  Gold, Silver, Beige, Blue, Pale Blue
  or Red, 'G-ACPT', open windows **£300-500**
  1939-39
- As previous model, but with
  'DH Leopard Moth' under wing.
  Green, Gold or Silver, 'G-ACPT'....... **£200-300**

1939-41
- As previous model, but blank side windows. Green, Gold or Silver, 'G-ACPT', (reissued as 66b) **£200-300**

60c Percival 'Gull' Monoplane
1934-36
- Cast fuselage, tinplate wings, large 2-blade propeller. Reissued as 60k. Blue with Red tail and wingtips, Red/Blue, Buff/White, Buff/Blue, Buff/Red, Gold/Green, Red/White, Silver/Green, White/Green, White/Blue, open windows, no registration markings **£100-150**
1936-39
- White, Red, Yellow, Light Blue, Blue, Silver, Buff, 'G-ADZO' in Black, open windows, (Silver version renumbered to 60k). **£100-150**
1939-39
- As 1936-39 version above, but with underwing stamped 'PERCIVAL GULL'. White, Red, Yellow, Blue, 'G-ADZO' in Black............................. **£200-300**
1939-41
- Same but blank or open side windows, 'Percival Gull' under wing, (reissued as 66c)............................ **£200-300**

60c 'Lewis's' 'Amy Mollinson'
1936-36
- Souvenir Issue. Mid-Blue with Silver wings and a Blue 'G-ADZO' marking. Sold at Lewis's of Liverpool department store in special 'LEWIS' yellow box. (Renumbered 60k when sold in normal yellow box) **£400-500**

60d Low Wing Monoplane (Vickers Jockey)
1934-36
- Cast body, tinplate wings, 2-blade propeller. Red with Cream tail and wingtips, Orange/Cream, Blue/Yellow, Silver/Red or Gold/Blue, no markings, no pilot....................... **£100-150**
1936-41
- Red, Orange, Blue, Gold, Silver, Black or Yellow, 'G-AVYP', pilot's head cast-in, (reissued as 66d)................. **£100-150**
- Red with cream tail and wingtips, no pilot, with 'G-AVPY' marking............ NGPP
- As previous but with pilot .... NGPP

60e General 'Monospar'
1934-36
- Two-piece diecasting, 2 x 2-blade propellers. Pale Blue with White tail and wingtips, Cream/Red, Red/Cream, Salmon/Blue or Silver/Blue, Gold/Red, no markings **£100-150**
1936-41
- Silver, Lilac or Gold, 'G-ABVP' in Black, (reissued as 66e) **£100-150**
- Same but with 'General Monospar', Cream, Gold, Lilac, Silver or Blue.... **£100-150**

60f Cierva 'Autogiro'
1934-36
- Gold body with Blue rotors and trim, no pilot...................................... **£200-300**
1936-41
- Gold body with Blue trim, unpainted rotors, pilot cast-in, (reissued as 66f) **£150-200**
1936-41
- Red body with Cream trim, Cream or Silver rotors, pilot cast-in **£150-200**

60g De Havilland 'Comet'
1935-36
- Cast fuselage and wings, enclosed wheels, 2 x 2-blade propellers. Silver, Red or Gold with Black registration 'G-ACSR' (no underwing description).................... **£100-125**
1936-41
- Silver, Red or Gold with Black

registration 'G-ACSR', ('DH COMET' underwing)............. **£100-125**

60g Light Racer (DH 'Comet')
1945-49
- Yellow, Red or Silver, 'G-RACE', 'Light Racer' under wing, 2 x 3-blade propellers **£175-225**

60h 'Singapore' Flying Boat
1936-36
- Cast fuselage (126 mm.), tinplate wings, 4 x 2-blade propellers (early hulls lead). Fully-moulded bow, no roller, Silver with stencilled RAF roundels..................................... **£350-450**
1936-37
- As previous model but with Red or Green plastic roller **£350-450**
1937-39
- As previous model (with Red or Green plastic roller) and with 'Gliding Game' hole **£350-450**
1939-40
- With Red or Green plastic roller, 'Gliding Game' hole and waterslide transfer RAF roundels...................... **£350-450**
1940-40
- Hollowed bow, wooden roller, no 'Gliding Game' hole, painted or transfer roundels **£350-450**
1940-41
- As previous model, but in Pale Grey with transfer roundels **£350-450**
1941 ?
- Same but with name under wing..... **£350-450**

No 60k Percival Gull 'Amy Mollison' - mid blue body, silver tinplate wings, G-ADZO.

60k Percival 'Gull' (Amy Mollison)
1936-41
- Blue/Silver version of 60c, 'G-ADZO' in Blue, special box **£300-400**

60k Percival 'Gull' (H. L. Brook)
1936-41
- Blue/Silver version of 60c, 'G-ADZO' in Black, special box........ **£300-400**

60k Light Tourer (Percival 'Gull')
1945-48
- Red, Silver or Dark or Light Green, 'Light Tourer' or 'Percival Tourer' under wing, no markings, small or large 2-blade propeller, (renumbered from 60c) **£150-200**

60m Four Engined Flying Boat
1936-41
- Red, Pale Blue, Light Blue, Mid Blue, Dark Blue, Light Green, Mid-Green, Dark Green, Gold, Cream or Silver. 'Civilian' version of 60h with 'G-EUTC', 'G-EUTG', 'G-EVCU', 'G-EXCF', 'G-EXGF', 'G-EXFE', 'G-EYCE' or 'G-EYTV' **£175-225**
NB With or without bow hollow, wood or plastic roller or gliding hole.

60m Four engined Flying Boat - dark blue fuselage and tinplate wings, G-EVCU in white.

60n Fairey 'Battle' Bomber
1937-40
- Silver or Grey, RAF roundels, 1 x 3-blade propeller, undercarriage . **£90-120**
1938-41
- Silver or Grey, RAF roundels, 1 x 3-blade propeller, without undercarriage, (reissued as 60s) **£120-150**
NB Early issues did not have name of plane cast in.

60p Gloster 'Gladiator'
1936-39
- Silver, stencilled roundels, Red 1 x 2-blade propeller, no name under wing......................... **£100-140**
1939-41
- Silver or Grey, transfer roundels, 'Gloster Gladiator' under wing **£100-140**

60r Empire Flying Boat
1937-40
Silver, 4 x 3-blade propellers, Red plastic roller, hole, own box. Liveries:
- 'CALEDONIA' ('G-ADHM') **£250-350**
- 'CALPURNIA' ('G-AETW') **£250-350**
- 'CALYPSO' ('G-AEUA') **£250-350**
- 'CAMBRIA' ('G-ADUV') **£250-350**
- 'CAMILLA' ('G-AEUB') **£250-350**
- 'CANOPUS' ('G-ADHL')..................... **£250-350**
- 'CAPELLA' ('G-ADUY') **£250-350**
- 'CENTURION' ('G-ADVE') **£250-350**
- 'CERES' ('G-AETX')........................... **£250-350**
- 'CHALLENGER' ('G-ADVD') **£250-350**
- 'CHEVIOT' ('G-AEUG') **£250-350**
- 'CLIO' ('G-AETY') **£250-350**
- 'CORDELIA' ('G-AEUD')................... **£250-350**
- 'CORINNA' ('G-AEUC')..................... **£250-350**
- 'CORSAIR' ('G-ADVB')...................... **£250-350**
1940-49 (reissued as 60x)
As previous models but plastic, wood or brass roller, no hole.
- 'CALEDONIA', ('G-ADHM') **£200-250**
- 'CAMBRIA', ('G-ADUV') **£200-250**
NB Camouflage issues: Early issues have Red/White/Blue roundels with a Yellow outer ring. The later (rarer) issues have a darker camouflage with just Blue/Red roundels.

60s Medium Bomber
1938-40
- Camouflaged 60n with undercarriage, single roundel has Yellow ring, (reissue of 60n)................................ **£100-150**

60s Fairy 'Battle' Bomber
1940-41
- Camouflaged body, two Blue/Red roundels, no undercarriage, 1 x 3-blade propeller **£150-200**
NB Early issues did not have the name of the plane cast in.

60t Douglas DC3 Air Liner
1938-41
- Silver, 'PH-ALI' 2 x 3-blade propellers, 'Gliding Game' hole, tail wheel on some, own box................................. **£200-300**

60v   Armstrong Whitworth Bomber
1937-41
- Silver body, 'Gliding Game' hole in some,
  RAF roundels, 2 x 3-blade propellers,
  (reissued as 62t) **£200-300**

60w   Flying Boat 'Clipper III' (Sikorsky S32)
1938-40
- Silver body, 'USA NC16736',
  4 x 3-blade propellers,
  plastic roller, 'gliding' hole **£150-200**
- US issue: Silver body,
  'NC 16736' markings, 'gliding' hole,
  Red plastic roller, leaflet **£250-350**

60w   Flying Boat
1945-48
- Silver, Blue or Green, no markings,
  4 x 3-blade propellers, brass roller .. **£150-200**

60x   Atlantic Flying Boat
1937-41   (reissue of 60r)
- Blue/Cream, 4 x 3-blade propellers,
  'DAUNTLESS' ('G-AZBP'),
  name under wing **£500-750**
- Green/Cream,
  'WHIRLWIND' ('G-AZBT') **£500-750**
- Black/White,
  'DREADNOUGHT' ('G-AZBV') **£500-750**
- Orange/Cream,
  'SWIFTSURE' ('G-AZBU') **£500-750**
- Blue/Cream,
  'ENTERPRISE' ('G-AZBR') **£500-750**
- Black/Cream,
  'ENDEAVOUR' ('G-AZBQ') **£500-750**
- Red/Cream,
  'VALORIUS' ('G-AZBS') **£500-750**

62a   Vickers-Supermarine 'Spitfire'
1939-41
- Silver body (short nose), RAF
  roundels, 1 x 3-blade propeller **£100-130**
1940-41   **'Meccano Spitfire Fund'**
- Model 62a in special souvenir box
  (at 2/6 each). Brass ring through fin
  allows use as badge or pendant.
  Proceeds went to Spitfire Fund.
  Blue, Green, Grey, Magenta, Red,
  Yellow, or Camouflage **£500-750**
- Chromium plated version
  (originally 10s.6d.) **£1,000-1,200**

62a   'Spitfire'
1945-49
- Silver, (long nose, bubble cockpit),
  RAF roundels, 1 x 3-blade propeller **£35-45**

62b   Bristol 'Blenheim' Bomber
1939-41
- Silver body, RAF roundels, Red
  2 x 3-blade propellers,
  name under wing **£100-150**

62b   Medium Bomber
1945-49
- Silver body, RAF roundels, 2 x 3-blade
  Red propellers, name under wing **£60-80**

62d   Bristol 'Blenheim' Bomber
1940-41
- 62b in Camouflage/Black/White,
  RAF roundels,
  2 x 3-blade propellers **£100-150**

62e   Vickers-Supermarine 'Spitfire'
1940-41
- 62a in Camouflage/Black/White, RAF
  roundels, 1 x 3-blade propeller **£100-150**

62f   D.H. Flamingo Airliner
1939 ?
  Not issued (some unofficial non-Meccano
  'Flamingos' in white-metal may be found)
  .... NPP

62g   Boeing 'Flying Fortress'
1939-41
- Silver, 4 x 3-blade propellers,
  'Gliding Game' hole, name under
  wing, 'U.S.A.A.C.'/stars, own box **£200-250**
- Pale Grey version,
  no 'Gliding Game' hole .... NGPP

62g   Long Range Bomber

1945-48
- Silver body, Red 4 x 3-blade propellers,
  no 'Gliding Game' hole, not boxed.. **£125-150**

62h   Hawker Hurricane Fighter
1938-41
- Camouflaged body, RAF roundels,
  1 x 2-blade propeller,
  undercarriage on some.................... **£100-130**

62k   The King's Aeroplane
1938-41
- Airspeed 'Envoy', Silver/Red/Blue,
  'G-AEXX', 2 x 2-blade propellers,
  own box **£300-400**

62m   Airspeed 'Envoy' Monoplane
1938-41
- Red ('G-ABDA' or 'G-ACVJ')............. **£300-400**
- Yellow ('G-ACMJ', 'G-ACMT' or
  'G-ACVJ')... **£300-400**
- Silver ('G-ACVI' or 'G-ADCB')........... **£300-400**
- Blue ('G-ADAZ' or 'G-ADCA').......... **£300-400**
- Pale Green ('GADCA')....................... **£300-400**
- Pale Green ('G-AENA').................... **£300-400**
- Mid-Green ('G-AENA') **£300-400**
- Gold ('G-AMTC')............................... **£300-400**

62m   Light Transport Plane
1945-48
- Red, Yellow, Silver or Blue,
  'G-ATMH', 2 x 2-blade propellers,
  name under wing **£100-125**

62n   Junkers 'Ju90' Air Liner
1938-41
  Silver, 4 x 3-blade propellers, own box.
- 'D-AALU'.. **£200-300**
- 'D-ADLH'.. **£250-350**
- 'D-AIVI'... **£250-350**
- 'D-AURE'.. **£250-350**

*62p Armstrong Whitworth Ensign Airliner 'Ensign' -
silver fuselage and wings.*

62p   'Ensign' Air Liner
1938-41
  Silver, Red 4 x 3-blade propellers,
  gliding hole in some, own box. Liveries:
- 'ECHO' ('G-ADTB') **£250-350**
- 'ELSINORE' ('G-ADST').................... **£250-350**
- 'ELYSIAN' ('G-ADSZ') **£250-350**
- 'ENSIGN' ('G-ADSR')........................ **£250-350**
- 'ETTRICK' ('G-ADSX')....................... **£250-350**
- 'EXPLORER' ('G-ADSV') **£250-350**

62p   Armstrong Whitworth Air Liner
1945-49
  As previous casting but no 'Gliding Game'
  hole, name under wing, no box,
  Silver, Blue or Green, with Silver or
  Grey/Green trim.
- 'ECHO' ('G-ADTB') **£300-400**
- 'EXPLORER' ('G-ADSV').................. **£300-400**

62r   D.H. 'Albatross' Mail Liner
1939-41
- Silver, 'G-AEVV', 4 x 3-blade Red
  propellers, 'Gliding Game' hole,
  name under wing, own box.............. **£300-400**

62r   Four Engined Liner
1945-49
- Grey, Light Blue (Red trim) or
  Silver (Red trim), no markings,
  no hole, not boxed **£100-130**

- Grey, Fawn, Light Blue or Silver,
  'G-ATPV',
  4 x 3-blade Red propellers............... **£100-130**

62s   Hawker 'Hurricane' Fighter
1939-41
- Silver body, RAF roundels,
  with or without undercarriage,
  single propeller with 2 or 3 blades..... **£90-120**
1945-49
- Silver body, RAF roundels, no
  undercarriage, 1 x 3-blade propeller ... **£60-70**

62t   Armstrong Whitley Bomber
1939-41   (reissue of 60v)
- Light Green/Brown camouflage,
  Yellow ring roundels,
  2 x 3-blade propellers, box **£200-300**
- Dark camouflage, Yellow roundels .. **£200-300**
- Dark camouflage,
  Red / Blue roundels **£200-300**

*62w Imperial Airways Liner Frobisher Class - silver
fuselage and wings, G-AFDI.*

62w   'Frobisher' Class Air Liner
1939-41   (renumbered 68b)
  Silver (casting as 62r),
  4 x 3-blade propellers, 'Gliding Game'
  hole, own box, 3 liveries:
- 'FALCON' ('G-AFDJ') **£250-350**
- 'FORTUNA' ('G-AFDK') **£250-350**
- 'FROBISHER' ('G-AFDI') **£250-350**

62x   British 40 Seat Airliner
1939-41   (renumbered 68a)
  'G-AZCA', not boxed, with or without
  'Gliding Game' hole. Colours:
- Grey/Green, Red/Maroon,
  Two-tone Green, Two-tone Blue,
  Blue/Silver, Yellow/Maroon **£200-250**

62y   Giant High Speed Monoplane
1939-40
- 'D-AZBK', 'Gliding Game' hole,
  not boxed. Colours:
  Blue/Brown, Blue/Silver, Blue/Cream,
  Olive/Green, Yellow/Maroon,
  Red/Maroon, Two-tone Blue or
  Two-tone Green **£500-750**
1945-49
- 'G-ATBK', no hole or box. Colours:
  Light/Dark Green, Grey/Green
  or Silver **£100-125**

63   Mayo Composite Aircraft
1939-41
- Models 63a (fitted with special
  tinplate clip) and 63b together in
  special box (see below).................... **£700-800**

63a   Flying Boat 'MAIA'
1939-41
- Silver, 'G-ADHK', 'Mayo Composite'
  under wing, own box **£100-150**

63b   Seaplane 'MERCURY'
1939-41
- Silver, 'G-ADHJ', 'Mercury Seaplane'
  under wing, 'Gliding Game' hole
  in some.. **£75-100**

63b   Seaplane
1945-49
- Silver, 'G-AVKW', 'Seaplane' under
  wing, no 'Gliding Game' hole **£90-120**

1952-57
- Reissue of 63b Seaplane, same as previous model, (renumbered 700)... **£90-120**

66a Heavy Bomber
1940-41 (reissue of 60a)
- Camouflaged, RAF roundels, 4 x 2-blade propellers, no name under wing.......................... **£250-300**

66b Dive Bomber Fighter
1940-41 (reissue of 60b)
- Camouflaged, RAF roundels, 1 x 2-blade propeller.......................... **£150-200**

66c Two Seater Fighter
1940-41 (reissue of 60c)
- Camouflaged, RAF roundels, 1 x 2-blade propeller.......................... **£150-200**

66d Torpedo Dive Bomber
1940-41 (reissue of 60d)
- Camouflaged, RAF roundels, 1 x 2-blade propeller.......................... **£150-200**

66e Medium Bomber
1940-41 (reissue of 60e)
- Camouflaged, RAF roundels, 2 x 2-blade propellers, 'General Monospar' under.............. **£150-200**

66f Army Co-operation Autogiro
1940-41 (reissue of 60f)
- Silver body and blades, Red/White/Blue roundels **£150-200**

67a Junkers Ju89 Heavy Bomber
1940-41
- Matt-Black with Light Blue underside, Red propellers, Silver cockpit area, Luftwaffe insignia, with or without 'Gliding Game' hole **£750-1,000**

68a 'Ensign' Air Liner
1940-41
- Camouflaged, RAF roundels, no 'Gliding Game' hole, 4 x 3-blade propellers **£300-400**

68b 'Frobisher' Class Air Liner
1940-41 (renumbered from 62w)
- Light or Dark Camouflage, RAF roundels, 4 x 3-blade propellers, 'Gliding Game' hole in some............ **£150-200**

70a/No 704 Avro York Airliner - silver fuselage and wings, G-AGJC

70a Avro 'York' Airliner
1946-49 (renumbered 704)
- Silver body, 'G-AGJC', Red 4 x 3-blade propellers. Early version has Silver propeller pins, tinplate base and blue wash cockpit **£125-150**

70b Tempest II Fighter
1946-49 (renumbered 730)
- Silver with blued canopy, Yellow band on fuselage roundels, pointed spinner..................................... **£35-45**

70c Viking Air Liner
1947-49 (reissued as 705)
- Silver or Grey body, 'G-AGOL', Red 2 x 4-blade propellers, large pointed spinners........................... **£55-65**

70d Twin-Engined Fighter
1946-49 (reissued as 731)
- Silver body with blued canopy............ **£35-45**
- Variation: As previous model but 'N' in 'MECCANO' is reversed **£35-45**

70e Gloster 'Meteor'

1946-49 (renumbered 732)
- Silver body with blued canopy, Black engine intakes, large roundels... **£35-45**

70f Lockheed 'Shooting Star'
1947-49 (renumbered 733)
- Silver body with blued canopy, Black air intakes, USAF star on port wing **£35-45**

700 Seaplane
1954-57 (renumbered from 63b)
- Silver body, 'G-AVKW' marking **£75-100**
- Silver body, 'G-AVKW', no 'Gliding Game' hole, 'Seaplane' under wing **£75-100**

700 Spitfire Mark II ('Jubilee')
1979
- Plated model on plinth, 1 x 3-blade propeller, 'Diamond Jubilee of the RAF', Blue card display box.............. **£150-175**

701 Short 'Shetland' Flying Boat
1947-49
- Silver, 'G-AGVD', 4 x 4-blade Black propellers, first Supertoys aircraft, own box................................... **£500-600**

702 DH 'Comet' Jet Airliner 'BOAC'
1954-55 (renumbered in 1954 to 999)
- White/Blue body, Silver wings and tail, 'G-ALYV', Gold wheels. Blue/white box **£110-130**

704 Avro 'York' Airliner
1954-59 (renumbered in 1954 from 70a)
- Silver, 'G-AGJC', 4 x 3-blade Red propellers, ('704' beneath wing) **£125-150**

705 'Viking' Air Liner
1952-62 (renumbered from 70c)
- Silver body with 'G-AGOL' marking, flat head spinners........................... **£60-75**
- Silver or Grey body, 'G-AGOL', 2 x 4-blade Red propellers.................. **£60-75**

706 Vickers 'Viscount' Airliner
1956-57
- Silver/Blue/White, 'AIR FRANCE', 'F-BGNL', 4 x 4-blade Red propellers.............. **£100-125**

708 Vickers 'Viscount' Airliner
1957-65
- Silver/White or Metallic Grey/White, 'B.E.A.', 'G-AOJA' **£100-125**

710 Beechcraft S35 'Bonanza'
1965-76
- Red/White, Bronze/Yellow, or Red/Blue/White body, 1 x 2-blade propeller **£40-50**
- German promotional: Green/White, 'GLUCK MIT WICKULER' on towing pennant and box.................. **£400-500**

712 US Army T.42A
1972-77
- Military Green (715), Beechcraft plus wing-tip tanks, 2 x 2-blade propellers . **£60-75**

715 Bristol 173 Helicopter - G-AUXR.

715 Bristol 173 Helicopter
1956-62
- Turquoise body with Red stripe and Red rotors, 'G-AUXR' **£65-75**

715 Beechcraft C55 'Baron'
1968-76
- White/Yellow or Red/Yellow body,

Yellow 2 x 2-blade propellers **£40-50**

716 Westland Sikorsky 'S-51'
1957-62
- Red and Cream helicopter body, 2 x 3-blade rotors................................. **£40-50**

717 Boeing '737'
- White/Blue body, 'LUFTHANSA', White or Blue engine pods.................. **£65-75**

718 Hawker 'Hurricane' Mk.IIc
1972-75
- Camouflaged body, RAF roundels, Black 1 x 3-blade propeller, guns......... **£75-95**

719 Spitfire Mk.II
1969-77 (renumbered 741)
- Camouflaged, RAF roundels, Black 3-blade propeller is battery-operated **£90-110**
- Early issues in 'Battle of Britain' pictorial card box **£75-95**

721 Junkers Ju87b Stuka
1969-80
- Camouflage/Yellow, German markings, 1 x 3-blade propeller, cap-firing bomb **£150-175**
- Early issues in 'Battle of Britain' pictorial card box **£90-110**

722 Hawker 'Harrier'
1970-80
- Metallic Blue/Olive camouflage, RAF markings, pilot, aerial **£80-100**

723 Hawker Siddeley HS 125
1970-73
- Yellow/White/Blue or Metallic Blue/White, drop-down door/steps **£35-45**
1973-73
- 'Hawker Executive Jet'. Yellow/White/Blue. In bubble-pack with English and French text. Possibly a promotional sample........ **£400-600**

724 'Sea King' Helicopter
1971-79
- Metallic Blue/White, 5-blade rotors, with 'Apollo' space capsule **£50-60**
- Early issues in card picture box with pictorial inner stand **£40-50**

725 Royal Navy 'Phantom II'
1972-77
- Dark Blue body, Black nose, roundels, decals in bubble-pack.......... **£80-90**

726 Messerschmitt Bf-109E
1972-74
- Desert camouflage, single 3-blade propeller, decals in bubble-pack **£200-250**
1974-76
- Grey/Green camouflage, Yellow wing-tips/nose, decals in bubble-pack...................... **£200-250**

727 U.S.A.F. Phantom F4 Mark II
1976-77
- Brown/Olive camouflage, 2 missiles, 2 figures, no transfers, US market.... **£500-750**

728 R.A.F. 'Dominie'
1972-75
- Metallic Blue and camouflage, roundels, retractable wheels, bubble-pack.......... **£40-50**

729 Multi-Role Combat Aircraft
1974-76
- Grey/Camouflage, swing-wings, decals in bubble-pack.......................... **£40-50**

730 Tempest II Fighter
1952-55 (renumbered from 70b)
- Same as 70b but without blued canopy and with flat spinner **£40-50**

730 US Navy 'Phantom II'
1972-76
- Grey/Red, 'NAVY', 'USS Saratoga', fires missiles, retractable wheels **£80-90**

731 Twin-Engined Fighter
1952-55 (reissue of 70d)
- Silver body, no blued canopy.............. **£25-35**

731 S.E.P.E.C.A.T. 'Jaguar'
1973-76
- Metallic Blue and camouflage body, Orange pilot, opening cockpit............. **£40-50**

732 Gloster 'Meteor'
1952-62 (reissue of 70e)
- Silver body without blued canopy, small roundels...................................... **£25-35**
- Shiny Silver body with large roundels... NGPP

732 Bell 'POLICE' Helicopter
1974-80
- Orange/Blue/White or Red body, sign boards and cones **£35-45**

732 'M.A.S.H.' Helicopter
1979
- Green body with 'M.A.S.H.' stickers ...... NGPP

733 Lockheed 'Shooting Star'
1952-62 (reissue of 70f)
- Silver body with blued canopy............. **£25-35**
- Variant with the word 'in' of 'Made in England by Meccano Ltd' missing......... NGPP

733 German 'Phantom II'
1973-76
- Grey/Green camouflage body, 'Bundesluftwaffe', two white missiles, instructions and transfers, (German/Austrian market) **£500-600**
1976-77
US F-4K 'Phantom II'
- Brown camouflage, retractable wheels, fires missiles, (US market only) **£80-90**

734 Supermarine 'Swift'
1955-62
- Grey/Green camouflaged body, RAF markings **£30-40**

734 P47 'Thunderbolt'
1975-78
- Metallic Silver/Black, Red 4-blade propeller, retractable wheels, 'U.S.A.A.F.' **£125-175**

735 Gloster 'Javelin'
1956-66
- Camouflaged 'delta-wing' body, RAF markings, smooth (later treaded) wheels **£40-60**

736 Hawker 'Hunter'
1955-63
- Camouflaged body, RAF markings...... **£30-40**

736 Bundesmarine 'Sea King'
1973-78
- Grey/Orange helicopter, German markings, decals in bubble-pack......... **£45-55**

737 P.1B 'Lightning' Fighter
1959-68
- Silver, with metal wheels **£60-80**
- Met. Grey, Black plastic wheels **£100-125**

738 DH 110 'Sea Vixen' Fighter
1960-65
- Grey/White body, Black nose, RAF roundels, 'ROYAL NAVY' **£60-80**

739 A6M5 'Zero Sen'
1975-78
- Metallic Blue/Black, Japanese markings, decals in bubble-pack......... **£60-80**
- Same, but in Metallic Green/Black.. **£125-175**

741 Spitfire Mk.II
1978-80
- Camouflaged body, (non-motorised version of 719)......... **£80-100**

749 RAF Avro 'Vulcan' Bomber
1955-56 (renumbered 992)
- Silver body (aluminium). Only 500 models were made (for Canadian market). 992 is the catalogue (and box) number, '749' is cast into the model. Two castings exist; one has pointed wingtips, the other is more rounded **£1,500-2,000**

997 Caravelle SE 210 Airliner
1962-65
- Silver/White/Blue, 'AIR FRANCE', 'F-BGNY', metal or plastic wheels, Yellow lidded picture box with card support **£100-150**

998 Bristol 'Britannia'
1959-64
- Silver with 'CANADIAN PACIFIC' livery in Blue/White, 'CF-CZA' in Blue on wing, striped picture box with card support.............................. **£250-275**

1964-65
- As previous model but with Silver-Grey wings. Yellow lidded picture box, card support **£200-250**

999 DH 'Comet' Jet Airliner
1955-65 (reissue of 702)
- White body, Blue fin, Silver wings, 'G-ALYV', 'No. 999' cast in underwing.
- Early issues came in Blue/White striped box with an oval '999' sticker over the '702' print. Later boxes were Yellow/Red with printed '999'.......... **£100-125**
- As above, but with 'G-ALYX' **£100-125**
- As previous but Silver-Grey wings ... **£100-125**

BOX TYPES:
Many 1970-79 issues were 'vacuform' packed and these include model nos: 710,712, 715, 717, 718, 721 to 734 inclusive, plus 736 and 739.

998 Bristol Britannia Airliner 'Canadian Pacific' - silver grey, red, blue and white fuselage, silver grey wings, CF-CZA.

Dinky Toys Public Transport Vehicles

Model and details	MPR
16 Silver Jubilee Set	
1936-37	
• Locomotive and two interlocking coaches, 'LNER' and '2590' cast-in, open windows, smooth hubs with White tyres, special box. Silver loco and coaches, Grey, Mid-Blue, Dark Blue, Red or Orange trim..........	**£200-250**
• Silver loco and coaches, Dark Blue trim	**£200-250**
• Cream loco and coaches with Red trim	**£250-275**
• Blue loco and coaches, Dark Blue trim	**£250-275**
• Green loco / coaches, Dark Green trim	**£250-275**
16 Streamlined Train Set	
1937-40	
• As previous models but changed name and box	**£200-250**
1946-52	
• Blue/Black loco, 'LNER', Brown/Grey coaches, filled windows, Black tyres. Individually boxed in buff box with divisions, yellow label lid end	**£125-150**
1952-54	
• As previous model but with 'BR' crest on tender	**£100-125**
1954 Model renumbered to 798	
16z Articulated Train	
1935-40	
• Two-tone Blue, or Gold/Red, or	

Model and details	MPR
Cream with Red, Blue or Orange. French issue sold in UK	**£200-250**
17 Passenger Train Set	
1935-40	
• Black/Maroon loco 17a, Maroon tender 17b, Maroon/Cream coaches 20a/20b	**£200-300**
• Black/Green loco 17a, Green tender 17b, 2 Green/Cream coaches 20a/20b	**£200-300**
• Lead and mazak set in 2nd type box with correct colour spot..............	**£400-500**
17a Locomotive	
1934-40	
• Black/Maroon or Black/Green, diecast cab/boiler, lead chassis	**£100-125**
17b Tender	
1934-40	
• Maroon or Green diecast body.............	**£40-50**
18 Tank Goods Train Set	
1935-40	
• Green/Black loco (21a), and 3 Green/Black open wagons (21b)....	**£200-300**
19 Mixed Goods Train	
1935-40	
• Maroon/Black loco (21a), Green/Red open wagon (21b), Red/Blue 'SHELL' tanker wagon (21d), Yellow/Red/Green lumber wagon (21e)	**£400-500**
• Set 19 in 3rd type pictorial landscape box	**£800-1,000**

Model and details	MPR
20 Tank Passenger Set	
1935-40	
• Green/Black loco (21a), 2 Brown/Green coaches (20a), Guard's van (20b)	**£300-400**
20a Coach	
1935-40	
• Brown/Cream or Green/White roof, diecast body, lead chassis.....................	**£60-75**
20b Guard's Van	
1935-40	
• Brown/Cream or Green/White roof, diecast body, lead chassis.....................	**£60-75**
21 Hornby Train Set	
1932-33	
• Blue/Red loco (21a), Green open wagon (21b), Green/Blue crane wagon (21c), Red/Blue 'SHELL' tank wagon (21d), Yellow/Red/Green lumber wagon (21e), 'HORNBY SERIES' cast into lead body. Red card box............................	**£500-600**
21 Modelled Miniatures Train Set	
1934-35 Contents as previous set, in Red card box	**£400-500**
21a Tank Locomotive	
1932-34	
• Red/Blue 0-6-0 tank loco, 'HORNBY SERIES' cast into lead body.................	**£75-100**
1934-41	
• Maroon/Black or Green/Black,	

'DINKY TOYS' cast into lead body...... **£75-100**

21b Open Wagon
1932-34
- Green/Red, Green/Blue, Green/Black, Maroon/Black, 'HORNBY SERIES' cast into lead body **£50-70**
1934-41
- Green/Red, Green/Blue, Green/Black, Maroon/Black, 'DINKY TOYS' cast into lead body **£50-70**

21c Crane Wagon
1932-34
- Green body, Blue chassis, 'HORNBY SERIES' cast-in, lead **£50-70**

21d Tanker Wagon
1932-34
- Red tank, Blue or Black chassis, 'HORNBY SERIES' cast-in, lead **£50-70**
1934-41
- Red tank, Blue or Black chassis, 'DINKY TOYS' cast-in, lead **£50-70**

21e Lumber Wagon
1932-34
- Brown/Blue, Yellow/Red or Yellow/Black, 'HORNBY SERIES' in lead..................... **£50-70**
1934-41
- Brown/Blue, Yellow/Red or Yellow/Black, 'DINKY TOYS', lead **£50-70**

26 G.W.R. Rail Car
1934-40
- Early issues are lead, later issues mazak, plastic rollers. Cream roof, Brown, Green, Yellow or Red body **£125-150**
- Green body with Red roof.................. **£125-150**

26z Diesel Road Car
1937-40
- Cream roof, Red, Green, Orange, Yellow or Blue body. (French)........... **£100-125**

27 Tram Car
1934-38
- Plastic or metal wheels, Red 'OVALTINE' or 'LIPTONS TEA' or no logo. Red, Orange, Green, Yellow or Light or Dark Blue body, Cream upper windows and roof **£200-250**
- Light Blue or Dark Blue body, Cream lower/upper windows and roof......... **£200-250**

29 Motor Bus
1934-38 (renumbered to 29a)
- Plastic or metal wheels, no logo, or Silver or Red 'MARMITE'. Blue, Green, Maroon, Yellow or Red body, Cream or Silver roof **£200-250**

29b Streamlined Bus
1936-46
- Green, Orange or Red coach body, all with Cream wheel covers, Black or White tyres, smooth hubs ... **£100-125**
- Two-tone Blue, Yellow/Orange, Red/Maroon, Two-tone Green, or Turquoise/Red, smooth Black hubs, open rear window **£100-125**
1946-47
- Cream and Dark Blue, smooth hubs, open windows **£100-125**
1947-50
- Grass Green/Light Green, Light Green/Dark Green, Grey/Blue, Grey/Red or Two-tone Blue body, Black tyres on ridged hubs, filled-in rear window **£100-125**

29c Double Decker Bus
The different casting types are shown in the attached diagrams.
1938-40
'DUNLOP TYRES'
1st Type AEC/STL, cutaway wings, stairs cast-in, smooth hubs, White tyres, crimped axle ends. Advertisement in Black on Yellow rectangle.
- Regular issues:
Cream upper deck and roof with

Red, Light Blue, Maroon, Green or Orange lower deck.............. **£300-400**
1938
- Early Grey roof issues:
As previous but with Grey roof.......... **£300-400**
Cream upper body, Grey roof, Mid-Green lower body, Black smooth hubs............................ **£600-800**
- Late issue: Dark Blue lower deck, Cream upper deck and roof.............. **£300-400**
1938-40
- Without advertisements:
As above but no advertisements **£200-300**
NB Baseplates:
1st issue 'Made in England', 29 x 2 mm.
2nd issue 'Made in England', 28 x 1.5 mm.
1946
Without advertisements:
1st type AEC/STL grille, cutaway wings, no staircase, six vertical inside body ribs, smooth Black hubs. Colours:
- Green lower deck with Cream or Grey upper-deck, Green hubs **£150-200**
- Red lower deck with Cream or Grey upper deck, Red hubs **£150-200**
1947-48
Without advertisements:
- As previous model but with post-war Black ridged hubs **£100-125**
- As previous model but with Two-tone Green body **£160-190**
1948-49
Without advertisements:
- 3rd type, Leyland or AEC grille, straight-across wings, Black ridged hubs. Early issues had 6 vertical inside body ribs, later issues had 5 (3 on n/s, 2 on o/s). Red or Green lower deck, Cream upper deck **£100-125**
1949-53
Without advertisements:
- 2nd type, AEC/Regent grille, straight-across wings, lengthwise chassis strengthener with hole in chassis centre, or (1952) eight vertical inside body ribs, ridged hubs, plus (in 1953) '29c' cast in chassis. Red or Green lower deck, Cream or White upper deck, hubs match the lower deck colour.... **£100-125**

29c Double Decker Bus. Pre-war model with 1st type AEC grille and cutaway wings.

29c 'DUNLOP' (renumbered to 290)
1954-54
- 3rd type Leyland Titan grille and straight-across wings, early issues have recessed stop lights, late issues (1959) protrude. Logo: 'DUNLOP -The World's Master Tyre' in Black and Red. Sloping and upright designs exist. Red or Green lower deck, Cream upper deck, hubs match lower deck colour **£200-250**

29dz Autobus
1939-40
- Green or White body, metal wheels, (French issue sold in UK) **£80-90**

29e Single Deck Bus
1948-52
- Mid-Blue body, Dark Blue flashes, Black hubs **£80-90**
- Mid-Blue body / hubs, Dark Blue flashes **£90-110**
- Cream body and hubs, Red flashes....... **£60-80**
- Cream body, Blue flashes, Blue or Black hubs **£60-80**
- Light Green body, Dark Green flashes, Black hubs **£80-90**
- Light Green body and hubs, Dark Green flashes **£140-160**

29f Observation Coach
1950-54 (renumbered in 1954 to 280)
- Grey body and hubs, Red flashes **£70-80**
- Grey body, Red flashes, Red hubs **£70-80**
- Cream body, Red flashes, Red hubs **£80-90**
- Cream body and hubs, Red flashes......... **£80-90**
- Cream body, Red flashes, Maroon hubs **£80-90**

29g Luxury Coach
1951-54 (renumbered in 1954 to 281)
- Maroon body, Cream flashes / hubs..... **£70-80**
- Orange body, Cream flashes / hubs.... **£80-100**
- Fawn body with Orange flashes, Cream or Green hubs.......................... **£80-100**
- Fawn body, Cream flashes / hubs **£100-130**
- Blue body, Cream flashes, Yellow hubs **£130-160**
- Cream body, Blue flashes and hubs ... **£80-100**
- Cream body, Red flashes and hubs **£100-130**
- Cream body, Orange flashes, Green hubs...................................... **£100-130**
NB Market Price Ranges for models 29f, g and h are based on their being unboxed, as compared to prices for the boxed renumbered issues 280, 281 and 282.

29h Duple Roadmaster Coach
1952-54 (renumbered in 1954 to 282)
- Dark Blue body, Light Blue hubs, Silver coachlines **£80-100**
- Red body and hubs, Silver coachlines **£80-100**
- Green lower body, Cream upper body and hubs............. **£150-200**
NB Early issue had a flat roof underside. Later issues have a rib front to back.

36g Taxi with Driver
'TAXI' cast into Black roof, driver cast into chassis.
1936-46
- Grey, Dark Blue, Green, Maroon or Red body, Black roof, open rear window.............................. **£200-250**
- Yellow or Violet body, Black roof, open rear window.............................. **£500-750**
1947-50
- Dark Blue, Green, Light Green, Red, Maroon or Brown body, Black roof on all, filled rear windows (a few open rear window versions exist) **£80-100**

40h Austin (FX3) Taxi
1952-54
Diecast chassis with cast-in driver and model number. Not boxed.
- All-Yellow body and hubs, Black chassis, interior and driver **£100-125**
- All-Yellow body and hubs, Brown chassis, interior and driver **£150-250**
- Dark Blue body, Light Blue hubs, Black chassis, interior and driver **£250-350**
- Mid-Blue body and hubs, Black chassis, interior and driver **£400-600**
1954 - 40h was renumbered to 254

067 Austin Taxi (FX3)
1959-64 See ref. 067 in the 'Dublo Dinky' section.

115 United Biscuits Taxi
1979-79
- Yellow/Blue/Black, casting as 120, promotional model **£45-55**

120 Happy Cab

1979-80
- White/Yellow/Blue, solid wheels, 'flower-power' stickers £45-55

241 'SILVER JUBILEE TAXI'
1977-77
- Silver body and hubs, Union Jack on bootlid, 284 casting £30-35

254 Austin (FX3) Taxi
1956-59 (renumbered from 40h)
- Dark Blue body, Light Blue hubs £500-750
- Black body, spun hubs, Grey chassis ('254'), interior and driver £140-170

Two-tone issue:
- Yellow upper body and hubs, Dark Green lower body, Black chassis ('254'), interior and driver £140-170

265 Plymouth U.S.A. Taxi
1960-64
- Yellow/Red body, Blue interior, windows, '25c First 1/5 Mile, 5c Additional', roof sign, white treaded tyres, spun hubs £150-175

266 Plymouth Canadian Taxi
1960-66
- Yellow/Red body with 'Taxi' and '450 Metro Cab' £100-125

268 Renault Dauphine Mini Cab
1962-67
- Red body with 'Meccano', 'Kenwood', and 'Britax Safety Belts' adverts £130-150

278 Plymouth Yellow Cab
1978-80
- Yellow body, 'Yellow Cab Co', plastic chassis and wheels £20-30

280 Observation Coach
1954-60 (renumbered in 1954 from 29f)
- Grey body, Red flashes and hubs...... £125-150
- Cream body and hubs, Red flashes ... £125-150
- Cream body, Red flashes, Red or Maroon hubs £130-160

Dinky 281 Luxury Coach.

281 Luxury Coach
1954-59 (renumbered in 1954 from 29g)
- Cream body, Blue flashes / hubs £125-150
- Cream body, Red flashes and hubs... £175-225
- Cream body, Orange flashes, Green hubs... £200-250
- Cream body/hubs, Orange flashes ... £125-150
- Maroon body, Cream flashes and hubs £90-120
- Mid-Blue body, Cream flashes, Yellow hubs....................................... £200-250
- Fawn body, Orange flashes, Green hubs... £125-150
- Fawn body, Cream flashes / hubs £125-150

NB Prices shown assume that models are in boxes with correct colour spot.

282 Duple Roadmaster Coach
1954-60 (renumbered in 1954 from 29h)
- Dark Blue body, Light Blue hubs, Silver coachlines.................................. £90-110
- Red body / hubs, Silver coachlines..... £90-110
- Light Blue body and hubs, Silver coachlines.................................. £90-110
- Yellow body, Red or Silver coachlines, Red hubs £125-150

US issues:
- Dark Green lower body, Cream upper body, Pale Green hubs..................... £300-350
- Same model but with Red hubs £300-350

Dinky 282 Duple Roadmaster Coach.

282 Austin 1800 Taxi
1967-69
- Blue/White body, Red/White 'TAXI' labels on doors and roof £65-75

Dinky 283 B.O.A.C. Coach.

283 B.O.A.C. Coach
1956-63
- Dark Blue/White, '*British Overseas Airways Corporation*', White tyres after 1960....................... £125-150

283 Single Deck Bus
1971-77
- Metallic Red body, Blue interior, 'RED ARROW'. Card box with instructions and packing £40-50
- Same, but in bubble pack with unused decal sheet............................... £35-45
- Metallic Red body, Yellow interior. Bubble pack £45-55
NB Also available in kit form with 'GREEN LINE' decals. See 1023 in the Dinky Action Kits section.

284 London Taxi (FX4)
1972-79
- Black (or very Dark Blue) body, detailed boot on some, Speedwheels, driver, 'TAXI'... £30-40

289 Routemaster Bus
'London Transport', Route '221', 'KINGS CROSS', driver/conductor, cast hubs, spun hubs or Speedwheels.
1964-65
- 'TERN SHIRTS', Red body, 'FOR 8am CRISPNESS' transfers......... £80-100
1966-69
- 'SSSCHWEPPES' Red body, Blue-Green logo on White transfers ... £80-100
1969-80
- 'ESSO' Red body, 'ESSO SAFETY-GRIP TYRES' White label....... £60-75
- Same but with transfers £100-150
- Deep Purple body, 'London Transport' and 'ESSO SAFETY-GRIP TYRES' logos, Blue driver and clippie............ £300-400
1968-68
- 'LONDON STORES' Promotional, Red body, Black/Gold logo, 'Festival of London Stores'................ £100-150
1970
- 'INGERSOLL RAND' Promotional, Red body £100-125
1974-74

- 'MECCANO' Gold body, 'MECCANO - DINKY TOYS'. (Very few issued - to Press only) .... NGPP
1977-79
- 'MADAME TUSSAUDS' Red body, driver/conductor, White lower deck seating, Blue on White advert., cast wheels £80-100
- Red body, driver/conductor, Dark Blue lower deck seating, White on Blue advert., plastic wheels......................... £80-100
- Red body, with figures, packed in 'SCHWEPPES' picture box................. £100-120
1977-77
- 'WOOLWORTHS' Silver body, (Silver Jubilee limited issue), figures in some...................................... £25-30
1977-77
- 'EVER READY' Silver body, (New Zealand Silver Jubilee issue), no figures... NGPP
1979
- 'THOLLEMBEEK & FILS' Gold body, Pale Blue upper interior, Darker Blue lower interior, 'Thollembeek 1929-79', Belgian promotional............................. £80-90
- 'FORDATH' Promotional. Red body, Light Blue upper deck seating, Deep Blue lower deck seating. In plain White box with 'WITH THE COMPLIMENTS OF FORDATH LTD' labels to box ends £175-225
1979
- 'GREENLINE JUBILEE' Promotional. All-Green body, 'GREENLINE GOLDEN JUBILEE' £70-80
- 'VISIT BLACKPOOL ZOO' Promotional. Cream body, plastic wheels, 'BLACKPOOL TRANSPORT' £90-110
19??
- 'NEW ZEALAND CLUB' Red body, Blue/White interior, 'CAR CLUB'S 10th ANNIVERSARY' £90-110

290 Double Decker Bus (renumbered from 29c)
Type 2 (AEC grille), 'DUNLOP - The World's Master Tyre' advert. may be upright or sloping, '290' cast on base, diecast hubs match lower deck.
1954-59
- 'DUNLOP' Green lower deck, Cream upper deck, Light Green hubs £120-140
- Red lower deck/hubs, Cream upper deck £120-140
1959-61
- 'DUNLOP' Type 3 (Leyland grille), diecast hubs match lower deck colour, roof route box added, Mid Green or Dark Green lower deck, Cream upper deck.......... £100-125
- Red lower deck, Cream upper £100-125
1961-63
- Same colours with sloping lettering but with spun hubs £150-200
1963
- Same body colours but Green or Red plastic hubs £175-200
1963
- 'EXIDE BATTERIES' Red or Green lower deck, Cream upper deck with '290' cast into base....... NGPP

291 London Bus
Type 3 (Leyland grille) with route '73' on destination board.
1961-62
- 'EXIDE BATTERIES' Red body with Red diecast hubs, logo in Black and Yellow £125-150
- Factory error:
As previous model, but with 'CORPORATION TRANSPORT' transfers on sides, crimped axles .... NGPP
- Promotional: Red body and ridged hubs,

White treaded tyres, no route number,
Exide dealer promotional leaflet............. NGPP
1962-63
- Same body colours as previous model
but with spun aluminium hubs.
Plain Yellow box.................................. **£150-175**
1963
- Same body colours as previous but with
Red plastic hubs. Box has alternating
Red and Yellow panels **£175-225**

291 London Bus.

291 - 293 Atlantean City Bus
A Leyland double-decker bus available
in several versions:
291 1974-77
'KENNINGS'
- Orange body, Blue interior and rear
engine cover, Speedwheels.................... **£30-40**
- Same but with White engine cover **£30-40**
- With White engine cover and interior .. **£30-40**
- As earlier model but with
'Yellow Pages' stickers............................. NGPP
- White body and lower deck interior,
Light or Pale Blue upper deck
interior. Bubble pack **£40-50**
1977
**'LONDON & MANCHESTER
ASSURANCE'**
- White model on plinth. 'Your Best Man
For Life'. (500 issued to agents).......... **£400-500**
292 1962-65
- **'RIBBLE'** Red and White body,
'REGENT' advert. on some **£80-100**
- Red and Cream, 'CORPORATION
TRANSPORT' fleetname **£80-100**
- Same but no fleetname or logo **£80-100**
292 1977
- **'LONDON COUNTRY'** Green body,
shown in 1977 catalogue, but not issued.
293 1963-65
- **'BP'** Green/Cream body, Yellow logo and
smooth roof, 'BP IS THE KEY' **£80-100**

- Same model but with ribbed roof **£100-120**
293 Swiss Postal Bus 'PTT'
1973-78
- Yellow body with Cream roof, clear
or tinted windows, (296 casting) **£25-35**
295 Atlas Kenebrake Bus
1963-69
- Light Blue/Grey body, windows........... **£50-70**
- All Blue body, Red interior **£125-150**
- Blue body, Lemon interior................. **£150-175**
295 Atlantean Bus
1973-74
- **'YELLOW PAGES'** Yellow body,
'Let Your Fingers Do The Walking',
Blue or off-White interior,
Speedwheels **£40-50**
1974-76
- Same, but deeper shade of Yellow **£40-50**
- Same model but finished in Silver,
no front or rear destination blinds.......... NGPP
296 Duple Viceroy 37 Coach
1972-75
- Metallic Blue body, clear or tinted
windows, bubble-packed....................... **£25-35**
- Yellow and Cream body 'P.T.T.',
bubble-packed, (see also 293)............... **£30-40**
297 Silver Jubilee Bus
1977-77
- Leyland Atlantean (291) Silver/Black
body, 'National' **£30-35**
- 'WOOLWORTHS' Silver Jubilee
Bus, promotional **£30-35**
784 Dinky Goods Train Set
1972-74
- Blue loco 'GER', one Red Truck,
one Yellow Truck **£30-40**
798 Express Passenger Train Set
1954-59 (renumbered in 1954 from 16)
- Green/Black loco, BR crest,
Cream/Maroon coaches (Grey roofs),
Black hubs/tyres **£125-150**
- Green/Black loco, BR crest,
Cream/Maroon coaches/roofs/hubs,
Black tyres **£125-150**
- Same but Red hubs, White tyres **£125-150**

949 Wayne School Bus.

949 Wayne 'SCHOOL BUS'
1961-66
- Deep Yellow body, Red lines/rear
bumper, windows, Red plastic hubs.
Supertoy **£160-190**
- Same but Black lines/rear bumper ... **£200-300**
952 Vega Major Luxury Coach
1964-71
- Pale Grey body, Cream interior,
Maroon side flash, cast hubs,
flashing indicators **£80-100**
- Off-White body, Deep Blue interior,
Maroon flash, flashing indicators **£80-100**
- Late issues:
Red interior, clear indicators **£70-90**

953 Continental Touring Coach.

953 Continental Touring Coach
1963-65
- Pale Blue body, White roof, '*Dinky
Continental Tours*', Supertoy **£300-350**
954 Vega Major Luxury Coach
1972-77
- White body, Mid-Blue interior, Maroon
flash, Lemon-Yellow base, cast hubs **£70-90**
- White body, Yellow interior,
Black base, cast hubs........................... **£90-110**
- White body, Red interior,
Black base, later cast hubs **£90-110**
961 Vega Major Coach 'PTT'
1973-77
- Yellow body, Cream roof, Blue interior,
'P.T.T.' and emblem, Swiss model
(in normal box)................................... **£100-125**
- Swiss Postal Bus variant:
Swiss box (Red/White/Yellow,
'Autocar Postal', 'Postauto', etc),
plus label: 'Special contract run 1973
Swiss Post Office Bus', also:
'Specially boxed for Swiss Meccano
Agent for sale under their name'...... **£250-300**

'Dublo Dinky' Models

'Dublo Dinky' models were made in a scale of 1:76. All their wheels are plastic: smooth wheels are fairly soft and treaded wheels are harder.
The late issues with black treaded ('knobbly') wheels are rarer and may attract a premium.
These versions should all be housed in the later issue lighter yellow boxes.

Model and details	MPR
061 Ford Prefect 1958-59	
• Fawn or Grey body, Silver trim, Grey smooth wheels...............................	**£50-60**
• With Grey treaded wheels.....................	**£65-75**

062 Singer Roadster.

Model and details	MPR
062 Singer Roadster 1958-60	
• Orange body, Red interior, Grey smooth or knobbly wheels	**£65-75**
• Fawn body, Red interior, Grey smooth or knobbly wheels..........	**£65-75**
• Yellow body, Grey knobbly wheels	**£75-85**
063 Commer Van 1958-60	
• Blue body, Silver trim, Grey smooth or knobbly wheels	**£100-125**
064 Austin Lorry 1957-62	
• Green body, Black or Grey smooth or knobbly wheels	**£60-70**

Model and details	MPR
065 Morris Pick-up 1957-60	
• Red body, Silver trim, Grey smooth or knobbly wheels	**£60-80**

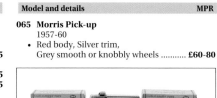

066 Bedford Flat Truck.

066 Bedford Flat Truck
1959-66
- Grey body, Silver trim, hook on some,
Grey smooth or knobbly wheels **£50-60**
067 Austin 'TAXI' (FX3)
1959-64
- Blue lower body, Cream upper body,
Black or Grey knobbly wheels **£70-80**

Dinky Dublo models with grey and later black wheel versions, 064,067 & 068.

068 'ROYAL MAIL' Morris Van
1959-64
- Red body, 'E II R' crest,
Grey knobbly wheels **£120-150**
- Red body, 'E II R' crest,
Black knobbly wheels **£100-120**
069 Massey Harris Tractor
1959-64
- Blue body, Silver trim, Grey knobbly

wheels, hole for driver **£90-110**
- With Grey knobbly wheels on front
and very Light Tan rear wheels **£100-120**
070 A.E.C. Mercury Tanker 'SHELL-BP'
1959-64
- Green cab (glazing in some), Red tank,
Black or Grey knobbly wheels **£100-125**
071 VW Delivery Van 'HORNBY DUBLO'
1960-64
- Yellow body with Red logo,
Black or Grey knobbly wheels **£70-90**
072 Bedford Articulated Truck
1959-64
- Yellow cab, Red semi-trailer, Black
or Grey smooth or knobbly wheels **£70-90**

073 Land Rover with Horsebox on Trailer.

073 Land Rover/Trailer/Horse
1960-64
Green car (Grey or Black knobbly wheels),
Tan or White horse. Trailers:
- with Bright Green trailer (Green
ramp, smooth Grey wheels) **£120-135**
- with Green trailer (Brown ramp,
knobbly Grey wheels) **£120-135**
- with Bright Green trailer (Black
ramp, knobbly Black wheels) **£120-135**
- with Orange trailer
(Grey plastic wheels and ramp) **£120-135**
- with Orange trailer (knobbly
Black plastic wheels and ramp) **£150-175**
076 Lansing Bagnall Tractor & Trailer
1960-64
- Maroon tractor/trailer, Blue driver/seat,
Black smooth or knobbly wheels **£70-90**
078 Lansing Bagnall Trailer
1960-64
- Maroon body, Black smooth or
knobbly wheels, hook, wire drawbar **£40-50**
Shop Display Stand
c1959
- Pale Yellow with Red logo and wording:
'NEW SERIES / DUBLO DINKY',
etc. 28 x 19cm overall **£300-400**

Dinky Toys Ships, Boats and Hovercraft

Model and details	MPR

50a Battle Cruiser 'HMS Hood'
1934-39
- Battleship Grey, 146 mm,
'HMS Hood' cast underneath............... **£30-35**
1939-41
- Without name cast underneath **£30-35**
50b Battleship 'Nelson' Class, 'HMS Nelson'
1934-39
- Battleship Grey, 117 mm,
'HMS Nelson' cast underneath **£30-35**
1939-41
- Without name cast underneath **£30-35**
50b Battleship 'Nelson' Class, 'HMS Rodney'
1934-39
- Battleship Grey, 117 mm,
'HMS Rodney' cast underneath **£30-35**
1939-41
- Without name cast underneath **£30-35**
50c Cruiser 'HMS Effingham'
1934-39
- Battleship Grey, 100 mm,
'HMS Effingham' cast underneath........ **£30-35**
1939-41
- Without name cast underneath **£30-35**
50d Cruiser 'HMS York'
1934-39
- Battleship Grey, 98 mm,
'HMS York' cast underneath **£30-35**
1939-41
- Without name cast underneath **£30-35**
50e Cruiser 'HMS Delhi'
1934-39
- Battleship Grey, 81 mm,
'HMS Delhi' cast underneath............... **£30-35**
1939-41
- Without name cast underneath **£30-35**
50f Destroyer 'Broke' Class
1934-41
- Battleship Grey,
no wording underneath, 57 mm **£15-20**
50g Submarine 'K' Class
1935-41
- Battleship Grey, wire mast,
no wording underneath, 57 mm **£15-20**
50h Destroyer 'Amazon' Class
1935-41
- Battleship Grey,
no wording underneath, 52 mm **£15-20**

50k Submarine 'X' Class
1935-41
- Battleship Grey, wire mast,
no wording underneath, 61 mm **£15-20**
51b Norddeutscher-Lloyd 'Europa'
1934-40
- Black hull, White superstructure,
Brown funnels, name under, 165 mm .. **£35-45**
51c Italia Line 'Rex'
1934-40
- Black hull, White decks, name under,
Red/White/Green funnels, 152 mm **£35-45**
51d CPR 'Empress of Britain'
1934-40
- Canadian Pacific Railway colours –
White hull, Cream funnels, 130 mm ... **£30-35**
51e P & O 'Strathaird'
1935-40
- White hull, Cream funnels,
name underneath, 114 mm **£30-35**
51f Furness-Withy Line 'Queen of Bermuda'
1934-40
- Grey and White hull,
Red/Black funnels, 99 mm.................... **£30-35**
51g Cunard 'White-Star' Liner 'Britannic'
1934-40
- Black/White/Brown hull,
Black/Tan funnels, 121 mm **£30-35**
52 Cunard White-Star Liner 'No. 534'
1934-35
- Black/White/Red, '534' cast under,
boxed, no rollers, 175 mm **£70-80**
- Same model but '534 Queen Mary'
cast underneath...................................... **£70-80**
52 1935-35 (renumbered in 1935 to 52b)
- As previous model with 'Queen Mary'
cast underneath, but without '534'
.... **£70-80**
52a Cunard White-Star Liner 'Queen Mary'
1935-41
- Black/White/Red, boxed,
with plastic rollers, 175 mm.................. **£70-80**
1946-49
- Same but with brass rollers **£70-80**
52b Cunard 'Queen Mary'
1935-36 (renumbered in 1935 from 52)
- Black/White/Red, boxed,
without rollers..................................... **£70-80**

Model and details | MPR

52a Cunard White Star Liner 'Queen Mary.'

52c 'La Normandie'
1935-40
- Black/White, Red/Black funnels, boxed,
made in France, pictorial insert
.... **£70-80**
52c Cunard 'Queen Elizabeth'
1939 Announced in 1939 catalogue
but not produced...................................... NPP
52m Cunard 'Queen Mary'
1936-40
- Renumbered from 52b,
without rollers, supplied unboxed........ **£40-50**
53az Battleship 'Dunkerque'
1938-39
- Battleship Grey, with or without
plastic rollers, boxed French issue........ **£40-60**
281 Military Hovercraft
1973-76
See 'Military Vehicles' section.
290 SRN-6 Hovercraft
1970-76
- Red body, Blue or Black skirt................ **£20-25**
- Same but Metallic Red body................. **£20-25**
671 Mk.1 Corvette
1976-78
- White/Grey/Brown/Black plastic
body, fires missiles **£20-25**
672 OSA-2 Missile Boat
1976-77
- Grey/Whit/Black, fires missiles **£20-25**
673 Submarine Chaser
1977-78
- Grey/White/Black,
fires depth charges **£20-25**

674 Coastguard Missile Launch
1977-78
- White/Blue/Red/Yellow,
'Coastguard', fires missiles **£20-25**

675 Motor Patrol Boat
1973-77
- Grey hull with Cream/Black/Red......... **£20-25**

678 Air-Sea Rescue Launch
1974-77
- Grey/Black/Yellow, Orange dinghy,
pilot/launch **£20-25**

796 Healey Sports Boat on Trailer
1960-62   All have an Orange cast trailer.
- Mid-Green body, Cream hull **£50-75**

- Dark Green body, Deep Cream hull **£50-75**
- Red body, Deep Cream hull **£150-175**
- Yellow body, Cream hull.................... **£150-175**

797 Healey Sports Boat
1966
- Sold without trailer from trade box of 6.
See entry above (796)............................... NGPP

Dinky Toys Novelty, Space, Film and TV-related Models

Model and details	MPR

100 Lady Penelope's 'FAB 1'
1967-75 (TV series 'Thunderbirds')
Non-fluorescent Pink body, clear or tinted
sliding roof (Pink stripes on early issues),
rockets/harpoons,
'Lady Penelope' and 'Parker' figures.
- With ridged cast wheels. Card picture
box with pictorial inner stand **£300-350**
- With ridged cast wheels.
Supplied in a bubble pack **£200-250**
- With Fluorescent Pink body **£500-700**
NB Rare White version reported (but not
seen) sold at auction.
Details welcomed, please.

101 Thunderbirds II and IV
1967-73
- Gloss Dark Green (including loading
door), Red thrusters, Yellow legs.
Separate plastic Yellow/Red
Thunderbird IV model inside.
Card box, pictorial inner stand **£700-900**
- Turquoise Green body, Black door,
Red thrusters, Yellow legs.
Bubble-packed................................... **£200-300**

102 Joe's Car
1969-75 (TV series 'Joe 90')
Metallic Green, White driver,
Red engine thruster, battery powered.
- Card picture box with
pictorial inner stand.......................... **£250-300**
- Same model, but in bubble-pack...... **£150-200**
NB Blue, Silver, Grey version reported
(but not seen) sold at auction.
Details welcomed, please.

103 Spectrum Patrol Car
1968-75 (TV series 'Captain Scarlet')
Shaped hubs, 'screaming motor'.
- Red body with Yellow base, Yellow or
Cream plastic interior. Card picture
box with pictorial inner stand **£175-200**
- Metallic Red body, White base,
Blue tinted windows, Yellow or
Cream interior **£250-300**
- Metallic Gold body, Blue tinted
windows, Yellow or Cream interior... **£175-200**
- Pre-production prototype:
Yellow (resin) body, Lemon interior,
aerial, cast wheels............................. **£400-500**
NB Metallic Blue and Silver versions
reported (but not seen) sold at auction.
Details welcomed, please.

104 Spectrum Pursuit Vehicle
1968-75
- Metallic Blue, Black base,
Black or White front bumper, 'SPV'.
Card box has inner pictorial stand.... **£240-280**
- Metallic Blue body, Black base,
White front bumper. Bubble-pack **£175-200**
- Blue body, Light Green base,
White front bumper. Bubble-pack **£110-140**
- Blue body and base, White front
bumper. Bubble-packed **£100-125**

105 Maximum Security Vehicle
1968-75 (TV series 'Captain Scarlet')
- White body, Red base and side stripes,
Red or Blue interior,
'RADIOACTIVE' crate **£200-250**
- Late issue without Red stripes........... **£200-250**

Model and details	MPR

NB All issues should include a
complete and unused decal sheet.
NB Grey version reported (but not seen)
sold at auction. Details welcomed, please.

106 'The Prisoner' Mini-Moke
1967-70
White body, Red/White canopy,
'bicycle' decal on bonnet, card box.
- With Black windscreen frame............ **£250-300**
- With Silver windscreen frame and
Brown side panels **£200-250**

106 Thunderbird 2 with Thunderbird 4.

106 Thunderbirds II and IV
- Metallic Blue body, Black metal
base, Yellow legs. Vacuum-packed
.... **£150-200**
- Metallic Blue body, White plastic
base, Yellow legs **£150-200**
1977-79
- Metallic Blue body, Black plastic
base, Red legs.................................... **£150-175**
NB Bubble-packed issues have card
bases with Dark Blue sides and
(usually) a Light Blue top.
Rarer issues have a Yellow top.

107 'Stripey the Magic Mini'
1967-68
- White/Red/Yellow/Blue stripes, with
Candy, Andy and the Bearandas. Card
picture box, pictorial inner stand...... **£350-450**

108 Sam's Car
1969-71 (TV series 'Joe 90')
Card box with tray, pictorial backing,
'WIN' badge, instructions.
- Chrome body, Lemon interior **£100-130**
- Gold body, Lemon interior............... **£120-140**
1971-75
- Pale (Powder) Blue body, Lemon
interior, Red engine cover................. **£140-160**
- Metallic Red body, Red or Silver
trim, Lemon interior **£140-160**
- Wine Red body, Lemon interior........ **£150-175**

109 Gabriel's Model 'T' Ford
1969-71 (TV series 'The Secret Service')
- Yellow/Black. Card picture box with
pictorial inner stand.............................. **£75-85**

111 Cinderella's Coach
1976-78 (from 'The Slipper & The Rose')
- Pink/Gold, plastic figures and horses... **£20-25**

112 Purdey's TR7
1978-80 (TV series 'The New Avengers')
- Yellow body, Black 'P' logo,

Model and details	MPR

Speedwheels **£55-65**
- As previous model but with Yellow
'P' in Black logo on bonnet............... **£100-125**
- As previous model but with
Silver 'P' logo on bonnet....................... **£35-45**

*'The New Avengers' pre-production John Steed's Jaguar
XJ5.3C with John Steed figure.*

**113 'The New Avengers'
John Steed's Jaguar XJ 5.3 Coupé**
- Metallic Dark Blue, Black interior and
base, plastic 'Steed' figure + another.
Pictorial window box, inner card tray.
Approx. 36 issued unofficially
.... **£4,000-5,000**

? John Steed's Ford Granada
- Approximately 6 pre-production
samples issued unofficially.
No details at present................................ NGPP

115 United Biscuits Taxi
1979-79 (promotional)
- Yellow/Blue/Black, casting as 120 .... **£50-60**

120 Happy Cab
1979-80
- White/Yellow/Blue, solid wheels,
'flower-power' stickers **£50-60**

281 'PATHE NEWS' Camera Car (Fiat 2300)
1968-70
- Black body, Red interior, cast wheels,
cameraman with Brown trousers,
camera and stand **£150-175**
- As previous model but cameraman
has Dark Grey trousers...................... **£175-225**

350 Tiny's Mini Moke
1970-71 (from 'The Enchanted House')
- Red body, White/Yellow
striped top **£150-175**

351 U.F.O. Interceptor
1971-79
(from Gerry Anderson's TV series 'U.F.O')
Light Metallic Green body,
'S.H.A.D.O.' labels. Initially packed
in card box with pictorial inner mount
(prices 20% higher), later bubble-packed.
- with Black missile holder,
White/Black missile, clear canopy,
Red legs/skids **£175-200**
- with Black missile holder,
White/Black missile, Blue canopy,
Red legs/skids **£175-200**
- with Red missile holder, Yellow/Black
missile, clear canopy, Orange
legs/skids. Bubble packed only **£175-200**
- with Red missile holder, Yellow/Black
missile, Blue canopy, Orange
legs/skids. Bubble packed only **£175-200**

352 Ed Straker's Car
1971-75 (TV series 'U.F.O.')
- Gold plated body, Blue interior,

keyless motor **£100-120**
- Yellow body, Pale Grey interior,
Black engine covers **£150-175**
- Red body, Silver trim **£70-80**

353 'SHADO 2 Mobile'
1971-79 (TV series 'U.F.O.')
- Green body, Red interior, Brown rollers,
Silver tracks, Light Green base.
All card box **£120-140**
- Green body, Black roof, Off-White
interior, Dark Green rollers,
Black tracks. Bubble-packed **£250-300**
- Green body, Yellow interior,
Light Green rollers and base,
Silver tracks **£120-140**
- Metallic Blue body, Off-White interior,
Light Green or Black base,
Green or Black rollers, tracks and roof.
Window box, internal card base........ **£250-300**

354 1st issue Pink Panther.

354 Pink Panther
1972-77
- Pink car and Panther, flywheel drive,
card endflap box **£35-45**
1977-79
- Similar to previous model but without
flywheel, bubble-packed........................ **£35-45**
NB A single experimental Green diecast
version exists (Christie's sale 4/95).

355 Lunar Roving Vehicle
1972-75
- Metallic Blue, White astronauts,
front/rear steering **£35-45**

357 Klingon Battle Cruiser
1977-80 (from TV series 'Star Trek')
- Metallic Blue body,
fires 'photon torpedoes' **£45-55**

358 'Star Trek' - USS Enterprise.

358 'USS Enterprise' ('NCC 1701')
1976-80
- White body, shuttlecraft,
Yellow or White 'photon torpedoes' **£70-90**
359 Eagle Transporter
1975-79 (from TV series 'Space 1999')
- White/Green body, Red rear and
side thrusters, clear windows **£100-125**
- White/Green body, Chrome rear
thrusters, Yellow side thrusters,
Orange windows................................. **£100-125**
- White/Green body, Chrome rear
thrusters, Yellow side thrusters,
Red windows...................................... **£100-125**
- White/Green body, Red rear
thrusters, side thrusters
and windows...................................... **£100-125**
NB All issues should include a complete
and unused decal sheet.
360 Eagle Freighter
1975-79 (from TV series 'Space 1999')
- White/Red, including rear and side
thrusters, 'RADIOACTIVE' drums **£100-125**
- White/blue, Red rear and
side thrusters **£100-125**
NB All issues should include a complete
and unused decal sheet.

360 'Space 1999' - Eagle Freighter.

361 Zygon War Chariot
1978-80
- Mid-Green body, two Red spacemen
and rocket motor **£35-45**
361 Galactic War Chariot
1978-80
- Metallic Green body, two White/Yellow
spacemen, Silver rocket motor.............. **£35-45**
NB Light Yellow-Green version
reported (but not seen) sold at auction.
Details welcomed, please.
361 Missile-firing War Chariot
1978-80
- Metallic Blue body, two Red
spacemen/rocket motor, blister card.... **£35-45**
362 Trident Star Fighter
1978-79
- Black/Orange, fires rockets,
drop-down stairway **£35-45**
- Metallic Gold.
500 only issued to guests at a special
Meccano Dinner in 1979.................... **£100-150**

363 Cosmic Interceptor
1979-79
- Metallic Silver/Blue, 2 pilots, Marks
& Spencer model ('St.Michael' box) **£45-55**
363 Zygon Patroller
1979-80
- Metallic Silver/Blue, 2 pilots, ('368' in
some catalogues, '363' on box) **£35-45**
- Yellow/Red/Blue version in
'U.S.S. Enterprise' box .... NGPP
364 NASA Space Shuttle
1979
- White booster and shuttle, decals,
instructions, plastic Orange satellite.
Pictorial window box.......................... **£100-150**
366 Space Shuttle
1979
- unboxed version of 364 without booster,
with plastic or cardboard load **£35-45**
367 Space Battle Cruiser
1979-80
- White/Red body, pilot, plastic weapons **£35-45**
368 Cosmic Cruiser
1979-79
- Blue body, Marks & Spencer model
(in 'St.Michael' box) **£35-45**
368 Zygon Marauder
1979-80
- Red/White, 4 spacemen, ('363' in
some catalogues, '368' on box) **£30-35**
371 Pocket-size 'USS Enterprise'
1980 (renumbered in 1980 to 801)
- Small version of 358, bubble-packed,
released after factory closure **£45-55**
372 Pocket-size Klingon Cruiser
1980 (renumbered in 1980 to 802)
- Small version of 357, bubble-packed,
released after factory closure **£45-55**
477 Parsley's Car
1970-72
(TV series 'The Adventures of Parsley')
- Green/Black/Yellow, head swivels. Card
picture box, pictorial inner stand...... **£100-120**
485 Santa Special Model 'T' Ford
1964-67
- Red/White body, Santa Claus,
Christmas tree/toys/decals................ **£100-120**
486 'Dinky Beats' Morris Oxford
1965-69
- Pink/Green, 'Da gear',
3 beat-group figures **£100-150**
602 Armoured Command Car
1976-77 (TV series 'The Investigator')
- Green or later Blue-Green body, White
star, driver, scanner, fires sparks........... **£35-45**
802 Pocket-size Klingon Cruiser
1980 (renumbered in 1980 from 372)
- Small version of 357, bubble-packed,
released after factory closure **£45-55**
803 Pocket-size 'USS Enterprise'
1980 (renumbered in 1980 from 371)
- Small version of 358, bubble-packed,
released after factory closure **£45-55**

Dinky Toys 'Action Kits'

These Action Kits were issued in the 1970s. Screws were usually included to attach their bases (which have no model numbers).
Paint supplied with the kit is not always the same colour or shade as on the relative model when supplied built and finished.

Model and details	MPR
1001 Rolls-Royce Phantom V 1971-77 Casting as 152	
• Various colours (usually Blue)............	**£30-35**
1002 Volvo 1800s Coupé 1971-75 Casting as 116	
• Yellow paint	**£30-35**

Model and details	MPR
1003 Volkswagen 1300 1971-75 Casting as 129	
• Red and White paint supplied	**£30-35**
1004 Ford Escort Police Car 1971-77 Casting as 270	
• Blue and White paint,	

Model and details	MPR
'POLICE' transfers	**£30-35**
1006 Ford Escort Mexico 1973-77 Casting as 168	
• Red paint and 'MEXICO' transfers.....	**£45-55**
1007 Jensen FF 1971-75 Casting as 188	

- Various paint colours (usually Blue) .. **£30-35**
1008 Mercedes-Benz 600
1973-77 Casting as 128
- Red, Yellow or Green paint supplied.. **£30-35**
1009 Lotus F1 Racing Car
1971-75 Casting as 225
- Green paint and 'gold leaf' transfers .. **£30-35**
1012 Ferrari 312-B2
1973-75 Casting as 226
- With Red paint + 'SHELL' transfers **£50-60**
1013 Matra Sports M530
Catalogued but not issued .... NPP
1014 Beach Buggy
1975-77 Casting as 227
- Blue paint included **£20-30**
1017 Routemaster Bus
1971-77 Casting as 289
- Red paint and
'ESSO Safety-Grip Tyres' transfers **£30-40**
1018 Leyland Atlantean Bus
1974-77 Casting as 295
- Various (mostly White) paint,
usually 'NATIONAL' transfers **£40-50**
**? Leyland Atlantean Bus
'YELLOW PAGES'**
- Three variations of transfers exist:
1) Mid-Blue interior, reversed front
'Yellow Pages' **£40-50**
2) White interior, reversed front
'Yellow Pages' sign **£40-50**
3) White interior, correct reading front
'Yellow Pages' **£40-50**
1023 A.E.C. Single Decker Bus
1972-77 Casting as 283

- Green paint and 'GREEN LINE'
transfers included **£30-35**
1025 Ford Transit Van
1971-75 Casting as 407
- Red paint and 'Avis Truck Rental'
transfers included **£30-35**
1027 Lunar Roving Vehicle
1972-75 Casting as model 355
- Blue/White paint supplied **£30-35**
1029 Ford D800 Tipper Truck
1971-77 Casting as 438
- Green or Yellow paint supplied **£30-35**
1030 Land Rover Breakdown Truck
1974-77 Casting as 442
- Red or White paint in kit **£30-35**
1032 Army Land Rover
1975-77 Casting as 344
- Military-Green paint and various
'ARMY' transfers in kit **£30-35**
1033 U.S.A. Army Jeep
1971-77 Casting as 615
- Military-Green paint and transfers
supplied in kit...................................... **£30-35**
1034 Mobile Gun
1975-77 Casting as 654
- Military-Green paint included........... **£30-35**
1035 Striker Anti-Tank Vehicle
1975-77 Casting as 691
- Military-Green paint and transfer
supplied **£30-35**
1036 Leopard Tank
1975-77 Casting as 692
- Military-Green paint and transfers
supplied **£30-35**

1037 Chieftain Tank
1974-77 Casting as 683
- Military-Green paint and transfers..... **£30-35**
1038 Scorpion Tank
1975-77 Casting as 690
- Military-Green paint and transfers..... **£35-45**
1039 Leopard Recovery Tank
Catalogued but not issued .... NPP
1040 Sea King Helicopter
1971-77 Casting as 724
- White with Blue or Orange paint plus
'USAF' transfers.................................... **£30-35**
1041 Hawker Hurricane Mk.IIc
1973-76 Casting as 718
- Camouflage paints and
RAF roundels in kit **£50-75**
1042 Spitfire Mk.II
1971-77 Casting as 719
- Camouflage paints and
RAF roundels in kit **£50-75**
1043 S.E.P.E.C.A.T. Plane
1974-76 Casting as 731
- Blue and Green paints, transfers **£40-60**
1044 Messerschmitt BF-109e
1972-75 Casting as 726
- Brown paint, Luftwaffe transfers **£80-100**
1045 Multi-Role Combat Aircraft
1975-76 Casting as 729
- Camouflage paints, transfers **£40-60**
1050 Motor Patrol Boat
1975-77 Casting as 675
- Black/Blue/White paints and stickers **£20-30**

Dinky Toys Gift Sets

Box types

Sets 001-006:
Housed in Green card boxes with
plain Yellow inserts.

Sets 1, 2, 3, 4, 5, 6:
Oblong boxes with Yellow insert card and
train picture on lid.
c 1932 Purple marbled
'Modelled Miniatures' box.
c 1936 Blue patterned 'MECCANO
DINKY TOYS' box, pictorial insert card.
c 1939 Green box with plain insert,
'DINKY TOYS' label.
1952-56 Green box with Yellow insert,
stripe lid label.

Train sets 17, 18, 19 and 20 box sequence:
'Modelled Miniatures' :
'Meccano Dinky Toys' :
'Dinky Toys'.

Sets 24, 25 and 30 series:
c 1934 Purple marbled
'Modelled Miniatures' box.
c 1935 Purple marbled
'MECCANO DINKY TOYS' box with
Yellow/Red label picturing eight assorted cars
and lorries. Purple insert with Gold script on two
central lines 'MECCANO DINKY TOYS
No '24', '25' or '30'.
NB The 24 Series and 30 series sets also
contained a purple packing card stating:
'PLEASE REMOVE THIS PACKING CARD
TO DISPLAY CONTENTS.'
c 1936 Blue patterned box lid with Yellow/Red
label picturing eight assorted cars and lorries.
Purple insert with no Gold Script on 25 series
(no details available on 24 and 30 series).

Sets 12, 42, 43, 44 and 49 (Pre-war issue):
Blue landscape boxes with inner
Blue/Green pictorial inserts.

Sets 151, 152, 156, 161, 162:
Grey/Blue or Blue (152) display boxes
with inner pictorial scenic backdrop and
packing boards.

Pre-war USA Sets:
may display 'FAO Schwarz' labels on base of
box and 'Meccano Co. of America Inc.' on
box lid (e.g., 62h Hurricane Set).

Early Post-war USA Special Sets:
Sets for the US market were distributed by
H. Hudson Dobson of New York. They are
housed in flat boxes with a mottled greenish-
blue lid. The picture label on the lid depicts a
boy's face plus line drawings of various models.
The lid often still retains a red 'H. Hudson
Dobson' label. The Set number and type are
shown on the main label, e.g. 'No. 6 Commercial
Vehicles'. Sets 1, 2, 3 and 6 are listed – the
Editor would welcome any new information on
the contents of these, and of Sets 4 and 5.

Set and details	MPR

Pre-war sets without 'fatigue' and with pristine
boxes attract a premium, as do early Accessory
Sets in 'Modelled Miniatures' boxes.

001 Station Staff ('0' gauge) (35mm)
1954-56 (renumbered in 1954 from 1)
- 1b Guard (flag in right hand),
1c Ticket Collector (right arm extended),
1d Driver, 1e Porter (with oblong bags),
1f Porter (standing) **£90-120**
002 Farmyard Animals (6)
1954-56 (renumbered in 1954 from 2)
- 2 x 2a horses, 2 x 2b cows, 1 x 2c pig,
1 x 2d sheep, simplified painting....... **£300-400**
003 Passengers ('0' gauge) (35mm)
1954-56 (renumbered in 1954 from 3)
- 3a Woman (with child on left),

3b Businessman (Brown suit and case),
3c Male hiker (no stick),
3d Female hiker (Blue shirt),
3e Newsboy (Grey tray),
3f Woman (Light Red coat,
round case) **£90-120**
004 Engineering Staff ('0' gauge) (35mm)
1954-56 (renumbered in 1954 from 4)
- 2 x 4b Fitter (all-Blue and all-Brown),
4c Storekeeper (all-Brown), 4d Greaser,
4e Engine-Room attendant.................. **£80-100**
005 Train and Hotel Staff ('0' gauge) (35mm)
1954-56 (renumbered in 1954 from 5)
- 5a Conductor, 2 x 5b waiters,
2 x 5c Porter (both Brown or Blue) **£90-120**
006 Shepherd Set
1954-56 (renumbered in 1954 from 6)

- 6a Shepherd (Green hat),
6b sheepdog (all-Black),
4 x 2b sheep.................................... **£250-350**
007 Petrol Pump Attendants (35 mm. tall)
1960-67
- 1 male (White overalls),
1 female (White coat), plastic **£30-40**
008 Fire Station Personnel (35 mm. tall)
1961-67
- Set of 6 plastic fire-fighters in
Blue uniforms plus hose **£30-40**
009 Service Station Personnel (35 mm. tall)
1962-66
- Set of 8 plastic figures in various
colours and stances.............................. **£30-40**
010 Road Maintenance Personnel (35 mm. tall)
1962-66

- Set of 6 plastic workmen using pick, barrow, shovels, drill etc, plus hut, brazier, barrier, and 4 lamps.................. **£60-70**

050 Railway Staff ('00' gauge)
1961-68
- 12 Blue plastic figures in a clear plastic box. Early issues contained a Policeman, later ones a Shunter **£40-50**

051 Station Staff ('00' gauge)
1954-59 (renumbered in 1954 from 1001)
- 6 plastic figures in a green card box (re-issue of pre-war Hornby-Dublo Set D1).......................... **£35-45**

052 Railway Passengers ('00')
1961-69
- 11 plastic figures plus a seat, in a clear plastic box.............................. **£35-45**

053 Passengers ('00' gauge)
1954-59 (renumbered in 1954 from 1003)
- 6 coloured plastic figures (re-issue of pre-war Hornby-Dublo Set D2)........ **£35-45**

054 Railway Station Personnel ('OO' gauge)
1962-70
- 4 plastic figures plus 8 pieces of furniture in a clear plastic box............... **£35-45**

1 Station Staff (6) (large) (40mm)
1931-39
- 'HORNBY SERIES' (early issues), 'DINKY TOYS' (later)
1a Station Master,
1b Guard (flag in left hand),
1c Ticket Collector (with open arms),
1d Driver, 1e Porter (round/oblong bags), 1f Porter (walking).................. **£150-200**

1 Station Staff (6) (small) (35mm)
1939-41
- As previous set but smaller figures ... **£100-125**

1 Station Staff (6) (35mm)
1939-41
- 1a and 1d as above,
1b Guard (flag in right hand),
1c Ticket Collector (right arm extended),
1e Porter (oblong bags),
1f Porter (standing) **£150-200**

1 Station Staff (5) (35mm)
1946-54 (renumbered in 1954 to 001)
- 1b Guard (flag in right hand),
1c Ticket Collector (right arm extended),
1d Driver, 1e Porter (with oblong bags),
1f Porter (standing) **£90-120**

1 Military Vehicles (1) Set
1954-55 (renumbered in 1954 to 699)
- 621 3-ton Wagon, 641 1-ton Truck, 674 Austin Champ, 676 Armoured Car. Blue/White box with Blue cut-out base plus packing piece on top................. **£400-600**

No.1 Railway Accessories Set
1934-39
- 'Miniature Luggage and Truck'. A Porter's truck and 4 pieces of luggage (tinplate and cast), items not available separately **£100-125**

No.1 Commercial Vehicles Set
1946-48
- 29c Bus, 25b Wagon, 25d Tanker, 25e Tipper and 25f Market Gardeners Lorry. In mottled Green, Blue and Fawn box with inner Green card cut-out base. Box lid has Light Green and Blue silhouette label.. **£2,500-3,500**

No.1 Farm Gear Gift Set
1952-54 (reissued in 1964 as 398)
- 27a Massey-Harris Tractor, 27b Harvest Trailer, 27c Manure Spreader, 27h Disc Harrow, 27k Hay Rake. In Blue/White box with inner cut-out base plus packing piece on top **£2,500-3,500**

2 Farmyard Animals
1934-35
- 2 x 2a horses, 2 x 2b cows, 1 x 2c pig, 1 x 2d sheep,

in 'Modelled Miniatures' box **£750-1,000**
1935-40
- Same set but in 'Dinky Toys' box....... **£600-800**
1946-54 (renumbered in 1954 to 002)
- Same set but less detailed painting... **£200-300**
NB Boxes with a 'H. Hudson Dobson' (of New York) label may sell at a premium of 30% to 35% more.

No.2 Railway Accessories Set
1934-?
- 'Milk Cans and Truck'. A 4-wheel barrow and 6 milk churns, not available separately .... NGPP

No.2 Private Automobiles Set
1946-48
- 39a Packard, 39b Oldsmobile, 39c Lincoln, 39d Buick, 39e Chrysler. Inner Green card base in Green, Blue and Orange mottled box, Green and Blue silhouette lid label (export only issue) **£2,500-3,500**

No.2 Commercials Vehicles Set
1952-53
- 25m Bedford End Tipper, 27d Land Rover (Dark Brown), 30n Farm Produce Wagon, 30p 'Mobilgas' Tanker, 30s Austin Covered Wagon. In Blue/White box with inner cut-out base plus packing piece on top ... **£2,500-3,500**

3 Railway Passengers (large) (40mm)
1932-39
- 'HORNBY SERIES' (early issues), 'DINKY TOYS' (later).
3a Woman (with child on right),
3b Businessman (left hand on chest),
3c Male hiker (with stick),
3d Female hiker (White shirt),
3e Newsboy (running), 3f Woman (Red jacket, oblong case) **£225-275**

3 Railway Passengers (small) (35mm)
1932-39
- As previous set but smaller figures. Oblong Green box, scenic background **£150-175**

3 Railway Passengers
1939-41
- 3a Woman (with child on left),
3b Businessman (case in left hand),
3c Male hiker (no stick),
3d Female hiker (White shirt),
3e Newsboy (standing),
3f Woman (Red coat, round case)..... **£125-175**

3 Railway Passengers
1946-54 (renumbered in 1954 to 003)
- 3a Woman (with child on left),
3b Businessman (Brown suit and case),
3c Male hiker (no stick),
3d Female hiker (with Blue shirt),
3e Newsboy (Grey tray), 3f Woman (Light Red coat, round case)............... **£90-120**

No.3 Railway Accessories Set
1934-?
- 'Platform Machines Etc'. A posting box, ticket machine, label machine and two benches, not available separately .... NGPP

No.3 Private Automobiles Set
1947-52
- (i) 30d Vauxhall, 36a Armstrong, 36b Bentley, 38a Frazer-Nash, 39b Oldsmobile. (Export only issue). Green, Blue and Orange mottled box with inner Green card cut-out base, Green and Blue silhouette lid label **£2,000-2,500**

No.3 Private Automobiles Set
1947-52
- (ii) 30d Vauxhall, 36b Bentley, 36d Rover, 38a Fraser Nash, 38c Lagonda. (Export only issue). Green, Blue and Orange mottled box with inner Green card cut-out base, Green and Blue silhouette lid label **£2,500-3,000**

Dinky Gift Set No 3 Passenger Cars 1952-54. Shows rare red Rover version with maroon wheels.

No.3 Passenger Cars Set
1952-54
- 27d Estate Car, 30h Daimler Ambulance, 40e Standard Vanguard, 40g Morris Oxford, 40h Austin Taxi, 140b Rover 75. Blue/White box with cut-out tray plus packing piece on top **£3,000-4,000**

4 Engineering Staff (6) (large) (40mm)
1932-41
- 'HORNBY SERIES' (early issues), 'DINKY TOYS' (later)
4a Electrician, 2 x 4b Fitter (Blue/White and Brown/White), 4c Storekeeper (Brown/Black), 4d Greaser, 4e Engine-Room attendant............... **£150-200**

4 Engineering Staff (6) (small)
1932-41
- As previous set but smaller figures ... **£150-175**

4 Engineering Staff (5)
1946-54 (renumbered in 1954 to 004)
- 2 x 4b Fitter (all-Blue and all-Brown), 4c Storekeeper (all-Brown), 4d Greaser, 4e Engine-Room attendant............... **£125-175**

No.4 Railway Accessories Set
1934-?
- A combination of No.1 ('Miniature Luggage & Truck'), No.2 ('Milk Cans & Truck'), and No.3 ('Platform Machines Etc.'). Individual items not available separately .... NGPP

No.4 Racing Cars Set
1953-54 (renumbered in 1954 to 249)
- 23f Alfa-Romeo, 23g Cooper-Bristol, 23h Ferrari, 23j HWM & 23n Maserati. Blue/White striped box with over packing piece **£2,000-2,500**

No.4 Commercial Vehicles Set
1948-48
- Contains 25d, 25f, 25w, 29c and 30e. Brown/Green box with silhouette lid label. (US export)....................**£2,500-3,000**

5 Train and Hotel Staff (large) (40mm)
1932-39
- 'HORNBY SERIES' (early issues), 'DINKY TOYS' (later)
5a Conductor, 2 x 5b waiters, 2 x 5c Porter (1 Red, 1 Green)............ **£300-350**
NB Also sold in USA - boxes often display 'H. Hudson Dobson' label.

5 Train and Hotel Staff (small)
1932-39
- As previous set but smaller figures ... **£150-175**

5 Train and Hotel Staff
1939-41
- 5a Conductor, 2 x 5b waiters, 2 x 5c Porter (both Brown or Blue) ... **£125-175**

5 Train and Hotel Staff
1946-54 (renumbered in 1954 to 005)
- 5a Conductor, 2 x 5b Waiter, 2 x 5c Porter (Brown or Blue), less detail **£90-120**

5 Military Vehicles Set
c1950
- 153a (672) US Army Jeep,
161b (690) Mobile AA Gun,
151a Medium Tank,
151b (620) Transport Wagon,
152b (671) Reconnaissance Car.
Green box, inner Green card base and
card cut-out packing piece. Blue,
Light Green and Red mottled
lid has Purple and Yellow label ...**£2,500-3,000**

6 Shepherd Set
1934-36
- 6a Shepherd (Dark Brown smock, hat
and leggings, Black boots, lamb under
arm), 6b Collie dog (Black/White),
4 x 2b sheep (Beige, 'Hornby Series'
cast-in), set presented in
'Modelled Miniatures' box.................**£500-750**

6 Shepherd Set
1936-40
- As previous set but in
'Dinky Toys' box...............................**£250-350**

6 Shepherd Set
1946-54 (renumbered in 1954 to 006)
- 6a Shepherd (all Brown below neck,
Green hat), 6b Collie dog (all Black),
4 x 2b sheep (without
'Hornby Series')................................**£150-200**

No.6 Commercial Vehicles Set
1946-48
- 29c Bus, 29b Streamline Bus,
25h Fire Engine, 30e Breakdown Car,
30f Ambulance. (US export issue).
Mottled Purple-Blue box with inner
Purple cut-out card base, Yellow
and Maroon silhouette lid label ..**£2,500-3,000**

12 Postal Set
1937-41
- 12a GPO Pillar Box,
12b Air Mail Pillar Box,
12c Telephone Call Box,
12d Telegraph Messenger,
12e Postman, 34b Royal Mail Van.
Blue box with Yellow insert **£600-800**

13 'HALL'S DISTEMPER'
1931-40
- Advertisement board, White overalled
figures (one with Green brush, the
other with Blue brush). 'Hornby Series'.
Box ('A898') **£300-400**

15 Railway Signals Set
1937-41
- 1 x 15a 'Home' (single-arm signal),
1 x 15a 'Distant' (single-arm signal),
2 x 15b 'Home/Distant' (double-arm signals),
1 x 15c 'Home' (double-arm signal),
1 x 15c 'Distant' (double-arm signal).
Yellow box with Purple insert,
'DINKY TOYS' on lid **£150-175**

16 Silver Jubilee Train Set
1936-37
- Locomotive and two interlocking
coaches, 'LNER' and '2590' cast-in,
open windows, smooth hubs with
White tyres, special box, 300 mm.
  1: Silver loco / coaches, Grey, Mid-Blue,
  Dark Blue, Red or Orange trim.........**£250-350**
  2: Silver loco and coaches with
  Dark Blue trim **£250-350**
  3: Cream loco and coaches, Red trim ..**£250-350**
  4: Blue loco/coaches, Dark Blue trim ..**£250-350**
  5: Green loco and coaches with
  Dark Green trim..................................**£250-350**

16 Streamlined Train Set
1937-40
- As previous models but with a
change of name and box...................**£250-350**
1946-52
- Blue/Black loco, 'LNER',
Brown/Grey coaches,
solid windows, Black tyres.................**£150-175**

1952-54 (renumbered in 1954 to 798)
- As previous model but with 'BR' crest
on tender. Long portrait 'ladder'
box with train picture........................**£125-145**

17 Passenger Train Set
1934-40
- Black/Maroon loco 17a, Maroon
tender 17b, Maroon/Cream coaches
20a/20b. Long portrait 'ladder'
box with train picture........................**£300-400**
- Black/Green loco 17a, Green tender
17b, two Green/Cream coaches 20a/20b.
Long portrait 'ladder' box with
train picture **£300-400**
- Lead and Mazak set in 2nd type
box with correct colour spot.............**£400-500**

18 Tank Goods Train Set
1934-40
- Green/Black loco (21a), 3 Green/Black
open wagons (21b). Long portrait
'ladder' box with train picture...........**£300-400**

19 Mixed Goods Train
1935-40
- Maroon/Black loco (21a),
Green/Red open wagon (21b),
Red/Blue 'SHELL' tanker wagon (21d),
Yellow/Red/Green lumber wagon (21e).
Long portrait 'ladder' box with
train picture **£400-500**
- Rare box version: Set in 3rd type
pictorial landscape box.................**£800-1,000**

20 Tank Passenger Set
1934-40
- Green/Black loco (21a),
2 Brown/Green coaches (20a),
Guard's van (20b). **£300-400**

21 Hornby Train Set
1932-33
- Blue/Red loco (21a),
Green open wagon (21b),
Green/Blue crane wagon (21c),
Red/Blue 'SHELL' tank wagon (21d),
Blue/Red/Black lumber wagon (21e).
In plain Red 'Hornby Series' box **£500-750**

21 Modelled Miniatures Train Set
1934-35
- As previous set, but in 'Modelled
Miniatures' Red card box...................**£500-750**

22 Motor Vehicles Set
1933-35
- 22a and 22b Cars, 22c Motor Truck,
22d Delivery Van, 22e Tractor,
22f Tank, with 'Hornby Series' or
'Dinky Toys' cast-in.
'Modelled Miniatures' box, Purple
lid, full-size full-colour label
with pictures of models **£7,500-10,000**

23 Racing Cars Set
1936-40
- 23c Mercedes-Benz,
23d Auto-Union,
23e 'Speed of the Wind'.
Blue box ('A2144')...............................**£500-750**

24 Motor Cars Set
1934-40
- 1st issue: 24a Ambulance, 24b Limousine,
24c Town Sedan, 24d Vogue Saloon,
24e Super Streamlined Saloon,
24f Sportsman's Coupé,
24g Sports Tourer (2 seater),
24h Sports Tourer (4 seater).
Purple and Gold marbled box, lid has
colour top label and Yellow/Red
end label with code 'DT24'.......**£7,500-10,000**
- Later issue: Blue marbled box
lid (with colour label),
Purple inner ('A2205') **£6,000-8,000**

25 Commercial Motor Vehicles
1934-37
- 25a Wagon, 25b Covered Wagon,
25c Flat Truck, 25d Tank Wagon,
25e Tipper, 25f Market Gardener's

Lorry.   Mauve 'grained' box lid
(colour label) ('A1052')................**£5,000-7,000**
- Revised set:
Contains 25b, d, e, f, g and h........**£4,000-5,000**

*Dinky pre-war Gift Set No 24 Motor Car Set - 2nd issue
with purple inner card containing – No 24a Ambulance,
No 24b Limousine, No 24c Town Sedan, No 24d Vogue
Saloon, No 24e Super Streamline Saloon, No 24f
Sportsman's Coupe, No 24g 2-seater Sports Tourer and
No 24h 4-seater Sports Tourer.*

27ak 'MASSEY-HARRIS' Tractor and Hayrake
1952-54 (renumbered in 1954 to 310)
- 27a Tractor and 27k Hayrake.............**£150-200**

28/1 Delivery Vans Set in Trade Box
1934-40
- (1st type castings)
28a Hornby Trains,
28b Pickfords,
28c Manchester Guardian,
28d Oxo,
28e Ensign Lukos,
28f Palethorpes Sausages
Box numbered 'A1008' **£17,500-20,000**
- Revised set:
28a Hornby Trains,
28b Pickfords,
28c Manchester Guardian,
28e Firestone,
28f Palethorpes,
28n Atco Mowers **£17,500-20,000**

28/2 Delivery Vans Set in Trade Box
1934-40
- (1st type castings)
28g Kodak,
28h Sharps Toffees,
28k Marsh & Baxter,
28L Crawfords Biscuits,
28m Wakefield's Castrol,
28n Meccano.
Box numbered 'A1008' **£17,500-20,000**
- Revised set:
28d Oxo,
28g Kodak,
28h Dunlop Tyres,
28k Marsh's,
28m Wakefield's Castrol,
28p Crawfords Biscuits............**£17,500-20,000**

28/3 Delivery Vans Set in Trade Box
1936-40
- (2nd type castings)
28r Swan Pens,
28s Frys Chocolate,
28t Ovaltine,
28w Osram Lamps,
28x Hovis,
28y Exide Batteries **£3,000-4,000**

30 Motor Vehicles
1935-37
- 30a Chrysler Airflow,
30b Rolls-Royce,
30c Daimler,
30d Vauxhall,
30e Breakdown Car,

30f Ambulance.............................**£5,000-6,000**
1937-41
- As previous set but 30g Caravan
replaces 30f Ambulance..............**£4,500-5,000**

**33/1 Mechanical Horse and
Five Assorted Trailers**
1935-37
- 33a Mechanical Horse,
33b Flat Truck,
33c Open Wagon,
33d Box Van,
33e Dust Wagon,
33f Petrol Tank 'WAKEFIELD CASTROL'
or 'ESSO' logo.
Blue or Green 'grained' box
lid, large colour label...................**£1,500-2,000**

**33/2 Mechanical Horse and
Four Assorted Trailers**
1935-37
- 33a Mechanical Horse, 33b Flat Truck,
33c Open Wagon and 33e Dust Wagon.
In Green display box (code 'A2036')
with Yellow inner tray **£1,250-1,500**

35 Small Cars Set
1935-41
- 35a Saloon Car, 35b Racer and
35c MG Sports Car. In display type
box ('A2222') with tuck-in flap
and scenic backdrop **£800-1,100**

**36 Motor Cars with Drivers,
Passengers and Footmen**
1936-41
- 36a Armstrong-Siddeley with figures,
36b Bentley with figures,
36c Humber with figures,
36d Rover with figures,
36e British Salmson 2-seater with figures,
36f British Salmson 4-seater, with figures.
Set housed in Blue landscape box with
Yellow tray with Purple inner and Brown
board top packing piece. Box code
'A2205', dated '6-38' **£7,500-10,000**

37a Motor Cycles Set
1937-41
- Six of 37a civilian Motor Cyclists in
various colours, hand-painted detail,
solid White rubber wheels.
Blue box with Green and White
pictorial inner **£400-600**

37 Motor Cycles Set
1938-40
- 37a (civilian), 37b (Police),
37c (Signals Despatch).......................**£400-600**

*Dinky 39e Chrysler including four scarce US export
versions in background.*

39 USA Saloon Cars Set
1939-41
- 39a Packard, 39b Oldsmobile,
39c Lincoln, 39d Buick,
39e Chrysler, 39f Studebaker.
Mauve box with full colour
label on lid **£2,500-3,500**

42 Police Set
1935-40
- 42a Police Box, 42b Motor Cycle Patrol,
42c Point-Duty Policeman (White coat),
42d Point-Duty Policeman (Blue uniform),

Blue box with pictorial
inner ('A2114') **£400-600**

*43 RAC Set containing – No 43a tinplate RAC Box, No
43b RAC Motorcycle Patrol, No 43c RAF Guide directing
traffic and No 43d RAC Guide saluting.*

43 'R.A.C.' Set
1935-41
- 43a RAC Box, 43b RAC Motor Cycle Patrol,
43c RAC Guide directing traffic,
43d RAC Guide saluting. Blue box,
pictorial inner part, ('A2064') **£500-600**

44 'A.A.' Set
1935-41
- 44a AA Box, 44b AA Motor Cycle Patrol,
44c AA Guide directing traffic,
44d AA Guide saluting. Blue box,
pictorial inner part, ('A2065') **£500-600**

46 Pavement Set
1937-41
- Dark Grey 'stone' effect (cardboard)
pavement pieces in a box **£100-150**

47 Road Signs Set
1935-41
- 12 road signs, 47e to 47t, (White under
base, triangles usually filled-in).
Yellow box and inner,
box code 'A2073' **£200-250**
1948-54 (renumbered in 1954 to 770)
- US issue: 12 road signs, 47e to 47t,
(Black under base, open triangles). Plain
card box with Yellow label on end
of lift up lid, or in slide-tray box........**£100-125**
- US issue: White under bases, filled-in
triangles, in a plain box marked 'Made in
England'. Made for sale by H. Hudson
Dobson, 200 5th Avenue, New York........NGPP

49 Petrol Pumps Set
1935-41
- 'Pratts': 49a, 49b, 49c, 49d, 49e.
White rubber hoses, Blue box **£250-300**
1946-50 (renumbered in 1950 to 780)
- Plain: 49a, 49b, 49c, 49d, 49e.
Yellow plastic hoses, Yellow box **£100-125**
- 'Pratts': 49, 49b, 49c, 49d, 49e.
White rubber hoses, Yellow box........**£150-200**
- Plain: 49, 49b, 49c, 49d, 49e.
White plastic hoses, Yellow box **£100-140**

*Dinky pre-war Gift Set No 50 Ships of the British Navy
containing No 50a 'Hood', No 50b 'Nelson', No 50b
'Rodney', No 50c 'Effingham', No 50d 'York', No 50e
'Delhi', 3 x 50f 'Broke', No 50g X Class Submarine, 3 x No
50h 'Amazon' and No 50k K Class Submarine.*

50 Ships of the British Navy
1934-42
- 50a 'Hood', 50b 'Nelson', 50b 'Rodney',
50c 'Effingham', 50d 'York',
50e 'Delhi', 3 x 50f 'Broke',
50g 'X'-class Submarine,

3 x 50h 'Amazon',
50k 'K'-class Submarine. Blue box
with Green/Blue label on lid **£250-300**

51 Great Liners Set
1934-40
- 51b 'Europa', 51c 'Rex',
51d 'Empress of Britain',
51e 'Strathaird',
51f 'Queen of Bermuda',
51g 'Britannic'...................................**£250-300**

60 Aeroplanes Set
1934-35
- (1st issue)
60a Imperial Airways,
60b Leopard Moth,
60c Percival Gull,
60d Low-Wing Monoplane,
60e General Monospar,
60f Autogiro, no registration letters.
Dark Blue box with Green, Blue
and White 'Atalanta' airliner on
lid label, Yellow/Green side
label dated '5-34' **£2,000-2,500**

60 British Aeroplanes Set
1936-41
- (2nd issue)
60a Imperial Airways, 60b Leopard Moth,
60c Percival Gull,
60d Low-Wing Monoplane,
60e General Monospar, 60f Autogiro.
All the planes in this set (except
60f) have 'GA-' markings **£1,500-2,000**
Box Type i) Blue box with multicoloured
label plus '150 varieties' slogan.
Box Types ii) and iii) Same as previous
but with '200' or '300 varieties'
slogans (code 'A1040').

60p Gloster Gladiator Set
1938-41
- 6 Silver planes with RAF roundels **£400-600**

60s 'Medium Bomber' Set
1938-41
- Two renumbered 62n Fairey 'Battle'
Bombers with camouflage finish.
In Stone-colour box...........................**£250-350**

60z 'Avions' Set
1937-41
- French Aeroplanes Set with
60az 'Arc-en-Ciel', Potez 58,
Hanriot 180t, 61az DeWetoine 500,
Breguet Corsair, 60f Cierva
Autogiro. Blue box **£900-1,200**

61 R.A.F. Aeroplanes Set
1937-41
- 60h 'Singapore' Flying Boat,
2 x 60n Fairey 'Battle' Bombers,
2 x 60p Gloster 'Gladiator' Biplanes.
Contained in Blue box with full
colour label on lid..........................**£900-1,200**

61z 'Avions' Set
1937-40
- French Aeroplanes Set with DeWoitine
D338, Potez 56, Potez 58,
61az DeWetoine 500d, Farman F360,
60f Cierva Autogiro. Blue box **£900-1,200**

62d Bristol Blenheim Bomber Set
1939
- Six planes, camouflaged, mounted on
card base with 'BRISTOL BLENHEIM
BOMBER MARK IV -
DINKY TOYS 62d'. Green box **£400-600**

62h Hawker Hurricane Set
1939
- Six planes, camouflaged tops, Black
undersides, mounted on card base with
'DINKY TOYS No.62h HAWKER
HURRICANE SINGLE SEATER
FIGHTER'. Green box, date'7-39'.......**£500-750**
- US issue: with
'Meccano Co. of America Inc.' label
on box lid and 'FAO Schwarz'
on box base **£500-750**

62s Hurricane Fighters Set
1939-41
- Six Fighters, Silver fuselages, RAF roundels, undercarriages, Blue box .. **£300-400**

64 Aeroplanes Set
1939-41
- 60g Light Racer, 62h 'Hurricane' (Camouflaged), 62k 'Kings Aeroplane', 62m Light Transport, 62s 'Hurricane' (Silver), 63b Seaplane 'Mercury'.
NB (In 1940 either 62a 'Spitfire' or 62s were substituted for 62h and 62s).................................**£1,000-1,250**

64z 'Avions' Set
193?-4?
- French Aeroplanes Set with 61az Dewoitine 'F-ADBF', 64a Amiot 370, 64b Bloch 220 'F-AOHJ', 64c Potez 63, 64d Potez 662 'F-ARAY'. Blue box, Yellow inner **£2,000-2,500**

65 Aeroplanes Set
1939-41
- 60r Flying Boat, 60t 'DC3', 60v 'Whitely' Bomber, 60w 'Clipper III', 62n Junkers, 62p 'Ensign', 62r 'Albatross', 62w 'Frobisher'. Blue box, illustrated leaflet enclosed..........**£1,750-2,000**

66 Camouflaged Aeroplanes Set
1940-41
- 66a Heavy Bomber, 66b Dive Bomber Fighter, 66c Fighter, 66d Torpedo, 66e Medium Bomber, 66f Army Autogiro (Silver). Yellow-Brown box.......................**£2,000-3,000**

68 Camouflaged Aeroplanes Set
1940-41
- 2 x 60s 'Battle' Bombers, 2 x 62d 'Blenheim', 3 x 62h 'Hurricane' (Camouflage), 3 x 62s 'Hurricane' (Silver), 62t 'Whitely', 68a 'Ensign', 68b 'Frobisher'. Blue or Yellow box, light or dark camouflage. Models have two roundels: Red inside Blue on the wings, and White/Blue/Red on the fuselage sides.........................**£2,500-3,500**
1940-41
- US issue: Camouflaged versions of: 60s, 62d, 62e, 62h, 62t, 68a and 68b. Box picture shows civilian aircraft. Red label states 'Sold by Meccano Company of America Inc., 200 5th Avenue, New York' **£2,500-3,500**

101 Dining-Room Furniture
1936-40
- 101a Table, 101b Sideboard, 2 x 101c Carver Chair, 4 x 101d Chair **£400-500**

102 Bedroom Furniture
1936-40
- 102a Bed, 102b Wardrobe, 102c Dressing Table, 102d Dressing Chest, 102e Dressing Table Stool, 102f Chair. Brown or Pink. Green box.................**£400-500**

103 Kitchen Furniture
1936-40
- 103a Refrigerator, 103b Kitchen Cabinet, 103c Electric Cooker, 103d Table, 103e Chair. Light Blue/White or Light Green/Cream ... **£400-500**

104 Bathroom Furniture
1936-40
- 104a Bath, 104b Bath Mat, 104c Pedestal Basin, 104d Stool, 104e Linen Basket, 104f Toilet. Brown or Pink. Green box.................**£400-500**

118 Towaway Glider Set
1965-69
- 135 Triumph 2000 (White/Blue), Cream/Red trailer, Yellow glider **£150-200**

121 Goodwood Racing Set
1963-66
- 112 Austin-Healey Sprite, 113 MGB, 120 Jaguar, 182 Porsche, 9 Service Station (009) plastic figures plus seated and standing drivers. In Buff/Red display box with stepped insert...**£1,250-1,500**

122 Touring Gift Set
1963-65
- 188 Caravan, 193 Station Wagon, 195 Jaguar, 270 'AA' Patrol, 295 Atlas Kenebrake, 796 Healey Sports Boat on Trailer. In Buff/Red display box with stepped insert...............**£1,500-2,000**

123 Mayfair Gift Set
1963-65
- 142 Jaguar, 150 Rolls-Royce, 186 Mercedes-Benz, 194 Bentley, 198 Rolls-Royce, 199 Austin Mini Countryman, plastic figures (3 male, 1 female). Buff/Red display box with stepped insert...............**£2,000-2,500**

124 Holidays Gift Set
1964-66
- 952 Vega Luxury Coach, 137 Plymouth, 142 Jaguar, 796 Healey Sports Boat. In Buff/Red display box with stepped insert...............**£1,500-2,000**

Dinky 130 Ford Corsair.

125 Fun Ahoy! Set
1964-66
- 130 Ford Corsair with driver, 796 Healey Sports Boat with pilot. Window box **£350-450**

126 Motor Show Set
1967-68
- 127 Rolls-Royce (Gold, Chrome hubs), 133 Cortina (Lemon, spun hubs), 151 Vauxhall Victor (Metallic Red, Cream interior, Chrome hubs, 171 Austin 1800 (Metallic Blue, Red interior, Chrome hubs). In Buff/Red display box with stepped insert **£1,750-2,500**
1968-69
- As above, but 133 Ford Cortina is finished in Lemon Yellow.........**£1,250-1,750**

149 Sports Cars Set ('Competition' finish)
1958-61
- 107 Sunbeam Alpine, 108 MG Midget, 109 Austin-Healey, 110 Aston-Martin, 111 Triumph TR2, Blue/White striped box................**£2,500-3,000**

150 Royal Tank Corps Personnel
1937-41
- 150a Officer, 2 x 150b Private, 2 x 150c Private, 150e N.C.O. Attached by cord to Yellow card in Yellow box or Grey/Blue box with Yellow inner, code 'A2187' **£200-300**
1946-50
- US export only Set: Post-war issue of pre-war figures in original Green box with 'H. Hudson Dobson' label.........**£200-300**
1952-55

- Reissue, US only: Contains 1 x 150a, 2 x 150b, 2 x 150c, 1 x 150e. Green box with one packing piece.... **£200-300**

151 Medium Tank Set
1937-41
- 151a Tank, 151b 6-wheel Wagon, 151c Cooker Trailer, 151d Water Tank Trailer, 150d Royal Tank Corps Driver. Drop-front Blue box with pictorial inner, one packing piece with cut-outs **£300-400**

152 Light Tank Set
1937-41
- 152a Tank, 152b Reconnaissance Car, 152c Austin 7 Car with 150d Royal Tank Corps Driver. Drop-front Blue box with pictorial inner, one packing piece with cut-outs **£300-400**

156 Mechanised Army Set
1939-41
- 151a Tank, 151b 6-wheel Wagon, 151c Cooker Trailer, 151d Water Tank Trailer, 152a Tank, 152b Reconnaissance Car, 152c Austin 7 Car with 150d Royal Tank Corps Driver, 161a Lorry with Searchlight, 161b AA Gun on Trailer, 162a Light Dragon Tractor, 162b Ammunition Trailer, and 162c 18-lb Gun. Drop-front Grey-Blue box (codes: '11-39', 'A2308') with contents shown on lid, four packing pieces. **£4,000-5,000**

160 Royal Artillery Personnel
1939-41 (reissued in 1954 to 606)
- 160a N.C.O., 2 x 160b Gunner, 160c Gunlayer, 2 x 160d Gunner (standing). Grey-Blue box (code: A2308) dated 11-39, Yellow box (code: A2303) dated 12-39. Production of this set continued post-war but only for export to USA **£200-300**
1952-55
- Reissue, US only: 1 x 160a, 3 x 160b, 2 x 160d, 1 x 150e. Green box with inner card stand.......**£200-300**

161 Mobile Anti-Aircraft Unit
1939-41
- 161a Lorry with Searchlight and 161b A.A. Gun on Trailer. Blue or Green box ('A2257' on some), 1 packing piece with cut-outs...........**£500-750**

162 18-pounder Field Gun Unit
1939-54
- 162a Light Dragon Tractor, 162b Trailer, 162c Gun. Blue box, 1 packing piece with cut-outs...........**£150-200**

201 Racing Cars Set
1965-68
- 240 Cooper, 241 Lotus, 242 Ferrari, 243 B.R.M.....................**£800-1,000**

237 Dinky Way Set
1978-79
- 178 Mini Clubman, 211 Triumph TR7, 382 Convoy Truck, 412 Bedford 'AA' Van.
NB Export only version of Set 240..........**£80-100**

240 Dinky Way Set
1978-80
- 211 Triumph TR7, 255 Police Mini, 382 Dump Truck, 412 Bedford, decal sheet, 20ft 'roadway', 20 road signs **£60-80**

245 Superfast Gift Set
1969-73
- 131 Jaguar 'E'-type, 153 Aston-Martin, 188 Jensen FF.....................................**£125-150**

246 International Gift Set
1969-73
- 187 De Tomaso Mangusta, 215 Ford GT, 216 Ferrari Dino.............................**£125-150**

249 World Famous Racing Cars
1962-63
- 230 Talbot-Lago, 231 Maserati, 232 Alfa-Romeo, 233 Cooper-Bristol, 234 Ferrari, 239 Vanwall. Bubble-packed onto large display card....**£4,000-5,000**

249 Racing Cars Set
1955-58 (renumbered in 1954 from 4)
- Cars: 231, 232, 233, 234, 235 ....**£1,000-1,250**

294 Police Vehicles Gift Set
1973-77 (Replaces Set 297)
- 250 Mini-Cooper, 254 Range-Rover,
287 Accident Unit **£200-250**

297 Police Vehicles Gift Set
1963-73 (Replaced by Set 294)
- 250 Mini-Cooper, 255 Ford Zodiac,
287 Accident Unit **£200-250**

298 Emergency Services Set
1963-66
- 258 Ford Fairlane, 263 Ambulance,
276 Fire Tender, 277 Ambulance,
Ambulance-man, Ambulance-woman
and Policeman **£500-750**

Dinky 299 Post Office Gift set.

299 Post Office Services
1957-59
- 260 'Royal Mail' Morris Van,
261 'GPO Telephones' Van,
750 Call Box, 011 Messenger,
012 Postman (but no Pillar Box!).
Blue and White striped box **£400-500**

299 Motorway Services Set
1963-66
- 434 Bedford Crash Truck, 269 Motorway
Police Car, 257 Fire Chief's Car,
276 Airport Fire Tender, 263 (later 277)
Criterion Ambulance **£1,500-1,800**

299 'Crash Squad' Action Set
1978-79
- 244 Plymouth Police Car and
732 Bell Helicopter **£45-55**

300 London Scene Set
1973-77
- 289 Routemaster Bus 'ESSO' and
284 London Taxi **£80-95**

302 Emergency Squad Gift Pack
1979-?
- Paramedic Truck, Fire Chief Car,
figures of Gage and DeSoto. Not issued ....NPP

303 Commando Squad Gift Set
1978-80
- 687 Convoy Army Truck, 667
Armoured Car, 732 Helicopter **£75-100**

304 Fire Rescue Gift Set
1978-79
- 195 Fire Chief Range Rover, 282 Land
Rover, 384 Convoy Fire Truck...............**£70-90**

306 'Space' Gift Pack
1979-?
- 358 'USS Enterprise', 357 Klingon
Battle Cruiser, and Galactic
War Chariot. Not issued ....NPP

307 'New Avengers' Gift Pack
1979-?
- Purdey's TR7, John Steed's Special
Leyland Jaguar, plus a 'fly-off'
assailant! Not issued...................................NPP

309 Star Trek Gift Set
1978-80
- 357 Klingon Battle Cruiser and
358 'USS Enterprise' **£125-150**

310 Tractor and Hayrake
1954-60
- 1st issue: Red 300 Tractor and 310
Hayrake. Blue/White striped box **£250-350**
- 2nd issue: Cherry Red 300 Tractor
with Yellow hubs. Late issue Yellow
box with lift-off lid **£300-400**

325 'DAVID BROWN' Gift Set
19??-??
- White 305 Tractor,
Red 322 Harrow **£150-200**
- Yellow 305 Tractor,
Red 322 Harrow **£175-225**

398 Farm Equipment Gift Set
1964-65 (reissue of Set No.1)
- 300 Massey-Harris Tractor,
320 Harvest Trailer, 321 Manure Spreader,
322 Disc Harrow, 324 Hay Rake.
Grey box with hinged lid.............**£1,250-1,750**

399 Farm Tractor and Trailer
1969-73
- 300 Massey-Harris Tractor and
428 Large Trailer (Red/Silver).
Yellow window box...........................**£225-275**

399 'Convoy' Gift Set
1977-79
- 380 Skip Truck, 381 Farm Truck,
382 Dumper Truck. 'Window' box........**£35-45**

606 Royal Artillery Personnel
1954-55 (reissue of 160)
- 1 x 160a, 2 x 160b, 1 x 160c,
2 x 160d. Export only (to USA)...........**£150-200**

607 25-pounder Field Gun Set
1957-71
- Tractor, Gun, Ammunition Trailer....**£125-150**

616 AEC Articulated Transporter with No 683 Chieftain Tank and camouflage net.

616 AEC Transporter and Tank
1976-82
- Militarised version of 974 with
683 Chieftain Tank + camouflage net
....**£65-80**

618 Transporter and Helicopter
1976-79
- Militarised versions of 974 and
724 with camouflage netting **£70-80**

619 Bren-Gun Carrier Set
1976-78
- 622 Bren-Gun Carrier and
625 6-pounder Anti-Tank Gun...............**£35-45**

677 Task Force Set
1972-75
- 680 Ferret Armoured Car, 681 D.U.K.W.,
682 Stalwart Load Carrier **£35-45**

695 Howitzer and Tractor
1962-66
- 689 Medium Artillery Tractor and
693 7.2in. Howitzer............................**£350-450**

697 Field Gun Set
1957-71
- 688 Field Artillery Tractor, 687 Trailer,
686 25-pounder Field Gun,
cast ridged or plastic hubs..................**£80-100**

698 Tank Transporter Set
1957-65
- 660 Mighty Antar Tank Transporter
and 651 Centurion Tank.
One packing piece in box **£200-250**

699 Military Vehicles (1) Set
1955-58 (renumbered in 1954 from No.1)
- 621 3-ton Wagon, 641 1-ton Truck,
674 Austin Champ, 676 Armoured Car.

Blue/White Striped box with inner
lining and stand **£350-450**

698 Gift Set No 660 Tank Transporter with No 651 Centurion Tank.

754 Pavement Set
1958-62
- Twenty various Grey cardboard
pieces representing paving...................**£30-40**

766 British Road Signs
1959-64
- Country Set 'A'. Six signs of the times,
mostly 55 mm high. Yellow box...........**£80-100**

767 British Road Signs
1959-64
- Country Set 'B'. Six signs of the times,
mostly 55 mm high. Yellow box...........**£80-100**

768 British Road Signs
1959-64
- Town Set 'A'. Six signs of the times,
mostly 55 mm high. Yellow box...........**£80-100**

769 British Road Signs
1959-64
- Town Set 'B'. Six signs of the times,
mostly 55 mm high. Yellow box...........**£80-100**

770 Road Signs Set
1950-54 (renumbered in 1954 from 47)
- 12 road signs, 47e to 47t, (Black under
base, open triangles) US export **£125-175**

771 International Road Signs
1953-65
- Set of 12 road signs with Silver posts
and bases. Yellow box with leaflet.....**£100-125**

772 British Road Signs
1959-63
- (Sets 766, 767, 768 and 769). 24
road signs in a Red/Yellow box **£150-200**

780 Petrol Pumps Set
1950-54 (renumbered in 1950 from 49)
- 49a, 49b, 49c, 49d, 49e (plain).
Yellow plastic hoses, export only **£90-110**
- Version issued in picture box **£100-150**

784 Dinky Goods Train Set
1972-74
- Blue loco 'GER', one Red Truck,
one Yellow Truck **£40-60**

798 Express Passenger Train Set
1954-59 (renumbered in 1954 from 16)
- Green/Black loco, 'BR' crest, Cream
coaches (Grey roofs), Black tyres **£100-125**
- Green/Black loco, 'BR' crest, Cream
coaches/roofs/hubs, Black tyres **£100-125**
- Green/Black loco, 'BR',
Cream coaches/roofs, Red hubs,
White tyres **£100-125**

851 Sets of vehicle 'Loads'
1961-
- 2 each of 846 Oil Drums, 847 Barrels,
849 Packing Cases and 850 Crates **£30-40**

900 'Site Building' Gift Set
1964-70
- 437 Muir-Hill Loader, 960 Albion
Mixer, 961 Blaw-Knox Bulldozer,
962 Muir-Hill Dumper,
965 Euclid Rear Dump Truck.
Grey/Red/Yellow box **£900-1,200**

950 Car Transporter Set
1969-70
- 974 AEC Car Transporter, 136 Vauxhall
Viva, 138 Hillman Imp, 162 Triumph
1300, 168 Ford Escort, 342 Austin
Mini-Moke. Not issued................................NPP

957 Fire Service Gift Set containing – No 257 Fire Chief's Car, No 955 Fire Engine and No 956 Turntable Fire Escape.

Dinky No 990 Pullmore Car Transporter with four cars and loading ramp.

957 Fire Services Gift Set
1959-65
- 257 Fire Chief's Car, 955 Fire Engine, 956 Turntable Fire Escape.... **£350-400**

990 Car Transporter Set
1956-58
- Contains 982 Pullmore Car Transporter, one packing piece, and these cars:

154 Hillman Minx (Light Green/Cream),
156 Rover 75 (Cream/Blue),
161 Austin Somerset (Red/Yellow),
162 Zephyr (Green/White)
....**£2,000-2,500**

1001 Station Staff ('00' gauge)
1952-54 (renumbered in 1954 to 051)
- Six Blue figures, Green card box........... **£45-55**

1003 Passengers ('00' gauge)
1952-54 (renumbered in 1954 to 053)
- Six coloured figures, Green card box
.... **£45-55**

49N2269 'Road Racers' Set
1965
- 113 MGB, 114 Triumph Spitfire, 120 Jaguar E-type, 237 Mercedes-Benz, 238 Jaguar D-type, 242 Ferrari Racing Car, 243 BRM Racing Car. Special set for US mail-order company Sears-Roebuck .... NGPP

Dinky Toys Accessories (Pre-War)

See also: Public Transport Models, Ships, Motor Cycles and Gift Sets sections. Approximate size of figures: large 40mm (scale 1:42); small 35mm (scale 1:48). Pre-war box title sequence: 'Modelled Miniatures'; 'Meccano Dinky Toys'; 'Dinky Toys'.

Model and details	MPR

No 1 Station Staff Set containing six figures including Station Master, Guard with flag, Ticket Collector, Driver with oil can and two Porters, one walking and the other carrying cases.

1 1939-41 **Station Staff** (large) see Gift Sets.
1 1939-41 **Station Staff** (small) see Gift Sets.
1a 1932-41 **Station Master** (large)
- Dark Blue uniform with Gold or Silver buttons on long coat **£30-35**
1a 1932-41 **Station Master** (small)
- As previous model but smaller **£20-25**
1b 1932-39 **Guard** (large)
- Dark Blue coat (Gold or Silver buttons), blowing whistle, flag in left hand **£30-35**
1b 1932-39 **Guard** (small)
- As previous version but smaller **£20-25**
1b 1939-41 **Guard** (large)
- Dark Blue coat (Gold or Silver buttons), blowing whistle, flag in right hand....... **£30-35**
1b 1939-41 **Guard** (small)
- As previous version but smaller **£20-25**
1c 1932-41 **Ticket Collector** (large)
- Dark Blue uniform (Gold or Silver buttons), slightly open arms **£30-35**
1c 1932-41 **Ticket Collector** (large)
- As before but only right arm extended **£30-35**
1c 1932-41 **Ticket Collector** (small)
- As previous version but smaller **£20-25**
1d 1932-39 **Driver** (large)
- Mid-Blue uniform (Gold or Silver buttons), holding oil-can............ **£30-35**
1d 1939-41 **Driver** (small)
- As previous version but smaller **£20-25**
1e 1932-39 **Porter with Bags** (large)
- Dark Blue uniform, oblong case in right hand, round hat-box in left.................. **£30-35**

1e 1939-41 **Porter with Bags** (small)
- Dark Blue, small oblong case in each hand.. **£20-25**
1f 1932-39 **Porter** (large)
- Dark Blue, walking, no luggage **£30-35**
1f 1939-41 **Porter** (small)
- Dark Blue, standing, no luggage........... **£20-25**
2a 1932-41 **Horses**
- One Light Brown or Dark Brown horse, one White horse **£20-30**
2b 1932-41 **Cow**
- 3 versions were available; Light Brown, Dark Brown, or Black and White.......... **£20-25**
2c 1932-41 **Pig.** A Pink porker.................. **£15-20**
2d 1932-41 **Sheep**
- White sheep, Black detailing................. **£15-20**
3a 1932-39 **Woman and Child** (large)
- Woman in Green coat, child (in Red) is on woman's right **£30-35**
3a 1939-41 **Woman and Child** (small),
- Woman in Green suit with Grey scarf and Red hat, child on woman's left...... **£20-25**
3b 1932-39 **Business Man** (large)
- Dark Blue suit/hat, walking stick in right hand, left hand holds lapels......... **£30-35**
3b 1939-41 **Business Man** (small)
- Grey suit, left hand holds attaché case **£20-25**
3c 1932-39 **Male Hiker** (large)
- Brown clothing, Grey, Brown or Khaki rucksack, walking stick in right hand... **£30-35**
3c 1939-41 **Male Hiker** (small)
- Brown clothing, Khaki rucksack, no walking stick **£20-25**
3d 1932-39 **Female Hiker** (large)
- Blue skirt, White blouse, walking stick in right hand................... **£30-35**
3d 1939-41 **Female Hiker** (small)
- All Blue clothing, or Dark Blue skirt, White blouse **£20-25**
3e 1932-39 **Newsboy** (large)
- Brown or Blue clothing, running, papers in right hand and under left arm.......... **£30-35**
3e 1939-41 **Newsboy** (small)
- Dark Blue clothing, standing, papers in Cream tray **£20-25**
3f 1932-39 **Woman**

- Red jacket, White skirt, coat over left arm, oblong case in right hand **£25-30**
3f 1939-41 **Woman**
- Dark Red coat, Black collar, round case in right hand **£25-30**
4 1932-39 **Engineering Staff**
See Gift Sets section.
4a 1932-39 **Electrician** (large)
- Blue overalls, White sleeves, carrying equipment............................... **£30-35**
4a 1939-41 **Electrician** (small)
- Blue overalls, White sleeves, carrying equipment............................... **£20-25**
4b 1932-39 **Fitter** (large)
- All-Blue overalls, or Brown overalls with White sleeves, carrying equipment...... **£30-35**
4b 1939-41 **Fitter** (small)
- As previous model but smaller **£20-25**
4c 1932-39 **Storekeeper** (large)
- Brown coat, Black trousers, holding forms in right hand, casting as 1a **£30-35**
4c 1939-41 **Storekeeper** (small)
- Brown coat, Black trousers, holding forms in right hand, casting as 1a **£20-25**
4d 1932-39 **Greaser** (large)
- Brown overalls, holding oil-can in right hand, casting based on 1d **£30-35**
4d 1939-41 **Greaser** (small)
- Brown overalls, holding oil-can in right hand, casting based on 1d **£20-25**
4e 1932-39 **Engine-Room Attendant** (large)
- Blue overalls, White sleeves on some .. **£30-35**
4e 1939-41 **Engine-Room Attendant** (small)
- Blue overalls, White sleeves on some .. **£20-25**
5 1932-39 **Train and Hotel Staff.**
See the Gift Sets section.
5a 1932-39 **Pullman Car Conductor** (large)
- White jacket, Blue trousers, slightly open arms, casting as 1c **£30-35**
5a 1939-41 **Pullman Car Conductor** (small),
- White jacket, Blue trousers, slightly open arms, casting as 1c **£20-25**
5b 1932-39 **Pullman Car Waiter** (large)
- White jacket, Blue trousers, two slightly different poses were available **£30-35**
5b 1939-41 **Pullman Car Waiter** (small)
- White jacket, Blue trousers, two slightly

different poses were available **£20-25**

5c 1932-39 **Hotel Porter** (large)
- Red jacket/Brown trousers, or Green jacket/Blue trousers, casting as 1e **£30-35**

5c 1939-41 **Hotel Porter** (small)
- Red jacket/Brown trousers, or Green jacket/Blue trousers, casting as 1e **£20-25**

6 1933-40 **Shepherd Set**
See the Gift Sets section.

6a 1932-41 **Shepherd**
- Brown with Dark Brown hat **£50-75**

6b 1932-41 **Sheep-dog**
- Black and White sheep-dog **£20-30**

12 1937-41 **Postal Set** See Gift Sets section.

12a 1935-40 **GPO Pillar Box 'GR'**
- Red, with or without Red/Yellow 'Post Office' sign on top, White panel .. **£25-30**

12b 1935-40 **Air Mail Pillar Box**
- Blue body, 'Air Mail', White panel, casting as 12a **£35-40**

12c 1936-40 **Telephone Box**
- Cream with Silver windows **£20-30**

12d 1938-40 **Telegraph Messenger**
- Dark Blue body, picked out detail in darker Blue, Brown pouch, 35 mm **£20-25**

12e 1938-40 **Postman**
- Dark Blue body, darker Blue detail, Brown post bag and badge, 35 mm **£20-25**

13 1931-40 **'HALLS DISTEMPER'**.
- Cream card with Red lettering, 2 painter figures (lead, usually White/Red/Grey), Silver/Green buckets/brushes. 'Hornby Series'. Boxed ('A898') **£300-400**

15 • 1937-41 **Railway Signals Set**.
See the Gift Sets section.

15a 1937-41 **Single Arm Signal**
- One Red 'Home' signal, or Yellow 'Distant' signal **£30-40**

15b 1937-41 **Double Arm Signal**
- One Red 'Home' signal and one Yellow 'Distant' signal on single pole .. **£40-50**

15c 1937-41 **Junction Signal**
- Two Red 'Home' signals, OR two Yellow 'Distant' signals on a single pole **£65-75**

30g 1936-39 **Caravan Trailer**
- 2 wheels, drawbar, body length 81 mm., open roof windows, Blue/Cream, Red/Cream, Green/Cream, Orange/Cream, TT-Green **£90-120**
- Chocolate and Beige, Blue hubs **£150-175**
  1939-40
- Same, but filled-in roof windows **£80-110**

42 1935-41 **Police Set** ..See the Gift Sets section.

42a 1936-40 **Police Box**
- Dark Blue box, 'POLICE' in Silver **£25-35**

42c 1936-40 **Point Duty Policeman**, (42 mm)
- Lead. White coat, Black helmet **£25-35**

42d 1936-40 **Point Duty Policeman** (40mm)
- Dark Blue, White gauntlets, lead **£25-35**

43 1935-41 **'RAC' Set** ...See the Gift Sets section.

43a 1935-40 **'RAC' Box**
- Blue and White (tinplate) call-box with 'RAC' emblem **£90-110**

43c 1935-40 **'RAC' Guide**. (37mm)
- Blue uniform, Red sash, directing traffic, (cast in lead) **£25-35**

43d 1935-40 **'RAC' Guide** (saluting) (36mm)
- Blue uniform, Red sash, cast in lead **£25-35**

44 1935-41 **'AA' Set** See the Gift Sets section.

44a 1935-40 **'AA' Box**
- Black/Yellow tinplate box with 'AA' badge and 3 signs **£90-110**

44c 1935-40 **'AA' Guide** (37mm)
- Tan uniform, Blue sash, directing traffic, cast in lead **£20-25**

44d 1935-40 **'AA' Guide** (saluting) (36mm)
- Tan uniform, Blue sash, cast in lead **£20-25**

45 1935-40 **Garage**
- Cream/Orange (tinplate), Green opening doors, boxed, 127 x 90 mm **£500-600**

46 1937-40 **Pavement Set**
- Dark Grey 'stone' effect (cardboard) pavement pieces in a box **£45-55**

47 1935-41 **Road Signs Set** See Gift Sets.

47a 1935-41 **4-face Traffic Lights**
- Black on White post, Yellow beacon, White base, 62 mm high **£15-20**

47b 1935-41 **3-face Traffic Lights**.
- Black on White post, Yellow beacon, White base, 62 mm high **£15-20**

47c 1935-41 **2-face Traffic Lights**
- Back-to-back lights, Black on White post, Yellow beacon, White base **£15-20**
  1935-41
- Lights at 90 degrees, Black on White post, Yellow beacon, White base **£15-20**

47d 1935-41 **Belisha Beacon**
- Black on White post, Orange globe, White base, 51 mm high **£15-20**

47e 1935-41 **'30 MPH' Limit Sign**
- Black on White post, Red top, 52 mm .. **£15-20**

47f 1935-41 **De-restriction Sign**
- Black on White post, diagonal Black bar on White circle, 52 mm high **£15-20**

47g 1935-41 **'School' Sign**
- Black on White post, Red top, Black 'beacon' design, 51 mm high **£15-20**

47h 1935-41 **'Steep Hill' Sign**
- Black on White post, Red top, Black 'incline' design, 51 mm high **£15-20**

47k 1935-41 **'S-Bend' Sign**
- Black on White post, Red top, Black 'S-Bend' design, 51 mm high **£15-20**

47m 1935-41 **'Left-Hand Bend' Sign**
- Black on White post, Red top, Black 'curve' design, 51 mm high **£15-20**

47n 1935-41 **'Right-Hand Bend' Sign**
- Black on White post, Red top, Black 'curve' design, 51 mm high **£15-20**

47p 1935-41 **'T-Junction' Sign**
- Black on White post, Red top, Black 'T' design, 51 mm high **£15-20**

47q 1935-41 **'No Entry' Sign**
- Black on White post, Red 'bar' design, 48 mm high **£15-20**

47r 1935-41 **'Major Road Ahead' Sign**
- Black on White post, Red top, Black lettering, 54 mm high **£15-20**

47s 1935-41 **'Crossing No Gates' Sign**
- Black on White post, Red top, Black 'loco' design, 51 mm high **£15-20**

47t 1935-41 **'Roundabout' Sign**
- Black on White post, Red top, Black 'arrows' design, 51 mm high **£15-20**
NB Pre-war issues have filled in triangles.

Dinky No 48 Pre-War Petrol Station, 36f, 36e and 24h also shown.

48 1935-41 **Filling and Service Station**. Tinplate construction with 'FILLING AND SERVICE STATION' logo. Orange box.
- Green roof and base **£500-600**
- Turquoise roof and base **£500-600**
- Yellow roof, Green base **£500-600**

49 1935-41 **Petrol Pumps Set**. See Gift Sets.

49a 1935-40 **Bowser Petrol Pump**
- Green pump, White rubber hose, 46 mm tall **£35-45**

49b 1935-40 **Wayne Petrol Pump**
- Turquoise pump, White rubber hose, 39 mm tall **£35-45**

49c 1935-40 **Theo Petrol Pump**
- Blue, White rubber hose, 58 mm **£35-45**

49d 1935-40 **'SHELL' Petrol Pump**
- Red, White rubber hose, 53 mm **£35-45**

49e 1935-40 **'Pratts' Oil Bin**
- Yellow bin body and opening tinplate lid, 'Pratts Motor Oil', 32 mm **£40-50**
- Post-war, 49e was only available in Set 49 (without 'Pratts' logo)..................... GSP

101 1935-40 **Dining Room Set** See Gift Sets.

101a 1935-40 **Dining Table**
- 'Wood' effect dining table, 64 mm **£30-35**

101b 1935-40 **Sideboard**
- 'Wood' effect sideboard with opening doors, tinplate back, 63 mm **£30-35**

101c 1935-40 **Carver Chair**
- 'Wood' effect chair with armrests, 33 mm high **£15-20**

101d 1935-40 **Dining Chair**
- 'Wood' effect chair without armrests, raised 'leather' cushion **£10-15**

102 1935-40 **Bedroom Set** See Gift Sets section.

102a 1935-40 **Bed**
- Brown or Pink double bed **£30-35**

102b 1935-40 **Wardrobe**
- Brown or Pink wardrobe with opening door, tinplate back, 63 mm **£30-35**

102c 1935-40 **Dressing Table**
- Brown or Pink, opening drawers, tinplate mirror, 51 mm **£30-35**

102d 1935-40 **Dressing Chest**
- Brown or Pink, opening drawer, tinplate back, 40 mm high **£30-35**

102e 1935-40 **Dressing Table Stool**
- Brown or Pink stool, 13 mm high **£15-20**

102f 1935-40 **Chair**
- Brown or Pink **£10-15**

103 1935-40 **Kitchen Set** See Gift Sets section.

103a 1935-40 **Refrigerator**
- Light Blue/White or Light Green/Cream, door, tinplate back and food tray **£35-45**

103b 1935-40 **Kitchen Cabinet**
- Light Blue/White or Light Green/Cream, opening doors/drawer, tin back **£35-45**

103c 1935-40 **Electric Cooker**
- Light Blue/White or Light Green/Cream, opening door, tinplate back **£35-45**

103d 1935-40 **Kitchen Table**
- Light Blue/White or Light Green/Cream, 34 mm high **£30-35**

103e 1935-40 **Kitchen Chair**
- Light Blue/White or Light Green/Cream, casting as 102f **£10-15**

104 1935-40 **Bathroom Set** See Gift Sets.

104a 1935-40 **Bath**
- Pink/White or Light Green/White, Gold taps, 69 mm.................................. **£35-45**

104b 1935-40 **Bath Mat**
- Mottled Green rubber, 50 x 37 mm **£10-15**

104c 1935-40 **Pedestal Hand Basin**
- Pink/White or Light Green/White, Gold taps, tinplate mirror, 63 mm **£30-35**

104d 1935-40 **Bathroom Stool**
- Pink/White or Light Green/White, 15 mm high **£15-20**

104e 1935-40 **Linen Basket**
- Pink/White or Light Green/White, hinged lid, 22 mm high **£15-20**

104f 1935-40 **Toilet**
- Pink/White or Light Green/White, hinged lid, 34 mm high **£35-45**

--- 1935-40 **'Dolly Varden' Dolls House**
- Not given a reference number, made of 'leather board' (heavy reinforced cardboard), and supplied packed flat. Cream/Brown upper storey, Red brick ground floor, Red roof, 476 x 260 mm base, 476 mm high **£500-750**

NB It is not really possible to give individual prices for single 'Dolly Varden' items as they are very rarely available in collectable condition. Boxed sets sell for £200-300, for example. See also the Gift Sets section.

Dinky Toys Accessories (Post-War)

See also: Public Transport Models, Ships, Motor Cycles and Gift Sets sections.

Model and details	MPR

No 1 Station Staff post-war issue with Guard, Ticket Collector, Locomotive Driver, Porter with cases and another Porter

001 1954-56 **Station Staff ('O' gauge)**
(renumbered in 1954 from 1)
- 1b Guard (flag in right hand),
1c Ticket Collector (right arm extended),
1d Driver, 1e Porter (with oblong bags),
1f Porter (standing) **£90-120**

001 1979-80 **'Space War Station'**
- Dinky Builda card ('54001') **£15-20**

002 1954-56 **Farmyard Animals (6)**
(renumbered in 1954 from 2)
- 2 x 2a horses, 2 x 2b cows, 1 x 2c pig,
1 x 2d sheep, simplified painting
.... **£200-300**

002 1979-80 **'Blazing Inferno'**
- Dinky Builda card ('54002') **£15-20**

003 1954-56 **Passengers ('O' gauge)**
(renumbered in 1954 from 3)
- 3a Woman (with child on left),
3b Businessman (Brown suit and case),
3c Male hiker (no stick),
3d Female hiker (Blue blouse),
3e Newsboy (Grey tray), 3f Woman
(Light Red coat, round case)............... **£90-120**

004 1954-56 **Engineering Staff ('O' gauge)**
(renumbered in 1954 from 4)
- 2 x 4b Fitter (all-Blue and all-Brown),
4c Storekeeper (all-Brown), 4d Greaser,
4e Engine-Room Attendant **£90-120**

No 5 Train and Hotel Staff containing Conductor, two Waiters and two Porters carrying bags.

005 1954-56 **Train and Hotel Staff ('O' gauge)**
(renumbered in 1954 from 5)
- 5a Conductor, 2 x 5b waiters,
2 x 5c Porter (Brown or Blue) **£90-120**

006 1954-56 **Shepherd Set**
(renumbered in 1954 from 6)
- 6a Shepherd (Green hat), 6b sheepdog
(all-Black), 4 x 2b sheep **£250-350**

007 1960-67 **Petrol Pump Attendants**
- 1 male (White overalls),
1 female (White coat), plastic **£15-20**

Model and details	MPR

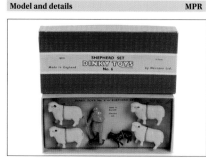

No 6 Shepherd set - comprising shepherd, sheep dog and four sheep.

008 1961-67 **Fire Station Personnel**
- Set of 6 plastic fire-fighters in Blue
uniforms plus hose, supplied in a bag.
(Also present in GS 298)...................... **£65-75**

009 1962-66 **Service Station Personnel**
- Set of 8 plastic figures in various
colours and stances. Supplied in a
bag or a Yellow box.............................. **£65-75**

010 1962-66 **Road Maintenance Personnel**
- Set of 6 workmen (35 mm tall) using
pick, barrow, shovels, drill etc, plus hut,
brazier, barrier, and 4 lamps. Plastic.
Supplied in a bag or a Yellow box **£65-75**

011 1954-56 **Telegraph Messenger**
(renumbered in 1954 from 12d)
- Mid-Blue uniform, detailing in darker
Blue, Brown pouch, 35 mm **£10-15**

012 1954-56 **Postman**
(renumbered in 1954 from 12e)
- Mid-Blue body, darker Blue detail,
Brown post bag and badge, 35 mm **£15-20**

013 1954-56 **Cook's Man**
(Agent for the Thomas Cook travel
company). (renumbered in 1954 from 13a)
- Dark Blue coat, 40 mm tall **£20-30**

050 1961-68 **Railway Staff ('OO' gauge)**
- 12 Blue plastic figures in a clear plastic
box. Early issues contained a
Policeman, later ones a Shunter **£40-50**

051 1954-59 **Station Staff ('OO' gauge)**
(renumbered in 1954 from 1001)
- 6 plastic figures in a clear plastic box ... **£35-45**

052 1961-69 **Railway Passengers ('OO' gauge)**
- 11 plastic figures plus a seat, in a
clear plastic box **£35-45**

053 1954-59 **Passengers ('OO' gauge)**
(renumbered in 1954 from 1003)
- 6 Blue plastic figures **£35-45**
US issue: 6 metal figures in 'Dark Red'
box marked 'Made in England, For sale
in the United States by H.Hudson Dobson,
P.O. Box 254 - 26th Street and Jefferson
Avenue, Kenilworth, New Jersey' .... NGPP

054 1962-70 **Railway Station Personnel**
- 4 plastic figures plus 8 pieces of furniture
in a clear plastic box, ('OO' gauge)....... **£35-45**

1 1946-54 **Station Staff** See Gift Sets section.

1a 1946-54 **Station Master**
- Dark Blue uniform (cap, long coat),
(in Set 001 till 1956).......................... **£20-25**

1b 1946-54 **Guard**
- Dark Blue uniform, blowing whistle,
flag in right hand (see Set 001) **£15-20**

1c 1946-54 **Ticket Collector**
- Blue uniform, only right arm is
extended (in Set 001 till 1956) **£15-20**

1e 1946-54 **Porter with Bags**

Model and details	MPR

- Blue uniform, oblong case in each
hand. (In Set 001 till 1956)..................... **£15-20**

1f 1946-54 **Porter**
- Dark Blue uniform, standing,
no luggage (in Set 001 till 1956) **£15-20**

2 1946-54 **Farmyard Animals** See Gift Sets.

2a 1946-54 **Horses**
- 3 versions: Dark Brown horse (Black
tail / mane), Light Brown horse (Light
Brown tail / mane), White horse (2 in
Set 002 till 1956)................................. **£20-25**

2b 1946-54 **Cows**
- Light Brown, Dark Brown, or
Black/White (2 in Set 002 till 1956)....... **£20-25**

2c 1946-54 **Pig**
- Cream body (in Set 002 till 1956) **£15-20**

2d 1946-54 **Sheep**
- White body with Black hand-painted
detail (in Set 002 till 1956) **£15-20**

3 1946-54 **Passengers** See Gift Sets section.

3a 1946-54 **Woman and Child**
- Woman in Green suit and hat (Brown
scarf), child on left (see Set 003)........... **£20-25**

3b 1946-54 **Business Man**
- Brown suit, left hand holds attaché
case (in Set 003 till 1956)....................... **£20-25**

3c 1946-54 **Male Hiker**
- Brown clothing, Brown or Khaki rucksack,
no stick (in Set 003 till 1956)................. **£20-25**

3d 1946-54 **Female Hiker**
- Blue or Dark Blue skirt and shirt,
stick in right hand (see Set 003) **£20-25**

3e 1946-54 **Newsboy**
- Dark Blue clothing, standing, papers
in Grey tray (in Set 003 till 1956) **£20-25**

3f 1946-54 **Woman**
- Light Red coat, round case in
right hand (in Set 003 till 1956) **£20-25**

4 1946-54 **Engineering Staff** See Gift Sets.

4a 1946-54 **Electrician**
- Blue overalls, White sleeves, carrying
equipment (in Set 004 till 1956) **£15-20**

4b 1946-56 **Fitters**
- 2 versions; one in Blue, the other
Brown, carrying equipment (Set 004)... **£15-20**

4c 1946-56 **Storekeeper**
- Brown coat, Black trousers,
holding forms in right hand **£15-20**

4d 1946-56 **Greaser**
- Brown overalls, oil-can in right hand ... **£15-20**

4e 1946-56 **Engine-Room Attendant**
- Blue overalls, Blue sleeves **£10-15**

5 1946-54 **Train and Hotel Staff** (Gift Sets).

5a 1946-56 **Pullman Car Conductor**
- White jacket, Blue trousers,
slightly open arms, casting as 1c **£20-25**

5b 1946-56 **Pullman Car Waiter**
- White jacket, Blue trousers, two
slightly different poses are known **£20-25**

5c 1946-56 **Hotel Porter**
- Red jacket/Brown trousers, or Green
jacket/Blue trousers, casting as 1e **£20-25**

6 1946-56 **Shepherd Set** See Gift Sets section

6a 1946-56 **Shepherd**
- Brown with Green hat **£40-50**

6b 1946-56 **Sheep-dog**
- All-Black sheep-dog **£20-30**

12c 1946-54 **Telephone Box**
(renumbered in 1954 to 750)
- Red call-box with Black window
frames, 58 mm high............................. **£20-30**

12d 1946-54 **Telegraph Messenger**
(renumbered in 1954 to 011)
- Dark Blue body, picked out detail in darker

Blue, Brown pouch, 35 mm tall **£15-20**

12e 1946-54 **Postman**
(renumbered in 1954 to 012)
- Mid-Blue body, darker Blue detail,
Brown post bag/badge, 35mm tall **£15-20**

13a 1952-54 **Cook's Man**
(Agent for Thomas Cook travel company)
(renumbered in in 1954 to 013)
- Blue coat, 40 mm tall **£20-30**

30g 1948-50 **Caravan**
- Orange/Cream, 'Caravan Club',
steel drawbar **£45-55**

42a 1954-60 **Police Hut**
(renumbered in 1954 to 751)
- Dark Blue hut, 'POLICE', 66 mm **£20-30**

47 1946-50 **Road Signs Set** See Gift Sets.

*No 49 Petrol Pumps and Oil Bin set: post-war version
containing No 29a Petrol Pump in green, No 49b Wayne
Petrol Pump in pale blue, No 39c Theo Petrol Pump in
brown and No 49d Shell Petrol Pump in red, together with
49e Pratt's Oil Bin.*

49 1946-50 **Petrol Pumps Set** See Gift Sets.

49a 1946-53 **Bowser Petrol Pump**
- Green, White rubber hose, 46 mm........ **£35-45**

49b 1946-53 **Wayne Petrol Pump**
- Pale Blue,Yellow plastic hose, 39mm **£25-35**

49c 1946-53 **Theo Petrol Pump**
- Brown, Yellow plastic hose, 58 mm **£25-35**

49d 1946-53 **'SHELL' Petrol Pump**
- Red, Yellow plastic hose, 53 mm **£25-35**

49e 194?-? **Oil Bin**
- As pre-war 'Pratts' Oil Bin but only
available post-war in Set 49 and
without 'Pratts' logo **£25-35**

117 1963-69 **Four Berth Caravan**
- Blue/Cream, clear roof,
Fawn plastic interior and door **£35-45**
- Primrose Yellow/Cream, Red plastic
interior, Yellow plastic door **£35-45**
- Primrose Yellow/Cream, Red plastic
interior, Grey plastic door **£35-45**

188 1961-63 **Four Berth Caravan**
- Green/Cream or Blue/Cream,
windows, detailed interior **£35-45**
- 1963-63 As previous model but larger
windows, (model replaced by 117) **£35-45**

190 1956-62 **Streamline Caravan**
- Mid-Blue lower body, Deep Cream
upper body, Cream hubs, drawbar,
metal jockey wheel **£35-45**
- Yellow lower body, Cream upper body,
Cream hubs, metal jockey wheel **£35-45**
- 1962-64 As previous models but with
knobbly Grey or Black plastic jockey
wheel. Two packing rings also in box ... **£35-45**

386 1954-?? **Lawn Mower**
(renumered in 1954 from 751)
- Green and Red, 140mm. **£50-75**

502 1961-63 **Garage**
- Blue/Grey plastic garage, opening
door, 272 mm. (French issue) **£70-80**

750 1954-62 **Telephone Box**
(renumbered in 1954 from 12c)
- Red call-box with Red window
frames, 58 mm high **£25-35**

751 1949-54 **Lawn Mower**
(renumbered in 1954 to 386)
- Green and Red, 140mm. **£50-75**

751 1954-60 **Police Box**
(renumbered in 1954 from 42a)
- Dark Blue hut, 'POLICE', 66 mm. **£25-35**

752 1953-54 **Goods Yard Crane**
(renumbered in 1954 to 973)
- Yellow with Blue or Dark Blue,
mazak or cast-iron base **£40-50**

*Dinky 753 Police Controlled Crossing. The policeman
can be rotated by the knurled ring shown.*

753 1962-67 **Police Crossing**
- Black/White box on traffic island
with policeman directing traffic **£80-100**

754 1958-62 **Pavement Set**
- 20 Grey cardboard paving slabs, box **£50-60**

755 1960-64 **Lamp Standard (Single)**
- Grey/Fawn/Orange, plastic single-arm
lamp on metal base **£20-30**

757 1960-?? **Chocks**
- Pack of 10 for 974 Car Transporter........ **£15-20**

756 1960-64 **Lamp Standard (Double)**
- Grey/Fawn/Orange, plastic double-arm
lamp on metal base **£30-40**

760 1954-60 **Pillar Box**
- Red/Black pillar box, 'E II R' cast-in **£25-35**

763 1959-64 **Posters for Hoarding**
- Six different coloured poster
advertisements (on paper) **£25-35**

764 1959-64 **Posters for Hoarding**
- Six different coloured poster
advertisements (on paper) **£25-35**

765 1959-64 **Road Hoardings (6 Posters)**
- Green plastic hoarding,
'David Allen and Sons Ltd' **£50-60**

766-772 Road Sign Sets See Gift Sets section.

773 1958-63 **4 face Traffic Lights**

- Black/White, Black base, similar to
47a but without beacon, 62 mm........... **£15-20**

777 1958-63 **Belisha Beacon**
- Black/White post on Black base,
Orange globe, casting as 47d, 51 mm ... **£10-15**

778 1962-66 **Road Repair Boards**
- Green and Red plastic
warning signs, 6 different...................... **£30-40**

780 1950-54 **Petrol Pumps Set** See Gift Sets.

781 1955-62 **'ESSO' Petrol Station**
- 'ESSO' sign, no kiosk, 2 pumps
('ESSO' and 'ESSO EXTRA').............. **£100-150**

782 1960-70 **'SHELL' Petrol Station**
- 'SHELL' sign, Green/Cream kiosk,
4 Red/Yellow 'SHELL' pumps **£100-150**

783 1960-70 **'BP' Petrol Station**
- 'BP' sign, Green/Cream kiosk,
4 Green/White 'BP' pumps................ **£100-150**

785 1960-64 **'SERVICE STATION'**
- Fawn and Red plastic, with 'BP' sign,
335 x 185 mm. (unbuilt kit, boxed) ... **£200-250**

786 1960-66 **Tyre Rack with Tyres**
- Green tyre rack with 21 assorted tyres
and 'DUNLOP' on board **£35-45**

787 1960-64 **Lighting Kit**
- Bulb and wire kit for model buildings .. **£20-25**

788 1960-68 **Spare Bucket for 966**
- For Marrel Multi-Bucket Unit............... **£10-15**

790 1960-64 **Granite Chippings**
- Plastic gravel in plastic bag ('50790').... **£15-20**

791 1960-64 **Imitation Coal**
- Packed in a plastic bag........................ **£15-20**

792 1960-64 **Packing Cases (3)**
- White/Cream plastic packing cases,
'Hornby Dublo', 38 x 28 x 19 mm **£15-20**

793 1960-64 **Pallets**
- Orange, Black, Pale Green, Yellow, Lemon,
Red, Pink or mottled Purple. For 930
Pallet-Jekta and 404 Conveyancer......... **£15-20**

794 1954-64 **Loading Ramp**
(renumbered in 1954 from 994)
- Blue loading ramp for use with
582/982 Pullmore Car Transporter **£15-20**

846 1961- **Oil Drums**
- Pack of 6 oil drums. French issue **£15-20**

847 1961- **Barrels**
- Pack of 6 barrels. French issue **£15-20**

849 1961- **Packing Cases**
- Pack of 6 packing cases. French issue... **£15-20**

850 1961- **Crates of Bottles**
- Pack of 6 crates. French issue **£15-20**

851 1961- **Sets of vehicle 'Loads'**
- Two each of 846 Oil Drums, 847 Barrels,
849 Packing Cases and 850 Crates **£50-60**

954 Fire Station Kit (Plastic**)**
- Red doors, Cream roof, Grey floor,
clear roof, 'FIRE STATION'.
'DINKY TOYS' in Red **£200-250**

994 1954-55 **Loading Ramp**
- Renumbered from 794 to 994 then
back to 794 after only a year! **£15-20**

973 1954-59 **Goods Yard Crane**
(renumbered in 1954 from 752)
- Yellow with Blue or Dark Blue mazak or
cast-iron base, steps in early issues **£40-50**

10011952-54 **Station Staff** See Gift Sets section.

10031952-54 **Station Staff** See Gift Sets section.

Spare Tyres, Tank Tracks, Batteries and Bulbs

020	1968-75	**Spare tyre** .....Black tyre, 16 mm. dia. YB (12) **£15-20**
021	1970-75	**Spare tyre** .....Black tyre, 20 mm. dia. YB (12) **£15-20**
022	1971-76	**Spare tyre** .....Black tyre, 16 mm. dia. YB (12) **£15-20**
023	1971-76	**Spare tyre** .....Black tyre, 16 mm. dia. YB (12) **£15-20**
024	1971-76	**Spare tyre** .....Black tyre, 23 mm. dia. YB (12) **£15-20**
025	1976 only	**Spare tyre** .....Black tyre, 17 mm. dia. YB (12) **£15-20**
026	1976 only	**Spare tyre** .....Black tyre, 21 mm. dia. YB (12) **£15-20**
027	1976 only	**Spare tyre** .....Black tyre, 27 mm. dia. YB (12) **£15-20**
028		**Spare tyre** .....Not issued .... NPP

029	1976 only	**Track**................. Black Track. Box of 6.......................**£15-20**
030	1968-76	**Track**................. Black Track. Box of 6.......................**£15-20**
031	1976-78	**Track**................. Black Track. Box of 6.......................**£15-20**
032	1973-76	**Track**................. Black Track. Box of 6.......................**£15-20**
033	1973-76	**Track**................. Black Track. Box of 6.......................**£15-20**
034	1964-76	**Battery**..........1.5 volt battery .... NGPP
035	1970-76	**Battery**..........1.5 volt battery .... NGPP
036		**Battery**..........1.5 volt battery for use with 276 ....Fire Tender and 277 Ambulance.......... NGPP

037	**Lamp**............Red light-bulb for use with 277............ NGPP	
038	**Lamp**............Blue (or Orange) light-bulb for use ....with model 276 Airport Fire Tender .... NGPP	
039	**Lamp**............Clear light-bulb for 952 Vega Coach.... NGPP	
081	**Spare tyre**.....White fine tread tyre, 14 mm. dia......... NGPP	
082	**Spare tyre**.....Black narrow tread tyre, 20 mm. dia.... NGPP	
083 (as 099)	**Spare tyre**.....Grey tyre, 20 mm. in diameter .... NGPP	
084	**Spare tyre**.....Black 'recessed' tyre, 18 mm. dia......... NGPP	
085 (as 092)	**Spare tyre**.....White tyre, 15 mm. in diameter .... NGPP	
086	**Spare tyre**.....Black fine tread tyre, 16 mm. dia. .... NGPP	
087 (as 60687)	**Spare tyre**.....Black big 'tractor' tyre, 35 mm. dia...... NGPP	
089 (as 60689)	**Spare tyre**.....Black 'tractor front tyre', 19 mm. dia.... NGPP	
090 (as 60790)	**Spare tyre**.....Black fine tread tyre, 14 mm. dia. .... NGPP	
090 (as 60791)	**Spare tyre**.....White fine tread tyre, 14 mm. dia......... NGPP	
091 (as 60036)	**Spare tyre**.....Black block tread tyre, 13 mm. dia...... NGPP	
092 (as 14094)	**Spare tyre**.....Black block tread tyre, 15 mm. dia...... NGPP	
092 (as 14095)	**Spare tyre**.....White block tread tyre, 15 mm. dia...... NGPP	
093 (as 13978)	**Spare tyre**.....Black medium tractor tyre, 27mm. dia... NGPP	
094 (as 6676)	**Spare tyre**.....Black smooth tyre, 18 mm. diameter... NGPP	
095 (as 6677)	**Spare tyre**.....Black block tread tyre, 18 mm. dia....... NGPP	

096 (as 7067)	**Spare tyre**.....Tyre, 15 mm. in diameter .... NGPP
097 (as 7383)	**Spare wheel**.Solid rubber wheel, 12 mm. dia.......... NGPP
098 (as 10118)	**Spare wheel**.Solid rubber wheel, 12 mm. dia.......... NGPP
099 (as 10253)	**Spare tyre**.....Black block tread tyre, 20 mm. dia....... NGPP
099 (as 10253)	**Spare tyre**.....Grey block tread tyre, 20 mm. dia....... NGPP
6676 (as 094)	**Spare tyre**.....Black smooth tyre, 18 mm. diameter... NGPP
6677 (as 095)	**Spare tyre**.....Black block tread tyre, 18 mm. dia....... NGPP
7067 (as 095)	**Spare tyre**.....Tyre, 15 mm. in diameter .... NGPP
7383 (as 097)	**Spare wheel**.Solid rubber wheel, 12 mm. dia.......... NGPP
10118 (as 098)	**Spare wheel**.Solid rubber wheel, 12 mm. dia.......... NGPP
10253 (as 099)	**Spare tyre**.....Black block tread tyre, 20 mm. dia....... NGPP
13978 (as 093)	**Spare tyre**.....Black medium tractor tyre, 27mm. dia. NGPP
14094 (as 092)	**Spare tyre**.....Black block tread tyre, 15 mm. dia...... NGPP
14095 (as 092)	**Spare tyre**.....White block tread tyre, 15 mm. dia...... NGPP
60036 (as 091)	**Spare tyre**.....Black block tread tyre, 13 mm. dia...... NGPP
606087 (as 087)	**Spare tyre**.....Black big 'tractor' tyre, 35 mm. dia..... NGPP
606089 (as 089)	**Spare tyre**.....Black 'tractor front tyre', 19 mm. dia. ... NGPP
607090 (as 090)	**Spare tyre**.....Black fine tread tyre, 14 mm. dia. .... NGPP
607091 (as 090)	**Spare tyre**.....White fine tread tyre, 14 mm. dia......... NGPP

Dinky Toys Catalogues (UK issues)

PRICES: Please note that paper ephemera must be in clean, undamaged condition to achieve the prices shown. French Dinky Toys Catalogues are listed at the end of the French Meccano Dinky Toys section.

Pre-war catalogues, leaflets and listings

Hornby 'Modelled Miniatures' were introduced in 1931 as model railway accessories. The first catalogue listings appeared in Hornby Train catalogues, Meccano catalogues and in the 'Meccano Magazine.'

Year of intro, publication details	MPR
1932-33 no ref. **Hornby 'Book of Trains'** First 'Modelled Miniatures' listed as 'Railway Accessories'.................................. **£50-60**	
1932 no ref. **Meccano trade catalogue** First 'Modelled Miniatures' listed as 'Railway Accessories'.................................. **£50-60**	
1933 no ref. **'Meccano Magazine'** 42 Hornby 'Modelled Miniatures' listed in the December issue............................. **£20-25**	
1933-34 no ref. **Hornby 'Book of Trains'** Accessories are depicted in full colour.... **£50-60**	
1934 no ref. **Meccano trade catalogue** 'Modelled Miniatures' briefly renamed 'Meccano Miniatures'................................ **£70-90**	
1934 no ref. **'Meccano Magazine'** February issue contained the last published 'Modelled Miniatures' listing.................... **£30-40**	
1934 no ref. **'Meccano Magazine'** April issue contained the first 'Meccano Dinky Toys' listing.................... **£30-40**	
1934 no ref. **'Meccano Magazine'** The May, June, July, August, September and November issues each reflected the increasing number of varieties of 'Dinky Toys'.. **£15-20**	
1934 no ref. **'Meccano Magazine'** '150 varieties of Dinky Toys' on double pages in October and December issues .. **£15-20**	
1934-35 no ref. **Hornby 'Book of Trains'** Catalogue shows 150 'Dinky Toys' in full colour on a double page...................... **£50-75**	
1934-35 13/834/900. **Meccano Catalogue** Boat plane and model plus boy on cover, 3 pages of Dinky Toys **£40-50**	
1934-35 13/834/900. **'Halford's Toys of Interest'** Inc. Dinky, Hornby, Meccano, etc........ **£150-175**	
1934-35 16/934/100. **'Hornby Trains/Meccano' Catalogue** Blue cover, full colour design of 'The World', lists 150 models of Dinky Toys **£70-90**	
1934-35 no ref. **Meccano Book** Cover depicts viaduct over river, complete Dinky Toys range is listed......... **£70-90**	
1935 no ref. **'Meccano Magazine'**	

Year of intro, publication details	MPR
January to November issues have various Dinky Toys listings........................ **£15-20**	
1935 no ref. **'Meccano Magazine'** December issue shows 200 varieties of Dinky Toys in black and white................. **£15-20**	
1935-36 7/835/65. **Hornby 'Book of Trains'** Catalogue features 200 varieties of Dinky Toys in full colour **£40-50**	
1935-36 no ref. **Hornby/Meccano Catalogue** Same cover as the 1934-35 issue **£70-90**	
1936 no ref. **'Meccano Magazine'** The February and August issues featured a road layout and a competition; the May issue introduced the 'Queen Mary' model **£15-20**	
1936-37 no ref. **Hornby 'Book of Trains'** The catalogue features full colour pictures of the Dinky Toys range **£50-60**	
1937 no ref. **Hornby/Meccano** Catalogue with 1934-35 'World' cover again. Seven pages of listings **£50-70**	
1937 no ref. **'Meccano Magazines'** Details given in the monthly listings of the superb new 'Army' range................. **£15-20**	
1937 13/637/25. **8-page Leaflet** 8 page fold-out buff leaflet. Front page depicts the 1937 Army models **£35-45**	
1938 13/638/1150. **Hornby/Meccano** 74 page Catalogue, full Dinky Toys listings. Numerous black and white pictures **£30-40**	
1938 13/638/1150/UK. **'Wonder Book of Toys'** Two boys with Meccano models plus 11 pages with Dinky Toys................. **£30-40**	
1938 8/1238/25. **'DINKY TOYS' Catalogue** (Booklet). Cover shows boy and 6 models inc. 29c Bus, 151a Tank, and 63 Mayo Composite. Brown print on pale-yellow paper........ **£100-125**	
1938 no ref. **'Meccano Magazine'** Details of the full range (with pictures) are published each month........................ **£25-35**	
1939 1/439/10. **'DINKY TOYS' leaflet** 'New Products' leaflet detailing items such	

Year of intro, publication details	MPR
as the Presentation Aeroplane Sets Nos 64 and 65. Black printing on pinkish paper . **£40-50**	
1939 no ref. **'MECCANO' booklets** complete Dinky Toys listings, various...... **£40-50**	
1939 13/639/1. Hornby/Meccano Catalogue 74 pages, full Dinky Toys listings and black and white pictures **£100-125**	
1939 13/639/11500 UK. **'A Wonder Book of Toys'** Green and Yellow cover depicts two boys with their Meccano models. The booklet includes 13 pages of Dinky Toys information..... **£100-125**	
1939 2/739/10 (1P). **'DINKY TOYS' Catalogue** Famous Red/Yellow cover picture of schoolboy with outstretched arm and 17 models. Contains 14 black and white pages...... **£150-175**	
1939 Same catalogue, but a version with only 10 black and white pages **£140-160**	
1939? no ref. **'Toys Of Quality'** Maroon Express train features on cover plus 'The Hornby Railway Co' logo. 13 pages of Dinky Toys listings included **£40-50**	
1939 no ref. **Trade catalogue** Cover depicts boy with Dinky Toys and Hornby pictures with 'MECCANO TOYS OF QUALITY' logo **£40-50**	
1939 2/939/20. **'Halford's Toys of Interest'** Inc. all Dinky, Hornby, Meccano, etc... **£150-200**	
1939 2/1139/20(3P) UK **'DINKY TOYS' Catalogue** Superb Red and Yellow cover picture of schoolboy with outstretched arm and 17 models. Contains 10 black/white pages of listings and pictures........ **£150-200**	
1939 no ref. **'Meccano Magazine'** Each month had Dinky Toys listings........ **£15-20**	
1940 1/440/100. **'Meccano Products'** 4 page leaflet, buff paper, brown printing... **£20-30**	
1940 16/1040/100. **'Meccano Products'** Four page leaflet, off-white paper, green printing (no pictures) **£20-30**	
1940 16/1040/200. **'DINKY TOYS' leaflet**	

Listing of models with pictures **£20-30**

1940 no ref. **'Meccano Magazine'**
Wartime Dinky aircraft and the
Meccano 'Spitfire Fund' are featured....... **£20-30**

1941 **16/541/25 UK. 'DINKY TOYS' leaflet**

Wartime camouflaged aircraft featured... **£20-30**

1941 **16/641/20 UK. 'DINKY TOYS' leaflet**
Similar to previous leaflet,
military models listed.............................. **£20-30**

1941 **16/1141/20 UK. 'DINKY TOYS' leaflet**
Listing of models and retail prices **£20-30**

Full Dinky Toys listings also appeared in the
toy catalogues of major retailers such as
Gamages and Bentalls. These are now
difficult to find. Each: **£30-40**

Post-war catalogues, leaflets and listings early post-war period, 1945–1954

There were at least two editions per annum so the following listings are not complete. The 'leaflet' approach reflects the shortage of paper in early post-war years.

Year of intro, publication details	MPR
1945 **16/1145/75 UK. Meccano leaflet** Leaflet lists the models to be reintroduced after the War and features pictures of 23e, 29c, 39a, 62s, 62p. Sepia print on cream paper	**£15-25**
1946 **16/546/30 UK. Meccano leaflet** Sepia printed listing on cream paper featuring pictures of models 70a, 38c, 29c, 23e...........................	**£15-25**
1946 **16/1146/65 UK. Meccano leaflet** Blue/Black print on cream paper, featuring models 70a, 38c, 70b, 38e.....	**£15-25**
1947 **16/347/50 UK. Meccano leaflet** Brown print on light cream paper. Models depicted are 70a, 70b, 70c, 70e, 38c, 38e, 38f, and 153a Jeep......	**£15-25**
1948 **16/448/30. Meccano General Products** Booklet with green printing on light cream paper	**£15-25**
1948 **16/948/200.** As previous issue but mauve print on light cream paper......	**£15-25**
1948 **16/1248/5. 'Dinky Toys Tyre Sizes'** Simple Leaflet giving information on Dinky Toys spare tyres....................	**£15-25**
1949 **16/449/100. Meccano General Products** Booklet with brown printing on light cream paper	**£15-25**
1949 **13/1049/150. Meccano General Products** 8 pages, cover has boys looking at globe circled by Hornby Trains, Meccano	

Year of intro, publication details	MPR
items and Dinky Toys	**£15-25**
1949 no ref. **Independent shop listings** Full Dinky Toys listings and pictures featured in catalogues published by the larger toy shops such as Bentalls, Gamages, etc	**£15-25**
1950 **16/250/100. Meccano Leaflet** A leaflet of two pages, printed in purple with drawings of 22 models	**£15-25**
1950 **16/450/150. Meccano General Products** booklet with pale Blue/Black printing on light cream paper............................	**£15-25**
1950 **16/550/75. Meccano Leaflet** A leaflet folded into three 'pages', with listings all Meccano items including Dinky Builder	**£15-25**
1950 **13/1050/80 UK. Dinky Toys Leaflet** 12pp catalogue, printed on cream paper with sepia pictures, 5"x3" approx.	**£25-35**
1950 no ref. **Independent shop listings** Full Dinky Toys listings and pictures featured in catalogues of the larger toy shops such as Gamages, Bentalls, etc	**£15-25**
1951 **16/251/33. Meccano General Products** Booklet with brown printing on light cream paper	**£10-15**
1951 no ref. **Independent shop listings** Full Dinky Toys listings and pictures featured in catalogues of the larger toy shops such as Bentalls, Gamages, etc	**£15-20**

Year of intro, publication details	MPR
1952 **16/352/120. Price List** A single sheet printed both sides in dark blue, listing 66 models with 23 model drawings.............................	**£10-15**
1952 **13/952/250. Price List** Beige leaflet with pictures and prices	**£10-15**
1953 **13/953/678. Meccano Catalogue** Includes Dinky Toys, Meccano and Hornby Dublo. '1st October 1953'	**£15-20**
1953 **16/453/500. 4-page Leaflet** Buff leaflet; front page shows date '15th April 1953' and boy shouting 'DINKY TOYS'	**£15-25**
1953 **16/753/75 (2P). 4-page Leaflet** Dark brown print, good illustrations..	**£15-20**
1953 **16/853/25. Price List** Beige leaflet with pictures and prices	**£15-20**
1953 **16/953/200. Price List** no details at present............................	**£10-15**
1954 **16/454/50 (7P). 4-page Leaflet** Dark brown print, good illustrations..	**£10-15**
1954 **16/854/25. Price List** Beige leaflet with pictures and prices	**£10-15**
1955 **16/255/100 (1P). 4-page Leaflet** Dinky Toys and Dinky Supertoys listed; sepia printing	**£10-15**

UK catalogue editions, 1952–1965

The series included fourteen editions although not all issues were given an edition number. More than one catalogue was issued in some years. It was common for catalogues to be overprinted with the name and address of the toy retailer. Original retail prices can be found under each model reference,

or on a stapled-in price list in the centre of the catalogue (except for 1956 and 1957 which have separate loose-leaf price lists). In addition to issuing Dinky Toys catalogues, Meccano Ltd continued to issue 'Meccano Toys Of Quality' leaflets which provided a full listing of Dinky Toys with their retail

prices plus details of their 'Hornby', 'Hornby-Dublo' and 'Meccano' products. As many as five printings per annum were produced using green, pink, blue or buff paper. When in perfect condition these leaflets sell for **£5-8** each.

1952	**16/152/50. (February) 16 pages** Cover features unknown 'C6321'........	**£55-65**
1952	**16/452/50. (April) 16 pages** As previous issue..................................	**£55-65**
1952	**15/852/165. (September) 16 pages** Cover shows hands holding 27f Estate Car, 'Dinky Toys' logo	**£55-65**
1953	**ref. ? 24 page catalogue** Cover shows boy wearing green sweater, 'Dinky Toys' and 'Price 3d'	**£55-65**
1953	**7/953/150. 24 page catalogue** As next item: 7/953/360.	
1953	**7/953/360. (1st October) 24 pages** (1) Cover features 555 Fire Engine, 522 Big Bedford Lorry and 25x Breakdown Lorry, price '2d'........	**£55-65**
1953	**13/953/678. (1st October)** (2) Cover shows 'Meccano Magic Carpet', two boys + globe with flag......	**£55-65**
1954	**7/754/600. (1st September) 24 pages** Cover features 157 Jaguar, 480 'Kodak' Van, 641 Army Truck, 'Dinky Toys' logo, price '2d'	**£40-50**
1955	**7/755/515. 24 page catalogue** 'Dinky Toys', 'Supertoys',	

	481 'Ovaltine' Van on cover, ('2d')	**£40-50**
1956	**7/456/800. (June) 32 pages** Cover has 942 'REGENT' Tanker, 255 Mersey Tunnel 'Police' Land Rover, 157 Jaguar XK120, 'Dinky Toys' and 'Dinky Supertoys', '2d'	**£40-50**
1956	**7/1056/125 (2P). (October) 32 pages** Same as previous issue, 2nd printing.	**£30-40**
1957	**7/657/820. (August) 28 pages** Cover shows 290 'DUNLOP' Double Decker Bus etc, 'Dinky Toys' and 'Dinky Supertoys', Price '2d UK'..........	**£40-50**
1958	**7/458/856. 28 page catalogue** Houses of Parliament shown on front cover with 'Dinky Toys' and 'Dinky Supertoys', price '2d UK'........	**£40-50**
1959	**7/559/900. 28 page catalogue** Red Jaguar XK120 Coupe (157) on front cover with 'Dinky Toys' and 'UK Seventh Edition', price '3d'..........	**£40-50**
1960	**7/3/800. 32 page catalogue** Motorway bridge on cover, 'Dinky Toys' and 'UK Eighth Edition'	**£40-50**
1961	**7/561/700. 32 page catalogue** Black/yellow cover with 6 models,	

	'Dinky Toys', 'UK 9th Edition'	**£40-50**
1962	**7/562/600. 32 page catalogue** Cover features 120 Jaguar 'E' type, 'Dinky Toys', price '2d'	**£40-50**
1963	**7/263/400** No details available for this reference number	**£25-35**
1963	**13/163/200. 32 page catalogue** Motor Show stands featured on cover, '11th Edition', 'UK', '2d'	**£25-35**
1963	**13/763/400. 32 page catalogue** 11th Edition, 2nd impression.............	**£25-35**
1964	**7/164/450. 8 page catalogue** 'Widest Range & Best Value In The World' and 'Dinky Toys' logos Price '3d'	**£25-35**
1964	**7/764/450 (2nd.Ptg.). 8 page catalogue** (2nd printing). As 7/164/450 except that page 8 shows Bedford TK instead of accessories	**£25-35**
1965	**7/265/200. 16 page catalogue** Rolls-Royce (127) on cover with 'Dinky Toys by Meccano' Price '3d'	**£25-35**
1965	**7/865/135 (2 ptg). 16 page catalogue** (2nd printing). Cover features cars 127, 128, 133, 151 and 178..................	**£25-35**

UK catalogue editions, 1966–1978

Up to 1972, original retail prices were on a refence listing stapled-in to the centre of the catalogue or bound-in at the back. However, no retail prices are shown on the lists for 1972 to 1978. For 1978, this list is found on the last three pages of the catalogue.

Year of intro, publication details	MPR
1966 **72561/2. 106 page catalogue** 1st Edition', '6d', 'Always Something New From Dinky' on the cover. Bound-in (pink) price list	£25-30
1966 **72561/2. (2nd edition, after 21st July)** Same cover as 1st, 104 pages plus bound-in (buff) price list	£20-25
1967 **72571. 104 page catalogue** 'No.3', '6d' 12 models on cover, same logo as 72561/2. Bound-in (pale-green) price list	£20-25
1967 As previous entry, but '2nd Printing' on the first page of the price list	£20-25
1968 **72580. 104 page catalogue** 'No.4', '6d', Spectrum Pursuit Vehicle (104) on cover. Logo as 72561/2. Buff price list	£20-25
1969 **72585. (May) 24 pages** 'No.5', '3d'. 102 'Joe's Car', and same logo as 72561/2. '1st Printing 1st May 1969'	£15-20

Year of intro, publication details	MPR
1969 **(Sept) 24 pages** 2nd run of 72585	£15-20
1970 **165000. (May) 24 page catalogue** 'No.6', '3d', many models on cover. Same logo as 72561/2	£15-20
1971 no ref. **(Feb) 24 page catalogue** '2nd Printing, 1st February 1971'. This is a '2nd printing' of 165000.	£15-20
1971 **100103. 24 page catalogue** 'No.7', '2p', '1971 Meccano Tri-ang Ltd' on rear cover. Same logo as on 72561/2. (Note the change to Decimal Currency in 1971)	£10-15
1972 **100107. (June) 28 page catalogue** 'No.8', '2p', 683 Chieftain Tank. '1st Printing, June 1972'	£10-15
1972 **100107.** 2nd printing of 100107	£15-20
1972 **100108. 28 page catalogue** 'No.8', 725 Phantom, 784 Goods Train, etc. on cover, but no date or price. No price list	£10-15

Year of intro, publication details	MPR
1973 **100109. 40 page catalogue** 'No.9', '3p', '1st Printing'. Shows 924 'Centaur', 'Dinky Toys'.	£10-15
1973 **100109. (October) 40 page catalogue** 2nd printing of 100109	£15-20
1974 **100113. (May) 48 page catalogue** 'No.10', '4p', cover shows 731 S.E.P.E.C.A.T. and 'Dinky Toys'.	£10-15
1975 **100115 UK. (June) 48 page catalogue** 'No.11', '5p', 'Dinky Toys' and 675 Motor Patrol Boat on cover	£10-15
1976 **100118 UK. 48 page catalogue** 'No.12', '5p', 'Dinky Toys' and 358 'USS Enterprise' on cover	£10-15
1977 **100122 (UK). 44 page catalogue** 'No.13' and '5p'. Cover features 357 Klingon Battle Cruiser	£5-10
1978 **100100. 44 page catalogue** 'No.14', '5p', 180 Rover 3500 on front cover. 'Airfix Group' logo on rear	£5-10

Leaflets and price lists, 1954–1978

Further information. It is known that other leaflets, literature and price lists were published. The Editor would welcome more information to add to these listings.

	MPR
1954 **16/854/25.** Price List - no details	£30-40
1955 **16/155/100. Leaflet / Price List** No details	£30-40
1955 **7/455/250. (May) 8 page leaflet** 251, 641, 170 and 401 on cover, 'Dinky Toys' and 'Dinky Supertoys'.	£20-30
1955 **16/655/25. 'Hamley's' Leaflet** No details	£30-40
1956 **16/156/225. Leaflet** - no details	£30-40
1956 **16/556/500. Leaflet / Price List** No details	£30-40
1956 **16/656/525. Leaflet / Price List** No details	£30-40
1957 no ref. **Booklet** Yellow cover, 'A NEW SERIES' and 'DUBLO DINKY TOYS' in red	£30-40
1957 **DT/CF/3 16/257/250 (1P) Leaflet and Price List** Yellow fronted leaflet '1st January 1957', pictures of 716, 162, 626, and 250 Fire Engine, 'Dinky Toys' and 'Dinky Supertoys' in Red	£30-40
1957 **DT/CF/4 UK 16/757/250 (2P) Leaflet and Price List** Yellow fronted folding leaflet. 'July 1957'. Pictures of 418 Leyland Comet, 923 'Heinz' Van, 164 Vauxhall plus 190 Caravan. 'Dinky Toys' and 'Dinky Supertoys' in Red	£30-40

	MPR
1957 **16/857/500. Leaflet / Price List**. No details	£30-40
1957 **DT/CL/20 16/1157/100 UK Two-sided Leaflet** 'Dublo Dinky Toys' in Red on Yellow. Pictures of first 3 issues: 064, 065, 066	£30-40
1958 **16/958/100. Leaflet** Car Carrier and Trailer leaflet	£30-40
1958 **10/758/450. Leaflet / Price List** No details	£30-40
1959 **DT/CF/5 16/159/100. Illustrated Price List** Colour cover showing 983 Transporter and cars, etc.	£30-40
1959 **DT/CF/6 16/759/100 2ndP. Price List with colour pictures** Leaflet cover shows nos. 998, 967, 968 and 986. Dated '1959/UK' on front	£30-40
1959 **10/1259/50.** Price List - no details	£30-40
1960 **DT/CF/7 16/160/100 (3P). Illustrated Price List** Colour cover with 666 Missile Vehicle and 785 Service Station, etc.	£30-40
1960 **DT/CF/8 16/160/100 (4P). Illustrated Price List** Colour cover with 930 Pallet-Jekta plus GS 951 Fire Service, etc.	£30-40

	MPR
1961 **DT/CF/11 8/561/100. Illustrated Price List** (72535/02) Colour cover with 4 cars and 'Purchase Tax Surcharges 26th July 1961'	£30-40
1965 **72557/02. Leaflet** Cover with 133, 127, 128, 151 and 171, with price list	£30-40
1966 **16/766/50M. Leaflet / Price List** No details	£30-40
1967 **72579. Trade Fair Leaflet** 'THUNDERBIRDS'	£30-40
1967 **72939. Leaflet / Price List** No details	£30-40
1968 **72569. Leaflet** Features 103-105 'Captain Scarlet'	£30-40
1971 **100217. Leaflet** Four page 'Action Kits' leaflet	£20-30
1971 **100261. Single sheet** Full-colour flyer featuring 'All Action Fighting Vehicles'	£20-30
72-75 no ref. **Dinky Driver's Diary** 6 models shown on the cover; descriptions and diagrams of 1970s models inside	£20-30
1979 no ref. **Trade Catalogue 1979** 'Fifty New Models', 11½ x 8¼ inches	£20-30

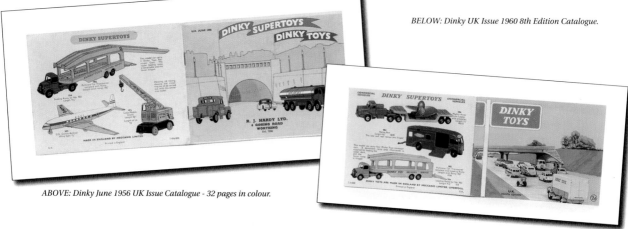

ABOVE: Dinky June 1956 UK Issue Catalogue - 32 pages in colour.

BELOW: Dinky UK Issue 1960 8th Edition Catalogue.

Meccano trade catalogues listing Dinky Toys

These were issued for many years but little information has been recorded. For example:
Ref. 100126 – 1978 Trade Catalogue with 'Todays World,' 'Todays Meccano' and Todays Dinky Toys' on the cover plus colour design of late 1970s models on Motorway with 'Meccano' buildings in background.
Ref. 100102 – 1979 Trade Catalogue 'Today's Meccano & Dinky'.

Meccano catalogues 1954–1958

With colour 'Dinky Toys' and 'Hornby-Dublo' listing. Details known to the compiler relate solely to issues in the mid-1950's period. 'MECCANO TOYS OF QUALITY' logo on each cover.

1954-55 13/654/995UK. 24 pages, price '2d'
Cover depicts 4 boys on a desert island. Black/white pictures **£20-25**

1955-56 13/655/797UK. 28 pages, price '2d'
Cover shows boys looking in toyshop window, black/white pictures **£20-25**

1956 13/756/525UK. 32 pages, price '4d'
Cover depicts Dinky Toys, Hornby-Dublo, and a Meccano helicopter. This is a large catalogue with colour printing **£30-35**

1957 13/757/500UK. 32 pages, price '4d'
Famous cover showing Meccano Tower, Hornby-Dublo train crossing a viaduct and Dinky Toys passing beneath.
Large, with colour pictures **£50-75**

1958 13/758/450UK. 20 pages, price '4d'
Cover depicts boy, Hornby-Dublo train, 8 Dinky Toys and a Meccano model. Includes some superb engine pictures................................ **£30-35**

The white price guide pictured (16/1055/500) is the Meccano/Dinky Toys Catalogue. Revised Prices, from October 1955 including information on Meccano, Dinky Toys, Hornby Clockwork Trains and Hornby Dubo Electric Trains.

The yellow guide pictured (16/857/500) is from September 1057 and includes information on Meccano, Dinky Toys, Dinky Supertoys, Hornby Clockwork Trains and Hornby Dublo Electric Trains.

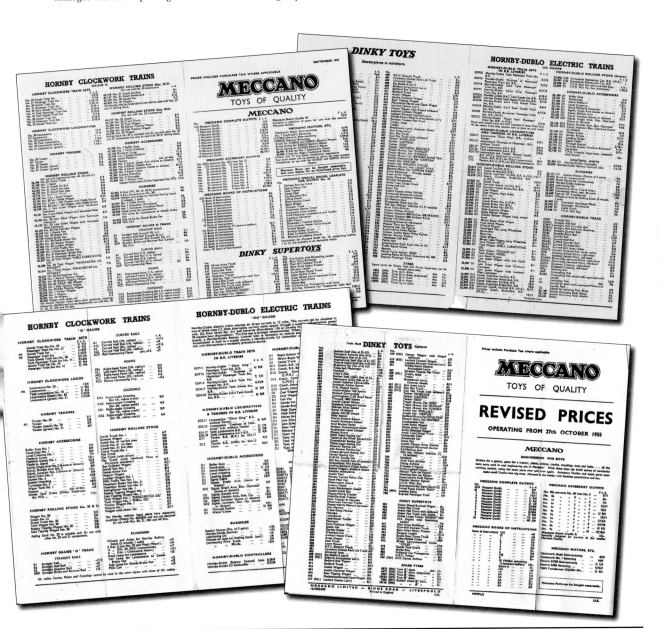

Meccano Magazines, 1942–1952

During the latter part of the war and especially during the early post-war years when Dinky Toys catalogues were not issued, the Meccano Magazine was the main source of new information for collectors. It advised on the reintroduction of models after the war and of the forthcoming new releases. Consequently the Magazines of this period are highly collectable in their own right.

1942 - September 1943. No Dinky Toys adverts or listings appeared.
September 1943 - December 1944. Back page adverts for Meccano incorporated listing and pictures of De Havilland Flamingo Aircraft and Buick 'Viceroy' Saloon.
January - November 1945. Back page adverts said 'Sorry, not available but will be ready after the war.'
December 1945. Advert on back page announced 'Ready during December.'
1946. Virtually every month a new model was added to the listing printed on the inside front cover. A picture of each model was shown.
January - September 1947. New models added regularly each month.
October 1947. First advert appears of Dinky Supertoys with pictures of 501 Foden Diesel Wagon, 502 Foden Flat Truck, 503 Foden Flat Truck with Tailboard, 511 Guy 4 ton Lorry, 512 Guy Flat Truck, 513 Guy Flat Truck with Tailboard, and 701 Short 'Shetland' Flying Boat.
1948. Single page advert every month, new models continually introduced.
1949, 1950, 1951. Double page advert each month listing new models.
1952. Double page advert each month. The December issue shows Gift Sets No.1 Farm Gear and No.2 Commercial Vehicles.
Prices for Meccano Magazines of this period range between **£10-15** each.

Factory drawings

UNISSUED MODELS
A number of models were planned but not actually produced by Meccano. This is list of known factory drawings and plans for such models.
Austin A40 Van 'OMNISPORT' drawing dated 31-8-57. **Guy Warrior Van** 'GOLDEN SHRED' drawing dated 26-3-57, Job No. 14794. **Leyland Fuel Tanker** drawing dated 30-9-65, Job No. 62520. **Single-Deck Bus** drawing dated 14-5-34, Job. No. 6763. **Jowett Javelin Saloon** drawing dated 10-10-47, Job No. 12886. **Renault Fregate** drawing dated 4-7-57, Job No. 20106. **Triumph Dolomite** (intended 38e) drawing dated 1939. **Vampire Jet** drawing dated 27-11-45, Job No. 12157. **Firebrand Aircraft** drawing dated 18-12-45, Job No. 12159.

PRODUCTION MODELS
In October 2000, Christie's South Kensington sold part of the Mike and Sue Richardson collection of Meccano General Assembly Drawings for the Dinky Toys range. The following is a small selection of items from that sale. The reference numbers are 'Job Numbers'.

Drawings – English Saloon Cars. 13866/7 **Jaguar XK120 and Base**, 20335 **Base XK150**, 20329 **Spring XK150**, 13381/3 **Austin Atlantic Body and Base**, 20121/2 and 20118/9 **Rolls-Royce Silver Wraith** (various parts), 62035/6/7 **Chauffuer**

Meccano Magazines, 1952–1975

With the introduction of yearly Dinky Toys catalogues from 1952 the Meccano Magazine lost its somewhat unique role as a combined magazine/catalogue. However, with the help of 'The Toyman' and his monthly articles plus superb colour advertising of new models, the Magazine continued to provide a valuable service for collectors. Meccano Magazines of this period are in the price range of **£5-10**.

Dinky Toys Club Licences, Newsletters, etc

no. ref.	19??-??	**Dinky Toys Club Certificate** (unused)	£100-125
no ref	1955-??	**Dinky Toys Club Enamel Badge**	£35-45
no ref	1955-??	**Dinky Toys Club 'Welcome' Letter**	NGPP

Dinky Toys Club Newsletters

?	195?	**Dinky Toys Club Newsletter No.1**, '3d', 'Greetings from Australia' on cover	£60-80
19/759/35	1959?	**Newsletter No.2**, '3d'. Stirling Moss on cover, 150 Rolls-Royce featured in centre-fold	£60-80
?	19??	**Newsletter No.3**, 'M1' on cover	£60-80
DTC/L/1	1958-59	**Collector's Licence**, Brown cover, 16 pages	£125-150
DTC/L/2	1959-60	**Collector's Licence**, Red cover, 16 pages	£100-125
DTC/L/3	1960-61	**Collector's Licence**, Green cover, 16 pages	£60-80
DTC/L/4	1961-62	**Collector's Licence**, Yellow cover, 16 pages	£60-80

and Passengers, 13360/1/2 **Rover 75**, 14844/5 **Spring and Base for Humber Hawk**, 14982/4 **Singer Gazelle Body and Base**, 14088/9 **Austin A30 Body and Base**, 14721/3 **Sunbeam Rapier Body and Base**, 14721/3 **Sunbeam Rapier Body and Base**, 14745/7 **Hillman Minx Body and Base**, 7889 **Ford Zephyr Body**, 14097/8 **Vauxhall Cresta Body and Base**, 14937/8 **Fiat 600 Body and Base**, 14847/8 **Austin A105 Body and Base**. (*All 1950s*). In all, 33 items sold in one lot for **£750**

Drawings – Buses. 10897/8 **Double Deck Omnibus Body and Base** (both with dyeline copies), **Memo** 15954 about 17693 **'Dunlop' Transfers**, 13480/2 **Luxury Coach and Base**, 13750/2 **Duple Roadmaster Coach and Base**, 13424/6 **Observation Coach and Base**. 12 items in one lot sold for **£420**

Drawings – Fodens. 12163/6 and 12822 **Cab and Chassis, Body and Tanker Body**, 12164/5/9 **Bogie, Clip and Washer for Spare Wheel** + 7 drawings for **Chains, Stanchions, Tank parts**, etc. 13 items sold for **£550**

Drawings – Leyland Octopus. 7874 **Cab and Chassis**, 7875 **Front Bogie**, and **Memo** 20649 **Label for 'ESSO'**. 3 items sold as one lot for **£120**

Dinky Toys Catalogues (Overseas Issues)

Catalogues were often adapted so that they could be switched for use in most countries in the world irrespective of the language or the currency used. An example of this is the 1965 catalogue:

1965	72257/02UK	**UK catalogue** 16 pages. Cover depicts 5 cars namely Nos.127, 128, 133 and 171 plus a description of various model features	£25-35
72557 1965		**Overseas edition** 16 pages. The cover is the same but replacing the features listing is a panel with 'Precision Diecast Scale Models' printed in English, German, French, Spanish, Italian and Swedish. The catalogue pages contain only the basic	

English model name and number - all the English text having been removed. The models are the same as 72257/02 .... **£25-35**

72559 1965		**Overseas edition** 24 pages. Whilst the cover is the same as 72557, the listings are entirely different for they feature both English and French Dinky Toys, including the French issues sold in the UK	£40-50

Price lists. Prior to the overseas editions being despatched, price lists in the correct language and currency would be inserted. The Editor would like to express his thanks to the many collectors around the world who have contributed to this listing. New information would be welcomed.

For French Dinky Toys Catalogues, please see the Catalogues listing at the end of the French Dinky Toys section.

AFRICA (Distributor unkown)
KENYA
1961 **Illustrated List** **£60-80**
RHODESIA
1953 **Illustrated Price List** **£60-80**
1954 **Illustrated Price List** **£60-80**
SOUTH AFRICA

1955 **Catalogue '7/655/20'**, Ovaltine Van + 7 others, 24 pages **£50-75**
TANGANYIKA & UGANDA
19?? **Combined Catalogue** **£60-80**

AUSTRALIA
Agents (in 1952): E. G. Page & Co. (Sales) Pty., Ltd., Danks Building, 324 Pitt Street, Sydney.

1950 **Meccano General Products Catalogue '13/550/68'**, as 1949 UK Catalogue, 'Meccano World-Famous Toys' **£70-90**
1952 **Catalogue '5/352/37.5'**, Cover has sepia drawings of hands holding 27f, with 139b, 25x and 532 .... **£50-75**
1952 **Catalogue '13/852/12'**, Cover shows

boy with green sweater. An example
sold at auction in 1998 for **£250**

1955 **Catalogue '7/655/30'**, 282, 591, 290,
961, 430, 251, 962 and 481 on cover ... **£40-60**

1956 **Leaflet '16/456/15'**, 8 page folded leaflet
with coloured drawings and price list.
Cover has 132, 255 and 781 .... **£25-35**

1957 **Leaflet '16/357/7.5 (1P)'**,
folded colour leaflet with 716,
162, 626, 955 on the front **£25-35**

1957 **Leaflet '16/757/15 (2P)'**,
folded colour leaflet with 932, 923,
164, 190 and 'Dinky Toys and
Dinky Supertoys' on billboard **£25-35**

1957 **Catalogue '7/757/30'**, Piccadilly Circus,
colour, vertical, no prices, 28 pages.... **£70-90**

1958 **Catalogue '7/658/40'**, UK cover **£30-45**

1959 **Catalogue '7/559/40'**, UK cover **£30-45**

1960 **Catalogue '23/560/40'**, UK cover **£30-45**

1961 **Catalogue '7/61/40'**, UK cover **£30-45**

1962 **Catalogue '7/662/40'**, UK cover **£30-45**

1963 **Catalogue '13/163/100'**, UK cover **£25-35**

1964 **Catalogue '7/364/100'**, UK cover **£25-35**

1969 **Catalogue '72585'**, UK cover **£25-35**

1971 **Catalogue '100103'**, UK cover **£20-25**

1978 **Catalogue '100100'** ('No.14'),
'20c' on cover, 44 pages. 'Liberty
Trading Pty Ltd, Surrey Hills,
Marshall St. NSW' on checklist **£20-25**

BELGIUM and LUXEMBOURG

French printing. Agents: P FREMINEUR et Fils,
Rue des Bogards 1, Bruxelles 1.

1936 **Meccano Catalogue '13/736/265'** **£150-200**

1954 **Catalogue '16/1053 /10'**,
Same cover as 1953 UK issue **£40-50**

1954 **Catalogue '16/1054 /2'**,
Same cover as 1954 UK issue **£40-50**

1956 **Catalogue '16/656/156'** (DT/CL/5).
Cover as 1956 UK issue **£40-50**

1958 **Leaflet '16/1258/12.5 Belgium'**
('DT/CL/32' on cover). Printed in
England. 168 Singer and 178 Plymouth
on cover. Text in French and Flemish **£40-50**

1959 **Catalogue '7/539/-'**,
Red Jaguar XK140 on cover **£30-40**

1960 **Catalogue** (no ref.).
English and French models in one
catalogue, 48 pages. Printed and issued
only in Belgium and Luxembourg.
Cover depicts Land Rover plus
two French Dinky cars. 'Frs 3-'. **£75-100**

BELGIUM French printing.

1954 **Illustrated price list '16/1054 /2'** **£40-50**

1966 **1st Edition price list '72551'**,
in French and Flemish, 164 pages **£40-50**

CANADA

Agents: Meccano Limited, 675 King Street West,
Toronto and 187 - 189 Church Street, Toronto.

1934 **Leaflet '10/34'**,
Yellow leaflet with 'LOCKE Bros.
of MONTREAL' stamp **£125-150**

1937 **Leaflet '13/637/5'**, Eight pages **£125-150**

1938 **Leaflet '7/38'**,
Ten page fold-out leaflet with
full range **£125-150**

1940 **Leaflet '13/840/5'**,
12 black and white pages, 8.75" x 5.875".
Cover shows boy with outstretched arms
plus 62h, 151a, 36g, 43a, and 33r. 'The
Fascinating Collecting Hobby' **£125-150**

1941 **Leaflet '6/41'**,
12 page fold-out leaflet
with full range **£125-150**

1951 **Catalogue '16/351/25'**,
16 pp, boy + 3 models, blue pictures .. **£60-70**

1953 **Catalogue '7/953/150'**,
555 Fire Engine, 522 Big Bedford,

25x Breakdown Truck, 28 pages **£50-60**

1955 **Illustrated price list: '16/355/90'**,
Off-White leaflet................................ **£30-35**

1955 **Catalogue '7/556/90'**,
Illustration of Bedford 'Ovaltine'
Van plus seven other models **£50-60**

1956 **Catalogue '7/556/90'**,
Regent Tanker/Tunnel,
1st June 1956 in colour, 32 pages **£50-60**

1956 **Illustrated price leaflet '16/656/18c'**,
(DT/CL/4) in colour, featuring 131
Cadillac and 660 Tank Transporter **£20-30**

1956 **Illustrated price leaflet '16/756/18'**,
in colour, featuring 706 Vickers
'Air France' Airliner............................ **£20-30**

1957 **Catalogue '7/757/90'**,
Piccadilly Circus, vertical, in colour,
with prices, 28 pages........................... **£50-60**

1959 **Catalogue '7/559/90'**,
Red Jaguar + 6 models on cover,
28 pages **£50-60**

1960 **Catalogue '7/560/90'**,
cover as UK issue **£40-50**

1961 **Catalogue '3/41/25 7252 3/42'**,
Black with 7 models and '9th' on
cover, Canada/English, 32 pages **£40-50**

1963 **Catalogue '13/163/100 7254 2/42'**,
Motor Show 11th, Canada/English,
32 pages **£40-50**

1963 **Catalogue '13/1063 /50 7254 8/42'**,
Flyer 8in x 10¼in. 10 models on
cover, 'Canada 1963', 8 pages............. **£30-40**

1964 **Trade Catalogue '7/364/150'**,
8 page catalogue plus 4 page trade price
list (half catalogue width, in centre)... **£30-40**

1964 **Catalogue '7/464/150 72550/42'**,
'12th', 8in x 11in,
Canada/English, 8 pp **£20-30**

1964 **Catalogue (no ref.)**, Flyer, 5½ x 3½,
shows 6 Hong Kong models, 12 pp..... **£10-15**

1965 **Catalogue (no ref.)** 1st Ed. 8½ x 5½in.,
5 models on cover, 16 pp **£20-25**

1966 **Catalogue '72561'**,
1st Edition, 108 pages **£30-40**

1966 **Catalogue '72561'**,
2nd Edition, 106 pages **£30-40**

1967 **Catalogue '72571'**,
3rd edition, 106 pages......................... **£30-40**

1968 **Catalogue '72580'**,
4th Edition, 106 pages **£30-40**

1969 **Catalogue '72585'**,
5th Edition, 24 pages **£20-30**

1970 **Catalogue '165000'**, UK cover.......... **£15-25**

1971 **Catalogue '100103'**, UK cover........... **£15-25**

CYPRUS

1969 **Catalogue** (no ref.),
Same as UK issue **£50-75**

EGYPT

1952 **Catalogue '5/652/2'**, Different p.9
from UK issue with pictures of
US 39 Series cars and British cars... **£100-150**

EIRE and Channel Islands

Agents until 1968:
S.J. Gearey, 1 St Stephens Green, Dublin.
Agents from 1969:
Kilroy Bros Ltd, Shanowen Road, Whitehall, Dublin
9.

1953 **Catalogue '7/953/9'**.
'Eire' and 'C.I.' on cover...................... **£40-50**

1955 **Catalogue '7/755/20'**.
'Eire' and 'C.I.' on cover...................... **£40-50**

1959 **Catalogue '7/659/75'**, 'Eire' on cover **£40-50**

1964 **Catalogue '7/364/7'**, 'Eire' on cover.. **£30-40**

1969 **Catalogue 'No.5'**, 'Irish' on cover,
(agents: Kilroy Bros Ltd)..................... **£30-40**

HONG KONG

Representatives: W.R.Loxley & Co. Ltd.,
Jardine House, 11th Floor, 20 Pedder Street,

Hong Kong.

1959 **Illustrated price list 'DT/CF/5'**,
same cover as UK issue **£50-75**

ITALY

Agents: Alfredo Parodi, Piazza 8, Marcellino 6,
Genova.

1957 **Leaflet '16/657/5'**, with 101-105 .... **£30-35**

1957 **Leaflet '16/3/57/5'**,
showing 677 and 472 'Raleigh'............ **£30-35**

1957 **Leaflet '16/357/5'**,
642 and 455 'Brooke Bond Tea'........... **£30-35**

1957 **Leaflet '16/857/5'**,
237 Mercedes front,
136, 236, 238 back **£30-35**

1957 **Leaflet '16/457/5'**, 697 Military Set ... **£30-35**

1957 **Leaflet '16/457/5'**,
661 and 919 'Golden Shred'................. **£30-35**

1957 **Leaflet** (no ref.), with 163, 236 and
238 on racing circuit **£30-35**

1957 **Leaflet** (no ref.), with 237, 661,
and 919 'Golden Shred' **£30-35**

1957 **Illustrated price list '16/357/5'**,
'Italy' printed after the ref. no. **£30-35**

1957 **Leaflet '12/757/20'** (DT/CL/15) 642
and 455 'Brooke Bond' **£30-35**

1957 **Catalogue '7/857/50'**,
Same cover as UK issue 7/657/820 ..... **£40-50**

1957 **Leaflet 'DT/CL/12'**,
with 677 and 472 on cover.................. **£30-35**

1958 **Catalogue '7/758/50'**,
Same cover as UK issue 7/458/856 ..... **£40-50**

1964 **Catalogue '7/364/40 7225 0/37'**,
12th, 8in x 11in, includes four pages
of French Dinky, 12 pages in total **£30-35**

MALAYA and SINGAPORE

Agents: King & Co, Singapore.

1957 **Catalogue '16/557/25 (1P)'** (DT/CF/3),
8 pages, cover depicts 170, 626, 716, 955,
other pictures within, price list in $.... **£40-50**

1958 **Catalogue '7/958/10'**, cover as UK,
4 pages with prices in $ **£40-50**

NETHERLANDS /HOLLAND

Agents: Hausemann & Hotte NV,
Kromboomssloot 57-61, Amsterdam.

Pre-War Editions

1936 **'1/736/5'**
Yellow paper with Black printing.... **£125-150**

1937 **'13/637/75'**
Yellow paper with Black printing.... **£125-150**

1938 **'13/738/22'**
Yellow paper with Black printing.... **£125-150**

Post-War Editions - Some black/white,
later coloured as per UK issues.

1954 **Illustrated price list '16/954/108'**,
Printed in French **£15-20**

1955 **'8/1255/50'** (DT/L/7), no details **£40-50**

1955 **'7/655/71.35'** - 24 pages with Dutch
text and prices by the pictures

1956 **'16/256/30n** (DT/CL/2), no details ... **£30-40**

1956 **'16/256/30n** (DT/L/9), no details **£30-40**

1958 **'16/1158 /20**, 'Nederland Frs 3-'.
Cover same as 1958 UK issue **£30-35**

1958 **'7/658/120'** - 28 pages with Dutch text
and prices by the pictures

1961 **'14/461/100'** - 48 pages with Dutch text
and prices by the pictures

1962 **'16/256/30 (72538/29)'**, no details **£20-25**

1963 **'13/163/80'** and **72545/29** - 48 pages with
English text and Dutch pricelist inserted in
the middle

1966 **1st edition 72561** - 164 pages - Dutch text
and prices by the pictures

1967 **Catalogue '72571'**, 3rd Ed., price list
in Dutch florins, 162 pages................. **£40-50**

1970 **Catalogue** (no ref.), 6th Edition includes
8pp of French Dinky, 32 pp in total.... **£20-30**

PORTUGAL

1956 **Illustrated Catalogue** (no ref.).......... **£40-50**

1957 **Illustrated Leaflet, 'DT/CF/4'**,
no details £50-70
1958 **Illustrated Catalogue '7/858/5'**,
Houses of Parliament on cover.......... £50-60
1959 **Illustrated Catalogue (no ref.)**.......... £40-50
1961 **Illustrated Catalogue '5/261/25'**,
9th edition £40-50
1963 **Illustrated Catalogue (no ref.)**.......... £30-40
1960s **Illustrated Catalogue '7255049'**,
group of 1960s cars on cover.............. £30-40
1969 **'No.5' Catalogue '72585'**,
cover features 'Joe 90's Car' £30-40

SPAIN
1957 **Illustrated Leaflet 'DT/CL15 SP 16/457/5'**,
Similar to Italian leaflet with
697 on colour front of single sheet,
unpriced list on reverse £10-15

SWEDEN
Agents: Ludvig Wigart & Cos, AB Helsingborg.
1954 **'7/654/14'**, 4 pages, 3 pages colour
pictures plus price list in Kroner
with Swedish text £40-50
1957 **Leaflet '16/357/15'**, Leaflet depicts 455
'Brooke Bond' Trojan plus 642 RAF Tanker.
Price list in Kroner; Swedish text........ £15-20
1957 **Catalogue**, 28 pages £70-90
1961 **Catalogue '14/561/60'**,
as 1961 UK issue, text in Swedish £30-40
1968 **Catalogue '72580'**, 162 pp,
as UK 1968 edition, but in Swedish £20-30

SWITZERLAND
Agents: Riva & Kunzmann SA Basel 2, Switzerland.
From 1965 address changed to Prattela,
Switzerland.
1956 **Catalogue '7/356/20'**, Ovaltine + 7
others, prices in Swiss francs, 24 pp... £40-50
1958 **Catalogue '7/858/80'**, UK cover £40-50
1962 **Catalogue '72537/25'**, 10th Edition,
48 pages, same as UK issue 72537/02
plus French Dinky Toys £40-50
1963 **Catalogue '13/163/175'**,
11th Edition, 48 pages, as UK issue
13/163/20 plus French Dinky £40-50
1965 **Catalogue '72559'**, 24 pp, cover as
UK 72557 + French Dinky Toys £40-50

USA
Agents: H. Hudson Dobson, PO Box 254, 26th St
and Jefferson Avenue, Kenilworth, NJ.
In 1952 the address was: PO Box 254, 906 Westfield
Avenue, Elizabeth, NJ.
From 1957 the address changed to 627 Boulevard,
Kenilworth. New York showroom: 200, Fifth Ave.,
PO Box 255. Models sold by this distributor will
often be found with an 'H.Hudson Dobson' label
From 1963: Lines Bros Inc, 1107 Broadway, New
York. **From ?**: AVA International, Box 7611, Waco,
Texas 76710.

War-Time Issue
1941 **Large leaflet**
(no ref.), no details available................. NGPP
Post-War Editions
1951 **Catalogue** (no ref.), boy's side face,
5 models, black and white,
green printing, 16 pages £70-90
1952 **Catalogue** (no ref.), hands holding 27f
(139b and 25x in picture). Unlike the
UK edition, 39b, 39c and 39e are
shown in two-tone colours £70-90
1953 **7/953/150** - 28 pages with loose American
pricelist
1953 **Catalogue '7/753/150'**, same cover as
1953 UK issue 7/953/360..................... £50-75
1954 **Catalogue '7/954/150'**, same cover as
1954 UK issue 7/754/600..................... £50-75
1954 **Catalogue '7/753/150'**, 157 Jaguar,
480 Kodak, 641 Army,
separate price list, 28 pages £50-75

1955 **Catalogue** (no ref.), 20 models on
cover, 5 French, black and white,
prices in $, 32 pages............................ £50-75
1956 **Catalogue** (no ref.), 'Ever-Ready'
plus 11 others, Feb 57, black/white,
prices in $, 32 pages............................ £50-75
1957 **Catalogue** (no ref.), Yellow/Red cover
shows model 697 plus Red lined sections
displaying English and French models.
Red panel with US address of H.Hudson
Dobson. 36 black/white pages of
English and French models £70-90
1957 **Catalogue** (no ref.),
Yellow, Red lines, black/white,
'9-30-57', prices in $, 36 pp £50-75
1958 **Catalogue '7/958/250'**,
Houses of Parliament on cover,
prices in $, 32pp £50-75
1959 **Leaflet '7/7/125'**,
Colour, English and French,
prices in $ £20-30
1959 **USA Catalogue '7/559/250'**, Cover
depicts Red Jaguar XK140 etc. 26 pages
English models, 6 pages French £50-75
1959 **Leaflet '7/8/125'**, 3 pp of colour
pictures plus price list. English and
French items on cover,
(195 Jaguar 3.4, 265 Taxi).................... £45-55
1960 **Leaflet** (no ref.),
6 pages introducing 'Mini-Dinky'...... £40-45
1960 **Catalogue '7/3/30 NP'**, 32 pages,
motorway bridge on cover £40-50
1961 **Leaflet '16/161/100 72529/22'**,4pp. £20-30
1961 **Catalogue '14/561/200'**, Black with
7 models, USA 1961, 48 pp £50-75
1962 **Leaflet '9/762/50'**,
'72542/22' and 'D.T./CL 14' £10-15
1962 **Catalogue '725377/22'**, 10th Ed.,
48 pp, UK 7253702 + French £20-30
1962 **Catalogue '72537/22'**, 120 Jaguar
'E'-type, 10th Ed. '5c' 16 pages of
French Dinky, 48 pages in total £50-75
1963 **Catalogue '13/763/60'**, 11th Ed.,
48 pp, UK 13/763/400 plus French
Dinky Toys NGPP
1963 **Leaflet '16/163/50 7254 7/22'**,
illustrated flyer price list, b/w £20-30
1963 **Catalogue '13/763/10 7254 5/22'**,
Motor Show 11th USA, 16 pages of
French Dinky, 48 pages in total £25-35
1965 **Leaflet** (no ref. no.) Lines Bros flyer
8½in x 11in, Hong Kong on cover....... £20-30
1965 **'Lines Bros' leaflet** (no ref. no.), 4 pp,
Yellow/Red cover with 113 MGB £30-35
1967 **Leaflet '72577/3'**, 10in x 12³/₄in.
includes 5 Hong Kong Dinky £15-20
1971 **Catalogue '100103'**,
7th Edition, same as UK, 24 pages...... £10-15
1972 **Catalogue '100108'**,
8th Edition, same as UK, 28 pages...... £10-15
1973 **Catalogue '100110'**,
9th Edition, same as UK, 40 pages...... £10-15
1973 **Leaflet '100265'**,
4 pages Dinky Action Kits Catalogue.. £10-15
1974 **Catalogue '100114'**,
10th Edition, same as UK, 48 pages.... £10-15
1975 **Catalogue '100/117'**, 11th Ed.,
40 pages, same as UK 100115 .... £10-15
1976 **Catalogue '100/120'**, 12th Ed.,
40 pages, same as UK 100118 .... £10-15
1977 **Catalogue '100/135'**, 13th Ed.,
40 pages, same as UK 100122, but
background on cover is Blue not Red £10-15
1978 **Catalogue '100/101'**, 14th Ed.,
64 pages, same as UK 100/100 .... £10-15

WEST GERMANY
Agents: Bienngraeber of Hamburg.
1969 **Catalogue '72585'**, 32 pages, No.5 features
'Joe's Car' on cover, Catalogue in
English, price list in German £40-50

*Variety of Dinky international catalogues.
Top four Dutch catalogues. Bottom two USA 1953.*

Dinky Toys Trade Boxes

Virtually all Dinky Toys models were supplied in their own individual boxes from around 1954. Before then, most small models were supplied to shopkeepers in 'Trade Boxes' containing 3, 4, 6 or 12 identical models separated by strips of card. (Some aircraft and ship models were an exception to this general rule). A single item would be sold without further packaging except perhaps for a paper bag.

These Trade Boxes have become collectors items in their own right whether full or empty (the latter selling for between £20 and £50 depending on its rarity and that of its original contents. Most of these boxes that come to auction are full and the listing below derives mostly from surveys of such items undertaken for the 8th, 9th and 10th Editions. We are grateful to David Cooke and Tony Murphy for updating and enhancing

the listing for this Edition. The boxes listed here are only those observed or reported. It is known that other trade packaging of this type exists and the Editor would welcome any additional information on the subject.

Expect Trade Boxes containing rare colour variations to attract a corresponding premium. NB See also Gift Sets for 62h and 62d pre-war Aeroplane Trade Box items. NGPP = No guide price at present.

Model and details	MPR

Type 1 Pre-Second World War. Card boxes that have a four-digit reference code number preceded by the letter 'A'. Most have a covering of yellow paper. (The few exceptions that have orange-brown, blue or green paper coverings are noted in the list). Wording: 'Dinky Toys Made in England by Meccano Limited'. Printed information consists of model name and number, often with a date and quantity. The date code is usually a month number and year number separated by a full stop thus: '3.40', in this case indicating March 1940.

Model and details			MPR
22e	Tractor	6.... A966B	£400-500
22g	Streamline Tourer	6.... A2018	£1,500-1,750
23	Racing Car	6.... A1002	£1,500-2,000
24g	Sports Tourer	6.... A1017	£1,500-2,000
24h	Sports Tourer	6.... A1018	NGPP
25d	Petrol Wagon	6.... A1022	NGPP
25e	Tipping Wagon	6.... A1023	NGPP
25f	Market Gardener's Lorry	6.... A1024	NGPP
26	Rail Autocar	6.... A1001	NGPP
27	Tram Car	6....	£900-1,200
28/1	Delivery Vans, 1st Type	6.... A1008	£5,000-7,500
29a	('Q') Motor Bus	6....	£1,000-1,500
29c	Double-Deck Bus	6.... A2226	£1,200-1,600
30e	Breakdown Car	6.... A2060	£150-200
30g	Caravan	6.... A2106	£100-150
32	Chrysler Airflow	6.... A2032	£2,000-3,000
33a	Mechanical Horse, orange-brown	6.... A2037	NGPP
36f	British Salmson 4-str with Driver	6.... A2211	NGPP
37a	Civilian Motor Cyclist	A2229 6	£150-200
37c	Dispatch Rider	6.... A2237	£150-200
39e	Chrysler Royal	6.... A2290	£1,000-1,500
47d	Beacon	12.... A2058	NGPP
50a	HMS 'Hood'	12.... A1030	NGPP
50f/50h	Destroyers 'Broke' and 'Amazon' Class	12.... A1035	NGPP
50g/50k	Submarines 'K' and 'X' Class	12.... A1036	NGPP
62d	Bristol Blenheim Bombers, green	6....	£400-600
62h	Hawker Hurricane Fighters, green	6.... '7-39'	£400-600
62m	Airspeed Envoy	6.... A2234	NGPP
62s	Hurricane Fighters, blue	6....	£300-400
63b	'Mercury'	6.... A2253	NGPP
151a	Medium Tank	6.... A2190	£3,000-4,000
152c	RTC Austin Seven	6.... A2196	£400-500
160b	R.A. Gunners	12....	£200-250
160g	R.A. Personnel	?.... A2303	NGPP

Type 2 The first of the post-war trade boxes. Brown card box with yellow contents label affixed to one end (occasionally both ends) No box reference code in the main, but exceptions are noted below.

Model and details		MPR
14a	B.E.V. Truck	6.... £150-200
23a	Racing Car	6.... £500-750
23d	Racing Car	6.... £175-225
25b	Covered Wagon	6.... £500-750
25d	Petrol Wagon	6.... £200-300

Model and details		MPR
25e	Tipping Wagon	6.... £250-350
25f	Market Gardeners Lorry	6, 'VK29' / 'AS39' £250-350
25g	Trailer	6.... NGPP
25h	Fire Engine	6.... £300-400
25j	Jeep	6.... 'M26' £250-350
25p	Aveling Barford Diesel Roller	4.... 'M__' £150-200
25r	Forward Control Lorry	6.... 'M23' £300-350
25t	Flat Truck/Trailer	3.... £300-350
25v	Bedford Refuse Wagon	4.... £200-300
27a	M-H Tractor	3.... £150-200
29b	Streamlined Bus	6.... 'M24' NGPP
29c	Double Deck Bus (packed vertically)	6.... £400-500
29c	Double Deck Bus (laid flat)	6.... £200-300
29e	Single Deck Bus	6.... £300-350
30b	Rolls-Royce	6.... £300-400
30d	Vauxhall	6.... £300-400
30f	Ambulance, 'M28' / 'M35'	6.... £300-400
33w	Mechanical Horse and Open Wagon	3.... £200-250
34b	Royal Mail Van	6.... £300-400
34c	Loudspeaker Van	6.... 'VK49' £150-180
36a	Armstrong-Siddeley Limousine	6.... £350-400
38c	Lagonda Sports	6.... £250-300
39a	Packard Super 8 Touring Sedan	6.... £400-500
39d	Buick Viceroy	6.... 'M24' £400-500
40a	Riley	6.... 'M__' £350-450
40b	Triumph 1800	6.... £350-450
40e	Standard Vanguard	6 £350-450
40e	Standard Vanguard	6 'M50' £350-450
52a	'Queen Mary'	6.... £90-120
	(some seen with red 'Hudson Dobson' label).	
105a	Garden Roller	6.... £100-125
152b	Reconnaissance Car	6.... £400-500
161b	Mobile A-A Gun	6.... £300-400

Type 3 Second design of post-war box. All-yellow with direct printing (no label). All are pre-1953/54 renumbering. No box reference code.

Model and details		MPR
23b	Small Closed Racing Car	6.... £200-300
23c	Large Open Racing Car	6.... £200-300
23e	'Speed of the Wind' Racing Car	6.... £200-300
25h	Fire Engine	6.... NGPP
25m	Bedford End Tipper	4.... £400-500
25t	Flat Truck and Trailer	3.... £300-325
25v	Bedford Refuse Wagon	4.... £350-400
25w	Bedford Truck	4.... £400-500
25y	Universal Jeep	4.... £150-225
27a	Massey-Harris Tractor	3.... £150-200
27b	Harvest Trailer	3.... £75-85
27c	MH Manure Spreader	3.... £85-100
27d	Land Rover	4.... £150-200
27f	Estate Car	4.... £200-250
27g	Motocart	3.... £100-150
27h	Disc Harrow	4.... £60-80
29f	Observation Coach	6.... £350-450
30h	Daimler Ambulance	4.... £200-300

Model and details		MPR
30j	Austin Wagon	6.... £400-500
30m	Rear Tipping Wagon	6.... £150-200
30r	Thames Flat Truck	6.... £130-160
30s	Austin Covered Wagon	6.... £200-250
30v	Electric Dairy Van	6.... £250-300
30v	Electric Dairy Van 'NCB'	6.... £250-300
31a	Trojan 'Esso' Van	6.... £600-700
31b	Trojan 'Dunlop' Van	6.... £600-700
35c	MG Sports Car	6.... £250-300
36a	Armstrong-Siddeley	6.... £400-500
37b	Police Motor Cyclist	6.... £150-200
38b	Sunbeam-Talbot	6.... £400-500
38e	Armstrong-Siddeley	6.... £450-550
39e	Chrysler Royal Sedan	6.... NGPP
40b	Triumph 1800 Saloon	6.... £350-450
40d	Austin Devon	6.... £350-450
40f	Hillman Minx Saloon	6.... £350-450
40g	Morris Oxford Saloon	6.... £350-450
40j	Austin Somerset	6.... £350-450
42a	Police Box	6.... £140-170
47c	Two-face Traffic Lights	12.... £40-70
70d	Twin Engined Fighter	6.... £100-130
70e	Gloster Meteor	6.... £40-60
70f	Shooting Star	6.... £100-150
105a	Garden Roller	6.... £80-90
105b	Wheelbarrow	6.... £80-90
105c	4-wheeled Hand Truck	6.... £40-60
105e	Grass Cutter	6.... £90-110
107a	Sack Truck	6.... £90-110
139a	Ford Fordor	6.... £250-300
139b	Hudson Commodore	6.... £500-700
140a	Austin Atlantic	6.... £400-500
152b	Reconnaissance Car	6.... £400-500
161b	Mobile AA Gun	6.... £300-400
603a	Army Personnel (metal). NB early boxes long, later issues are square	12.... £80-110
603a	Army Personnel (plastic)	12.... £40-50

Type 4 As Type 3 but with the addition of a five-digit box reference code.

Model and details		MPR
23f	Alfa Romeo Racing Car '50189'	6... £400-500
23s	Streamlined R. Car, '50012'	4... £300-400
25h	Fire Engine, '50019'	6... £300-400
25m	Bedford Truck, '50021'	4... £400-500
25p	Aveling-Barford Diesel Roller, '50022'	4... £150-200
25y	Universal Jeep, '50159'	4... £150-225
27a	M-H Tractor, '50029'	3... £150-200
27h	Disc Harrow, '50035'	4... £60-80
27j	Triple-Gang Mower, '50156'	3... £150-200
27m	Land-Rover Trailer, '50161'	4... £90-110
29g	Luxury Coach, '50042'	6... £400-500
29h	Duple Roadmaster Coach, '50163'	6... £300-400
30h	Daimler Ambulance, '50049'	4... £200-300
30j	Austin Wagon, '50050'	6... £400-500
30m	Rear Tipping Wagon, '50052'	6... £200-250
30p	Mobilgas Tanker, '50051'	6... £500-600
30pa	Castrol Tanker, '50146'	6... £500-700
30pb	Esso Tanker, '50147'	6... £500-700
30w	Electric Artic. Lorry, '50059'	3... £300-400
31a	Trojan Esso Van, '50149'	6... £500-600
31c	Trojan Chivers Van, '50151'	6... £600-800
33w	Mechanical Horse and Open Wagon, '50060'	3... £200-250
34c	Loudspeaker Van, '50062'	6... £200-250

35a	**Saloon Car**		
	('Slide-tray' type box), '50063'...	6	**£300-400**
35b	**Racer**		
	('Slide-tray' type box), 'CZ35'...	6	**£280-330**
40f	**Hillman Minx**	6	**£350-450**
40g	**Morris Oxford**	6	**£350-450**
40h	**Austin Taxi**, '50097'	6	NGPP
70a	**Avro York Air-Liner**, '50123'	1	NGPP
70b	**Hawker Tempest**, '50124'	6	NGPP
70c	**Viking Air-Liner**, '50125'	6	NGPP
70f	**Shooting Star Jet**, '50128'	6	NGPP
105e	**Grass Cutter**, '50132'	6	**£90-110**
139b	**Hudson Commodore**, '50135'	6	**£500-700**
140a	**Austin Atlantic**, '50136'	6	**£500-700**
140b	**Rover 75**, '50137'	6	**£350-450**

Type 5 As Type 3 (all-yellow, direct printed, no reference code), but these display the 'dual numbering' of the models contained. They generally date from around 1954 when Meccano renumbered most of the Dinky Toys. They are listed here in the order of the earlier model numbering system.

12c/750	**Telephone Call Box**	6	**£150-200**
23a/220	**Racing Car**	6	**£400-500**
23e/221	**'Speed of the Wind'**	6	**£200-250**
23s/222	**Streamlined R. Car**	4	**£200-300**
25g/429	**Trailer**	6	**£80-120**
25h/250	**Fire Engine**	6	NGPP
25m/410	**Bedford End Tipper**	4	**£400-500**
25r/420	**Forward Control Lorry**	6	**£200-250**
25w/411	**Bedford Truck**	6	**£200-250**
25y/405	**Universal Jeep**	4	**£200-250**
27a/300	**Massey-Harris Tractor**	3	**£150-200**
27d/340	**Land-Rover**	4	**£200-250**
27g/342	**Motocart**	3	**£80-120**
27m/341	**Land-Rover Trailer**	4	**£80-120**
29g/281	**Luxury Coach**	6	**£300-350**
30r/422	**Fordson Thames**	6	**£70-100**
30s/413	**Austin Cov. Wagon**	6	**£250-300**
30v/490	**'Express Dairy' Van**	6	**£250-300**
30v/491	**'N.C.B.' Dairy Van**	6	**£120-160**
30w/421	**Electric Artic. Lorry**	3	**£125-150**
31b/451	**Trojan Van 'Dunlop'**	6	**£400-500**
31c/452	**Trojan Van 'Chivers'**	6	**£400-500**
35b/200	**Midget Racer**, 'CZ35'	6	NGPP
40b/151	**Triumph 1800 Saloon**	6	**£250-350**
40j/161	**Austin Somerset**	6	**£350-450**
42a/751	**Police Hut**	6	**£50-80**
63b/700	**Seaplane**	6	**£250-350**
70c/705	**Viking Airliner**	6	NGPP
70d/731	**Twin Engined Fighter**	6	NGPP
70e/732	**Meteor Jet Fighter**	6	NGPP
70f/733	**Shooting Star Jet**	6	**£80-100**
105a/381	**Garden Roller**	6	**£80-120**

105b/382	**Wheelbarrow**	6	**£60-80**
105c/383	**4-w. Hand Truck**	6	**£80-120**
105e/384	**Grass Cutter**	6	**£120-150**
107a/385	**Sack Truck**	6	**£50-70**
140a/106	**Austin Atlantic**	6	NGPP
140b/156	**Rover 75**	6	**£200-250**

Type 6 Post 1953-54, all-yellow printed box. These contain the newly-introduced (or re-introduced) models having just a single three-digit reference number.

270	**'AA' Motor Cycle**	6	**£200-300**
272	**'ANWB' Motor Cycle**	6	**£250-350**
603	**Army Personnel -**		
	Private (seated)	12	NGPP
673	**Scout Car**	6	**£65-85**
687	**Field Gun Trailer**	6	**£65-85**
705	**Viking Airliner**	6	**£200-300**
750	**Telephone Call Box**	6	**£200-300**
751	**Police Hut**	6	**£150-180**
755	**Lamp Standard,** single-arm	6	**£30-40**
756	**Lamp Standard,** double-arm	6	**£30-40**
760	**Pillar Box**	6	**£150-200**
768	**Racks with Tyres**	6	**£75-100**
773	**Robot Traffic Signal**	12	**£150-175**
777	**Belisha Beacon**	12	**£65-90**
786	**Tyre Rack**	6	**£120-160**
788	**Spare Bucket** for 966	6	**£175-225**
797	**Healey Sports Boat**	6	**£150-200**

Type 7 (Post-war).
Small boxes, covered in green paper; with 'flap' ends.

12d	**Telegraph Messenger**		
	'50175' on some	6	**£100-125**
12e	**Postman**, '50176' on some	6	**£100-125**
13a	**Cook's Man**, '50174' on some	6	**£100-125**
43b	**'RAC' M/c Patrol**	6	**£300-400**
44b	**'AA' M/c Patrol**	6	**£300-400**
760	**Pillar Box**	2	NGPP

Type 8 (Post-war).
A box specially designed for
3 x **551 Large Trailer**.

'Dinky Toys', brown, yellow label		**£80-120**
'Dinky Toys', blue card, '50551'		**£80-120**
'Supertoys', brown, '50551'		**£80-120**
'Supertoys', green, '(M49)'		**£80-120**
'Supertoys', green, '(IH89)'		**£80-120**
'Supertoys', blue card, '50551'		**£80-120**
'Supertoys' yellow card, '(M44)'		**£80-120**

Type 9 These began appearing from the mid-1950s. They are 'trade packs' rather than trade boxes as they contain quantities of individually boxed models. Thin grey (or brownish-grey) card construction with flap ends or tuck-in ends; direct printing mostly in black. The printing on outer boxes for Dublo Dinkys 067 and 069 is in red. The major exception here is 078 which has an outer box of similar design to the individual Dublo boxes inside.

067	**Austin Taxi**	6	NGPP
069	**Massey-Harris Tractor**	6	**£300-400**
070	**AEC Mercury Tanker**	6	**£500-600**
076	**Lansing-Bagnall Trailer**	6	**£300-400**
104	**'United Biscuits' Taxis**	?	NGPP
106	**'Prisoner' Mini-Moke**	6	**£300-400**
112	**Purdey's Triumph TR7**	6	**£150-200**
122	**Volvo 265 DL Estate**	6	**£55-65**
159	**Morris Oxford**	6	**£350-450**
161	**Austin Somerset**	6	**£600-800**
188	**Jensen FF**	6	**£150-200**
188	**4-berth Caravan**	6	**£175-200**
193	**Rambler Station Wagon**	6	**£400-500**
195	**Jaguar 3.4 Saloon**	6	**£400-500**
292	**Leyland Atlantean Bus**	6	**£350-450**
429	**Trailer**	6	**£100-150**
442	**Land-Rovers**	6	**£100-125**
471	**Austin Van 'NESTLE'**	6	**£300-400**
491	**Electric Dairy Van 'N.C.B.',**		
		6,	**£1,000-1,200**
491	**Electric Dairy Van 'JOB'S'**	6	**£600-800**
252/25v	**Refuse Wagon**	4	**£350-450**
260	**Royal Mail Van**	6	NGPP
260	**VW 'Deutsche Bundespost'**	6	**£150-200**
344/27f	**Estate Car**	4	**£200-250**
492/34c	**Loudspeaker Van**	6	**£200-250**
668	**Foden Army Trucks**	6	**£80-100**
675	**Ford US Army Staff Car**	6	NGPP
677	**Armoured Command Vehicle**	6	**£200-250**
755/6	**Lamp Standards,**		
	yellow/red box	6	**£100-120**
994	**Loading Ramp** (for 982)	3	**£55-80**

Type 10 Later 1970s trade packs without printing. A small yellow label is attached that shows the model number only. 432 and 662 are exceptions, being shrink-wrapped with no label.

305	**David Brown Tractor**	6	NGPP
308	**Leyland 384 Tractor**	6	NGPP
432	**Foden Tipping Lorry,**		
	factory shrink-wrapped pack	6	**£80-100**
662	**Foden Army Truck,**		
	factory shrink-wrapped pack	6	**£100-125**

Buying?
visit dinkystore.com

We let our photos do the talking

Because a picture's worth a thousand words...

dinkystore.com

Selling?
visit dinkysite.com

Jonathan Francis
07716 338228 or 01212 888697
jonathan.francis@dinkysite.com

Dinky Toys Trade Accessories

'World Famous Racing Cars'. Retailer's Shop Window / Counter Display Showcard with models 230, 231, 232 and 233 strung into place on the racetrack design.
Yellow and Red Showcard **£3,000-4,000**

Black wooden Trade Display Unit in plain cardboard box. 'Property of Meccano Ltd Liverpool' in black on gold; 3 shelves in light blue/white/yellow;
4 gold supports with 2 yellow and 2 red supports;
4 red tin flags 'DINKY TOYS'; 3 tin flags 'ASK FOR BOOKLET', 'OVER 200 MODELS', and 'ALWAYS SOMETHING NEW'; plus
2 red and 2 yellow balls.............................. **£400-500**

Glass Display Case. Oak frame with three glass shelves. Size approx. 32" (80 cm.) wide, 24" (60 cm.) high, 9" (22 cm.) deep. With 'DINKY TOYS' in green lettering on glass front **£350-450**

Large wooden Display Unit 'DINKY SHOWROOM', 50" x 22" x 38" **£1,000-1,200**

Dinky Dealers Trade Counter Display Box.

Trade Display Stand Large yellow folding cardboard stand which non-erected measures approx. 28" (70 cm.) x 14" (35 cm.); three display levels with 'DINKY TOYS' logo in green plus 'MECCANO PRODUCT' in red on top header board. Outer corrugated cardboard packing has green printed instruction leaflet. **£200-300**

Trade Display Stand Small yellow and red folding cardboard stand which non-erected measures approximately 12" (31 cm.) x 7" (15 cm.); with one 'DINKY TOYS' and two 'DINKY SUPERTOYS' logos in red plus yellow 'MASTERPIECES IN MINIATURE' logo on red background. **£100-125**

Display Stand (circa 1950 - 1960) Large metal stand measures approximately 36" x 21" x 22" (91.5 x 53 x 56 cm.); with nine display shelves covered in black plastic track. Metal advertisement affixed to top states in yellow/red/black 'A MOTOR SHOW FOR GIRLS AND BOYS', 'PRECISION DIE-CAST MODELS BY MECCANO', 'BEST RANGE', 'BEST VALUE IN THE WORLD'. Lower large transfer also in yellow/red/black repeats the message. **£500-750**

Window Sign (plastic), Dark blue top half with white 'MECCANO' logo, bottom half is yellow. Red 'Dinky Toys' logo. Approx. 18"x6"........ **£100-125**

Counter Display (cardboard), Small display stand for a single model, 'ALWAYS NEW MODELS' logo in white on red background, header states 'DINKY TOYS' in red on yellow. **£100-125**

Counter Display (cardboard), retailer's display stand in yellow/blue, 'ALWAYS NEW' logo, 'DINKY TOYS' in red....................... **£50-75**

Counter Display (cardboard) 'BATTLE OF BRITAIN' Blue/yellow displaying 719 Spitfire MkII and 721 Junkers JU 87b Stuka........... **£150-175**

Shop Display Carousel with tripod base supporting four stacks of clear plastic. **£200-300**

Illuminated Shop Display Sign with 'DINKY TOYS' in large red wooden letters above a glass panel lettered either 'Made by Meccano Ltd' or 'British and Guaranteed'. **£500-600**

Shelf Display Card in 'landscape' format, featuring the Hesketh 308E 'OLYMPUS' Racing Car **£100-150**

Display Card, 300 x 250mm, with 'The Wisest Choice Dinky Toys' on yellow background ... **£50-75**
Freestanding Card, 'Dinky Toys for Variety and Value', 33 x '17cm........................ **£50-75**

Illuminated Counter or Window display unit 13" x 9", perspex front 'DINKY TOYS' + 'NEW MODELS EVERY MONTH' logo............... **£100-1500**

Counter Carousel Unit with 'Always Something New from Dinky' around its edge. Red/Yellow 'DINKY TOYS BY MECCANO' sign on top, 26" high overall. **£200-250**

Metal Counter Display Sign, triangular in shape with red 'DINKY TOYS' on yellow background, approximately 8" x 1" x 1". **£30-40**

Electric Revolving 'Meccano' Wooden Display Stand. 'DINKY TOYS - LOOK FOR THE NAME ON THE BASE' logo, (28" square and 10" high) **£250-350**

Pre-War 'Meccano Dinky Toys' Advertising Sign. This double-sided hanging sign shows pictures and details of 22, 24, 25 and 28 series models available in 'Season 1934'. Date code: '16/734/1'.
Size: 11in x 9in (28cm x 23cm) **£500-600**

1938 Cardboard Display Stand shows boy with green jumper, and 'Dinky Toys 300 Varieties'... **£150-175**

1955 Wooden 3-tier Display Stand. Pale green. 'Dinky Toys' and 'Dinky Supertoys' **£300-400**

c.1959 'Dublo Dinky' Shop Display Stand. Pale yellow with red logo and wording 'NEW SERIES / DUBLO DINKY', etc. Stand dimensions: 28cm x 19cm overall ... **£300-500**

Dinky Toys Price Tickets. Aluminium tags to place on toys plus sheet of 200 self-adhesive labels showing model number and price.. **£200-250**

Wall Chart. 1963 Dinky Toys and Dinky Supertoys Wall Chart listing all tyre sizes for model vehicles **£100-125**

1961 'Mini Dinky' retailer's counter/window display card, 23 x 16.5cm **£100-125**

c1960 Electric 'Dinky Toys' Perspex Hanging Sign. Yellow sides, red letters, 1,300mm. .. **£250-350**

c1960 'Dinky Toys' Counter-top Stand for the Italian market. Steel tubular and metal sheet construction approx. 30cm high, triangular back, two shelves, 'Novita', 'Meccano'.
Dark cream and white................................. **£90-120**
1960s Metal and Perspex Display Case, (33 x 24cm), yellow with red letters with 'Dinky Toys' sign and window for models............ **£200-250**

c1970s Electric 'Dinky Toys' Perspex Hanging Sign. Yellow sides with red letters, 1,270mm long **£175-225**

1960s Window leaflets / posters / stickers

72569	Lady Penelope's 'FAB 1'	**£50-60**
72579	Captain Scarlett and Thunderbirds ..	**£50-60**
?	486 'Dinky Beats' Morris Oxford.......	**£30-40**
?	107 'Stripey, the Magic Mini'	**£30-40**
?	101 Thunderbirds	**£30-40**
?	153 Aston-Martin DB6.......................	**£30-40**
?	970 Jones Fleetmaster Crane	**£30-40**
?	281 Pathe News Camera Car.............	**£30-40**
?	158 Rolls-Royce Silver Shadow	**£20-30**
?	131 Ford 40-RV	**£20-30**
?	282 Austin 1800	**£20-30**
?	280 Midland Mobile Bank.................	**£20-30**
?	129 Volkswagen Beetle	**£20-30**
?	163 Volkswagen 1600TL...................	**£20-30**
?	166 Renault R16	**£20-30**
?	135 Triumph 2000 and	
	240 Cooper Racing Car.....................	**£20-30**
?	141 Vauxhall Victor Estate Car..........	**£20-30**

1970s Shop window self-adhesive posters

100362	1972 Double-sided poster featuring 'All Action Fighting Vehicles' and '10 Great Fighting Vehicles'	**£20-30**
100367	1973 Double-sided poster featuring 'Highway Action Models'.................	**£20-30**
100482	1971 Single-sided poster advertising '451 Road Sweeper'	**£20-30**
100524	Single-sided poster advertising 'No 410 Bedford Van'	**£20-30**
100537	Single-sided poster with 'No 654 155mm Mobile Gun'	**£20-30**
100595	Single-sided poster advertising 'No 694 Hanomag Tank Destroyer'.	**£20-30**
100602	Single-sided poster advertising 'No 293 Swiss PTT Bus'	**£20-30**
100604	Single-sided poster advertising 'No 656 88mm Gun'	**£20-30**
100734	Single-sided poster advertising 'No 668 Foden Army Truck'	**£20-30**
100741	Single-sided poster advertising 'No 432 Foden Tipper Truck'	**£20-30**
100742	Single-sided, advertising 'No 430 Johnson 2-ton Dumper'.....	**£20-30**
100523	Single-sided, advertising 'No 682 Stalwart Load Carrier'........	**£20-30**
100531	Single-sided poster advertising 'No 683 Chieftain Tank'	**£20-30**
100496	Single-sided poster advertising 'No 725 F-4K Phantom II'	**£20-30**
?	Poster advertising '442 Land-Rover Breakdown Crane'............................	**£20-30**
?	Poster advertising '967 Muir-Hill Loader and Trencher'.........................	**£20-30**
?	Poster advertising '915 AEC with Flat Trailer'...............	**£20-30**
?	Poster advertising 1/25th scale Ford Capri and Police Car	**£30-40**
?	Poster adv. 1/25th Saloon Car	**£30-40**
?	Poster advertising 724 Sea King Helicopter...................	**£20-25**
?	Poster advertising 984 Atlas Digger .	**£20-25**
?	Poster adv. 977 Shovel Dozer	**£20-25**
?	Poster adv. 963 Road Grader	**£20-25**
?	Poster adv. 726 Messerschmitt.........	**£20-25**
?	Poster adv. 730 US Phantom	**£20-25**
?	Poster advertising 731 S.E.P.E.C.A.T. Jaguar and 728 RAF Dominie	**£20-25**
?	Poster adv. 734 P47 Thunderbolt	**£20-25**
?	Poster advertising 739 Zero Sen.......	**£20-25**

All other late issued leaflets not listed . each: **£20-25**

Note: This section is far from complete and the Editor would welcome details of other trade stands, posters, display cards, promotional material and advertising signs.

Nicky Toys, 1968–1975

In the late 1960s Meccano shipped out to India obsolete model dies and tools. The objective was to overcome exporting difficulties by manufacturing toys in India itself. The Indian manufacturing company was S. Kumar & Co who traded as Atamco Private Ltd. For trade mark reasons the toys were sold as 'Nicky Toys' and the arrangement was that the words 'Meccano' and 'Dinky Toys' would be obliterated from the dies. Similarly an arrangement was agreed in respect of deleting 'Dinky Toys' from the original model boxes.

However, the removal process was not diligently implemented which resulted in Nicky Toys occasionally being sold with 'Dinky Toys' being displayed both on their baseplates and on their boxes. These models are sought after by collectors and attract a premium at auctions.

After S.Kumar & Co. had made the models from the original dies, they were finished by various firms of outworkers and as a result many different paint, decal and wheel versions exist. The details of the models listed are taken from various recent auction listings so their existence is confirmed.

The figures shown in the 'Market Price Range' column are based on recent auction results and reflect the prices achieved by mint models in good boxes.

Types of Nicky Toys Boxes
i) Original yellow box with 'Dinky Toys' on the front

and end flaps of the box and with a single model picture on front of box. This is the type of box which should have had all references to 'Dinky Toys' removed or overstamped.
ii) A plain yellow card box with 'Nicky Toys' stamped on the box end flaps and with 'Manufactured by: ATAMCO PRIVATE LTD. CALCUTTA' printed on the box sides.
iii) A yellow box with a full colour picture on the side. 'Nicky Toys' is clearly printed on all sides of the box and on the end flaps.
More information would be welcomed.

Model and details	MPR

A group of Nicky Toys.

050 Jaguar 'Police' Car
- Metallic Red body.........**£80-100**
- Red/White body..............**£80-100**

05 VW 'Police' Car
- Blue, white doors..........**£80-100**

051 Mercedes 220E 'Taxi'
- Black/Yellow, 'Taxi' headboard..........**£80-100**
- Same but Grey body........**£80-100**
- With Orange body.........**£80-100**

054 Standard Herald Mk.II
- Metallic Green body.....**£80-100**
- Red or Blue body..........**£80-100**
- Lemon-Yellow body......**£80-100**
- White/Red body............**£80-100**
- All-White body............**£150-175**

094 Rolls-Royce
- Gold body.....................**£80-100**

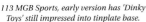

113 MGB Sports, early version has 'Dinky Toys' still impressed into tinplate base.

113 MGB Sports (with driver)
- Light Blue body..........**£100-125**
- Navy Blue body..........**£100-125**
- Metallic Red body.......**£100-125**
- Light Green body........**£100-125**

115 Plymouth Fury
- Metallic Green body.....**£80-100**
- Silver body..................**£80-100**
- Blue body.....................**£80-100**

120 Jaguar 'E'-type
- Metallic Green body...**£100-125**
- Red body....................**£100-125**
- Apple-Green body......**£100-125**
- Blue body..................**£100-125**
- Silver body.................**£100-125**

- Yellow body.................**£100-125**

134 Standard Herald Mk.II
(Triumph Vitesse)
- Red with White stripe...**£80-100**
- Turquoise with White body stripe...................**£80-100**
- Green with Red stripe....**£80-100**
- Blue with Red stripe.....**£80-100**

137 Plymouth Fury Convertible
- Red, Yellow interior......**£80-100**
- Yellow, Black interior...**£80-100**
- Apple-Green body........**£80-100**
- Metallic Green body.....**£80-100**
- Red body......................**£80-100**
- Cream body..................**£80-100**

137 Plymouth Fury Sports
- Silver, Blue interior.......**£80-100**
- Yellow body.................**£80-100**
- Blue body.....................**£80-100**
- Apple-Green body........**£80-100**
- Red body.....................**£80-100**
- Turquoise body............**£80-100**

142 Jaguar Mk.X
- Met. Blue, White int......**£80-100**
- Green, White interior...**£80-100**
- Metallic Red body........**£80-100**
- Metallic Turquoise.......**£80-100**
- Silver body..................**£80-100**
- Pale Yellow body..........**£80-100**

144 Volkswagen 1500
- Red body.....................**£80-100**
- White body...................**£80-100**
- Blue body.....................**£80-100**
- Metallic Green body......**£80-100**
- **'Police'** version, Blue / White body.........**£80-100**

146 Daimler V8 Saloon
(Jaguar 3.4 litre)
- No colour details..............NGPP
- **'Police'** version, Red / White body..........**£80-100**

170 Lincoln Continental
- Blue, White roof..........**£100-150**
- Silver, White roof........**£100-150**
- Pale Yellow body, Black roof....................**£100-150**
- Cream, Black roof.......**£100-150**
- Metallic Red body with White roof..........**£100-150**
- Metallic Turquoise, White roof..................**£100-150**

186 Mercedes Benz 220SE
- Metallic Red body, Light Grey interior........**£80-100**
- Grey, Light Grey int. **£80-100**
- Metallic Light Green.....**£80-100**
- Metallic Blue body........**£80-100**
- Silver, White int...........**£100-120**

194 Bentley 'S' Coupé
- Met. Red, White tonneau, Black interior..................**£80-100**
- Met. Green, Black tonneau, Red or Yellow int...........**£80-100**
- Cream with Red int.......**£80-100**
- Blue, Red interior..........**£80-100**
- Silver body...................**£80-100**
- Gold body.....................**£80-100**

195 Jaguar 3.4 litre
- Silver body, Light Grey interior........**£80-100**
- Cream, Red interior.......**£80-100**
- Blue, Red interior..........**£80-100**

238 Jaguar 'D'-type
(RN '35' on some)
- Light Blue body, Yellow plastic hubs.........**£70-90**
- Racing Green body.........**£70-90**
- Red body........................**£70-90**
- Silver body.....................**£70-90**
- Metallic Red body..........**£70-90**
- Metallic Green body.......**£70-90**

Vanwall Racing Car with 'Dinky Toys' impressed into tinplate baseplate.

239 Vanwall Racing Car
(All have a blue plastic driver)
- Dark Metallic Blue..........**£70-90**
- Red..................................**£70-90**
- Green **£70-90**
- Light Blue body...............**£70-90**
- Grey body........................**£70-90**
- Yellow body....................**£70-90**

295 Standard '20' Minibus
- Metallic Red body...........**£60-80**
- Green body......................**£60-80**
- Silver body......................**£60-80**

- Pale Blue body **£60-80**
- Red body **£60-80**
- Grey body **£60-80**
- **'Ambulance'** version. White, Blue rooflight, red crosses on roof/doors.....**£60-80**

405 Universal Jeep
(All have black windscreen frame)
- Gloss Brick Red...........**£100-125**
- Light Grey....................**£100-125**
- Blue..............................**£100-125**
- **Army** versions in Military Green.............**£100-125**

626 Military Ambulance
- Gloss Green body **£80-100**

660 Mighty Antar Tank Transporter
- Gloss Green (military)......NGPP
- Yellow/Grey (civilian version)........**£300-400**

693 Howitzer 7.2
- Dark Military Green ....NGPP

705 Viscount Airliner 'BEA'
- Red, White and Blue.........NGPP

Nicky Toys 194 Bentley S Coupé.

735 Gloucester Javelin
- RAF and camouflage liveries **£90-110**

738 Sea Vixen
- RAF and camouflage liveries **£80-100**

949 Wayne School Bus
- No details available ....NGPP

962 Dumper Truck
- No details available ....NGPP

999 Comet Airliner 'BOAC.'
- 'G-ALYX', boxed...........**£140-180**

Nicky Toys Catalogue Cover depicts Jaguar Mk.10 at Motor Show. Range of models shown in two-tone colour **£40-60**

French Meccano Dinky Toys

The history of French Meccano Dinky Toys mirrors that of the Liverpool parent company. The Meccano France subsidiary was set up by Frank Hornby at Rue Ambroise Thomas in Paris in 1912 primarily to import British-made Meccano outfits and components. Having successfully marketed Meccano in France the obvious next step was to manufacture it there and in 1921, a factory was duly established at Rue Rébéval in Paris. This was initially used as offices and warehousing until 1924 when French-made Meccano became available, the Meccano Guild having been created a year before.

Production on French soil proved even more successful and a major new factory was soon required. Building of the famous plant at Bobigny was started in 1929. In 1931, the year in which Frank Hornby became MP for Everton, French Hornby 'Lead Models' nos 1, 2 and 3 were introduced, followed by 'Miniature Models' nos 4 and 10 in 1932. 'Modelled Miniatures' made their appearance in England in these years. Early in 1934 'Hornby Modelled Miniatures' were announced in France. Originally intended to extend the growing range of Hornby railway accessories, they were very briefly renamed 'Meccano Miniatures'. Before the year was out they had acquired the name 'Dinky Toys' in both countries. In the same year the Bobigny factory took over all French Meccano production while the Rue Rébéval premises reverted to offices and warehousing.

In 1935, 'Dolly Varden' dolls house furniture was introduced in England and the following year in France. Military vehicles became part of the Dinky range in Britain in 1937 but plans to introduce models of this type in France came to nothing before the war. Some of the English model tanks and guns were sent there between 1938 and 1940 along with some aircraft and ships. A very small part of French production was imported into Britain in the late 1930s and most of their references were given a 'z' suffix.

During the late pre-war period the names were removed from aircraft dies and the models were given vague generic titles such as 'Long Range Bomber' and 'Medium Bomber'. Some planes, like the Gloster Gladiator, had no name at all and models of ships were given similar anonymity. It has been said that this was done for the cause of national security – to prevent Nazi intelligence from identifying the actual planes and ships by looking at the toys!

Among resources eagerly seized by the occupying German forces was naturally any factory that could turn instantly to the production of armaments. The French Meccano factory was thus commandeered in 1940 and required to produce various industrial items to satisfy the German war effort and even some toys to be sold under the Märklin name in German-occupied parts of the continent. Production of conventional Meccano products was, of course, prohibited. There were very many shortages by the time peace was declared, rubber being a particular problem in France from 1940 since Nazi activities had completely cut off supplies.

When Meccano haltingly returned to production in 1946, Dinky Toys tyres were noticeable by their absence. The metal wheel castings first used in 1940 continued to be fitted right up to the beginning of 1950. Even the 49 series Petrol Pumps had to be sold without hoses for a while! One of the most common vehicles on British and Continental roads during and after the war was the US Army Jeep. Thus in 1946 the 153a Jeep was introduced in England and the 24-M in France.

Any study of the history of Dinky Toys needs documentation from contemporary Meccano sources. Much of the required information is to be found in various catalogues and Meccano Magazines of the period but is not always reliable as an indicator of the date of introduction of models. Advertising did not always coincide with supply of models and distribution was not always even across the country. Most catalogues were generally accurate but occasionally announcements of forthcoming additions to the range could be just wishful thinking or proclamation of intent rather than actual production. Illustrations in early catalogues sometimes present problems with inaccurate line drawings and heavily retouched photographs. French catalogues suffered additional problems in having photos or drawings of English prototypes.

Many French catalogues were printed in England and some were actually English catalogues with a small amount of additional text in French plus a French currency price list. There is a marked similarity between French and English numbering systems and between actual castings, particularly before the war. However, it is important to remember that French castings are different from similar English ones, and come from French dies. All French Dinky Toys carry specific information either cast-in or stamped on a tinplate base as to the country of manufacture or assembly of the item.

In 1951, the Rue Rébéval factory closed and all French production was centralised at Bobigny. The French Meccano Magazine re-appeared in 1953 and 24-U Simca and 25-B Peugeot Van were introduced in their own individual yellow boxes. The first French Dinky Supertoy was issued in 1955.

Promotional opportunities were always being sought by Meccano and the idea of a society for young drivers of toy vehicles was welcomed by Roland Hornby who initiated the French Dinky Toys Club in 1957. 1960 saw the introduction of the French version of 'Dublo' trains ('Hornby ACHO'), production of which continued until 1974. French Hornby O gauge train manufacture came to an end in 1963.

The early 1960s was a time of diversification for Meccano in both England and France with Scalextric and other toys being added to the range of products. In a decade of changing fortunes they continued to design and manufacture an interesting range of Dinky Toys. In 1970 production was moved to a factory at Calais, partly to help relieve the industrial pressure in the Paris area and also to benefit from access to a major port. To cut costs in an increasingly difficult economic climate, manufacture of French Dinky cars was undertaken by Auto-Pilen of Spain in 1975. Other production continued at Calais until 1978 when all remaining French Dinky Toys manufacturing rights were signed over to the Spanish company.

Over the years, French and English Dinky Toys have had remarkable similarities and some quite paradoxical differences, reflecting the independence of the two companies. 'Speedwheels', for instance, were deemed essential in England to compete with Corgi's WhizzWheels and Lesney Superfast, while in France the need seems not to have been at all apparent. The range of ship models was quite extensive in England but very limited in France. The understandable dominance of French cars in the range resulted in a stream of taxi models in France while motorcycles were completely ignored after the Triporteur was withdrawn. The excellent French idea of a diamond shaped 'viewport' in the famous yellow boxes was restricted to that country and not tried in England. There is no 'Novelty' section in the French Dinky listings since the only models that would come under that heading would be imported British ones! Indeed, the only film or TV-related item to have originated in France is 1406 Michel Tanguy's Renault 4L Sinpar from the French TV series 'Les Chevaliers du Ciel'.

Some interesting models exist as accessories, particularly among the railway items. All the French castings of figures differ from English ones and have distinctly French characteristics; the 'Normandy' farmer and his French countrywoman spouse, the female railway crossing keeper, and the railway cook with his poultry dish are particularly pleasing. Road signs provide another area of interest, some of the later French versions being only available as a free addition with certain models and not sold individually.

Market Price Range
Please note that the prices shown refer to pristine models and boxes.
Items failing to match this standard will sell for less.
Note also that boxes must still contain all their original packing pieces
and additional contents where appropriate.

Cars – identification and casting differences

Although French and English reference numbers (particularly pre-war) are strikingly similar, it is very important to treat them as completely different systems in order to avoid confusion. The majority of French castings are different, as are the tyres. Surprisingly, small detail differences occur, as with steering wheels for instance. Post-war French-made open sports cars such as 22-A Maserati and 546 Austin-Healey have cast steering wheels with three spokes while those fitted to English made sports cars have four spokes. Many pre-war French made tyres have 'DUNLOP' moulded into the side-wall; post-war Spanish produced tyres similarly display the name 'PIRELLI'.

The 23b Streamlined Racing Car as made and sold in England from 1935 was based on a French Hotchkiss racing car. Unlike the English version, there were two French castings with the 23b reference. One is obviously the Hotchkiss (introduced in France in 1940). The other (pre-war) one is said by some to be modelled on a Renault Nervasport or possibly a Delahaye record car.

The 23 Racing Car is generally considered to have been inspired by the MG Magic Midget though it was never actually named as such by Meccano. Many modifications were made to the actual car in the 1930s in attempts to break various endurance and speed records, and both English and French models mirrored these changes during their production. Racing numbers on the French 23 and 23a models were never contained within a circle and were initially stencilled, later mask-sprayed. All the French 23 series castings have either 'Made in France' or 'Fab. en France' cast underneath

and also have a number of other differences from the English castings.

The first French Dinky Toys car model to be sold in its own box was the 24-U Simca Aronde in 1953. Many of the French boxes had a 'viewport' or aperture (usually diamond shaped) to allow a glimpse of the model. This enabled dealers and potential buyers to establish the colour of the model without the need to open the box. At the same time it saved the cost of printing a matching colour spot on the outside.

From 1969, a free 595 Traffic Sign was included as an additional attraction with certain models and these are noted in the listings that follow. More than 20 different plastic signs were made (see the 'Accessories' listing for details). They were not sold individually, but selections were available in Gift Sets 592 and 593.

French Dinky Toys Cars

Model and details	MPR
22a Roadster Sports	
1933-37 (scale 1:53)	
Lead two-seater open body, lead wheels.	
• Grey body / Blue wings	**£500-750**
• Blue body / Yellow wings	**£500-750**
• Silver body / Red wings	**£500-750**
• Green body / Yellow wings	**£500-750**
• Cream body / Red wings	**£500-750**
• Yellow body / Black wings	**£500-750**
22-A Maserati Sport 2000	
1958-58 (renumbered in 1958 to 505) (1:43)	
• Dark red body, Tan seats, plated convex hubs, white driver. Early bases are matt; later ones shiny	**£300-350**
1958-59	
• Dark red body, dark red seats, plated convex hubs, white driver	**£90-110**
• Same, but bright red body and seats	**£90-110**
22b Sports Coupé	
1934-37 (scale 1:53)	
Lead two-seater closed body, lead wheels.	
• Cream body with black wings	**£500-750**
• Blue body with red wings	**£500-750**

Model and details	MPR
• Red body with blue wings	**£500-750**
• Green body with yellow wings	**£500-750**
• Grey body with green wings	**£500-750**
• Buff body, Black wings and hubs	**£500-750**
22c Sports Roadster	
1934-37	
• As 22a, but with white rubber tyres on smooth silvered lead hubs	**£500-750**
22d Sports Coupé	
1934-37	
• As 22b, but with white rubber tyres on smooth silvered lead hubs	**£500-750**
23 Racing Car	
1933-35 (scale 1:53)	
• Lead body with contrasting colour flash over main colour, smooth lead hubs, 'DUNLOP' tyres coloured to match body flash. Indication of driver, 4 exhaust stubs, no exhaust pipe.	
• Orange (white, blue or green flash)	**£150-200**
• Cream (blue, green or red flash)	**£150-200**
• Blue (with silver or white flash)	**£150-200**
• Yellow (with blue flash)	**£150-200**

Model and details	MPR
1934-36	
Lead body with contrasting colour flash, smooth lead hubs, black or white or coloured tyres matching colour flash. Helmet detail, 4 exhaust stubs, no pipe.	
• Blue (white flash)	**£150-200**
• Green (orange flash)	**£150-200**
• White (blue flash)	**£150-200**
• Silver (blue flash)	**£150-200**
• Silver (red flash)	**£150-200**
• Cream (blue flash)	**£150-200**
• Cream (green flash)	**£150-200**
• Cream (red flash)	**£150-200**
23a Racing Car	
1936-37	
Diecast body and smooth hubs; black, white or coloured 'DUNLOP' tyres that match body flash. No driver, 4 exhaust stubs, no exhaust pipe.	
• Blue (white flash)	**£200-250**
• Green (orange flash)	**£200-250**
• White (blue flash)	**£200-250**
• Silver (blue flash)	**£200-250**

- Silver (red flash) **£200-250**
- Cream (blue flash) **£200-250**
- Cream (green flash) **£200-250**
- Cream (red flash) **£200-250**
1937-39
Diecast body and smooth hubs; black, white or coloured 'DUNLOP' tyres that match colour flash. Six branch exhaust pipe, driver helmet detail, 90mm. Racing numbers '1' or '12'.
- Blue (silver flash) **£200-250**
- Blue (white flash) **£200-250**
- Orange (green flash) **£200-250**
- Orange (blue flash) **£200-250**
- Yellow (blue flash) **£200-250**
- Cream (blue flash) **£200-250**
- Cream (green flash) **£200-250**
- Cream (red flash) **£200-250**
1939-40
As previous model but smooth diecast hubs in assorted colours, black or white tyres, RNs '1' or '12'.
- Blue (silver flash) **£200-250**
- Blue (white flash) **£200-250**
- Orange (green flash) **£200-250**
- Orange (blue flash) **£200-250**
- Yellow (blue flash) **£200-250**
- Cream (blue flash) **£200-250**
- Cream (green flash) **£200-250**
- Cream (red flash) **£200-250**
1940-40
As 1937-39 model but with unpainted diecast wheels.
- Blue (silver flash) **£200-250**
- Blue (white flash) **£200-250**
- Orange (green flash) **£200-250**
- Orange (blue flash) **£200-250**
- Yellow (blue flash) **£200-250**
- Cream (blue flash) **£200-250**
- Cream (green flash) **£200-250**
- Cream (red flash) **£200-250**

23b Streamlined Racing Car
1935-37 (scale 1:53)
Diecast body, plated smooth hubs, 'DUNLOP' tyres in the colour of the body flash.
- Blue (red flash, '1') **£200-250**
- Yellow (red flash, '2') **£200-250**
- Orange (blue flash, '3') **£200-250**
- Cream (blue flash '4') **£200-250**
- White (green flash '5') **£200-250**
- Red (green flash, '6') **£200-250**
1937-40
Diecast body, plated or black smooth hubs, white 'DUNLOP' tyres.
- Blue (red flash, '1') **£200-250**
- Blue (white flash, '11' or '12') **£200-250**
- Red (green flash, '6') **£200-250**
- Red (silver flash, '2') **£200-250**
- Yellow (red flash, '2') **£200-250**
- Cream (blue flash, '4') **£200-250**
- White (green flash, '5') **£200-250**
- Green (white flash, '7' or '8') **£200-250**
- Green (silver flash, '7' or '8') **£200-250**
- Orange (green flash, '9' or '10') **£200-250**
- Orange (blue flash, '3') **£200-250**
1940-40
As previous model but with cast metal wheels (black or unpainted) **£200-250**
NB Many of the pre-war 23b models listed left the factory without having the racing numbers applied. The rarity levels for these is much the same as the numbered ones, consequently prices are similar.
1949-49
- Re-issue of 1940 model with cast metal wheels (black or unpainted) **£130-180**
1949-49
As 1939 issue but cream painted smooth hubs, black tyres.
- Red body, silver flash, racing numbers '1' to '6' on cream background **£110-140**

1952-52
- Brief re-issue of previous model..... **£110-140**

23b Hotchkiss Racing Car
1940-40
- Red (silver flash, RNs '1' to '6'), unpainted mazak wheels, 1:53........ **£200-250**
1948-49
- As previous model but with painted mazak wheels **£200-250**
1950-51
- Same, but cream painted convex hubs, black tyres.............................. **£100-150**

23c Mercedes-Benz W154
1949-49 (scale 1:43)
- Silver, (RNs '1' to '6'), driver, painted or unpainted metal wheels (2 sizes known)................................... **£90-120**
1949-51
- As previous model but black or red painted convex hubs, black tyres.... **£350-450**

23d Auto-Union Record Car
1950-? (scale 1:43)
- Light green body, filler cap on some, RNs '1' to '6', red convex hubs, black tyres... **£90-120**
- Same model but with bright green convex hubs, black tyres, '2'......**£3,000-4,000**
NB Unlike the UK version, the rear axle ends are not visible.

23-H Talbot-Lago GP Car
1953-54 (scale 1:43)
- Blue, (RN's '1' to '6' in white paint), driver cast in, blue convex hubs, ribbed tyres...................................... **£100-125**
1954-55
- Same but numbers '1' to '6' on yellow transfers **£100-125**
1955-59 (renumbered in 1959 to 510)
- Blue, (RNs '1' to '6' and '22' to '27' on yellow transfers), plated convex hubs **£100-125**

23-J Ferrari GP Car
1956-56 (scale 1:43)
- Red, (RN's '1' to '6'), smooth grille, driver, plated convex hubs **£120-150**
1957-59 (renumbered in 1959 to 511)
- Dark red body (RNs '1' to '6' and '33' to '38'), squared grille, plated convex hubs **£150-200**

24A Chrysler New Yorker.

24-A Chrysler New Yorker
1956-57 (scale 1:48)
'CHRYSLER NEW YORKER' on base and on box. All have plated convex hubs.
- Lemon yellow body, green seats..... **£125-150**
- Red body, ivory body **£120-140**
1957-60 (renumbered in 1960 as 520)
'CHRYSLER NEW YORKER 1955' on base and on box. All have plated convex hubs.
- Lemon Yellow body, green seats **£300-400**
- Mustard Yellow body, green seats .. **£300-400**
- Red (or orange-red), ivory seats..... **£300-400**
- Light met. Blue body, ivory seats.... **£300-400**
- Light met. Blue, pale grey seats **£300-400**

24b Limousine
1934-35 (scale 1:53)
4 doors cast-in, horizontal bonnet louvres (aligned), large headlights, no sidelights, black or white 'DUNLOP' tyres on smooth hubs.
- Yellow body (with black wings) **£300-400**

- Yellow body (with red wings).......... **£300-400**
- Green body (with blue wings) **£300-400**
1936-39
4 doors cast-in, horizontal bonnet louvres (stepped), medium or small headlights, sidelights on wings, black or white 'DUNLOP' tyres on smooth hubs.
- Green body (with red wings) **£300-400**
- Grey body (with blue wings)........... **£300-400**
1940-48
As previous model but unpainted mazak wheels.
- Grey body (red wings) **£300-400**
- Yellow body (red wings) **£300-400**
- Red body (black wings) **£300-400**
- Blue body (black wings) **£300-400**
- Green body (black wings) **£300-400**

24B Peugeot 403 Berline.

24-B Peugeot 403 8cv
1956-58 (scale 1:43)
No window glazing, base without towing notch, plated convex hubs, smooth white tyres.
- Blue body **£80-100**
- Black body **£80-100**
1958-59 (renumbered in 1959 to 521)
Base has towing notch, plated convex hubs, smooth white tyres.
- Blue body.. **£100-120**
- Light grey body................................ **£100-120**
- Pale Yellow body **£150-200**

24C Citroën DS19.

24-C Citroën DS19
1956-58 (scale 1:43)
No window glazing, plated convex hubs, smooth white tyres.
- Green body with white roof **£110-130**
- Green body with pale grey roof **£110-130**
- Ivory body, very dark purple roof ... **£110-130**

Citroen DS19 - yellow body, pale grey roof, windows, chrome ridged hubs, white tyres. Very hard to find model.

24-CP Citroën DS19
1958-59 (renumbered in 1959 to 522)
As 24-C but with window glazing. In 24-C box with '24CP' sticker, later in own box.
- Green body (with white grey roof) . **£200-250**
- Green body (with pale grey roof) ... **£200-250**
- Ivory body (very dark purple roof). **£200-250**
- Dark orange body (cream roof)...... **£200-250**
- Brown body (cream roof)................ **£200-250**

- Yellow body, grey roof £300-350

24d   Vogue Saloon
1934-35 (scale 1:53)
Spare wheel in wing, large headlights,
no sidelights, smooth mazak hubs,
black or white 'DUNLOP' tyres.
- Blue body (with black wings).......... £300-400
- Green body (with red wings) £300-400
1936-37
Spare wheel in wing, medium headlights,
sidelights on wings, smooth mazak hubs,
black or white 'DUNLOP' tyres.
- Red body (black wings) £300-400
- Blue body (yellow wings) £300-400
- Blue body (black wings) £300-400
- Green body (yellow wings) £300-400
1938-39
No spare wheel, small headlights,
sidelights on wings, smooth mazak hubs,
black or white 'DUNLOP' tyres.
- Grey body (with black wings) £300-400
- Green body (with maroon wings)
.... £300-400
1940-48
No spare wheel, medium or small
headlights, sidelights on wings, painted
mazak wheels.
- Yellow body (red wings) £300-400
- Grey body (red wings) £300-400
- Red body (black wings) £300-400
- Blue body (black wings) £300-400

24D Plymouth Belvedere.

24-D   Plymouth Belvedere
1957-59 (renumbered in 1959 to 523) (1:48)
Plated convex hubs.
Model picture on some boxes.
- Green body, black roof and
side flash £100-120
- Tan body, brown roof / side flash
.... £110-135
- Grey body, Red roof and side flash
.... £80-100
- White body, blue roof / side flash
.... £275-325
- White body, blue roof / side flash
.... £350-400
- Pink body, Pale Maroon roof and
side flash £375-450

24e   Aerodynamic Saloon Car
1934-35 (scale 1:53)
Large headlights, no sidelights, smooth
hubs, black or white 'DUNLOP' tyres.
- Green body, blue wings.................. £200-250
- Green body, red wings.................... £200-250
1936-39
Medium or small headlamps, sidelights
in wings, smooth mazak hubs,
black or white 'DUNLOP' tyres.
- Blue body (with black wings).......... £200-250
- Red body (with black wings).......... £200-250
- Red body (with yellow wings)........ £200-250
1940-48
Medium or small headlamps,
sidelights in wings, cast metal wheels.
- Blue body (black wings) £200-250
- Green body (black wings) £200-250
- Red body (black wings) £200-250
- Yellow body (red wings) £200-250

24E Renault Dauphine.

24-E   Renault Dauphine
1957-59 (renumbered in 1959 to 524) (1:43)
No window glazing, plated convex hubs,
smooth black tyres.
- Olive-green body............................. £150-200
- Brick-red body................................. £150-200
- Raspberry-red body........................ £120-150
- Bright Blue body £400-500
- Turqoise body................................. £150-200

24f   Sportsman's Coupé
1934-35 (scale 1:53)
Two-door body with spare wheel in wing,
large headlights, no sidelights, smooth mazak
hubs, black or white 'DUNLOP' tyres.
- Green body (with yellow wings) £300-400
- Blue body (with black wings).......... £300-400
1936-37
Two-door body with spare wheel in wing,
medium headlights, sidelights on wings,
smooth mazak hubs,
black or white 'DUNLOP' tyres.
- Blue body (black wings) £300-400
- Blue body (yellow wings) £300-400
- Green body (yellow wings) £300-400
- Red body (black wings) £300-400
1938-39
Two-door body, no spare wheel, small
headlights, sidelights on wings, smooth
hubs, black or white 'DUNLOP' tyres.
- Red body (black wings) £300-400
- Yellow body (black wings).............. £300-400
- Yellow body (red wings) £300-400
- Blue body (maroon wings)............. £300-400
- Cream body (blue wings) £300-400
1940-40
Two-door body, no spare wheel,
medium or small headlights, sidelights
on wings, painted mazak wheels.
- Red body (black wings) £300-400
- Blue (black wings)........................... £300-400
- Green (black wings)........................ £300-400
- Yellow body (red wings) £300-400
1947-48
Re-issue of 1940 versions (with
cast metal wheels):
- Red body, black wings £300-400
- Blue body, black wings £300-400
- Green black wings........................... £300-400
- Yellow body, black wings £300-400

24-F   Peugeot 403-U Familiale
1958-59 (renumbered in 1959 to 525) (1:43)
- Sky Blue body, no windows,
plated convex hubs £100-120
1958
- Dark red body (no windows). Only
a few made as gifts for 1958
visitors to Meccano factory £2,000-3,000

24g   4-seat Sports Car
1934-35 (scale 1:53)
Spare wheel, open windscreen, large
headlights, no sidelights, black or white
'DUNLOP' tyres.
- Blue body (with black wings).......... £300-400
- Green body (with red wings) £300-400
1936-37
Spare wheel, solid windscreen, medium
headlights, sidelights in wings,
black or white 'DUNLOP' tyres.
- Yellow body (with red wings).......... £300-400
- Grey body (with blue wings).......... £300-400
1938-39
Spare cast-in, solid windscreen, small

headlights, sidelights in wings,
black or white 'DUNLOP' tyres.
- Green body, red wings.................... £300-400
- Cream body, red wings................... £300-400
1940-40
Spare wheel cast-in, solid windscreen,
medium or small headlights, sidelights
in wings, unpainted mazak wheels.
- Grey body (red wings) £200-300
- Yellow body (red wings) £200-300
- Red body (black wings) £200-300
1947-48
Re-issue of 1940 versions
(unpainted mazak wheels).
- Grey body (red wings) £200-300
- Yellow body (red wings) £200-300
- Red body (black wings) £200-300

24h   2-seat Sports Car
1934-35 (scale 1:53)
Spare wheel, open windscreen, large
headlights, no sidelights, black or white
'DUNLOP' tyres.
- Green body (blue wings)................. £300-400
- Black body, (blue wings) £300-400
- Black body, (red wings) £300-400
- Red body (black wings) £300-400
1936-37
Spare wheel, solid windscreen, medium
headlights, sidelights in wings,
black or white 'DUNLOP' tyres.
- Yellow body (black wings).............. £300-400
- Blue or green body (red wings) £300-400
1938-39
Spare cast-in, solid windscreen, small
headlights, sidelights in wings,
black or white 'DUNLOP' tyres.
- Green body (red wings) £300-400
- Red or body (black wings) £300-400
- Yellow body (black wings).............. £300-400
1940-40
Spare cast-in, solid windscreen, medium
or small headlights, sidelights in wings,
unpainted mazak wheels.
- Cream body (red wings) £200-300
- Yellow body (red wings) £200-300
- Green body (black wings) £200-300
- Red body (black wings) £200-300
1947-48
Re-issue of 1940 versions with
unpainted mazak wheels.
- Cream body (with red wings) £200-300
- Yellow body (with red wings) £200-300
- Green body (with black wings) £200-300
- Red body (with black wings).......... £200-300

24-H   Mercedes-Benz 190sl
1958-59 (renumbered in 1959 to 526) (1:43)
- Cream body (various shades), black
hard-top. Picture on some boxes.... £100-120
- Silver body, Black roof,
plated convex hubs £140-160

24-J   Alfa-Romeo 1900 Sprint
1959-59 (renumbered in 1959 to 527) (1:43)
- Red body, windows, plated convex
hubs, smooth black tyres.................. £80-100
- Blue body, windows, plated convex
hubs, smooth black tyres.................. £80-100

24k   Peugeot 402
1939-40 (scale 1:53)
No baseplate and no base retainers cast
inside body), black or white 'DUNLOP'
tyres on smooth painted mazak hubs.
- Maroon body £300-400
- Blue body.. £300-400
- Light blue body £300-400
- Red body £300-400
- Yellow body £300-400
1947-48
No baseplate (and no retainers cast
inside), unpainted mazak wheels.
- Maroon body £500-750
- Blue body.. £500-750
- Light Blue body £500-750

- Red body..**£500-750**
- Yellow body **£500-750**
1948-48
With tinplate base/front bumper (and
with base retainers cast inside body),
unpainted mazak wheels.
- Maroon body **£500-750**
- Blue body...**£500-750**
- Light Blue body **£500-750**
- Red body..**£500-750**
- Yellow body **£500-750**

24-K   Simca Vedette Chambord
1959-59 (renumbered in 1959 to 528) (1:43)
- Ivory/red body, plated convex hubs **£150-200**
- Light green/dark green body **£130-150**

24 I   Peugeot 402 Taxi
1939-40 (all have a tinplate taxi-meter)
- Royal Blue/Yellow, smooth cast
hubs, no base..................................**£500-700**
- Maroon/Cream, smooth cast hubs,
no base...**£500-700**
1947-47
- Royal Blue/Yellow, metal wheels,
no base...**£500-700**
- Maroon/Cream, metal wheels,
no base...**£500-700**
1948-48
- Royal Blue/Yellow, metal wheels,
with base...**£500-700**
- Maroon/Cream, metal wheels,
with base...**£500-700**

24L Vespa 2cv 400 Saloon.

24-L   Vespa 400 2cv
1959-59 (renumbered in 1959 to 529) (1:43)
- Blue/Grey or Orange/Grey,
plated convex hubs, '24L' on box........**£65-75**

24m   Military Jeep
1946-48 (scale 1:43)
- US Military olive-drab body and khaki
painted mazak wheels (mounted inside-out
for effect), white star on bonnet, cast star
at rear, tinplate windscreen frame (bonnet
castings exist with and without frame
supports), wire steering wheel........**£700-900**
NB 24m was the first new French made
Dinky Toys model to appear after the war.
They were supplied to shops in trade boxes
of twelve units. A trailer was designed to
complement the Military Jeep but was
never produced, nor did 24m ever
acquire a towing hook.

24m   Civilian Jeep
1948-49
Castings as military version, usually
with unpainted wheels (a few painted).
- Red body..**£400-500**
- Green body **£400-500**
- Blue body...**£400-500**
- Orange body **£400-500**
- Sand body..**£400-500**
- Yellow body **£400-500**
- Metallic Grey body.........................**£400-500**
- Metallic Gold body. **£400-500**

24-M   VW Karmann-Ghia
1959-59 (renumbered in 1959 to 530) (1:43)
- Black/Red, plated convex hubs **£90-120**

24-N   Citroën 11BL
1949-58 (scale 1:43)
1st version: Small rear window, small
lettering on base, widely spaced grille
bars, spare wheel cover, tinplate front
bumper, no direction indicators,

smooth roof interior.
2nd version: With 16mm wide rear window,
small lettering on base, boot replaces spare
wheel cover, shallow rear axle supports, with
direction indicators, smooth roof interior.
3rd version: With 17mm wide rear window,
large lettering on base, boot replaces spare
wheel cover, deep rear axle supports, cast
front bumper, with direction indicators,
hatched roof interior.
1949-49
- Navy blue, black mazak wheels **£750-900**
1950-51
As first version but the front wheel arch
casting extends below the baseplate.
- Metallic gold body, black convex
hubs, black tyres............................**£500-700**
- Metallic grey body and red convex
hubs, black tyres.............................**£450-650**
- Black body and yellow convex
hubs, black tyres.............................**£300-400**
1951-52
As first version but with large rear window.
- Black body, yellow or cream
hubs, black tyres.............................**£300-400**
1953-55
Integral front bumper, big or small rear
window, rounded boot, narrow grooves
on grille, small print on base, straight
windscreen base, smooth inside roof.
- Black body, cream convex hubs,
black tyres.......................................**£130-160**
1955-57
As 1953-55 model but large print and '24N'
on base. Inside of roof is cross-hatched.
- Black body, cream convex hubs **£100-125**
- Light grey, yellow convex hubs.......**£120-160**
1957-58
As 1953-55 model but large print and '24N'
on base, arched base to windscreen.
- Black body (cream convex hubs)....**£100-125**
- Light Grey body and convex hubs ..**£100-125**
1958-58
As previous but with plated convex
hubs, white tyres.
- Black body **£100-125**
- Light grey body, grey hubs **£120-140**
NB 24-N Citroën models were all
supplied to shops in grey trade boxes
each containing six models.

24N Citroen 11BL.

24-N   Fiat 1200 Grand Vue
Announced only in the 1959 Swiss
catalogue but not made as 24-N.
Renumbered and produced as 531.

24-O   Studebaker State Commander
1949-49 (scale 1:48)
Casting as the English 39f model but
the black tinplate base is marked
'Fabriqué en France'.
- Cream body,
painted mazak wheels **£800-1,100**
- Red body, painted mazak wheels **£800-1,100**
- Metallic blue-green body,
painted mazak wheels **£800-1,100**
1950-50
- Cream body, red convex hubs,
black tyres.......................................**£400-600**
- Metallic blue-green, red convex
hubs, black tyres.............................**£400-600**

- Cream or Red body, Black hubs **£175-250**
NB 24-O Studebaker was supplied to
shops in trade boxes of six units.

24-P   Packard Super 8 Limousine
1949-49 (scale 1:48)
Casting as English 39a but with black
tinplate base marked 'Fabriqué en France'.
Painted convex hubs.
- Blue body..**£750-850**
- Turquoise body **£750-850**
- Metallic Gold body **£750-850**
NB 24-P Packard was supplied to
shops in trade boxes of six units.

24-Q   Ford Vedette
1950-51 (scale 1:43)
- Navy blue body and convex
hubs, small baseprint **£900-1,000**
- Metallic blue body (red hubs) **£200-250**
- Grey body and hubs.........................**£200-250**
- Turquoise body and hubs **£200-250**
- Sand body and hubs **£200-250**
1952-55
- Metallic blue, red convex hubs,
large base print...............................**£150-175**
- Turquoise body and hubs **£150-175**
- Grey body and hubs.........................**£150-175**
- Sand body and hubs **£150-175**
NB 24-Q was supplied to shops in
trade boxes of six units.

24R Peugeot 203.

24-R   Peugeot 203
1951-52 (scale 1:43)
Small rear window, smooth inside roof,
round filler cap on right rear wing.
- Maroon body, cream convex hubs
....**£150-200**
- Metallic Gold body,
cream convex hubs **£450-600**
- Metallic Gold body,
red convex hubs **£450-600**
- Iridescent Violet body,
cream convex hubs **£750-1,000**
- Grey body, grey convex hubs
....**£2,000-3,000**
- Metallic Blue body,
cream convex hubs **£150-175**
- Metallic Blue body,
creamy-yellow convex hubs............**£150-200**
1953-55
Small rear window, cross-hatching
inside roof, no filler cap.
- Grey body, grey convex hubs **£140-160**
- Metallic Blue-Green body,
cream convex hubs **£140-160**
- Grey-Blue body,
cream convex hubs **£140-160**
1955-56
- Grey or Grey-Blue body, spun hubs,
white tyres, small rear window,
no filler cap.....................................**£100-130**
1956-57
- Grey-Blue, spun hubs, white tyres,
big rear window, square filler cap ..**£100-130**
- Pale Grey-Green, spun hubs,
white tyres, big rear window,
square filler cap..............................**£100-130**
1957-59
- Same but with Lime Green body
....**£800-1,000**
1959 (renumbered in 1959 to 533)
Promotional: Lime Green body,

'Club Dinky Toys' **£750-1,250**
NB 24-R was supplied to shops in trade boxes of six units.

24S Simca 8 Sport - Type 2 with thick windscreen frame.

24-S   Simca 8 Sport
1952-54 (scale 1:43)
1st type: thin windscreen frame, unpainted convex hubs, white tyres.
- Grey body, red seats, ... **£90-120**
- Black body, fawn seats..................... **£300-400**
- Black body, red seats **£100-130**
1954-56
- Grey body, red seats, chrome hubs, white tyres... **£80-100**
- Black body, red seats **£90-120**
1956-59
2nd type: thick windscreen frame, spun hubs, white tyres.
- Grey body, red seats.......................... **£150-200**
- Black body, red seats **£200-300**
- Ivory body, red seats **£100-120**
- Duck-egg Green body, red seats **£125-150**
- Duck-egg Blue body, red seats........ **£125-150**
NB 24-S was supplied to shops in trade boxes of six units.
1959 (renumbered in 1959 to 534)

24-T   Citroën 2cv (1951-53 car)
1952-52 (scale 1:43)
- Mid-Grey or Metallic Grey (grey hood), Grey-Gold hubs, one rear lamp, rear axle ends not rounded. Sold unboxed (supplied to shops in trade boxes of six units)...... **£90-120**
1953-54
- Mid-Grey or Metallic Grey (gloss or matt grey hood), grey-gold hubs, one rear lamp, rounded rear axle ends. In individual box with '24T' and 'MECCANO' in large print on ends **£80-90**
- Dark Grey body, matt grey hood, cream convex hubs **£80-90**
- Light Grey body, matt grey hood, cream convex hubs **£80-90**
1955-59
- Light Grey body, gloss or matt grey hood, cream hubs, three red rear lamps, rounded rear axle ends. In own box with '24T' and 'MECCANO' in small print on ends ... **£75-85**
- Maroon body, matt-grey hood, cream convex hubs **£75-85**
- Grey-Blue body, dark grey-blue hood, grey concave or convex hubs **£100-120**
1959 (renumbered in 1959 to 535)

24-U   Simca 9 Aronde
1953-55 (scale 1:43)
1st type: 'stepped' grille, painted convex hubs.
- Olive Green body **£100-150**
- Light Grey-Green body..................... **£90-120**
- Mid Grey or Light Grey body **£150-200**

24-U   Simca Aronde Elysée
1956-57
2nd type: 'wide' ('shark') grille, spun hubs.
- Light Grey or Light Grey-Green body................... **£150-200**
- Sky Blue body **£100-150**
1958-59
- Light Grey-Green body, dark green roof.............................. **£100-150**
- Blue or Sky-Blue body, white roof .. **£200-250**
NB 24-U Simca was the first French

Dinky Toy to be supplied in its own individual box (in 1953).
1959 (renumbered in 1959 to 536)

24U Simca Aronde 9 - Type 2.

24UT   Simca Aronde Elysée Taxi
1956-58 (scale 1:43)
- Red/Blue body, meter and roof sign, painted convex hubs, second grille .. **£90-120**
1958-59
- Same but with plated convex hubs... **£90-120**
NB 24-UT was supplied to shops in trade boxes of six units.
1959 (renumbered in 1959 to 537)

24V Buick Roadmaster.

24-V   Buick Roadmaster
1954-56 (scale 1:48)
1st type: smooth inside roof, unpainted convex hubs, white tyres.
- Blue body, dark blue roof **£160-200**
- Yellow body, green roof **£160-200**
1956-59
2nd type: cross-hatched inside roof, plated convex hubs, white tyres.
- Blue body, dark blue or cream roof................ **£160-200**
- Yellow body, dark blue roof **£160-200**
- Lemon-Yellow body, green roof **£750-1,000**
- Salmon-Pink body, black roof **£500-700**
- Ivory body, blue roof....................... **£400-600**
- Ivory/Metallic Blue body................ **£500-600**
- Red/Yellow with blue roof.........**£1,000-1,250**
1959 (renumbered in 1959 to 538)

24-X   Ford Vedette
1954-56 (scale 1:43)
With or without 'Made in France, Imprimé en France' on individual boxes.
- Dark Blue body and convex hubs **£120-140**
- Pale Grey-Blue body and convex hubs **£100-125**

24XT Ford Vedette Taxi.

24XT   Ford Vedette Taxi
1956-59
- Black body, Beige or Cream roof,

meter, taxi sign, spun hubs **£125-150**
1959 (renumbered in 1959 to 539)
NB 24-XT was supplied in trade boxes of six units. It was never individually boxed.

24-Y   Studebaker Commander Coupé
1955-57 (scale 1:48)
1st type: Base has no towing eye, plated convex hubs, smooth tyres. '24Y' on box but no illustration.
- Red body, dark cream roof.............. **£150-200**
- Light Green body, dark green roof . **£150-200**
- Ivory body, maroon roof.................. **£200-250**
- Orange body, tan roof...................... **£200-250**
1957-58
2nd type: Base has a towing eye, plated convex hubs, smooth tyres. '24Y' and picture of model on box.
- Red body, cream roof **£100-125**
- Light Green body, dark green roof . **£100-125**
- Ivory body, dark red roof................ **£300-350**
1958-59
3rd type: Towing eye in base, plated convex hubs, smooth tyres. '540-24Y' and picture of model on box.
- Red body, cream roof and panels... **£300-350**
- Ivory body, maroon roof / panels... **£300-350**
- Pale Grey body, maroon roof and wing panels........ **£300-350**
1959 (renumbered in 1959 to 537)
NB The 1959 catalogue shows a two-tone blue version of 24-Y/540 but it has not been seen. Also, a photo exists showing a 24-Y prototype of the 1953-54 Studebaker, but only the 1955 car was actually modelled.

24-Z   Simca Vedette 'Versailles'
1956-58 .... (scale 1:43)
1st type: No towing eye, plated convex hubs, white tyres, picture on some boxes.
- Yellow body, black roof.................... **£100-120**
- Light Blue body, white roof **£100-120**
24-Z   1958-59
2nd type: Base has towing eye, plated convex hubs, white tyres, picture on box.
- Yellow body, black roof.................... **£100-120**
- Light Blue body, white roof............. **£100-120**
1959 (renumbered in 1959 to 541)

24ZT   Simca Ariane Taxi
1959-59 (renumbered in 1959 to 542)
- Black body, red roof, plated concave hubs. '542-24ZT' on box **£120-140**

30a   Chrysler Airflow
1935-39 (scale 1:48)
English castings painted and assembled in France. Smooth hubs, black or white 'DUNLOP' tyres.
- Green body **£200-250**
- Blue body... **£200-250**
- Red body... **£200-250**

35a Simca 5.

35a   Simca 5
1939-40 (scale 1:50)
No base, black rubber wheels. Colours:
- Red, Dark Red, Maroon, Light Blue, Mid-Blue, Royal Blue, Grey, Grey-Blue, Green, Light Green, Brown, Silver, Yellow, Gold, Cream **£250-300**
1939-40
Export version of 35-A with white

rubber wheels. Body colours:

- Red, Dark Red, Maroon, Light Blue, Mid-Blue, Royal Blue, Grey, Grey-Blue, Green, Light Green, Brown, Silver, Yellow, Gold, Cream **£250-300**
1940-40
No base, black painted mazak wheels.
- Red, Dark Red, Maroon, Light Blue, Mid-Blue, Royal Blue, Grey, Grey-Blue, Green, Light Green, Brown, Silver, Yellow, Gold, Cream **£250-300**
1948-50 No base, black rubber wheels.
- Red, Dark Red, Maroon, Light Blue, Mid-Blue, Royal Blue, Grey, Grey-Blue, Green, Light Green, Mid-Brown, Silver, Yellow, Gold, Cream **£100-125**
- Green, Dark Brown **£150-200**

Numbers 100 to 106 were produced as 'Dinky Juniors' --a pocket-money budget series. Most fitted with spun steel hubs or Silver hubs with 'DUNLOP' tyres. Scale 1:43.

100 Renault 4L
1963-68
- Pale Green body **£400-500**

101 Peugeot 404 (553 casting)
1963-66
- Orange, no frame to rear number plate **£400-500**
1966-69
- Orange or Red-Orange, rear number plate has frame **£400-500**

102 Panhard PL17
1963-68
- Grey-Blue body **£400-500**
- Bright Blue body **£400-500**

103 Renault R8
1964-68
- Red body **£400-500**

103 Renault R8S Gordini
1969-69
- Red body, painted headlights **£450-600**

104 Simca 1000
1964-68
- Pale Yellow body **£300-400**
- Lime-Green body **£300-400**

105 Citroën 2cv
1964-68
- Grey body, light grey concave hubs **£400-500**

106 Opel Kadett
1965-69
- Yellow body **£1,600-1,900**

500 Citroën 2cv.

500 Citroën 2cv
1967-71
- Beige (dark grey open top), painted concave hubs. 'Made in France' on aperture box **£80-90**
- Blue-Grey body (dark blue open top) **£80-90**
- Pale Grey body (mid-grey open top) **£80-90**
1974-? Spanish issues:
1974-75 Beige (dark grey open top), painted hubs. 'Made in Spain' over-stamped on box, own box printed later **£80-90**
1975-76
- Beige (dark grey open top), painted hubs.

'Made in Spain' and 'Meccano' on large non-aperture box **£80-90**
1976-78
- Orange body, 'square' headlamps, rivetted base, plated concave hubs. 'Made in Spain, imprimeé en France, ref 500' on box . **£70-80**
1978-?
- Orange body, 'square' headlamps, screwed base, plated concave hubs. 'Made in Spain, imprimeé en Espagne, ref 011500' on box **£70-80**

501 Citroën DS19 Police Car.

501 Citroën DS19 'POLICE' Car
1967-70 (scale 1:43)
- Very dark blue/white, roof beacon, concave hubs **£200-250**

503 Porsche Carrera 6
1967-69 (scale 1:43)
- White/Red, 'Carrera' in black. Box has 'moteur...280km/h' printed outside of yellow lines **£100-120**
1969-71
- Same model but box has 'moteur.. 280km/h' within yellow lines **£100-120**

505 Maserati Sport 2000 (1:43)
1959-60 (renumbered in 1959 from 22a)
- Dark or Bright Red, shiny baseplate, convex chromed hubs, white driver **£100-125**
1960-61
- Same but concave chromed hubs .. **£125-150**

506 Aston-Martin DB3S
1960-61 (scale 1:43)
- Emerald Green, concave hubs, driver, racing numbers '1' to '17' **£100-130**
NB 506 used the English 104 body casting with 'Made in France' base and a French three-spoke steering wheel.

506 Ferrari 275 GTB
1967-72 (scale 1:43)
Cast base, cast detailed wheels, nylon tyres.
- Red body **£100-120**
- Yellow body **£110-130**
- Yellow body, 'hybrid' with Red doors/bonnet/boot **£90-110**

507 Simca 1500 Estate Car
1967-71 (scale 1:43)
- White, Metallic Dark Grey or Silver-Grey body, camping table, concave hubs, black tyres **£100-120**

507-P Simca 1500 'POLICE' Car
1967-71
- White and Dark Blue body, red interior, aerial at one side of roof **£5,000-6,500**

508 DAF 33.

508 Daf 33
1966-71 (scale 1:43)
- Dark Red body, cast base, concave hubs, black tyres, female driver **£80-100**
- Metallic Bronze, concave chromed

hubs, black tyres **£110-130**
- Beige body, concave chromed hubs, black tyres **£90-110**

509 Fiat 850
1966-68 (scale 1:43)
- Red body, white tilting seats, concave hubs **£70-90**
- Yellow body, red tilt seats, concave hubs **£100-125**
- White body, red tilt seats, concave hubs **£80-100**
1968-71 Spanish issues:
- Red, Yellow or White body, 'PIRELLI' tyres, Barcelona number plate. 'DINKY-POCH' on box. **£400-500**
- Turquoise-Green body, white interior, 'PIRELLI' tyres, Barcelona number plate. 'DINKY-POCH' on box.......... **£450-600**

510 Talbot-Lago GP Car
1959-59 (renumbered in 1959 from 23-H)
- Blue body, (RN's '1' to '6' and '22' to '27' on yellow transfers), driver cast in, plated convex hubs **£100-150**

510 Peugeot 204
1965-68 (scale 1:43)
Two-part rear bumper, rivetted floor, concave hubs.
- Metallic Dark Red body. 'Par autorisation des automobiles PEUGEOT' on box...................... **£100-125**
- Same but Greenish-Beige body **£100-125**
1968-68 Spanish issues:
Two-part rear bumper, rivetted floor, concave hubs, 'PIRELLI' tyres.
- Bright Red body, 'DINKY-POCH' on box. Assembled in Spain............ **£500-750**
1968-71
- Same, but White body. Made for export to Spain................. **£400-450**
1977-78
One-piece rear bumper, screwed floor.
- Beige-Pink body. Made in Spain, box printed in Spain **£50-75**
1981
Promotional issue:
Off-White body with 'VGE' in Blue/White/Red with Presidential Election decor **£400-500**

511 Ferrari Racing Car (1:43)
1959-63 (renumbered in 1959 from 23-J)
- Red body, 'cross-hatched' grille, racing numbers '1' or '22' to '27', driver, concave hubs, radial or block tread tyres **£150-200**

511 Peugeot 204 Cabriolet
1968-71 (scale 1:43)
Cast base, aluminium concave hubs, tilting seats.
- Sky-blue open body, black interior **£140-170**
- Red open body, black interior......... **£170-200**

512 Leskokart Midjet Kart
1962-66 (scale 1:43)
- Blue body, Black plastic wheels. Plastic driver (white with yellow jacket) **£80-100**
- Same but with blue jacket **£80-100**
- Same but driver with red jacket **£200-250**

513 Opel Admiral
1966-68 (scale 1:43)
- Metallic Blue or Metallic Red, detailed hubs, luggage...................... **£90-120**
1968-69 Spanish issue:
- Same but with 'PIRELLI' tyres. 'DINKY-POCH' on box **£250-300**

514 Alfa-Romeo Giulia 1600ti
1966-71 (scale 1:43)
Plated concave hubs, working windows, headlights and rear lights.
- Beige or White or Metallic Grey body, red interior **£100-130**
- Pale Green body, red interior.......... **£125-150**

- Spanish export issue:
Metallic Grey body, 'PIRELLI'
tyres, Barcelona number plate........ **£200-300**

515 Ferrari 250GT 2+2.

515   Ferrari 250GT 2+2
1963-70 (scale 1:43)
- Red body, white interior,
concave hubs, black tyres............... **£100-125**
- Metallic Blue body,
concave hubs, black tyres................. **£90-110**

516   Mercedes-Benz 230SL
1964-65
Removable hard-top, concave hubs,
'MERCEDES 230SL' on base,
French box.
- Metallic Silver/Cream body **£130-160**
- Metallic Red-Orange/Cream body. **£100-120**
- Metallic Red/Cream body **£120-140**
1965-66
- Same as previous model but with
'MERCEDES-BENZ 230SL' on
base. French box **£100-125**
1966-70
- Metallic Red-Orange/Cream as
1965-66 version but in British box
for export to UK and USA **£70-90**

517   Renault R8
1962-64 (scale 1:43)
- Blue body, concave hubs................ **£100-125**
- Primrose-Yellow, concave hubs...... **£100-125**
1964 (renumbered in 1964 to 1517)
NB Model was introduced on the
same day as the actual car.
1968-70 Spanish issues:
- Cream body, concave hubs, 'PIRELLI'
tyres, silver rear number plate.
'DINKY-POCH' on box **£400-600**
- Dark Blue body, concave hubs,
'PIRELLI' tyres, Silver rear number
plate. 'DINKY-POCH' on box **£400-600**

517-P   Renault R8 Police Car
1969
- Dark Blue/White, 'POLICE'.
Commissioned for use by Police **£600-700**

518   Renault R4L
1961-64 (scale 1:43)
- Pale Blue or Light Blue body,
first grille, concave hubs...................... **£50-60**
1964
- Brick-Red or Brown body **£50-60**
- Grey-Green body **£95-125**
1964 (renumbered in 1964 to 1518)
1964-64
- Red body, 'POMPIERS de PARIS'.
Commissioned by Fire Service . **£1,200-1,600**
1964-64
- Yellow/blue 'PTT' livery. Commissioned
for use by Postal Service **£500-600**
1968-70 Spanish issues:
- As standard 1964 French model but
Violet body, 'PIRELLI' tyres.
'DINKY-POCH' on box **£400-600**
1975-77
- Dark Blue, second grille,
concave hubs. 'Made in Spain' and
pink '4L' on box **£55-65**
1977-?
- Sky Blue, second grille, concave hubs.
'Made in Spain' and blue '4L' on box. **£55-65**

518-A   Renault 4L, 'AUTOROUTES'

1970-71
- Orange body, first grille, plated concave
hubs. Box also contains
595r Traffic Sign 'Road Works' **£200-250**

519   1961 ....**Facel Vega Facellia**
Announced in the 1961-62 catalogue
but not produced. ....NPP

519   Simca 1000
1962-63
- Red or Light Blue-Grey body,
cream interior, black base.
'519' in black oval on box **£70-90**
- Lime-Green body, cream interior .. **£220-260**
- Light Yellow body, cream interior .. **£220-260**
- Sky-Blue body, white interior **£80-90**
1962-64
- Light Blue-Grey body, red interior,
Black base, concave hubs, rubber tyres.
'519' in black oval on box **£55-65**
1963-64
- Metallic Grey body, black or green
interior. Existence not confirmed ....NPP
NB The 1962-64 version of 519 was
renumbered in 1964 as 1519.
Production of 519 continued as follows:
1964-66
- Light Blue-Grey body, white interior.
Anodised base, concave hubs, nylon
tyres. '519' in black band on box. **£70-90**
1966-68 South-African issues:
- Turquoise body, red interior,
concave hubs. Assembled / painted
in South Africa............................**£1,500-2,000**
- Dark Red body, white interior,
concave hubs. Assembled / painted
in South Africa............................**£1,500-2,000**
1968-70 Spanish issues:
- Metallic Blue body, Cream interior,
concave hubs, 'PIRELLI' tyres.
'DINKY-POCH' on box **£500-700**
- Red body, cream interior,
concave hubs, 'PIRELLI' tyres.
'DINKY-POCH'on box **£250-300**

520   Chrysler New Yorker (1:48)
1960-61 (renumbered in 1960 from 24-A)
'CHRYSLER NEW YORKER 1955' on
base and on box. Concave hubs.
- Yellow body, green seats **£200-250**
- Red body, ivory seats **£100-120**
- Light Met. Blue body, ivory seats.... **£275-350**

520   Fiat 600D
1963-64 (scale 1:43)
- White body, red int., concave hubs **£85-95**
1964-64
Red or Cream body, concave hubs
.... **£90-100**
1964 (renumbered in 1964 to 1520)
1968 Spanish export issues:
- Pale Yellow, concave hubs, 'PIRELLI'
tyres.'DINKY-POCH'on box **£200-250**
- Light Blue body, concave hubs, 'PIRELLI'
tyres. 'DINKY-POCH' on box **£300-400**
- Off-White body, concave hubs,
'PIRELLI' tyres, Silver number plate.
'DINKY-POCH' on box **£250-300**

521   Peugeot 403 8cv
1959-60 (renumbered in 1960 from 24-B)
No windows, base has towing notch,
plated convex hubs, smooth white tyres
- Light Grey body.............................. **£90-110**
- Cream body **£175-225**
1960-62
With windows and towing notch, plated
concave hubs, smooth or treaded white tyres.
- Light Grey body. (Light Blue-Grey
picture and Black picture on box) .. **£100-125**
- Cream body. (Light Blue-Grey
picture and Black picture on box) .. **£150-200**
1962-64
521 became individually unavailable in 1962
but was included in Gift Set 503 up to 1964.

---

522   Citroën DS19 (1:43)
1959-60 (renumbered in 1960 from 24-CP)
With windows, convex hubs, smooth
white tyres, '24CP' on box.
- Green/White.. **£225-275**
- Ivory/very Dark Purple.................... **£225-275**
- Yellow/Grey **£225-275**
- Orange/Cream **£225-275**
1960-63
With concave hubs, smooth white tyres.
'522' on box.
- Orange/Cream body........................ **£110-140**
- Yellow/Grey body............................ **£100-130**
1963-68
With concave hubs, treaded white tyres.
'522' on box.
- Orange body, Cream roof................ **£100-130**
- Yellowish-Beige body,
pale grey roof.................................. **£150-200**
- Pale Yellow body, grey roof **£100-130**

523   Simca Driving School Car
Announced (but not illustrated) in the
1962 price list. Not produced.................NPP

523   Plymouth Belvedere (1:48)
1959-60 (renumbered in 1960 from 24-D)
Convex hubs. Picture on some boxes.
- Green body, black roof and panel **£90-110**
- Tan body, metallic brown
roof and panel **£150-200**
- Grey body, orange-red roof / panel.. **£85-110**
- White body, blue roof and panel **£300-350**
1960-61 With concave hubs.
- Tobacco-Brown body,
maroon roof and panel.................... **£200-300**
- White body, blue roof and panel **£375-450**

523   Simca 1500
1963-64 (scale 1:43)
- Light-Blue body, concave hubs **£60-80**
1964 (renumbered in 1964 as 1523)
- Light Blue body, concave hubs.......... **£60-80**
- Metallic Grey body, concave hubs **£60-80**
1968-69 Spanish issue:
- Bright Blue body, plated concave hubs,
'PIRELLI' tyres.
'DINKY-POCH' on box **£400-600**

524   Renault Dauphine
1959-60 (scale 1:43)
With windows (some without), convex hubs,
smooth black tyres. '524 - 24E' on box.
- Turquoise body **£120-150**
- Brick-Red body **£120-150**
- Raspberry-Red body **£120-150**
- Ivory-White body **£150-200**
1960-60
As previous models but box has 'DINKY
TOYS' in upright lettering plus '524'.
- Turquoise body **£150-175**
- Brick-Red body **£100-120**
- Raspberry-Red body **£150-175**
- Ivory-White body **£150-200**
1960-61
Bright Blue-Green body. Box has 'DINKY
TOYS' in upright lettering plus '524'.
Special limited edition for Paris
Dinky Toys Club **£500-750**
1960-60
With windows, concave chromed hubs
with smooth or treaded black tyres.
Box has 'DINKY TOYS' in oblique
lettering plus '524'.
- Turquoise body **£100-140**
- Brick-Red body **£100-140**
- Raspberry-Red body **£100-140**
1961-64
524 became individually unavailable
in 1961 but remained in Gift Set 503
up till 1964.

524   Panhard 24CT
1964-66 (scale 1:43)
- Metallic Grey body, concave
chromed hubs, 'DUNLOP' tyres.
In French box **£80-100**

- Pale Yellow-Green body, concave chromed hubs, 'DUNLOP' tyres. In French box **£70-90** 1966-69
- Metallic Grey body; steel hubs, in English box (model made for export to UK and USA) **£80-100**

525   Peugeot 403 Estate Car
1959-60 (renumbered in 1960 from 24-F)
- Sky Blue, no windows, convex hubs, rear bumper over-riders **£80-100** 1960-62
- Sky Blue, concave hubs, no rear bumper over-riders............. **£120-140**
NB Model was originally shown in catalogues as being available in black. It was never produced in that colour.

525   Peugeot 404 Commercial Traveller's Car
1964-70 (scale 1:43)
With yellow or black rear number plate, spun hubs, windows.
- Ocean Blue body............................. **£100-125**
- Cream body **£100-125**

525   Peugeot 404 Fire Car
1964-64
- Red body, 'Pompiers de Paris', concave chromed hubs, 'DUNLOP' plastic tyres, aerial ..**£1,500-2,000**

526 Mercedes 190sl with windows.

526   Mercedes-Benz 190sl (1:43)
1959-60 (renumbered in 1960 from 24-H)
No windows, convex hubs.
Picture on some boxes.
All 526 models have a black hard-top.
- Cream body (various shades) **£75-100**
- Silver body **£100-120** 1960-62
With windows, convex hubs.
'526' and picture on box.
- Cream body (various shades) **£75-100**
- Silver body **£80-100**

526   Mercedes-Benz 190sl Hard-Top
1961-63
With windows, concave hubs.
'526' and picture on box.
- Cream body (various shades) **£80-100**
- Silver body **£100-130**

527   Alfa-Romeo 1900 Sprint (1:43)
1959-63 (renumbered in 1959 from 24-J)
- Red or Blue body, cream interior, windows, concave hubs, smooth (later treaded) black tyres ... **£80-100**
- Red body with red interior **£150-200**
- Turquoise body **£4,000-5,000**

528   Simca Vedette Chambord (1:43)
1959-60 (renumbered in 1959 from 24-K/2)
- Ivory and Red body, convex hubs .. **£150-200**
- Light and Dark Green, convex hubs .. **£75-90** 1960-61
- Ivory and Red body, concave hubs **£150-200**
- Light and Dark Green, concave hubs **£75-90**

528   Peugeot 404 Cabriolet
1966-71 (scale 1:43)
With female driver, steel hubs.
- White open body, red interior **£140-180**
- Metallic Blue body, red interior..... **£140-180**
- Pale Grey body, red interior **£170-200**
- Light Beige body, red interior **£170-200**

529   Vespa 400 2cv (scale 1:43)
1959-60 (renumbered from 24-L)

- Blue/Grey, plated hubs. '24L' on box . **£70-80** 1960-63
- Blue/Grey, convex hubs,'529' on box . **£70-80**
- Orange/Grey, convex hubs, '529' on box **£300-400**

530   VW Karmann-Ghia (1:43)
1959-59 (renumbered in 1959 from 24-M)
- Black/Red ('pointed' bonnet), convex hubs.................................. **£80-100** 1960-62
- Black/Red body ('rounded' bonnet), convex hubs.................................. **£100-120** 1961-62
- Same, but with concave hubs **£150-200**

530   Citroën DS19
1964-70
Steel hubs. French '522' box with '530' labels, later in own '530' box.
1964-64
- Metallic Grey body.....................**£1,500-2,000** 1964-66
- Red/Cream body, ivory interior, silver base **£175-225**
- Lime Green/Grey body, pale grey interior, silver base **£175-225** 1966-68
Steel hubs. British box. Model made for export to UK and USA.
- Red/Cream body, ivory interior, silver base **£90-110**
- Lime Green/Grey body, pale grey interior, silver base **£90-110**
1968-70 Spanish issues:
Spun hubs, 'PIRELLI' tyres.
'DINKY-POCH' on box.
- Red/Cream body, ivory interior, black base **£500-600**
- Lime Green/Grey body, pale grey interior, black base **£500-600**
- Bright Blue body **£700-900**
- Silver-Grey body.............................. **£700-900**

530   Citroën DS23
1976-78 (scale 1:43)
- Metallic Red/Black body, concave hubs. Made in Spain **£120-140**
NB 530 Citroën DS23 was shown in the 1974 catalogue but production did not start until Auto-Pilen took over the dies in 1976. The plastic base on this model (and some other Spanish models) was made in different colours and some are held in place by screws rather than rivets. Consequently, beware the 'rare combination' of base and body colours as they are easily interchanged.

531 Fiat 1200 Grande Vue.

531   Fiat 1200 Grande Vue (1:43)
1959-60 (renumbered in 1960 from 24-N)
With convex hubs, smooth tyres.
- Metallic Bronze/Cream body........... **£90-110**
- Cream/Metallic Blue body............. **£120-140**
NB 531 was shown in the 1959 Swiss catalogue with the reference '24N'.
1960-62
With concave hubs, smooth or treaded tyres.
- Metallic Bronze/Cream body........... **£90-100**
- Cream/Metallic Blue body............. **£130-160**

532   Lincoln Premiere
1959-60 (scale 1:43)
- Silver body, dark red roof, convex hubs. Box has no view window **£225-275**
- Light Blue body, silver roof **£100-125**
- Metallic Green, dark green roof...... **£100-125**

1960-65
- Bright Blue body, silver roof, concave hubs, white smooth or treaded tyres. View window in box........................ **£500-650**
- Light Blue body, silver roof **£90-100**
- Metallic Green, dark green roof........ **£90-100** 196?-?
- Export model: Dark Blue body, silver roof. In gold card and cellophane box **£300-400**
NB A dark green wooden prototype of 532 exists...NPP

532 Lincoln Premiere.

533   Peugeot 203
1959-59 (renumbered in 1959 from 24-R)
- Grey-Blue or Pale Grey-Green body, convex hubs, white tyres, big rear window, square filler cap **£90-120**

533   Mercedes-Benz 300 SE
1963-70 (scale 1:43)
With plated concave hubs.
- Metallic Blue body **£150-175**
- Metallic Orange-Red body **£150-175**
- Metallic Red body **£150-175**

534   Simca 8 Sport (1:43)
1959-59 (renumbered in 1959 from 24-S)
Thick windscreen, convex hubs.
- Grey body, red seats........................ **£100-125**
- Black body, red seats **£100-125**
- Pale Greenish-Blue body, red seats **£100-125**
- Cream body, red seats **£100-125**

534   BMW 1500
1963-68 (scale 1:43)
- Red body, steel hubs......................... **£90-100**
- Lime Green, plated concave hubs .. **£100-120** 1968-? Spanish issue:
- Metallic Blue, plated concave hubs, 'PIRELLI' tyres, 'DINKY-POCH' on box **£500-750**

535 Citroën 2cv.

535   Citroën 2cv
1959-60
- Red or Brighter Red body, painted steel hubs, glossy baseplate. Box has '535-24T' printing **£100-120**
- Maroon body, grey top **£100-120**
- Blue body with brighter blue roof .. **£150-175** 1960-63
- Red or Blue body, chromed steel hubs, blued-steel baseplate. Box has '535' printing **£90-110**

536   Simca Aronde Elysée (1:43)
1959-59 (renumbered in 1959 from 24-U)
- Light Grey-green/Dark Green, second grille, convex hubs **£100-125**
- Pale Green/Dark Green, second grille, convex hubs **£100-125**
- Blue body, ivory roof...................... **£100-125**
- Sky blue body, ivory roof **£300-400**
NB Though renumbered from 24-U to 536, no boxes have yet been seen bearing the new number.

536 Peugeot 404 and Trailer
1965-70 (scale 1:43)
- Red car, ivory interior, concave hubs, black skis on yellow rack (or yellow skis on black rack), cream plastic single-wheel trailer (no. 812), luggage................. **£250-300**

537 Simca Aronde Elysée Taxi (1:43)
1959-60 (renumbered in 1960 from 24-UT)
- Red/Blue body, convex plated hubs, second grille **£80-90**

537 Renault R16
1965-67 (scale 1:43)
Concave hubs, black treaded rubber tyres, '537' on base. Box has single viewport, R16 leaflet in early issues.
- Sky-Blue body, gloss Black base **£70-90**
- Metallic Grey body, gloss Black base . **£60-80**
1967-70
Concave hubs, 'DUNLOP' nylon tyres, '537' on base. Box has single viewport, R16 leaflet discontinued in 1967.
- Light Blue body, matt black base........ **£50-65**
- Metallic Grey body, matt black base
.... **£50-65**
1968-69 Spanish issue:
- Bright Blue, '537' on base, concave hubs, 'PIRELLI' tyres, 'DINKY-POCH' box.......................... **£250-350**
1969-70
- Sky-Blue body, matt black base without '537' reference, concave hubs, 'DUNLOP' plastic tyres.
Box has single viewport....................... **£60-75**
1974-78 Spanish issue:
- Metallic Grey body, base without '537', concave hubs, 'DUNLOP' plastic tyres. 'MECCANO' and 'Made in Spain' on box (no viewport) **£60-75**

538 Buick Roadmaster
1959-59 (renumbered in 1959 from 24-V)
All have convex hubs. Scale 1:48.
- Blue/Dark Blue body **£130-170**
- Yellow/Green body **£100-150**
- Blue/Cream body............................. **£100-150**
- Ivory/Metallic Blue body................ **£500-600**
- Salmon-Pink/Black body **£500-600**

538 Ford Taunus 12M
1963-70 (scale 1:43)
- Turquoise body, steel or spun hubs
.... **£90-110**
- Brick Red body, steel or spun hubs **£80-95**

538 Renault R16 TX
1976-78
- Metallic Plum, concave hubs, rear number plate on sticker. Made in Spain........... **£70-90**
NB 538 Renault R16 was shown in the 1974 French catalogue, but production was delayed until 1976.

539 Ford Vedette Taxi
1959-59 (renumbered in 1959 from 24-XT)
- Black/Beige (various shades), meter, taxi sign, plated convex hubs, white tyres. **£75-85**
NB 539 was never individually boxed (supplied to shops in trade boxes of six).

539 Citroën ID19 Estate
1963-66 (scale 1:43)
- Gold/Cream body, red or white seats, black or white steering wheel, steel hubs, black or white tyres....... **£100-125**
- Green-Gold body, darker cream roof, spun hubs **£125-150**

540 Studebaker Commander
1959-60 (renumbered in 1959 from 24-Y)
With convex hubs, smooth tyres. Tinplate base has towing notch. '540-24Y' and picture of model on box.
- Ivory body, maroon roof and wing panels **£120-150**
- Orange body, dark cream roof and panels **£140-180**
1960-61
With concave hubs, treaded tyres. Towing

notch in base. '540-24Y' and picture on box.

- Ivory body, maroon roof and wing panels **£150-200**
- Orange body, dark cream roof and wing panels. Existence not confirmed .... NPP

540 Opel Kadett
1963-64
- Red or Pale Green body, steel hubs.... **£85-95**
1964
- Bright Blue body, plated steel hubs **£200-300**
1964 (renumbered in 1964 to 1540)
NB 540 Opel was available with either the standard size hubs or smaller hubs. Both types were concave and were steel or spun aluminium with black tyres.

541 Simca Vedette Versailles
1959-60 (renumbered in 1959 from 24-Z)
With convex hubs, white tyres, towing notch. Picture on box.
- Yellow/Black body **£100-125**
- Light Blue/Ivory body...................... **£90-110**

542 Simca Ariane Taxi
1959-62 (renumbered in 1959 from 24-ZT)
'Ariane' on base, '542-24ZT' on box, window glazing, scale 1:43.
- Black body, red (later orange-red) roof, meter, taxi sign, convex hubs (concave from 1961) **£125-150**
- Reversed colours:
Red body, black roof **£300-400**

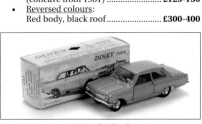
542 Opel Rekord.

542 Opel Rekord
1964-69
With concave hubs. Scale 1:43.
- Metallic Blue two door body............ **£80-100**
- Metallic Gold-Cream two door body
.... **£80-100**
- Metallic Grey two door body **£80-100**

543 Renault Floride
1960-63 (scale 1:43)
Concave hubs, smooth or treaded white tyres.
- Metallic Green body **£90-120**
- Metallic Green-Gold body **£90-120**
- Metallic Bronze body........................ **£90-120**
- White body **£750-1,000**
NB A wooden prototype of 543 is known to exist. It was painted pink...................... NPP

544 Simca Aronde P60.

544 Simca Aronde P60
1959-60 (scale 1:43)
Convex hubs.
Box without (later with) viewport.
- Two-tone Grey body (with silver flash)............................... **£90-110**
- Brick Red body (with cream or pinkish-cream roof) **£90-110**
1960-63
Concave hubs. Box with one viewport.
- Two-tone Grey body **£90-110**
- Brown body (with off-white roof and

silver flash) **£90-110**
- Cream body, red roof, smooth white tyres....................**£4,000-5,000**

545 De Soto Diplomat
1960-63 (scale 1:43)
Concave hubs, (usually) treaded white tyres.
- Salmon-Pink/Black body, silver flash **£100-125**
- Metallic Green body, ivory roof **£200-250**

546 Austin-Healey 100-6
1960-61 (scale 1:43)
- White body (different shades reported), driver, 3-spoke steering wheel, concave hubs.................................... **£120-150**

546 Opel Rekord Taxi.

546 Opel Rekord Taxi
1964-67 (scale 1:43)
- Black body, aluminium or steel concave hubs, white tyres. Box has German text as this model was made only for export to Germany for this period. The taxi sign lettering may be white or yellow..... **£400-500**

547 Panhard PL17
1960-64
1st type: Sidelights to front and rear of centre-hinged doors, black painted baseplate, steel hubs, rubber tyres.
2nd type: As 1st type but without rear sidelights.
3rd type: Front-hinged doors, sidelights under headlamps, black painted baseplate, steel hubs, rubber tyres.
4th type: As 3rd type but with blued-steel baseplate, steel or aluminium hubs.
5th type: Aluminium hubs with plastic 'DUNLOP' tyres.
1960-60
- 1st type, Violet body........................ **£130-160**
- 1st type, Brick Red body **£130-160**
1960-61
- 2nd type, Violet body....................... **£130-160**
- 2nd type, Brick Red or Orange........ **£130-160**
1962-63
- 3rd type, Violet body **£70-85**
- 3rd type, Orange body **£60-80**
1963-64
- 4th type, Violet or Brick-Red body.. **£100-120**
1964-64
- 5th type, Blue-Grey body................. **£120-150**
- 5th type, Blue body **£300-350**
1964 (renumbered in 1964 to 1547)

548 Fiat 1800 Familiale Estate Car
1960-63 (scale 1:43). Concave hubs.
- Lilac body with black roof................ **£90-120**
- Lavender body, black or blue roof.... **£90-120**
- Yellow body, metallic brown roof
.... **£100-125**
- Yellow body, black roof.................... **£100-125**
- Two-tone Blue body, black roof...... **£100-125**
1962 South African issues:
- Ivory body (with red interior) **£600-800**
- Lime Green body **£500-600**
- Green-Bronze body **£500-600**
- Yellow body, metallic maroon roof
.... **£400-500**

549 Borgward Isabella TS
1961-61 (scale 1:43)
Concave hubs, black or white tyres.
- Turquoise body **£110-140**
- Light Green body **£110-140**
- Metallic Grey body.......................... **£110-140**

550 Chrysler Saratoga
1961-65
Plated concave hubs,
smooth or treaded white tyres.
- Pale Pink with white flash **£120-140**
- Deep Pink with white flash **£120-140**
- Violet with black flash **£175-200**

551 Rolls-Royce Silver Wraith
1959-61 (scale 1:43)
- Light Grey/Dark Grey body,
  concave hubs...................................... **£90-100**

551 Ford Taunus 17M Police Car
1965-67 (scale 1:43)
- Dark Green/White, 'POLIZEI',
  concave hubs, German text on box **£500-700**

552 Chevrolet Corvair.

552 Chevrolet Corvair
1961-64 (scale 1:43)
Concave hubs, indication of filler
cap on some.
- Turquoise body, cream interior **£90-110**
- Blue-Grey body, cream interior **£90-110**
- Red body, cream interior **£120-140**
  1963 South African issues:
  (All have off-white interior)
- Silver body **£700-800**
- Light Grey-Blue body...................... **£700-900**
- Smokey-Green body **£1,000-1,500**
  1964 (renumbered in 1964 to 1552)

553 Peugeot 404
1961-68
1st type: Round 'O' on bonnet,
steel hubs, smooth black or white tyres,
painted baseplate.
2nd type: Squared 'O' on bonnet, steel hubs,
treaded black tyres, painted baseplate.
3rd type: As 2nd type with reinforcement
behind front number plate, revised glazing
moulding common to 536 with opening
roof, blued-steel baseplate. Aluminium hubs
and plastic 'DUNLOP' tyres.
1961-62 1st type,
- Cream body, dark red interior **£100-120**
- Cream body, dark brown interior... **£125-150**
- Pale blue body, bright red interior
  .... **£100-120**
  1962-64 2nd type,
- Cream body,
  dark (later bright) red interior **£100-125**
- Cream body, dark brown interior
  .... **£110-150**
  1963-66 3rd type,
- Pale Blue body, bright red interior
  .... **£100-120**
  1963 South African issues:
- Pale Green body,
  bright red interior **£1,000-1,250**
- Metallic Charcoal Grey body,
  bright red interior **£1,000-1,250**
- Cream body, dark red interior **£800-1,000**
  1964 (renumbered in 1964 to 1553)
  1968-68 Spanish assembled model:
- 3rd type, but with 'PIRELLI' tyres,
  'DINKY-POCH' on box.
  Bright Blue body, bright red interior,
  Barcelona number plate.............. **£900-1,100**

554 Opel Rekord
1961-63 (scale 1:43)
Concave hubs, (usually) white tyres.
- Coral-Pink/Ivory body...................... **£90-110**
- Dark Yellow/Ivory body.................. **£110-130**
- Beige body, cream roof................... **£115-135**
- Turquoise/Ivory body..................... **£500-600**

1962 South African issues:
- Pale Blue body, light grey int. **£800-1,000**
- Bright Blue body, light grey int
  .... **£800-1,000**
- Dark Blue body, light grey int. **£800-1,000**
- Metallic Dark Green body,
  grey interior **£1,000-1,250**

555 Ford Thunderbird
1961-69
1st type: Black painted baseplate,
steel hubs, smooth white tyres.
2nd type: Blued-steel baseplate,
steel hubs, treaded white tyres.
3rd type: Blued-steel baseplate,
aluminium hubs, treaded white tyres.
NB Driver may wear bright or dark suit,
steering wheel may be cream or black.
- White body, red interior **£110-130**
- Red body, sky-blue interior............. **£110-130**
- Dark Brown body, sky-blue int. **£110-130**
- Dark Brown body, pale green int.... **£100-150**
  1966-? South African issues:
- Bright Blue open body, red int..... **£900-1,200**
- Metallic Blue open body, red int. **£900-1,200**
- Sand open body, red interior **£900-1,200**
- Red open body, red interior **£900-1,200**

Citroën ID19 Ambulance.

556 Citroën ID19 Ambulance
1962-70
1st type: Steel hubs, metal steering wheel,
centred transfer lettering.
2nd type: As 1st type, but with plastic
steering wheel.
3rd type: As 2nd type, but with
aluminium hubs.
4th type: Aluminium hubs, plastic
'DUNLOP' tyres, plastic steering wheel,
transfer lettering aligned to left.
1962-67
- 1st/2nd/3rd types: Grey/cream body.
  In standard box until '64, then in
  'Super detail' box **£120-140**
  1967-70
- 4th type: Grey/cream body.
  In 'Super detail' box......................... **£100-125**

557 Citroën Ami 6
1962-70
1st type: Steel hubs, spare wheel under
bonnet, black painted base.
2nd type: Steel hubs, engine detail under
bonnet, black painted base.
3rd type: As 2nd type, but with
blued-steel baseplate.
4th type: As 3rd type, but with aluminium
hubs and plastic 'DUNLOP' tyres.
1962-62
- 1st type, Pale Green body,
  white or pale grey roof.................... **£120-140**
- Light Blue body,
  with white or pale grey roof **£120-140**
- Light Blue body, pale blue roof....... **£120-140**
  1963-64
- 2nd type. Pale Green body,
  white or pale grey roof...................... **£90-110**
- Light Blue body, pale blue roof........ **£90-110**
- Bright Blue body,
  white or pale grey roof...................... **£90-110**
  1964 (renumbered in 1964 to 1557)
  1964-70
- 3rd/4th types. Pale Green body,
  white or pale grey roof...................... **£90-110**

- Light Blue body,
  white or pale grey roof...................... **£90-110**

558 Citroën 2cv Azam
1962-64
- Yellow body, Brown roof **£100-125**
- Beige body, Brown roof **£150-175**
- Green body, Dark Green roof............. **£75-85**
- Greyish-Green body, Black roof **£75-85**
  1964 (renumbered in 1964 to 1558)

558 Citroën 2cv
1968-70 Spanish issues:
- Yellow/Maroon body, concave hubs,
  'PIRELLI' tyres,
  'DINKY-POCH' on box **£300-400**
- Green/Dark Green body, concave
  hubs, 'PIRELLI' tyres,
  'DINKY-POCH'on box **£300-400**

559 Ford Taunus 17M
1962-64 (scale 1:43)
Steel or aluminium hubs, smooth or
treaded black or white tyres.
- Ivory body **£80-100**
- Pale Grey body **£80-100**
- Metallic Brown body.......................... **£80-100**
- Metallic Grey-Brown body................ **£80-100**
  1964 (renumbered in 1964 to 1559)
  1968-69 Spanish issue: Yellow body,
  concave hubs, 'PIRELLI' tyres,
  'DINKY-POCH' on box **£1,400-1,600**

1400 Peugeot 404 G7 Taxi (536 casting)
1967-71 (scale 1:43)
- Black body, red top with sunroof, taxi
  sign and aerial, 'Ampere 28.30' and 'G7'
  shield on doors, concave hubs, black
  'DUNLOP' tyres, yellow box............ **£250-350**

1401 Alfa-Romeo Guilia 1600Ti (514 casting)
1967-70
- Dark Red 'rally' finish with yellow
  stripe, spotlights, concave hubs.
  Yellow box.. **£120-140**

1402 Ford Galaxie Sedan
1968-71 (scale 1:43)
Detailed wheels. Perspex box.
- Dark Red (cream interior)................ **£90-110**
- Metallic Gold body (red interior) **£90-110**

1402 Ford Galaxie Police Car
1968-68
- Black/white body, 'POLICE'.
  Commissioned for
  use by Police..............................**£2,000-3,000**

1403 Matra M530
1967-71
- White or Orange body, concave hubs,
  two-part roof can be stowed in boot.
  Perspex box.. **£80-100**

*Rare 1404 RTL Luxembourg Citroën ID19
estate car.*

1404 Citroën ID19 Estate Car
1968-69
- Grey/red, 'RADIO TELE LUXEMBOURG',
  camera/operator, concave hubs.
  Yellow box....................................... **£500-750**
  1969-71
- Grey/red, 'RTL LUXEMBOURG',
  ('RTL' in black), concave hubs.
  Yellow box....................................... **£500-750**
  1971-71
- Grey/red, 'RTL LUXEMBOURG'
  ('T' of 'RTL' in black/white check).
  Yellow picture box.....................**£3,500-4,500**

- Same model but with Grey and Orange-red body. Yellow box....**£2,000-2,500**

1405 Opel Rekord 1900s
1968-70 (scale 1:43)
- Metallic Blue body. In perspex box **£70-80**

1405E Opel Rekord 1900s
1970-71 (scale 1:43)
- Metallic Blue. Export model in card box **£150-250**

1405P Opel Rekord 1900s
1968-68
Prototypes using the 1405 casting were prepared for the 1420 Opel Commodore. '1405' on the base.
- Silver body, black 'vinyl' roof, Black interior, paper number plate **£85-95**
- Red body, black 'vinyl' roof, Black interior, paper number plate **£85-95**

1406 Renault 4L Sinpar 'Tanguy'
1968-71
- Khaki-green camouflage body, driver (Michel Tanguy), passenger, painted concave hubs. From TV serial 'Les Chevaliers du Ciel' ('Knights of the Sky')....................... **£140-170**

1407 Simca 1100
1968-71
- Metallic Grey body, concave hubs. 'Made in France' yellow viewport box......... **£80-100**
- Dark Red body. This was the intended colour when 1407 was introduced but its existence is doubtful .... NPP
1974-78 Spanish issue:
- Metallic Green body, concave hubs. 'Made in Spain' overprinted on French box (later in Spanish box also printed 'Made in Spain')................................... **£60-70**

1408 Honda S800
1969-70 (scale 1:43)
- Yellow body, concave hubs. Yellow box.. **£90-110**

1409 Simca 1800
1970. A prototype for the 1409 Chrysler 180 but with 'Simca 1800' on the base. Just a few were sold - they were finished in the same metallic blue-grey paint as the production version............... **£200-250**

1409 Chrysler 180
1970-71 (scale 1:43)
- Metallic Blue-Grey body, 'Chrysler' on base, 'DUNLOP' tyres. Yellow box...... **£75-90**
NB 595w Traffic Sign 'Danger - Cyclists' included with 1409.

1410 Moskvitch 408
1968-71 (scale 1:43)
- Red body, plated concave hubs. Yellow box.. **£50-60**

1411 Renault Alpine A310
1971-72 (scale 1:43)
- Bright Red body, plastic hubs. Yellow box.. **£70-90**

1413 Citroën Dyane
1968-70 (scale 1:43)
- Off-White body, luggage, concave hubs. Box has 'DYANE CITROËN' in white on yellow **£60-70**
1969-71
- Same model but box has 'DYANE CITROËN' in white on green **£60-70**
1977-78 Spanish issue:
- Off-White body, concave hubs............ **£50-60**

500 Citroën 2cv (open), 535 Citroën 2cv (closed) and 1413 Citroën Dyane.

1414 Renault R8 Gordini
1969-70
- Blue body, White stripes, driver, RN '36', jewelled lights, concave hubs **£200-300**

1414 Renault R8-S
1969-70
- Promotional model:
Yellow or Mustard-Yellow body, driver in some **£1,500-2,000**

1415 Peugeot 504
1969-71 (scale 1:43)
- Pale Blue body, concave hubs. Clear plastic box................................. **£90-110**
- Dark Blue body................................. **£500-600**
1974-76 Spanish issue:
- Pale Yellow body, concave hubs or special wheels. Card box **£60-80**

1416 Renault R6
1969-70
- Bright Red body, first grille (round headlamps), concave hubs. Side view of white model on box........................ **£60-70**
1970-74
- As previous model but with rear view of dark grey model on box.................. **£60-70**
1974-76 Spanish issue:
- Red or Yellow body, second grille (square headlamps), concave hubs. Side view of white model on box...... **£80-100**

1416 Renault Postal Car
1974-75
- Code 2 model based on Spanish-made components, commissioned by the Postal Service. Yellow, second grille (square headlamps), plated concave hubs. Side view of white model on box....... **£70-90**

1416P Renault R6 Fire Car
1970-70
- Code 2 model based on Spanish-made components, commissioned by the Fire Service. Red body and hubs, 'POMPIERS de PARIS', second grille, side view of white model on box. ... **£100-125**

1417 Matra V12 F1
1969-71 (scale 1:43)
- Blue body, driver (J.P.Beltoise), RN '17' (transfer, later on label), special wheels. Yellow box... **£60-70**
NB 595c Traffic Sign 'Dangerous Bend To Right' included with 1417.

1419 Ford Thunderbird
1969-71 (scale 1:43)
- Battery in base for rear lights, special wheels. Perspex box. Metallic green body (black 'vinyl' roof on some) **£75-85**
NB Prototype with Metallic Red body and black 'vinyl' roof. (Not issued) .... NPP
- Metallic Grey body, dark metallic grey roof.................. **£800-1,100**
NB 595g Traffic Sign 'Caution - Animals Crossing' included with 1419.

1420 Opel Commodore GS
1970-71 (scale 1:43)
- Red body, Black 'vinyl' roof, special wheels. Some boxes have a printed design in a panel...................................... **£90-100**
NB The Opel Commodore had a 6-cylinder engine, but as 1420 was produced using the 1405 casting, the model retains a 4-cylinder engine and the 'Rekord' badges. 595o Traffic Sign 'Customs' included with 1420.

1421 Opel GT 1900
1969-71 (scale 1:43)
- Dark Blue body, detailed chromed wheels, luggage rack. Yellow box.... **£100-140**
NB 595f Traffic Sign 'Speed Limit' included with 1421.

1422 Ferrari 3L V12 F1
1969-71 (scale 1:43)
- Red body, driver (Jacky Ickx), RN '26', detailed chromed wheels..... **£90-110**
NB 595e Traffic Sign 'Road Narrows'

included with 1422.

1423 Peugeot 504 Convertible
1969-71 (scale 1:43)
- Dark Blue, plastic base, plated concave hubs. Yellow box............... **£200-300**
NB 595i Traffic Sign 'Two Way Traffic' included with 1423.

1424 Renault R12
1969-70
- Mustard-Yellow body, opening doors, red interior, reversed 'V' shape on grille, aluminium concave hubs, sidelights. Yellow box... **£70-80**
NB 595h Traffic Sign 'Danger - End of Quay' included with French-made 1424.

1424 Renault R12-TL
1977-78
- Spanish issue:
Yellow body, fixed doors, alminium concave hubs, second (corrected) grille, no sidelights. Yellow box **£70-80**

1424G Renault R12 Gordini Rally Car
1971-71
- Blue, white stripes, RN '5', silver headlights, fixed doors, aluminium concave hubs, second grille, sidelights. Yellow box...................... **£125-150**
1974-78 Spanish issue:
- Blue (slightly darker than 1971 model), white stripes, yellow headlights, fixed doors, aluminium concave hubs, second grille, sidelights. Yellow box **£100-125**

1425 Matra 630 Le Mans
1969-71 (scale 1:43)
- French Blue body, driver (Pescarolo), RN '5'. Plastic box **£60-70**

1425E Matra 630 Le Mans
1971-71 (scale 1:43)
- French Blue body, driver (Pescarolo), RN '5'. Yellow card box **£80-100**
NB 595k Traffic Sign 'Road Narrows from Left' included with 1425.

1426 Alfa-Romeo Carabo P33
1969-71 (scale 1:43)
- Metallic Green/plain Green/Black/Orange, special wheels. Yellow box **£70-80**
- Orange-Yellow/Green/Black/Orange-red, special wheels. Yellow box **£100-125**
NB 595m Traffic Sign 'Danger - Loose Chippings' included with 1426.

1428 Peugeot 304
1970-74 (scale 1:43)
- White, concave hubs. Yellow box...... **£80-100**
NB 595p Traffic Sign 'Humpback Bridge' included with French made 1428.
1974-78 Spanish issue:
- Metallic Green, concave hubs. Yellow box.. **£70-90**

1429 Peugeot 404 Police Car
1970-71 (scale 1:43)
- Blue/White body, 'POLICE', plastic base, concave hubs. Yellow box...... **£250-350**
NB 595i Traffic Sign 'Cycling Prohibited' included with 1429.

1430 Fiat Abarth 2000
1970-71 (scale 1:43)
- Orange body, special wheels. Plastic box also contains a 595u Traffic Sign 'Dangerous Bends'.............................. **£30-40**

1431 1970....................................**Porsche 917**
Model planned but not actually issued ..NPP

1432 Ferrari 312P
1970-71 (scale 1:43)
- Red body, no driver, RN '60', special wheels. Plastic box also has a 595v Traffic Sign 'All Vehicles Prohibited'...................... **£60-75**

1432E Ferrari 312P
1971-?
- Red body, no driver, '60', special wheels. Card box **£60-75**

1433 Surtees TS5 V8 F1
1971-74 (scale 1:43)

- Red body, white driver, yellow helmet,
  RN '5' or '14'. Yellow card box **£40-50**

1435 Citroën Présidentielle
1970-71 (scale 1:43)
- Metallic Grey and plain Charcoal Grey body,
  chauffeur, felt carpet, flag, electric interior
  light, Speedwheels. Special plastic
  and rigid card box **£450-600**

1435E Citroën Présidentielle
1971
- As 1435 but in blue
  presentation box (200 made) **£1,500-1,750**

*1450 Simca 1100 Police Car - of Spanish
manufacture.*

1450 Simca 1100 'POLICE' Car
1977-78
- Spanish issue: Blue/white or black/white
  body, plated concave hubs................. **£50-60**

1451 Renault R17-TS
1978-? (scale 1:43)
- Spanish issue:
  Orange-Yellow, plated concave hubs . **£50-60**
  NB 1451 was announced in the 1976 French
  catalogue but production only took place
  in Spain from 1978.

1452 Peugeot 504
1977-78 Spanish issues:
- Metallic Copper body, fixed doors,
  special wheels. 'réf. 1452' on box. **£50-60**
  1978-78
- Metallic Bronze body, fixed doors, special
  wheels. Box has: 'réf. 011452' and
  'conformité du produit aux normes
  francaises' **£50-60**
  NB Different registration numbers (on labels)
  may be found on 1452.

1453 Renault R6
1977-78
- Spanish issue:
  Blue-grey, fixed bonnet, square
  headlamps, concave hubs **£75-85**

NB Although only available in blue-grey,
1453 continued to be shown in yellow
in contemporary catalogues.

1454 Matra Simca Bagheera S
1978-78 (scale 1:43)
- Spanish issue:
  Green body, concave hubs................. **£35-45**

1455 Citroën CX Pallas
1978-78 (scale 1:43)
- Spanish issue:
  Metallic blue body, concave hubs...... **£50-60**
  NB 1455 was announced (but not
  illustrated) in the 1977 catalogue but
  was not available before May 1978.

1517 Renault R8 (1:43)
1964-65 (renumbered in 1964 from 517)
- Blue, concave hubs. In blister pack .. **£80-100**
- Yellow, concave hubs. Blister pack... **£80-100**

1518 Renault R4L
1964-65 (renumbered from 518)
First grille. Blister-packed.
- Pale Blue body **£80-100**
- Light Blue body **£80-100**
- Brick-Red body **£80-100**
- Maroon body **£80-100**
- Grey-Green body .... NGPP

1519 Simca 1000
1964-65 (renumbered in 1964 from 519)
- Light Blue-Grey, Red interior,
  Black painted base. Blister pack **£80-100**

1520 Fiat 600 D
1964-65 (renumbered in 1964 from 520)
- Red body, concave hubs. Bister pack . **£70-90**
- Pale Yellow, concave hubs.
  Blister pack **£70-90**

1523 Simca 1500 (1:43)
1964-65 (renumbered in 1964 from 523)
Blister-packed.
- Mid-Blue body, concave hubs **£70-90**
- Light Blue body, concave hubs.......... **£70-90**
- Metallic Grey body, concave hubs **£70-90**

1539 VW Scirocco
1980? .... (scale 1:43)
- Spanish issue: Metallic Light Green
  body, special wheels.......................... **£60-70**

1540 Opel Kadett
1964-65 (renumbered in 1964 from 540)
Blister-packed.
- Red body, concave hubs,
  sliding windows **£70-80**
- Pale Green body, concave hubs......... **£70-80**
- Blue body, concave hubs................. **£130-170**

1540 Renault R14
1980? (scale 1:43)
- Spanish issue:
  Metallic Bright Green body,
  special wheels **£60-70**

1541 Ford Fiesta
1981? (scale 1:43)
- Spanish issue:
  Metallic Light Blue body,
  special wheels **£50-60**

1542 Chrysler 1308 GT
1980? (scale 1:43)
- Spanish issue:
  Metallic Green, special wheels **£35-45**

1543 Opel Ascona
1980? (scale 1:43)
- Spanish issue:
  Orange-Yellow, special wheels........... **£60-70**

1547 Panhard PL17 (1:43)
1964-66 (renumbered in 1964 from 547)
- Violet body, anodised base, concave hubs,
  sidelights under headlights.
  In blister pack................................... **£80-100**
- Brick Red body, anodised base, concave
  hubs, sidelights under headlights.
  In blister pack................................... **£80-100**

1552 Chevrolet Corvair
1964-66 (renumbered in 1964 from 552)
Raised filler cap on some. Blister pack.
- Turquoise Blue body........................... **£65-75**
- Orange-Red body **£65-75**

1553 Peugeot 404
1964-66 (renumbered in 1964 from 553)
- Ivory body, dark red interior.
  Blister pack **£90-110**

1557 Citroën Ami 6
1964-66 (renumbered in 1964 from 557)
- Green/White, no spare wheel.
  Blister pack **£60-70**
- Blue/White, no spare wheel.
  Blister pack **£60-70**

1558 Citroën 2cv Azam (1:43)
1964-66 (renumbered in 1964 from 558)
- Yellow/Maroon body, grey concave
  hubs (black tyres). In blister pack **£45-60**
- Light Yellow/Maroon body, grey concave
  hubs (black tyres). In blister pack **£60-70**
- Green/Dark Green body, grey concave
  hubs (black tyres). In blister pack **£60-70**

1559 Ford Taunus 17M (1:43)
1964-69 (renumbered in 1964 from 559)
(All have concave hubs.)
- Metallic Gold body. Blister pack......... **£70-90**
- Metallic Grey-Gold. Blister pack......... **£70-90**
- Ivory body. Blister pack **£70-90**

Solido-Cougar Models

Cast by Solido in France, all the models are in
1:43 scale, all have plastic wheels and 'Dinky Toys
France' on the plastic base, and all were supplied
in a 'Dinky Toys GB' box. Compare this list with
the 'COUGAR Model Toys' list that follows it.

1401 1981 **Citroën 2cv6**
Orange-red body (beige open top)
with 'ducks' decal....**£25-35**
Green body (grey open top) with
'ducks' decal **£25-35**

1402 1981 **Citroën 2cv6**
Orange-red body (beige closed top)
with 'ducks' decal.................**£25-35**
Green body (grey closed top) with
'ducks' decal **£25-35**

1402 1981 **Citroën Visa**
Metallic jade green (white base,
tinted windows), no decals....**£25-35**
Metallic red, (grey base, clear
windows), no decals..............**£25-35**

1403 1981 **Fiat Ritmo/Strada**
Metallic orange body (dark cream
base), no decals **£25-35**

Metallic blue body (yellow base),
no decals **£25-35**

1404 1981 **BMW 530**
Metallic green with 'Cougar' decal.....
.... **£25-35**
Metallic purple with 'flames' decal ....
.... **£25-35**

1405 1981 **Alfa-Romeo Alfetta GTV**
Red body, 'shamrock' decal .. **£25-35**
Yellow body, 'shamrock' decal**£25-35**

1406 1981 **Peugeot 504**
Metallic yellow with 'cougar' decal ....
.... **£25-35**
Metallic blue with 'flames' decal ....
.... **£25-35**
1983   Black body, 'Dinky France' decal,
plastic wheels.
(Lyons 1983 promotional)...... **£35-45**

COUGAR Model Toys. Many of the 'Airfix Dinky
Toys' appeared erratically in the early 1980s
(in France then in the UK) under the name of
'Cougar Model Toys'. Every one had a plastic
base marked 'Dinky Toys made in France' and
the code '1/43 07 80'. They were presented in

card backed blister-packs with 'Metal Cougar'
and 'Fabriqué par Solido' printing. Numbers
printed on card are 100 less than numbers
moulded on base.

1301-1401 **Citroën 2cv6**
Orange-red body with 'ducks' decal,
Grey base/interior/open top . **£15-25**
Green body, 'ducks' decal, grey base,
orange interior, tan open top. **£15-25**

1302-1402 **Citroën Visa**
Metallic jade green, no decal, white
base, dark cream interior **£15-25**
Metallic red body, no decal, grey base
and interior **£15-25**

1303-1403 **Fiat Ritmo**
Metallic orange (dark cream base/
interior), no decal.................. **£15-25**
Metallic blue (yellow base/interior),
no decal **£15-25**

1304-1404 **BMW 530**
Metallic green, 'cougar' decal, grey
base, black/grey interior, green tinted
windows **£15-25**
Metallic purple, 'flames' decal, grey

base, black/grey interior, yellow
tinted windows **£15-25**
1305-1405 Alfetta GTV
Red body, 'shamrock' decal, tan base,
black/tan interior, yellow tinted
windows **£15-25**

Yellow body, 'shamrock' decal, tan
base, black/tan interior, blue tinted
windows **£15-25**
1306-1406 Peugeot 504 Berline
Metallic yellow, 'cougar' decal, brown
base and tinted windows, black/

brown interior **£15-25**
Metallic blue body, 'flames' decal,
blue base and interior, clear
windows **£15-25**

French Dinky Toys Commercial Vehicles

French Dinky commercial vehicles (in keeping with other ranges) have very similar series numbering to their English counterparts. But, like the cars, the French castings are different in many ways from the Liverpool produced versions and, of course, are marked 'Made in France' or 'Fab. en France'.

An interesting point about the 25 Series is that although there was a range of body styles on offer at any one time, there was only one chassis casting for a particular period. This meant that the chassis dies wore out at a disproportionate rate to the body dies. Chassis castings are found that come from either a crisp new die or from one that is weary from over-use, and the appearance can be so different that

some collectors have thought these to be the result of intentional design changes. The only differences however, are the ones noted in this listing.

On the French 25 series the headlights are larger and more pointed than the English equivalent. They were originally silver plated, later silver painted. The size of the headlights was reduced over the years and are best classed as large, medium and small. Modern replacement parts (radiator/grille/bumper) which are intended for the English lorries are not suitable for use on the French 25 series. Like the cars, the lorries had 'DUNLOP' tyres, first in the colour of the body, later black or white. The problem of shortage of rubber affected the lorry production in 1940 and for four years after the war ended, so that in those

periods the lorries had to be produced with all-metal wheels. Metal failure affects pre-war mazak castings whether they are of French or English origin though the commercial vehicles seem not to be so drastically affected as, for instance, aircraft or ship models.

The first French Dinky Toys commercial vehicle model to be issued in an individual yellow box was 25-B Peugeot D3a Van in 1953. In England the Supertoys range was introduced in 1947 but it was not till 1955 that a French Supertoys model appeared. The 'Auto-Echelle de Pompiers' (Delahaye Fire Escape) was the first French model to be presented in the famous blue and white striped Supertoys box and was given the number 32-D.

Model and details	MPR

14 Triporteur

14 Triporteur
1935-39
Tinplate base, smooth hubs (various colours), black or white 'DUNLOP' tyres, scale 1:40. The driver may be found as a solid casting or hollow-cast. His cap is usually the same colour as his jacket. His trousers and boots were black or very dark brown (hand applied paint that may vary in shade or extent).
* Vehicle colours: Yellow, Red, Light Blue, Navy Blue. Driver's jacket: Blue, Grey or Green **£750-1,000**
NB The 1935 catalogue illustration (a drawing) shows 14 with a front bumper but the existence of this version is very much in doubt.
1940-49
Plain cast wheels (black or unpainted), tinplate base, scale 1:40. Vehicle colours:
* Yellow, Red, Light Blue, Navy Blue. Driver's jacket: Blue, Grey or Green **£500-750**
1950-52
* Painted ridged hubs with black rubber tyres, no base. Vehicle colours: Yellow, Red, Light Blue, Navy Blue. Driver's jacket: Blue, Grey or Green **£250-500**
14-C Coventry Climax Fork Lift Truck
1950-59 (scale 1:43)
* Orange/green/black, painted ridged hubs, grey tyres, made in England. French box (orange-red outer, yellow inner) **£40-50**
NB 14-C was renumbered in 1959, then assembled in France and issued as 597.
25a Open Lorry
1935-39 (scale 1:65)
Open chassis, grille/headlights casting, front bumper, cast-in tow hook, painted smooth hubs, black or white 'DUNLOP' tyres.
* Green/black **£250-350**

* Blue/black **£250-350**
* Yellow/brown **£250-350**
25a Open Lorry
1940-48
Same, but with unpainted cast wheels.
* Green/black or Red/black **£250-350**
* Red/grey or Brown/grey................... **£250-350**
25-A Ford Livestock Truck
1950-52 (scale 1:65)
* Metallic Grey or Metallic Light Blue body, painted ridged hubs.............. **£150-200**
* Silver body, red ridged hubs............ **£250-350**
* Yellow cab, Red back and ridged hubs **£3,000-4,000**
25b Covered Lorry
1935-39 (scale 1:65)
Open chassis, grille/headlights casting, front bumper, cast-in tow hook, smooth hubs, black or white 'DUNLOP' tyres, removable tilt.
* Green/black (green tilt), Blue/black (beige tilt), Red/brown (green tilt), Blue/red (beige tilt) **£350-450**
25b Covered Lorry
1940-48
Open chassis, grille/headlights casting, front bumper, cast-in hook, unpainted cast (or Cream) wheels, removable tilt.
* Red/black (green tilt), Blue/black (green tilt), Red/black (cream tilt), Red/grey (green tilt) **£150-200**
25-B Peugeot D3a Van
1953-53 (scale 1:50)
* Navy blue body (cross-hatching on inside of roof), no advertising, red ridged hubs................................ **£600-750**
* Grey body (cross-hatching on inside of roof), no advertising, red ridged hubs................................ **£600-750**
1953-54
* Yellow and Green body (smooth inside roof), 'LAMPE MAZDA' logo, painted ridged hubs **£200-300**
NB This was the first French Dinky Toys commercial vehicle model to be issued in an individual yellow box.
25BV Peugeot Post Van
1954-59 (renumbered in 1959 as 560)
* Dark Green body (smooth or cross-hatched inside roof), 'POSTES' (thin lettering, tampo). Box print: '25BV, marque déposée' only............ **£130-160**

* Same model, but with box print: '25BV, marque déposée, Made in France, Imprimé en France' **£130-160**
25c Flat Truck
1935-39 (scale 1:65)
Open chassis, grille/headlights casting, front bumper, cast-in tow hook, smooth hubs, black or white 'DUNLOP' tyres.
* Turquoise/black, Blue/black, Grey/red, Green/black or Red/brown.............. **£225-275**
1940-48
Open chassis, grille/headlights casting, front bumper, cast-in tow hook, unpainted mazak wheels.
* Blue/black, Green/black, Cream/red or Grey/red **£100-125**
25-C Citroën H Van
1954-57 (scale 1:50)
* Metallic Grey and Gold body (official Citroën colours), painted ridged hubs. Yellow box (grey model shown) **£100-125**

25CG 'Cibie' Citroën H van.

25CG Citroën H Van
1957-59
* Cream body, 'FROMAGE CH GERVAIS', in 25-C yellow box but with '25CG' sticker **£160-190**
1959-59 (renumbered in 1959 as 561)
* Turquoise body (various shades), 'CIBIE', ridged or concave hubs, box with '25C' or '25CG' printed...... **£300-400**
25d Tanker Lorry
1935-35 (scale 1:65)
* Red body (smooth inside tank), no advertising, maroon open chassis (no hook), grille/headlights casting, front bumper, smooth hubs, red 'DUNLOP' tyres... **£300-400**
1936-37
* Red body (smooth or ridged inside tank), 'STANDARD ESSOLUBE', black open

chassis, smooth hubs, black or white
'DUNLOP' tyres **£300-400**
1938-39
- Red body (ridged inside tank),
'ESSOLUBE - ESSO', black or red open
chassis, smooth hubs, black or white
'DUNLOP' tyres **£300-400**

25d Tanker Lorry
1940-49
- Red body (ridged inside tank),
'ESSOLUBE - ESSO', black open
chassis, mazak wheels **£200-300**
- Maroon body (ridged inside), 'ESSO'
or 'ESSOLUBE', grey or black open
chassis, mazak wheels **£200-300**

25-D Citroën 2cv Van 'BÉBÉ LORRAIN'
1959-59
- Grey body, cream hubs.
Only 80 made of this Code-2
promotional (see 562) **£6,000-8,000**

25e Tipping Lorry
1935-39 (scale 1:65)
Tipping rear truck body, open chassis,
grille/headlights casting, front bumper,
cast-in tow hook, smooth hubs, black or
white 'DUNLOP' tyres.
- Blue cab, Yellow body,
black or brown chassis **£240-300**
- Green cab, Blue body,
black or red chassis **£240-300**
- Green cab, Yellow body,
red, black or brown chassis.............. **£240-300**
1940-48
As previous version, but with painted
mazak wheels. Cab/body/chassis colours:
- Blue/yellow/black, Green/yellow/brown,
or Cream/green/red **£130-180**

25f Market Gardener's Lorry
1935-39 (scale 1:65)
Open chassis, grille/headlights casting,
front bumper, cast-in tow hook, smooth
hubs, black or white 'DUNLOP' tyres.
- Violet body (black chassis) **£240-300**
- Cream body (black chassis)............. **£240-300**
- Green body (red chassis) **£240-300**
- Grey body (black chassis) **£300-400**
1940-48
As previous version, but with unpainted
mazak wheels. Body/chassis colours:
- Cream/Red, Turquoise/Black,
Yellow/Red, Light Green/Grey **£240-300**

25g Flat Trailer with Headboard
1935-39 (scale 1:65)
- Blue, red or green, 4 mazak hubs,
black or white tyres................................ **£30-40**
1940-48
- Turquoise, red or green, two axles,
unpainted or black mazak wheels........ **£30-40**
1949-50
- Red or green, two axles, painted
ridged hubs, black tyres. **£30-40**

25-H Ford Beverage Truck
1949-49 (scale 1:65)
Flat truck with removable tailboard,
cast-in tow hook, spare wheel.
- Blue, Cream, Turquoise, Red, Brown,
Metallic Green, Bright Green body,
painted mazak wheels....................... **£250-350**
1950-50
- Blue, Cream, Red, Brown, Bright
Green body, with ridged hubs **£300-400**
- Metallic green, bright green hubs **£300-400**
- Turquoise body, ridged hubs......... **£750-1,000**

25-I Ford Open Wagon
1949-49 (scale 1:65)
- Blue, Red, Green, Dark Grey, Maroon,
or Brown body, cast-in towing hook,
painted mazak wheels....................... **£150-200**
1950-50
- Beige or Metallic Grey body,
cast-in hook, painted ridged hubs
(colour as body) **£300-400**

1951-52
- Dark Red or Light Blue body, separate
rivetted hook and spare wheel,
matching ridged hubs **£200-300**
- Cream body, separate rivetted hook
and spare wheel, matching
ridged hubs.............................**£2,000-2,500**

25-J Ford Covered Wagon
1949-50
(plain) Tinplate tilt (no advertising),
cast-in towing hook, spare wheel,
painted mazak wheels or ridged hubs.
- Metallic Gold (green tilt).................. **£375-475**
- Red (green or red tilt) **£375-475**
- Light Blue (cream tilt) **£375-475**
- Dark Blue (brown tilt) **£375-475**
- Brown (brown tilt) **£375-475**
- Brown (green tilt)............................. **£375-475**
- Cream body, brown tilt **£375-475**

25-JB 'SNCF'
1949-50
- Blue (dark blue tilt), 'SNCF' round logo,
cast-in hook, black mazak wheels or
ridged hubs **£1,000-1,500**
1951-52
- Blue (dark blue tilt), 'SNCF' round logo,
separate hook, black ridged hubs **£400-500**

25-JJ 'CALBERSON'
1949-52 (scale 1:65)
Wide spacing to letters, plus map of
France, cast-in (later separate) hook.
- Yellow or Yellow Ochre body with black
tilt, painted mazak wheels or Red or
Black ridged hubs **£600-800**

25-JV 'GRAND MOULINS DE PARIS'
1953-53
- Grey body, black tilt, separate hook,
painted ridged hubs **£300-400**

25-K Studebaker Farm Produce Truck
1949-49 (scale 1:55)
Short lateral bonnet mouldings, small
windows, tool-box, painted mazak
wheels (usually black).
- Red/Blue, Blue/Turquoise,
Red/Yellow, Turquoise/Red.............. **£350-450**
- Blue/Greyish-Green **£350-450**
1950-50
- Red/Blue, Blue/Red, Blue/Turquoise,
Red/Turquoise-Green,
painted ridged hubs **£200-250**
1951-52
Long curved bonnet mouldings, large
windows, outline of tool-box only,
painted ridged hubs.
- Red/Yellow, Blue/Red,
Blue/Maroon **£150-200**
- Red cab, Blue back............................ **£400-500**

25-L Studebaker Covered Truck
1949-50
Short lateral bonnet mouldings, small
windows, tinplate tilt, tool-box,
painted mazak wheels or ridged hubs.
- Red body, yellow tilt **£750-1,000**
- Blue body, yellow or brown tilt......**£750-1,000**
- Turquoise body, cream or yellow
tilt, red or cream hubs **£750-1,000**
1951-52
Long curved bonnet mouldings,
large windows, tool-box outline only,
painted ridged hubs
- Blue (brown tilt, blue hubs)............. **£300-400**
- Red (yellow tilt, red hubs)................ **£300-400**

25-M Studebaker Tipping Truck
1949-50 (scale 1:55)
Short bonnet mouldings, small windows,
tool-box, painted mazak wheels or
ridged hubs.
- Dark Green/Metallic Grey **£100-130**
- Dark Green/Plain Grey..................... **£100-130**
1951-52
Long bonnet curved bonnet mouldings,
large windows, tool-box outline only,

painted ridged hubs.
- Dark Green/Metallic Grey **£70-85**
- Dark Green/Plain Grey......................... **£70-85**
- Khaki/silver (cream hubs) **£700-900**

25-M Ford Tipping Truck
1950-55 (scale 1:65)
- Green cab, Metallic or Plain Grey
tipper, black or green ridged hubs. **£65-75**

25-O Studebaker Milk Truck
1949-50 (scale 1:55)
- Blue/Eggshell Cream or Blue/White,
'NESTLÉ' (transfer), short bonnet
mouldings, small windows, tool-box,
painted wheels or ridged hubs,
ten milk churns. Red box with
yellow interior **£400-600**
1951-54
- Blue/White, 'NESTLÉ' advertising on
some, long curved bonnet mouldings,
large windows, tool-box outline only,
painted ridged hubs, ten churns.
Red box with yellow inner **£350-450**

25-O Ford Milk Truck.

25-O Ford Milk Truck
1950-50
- Blue/White body, 'NESTLÉ' (transfer,
thick lettering). Long red box with
yellow inner, card spacer **£400-500**
1954-55
- Blue/white body, 'NESTLÉ' (tampo,
plain or later lettering).
Shorter (correct length) box............. **£450-550**

25-P Studebaker Pick-Up
1949-49 (scale 1:55)
- Mustard-Yellow and Dark Red body, painted
mazak wheels, short bonnet mouldings,
small windows, tool-box **£500-600**
1950-55
- Yellow/Red, ridged hubs, short or long
bonnet mouldings, small or large
windows, box outline only. **£100-150**

25-Q Studebaker Covered Pick-Up
1949-49 (scale 1:55)
- Green cab and tilt, Red body, short bonnet
mouldings, small windows, tool-box,
painted wheels **£500-750**
- Dark Grey-Green cab and tilt, Yellow
ochre body, painted wheels.............. **£500-750**
1950-52
- Green/Yellow, Green hubs, short or long
bonnet mouldings, small or large
windows, outline only **£500-700**

25-R Studebaker Breakdown Truck
1949-50
- Red body, 'DINKY SERVICE' on some,
short bonnet mouldings, small windows,
tool-box, painted mazak wheels or
ridged hubs **£400-500**
1951-54
- Red body, 'DINKY SERVICE', long curved
bonnet mouldings, large windows, tool-box
outline only, painted ridged hubs
.... **£150-200**

25-R Ford Breakdown Truck
1954-54 (scale 1:65)
- Red body, 'DINKY SERVICE',
red ridged hubs, black tyres............. **£300-400**
1954-55
- Red body, no logo, plated ridged
hubs, white tyres. .... NGPP

25-S Single-axle Trailer
1949-49 (scale 1:55)
- Red body, concave rear lamps,
painted wheels......................................**£30-35**
1950-50
- Red (Cream hubs), Yellow (Red hubs),
Green (Yellow hubs). Concave or
raised rear lamps **£30-35**

25-T Single-axle Covered Trailer
1949-49
As 25-S but with tinplate tilt, concave
rear lamps, painted mazak wheels.
- Red body (green tilt), or
Yellow body (brown tilt)........................**£30-35**
1950-55
- Red (green tilt, green ridged hubs),
Yellow (brown tilt, yellow ridged hubs).
Concave or raised rear lamps **£30-35**

25-U Ford Tanker
1950-50 (scale 1:65)
- Red body, 'ESSO', painted ridged
hubs, hook and spare wheel support,
pierced base **£400-500**
1951-51
- As previous model but without the
support for hook/spare wheel **£120-140**
1952-53
- As 1951 version but with smaller
transfers and non-pierced base........**£100-125**

25-V Ford Refuse Tipper
1950-51 (scale 1:65)
- Dark Green body, Dark or Mid-Green
ridged hubs, smooth tailgate
interior surface....................................**£80-100**
1952-55
- Dark Green body, dark-green ridged
hubs, cross-braced tailgate
interior surface **£70-90**

**27AC Massey-Harris Tractor
and Manure Spreader**
1950-50 (scale 1:43)
- Red tractor and implement made in
England, painted wheels,
French display box (Red) **£400-600**

30e Breakdown Lorry
1936-39 (scale 1:65)
Fitted with the (lead) crane from 21d
Railway Crane Truck. , smooth hubs,
'DUNLOP' tyres.
- Yellow body, green crane, brown or
black chassis.......................................**£300-350**
- Red body, green crane, red or Black
chassis; or Blue body, green crane,
black chassis.......................................**£300-350**
1938-39
- Green body, green crane, brown
chassis; or Red body, red crane,
black chassis.......................................**£300-350**
1940-40
- With mazak wheels. Blue body
with blue crane, or Yellow body,
black chassis....................................**£900-1,200**

PANHARD ARTICULATED LORRIES:
32-A (plain) (scale 1:60)
1952-52
- Blue body, plain or silver grille,
painted ridged hubs. Sold unboxed . **£200-250**

32-AB 'SNCF'
1952-52
- Blue body, 'SNCF' (locomotive in round
logo), painted ridged hubs.
Sold unboxed (3 to a trade box) **£400-500**
1954-59 (renumbered in 1959 as 575)
- Blue body, 'SNCF' (pale green French
map logo), painted ridged hubs.
Sold unboxed (three to a trade box)
or later in own yellow box
(add £30 to price)..............................**£150-200**

32-AJ 'KODAK'
1952-53
- Yellow body (smooth inside cab roof),
'KODAK', painted ridged hubs,

Sold unboxed (supplied to shops in
trade boxes of three)..........................**£400-500**
1955-57
- Yellow body (cross-hatching in cab roof),
'KODAK', painted ridged hubs. Sold
unboxed (supplied to shops in
trade boxes of three)..........................**£450-550**
- US issue:
Yellow body, (different letter shape
from the French issue) **£800-1,100**

32AJ 'Kodak' Panhard articulated lorry.

32C Panhard Titan-Coder Tanker, 'ESSO'
1954-55
- Red body, 'ESSO' (large transfers), painted
ridged hubs, '32C TRACTEUR
PANHARD' on Yellow box......**£160-200**
1956-59 (renumbered in 1959 as 576)
- Red body, 'ESSO' (medium transfers), '32C
TRACTEUR PANHARD' in 5 languages
on Yellow box **£130-160**

33A Simca Cargo Van
1955-56 (scale 1:55)
Indented (early) or raised (later) cab
step-plate, no hook mounting,
spare wheel held by screw.
- Olive-Green/Yellow (green/yellow
picture on yellow box), painted
ridged hubs **£140-200**
- Olive-Green/Orange (green/orange
picture on yellow box), painted
ridged hubs **£140-200**

33AN Simca Cargo Van, 'BAILLY'
1956-59 (renumbered in 1959 as 577)
Indented or raised cab step-plate, with hook
and mounting, spare wheel held by screw.
- Yellow/White body, 'BAILLY
DEMENAGEMENTS' logo, painted
ridged hubs, yellow box **£200-250**

33B Simca Cargo Tipping Truck.

33-B Simca Cargo Tipper Truck
1955-59 (renumbered in 1959 as 578)
Indented (later raised) cab step-plate, no
hook mounting, smooth or grooved tipper
surface, indented (later raised) tailgate
central reinforcement, painted ridged hubs.
- Dark Green/Grey, Dark Green/Metallic
Grey, Metallic Dark Green/Metallic
Grey. Yellow box **£90-110**
- Later version of previous models, with
hook and mounting. Yellow box.........**£90-110**

*33C Simca Glazier's Lorry and 25V Ford
Refuse Truck.*

33-C Simca Glazier's Truck
1955-59 (renumbered in 1959 as 579)
- Grey/Dark Green, indented or raised cab
step-plate, hook mounting on later issues,
grey ridged hubs. Scale 1:55.
'MIROITIER SAINT-GOBAIN'.
Yellow box has '33C MIROITIER'
in French, later in 5 languages **£120-170**

34-A Berliet Quarry Truck
1955-59 (renumbered in 1959 as 580)
No spare wheel support, ridged and concave
painted hubs, scale 1:55.
- Blue/black, orange tipper. Box first
without then with picture and '34A'... **£90-110**
1957-59
Promotional: Blue/black, Orange tipper.
In 'BERLIET' yellow box...................**£500-750**

34-B Berliet Container Truck
1956-57 (renumbered in 1959 as 581)
Spare wheel screwed on, iron container-
lifting eye, ridged and concave painted hubs.
- Red/Black/Light Grey, matt grey container.
No picture on yellow box **£100-120**
1957-59
- As previous model but with cast-in lifting
eye, yellow box has picture and
'34B plateau avec container'............**£100-120**
- Promotional: Yellow body,
'BAILLY' on container **£120-140**

35-A Citroën U23 Breakdown Truck
1955-55 (scale 1:50)
- Red body, large tool-box, closed fuel
tank, yellow 'DINKY TOYS' logo.
'35A' on box **£110-140**
1956-59 (renumbered in 1959 as 582)
- Dark Red body, small tool-box, open fuel
tank, Yellow 'DINKY TOYS' logo.
'35A' on box **£110-140**

36-A Willeme Log Lorry
1956-59 (renumbered in 1959 as 897)
- Orange cab, Yellow semi-trailer (pierced
beam), wooden logs, black painted base,
painted ridged and concave hubs,
radial tread tyres, scale 1:55.
'36A' on Supertoys box **£100-130**

36B Tracteur Willeme.

36-B Willeme Tractor & Closed Trailer
1958-59 (renumbered in 1959 as 896)
- Red tractor, Orange semi-trailer with
removable green plastic tilt, painted ridged
and concave hubs, 4 rollers on trailer
prop. '36B' on Supertoys box **£150-200**

38A Unic Skip Lorry.

38-A Unic Marrel Multi-Skip Truck
1957-59 (renumbered in 1959 as 895)
- Grey and Golden-Yellow (or Lemon-Yellow)
body (windows in some), fixed skip,
ridged and concave painted hubs, black
radial or block tread tyres.
'38A' on Supertoys box **£130-170**

39A Unic Boilot car transporter.

39-A Unic Boilot Car Transporter
1957-59 (renumbered in 1959 as 894)
• Silver/orange, ridged and concave hubs, black radial tread tyres, scale 1:55, '39A' on Supertoys box **£180-200**
• With all-Red trailer, Black hubs .. **£500-750**

39-B Unic Sahara Pipe Transporter
1959-60 (renumbered in 1960 as 893)
• Beige body (various shades), White roof, 'open' trailer, painted ridged and concave hubs, 6 black tubes, scale 1:55. '893' on Supertoys box **£120-150**

50 Salev Mobile Crane
1957-59 (1:43) (renumbered in 1959 as 595)
• Grey body, Red crane, Blue driver, ridged and concave painted hubs ... **£120-150**

70 Two-Axle Covered Trailer
1957-59 (1:60) (renumbered in 1959 as 810)
• Red or Yellow, green tilt, ridged or concave hubs. '70' on yellow box **£30-40**

90-A Richier Diesel Roller
1958-59 (renumbered in 1959 as 830)
• Yellow body, blue driver, red roller wheels, '90A' on Yellow box. Supertoy **£90-110**

560 Muir-Hill Dumper
1951-?
• Yellow body, metal wheels. Imported from England; sold in special blue box, French printing on label **£55-65**

560 Peugeot D3A Van
1959-60 (1:50) (renumbered from 25-BV)
• Dark or Light Grey body, painted ridged hubs **£550-625**

560 Peugeot Post Van, 'POSTES'
1959-60
• Dark Green body, 'POSTES' (thick letters, transfer). Box print: '25BV, marque déposée' only **£150-200**
• Same model, but box print reads: '25BV, marque déposée, Made in France, Imprimé en France' **£150-200**
1960-61
• Same model, but 'POSTES' transfer has oval or more square letter 'O'. Box reads '25BV/560' **£150-200**
1960-61
• Same model (transfer with oval 'O' of 'POSTES'), concave painted hubs. '560' on box **£150-200**

560 Peugeot D3a Van 'CIBIE'
1960
• Promotional: Turquoise body, yellow ridged hubs **£2,500-3,500**

560-P Citroën 2cv Van 'PHILIPS'
1961
• Promotional: Yellow cab, Silver back, red logo and design on door **£4,000-5,000**

560 Citroën 2cv Postal Service Van
1963-70
• Yellow body and concave hubs, blue 'swallow' logo. Yellow box print reads: 'C'est une fabrication MECCANO,' or (later): 'C'est une fabrication MECCANO TRI-ANG'........................**£125-150**

560-E Citroën 2cv Azam Van
1968-70
• Pale Green body, plated concave hubs, 'PIRELLI' tyres, 'DINKY-POCH' on box. Export to Spain **£1,750-2,250**

---

561 Blaw-Knox Bulldozer
1951-59 (renumbered in 1959 as 885)
• Red/black, with driver. Model made in England, Blue box made in France .. **£100-125**

561 Citroën H Van
1959-59 (1:50) (renumbered from 25-CG)
• Cream body, 'FROMAGE CH GERVAIS,' In own box with '25CG GERVAIS' print **£200-250**
1959-63
• Turquoise body (various shades), 'CIBIE,' painted ridged hubs (concave from 1961). In 25CG box with '561 CIBIE' sticker over the number **£300-400**
1963-66
• White/blue body, 'GLACES GERVAIS,' blue concave hubs. Picture box........ **£400-500**
1964-64
• Code-2 promotional: Blue body, 'BAROCLEM,' aluminium concave hubs. Special picture box............**£4,000-6,000**

561 Renault 4L Van
1972-72 (scale 1:43)
• Yellow body, 'PTT,' first grille, grey security window, plastic base, chromed concave hubs **£2,500-3,000**

562 Muir-Hill Dumper
1951-? (scale 1:43)
• Golden Yellow, with driver, model made in England, Blue box made in France .. **£50-60**

562H Citroën 2cv Van, 'WEGENWACHT'
1965-68
• Yellow body, concave hubs, '25D' on black painted base or anodised base without '25D'. Model made for export to Netherlands. Yellow box marked 'WW' from 1968 .... **£500-750**

563 Renault Estafette Pick-Up
1960-62 (scale 1:43)
• Orange or Green body, green tilt, painted concave hubs. Yellow box without, later with, illustration **£60-80**

564 Renault Mirror Truck
1963-65 (scale 1:43)
• Red-Orange body, 'SAINT-GOBAIN / MIROITIER,' painted concave hubs. Yellow box **£150-175**
• As previous model but with Brick Red body. Yellow box.............. **£150-175**

565 Renault Estafette Camper.

565 Renault Estafette Camper
1965-71 (scale 1:43)
• Blue body, Ivory plastic roof, chromed concave hubs. Yellow box **£200-250**

566 Citroën H Currus Van 'POLICE'
1965-70
• Blue/White body, painted concave hubs, working warning lights **£200-300**

567 Unimog Snow Plough
1967-70 (scale 1:50)
• Yellow/black body, brown removable top, painted concave hubs. Yellow box ... **£120-140**

569 Berliet Stradair Side Tipper
1967-71 (scale 1:43)
• Light Green/Dark Green body, painted hubs, green or black motor. Yellow box, instruction leaflet **£250-400**

---

570 PEUGEOT J7 TAXI VANS:
570 'ALLO-FRET'
1967-67 (scale 1:43)
• Blue body, blue or white roof, aluminium concave hubs, aerial. Yellow box...... **£300-400**

570 'IMPERIAL CHEMICAL INDUSTRIES'
1968-68
• Blue/White. Code 2 promo **£1,000-1,500**

570A 'AUTOROUTES'
1970-71 (scale 1:50)
• Orange body, two workmen plus equipment, On diorama base in yellow box (also containing a 595s Traffic Sign 'Pedestrians Prohibited') **£600-750**

571 Coles Mobile Crane
1951-59 (1:50)
• Yellow and Black, painted hubs. Model made in England, Blue box made in France (see 972) **£70-80**

571 Saviem Goelette Horse Box and Sulky
1969-71 (scale 1:43)
• Blue/'wood'/White, painted concave hubs, racehorse, Green two-wheel racing cart (sulky) with driver. Yellow picture box **£900-1,200**

572 Berliet Quarry Truck
1970-71 (scale 1:43)
• Red body, Yellow plastic tipper, plastic hubs, 595d Traffic Sign 'No Overtaking For Heavy Vehicles' also in yellow box **£400-650**

575 Panhard Articulated Lorry, 'SNCF'
1959-63 (renumbered in 1959 from 32-AB)
• Blue body, 'SNCF' on Pale (later Dark) Green French map logo, painted ridged or concave hubs. Sold unboxed (three to a trade box), later in own Yellow box (add £30 to price).............................**£120-150**

576 Panhard Tanker 'Esso'.

576 Panhard Titan-Coder Tanker, 'ESSO'
1959-60 (renumbered in 1959 from 32-C)
• Red body, 'ESSO' (medium lettering), painted ridged hubs. '32C TRACTEUR PANHARD' in 5 languages on yellow box **£175-200**
1960-61
• Red or Dark Red body, 'ESSO' (smaller lettering), painted ridged hubs (concave from 1961). Yellow box has 'DINKY TOYS' in italics, '576' and description in 5 languages on flap...................... **£160-200**
1961-61
• Same, but with concave hubs **£200-250**

577 Simca Cargo Van, 'BAILLY'
1959-61 (renumbered in 1959 from 32AN)
• Yellow/White body, 'BAILLY DEMENAGEMENTS.' Indented or raised cab step-plate, with hook support, spare wheel held by screw (later by rivet), painted ridged hubs (later concave) **£540-200**

577 Berliet Livestock Truck
1965-71 (scale 1:43)
• Yellow and Green, two black and white cows, painted concave hubs. Yellow box **£150-200**

578 Simca Cargo Tipper Truck
1959-70 (renumbered in 1959 from 33-B)
• Dark or Mid-Green/Metallic Grey, indented or raised cab step-plate, with hook mounting, spare wheel held by screw (later by rivet), scale 1:55. Yellow box **£80-100**

577 Berliet Cattle Truck.

579 Simca Mirror Truck, 'SAINT-GOBAIN'
1959-61 (renumbered in 1959 from 33C)
• Grey/Dark Green, 'MIROITIER SAINT-GOBAIN'. Indented or raised cab step-plate, with hook mounting, spare wheel screwed on, Grey or Yellow ridged hubs, scale 1:55. Yellow box has '33C MIROITIER' in 5 languages **£120-160**
1961-67
• Yellow/Dark Green, Yellow ridged hubs, spare wheel rivetted. Yellow box changed to read: '579-33C'.............................. **£140-180**
• Yellow/Dark Green or Grey/Dark Green, Grey ridged hubs or Cream concave hubs **£150-200**
196?-6?
• Export model: Pale Grey/Pale Green, without 'SAINT-GOBAIN', Cream ridged or concave hubs. **£100-150**

580 Berliet Quarry Truck
1959-61 (renumbered in 1959 from 34A)
• As 34-A but with spare wheel support, ridged and concave painted hubs, block tread tyres. Blue/Black, Orange tipper. Picture on yellow box **£150-175**
1961-70
• Same model but with cast-in spare wheel location, concave painted hubs and anodised base **£150-175**

581 Berliet Container Truck
1959-60 (renumbered in 1959 from 34B)
Spare wheel held by screw, ridged and/or concave painted hubs, round (later square) section tyres.
• Red/Black/Light Grey, Dark Grey container. Picture on yellow box **£100-120**
1960-65
• Same, but spare wheel rivetted on. Yellow box has picture and '34B plateau avec container' in 7 languages **£120-140**

582 Citroën 'Dinky Toys Breakdown Lorry.

582 Citroën Breakdown Truck, 'DINKY TOYS'
1959-69 (renumbered in 1959 from 34A)
Painted ridged hubs, smooth black tyres, small tool-box, open fuel tank, 1:50.
• Dark red body, yellow 'DINKY TOYS' logo. '35A' on box.............................. **£100-150**
1969-71
• Red body and concave hubs, yellow logo, plastic hook, smooth or treaded black tyres. '582' on box **£120-160**

584 Berliet Covered Lorry
1961-65 (scale 1:43)
• Red or Yellow body (either with Green tilt), concave hubs. Yellow box (picture on later ones) **£100-120**

585 Berliet Builders Lorry
1961-64 (scale 1:43)

• Blue/Orange/Grey, wide (later narrow) boards in tipping body, painted concave hubs. Yellow box **£100-125**

586 Citroën 55 Milk Lorry
1961-65 (scale 1:43)
• White/Blue body, 30 bottle crates, painted concave hubs. Yellow box ... **£500-700**

587 Citroën H Display Van, 'PHILIPS'
1964-70 (scale 1:43)
• Yellow/Silver body, red concave hubs, household appliances. Yellow picture box **£600-800**

588 Berliet Beer Lorry
1964-70 (scale 1:43)
• Yellow/Red/Brown, 'BIERES, LIMONADES, EAUX MINÉRALES', painted concave hubs, crates and barrels. Yellow picture box............... **£250-300**
588K 1970-71
• Code 1 Promotional: Red body, 'KRONENBOURG LE GRAND NOM des BIERES d'ALSACE'...............**£3,500-4,500**

589 Berliet Breakdown Lorry
1965-69 (scale 1:43)
• Red body, 'DEPANNAGE' in yellow or white, chromed concave hubs **£250-300**
1970-71
• Orange body, 'DEPANNAGE AUTOROUTES', chromed concave hubs, aerial. 595t Traffic Sign 'Maximum Height 3.5 metres' included in box .. **£250-300**

595 Salev Mobile Crane
1959-61
• As reference 50 but crane pillar not held by rivet, painted concave hubs
.... **£80-110**

596 LMV Road Sweeper.

596 LMV Road Sweeper/Washer
1960-63 (scale 1:43)
• Cream and Green body, rotating and pivoting brush mechanism. Yellow box **£80-110**

597 Coventry Climax Fork Lift Truck
1959-61 (renumbered in 1959 from 14-C)
• Orange/Yellow (or Green)/Black, ridged and concave hubs, 'assemblé en France' on base **£60-75**

803 Unic Articulated Lorry, 'SNCF'
1967-69 (scale 1:43)
• Dark Blue body, cream trailer roof, 'SNCF' and 'PAM-PAM', plastic hubs. Yellow picture box **£250-350**

805 Unic Multi Skip and Gas Tanker
1966-71 (scale 1:55)
• Red/Black/White, interchangeable skip and 'PROPANE-PRIMAGAZ' gas tank (from Hornby ACHO range), painted concave hubs. Yellow picture box **£300-400**

810 Two-Axle Covered Trailer
1959-62 (renumbered in 1959 from 70)
• Red or Yellow, Green tilt, ridged or concave hubs, scale 1:60. '70' (later '810') on Yellow box.............. **£40-50**
1962-?
• **Two-Axle Covered Trailer, 'ESSO'**
Red body and tilt, 'ESSO' transfers, painted concave hubs. Yellow box **£55-65**

830 Richier Diesel Roller
1959-69 (renumbered in 1959 from 90A)

• Yellow body, Blue driver, Red wheels, '90A-830' (later '830') on Yellow box, scale 1:43. Supertoy **£90-120**

881 GMC Circus Truck and Animal Trailer
1969-70 (scale 1:43)
• Red/Yellow/Black, 'PINDER FAUVES', no hole in seat for driver, plastic animals, card supports, 'SUPER DINKY MECCANO FRANCE' on chassis, painted concave hubs. Yellow box **£1,000-1,500**
1970-71
• Same, but with hole in seat for driver, and 'DINKY-TOYS MECCANO TRI-ANG' on chassis **£1,000-1,500**

882 Peugeot 404 + Circus Caravan
1969-70
• Red/Yellow/White Peugeot 404 (536) and Caravelair Armagnac 420 Caravan (564), 'Le SUPER CIRQUE PINDER' roof hoardings, chromed concave hubs. Yellow box also contains : a 595L Traffic Sign 'Maximum Width 2 metres', 'Martin' the circus bear and a leaflet........**£1,500-1,800**

885 Blaw-Knox Bulldozer
1959-61 (scale 1:43)
• Orange/Grey/Black, driver. 'Assemblé en France' on base (see 561). Blue/White striped picture box **£150-175**

885 Saviem Sinpar Steel Carrier
1966-71 (scale 1:43)
• Red cab, grey chassis, driver, plastic hubs, steel load held by magnets. Yellow picture box (showing yellow/grey vehicle) **£300-350**

886 Richier Road Profiler
1960-65 (scale 1:43)
• Yellow body, driver, plastic hubs. Supertoys box................................... **£200-250**

887 Muir-Hill Dumper
1959-61 (scale 1:43)
• Yellow-Cream body, driver, painted ridged hubs. English components, 'Assemblé en France' on base............... **£40-50**

887 Unic Articulated Tanker, 'BP'
1963-71 (scale 1:43)
• White/Green/Lemon Yellow, 'AIR BP', plastic hubs, hoses for filling tank, electric lights switched by spare wheel. Supertoys blue/white box with full colour picture on lid **£150-200**

888 Berliet Sahara Pipe-Layer
1960-66 (scale 1:50)
• Sand yellow (various shades), White roof, operable crane, most with White or Beige plastic hubs (a few cast metal), most with tow hook (a few without).......... **£175-225**
1968
• Promotional: As previous model but with 'Société Languedocienne de Forages Pétroliers' **£1,000-1,200**

889 Coles Mobile Crane
1959-62
• Orange/Yellow, 2 drivers, painted concave hubs, 'Assemblé en France' on base. Renumbered in 1959 from 972; reissued in 1962 as 972......................... **£60-80**

893 Unic Sahara Pipe Transporter
1960-70 (renumbered in 1960 from 39B)
• Beige body (various shades), White roof, window glazing, pierced (later solid) trailer painted ridged and concave hubs, 6 tubes, scale 1:55. Supertoys box without (later with) '893'................................ **£150-175**
196?
• Code 2 Promotional: Beige body, White roof, window glazing, 'solid' trailer, painted concave hubs. 'DESTINATION: PETROLE DU SAHARA' on box.............................. NGPP

894 Unic Boilot Car Transporter
1959-68 (renumbered in 1959 from 39A)
• Silver/Orange, 'DINKY TOYS SERVICE LIVRAISON', painted concave hubs,

black block tread tyres, scale 1:55.
'894' on Supertoys box **£150-180**

895 Unic Marrel Multi-Body Truck
1959-65 (renumbered in 1959 from 38A)
• Grey and Golden-Yellow body, fixed skip, ridged and concave (or all concave) painted hubs, black block tread tyres, scale 1:55.
'895' on Supertoys box **£120-140**

896 Willeme Tractor and Covered Trailer
1959-71 (renumbered in 1959 from 36B)
• Red tractor, inclined (later straight) chassis members, Orange semi-trailer, Green tilt, painted ridged and/or concave hubs,

4 (later 2) rollers on trailer prop.
'36B-896' (later just '896') on
Supertoys box.................................. **£140-180**

897 Willeme Log Lorry
1959-71 (renumbered in 1959 from 36A)
• Orange tractor (chassis members on spindle), Yellow semi-trailer (pierced, later solid), black painted base, painted concave hubs, radial or block tread tyres, 1:55.
'897-36A' (later just '897') on
Supertoys box.................................. **£125-165**

898 Berliet Transformer Carrier,'ALSTHOM'
1961-65

• Orange body, Grey transformer (loose parts within), painted ridged (later concave) hubs.
Supertoys box.................................... **£400-500**

972 Coles Mobile Crane
1957-62 (renumbered in 1959 to 889)
• Orange and Yellow, two drivers, painted concave hubs, scale 1:50. English parts,
'Assemblé in France' on base............... **£60-80**

1412 Hotchkiss Willys Recovery Jeep
1968-71 (scale 1:50)
• Red and Yellow body, Orange or Black jib with lamp, painted concave hubs **£100-130**

French Dinky Toys Emergency Vehicles *See also Gift Sets section.*

Model and details	MPR

25BR Peugeot D3a Fire Service Van
1959
• A prototype exists with a light red body (cross-hatching inside roof), dark red ridged hubs and identical transfers to the 25D Citroën van.............................. NPP

25D Citroën 2cv Fire Service Van
1958-59 (1:43) (renumbered in 1959 to 562)
• Red body and ridged hubs, 'Pompiers Ville de Paris'. Yellow box.................. **£130-170**
1959-59
Grey body, 'BÉBÉ LORRAIN', cream hubs. Only 80 were made of this Code-2 promotional model..................... **£3,500-5,000**

32D Delahaye Turntable Fire Escape.

32D Delahaye Fire Escape
1955-59 (renumbered in 1959 to 899)
• Red body, chromed ladder, painted ridged hubs, smooth White tyres (specially made for this model), scale 1:55.
Blue/White striped Supertoys box.
(32-D was the first of the French Dinky Supertoys)............................... **£150-200**

32E Berliet First-Aid Vehicle
1957-59 (renumbered in 1959 to 583)
• Bright Red (occasionally Brownish-Red) twin-cab body (no markings), detachable hose reel, painted ridged (concave through 1959) hubs, white tyes, scale 1:55,
'32E' on Supertoys box **£150-200**

80F Renault Military Ambulance
1959-59 (renumbered in 1959 to 820)
• Renault Goelette in Gloss or matt finish, painted ridged hubs, scale 1:55. Yellow box........................... **£60-75**

501 Citroën DS19 'POLICE' Car
1967-70
• Very dark blue/white, roof beacon, plated concave hubs, scale 1:43 .... **£160-200**

507P Simca 1500 'POLICE' Estate Car
1967-71
• Dark blue/white body. Commissioned for use by Police **£300-350**

517P Renault R8 'POLICE' Car
1969
• Dark blue/white. Commissioned for use by Police..................................... **£400-450**

518 Renault 4L

Model and details	MPR

1964-64
• Red body, 'POMPIERS de PARIS'.
Commissioned by Fire Service **£375-425**

525 Peugeot 404 Fire Car
1964-64
• Red body, 'Pompiers de Paris', concave chromed hubs. Commissioned for use by Fire Service. **£400-500**

551 Ford Taunus 17M Police Car
1965-67 (scale 1:43)
• Green/white, 'POLIZEI', plated concave hubs, German text on box.
Made for export to Germany and Benelux countries..........................**£800-1,000**

556 Citroën ID19 Ambulance
1964-67
• Same, but 'A' of 'Ambulance' and 'M' of 'Municipale' are not aligned.
'Super detail' box................................ **£80-100**
1967-70
• Grey/cream body, plated concave hubs, 'DUNLOP' nylon tyres, plastic steering wheel, without '556' on base, 'A' of 'Ambulance' and 'M' of 'Municipale' are not aligned. 'Super detail' box... **£110-140**

556 Citroën ID19 Ambulance; 32D Delahaye Fire Escape; and 32E Berliet First-Aid Vehicle.

562 Citroën 2cv Van
1959-61 (renumbered in 1959 from 25-D)
• Red body and ridged hubs, 'POMPIERS VILLE de PARIS', scale 1:43............... **£130-170**
1961-63
• Red body and concave hubs, 'POMPIERS VILLE de PARIS', smooth or treaded black tyres......... **£140-180**

566 Citroën H Currus Van, 'POLICE'
1965-70
• Blue/white body, painted concave hubs, working warning lights........... **£200-300**

568 Berliet Gak Fire Escape
1968-70 (scale 1:43)
• Red twin-cab body, extending chromed ladder, painted concave hubs.
Yellow picture box............................ **£250-300**

570P Peugeot J7 VSAB Fire Van
1971-72

• 'POMPIERS', Red body, painted hubs, 'MECCANO FRANCE SA' on diecast base. Yellow box **£300-450**
1972-
• Later version, with 'MECCANO TRI-ANG' on plastic base. Yellow box............... **£300-450**

583 Berliet First-Aid Vehicle
1959-63 (renumbered in 1959 from 32-E)
• Bright Red twin-cab body (no markings), detachable hose reel, painted concave painted hubs, white tyes, scale 1:55,
'32E' (later '583-32E') on Supertoys box **£140-180**
1962-63
• Fire Service promotional:
Red twin-cab body with 'POMPIERS de PARIS' shield, concave hubs **£200-250**

820 Renault Goelette Ambulance
1959-70 (renumbered in 1959 from 80-F)
• Gloss or matt finish, painted concave hubs, treaded rubber (later nylon) tyres, scale 1:55. Yellow box.......................... **£60-75**

899 Delahaye Fire Escape
1959-65 (renumbered in 1959 from 32-D)
• Red body, black steering wheel, painted ridged hubs, smooth white tyres, 1:55. '32D' on Supertoys box........... **£200-250**
1965-70
• Red body, white steering wheel, painted concave hubs, treaded white tyres.
'899' on Supertoys box..................... **£200-250**

1402 Ford Galaxie 'POLICE' Car
1968-68
• Black/white body. Commissioned for use by Police............................... NGPP

1416P Renault R6 Fire Car
'POMPIERS de PARIS'
1970-70
• Code 2 model based on Spanish-made components, commissioned by the Fire Service. Red body, second grille (square headlamps), red concave hubs. Side view of white model on box. **£400-500**

1429 Peugeot 404 'POLICE' Car
1970-71 (scale 1:43)
• Blue/White body, plastic base, plated concave hubs.
Yellow box..................................... **£200-300**
NB 595n Traffic Sign 'Cycling Prohibited' included with 1429.

1450 Simca 1100 'POLICE' Car
1977-78
• Blue/white or black/white body, plated concave hubs.
Made in Spain....................................... **£25-40**

French Dinky Toys Military Vehicles

A number of military vehicle models were designed in the late 1930s and the prototypes were shown in the June 1940 French catalogue. They were never put into production because of the Nazi Occupation.

It came as no surprise that, following liberation by the Allies, the first new French Dinky Toy to be introduced was a model of the US Army Jeep, so common at the time. The unavailability of rubber meant that all-metal wheels had to be used instead of hubs and tyres. The wheels used on the Jeep were mounted inside-out to give a heavy duty off-road effect. During the 1960s and 1970s a number of military models from the English range were imported into France.

These are listed in the Imports section. 681 DUKW Amphibious Vehicle was not one of those imported as the French factory produced a much more detailed version (number 825). Note that the letters 'DUKW' are not initials nor are they an abbreviation - they are simply part of the General Motors design reference system of the time.

All the models listed are finished in various shades of military green unless otherwise stated. The paint can be found to be either gloss, semi-gloss or matt but this does not affect the price range. Some military items are also noted in the Accessories section.

Model and details	MPR

24M Military Jeep
1946-48 (scale 1:43)
- US Military olive-drab body and mazak wheels (mounted inside-out for effect), white star on bonnet, tinplate windscreen frame (some bonnet castings have frame supports), wire steering wheel **£400-600**

NB 24-M was the first French made Dinky Toy to appear after the War. Trade boxes contained twelve units.

80A Panhard EBR75 FL11
1957-59 (renumbered in 1959 to 815) (1:55)
- Painted hubs, radial tread tyres, side headlamps or red lights. '80A' on base and box (picture on some boxes).......... **£50-70**

828 Jeep Missile Launcher and 80BP Hotchkiss Willys Jeep.

80-B Hotchkiss Willys Jeep
1958-59 (scale 1:50)
- No driver (but hole in some), no hook, convex or ridged painted hubs, smooth black tyres. '80B' printed on deep yellow end-flap box (picture on some) **£55-75**

80-BP Hotchkiss Willys Jeep
1959-59 (renumbered in 1959 to 816)
- With driver, no hook, convex or ridged painted hubs, smooth black tyres. There are two end-flap box types:
  1 - '80B' Yellow box (with picture) has '80BP' stickers
  2 - '80BP' printed on Yellow box (with picture) **£50-70**

80-C AMX 13 Tank
1958-59 (renumbered in 1959 to 817) (1:55)
- Gloss or matt finish, no aerial, rubber tracks, rear roller treads indented or raised. '80C' on Yellow end-flap box................ **£50-80**

80-D Berliet 6x6 All-Terrain Truck
1958-59 (scale 1:55)
- Tinplate tilt, black cab floor, painted hubs. '80D' (no picture) on yellow end-flap box............................ **£50-70**
1959-59 (renumbered in 1959 to 818)
- Tinplate tilt, khaki cab floor, concave painted hubs. '80D' and picture on yellow end-flap box............................ **£60-85**

80-E Obusier ABS 155mm Gun
1958-59 (renumbered in 1959 to 819) (1:55)
- Gloss or matt finish, painted concave hubs. Yellow end-flap box with or without picture, one packing piece.................... **£40-50**
- Same but with painted ridged hubs...... **£50-60**

80-F Renault Goelette Ambulance
1959-59 (renumbered in 1959 to 820) (1:55)
- Gloss or matt, no roof vent or red crosses, ridged hubs. Deep yellow end-flap box (model picture faces left)...................... **£60-75**

676 Daimler Armoured Car
1972-72 (scale 1:55)
- Painted concave hubs, camouflage net. Model first made in France though 'Made in England' wrongly stated on base. 'MECCANO FRANCE' on yellow box **£150-200**

NB 676 was replaced after a short time by the Liverpool-made model with new reference '676L'.

800 Renault 4x4 Sinpar
1974-? (revised and renumbered from 815)
- Khaki body, grey-green-khaki top, camouflage net, no gear lever, no aerial support, black or white plastic radio, painted concave hubs, scale 1:43. 'MECCANO' on base and box ('camouflage' effect on yellow end-flap box).. **£90-120**

801 AMX 13 Tank
1973-75 (renumbered in 1973 from 817)
- Matt Khaki body, grey nylon tracks, plastic rollers, camouflage net (a few without), scale 1:55. '801' on yellow, part camouflaged box **£55-75**

802 Obusier ABS 155mm Gun
1974-? (renumbered in 1974 from 819)
- Khaki body with camouflage net, 'OBUSIER 155' replaces '80E' on base, painted concave hubs. 'Camouflage' effect on yellow box **£40-50**

804 Mercedes-Benz Unimog
1973-?
(revised and renumbered from 821)
- Khaki body and camouflage net, 'MERCEDES TOUS TERRAINS, 804' on chassis, grey-blue base without '821', painted concave hubs, ridged tyres. 'MECCANO TRI-ANG' on yellow box with 'camouflage' effect (box also contains unused transfer sheet)........ **£110-140**

806 Berliet Recovery Truck
1973-?
(revised and renumbered from 826)
- Khaki body and base, driver, plastic hook, camouflage net, without 'TOUS TERRAINS BERLIET' on chassis, painted concave hubs. 'Camouflage' effect on yellow box **£200-250**

807 Renault All-Terrain Ambulance
1973-? (scale 1:55)
- Khaki body with roof vents and red crosses, plastic concave hubs and base. Later editions . with windows. Yellow end-flap box........................... **£110-120**

808 Dodge WC56 Command Car
Announced in the 1971 catalogue but made as reference 810 from 1972.

808 GMC US Army Recovery Truck
1972-74 (scale 1:43)
- Sand body (hole for driver), painted concave hubs, black removable top. Yellow box with insert **£200-250**
1974-?
- Olive-drab body (hole for driver in some), painted concave hubs, black top. Yellow box with insert **£200-250**

809 GMC US Army 6x6 Truck
1970- (scale 1:43)
- Olive drab/black body (white stars), driver (white or khaki helmet), painted concave hubs. Yellow box has design panel and insert.............. **£125-150**

809 GMC 6x6 Truck
197?-?
- Khaki/black (white stars), driver (grey helmet), painted concave hubs. 'MECCANO' on box but no design panel, box has insert **£175-225**

NB 595q Traffic Sign 'Automatic Level Crossing' included with 809, plus additional 'white star' transfer sheet.

804 mercedes Benz Unimog truck and 810 Dodge Command Car.

810 Dodge WC56 Command Car
1972-74 (scale 1:43)
- Removable top, soldier, camouflage net, antenna concave hubs. 'Camouflage' effect yellow box, transfers........................ **£170-200**

813 AMX with 155mm ABS Gun
1969-71 (scale 1:55)
- Gloss or matt finish, nylon tracks. Yellow end-flap box........................... **£140-190**
1972-?
- Gloss or matt finish, nylon tracks, simplified gun, camouflage net. 'Camouflage' effect on yellow box **£140-190**

814 Panhard Armoured Car
1963-71 (scale 1:52)
- Khaki finish, painted concave hubs, black (later Grey-Blue) base. 'C'est une fabrication MECCANO' printed on plain side of yellow end-flap box, insert, aerials in packet... **£45-55**

815 Panhard EBR75 FL11
1959-63 (renumbered in 1959 from 80-A)
- Gloss or matt finish, '80A' on base, painted hubs, block tread tyres, 1:55. Picture and '815' on box **£40-50**

815 Renault 4 Sinpar Gendarmerie
1969-74
(revised in 1974 and issued as 800) (1:43)
• Khaki body, green-khaki top, two military
policemen, gear lever, aerial, light grey
plastic radio, painted concave hubs.
'MECCANO TRI-ANG' on base **£140-170**

816 Hotchkiss Willys Jeep
1959-61 (renumbered in 1959 from 80-BP)
• Driver, no hook, painted ridged hubs,
smooth black tyres, scale 1:50. Picture
and '816-80BP' on yellow box **£50-70**
1962-63
• Driver, cast-in hook, concave hubs,
smooth or treaded black tyres.
Picture and '816' on yellow box **£50-70**

816 Berliet Rocket Launcher
1969-71 (scale 1:55)
• Khaki/grey body, white/red rocket
('NORD, R-20'), painted concave hubs.
Yellow end-flap box **£200-250**

817 AMX 13 Tank
1959-64 (renumbered in 1959 from 80-C)
• Gloss or matt khaki, no aerial, rubber
tracks, rear roller treads raised. 1:55.
'80C' on yellow box **£50-70**
1965-70
• Same but only in gloss khaki and with
aerial. With (later without) '80C' on
base. '817' on yellow box **£50-70**
1973-75 (renumbered in 1973 to 801)
• Same but matt khaki body, grey nylon
tracks on plastic rollers, Yellow box
with 'camouflage' effect **£50-75**

818 Berliet 6x6 All-Terrain Truck
1959-65 (renumbered in 1959 from 80-D)
• Tinplate tilt, khaki cab floor,
painted concave hubs, scale 1:55.
'80D' and picture on yellow box **£60-80**
1965-70
• Same, but 'TOUS TERRAINS BERLIET'
on base (a few without), '818' and
picture on yellow box **£60-80**

819 Obusier ABS 155mm Gun
1959-65 (renumbered in 1959 from 80-E)
• Khaki body, painted ridged hubs,
'80E' on base, scale 1:55.
Fully illustrated yellow box **£40-50**
1965-74
• Gloss khaki body, painted concave hubs.
Fully illustrated yellow box **£40-50**
1974 (revised in 1974; issued as 802)

See larger image on page 193.

820 Renault Goelette Ambulance
1959-70 (renumbered in 1959 from 80-F)
• No roof vents, no red crosses,
concave hubs, treaded plastic tyres,
Yellow box (picture faces left) **£65-85**
• Same but with roof vents/ crosses, plastic
windows.
(Model picture on later boxes faces right) **£80-110**

821 Mercedes-Benz Unimog
1960-63
• 'MERCEDES-UNIMOG' on chassis,
'821' on black painted base,
painted concave hubs, smooth tyres.
No picture on yellow end-flap box **£50-80**
1963-65
• 'MERCEDES-BENZ UNIMOG' on chassis,
'821' on black painted base, painted

concave hubs, smooth tyres. Picture and
'MECCANO' on yellow end-flap box **£45-55**
1965-66
• As previous model. but with ridged tyres.
Picture and 'MECCANO TRI-ANG'
on yellow end-flap box **£45-55**
1966-70
• Same but with grey-blue base without
'821'. Picture and 'MECCANO
TRI-ANG' on yellow box **£45-55**
1973 (revised in 1973 and issued as 804)

See larger image on page 193.

822 White M3 Half-Track
1960-63 (scale 1:50)
• Matt finish, no machine gun, black painted
chassis, painted concave hubs (smooth
black tyres). Picture of model on
yellow end-flap box **£70-80**
1963-65
• Matt or gloss finish, with machine gun,
anodised chassis, painted concave hubs
(treaded black tyres). Picture of model plus
scene and 'C'est une fabrication MECCANO'
on some yellow end-flap boxes **£70-85**
1965-71
• Same, but with picture of model plus scene
and 'C'est une fabrication
MECCANO TRI-ANG' on box **£70-80**

823 Marion Mobile Kitchen
1962-66 (scale 1:50)
• Khaki body, black or khaki base,
painted concave hubs.
'Cuisine Roulante' on Yellow box **£50-60**

*823 GMC Tanker, 810 Command Car, 80A Panhard
EBR Tank, 80B Hotchkiss Jeep, 80F Renault
Goelette Ambulance.*

823 GMC Military Tanker
1969-70 (scale 1:43)
• Khaki/Black, plastic tank, removable cab
canopy, painted concave hubs.
Yellow end-flap box has insert and also
contains a 595b Traffic Sign
'Maximum Weight 5.5 tonnes' **£200-300**

824 Berliet Gazelle 6x6 Truck
1963-64 (scale 1:55)
• Removable cab canopy and tilt, painted
concave hubs. 'Cabine vitrée' ('cab
window glazing') on illustrated
yellow end-flap box **£120-140**
1964-70
• Same model, but 'Cabine vitrée aménagée'
('cab window glazing fitted') on
yellow end-flap box **£120-140**

825 GMC DUKW Amphibian
1963-71 (scale 1:55)
• Gloss or matt finish, drums and boxes,
painted concave hubs, driver with later

issues. Yellow end-flap box
(picture on later boxes) **£120-140**

826 Military Recovery Truck.

826 Berliet Recovery Truck
1963-70 (scale 1:55)
• Plastic driver, metal hook, black base,
'TOUS TERRAINS BERLIET' on
chassis, painted concave hubs.
Deep yellow end-flap box also
contains a pink instruction leaflet **£140-170**
1973
(revised in 1973 and issued as 806).

827 Panhard EBR75 FL10
1964-71 (scale 1:55)
• Khaki body, aerial/aerial point in some,
painted concave hubs. Yellow scenic
end-flap, some with Eiffel Tower logo,
box with packing piece **£75-85**

828 Jeep SS10 Missile Launcher
1964-71 (scale 1:50)
• Driver, missile battery, concave hubs.
Yellow scenic end-flap box has
instructions printed on side **£55-70**

829 Jeep 106SR Gun Carrier
1964-71 (scale 1:50)
• Driver, plastic gun, painted concave hubs.
Yellow scenic end-flap box
(instructions on side) **£75-100**

834 Mobile Bridge Pack
1963-70 (scale 1:55)
• Khaki plastic 6 part bridge plus inflatable
boats (as supplied with 884) .... NPP

841 Tank Tracks Pack
1959-71
• Twelve tracks for AMX tanks .... NPP

843 Military Tyre Pack
1962-71
• Twelve treaded black tyres
(large for 818 and similar) .... NPP

852 Tank Tracks Pack
1962-71
• Ten replacement tracks for
822 White M3 Military Half-Track .... NPP

856 Machine Gun
1963-71
• Plastic armament for use on
822 White M3 Half-Track .... NPP

883 AMX Bridge Laying Vehicle.

883 AMX 13 Bridge Layer
1964-66 (scale 1:55)
• Gloss or matt, '13t AMX' on base.
Yellow box reference on black
oval, instructions enclosed **£150-200**
1966-71
• Same, but 'Char AMX poseur de pont,
réf.883' on base. Yellow box has
reference on violet band **£150-200**

884 Brockway Bridge Layer
1961-70 (scale 1:55)
• 10 element bridge, 2 inflatable boats.

Supertoys box ('884' on some) also
contains leaflet/map £275-325

890 Berliet T6 Tank Transporter
1959-63 (scale 1:55)

• Gloss or matt finish, painted ridged
hubs, Supertoys box has
no illustration..................................... £160-250
1963-70

• Gloss or matt finish, painted ridged or
concave hubs. Illustration on
blue/white Supertoys box.................. £160-200

French Dinky Toys Aircraft

In comparison with the English factory, Meccano France produced only a small range of model aircraft. They are nonetheless rather attractive and much sought after. Pre-war planes are especially difficult to find in good stable condition since the metal deterioration problem equally affected production on both sides of the Channel.

Some interesting models were designed at the end of the 1930s in the French 64 series (listed below). These were announced in the 1939 Meccano Magazine but with the advance of the occupying German forces production did not take place. Around this period a few small (normally silver) planes were given a camouflage finish and advertised as 'Reconnaissance' or 'Spotter' planes though it is very unlikely that serious production of these was actually undertaken.

Some of the English 60 series were imported into France before the war, and very few post-war (see the Imports section for details). Of the few new French made aircraft models to appear in the late 1950s, the Caravelle is perhaps the most desirable, particularly in the Swiss, Scandinavian or Algerian liveries with their specially printed Supertoys boxes.

As in England the French factory produced a number of boxed sets of model aircraft in the 1930s. They are fully described in the Gift Sets section.

60a DeWoitine D388 Rainbow ('L'Arc en Ciel')
1935-40
Three engines, each with 2-blade propellers
and no tinplate surrounds.
• Silver/Red £200-300
• Gold/Red £200-300
• Cream/Red £200-300
• Cream/Green....................................... £200-300
• Gold/Green.. £200-300
• Gold/Blue £200-300

60A Dassault Mystere IVa Jet
1957-59 (renumbered in 1959 to 800)
• Metallic Grey, single jet,
Blue cockpit. Yellow box....................... £70-80

60b Potez 58
1935-40
Tinplate main wings, 2-wheel undercarriage,
2-blade propeller, 2-part windscreen.
• Yellow/Grey £150-250
• Red/Silver £200-300

60B Sud Aviation Vautour 'SNCASO'
1957-59 (renumbered in 1959 to 801)
• Metallic Grey, twin jet,
Blue cockpit. Yellow box..................... £80-100

60c Henriot H180T
1935-40
Tinplate main wings, 2-wheel undercarriage,
2-blade propeller, 3-part windscreen.
• Green/White, Green/Red £150-250
• Blue/White, Red/Silver...................... £150-250

60C Lockheed Super G Constellation
1956-59 (renumbered in 1959 to 892)
• Silver, 'AIR FRANCE', 'FB-HBX',
4 x 3-blade propellers, scale 1:190.
Supertoys box £150-200

60d Breguet Corsaire
1935-40
Open two-seater fuselage with tinplate
main wings and 2-blade propeller.
• Silver/Red £200-300
• Red/Green £200-300
• Red/Yellow.. £200-300

60D Sikorsky S58 Helicopter
1957-59 (renumbered in 1959 to 802)
• White/Grey/Blue, 'SABENA',
Black rotors. Yellow box.................... £100-125

60e DeWoitine 500 Hunter
1935-40
Open cockpit, tinplate main wings,
2-wheel undercarriage, 2-blade propeller.
• Cream/Red or Light Cream/Green.. £200-300

60E Vickers Viscount
1957-59 (renumbered in 1959 as 803)
• White/Grey/Blue, 'AIR FRANCE',
'FB-GNX', 4 x 4-blade propellers,
scale 1:190. Yellow box...................... £125-175

60f Cierva Autogiro
1935-40
Cast body, with or without pilot.
• Gold (Red rotors) £200-300
• Cream (Red or Blue rotors) £200-300
• Silver (Red or Blue rotors)............... £200-300
• Red (Cream rotors) £200-300

60F Caravelle SE210 'Air France.'

60F Caravelle SE210, 'AIR FRANCE'
1959-59 (renumbered in 1960 to 891)
• Metallic Grey/White/Blue,
'FB-GNY', operable steps,
scale 1:190. Supertoys box................ £130-180

61a Dewoitine D338
1938-40
Casting as 60a L'Arc en Ciel but different
arrangement of decoration, 3 x 3-blade
propellers and tinplate engine surrounds.
• Green/Silver £150-250
• Red/Gold £150-250
1939-40
Different casting from first version of 61a
(and also has the reference 64). Three
engines, each with 3-blade propellers and
tinplate engine surrounds, gliding hole.
'FA-DBF' marking on body.
• Silver body £150-250
• Light Green body.............................. £150-250

61b Potez 56
1938-40
Fitted with 2 x 2-blade propellers.
• Blue/Silver £150-250
• Red/Silver £150-250
• Yellow/Silver...................................... £150-250

61c Farman F360
1938-40
Open two-seater, single 2-blade propeller.
• Silver/Blue or Silver/Red................. £150-250
• Silver/Yellow or Silver + roundels.... £150-250

61d Potez 58 Air Ambulance
1938-40
• Silver body with red cross on
Silver or White ground...................... £200-300

61e Henriot H180M
1938-40
• Silver wings and fuselage with
roundels, 2-blade propeller.............. £200-300

61f Dewoitine 500 Hunter
1938-40
• Silver wings and fuselage with
roundels, 2-blade propeller.............. £200-300

64 Dewoitine D338
1939-40
Different casting from previous version
with more prominent tailfin and also having
the reference 61a. Three engines, each with
2-blade propellers, gliding hole.
'FA-DBF' marking.
• Silver body £150-200
• Light Green body.............................. £150-200

64a Amiot 370
1939-40
Twin engine monoplane,
2 or 3-blade propellers, gliding hole.
• Beige, Pink, Red or Blue; or Pale Green
with red circles on wings; or
Silver with French roundels £150-250
1948-49
• A small number of pre-war castings
were issued in various colours......... £150-250

64b Bloch 220
1939-40
Twin engine airliner marked 'FA-OHJ',
2 x 3-blade propellers, gliding hole.
• Silver or Dark Red £150-250
• Pale Green or Ivory £150-250

64c Potez 63
1939-40
Twin engines, twin tailplanes,
3-blade propellers.
• Beige, Red, Blue, Silver,
Silver with French roundels £150-250
1948-49
• A small number of pre-war castings
were issued in various colours......... £150-250

64d Potez 662
1939-40
Four engines, 'FA-RAY', 3-blade propellers,
twin tailplanes, gliding hole.
• Silver, Red, Light Blue, Yellow £150-200

800 Dassault Mystere IVa Jet
1959-64 (renumbered in 1959 from 60-A)
• Metallic Grey, single jet,
Blue cockpit. Yellow box....................... £70-80

801 Sud Aviation Vautour 'SNCASO'
1959-64 (renumbered in 1959 from 60-B)
• Metallic Grey, twin jet,
Blue cockpit. Yellow box..................... £80-100

802 Sikorsky S58 Helicopter
1959-61 (renumbered from 60-D)
• White/Grey/Blue, 'SABENA',
Black rotors. Yellow box.................... £100-125

803 Vickers Viscount, 'AIR FRANCE'
1959-61 (renumbered in 1959 from 60-E)
• White/Grey/Blue, 'FB-GNX',
scale 1:190, 4 x 4-blade propellers.
Yellow box.. £125-175

804 SNCAN Noratlas (French military)
1959-63
• Metallic Grey, twin-fuselage,
2 x 4-blade propellers. Yellow box ... £150-200

891 Caravelle SE210
(renumbered in 1959 from 60-F)
All have 'Escalier escamotable' (operable

steps) and Supertoys box. Scale 1:190.
- 1959-59 **'AIR FRANCE'**
  Silver/White/Blue, 'FB-GNY' **£200-250**
- 1959-68 **'AIR FRANCE'**
  Metallic Grey/White/Blue. '60F' under
  wing of early issues only **£250-350**

- 1960-? **'SWISSAIR'** on box, 'HB-ICX',
  Metallic Grey/White/Red **£900-1,200**
- 1960-? **'SAS'** on box, 'SE-DAA',
  Metallic Grey/White/Blue **£900-1,200**
- 1960-? **'AIR ALGERIE'**
  Metallic Grey/White/Red. 'FO-BNH'.

Supertoys 'Air Algerie' on box **£900-1,200**
892 Lockheed Super G Constellation
- 1959-62 **'AIR FRANCE'**, (scale 1:190)
  Silver, 'FB-HBX', 4 x 3-blade propellers.
  Supertoys box **£200-250**

French Dinky Toys Trains

Model and details	MPR
16 Northern Sector Railcar	
1935-40	
'Autorail' with 3 articulated coaches in	
mazak, tinplate base, silvered or black lead	
hubs, white rubber tyres. Boxed.	
• Blue-Grey/Dark Blue	**£100-125**
• Grey/Blue	**£100-125**
• Grey/Red	**£100-125**
• Gold/Red	**£100-125**
• Cream/Red	**£100-125**
• Cream/Green	**£100-125**
16a 1940 Two-Car Railcar	
A two-part version of 16a. Advertised	
in the 1940 catalogue but not issued	NPP
17 1935-38 Electric Goods Train	See 'Gift Sets'.
18 1934-38 Steam Goods Train	See 'Gift Sets'.
19 1935-38 Electric Passenger Train	'Gift Sets'.
19a Electric Locomotive	
1935-36	
• Cast in lead. Various basic colours	**£60-80**
1936-40	
• Cast in mazak.	
Silver/Red; Light Green/Red; Green/Black;	
Gold/Blue; Two-tone Blue	**£50-70**

Model and details	MPR
20 1935-38 Steam Passenger Train	'Gift Sets'.
20a Passenger Coach	
1935-40	
Cast in lead	
• Red/Blue	**£25-35**
• Green/Blue	**£25-35**
21 1934-38 Steam Mixed Goods Train	
See 'Gift Sets'. section.	
21a Steam Tank Locomotive	
1934-40	
Cast in lead.	
• Red/Blue	**£30-45**
• Green/Blue	**£30-45**
• Green/Black	**£30-45**
21b Timber Wagon	
1934-40	
Red/Green wagon cast in lead,	
Yellow mazak 'log'	**£30-45**
21c Coal Wagon	
1934-40	
Cast in lead.	
• Green/Red wagon	**£30-45**
• Green/Black wagon	**£30-45**
21d Crane Wagon	

Model and details	MPR
1934-38	
Cast in lead, crane has 'open' jib.	
• Blue and Green	**£25-35**
• Green and Blue	**£25-35**
• Red and Blue	**£25-35**
• Yellow and Red	**£25-35**
1938-40	
Cast in lead, crane has 'solid' jib.	
• Blue and Green	**£25-35**
• Green and Blue	**£25-35**
• Red and Blue	**£25-35**
• Yellow and Red	**£25-35**
26 Bugatti Autorail	
1934-35	
Cast in mazak, smooth sides, small windows.	
May have silvered metal cast wheels or	
bakelite moulded rollers in red, green or blue.	
• Cream body with Blue, Yellow,	
Green, Red or Orange sides	**£90-120**
1934-40	
Same, but with ridged sides and	
larger windows.	
• Yellow body (Red or Green sides)	**£90-120**
• Green (Red sides)	**£90-120**

Caravans and Campers

564 1969-71 Caravelair Armagnac 420
Blue/white, plated concave hubs, scale
1:43. Yellow box has 595a Traffic Sign
'Danger of Falling Rocks'...............**£100-150**

565 1965-71 Renault Estafette Camping Car
Light blue body, ivory roof, floral curtains,
aluminium concave hubs, scale 1:43. Yellow

box   **£140-180**

811 1959-59 Caravan ('Henon' style)
Cream/White, smooth roof casting, window
glazing in most, tinplate drawbar, plated
ridged hubs, scale 1:43. .... **£80-100**
1960-63 As previous model, but with

ribbed body casting **£70-90**
812 1965-69 Camping Trailer
Cream body with luggage, single plated
ridged hub and black tyre, scale 1:43. Sold
only in plastic bag............................ **£40-50**

Ships

Most of the Dinky Toys model ships sold in France were imported English issues (see the Imports section for details). Those of French design and manufacture are listed below. No boxed sets made entirely in France appear to have been produced, though the Liverpool made castings of the British Naval Warships set were imported into France between 1938 and 1940. They were sold in a French version of the presentation box. The 'Locomotion Moderne' set was intended to contain ship models but was another of those proposals which fell victim to the outbreak of war (see the Gift Sets section for details).

52c Steamship 'Normandie'
1937-40
Black/white/red, no rollers, 175mm. Blue box
has coloured picture of the ship at sea on
the lid, and a picture of the ship and the
port of Manhattan on the inner part**£175-250**
1940-40
Black/white/red, no rollers, 175mm. Blue
box has no inner picture **£120-170**

52d Steamship 'Normandie'
1937-40
Black/white/red, with metal rollers,
175mm. Blue box has coloured picture of

the ship at sea on the lid, and a picture of
the ship and the port of Manhattan on the
inner part **£175-250**
1940-40 ....
Black/white/red, with metal rollers,
175mm. Blue box has no inner picture.........
....**£120-170**
1947-48 ....
Black/white/red, with metal rollers,
175mm. Blue box has no inner picture.........
....**£120-170**

53a Battleship 'Dunkerque'
1937-40
Battleship grey, with metal rollers, 120mm.
Light yellow one-piece illustrated box..........
....**£100-150**
53b Battleship 'Dunkerque'
1937-40 ....
Battleship grey, no rollers, 120mm. Light
yellow one-piece illustrated box .**£100-150**
870 Steamship 'France'
1962-71
White/black/red, scale 1:1200, 263mm. ....
....**£150-200**

'Dolly Varden' Dolls House Furniture

Models of 'Dolly Varden' dolls house furniture were available in France and England. They are very similar in range and appearance but are definitely different castings with a different finish. French boxed sets generally appear to have much bigger boxes than the English equivalent. It is thought that the 'Dolly Varden Dolls House' was never advertised in France and is consequently almost impossible to find there.

101	1936	**Dining Room Furniture Set** See 'Gift Set' section	
101a	1936-40	**Dining Table** Light or Dark mottled brown **£10-15**	
101b	1936-40	**Sideboard** Light or Dark mottled brown **£15-20**	
101c	1936-40	**Carver** Light or Dark mottled brown **£10-15**	
101d	1936-40	**Chair** Light or Dark mottled brown **£10-15**	
102	1936-40	**Bedroom Furniture Set**.....'Gift Sets'.	
102a	1936-40	**Bed**, Mottled lilac................... **£10-15**	
102b	1936-40	**Wardrobe**, Mottled lilac **£15-20**	

102c	1936-40	**Dressing Table** Mottled lilac, with mirror **£15-20**	
102d	1936-40	**Chest of Drawers**, Mottled lilac........................... **£15-20**	
102e	1936-40	**Stool**, Mottled lilac................. **£10-15**	
102f	1936-40	**Chair** (as 101d), Mottled lilac **£10-15**	
103	1936-40	**Kitchen Furniture Set**.See 'Gift Sets'.	
103a	1936-40	**Refrigerator** Pale green/cream or Blue/ivory. **£15-20**	
103b	1936-40	**Sideboard** Pale green/cream or Blue/ivory. **£15-20**	
103c	1936-40	**Cooker** Pale green/cream or Blue/ivory. **£15-20**	

103d	1936-40	**Table** Pale green/cream or Blue/ivory. **£10-15**	
103e	1936-40	**Chair** (casting as 101d) Pale green/cream or Blue/ivory **£10-15**	
104	1937-40	**Bathroom Furniture Set** ...'Gift Sets'.	
104a	1937-40	**Bath**, Pink **£10-15**	
104b	1937-40	**Bath Mat**, Pink rubber (prone to deterioration)......... **£10-15**	
104c	1937-40	**Hand Basin**, Pink, with mirror **£15-20**	
104d	1937-40	**Stool**, Pink.............................. **£10-15**	
104e	1937-40	**Linen Basket**, Pink **£10-15**	
104f	1937-40	**Toilet**, Pink............................ **£10-15**	

French Dinky Toys Buses

Model and details	MPR
29d **Renault TN4H Paris Bus** All have Dark Green cast lower body, Cream tinplate top, scale 1:80. Variations:	
1939-40	
• Base on some, cast hubs, black or white 'DUNLOP' tyres............................... **£300-400**	
1940-40	
• No base, painted mazak wheels **£200-250**	
1940-49	
• Base on some (may be black or silver painted), painted mazak wheels..... **£200-250**	
1950-51	
• Driver set high; with base (may be black or silver painted), yellow ridged hubs........................... **£250-300**	
29D **Somua-Panhard Paris Bus** 1952-54 (scale 1:70)	
• Dark Green/Cream, smooth inside roof, painted ridged hubs. Not boxed ... **£150-175**	
1954-59 (renumbered in 1959 to 570)	
• Dark Green/Cream, cross-hatched inside roof, painted ridged hubs. Yellow box marked '29D'................. **£150-175**	
29E **Isobloc Autocar** 1950-50 Smooth sides and roof, painted ridged hubs, scale 1:70.	
• Blue/Cream **£250-350**	
• Dark Green/Light Green **£200-250**	
• Blue/Silver **£250-350**	
1951-52 All have side detailing in this period.	
• Blue/Silver body, smooth roof........ **£185-225**	
1953-55 All have side detailing in this period.	

Model and details	MPR
• Red/Silver, smooth roof................... **£110-130**	
• Orange/Silver, smooth roof............ **£125-150**	
• Blue/Silver, ridged roof....................... **£75-95**	
29F **Chausson AP521 Autocar** 1956-58 (scale 1:65) Painted ridged hubs. Box flap reads '29F AUTOCAR CHAUSSON' in French only.	
• Blue/Cream body.............................. **£125-150**	
• Red/Cream body................................ **£125-150**	
1958-59 (renumbered in 1959 to 571)	
• As previous model, but concave hubs. Box flap reads '29F AUTOCAR CHAUSSON' in 4 languages............ **£125-150**	
541 **Mercedes-Benz Autocar** 1963-71 (scale 1:43) All have 18 seater body, chromed concave hubs. Yellow box.	
• Mid-Red and Cream **£90-110**	
• Orange-Red and Cream **£90-110**	
• Deep Pink (various shades) and Cream **£90-110**	
1966-? South African issue:	
• Blue/Cream body.........................**£800-1,200**	
19??... **'PTT SUISSE'**	
• Orange/Silver body..................**£3,500-4,500**	

541 Mercedes Benz Autocar.

Model and details	MPR
570 **Somua Paris Bus OP5** 1959-61 (renumbered in 1959 from 29-D)	
• Dark Green/Cream, cross-hatched inside roof, painted ridged hubs. In Yellow box marked '29D' **£90-120**	
571 **Chausson AP521 Autocar** 1959-60 (renumbered in 1959 from 29-F) Painted concave hubs, scale 1:65. Box flap reads '29F AUTOCAR CHAUSSON' in 4 languages.	
• Blue/Cream body.............................. **£130-150**	
• Red/Cream body................................ **£120-140**	
889 **Berliet Paris Autobus** 1965-70 (scale 1:49)	
• Green/Greenish-White, 'DUNLOP', 'PEPSI-COLA', painted concave hubs. Supertoys blue/white box, colour picture on lid **£200-250**	
889U **Berliet Urban Bus** 1965-70 'DUNLOP' and 'PEPSI-COLA' adverts., painted concave hubs. Supertoys blue/white box with colour picture of the Place Bellecour in Lyons.	
• Red/Cream **£225-275**	
• Orange/Cream **£225-275**	
NB 889 Paris Bus was modelled on a Berliet vehicle though the 1965-66 catalogue attributes it to Saviem.	

French Dinky Toys Accessories

Pre-war figures 1 to 10 inclusive were hollow cast in lead and individually hand painted. The colours stated are therefore those observed but any other colours and shades are possible especially with painted detail. The bases are usually brown, beige or grey (some blue ones seen) and are usually marked 'MECCANO DINKY TOYS' though some early ones may be found with 'HORNBY' marked under them. Early boxes were blue-grey (often marked 'Série Hornby'), later ones were red (usually printed 'Dinky Toys' and with various shades and degrees of surface gloss). They vary greatly as far as the printing is concerned. After the war, Meccano-France considered most of the figures to be primarily railway accessories so they reverted to listing them in the 'Hornby Railway Accessories' range. Their boxes generally reflect this thinking after 1948, and between 1950 and 1955 most of models 1 to 10 were issued in plastic as 'Hornby unbreakable figures'.

1	1934-40	**Station Staff Set**..........See 'Gift Sets'.	
1a	1934-40	**Station Master**	
• Dark blue coat, grey or grey-green trousers **£30-35**			
1b	1934-40	**Porter**	
• Light blue uniform with red belt, no luggage.. **£30-35**			
1c	1934-40	**Railway Guard**	

• Dark blue coat, grey or grey-green trousers **£30-35**			
1d	1934-40	**Policeman**	
• Dark blue uniform **£30-35**			
1e	1934-40	**Controller**	
• Dark blue coat, grey or grey-green trousers **£30-35**			

2	1934-40	**Railway Passengers Set** ... 'Gift Sets'	
2a	1934-40	**Normandy Farmer**	
• Various rustic colours **£30-35**			
2b	1934-40	**Farmer's Wife**	
• A 'Peasant type Bécassine' with basket and umbrella, red or orange dress (later turquoise) **£30-35**			

2c 1934-40 **Young Woman**
- Bag under right arm, various colours.. **£30-35**

2d 1934-40 **Boy Scout**
- Boy in French scout uniform (all khaki or khaki shorts/green shirt) **£30-35**

2e 1934-40 **Boy (sitting)**
- Satchel under right arm, var. colours .. **£30-35**

2f 1934-40 **Girl (sitting)**
- Bag under left arm, various colours ... **£30-35**

2g 1934-40 **Bench Seat**
- Green or brown painted tinplate **£30-35**

3 1934-40 **Animals Set**.... See 'Gift Sets' section

3a 1934-40 **Pig**. Pink (shades may vary).. **£20-30**

3b 1934-40 **Sheep**
- Cream, white or dark brown (shades). **£20-30**

3c 1934-40 **Horse**
- Grey or reddish-brown 'mottled' finish (painted using a 'run' technique). Various shades known **£20-30**

3d 1934-40 **Bull**
- White or reddish-brown 'mottled' finish (painted using a 'run' technique). Various shades known **£20-30**

4 1934-40 **Railway Personnel Set** ..... 'Gift Sets'

4a 1934-40 **Cook**
- White cook's outfit, carrying a (usually gold painted) fowl on a dish . **£30-35**

4b 1934-40 **Engine Fireman**
- Dark blue overalls, coal shovel **£30-35**

4c 1934-40 **Greaser**.
- Dark blue overalls, oilcan **£30-35**

4d 1934-40 **Wheel Tapper**
- Dark blue overalls, sounding mallet.... **£30-35**

4e 1934-40 **Gate Keeper** (Female)
- Green shirt, black skirt, with red flag... **£30-35**

4f 1934-40 **Porter with Luggage**
- Dark blue uniform, carrying case and hat-box (various shades seen)...... **£30-35**

5 1934-40 **Railway Passengers Set** ....'Gift Sets'.

5a 1934-40 **Woman and Child**
- Green or brown (various shades). Single hollow casting **£30-35**

5b 1934-40 **Businessman**
- Grey or brown (shades), with briefcase .. **£30-35**

5c 1934-40 **Male Tourist**
- Brown (various shades), with walking stick and camera............. **£30-35**

5d 1934-40 **Clergyman**
- Black garb, brolly (usually red/grey) ... **£30-35**

5e 1934-40 **Newsboy**
- Grey or brown (various shades known), papers under left arm **£30-35**

5f 1934-40 **Woman with Tennis Racket**
- Green, grey or beige (various shades), tennis racket in right hand **£30-35**

6 1934-40 **Shepherd Set**. See 'Gift Sets' section

6a 1934-40 **Shepherd**
- Light brown (various shades), with crook in right hand and lamb under left arm **£30-35**

6b 1934-40 **Sheepdog**
- Black, with or without white detail...... **£30-35**

10 1934-40 **Assorted Figures Set**
- Consists of Sets 1, 2 and 4. Box has two illustrations.................. **£250-350**
- 1938-40 Same set but box has no illustration **£220-270**

40 1953-59 **Traffic Signs 'Town' Set** ... 'Gift Sets'

41 1953-59 **Traffic Signs 'Route' Set**... 'Gift Sets'

49 1935-40 **Set of Fuel Pumps**.......See 'Gift Sets'

49 1949-50 **Set of Fuel Pumps**.......See 'Gift Sets'

49a 1935-40 **Pillar type Fuel Pump**
- Blue, green, yellow, red, cream, gold or white. White rubber hose, wire crank handle, scale 1:43, 60mm. **£75-100** 1948-53
- Reissue of pre-war version (sold without the hose between 1948-50) **£30-35**

49b 1935-40 **'SHELL' Mobile Oil Pump**
- Blue, green, yellow, red, cream, gold or white. White rubber hose, 1:43, 47mm. **£75-100** 1948-50
- Reissue of pre-war version (without hose) **£30-35**

49c 1935-40 **Double Output Fuel Pump**
- Blue, green, yellow, red, cream, gold or white. Two white rubber hoses, scale 1:43, 55mm. **£75-100** 1948-52
- Reissue of pre-war version (without hoses 1948-50) **£30-35**

49D 1954-59 **Pump Island, 'ESSO'** (renumbered in 1959 to 592)
- Two pumps (red/white and blue/white), 'ESSO' sign. Yellow box....................... **£80-100**

502 1959-66 **Garage**
- Yellow/grey, sky-blue/grey or all light grey, plastic, with parking numbers '0' to '9'. Yellow box.. **£100-120**

590 1959-68 **Traffic Signs 'Town' Set** ....'Gift Sets'.

591 1959-68 **Traffic Signs 'Route' Set**....'Gift Sets'.

592 1959-63 **Pump Island, 'ESSO'** (renumbered in 1959 from 49-D)
- Two pumps (red/white and blue/white), 'ESSO' sign, scale 1:43. 'DINKY TOYS 592-49D' on box............ **£65-75**

592 1969-71 **Traffic Signs 'Town' Set** ....'Gift Sets'.

593 1969-71 **Traffic Signs 'Route' Set**....'Gift Sets'.

594 1969-71 **Traffic Lights (3-colour)**
- Battery operated grey/black plastic traffic lights, scale 1:43. Yellow box...... **£65-75**

TRAFFIC SIGNS. Since the messages given on road signs are often more graphical than textual, the list that follows contains literal interpretations that reflect the general meaning of the signs rather than attempting accurate translations. **Traffic Signs 595a to 595w** were not available for purchase; they were included free in the box of the model mentioned. Scale 1:43.
595a - 595L were available from 1969-72,
595m - 595w were available from 1970-72.

595a **'Danger of Falling Rocks'**, (with model 564 Caravan)...................... NPP

595b **'Maximum Weight 5.5 tonnes'**, (823 GMC Tanker).............................. NPP

595c **'Dangerous Bend to Right'**, (1417 Matra F1)................................. NPP

595d **'No Overtaking for Heavy Vehicles'**, (572 Berliet Truck)............................ NPP

595e **'Road Narrows'**, (1422 Ferrari F1) .... NPP

595f **'Speed Limit'**, (with 1421 Opel GT)........ NPP

595g **'Caution - Animals Crossing'**, (with 1419 Ford Thunderbird) .... NPP

595h **'Danger - End of Quay'**, (1424 Renault R12)................................... NPP

595i **'Two-Way Traffic'**, (1423 Peugeot 504) .. NPP

595k **'Road Narrows from Left'**, (with 1425 Matra).............................. NPP

595L **'Maximum Width 2 metres'**, (with 882 Peugeot 'Pinder') .... NPP

595m **'Danger - Loose Chippings'**, (1426 Alfa)... NPP

595n **'Cycling Prohibited'**, (1429 Peugeot)..... NPP

595o **'Customs'**, (1420 Opel Commodore)...... NPP

595p **'Humpback Bridge'**, (1428 Peugeot 304)............................... NPP

595q **'Automatic Level Crossing'**, (809 GMC)... NPP

595r **'Road Works'**, (518 Renault 'Autoroutes')...................... NPP

595s **'Pedestrians Prohibited'**, (with 570 Peugeot 'Autoroutes')............. NPP

595t **'Max. Height 3.5 metres'**, (with 589 Berliet 'Autoroutes') .... NPP

595u **'Dangerous Bends'**, (1430 Abarth)......... NPP

595v **'All Vehicles Prohibited'**, (1432 Ferrari)..................................... NPP

595w **'Danger - Cyclists'**, (1409 Chrysler 180)............................. NPP

833 1962- **Transformer** (scale 1:55) Grey plastic 'ALSTHOM' transformer (as supplied with 898). In yellow box.. **£30-50**

834 1963-70 **Mobile Bridge Pack** Khaki plastic six part bridge plus inflatable boats (as with 884) **£20-30**

835 1959-71 **Tyre Pack**. Twelve large black treaded tyres for racing cars and commercial vehicles (smooth till 1961). Was 6676 ....**£5-10**

836 1959-71 **Tyre Pack**. Twelve white treaded tyres (smooth till 1960). Previously 6677**£5-10**

837 1959-71 **Tyre Pack**. Twelve black smooth tyres (small). Previously 7067.................**£5-10**

837 1961-71 **Tyre Pack**. Twelve black treaded tyres (small) **£5-10**

837 1965-71 **Tyre Pack**. 12 black nylon tyres (small). French versions often marked 'DUNLOP', Spanish usually 'PIRELLI' **£5-10**

838 1961-71 **Tyre Pack**. Twelve white treaded tyres (small). 'DUNLOP' or 'PIRELLI' markings not seen...............**£5-10**

839 1959-63 **Tyre Pack**. Twelve tyres, round or square section (treaded version of 11190). Sold in paper (later, plastic) packet **£10-15**

839 1971-71 **Rally Pack**. Two sheets of rally transfers, scales 1:32 and 1:24 .... **£15-20**

840 1959-70 **Elastic Cord Pack**. Pack of 6 (later 10) elastic cords for 32D and 899 Delahaye Fire Escape. Was 11146 ....**£5-10**

841 1959-71 **Tank Tracks Pack**. 12, black rubber, for AMX tanks. Was 11924....... **£10-15**

842 1959-64 **Tyre Pack**. Twelve tyres for 24-L Vespa. Was 12110........................ **£10-15**

843 1962-71 **Military Tyre Pack**. Twelve treaded black tyres (large square section for 818 and similar) **£10-15**

844 1959-70 **Pipe-Line Pack**. Six black tubes (as with 893 Sahara Pipe Transporter) **£15-20**

845 1959-70 **Barrier Pack**. Ten grey plastic barriers (Vauban-Samia), scale 1:43.... **£15-20**

846 1959-70 **Oil Drum Pack**. Ten grey plastic oil drums **£15-20**

847 1959-70 **Barrel Pack**. Ten brown plastic barrels **£15-20**

848 1959-70 **Trunk Pack**. Ten brown plastic travelling trunks with hinged lids **£15-20**

849 1959-70 **Packing Case Pack**. Ten ivory plastic packing cases with lifting lids, in plastic 'Bobigny' bag **£15-20**

850 1959-70 **Bottle Crate Pack**. Ten white or cream plastic crates with transparent or orange bottles....................................... **£20-25**

851 1959-70 **Assortment Pack**. Ten items - two each of: 846 (barrels), 847 (barrels), 848 (trunks), 849 (packing cases), 850 (bottle crates) **£20-25**

852 1962-71 **Half-Track Tracks Pack**. Ten replacement tracks for 822 White M3 Half-Track, (black rubber) **£10-15**

853 1962-64 **Tyre Pack**. Twelve extra large black tyres for use on 803 Unic and 888 Berliet...................................... **£10-15**

854 1962-68 **Milk Crates Pack**. Ten grey plastic milk crates with white bottles, as with 586 Citroën P55 Milk Lorry **£20-25**

855 1962-65 **Tyre Pack**. Twelve small black rubber treaded tyres (Renault R4, etc.)..**£10-15**

855 1965-70 **Tyre Pack**. As previous, but made of black nylon............................ **£10-15**

856 1963-71 **Machine Gun**. Black plastic (822 White Half-Track) ... **£10-15**

857 1970-71 **Racing Tyre Pack**.
Two small tyres for use on the
front wheels of Formula 1 racing cars . **£10-15**
858 1970-71 **Racing Tyre Pack**.
Two larger tyres for F1 rear wheels...... **£10-15**
859 1970-70 **Tyre Pack**.
4 tyres for 1419 Ford............................. **£10-15**
860 1963-? **1.5 volt Battery** for 276L **£5-10**
861 1964-? **Lamp Bulb**.
1.5 volt bulb for 887 BP Tanker **£5-10**
862 1965-? **Lamp Bulb**.
1.5 volt bulb for use with 566 Citroën.....**£5-10**
863 1964-? **Battery**. Mazda battery for use
with 887 then 952L **£5-10**
864 1968-? **Lamp Bulb**. Bulb for use with
276L, 160L and 952L **£5-10**
6676 1950-59 **Tyre Pack**. Twelve large black
smooth or treaded tyres (racing cars,
articulated commercials). With letter
'M' on sidewall till 1958.
(Renumbered to 835) **£10-15**

6677 1950-59 **Tyre Pack**. Twelve large
white treaded tyres (some smooth).
'M' on sidewall till 1958.
(Renumbered to 836 in 1959) **£10-15**
7067 1950-59 **Tyre Pack**. Twelve smooth
black tyres (small) for touring cars
25-BV, 25-CG, 25-D, 29-D and 80-BP.
'M' on sidewall till 1958.
(Renumbered to 837 in 1959) **£10-15**
7068 1953-59 **Tyre Pack**
Twelve smooth white tyres (small).
Letter 'M' on sidewall till 1958.
(Renumbered in 1959 to 837) **£10-15**
11146 1958-59 **Elastic Cord Pack**
Six elastic cords for 32-D and
899 Delahaye Fire Escape.
(Renumbered in 1959 to 840) **£5-10**

11190 1953-59 **Tyre Pack**. Twelve large
black ribbed tyres originally for racing cars.

Design was changed in 1958 to make them
suitable for use with military vehicles.
Paper packets marked either 'Racing Tyres'
or 'Cross Country Tyres'.
(Renumbered in 1959 to 839) **£10-15**
11924 1958-59 **Tank Tracks Pack**.
Twelve black rubber tracks for AMX Tanks.
(Renumbered to 841 in 1959) **£10-15**
12110 1959-59 **Tyre Pack**
Twelve tyres for 24-L Vespa.
(Renumbered to 842 in 1959) **£10-15**

--- 1935-40 **Milk Churn (large)**.
2 fixing holes in base, scale 1:43 .... **£30-40**
--- 1948-50 **Milk Churn**. Smaller churn,
scale 1:43, as supplied with
25-O 'NESTLE' Trucks.............................. **£30-40**
--- 1969-? **Driving Test Circuit**.
Printed road layout with town and
country elements, 1:43, boxed.................. **£25-40**

French Dinky Toys Gift Sets

Set and details	MPR
1 **Station Staff Set** 1934-40	
• Six figures: 1 x 1a Station Master, 2 x 1b Porter (no luggage), 1 x 1c Guard, 1 x 1d Policeman, 1 x 1e Inspector. Two pictures on lid of card box......	**£250-300**
1 **Station Staff Set** 1938-40	
• Same but box has no illustration ...	**£225-275**
2 **Railway Passengers Set** 1934-40	
• Contains a tinplate bench (2g) and six figures: 2a Normandy Farmer, 2b Farmer's Wife, 2c Young Girl, 2d Boy Scout (with stick), 2e Boy (sitting), 2f Girl (sitting). Red box has illustrations, yellow inner .	**£225-275**
1938-40	
• Same set but in red box (yellow inner) with no illustration	**£200-250**
3 **Animals Set** 1934-40	
• Contains six animals: 3a Pig, 3b Sheep (dark brown), 3c Horse (grey), 3c Horse (brown), 3d Bull (mottled White), 3d Bull (mottled reddish-brown). Box has two pictures on lid............	**£300-350**
1938-40	
• Same but box has no illustrations ..	**£250-300**
4 **Railway Personnel Set** 1934-40	
• Six figures: 4a Cook (with fowl), 4b Engine Fireman, 4c Greaser (with oilcan), 4d Wheel Tapper (with mallet), 4e Female Gate-Keeper (with flag), 4f Porter (with luggage). Box has two illustrations.................	**£225-275**
1938-40	
• Same but box has no illustration ...	**£175-225**
5 **Railway Passengers Set** 1934-40	
• Contains six figures: 5a Woman and Child, 5b Businessman, 5c Male Tourist (with camera), 5d Clergyman, 5e Newsboy, 5f Female Tennis Player. Two different pictures on box	**£225-275**
1938-40	
• Same but box has no illustration ...	**£175-225**
6 **Shepherd Set** 1934-40	
• 6a Shepherd (light brown), 6b Sheepdog (black), 4 x 3b Sheep (white or cream). Box has two illustrations................	**£400-500**
1938-40	
• Same but box has no illustration ...	**£300-400**

Set and details	MPR
10 **Assorted Figures Set** 1934-40	
• Consists of Sets 1, 2 and 4. Box has two illustrations................	**£250-350**
1938-40	
• Same but box has no illustration ...	**£220-270**
17 **Electric Goods Train** 1935-38	
• 19a Electric Locomotive, 21b Timber Wagon, 21c Coal Wagon, 21d Crane Wagon. Diorama box	**£250-300**
1938-40	
• Same but box has no diorama........	**£175-225**
18 **Steam Goods Train** 1934-38	
• 21a Steam Tank Locomotive, 3 x 21c Coal Wagon, diorama box..	**£250-300**
1938-40	
• Same but box has no diorama........	**£175-225**
19 **Electric Passenger Train** 1935-38	
• 19a Electric Locomotive, 3 x 20a Coach, diorama box	**£250-300**
20 **Steam Passenger Train** 1935-38	
• 21a Steam Tank Locomotive, 3 x 20a Coach, diorama box............	**£250-300**
1938-40	
• Same but box has no diorama........	**£175-225**
21 **Steam Mixed Goods Train** 1934-38	
• 21a Tank Locomotive, 21b Timber Wagon, 21c Coal Wagon, 21d Crane Wagon, diorama box....................................	**£350-450**
1938-40	
• Same but box has no diorama........	**£225-275**
24 **Passenger Cars Set** 1935-36	
• 6 cars: 24b Limousine, 24d Vogue Saloon, 24e Aerodynamic Saloon, 24f Sportsman's Coupé, 24g 4-seat Sports Car, 24h 2-seat Sports Car. Yellow box / no illustration.....	**£8,000-11,000**
NB The basic box for this set was adapted to contain the 25 series Commercial Vehicles Set. 1936-39	
• 6 cars: 24b Limousine, 24d Vogue Saloon, 24e Aerodynamic Saloon, 24f Sportsman's Coupé, 24g 4-seat Sports Car, 24h 2-seat Sports Car. Purple box with picture (two different designs exist)	**£7,000-8,000**

Set and details	MPR
1940-48	
• The same set, but in Blue box without illustration....................	**£6,000-7,000**
24-55 **Touring Cars Gift Set** 1955-55	
• 24-R Peugeot 203, 24-T Citroën 2cv, 24-U Simca Aronde 9, 24-V Buick Roadmaster, 24-X Ford Vedette......................	**£1,500-2,000**
24-56 **Touring Cars Gift Set** 1956-56	
• 24-R Peugeot 203, 24-T Citroën 2cv, 24-U Simca Aronde Elysée, 24-Y Studebaker Commander, 24-Z Simca Vedette Versailles...	**£1.500-2,000**
24-57 **Touring Cars Gift Set** 1957-57	
• 24-A Chrysler New Yorker, 24-B Peugeot 403 8cv, 24-E Renault Dauphine, 24-Y Studebaker Commander, 24-Z Simca Vedette Versailles...	**£1,500-2,000**
24-58 **Touring Cars Gift Set** 1958-58	
• 24-B Peugeot 403 8cv, 24-C (or 24-CP) Citroën DS19, 24-D Plymouth Belvedere, 24-E Renault Dauphine, 24-Z Simca Vedette Versailles. Red/yellow/green/black box....	**£1,500-2,000**
NB The annual '24 series' of Gift Sets was renumbered in 1959 ; the next issue in the series is 500.	
25 **Commercial Vehicles Gift Set** 1935-37	
• 25a Open Lorry, 25b Covered Lorry, 25c Flat Lorry, 25d Tanker Lorry, 25e Tipping Lorry, 25f Market Gardeners Lorry. Purple and gold box.	**£2,000-2,500**
NB The basic box for this set was adapted from that used for the 24 series Passenger Cars Set. 1938-39	
• Same, but in a long Blue box.	**£1,500-2,000**
1940-48	
• Same set, but all wheels are solid metal. Long blue box with printed ends (yellow base, blue inner).	**£1,500-2,000**
25S **Commercial Vehicles Gift Set** 1948-48	
• The same set, all models having solid metal wheels. Light blue box....	**£2,500-3,500**
25N **Commercial Vehicles Gift Set** 1949-49	

- 25-H Ford Beverage Truck,
  25-I Ford Open Wagon,
  25-J Ford Covered Wagon,
  25-K Studebaker Market Gardeners Truck,
  25-L Studebaker Covered Delivery Truck,
  25-M Studebaker Tipping Truck.
  Blue or yellow box. **£3,500-5,000**
  1950-50
- The same set, but in a Red box. **£3,500-5,000**

40 Traffic Signs 'Town' Set
1953-59 (renumbered in 1959 to 590)
- 6 diecast signs: 'No Entry', 'No Waiting',
  '30km/hr', 'No Overtaking',
  'Maximum Weight 5.5 tonnes',
  'Right (or Left) Turn'. Each 55mm. high,
  scale 1:43. Yellow box with
  'Code de la Route' leaflet **£65-75**

41 Traffic Signs 'Route' Set
1953-59 (renumbered in 1959 to 591)
- 6 diecast signs: 'Danger - Crossroads',
  'Priority' marker, 'Dangerous Bends',
  'Caution - School', 'Level Crossing with
  Gates'. Small signs 37mm. high; large
  signs 52mm., scale 1:43.
  Yellow box with leaflet **£65-75**

49 Set of Fuel Pumps (5)
1935-40
- 2 x 49a Pillar type Fuel Pump,
  1 x 49b Mobile Oil Pump,
  2 x 49c Double Output Pump.
  Blue box, later Yellow **£400-500**
  1949-50
- Same set, Yellow box **£300-400**

50 British Naval Warships Set
1938-40
- 14 English-made models in French
  printed box:
  50a 'Hood', 50b 'Nelson', 50b 'Rodney',
  50c 'Effingham', 50d 'York', 50e 'Delhi',
  3 x 50f 'Broke', 50g 'X' class Submarine,
  3 x 50h 'Amazon',
  50k 'K' class Sub **£200-300**

60 Aircraft Presentation Set
1935-37
- 6 models: 60a DeWoitine D338 Rainbow,
  60b Potez 58, 60c Henriot H180T,
  60d Breguet Corsaire,
  60e DeWoitine 500 Hunter, 60f Cierva
  Autogiro. Purple and gold box (models
  are set out in a straight formation along
  the length of the box).
  Picture on lid.............................**£1,500-1,750**
  1937-39
- The same 6 models but set out in a
  diagonal formation within a bright
  blue box. Picture on box lid......**£1,500-1,750**
  1939-40
- The same 6 models but set out in a
  diagonal formation within a Dark
  Green box. Picture on box lid...**£1,500-1,750**
  1957-59 (renumbered in 1959 to 501)
- 4 models: 60-A Dassault Mystere IVa,
  60-B Sud Aviation Vautour,

60-D Sikorsky S58, 60-E Vickers Viscount.
Supertoys box, picture on lid.......... **£300-400**

61 Aircraft Presentation Set
1938-39
- 5 models: 61a DeWoitine D338,
  61b Potez 56, 61d Potez 58,
  61e Henriot H180M,
  61f DeWoitine 500 Hunter.
  Blue box.................................... **£1,500-2,000**
  1939-46
- 6 models: 61a DeWoitine D338,
  61b Potez 56, 61c Farman F360,
  61d Potez 58, 61e Henriot H180M,
  61f DeWoitine 500.
  Green box.................................. **£1,250-1,750**

64 Aircraft Presentation Set
1939-48
- Five models: 61a DeWoitine D338,
  64a Amiot 370, 64b Bloch 220,
  64c Potez 63, 64d Potez 662.
  Green box with illustration.......**£1,250-1,750**

**70 Modern Travel Set
('Locomotion Moderne')**
1939?
- Five different forms of travel represented by:
  23b Racing Car, 26 Railcar,
  52c Steamship 'Normandie',
  53a Steamship 'Dunkerque',
  60a DeWoitine Rainbow.
  Advertised in 1939(?)
  catalogue but no production known ...... NPP

101 Dining Room Furniture Set
1936
- 101a Table, 101b Sideboard, 2 x 101c
  Carver, 4 x 101d Dining Chair.
  Light or dark mottled brown **£300-350**

102 Bedroom Furniture Set
1936-40
- 102a Bed, 102b Wardrobe, 102c Dressing
  Table, 102d Chest of Drawers,
  102e Stool, 102f Chair. Lilac............ **£300-350**

103 Kitchen Furniture Set
1936-40
- 103a Refrigerator, 103b Sideboard,
  103c Cooker, 103d Table, 103e Chair.
  Pale Green/Cream or Blue/Ivory..... **£300-350**

104 Bathroom Furniture Set
1937-40
- 104a Bath, 104b Bath Mat, 104c Hand
  Basin, 104d Stool, 104e Linen Basket,
  104f Toilet. Pink veined **£300-350**

500 Touring Cars Gift Set
1959-59
- 521 Peugeot 403 8cv, 522 Citroën DS19,
  523 Plymouth Belvedere,
  524 Renault Dauphine,
  541 Simca Vedette Versailles **£2,000-3,000**

501 Aircraft Presentation Set
1959-62 (renumbered in 1959 from 60)
- 800 Dassault Mystere IVa, 801 Sud
  Aviation Vautour, 802 Sikorsky S58,
  803 Vickers Viscount **£300-400**

503 Touring Cars Gift Set
1963-64
- 521 Peugeot 403 8cv, 522 Citroën DS19,
  543 Renault Floride, 544 Simca Aronde,
  545 DeSoto Diplomat.
  Blue/Yellow/Grey box..............**£2,000-3,000**

536 Peugeot 404 and Trailer
1965
- Red car, Black skis on Yellow rack or
  Yellow skis on Black rack, Cream
  plastic trailer (no. 812), luggage **£175-200**

590 Traffic Signs 'Town' Set
1959-68 (renumbered in 1959 from 40)
- 6 signs 55mm. high: 'No Entry', 'No
  Parking', 'Maximum Weight 5.5 tonnes',
  'Right (or Left) Turn', '30km/hr',
  'No Overtaking'. Yellow box
  with 'Code de la Route' leaflet........... **£70-80**

591 Traffic Signs 'Route' Set
1959-68 (renumbered in 1959 from 41)
- 6 metal signs: 'Danger - Crossroads',
  'Priority' marker, 'Dangerous Bends',
  'Caution - School',
  'Level Crossing with Gates'.
  Signs 37mm. and 52mm. high.
  Yellow box, leaflet................................ **£70-80**

592 Traffic Signs 'Town' Set
1969-71 (scale 1:43)
- Twelve plastic signs on diecast bases:
  'Caution - Gyratory System', 'No Entry',
  'Parking', 'No Parking', 'Caution - School',
  'No U-Turn', '45km/hr', 'No Overtaking',
  'Do Not Use Horn', 'Blue Zone', 'Taxis',
  'No Left Turn'. In 'window' box **£100-125**

593 Traffic Signs 'Route' Set
1969-71 (scale 1:43)
- Twelve plastic signs on diecast bases:
  'Autoroute', 'End of Autoroute', 'Autoroute
  Toll Point', 'End of Speed Limit',
  'Crossroads - Give Way', 'Dangerous
  Crossing', 'Stop', 'Priority' marker,
  'Dangerous Bend', 'Caution',
  'Gradient 10%', 'Low Flying Aircraft'.
  In 'window' box **£100-125**

1460 Touring Cars Gift Set
1969-70
- 6 models: 501 Citroën DS19 'POLICE',
  507 Simca 1500GLS Estate, 508 Daf 33,
  509 Fiat 850, 513 Opel Admiral,
  514 Alfa-Romeo 1600.
  Blue/yellow box........................**£2,500-3,500**

1462 'Three Days' Gift Set
1969-69
- 4 models: 507 Simca 1500GLS Estate,
  508 Daf 33, 509 Fiat 850,
  514 Alfa-Romeo 1600. Sold in a special
  'Sac-cadeau'(plastic Gift-Bag)........ **£600-800**
  NB 'Galeries Lafayette' is a Paris department
  store with branches in several French towns.
  Annually '3J' sales are held in these shops.
  Selection 1462 was specially made for the
  1969 'Trois Jours' ('Three Days') sale.

French Dinky Toys 500 Citroën 2cv (open), 535 Citroën 2cv (closed) and 1413 Citroën Dyane.

French Dinky Toys Trade Boxes

Meccano distributed Dinky Toys, from factories to shops via warehouses, in the same way in France as in England, through the use of Trade Boxes. Our knowledge of the French versions is not extensive and readers' help is required in adding to this short list of known French Trade Boxes and Packs.

Model ref. and name	Quantity in box	MPR
507 Simca 1500 (Estate Cars)	6 indiviually boxed models	£400-500
24UT Taxi (Simca) Aronde	6	£700-800
24R 203 Peugeot	6	£600-700
245 Simca 8 Sport	6	£600-700
24N Citroën Traction Avant 3rd type	6	£700-800
23H Talbot-Lago Racing Cars	6	£500-600
24XT Taxi (Ford) Vedettes	6	£500-600
508S Dafs	6 indiviually boxed models, outer shrink wrapped	£400-500
24V Buick Roadmasters	6 indiviually boxed models	£700-800
828 Rocket-Carrier Jeeps	6 indiviually boxed models	£300-350
810 Military Command Car	3 indiviually boxed models	£600-700
25P Studebaker Open Lorries	6	£1,000-1,200
32AB Panhard Tractors and 'SNCF' Semi-Trailers	6	£400-500
29D Paris Buses	6	£350-400
25V Ford Dust Carts	6	£600-700
1412 Breakdown Jeeps	6 indiviually boxed models	£600-700

French Dinky Toys Catalogues and Magazines

Note that some post-war catalogues have '57B.16273' or '60B.3844' printed at the bottom of the back cover or in some inconspicuous corner. These are not catalogue reference numbers but a form of 'registered design' for publicity material. As they have no other meaning to collectors they are therefore not shown in the following list. French Dinky Toys are also mentioned in catalogues from other countries, notably Spain and Holland. We are in need of details of Meccano advertising in other countries and would welcome any help our readers could provide.

Year of intro, publication details	MPR
1949 **Catalogue** (no ref.) Sepia cover, 'Nouveauties Dinky Toys'	£50-60
1950 **Catalogue** (no ref., 12 page booklet) Blue on white cover shows 'Dinky Toys Miniatures' issuing from Meccano factory through arched gateway. 'Meccano 78-80 Rue Rébéval Paris (XIX)' on back cover. No price list	£50-60
1951 **Catalogue** no ref. Green / sepia, 'Miniatures Dinky Toys'in black	£60-70
1952 **Catalogue** '175-5-52' (10 page booklet) Glossy pages fold out to twice the size of the cover. Cream cover with green and red printing. Black and white photographic illustrations, no prices, 'Imp. HENON PARIS' on last page	£60-70
1953 **Catalogue** (no ref., 20 page booklet) Pale grey stylized car of the period and trees on cover overprinted with 'Miniatures Dinky Toys' and 'C'est une fabrication Meccano' in red. Black and white inside pictures; no price list	£40-50
1954 **Catalogue** (no ref., 20 pages). Blue and white striped cover with Buick Roadmaster, Esso Tanker and Citroën 'H' van. Black and white pictures inside. No prices	£40-50
1954 **Leaflet** (no ref.) Various, advertising new issues	£10-15
1955 **Catalogue** (no ref., 16 page booklet) No price list. Blue/white stripes on cover, plus Marrel truck and 32-D Delahaye fire appliance	£40-50
1956 **Catalogue** (no ref., April, 16 pages) Colour printing inside, no prices. 'Supertoys look' covers with Berliet Container Truck, Autocar Chausson and Citroën car on front with Willème Log Lorry and rear view of 32-D on back cover	£40-50
1956 **Catalogue** (no ref., September, 20 pages) Similar to April catalogue but cover has Log Lorry, Citroën car and Dassault plane. No price list	£40-50
1957 **Summer Catalogue** (no ref., 16 pages)	

Driverless vehicles emerging from tunnel on front cover. Printed in France £40-50

16-page catalogue, 1958 issue in colour.

Year of intro, publication details	MPR
1958 **Summer Catalogue** (no ref., 16 pages) Maserati and Mercedes on front cover. Two to five models per page (drawn). Printed in France	£40-50
1958 **Meccano Catalogue 'DL 1958/3'** (32 pp). The colourful cover shows a boy's face, an electric train at speed on a blue/gold Meccano track and three Dinky Toys. 8 pages of Dinky Toys. September price list enclosed. Printed in France	£40-50
1959 **Catalogue** (no ref., 20 pages) Colour booklet like 1958 issue. Cover shows Simca and lorry at an Esso station. No price list	£40-50
1960 **Catalogue** (no ref., 24 page booklet) Full colour with Renault Floride and Panhard on the front cover. Printed at Mulhouse in France	£40-50

1961 catalogue - 20 pages in colour.

Year of intro, publication details	MPR
1961 **Catalogue** (no ref., 20 pages) Full colour booklet printed in Belgium. Pictures of real vehicles plus parts of a	

road map of France with various Dinky Toys on it. No price list £30-40

Year of intro, publication details	MPR
1962 **Catalogue** (no ref.) Includes mention of Hornby boats and Hornby Acho trains	£30-40
1962 **Catalogue** (no ref., 24 pages) Cover shows Renault R4 parked on quayside next to Steamship 'France'. Printed in Belgium	£30-40
1963 **Catalogue** (no ref., 32 pages) 'First half' catalogue. Cover shows Dinky Mercedes against photo of the actual car. February price list (on very pale green pages) stapled in. Printed in England	£30-40
1963 **Catalogue** (no ref., 32 pages) 'Second half' catalogue (cover as 'first half'). Includes price list dated 'Juillet 1963' in centre	£30-40
1964 **Catalogue** (no ref., 16 pages) Full colour pages with April price list (on orange paper) stapled in. Five new models pictured and described on the cover which also has photo of car showroom interior. Printed in England	£25-35
1964 **Catalogue** (no ref., 16 pages) Booklet with October price list	£25-35
1965 **Catalogue** (no ref., 20 pages) Full colour 'first half' catalogue. Front cover shows 128L Mercedes and 537 Renault. April price list (1965/1, orange paper) stapled in. Printed in England	£25-35
1965 **Catalogue** (no ref., Winter 1965-66) 28 pages; includes October price list 1965/2 on red paper. Cover depicts 889 Autobuses and 510 Peugeot. The only photo within is of an actual AMX Bridge-Layer in action. Printed in England	£25-35
1966 **Catalogue** (no ref.) 'First half'	£25-35
1966 **'Second half' Catalogue** (no ref., 122 pages). Simca and Opel on the cover. September price list on blue paper. Printed in England	£25-35
1967 **'First half' Catalogue** (no ref.)	£25-35

1967 **Catalogue** (no ref., 128 pages)
Porsche Carrera on cover. September
price list (on pink paper) fixed in at rear.
Lady Penelope's 'FAB 1' shown as newly
introduced. Printed in England. '2e édition'
printed inside back cover **£25-35**

1968 **'First half' Catalogue** (no ref.,
130 pages). With February price list.... **£25-35**

1968 **'Second half' Catalogue** (no ref.,
122 pages). Simca and fast-cornering Opel
on the cover. Printed in England **£15-20**

*1969 2nd Edition Catalogue, 24 pages in colour with
flyer to the centre detailing examples of the other toys in
the Meccano Tri-ang range of the period.*

1969 **'First half' Catalogue** (no ref., 24 pages).
Front cover shows hard-braking Ford
Thunderbird avoiding errant daschund,
yellow Opel GT in foreground. Rear cover
advertises 'free' Traffic Signs.
Printed in England **£25-35**

1969 **'Second half' Catalogue** (no ref.) **£20-30**

1970 **Catalogue '91.761'** (24 pages)
'1970.1' printed on cover which also shows
a Porsche and a Ferrari 312P racing round
a banking which has 'La Marque du
Connaisseur' on it in yellow.
Printed in England **£20-30**

1970 **Catalogue '91.762'**
As previous catalogue but with '1970.2'
on front cover. Printed in England **£20-30**

1971 **Catalogue '91.786'** (24 pages)
Cover depicts a Citroën Présidentielle and
a Renault R12. Printed in England **£20-30**

1971 **Meccano Tri-ang leaflet '91.780'**
(full colour). Nearly A4 size; one side
depicts 1971 Dinky Toys. 'Gyro-Jets'
and 'Spirofoil' on reverse........................**£6-10**

1976 **Meccano Catalogue** (no ref., 108 pages)
Only 10 pages of Dinky Toys
(English and French). Brown cover.... **£25-35**

MAGAZINES

1924-38 **Meccano Magazine**
Published monthly from 1924 to 1938,
large format **£5-10**

1953-57 **Meccano Magazine**
Published monthly from October 1953
to October 1957, small format **£5-10**

1957-59 **Meccano Magazine**
Published monthly from November
1957 to September 1959, large format...**£5-10**

1959-60 **'Actualités Meccano' Journal**
Published between October 1959 to
October 1960 (5 issues), each **£5-10**

Promotional material

1957- **Membership Certificate**. 'Parchment' style
'CLUB DINKY TOYS' certificate **£45-55**

1960- **Membership Certificate**. As above, but amended **£45-55**

1960- **Subscription Reminder**. Reminder form **£10-20**

1961- **Subscription Reminder**. As above, but updated....................... **£10-20**

1957- **Membership Document**. Printed details of Club membership**£10-20**

1954- **Dinky Toys Driver's Licence** **£35-45**

1957- **Button Insignia**. A round metal badge, 'CLUB DINKY TOYS',
screw fitting through button-hole **£35-45**

1957- **Brooch Insignia**. As above, but with 'safety pin' lapel fitting... **£35-45**

1957- **Key Ring**. Round metal badge within stitched 'leather' surround **£35-45**

1957- **Key Ring**. Round metal badge encapsulated in clear plastic.... **£35-45**

Display Case. A small display case (no other details) **£150-250**

1961- **ESGE Display Case**. A larger display case (cream/yellow/red)
with 5 shelves, 'DINKY-TOYS MECCANO' on glazing **£400-500**

? **Illuminated Display Case**. Large display case with
6 shelves and electric lighting **£450-600**

? **Illuminated Curved Case**. Large curved display case with
6 shelves and electric lighting **£450-600**

? **Counter Sign**. Diecast triangular block painted red/cream,
'DINKY TOYS' **£75-100**

1950s/60s **Shop Display Stand**, freestanding 68 x 16 x 49cm.,
'DINKY TOYS' and 'MECCANO' logos, Yellow/Red **£1,500-2,000**

1950s/60s **Electric Metal Display Stand**, 'DINKY TOYS' and
'MECCANO', illuminated centre piece with 5 shelves.....**£1,500-2,000**

English Dinky Toys imported into France

The models in the following list were those manufactured in Liverpool and sent to France for sale over different periods of time. In the main they were complete English made models but some were supplied in component form for assembly in the French factory.

It is understood that the boxes were either made in England and printed 'Fabriqué en Angleterre' and 'Imprimé en Angleterre', or were made in France and printed 'Fabriqué en Angleterre' and 'Imprimé en France'. In some cases the model and the box were sold just as they came from Binns Road with no modification or overprinting of any kind. It is therefore important when seeking variations to make sure whether the model was only imported fully built, imported as plain castings for assembly in France, or both (at different times). They were also on occasions supplied complete except for the baseplate which was fitted in France. The degree of painting often varied, some items being supplied fully finished while others were still 'raw' from the dies.

Some models were supplied with English tyres, some without, so that French tyres could be fitted. Body colours were much the same as the UK versions though could be different shades, unique colours or a different range of colours. The 60h Singapore Flying Boat was for instance, painted in a camouflage finish

for the French market, and 108L Sam's Car was only available in silver or blue in France. Some renumbering also took place when models previously assembled in France (imported only as components) were later imported ready made. A couple of examples of this practice are 150/551 and 885/961. Virtually every post-war import from England carries the suffix 'L' after its reference number to indicate its Liverpool origin.

Note also that from time to time various factory items were exchanged between Liverpool and Bobigny (this included equipment components and complete or partial dies and tools). This was done either to make up an end of run deficiency, to replace worn or broken dies, to experiment with prototypes or simply to evaluate a new idea. Consequently there may well be oddities still to be found which do not conform to the known output. If you have knowledge of any item or variation not listed, do please communicate it to the Editor so that we may share the information with others in the collecting fraternity. Thank you.

The prices you should expect to see asked for these essentially English productions are likely to be much the same as for the same items sold in British shops or auction houses.

French ref.no	Years imported	Model
14-C	50-51	Coventry Climax Fork Lift Truck
23c	38-39	Mercedes Racing Car
23d	38-39	Auto-Union Record Car
23e	38-39	'Speed of the Wind'
23m	38-39	'Thunderbolt'
25h	38-39	Streamlined Fire Engine
27AC	50-50	Tractor and Manure Spreader
29b	39-39	Streamlined Bus
30a	35-39	Chrysler Airflow
30b	35-37	Rolls-Royce
30g		Camping Trailer
50	37-38	Battleship Gift Set
51b	37-39	Norddeutscher-Lloyd 'Europa'
51c	37-39	Italia Line 'Rex'
51d	37-39	'Empress of Britain'
52a	36-39	'Queen Mary'
60h	38-38	Singapore Flying Boat (camouflaged)
60m	38-39	Singapore Flying Boat (civilian)
60r	38-39	'Empire' Flying Boat
60w	38-39	'Clipper III' Flying Boat
62k	38-39	'King's Aeroplane'
62n	39-39	Junkers 'Ju90'
62p	39-39	'Ensign' Air Liner
63	39-39	Mayo Composite
100L	68-71	Lady Penelope's 'FAB 1'
101L	68-69	Thunderbirds II / IV
104L	69-71	Spectrum Pursuit
106L	69-70	'The Prisoner' Mini-Moke
108L	70-71	Sam's Car
110L	65-68	Aston-Martin DB5
114L	64-66	Triumph Spitfire
116L	67-71	Volvo P1800
118L	67-70	Towaway Glider
127L	65-68	R-R Silver Cloud
128L	65-70	Mercedes 600
129L	68-68	Volkswagen 1300
131L	69-71	Jaguar 'E'-type
132L	68-71	Ford RV40
142L	63-67	Jaguar Mark 10
150L	62-64	R-R Silver Wraith
151a	38-38	Medium Tank
152a	38-38	Light Tank
152L	67-70	R-R Phantom V
153L	68-70	Aston-Martin DB6
155L	62-65	Ford Anglia
160L	68-71	Mercedes 250
161	39-40	Mobile A-A Gun
161L	67-71	Ford Mustang
162	39-40	Light Dragon Tractor
163L	70-71	VW 1600TL
165L	69-70	Ford Capri 1600
172L	67-71	Fiat 2300 Estate

173L	69-71	Pontiac Parisienne	218L	70-71	Lotus Europa GT			Manure Spreader	665L	65-71	Honest John Carrier
174L	69-70	Ford Mercury	220L	70-71	Ferrari P5	324L	62-64	Hay Rake	666L	61-65	Corporal Missile
		Cougar	221L	70-71	Chevrolet Corvette	340L	62-67	Land Rover	667L	62-64	Servicing Platform
175L	69-71	Cadillac Eldorado	223L	70-71	McLaren Can-Am	341L	62-67	Land RoverTrailer	676L	72-?	Scout Car
176L	69-71	NSU Ro80	224L	71-?	Mercedes C111	344L	71-?	Land Rover Pick-up	697L	62-70	Artillery Set
182L	62-64	Porsche 356a	225L	71-?	Lotus 49B F1	351L	71-?	'SHADO' Interceptor	719L	70-71	Spitfire
186L	62-63	Mercedes 220	238L	71-?	Ferrari 3L F1	370L	70-71	Dragster / Launcher	721L	70-71	Stuka Ju 87b
187L	69-71	De Tomaso Mangusta			(not issued)	401L	62-64	Coventry Climax	722L	70-71	Hawker Harrier
188L	69-71	Jensen FF 542	240L	63-70	Cooper RacingCar			Fork Lift Truck	724L	71-?	Sea Rescue
189L/1	62-64	Triumph Herald	241L	63-70	Lotus Racing Car	437L	63-71	JCB Shovel			Helicopter
189L/2	69-71	Lamborghini Marzal	242L	63-70	Ferrari Racing Car	439L	71-?	Ford Snow Plough	796L	62-68	Dinghy on Trailer
190L	71-?	Monteverdi 375L	243L	64-70	BRM Racing Car	449L	62-63	El Camino Pick-up	930L	61-64	Bedford
192L	71-?	Range Rover	252L	62-64	Bedford Refuse Truck	451L	71-?	Ford D800 Johnston			'Pallet-Jekta'
194L	62-63	Bentley 'S'	253L	62-62	Daimler Ambulance			Road Sweeper	936L	65-68	Leyland Test Chassis
195L	62-65	Jaguar 3.4	258L	62-63	De Soto USA Police	475L	64-68	Ford Model 'T'	952L	64-70	Vega Major Coach
198L	63-66	R-R Phantom V	258L	63-64	Dodge USA Police			1908	958L	62-65	Guy Snow Plough
199L	62-67	Austin 7	258L	65-66	Cadillac USA Police	476L	65-69	Morris Oxford	960L	62-69	Albion Cement Mixer
		Countryman	258L	67-68	Ford Fairlane USA			1913	961L	62-63	Blaw-Knox Bulldozer
200L	71-?	Matra 630			Police Car	485L	64-70	Ford Model 'T'	962L	62-64	Muir-Hill Dumper
202L	71-?	Fiat Abarth 2000	263L	63-68	Super Criterion			'Father Christmas'	964L	62-63	Elevator Loader
204L	71-?	Ferrari 312 P			Ambulance	601L	67-70	Austin Para-Moke	965L	61-64	Euclid Quarry Truck
205L	69-71	Lotus Cortina	270L	69-71	Ford Escort Police	615L	68-71	Jeep / Field Gun	971L	62-63	Coles Mobile Crane
208L	71-?	VW Porsche 914	276L	63-69	Airport Fire	617L	69-71	VW KDF /	972L	62-69	Coles Lorry Crane
210L	71-?	Alfa-Romeo 33	300L	62-70	Massey-Harris			Field Gun	973L	71-?	Yale Diesel Shovel
213L	70-71	Ford Capri 1600			Tractor	620L	71-?	Berliet Gazelle	974L	69-71	AEC Hoynor
215L	65-71	Ford GT Le Mans	308L	71-?	Leyland Tractor			with Missile			Car Transporter
216L	68-71	Ferrari Dino	320L	62-70	Halesowen Trailer	651L	62-70	Centurion Tank	976L	69-71	Michigan Shovel
217L	69-71	Alfa-Romeo Scarabeo	321L	62-71	Massey-Harris	661L	62-63	Recovery Tractor			Dozer

English and French Dinky Toys military models.

Group of military related vehicles: No 820 Renault 'Ambulance'; No 828 Jeep; and No 829 Jeep with cannon.

Robert Newson has provided the following information on Lone Star models.

'Lone Star' was the trade name of Die Casting Machine Tools Ltd (DCMT) who started in 1939 as manufacturers of diecasting machines. They were based at Palmers Green in North London. After the war they started making diecast toys which were distributed by The Crescent Toy Co Ltd. In the Crescent Toys section of this catalogue, the items listed as 'early post-war models' were all made by DCMT with the exception of the Locomotive and the Racing Car. From 1950 DCMT arranged their own distribution direct to wholesalers. Over the next four decades DCMT Lone Star made several ranges of diecast vehicles including 'Slikka Toys' (early 1950s), 'Modern Army Series' (mainly 1960s), 'Roadmaster Majors' (1960s and 1970s), 'Farmer's Boy' (1980s) and the well known 'Lone Star Locos' miniature railway system (later called 'Treble-O-Lectric' or 'Treble-O-Trains'). The four ranges of most interest to collectors are listed here - the original DCMT 'Roadmasters' of 1956, the 1:50 scale 'Roadmasters' (1960s), the 'Impy' and 'Flyers' series made in various forms from 1966 to the mid 1980s, and the miniature 'Tuf-Tots' (1970s). The editor would welcome any further information on Lone Star products.

Model and details	MPR

DCMT Lone Star Roadmasters

This was a short-lived series introduced in 1956, consisting of three sports cars and four veteran cars, all around 1:35 to 1:40 scale. The models had diecast bodies but all other components were plastic. Plastic drivers and passengers were included with the models.

- **1904 Darracq 'Genevieve'**
  Black or Red body, Yellow plastic chassis;
  Metallic Blue or Silver body,
  Black plastic chassis **£250-350**
- **1904 Daimler 'Windsor' Phaeton**
  Red body, Yellow plastic chassis **£70-80**
- **1912 Ford Model 'T'**
  Silver body, Black plastic chassis **£70-80**
- **1912 Morris Oxford 'Bullnose'**
  Met. Blue body, Black plastic chassis **£80-100**
- **Daimler Conquest Roadster**
  Red, Metallic Light Blue, Pale Yellow,
  Pale Green or Pale Blue........................... **£80-100**
- **Ford Thunderbird**
  Red, Metallic Light Blue, Pale Yellow,
  Pale Green or Pale Blue........................... **£80-100**
- **MG Midget TF**
  Metallic Light Blue or Red **£80-100**

Lone Star Roadmasters

In 1960 Lone Star produced four American cars on behalf of the US firm of Tootsietoy. These were

Model and details	MPR

the first four models listed below and they had 'Tootsietoy Classic Series' cast underneath. This arrangement only lasted for a couple of years, as by 1962 there were eight models available, all now marked 'Lone Star Roadmasters'. The models featured plated grilles, bumpers and wheels, and had windows but no interior detail. Around 1964 the plated parts were replaced by less attractive painted or self-coloured plastic, and vacuum-formed interiors were fitted. Later issues have yellow interiors, white wheels, plastic grille and bumpers. Five further numbers were added to the range before they were withdrawn around 1966.

1258 **Farm King Tractor and Trailer**
  Red tractor, 'Farm King' paper label,
  Blue trailer, 'Farm Estates Co.'
  paper label. (Roadmaster Major) **£70-80**
1470 **Chevrolet Corvair**
  Red or Orange-Red................................... **£70-80**

A pair of Rambler Station Wagon Ambulance variations - white with red cross to bonnet, blue beacon and scarce military green version with tan interior.

Model and details	MPR

1471 **Rambler Rebel Station Wagon**
  Sea-Green, Metallic Blue-Green or
  Green with Cream roof, Metallic
  Brown with White roof or all Green **£70-80**
1472 **Cadillac 62**
  Pale Blue, Blue (Cream roof) or all Blue .. **£70-80**
1473 **Ford Sunliner Convertible**
  White or Light Blue; Red interior **£70-80**
1474 **Chevrolet El Camino Pick-Up**
  Yellow or Orange **£70-80**
1475 **Dodge Dart Phoenix**
  Metallic Dark Blue or Mid Blue................ **£70-80**
1476 **Rolls-Royce Silver Cloud II**
  Grey with Black upper half or
  Metallic Blue **£70-80**
1477 **Dodge Dart Police Car**
  Black, 'POLICE PATROL' or 'POLIZEI'...... **£70-80**
1478 **Rambler Ambulance**
  White, Red Cross transfer on bonnet........ **£70-80**
1479 **Chevrolet Corvair**
  Red, 'FIRE CHIEF', 'FEUERWEHR'
  or 'BRANDWEER' **£70-80**
1480 **Chevrolet Corvair**
  Army Staff Car (continued after 1966 as
  no.1273 in 'Modern Army' series),
  Olive Green **£70-80**
1481 **Rambler Military Ambulance**
  (continued after 1966 as no.1274 in
  'Modern Army' series), Olive Green **£70-80**
1482 **Citroën DS19**
  Turquoise **£70-80**
- **Rambler Police Car**
  White body, 'POLIZEI' on bonnet............ **£70-80**

Lone Star 'Tuf-Tots'

The first thirteen Tuf-Tots were introduced in 1969, and the next five followed in 1970. The remainder had appeared by 1972. They were available boxed or bubble-packed, and when bubble-packed there was an additional '2' in front of the model number to give a four-digit reference. Later, models were sold in open counter-top trays.

The trucks were based on a common US Ford chassis. Most models exist in numerous colour variations. The series was discontinued after 1980. Market Price Range is **£10** to **£15**.

601 **Ford Petrol Tanker**
  'ESSO' labels ....
  Same, but 'ESSO' cast into sides ....
602 **Citroën DS Convertible with Driver** ....
603 **Chevrolet Corvette Stingray Conv.**
  with Driver ....

604 **Dodge Dart Convertible with Driver** ....
605 **Mercedes-Benz 280SL Convertible**
  with Driver ....
606 **Ford 'TT' Tow Truck** ....
607 **Ford 'Big L' Dumper Lorry** ....
608 **Jeep and Trailer** 'Herts. Farm', scale 85:1.........
609 **Ford 'Autos' Flat Truck**
  with metal petrol pump island ....
  with plastic petrol pump island ....
610 **Ford Tipper Lorry**
  'LS Construction Co.' labels ....
  with ribs cast onto body instead of labels ....
611 **Ford Luton Van**
  with 'Express Freight' labels ....
  with ribs cast onto body instead of labels ....
612 **Ford Articulated Low-Loader** 'Apache' ....
613 **Chris Craft Capri Speedboat** (plastic)
  on Trailer, scale 86:1 ....

614 **Ford Refuse Lorry**
  with 'City Refuse' labels ....
  with 'City Refuse' cast lettering ....
615 **Ford Cement Mixer** ....
616 **Ford Milk Float**
  'Milk, Milk, Milk' cast on each side................
617 **Ford Cattle Transporter** ....
618 **Ford Skip Lorry** ....
619 **Citroën DS Coupé** ....
620 **Chevrolet Corvette Stingray Coupé**................
621 **Dodge Dart Coupé** ....
622 **Mercedes-Benz 280SL Coupé**, scale 86:1 ....
623 **Routemaster Bus**...
  with 'London Bus' advertisements ....
624 **ERF Fire Engine**
  with ladder, 'Fire Brigade' labels ....
625 **Caravan** ....
626 **Ford Circus Cage Lorry**

627 **Tractor Shovel** ....

with plastic lion, 'Circus' cast-in ....

Gift Sets
579 **Commercial Vehicle Set** 6 models...................
580 **Car and Trailer Set** 6 models ....
581 **12 Vehicle Set** 12 models ....
582 **Highway Set**
   3 models plus sand hopper, car ramp,

street and traffic lights...........................
583 **Travel Set**
   3 models plus girder bridge,
   windmill and 'Stop' barrier........................
2570 **Building Site Playset**
   4 models plus sand hopper ....
2571 **Garage Playset**
   4 models plus car ramp...........................

2572 **Highway Playset**
   4 models plus street and traffic lights................
2573 **Travel Playset**
   4 models plus 'Stop' barrier........................
2574 **Dutch Farm Playset**
   4 models plus windmill...........................
2575 **Bridge Playset**
   4 models plus girder bridge........................

Lone Star 'Impy' and 'Flyers' series, Lone Star Sets and Miscellaneous

In the following listing the year shown is the date of introduction. Most models remained in production until 1976. **IW** = Impy wheels, **FW** = Flyers wheels, **HSW** = Hi-Speed wheels, **BPW** = black plastic wheels.

7	71	**Vauxhall Firenza** IW / FW, RHD and LHD.....................	**£25-30**
8	-	**Ford Capri,** not issued	**NPP**
9	70	**Maserati Mistral**, IW or FW...............	**£20-30**
10	66	**Jaguar Mk.X**, IW or FW	**£20-30**
11	66	**Chevrolet Corvette Stingray GT** IW or FW..	**£20-30**
12	66	**Chrysler Imperial**, IW or FW.............	**£20-30**
13	-	**Ford Thunderbird**, not issued	**NPP**
13	71	**Toyota 2000 GT**, Flyers wheels...........	**£20-30**
14	66	**Ford Zodiac Mk.III Est.**, IW or FW...	**£20-30**

No 15 Volkswagen Microbus - blue, No 124 Foden Openback Tipping Truck - blue cab, black chassis, grey back (incorrect box illustrated) No 401 Car Ramp - red, grey, blue plus plain mailaway box.

15	66	**VW Microbus**, IW or FW.....................	**£20-30**
16	66	**Ford Zodiac Mk.III Est.** 'POLICE' Car. IW or FW......................	**£20-30**
16	-	**Chrysler Imperia 'POLICE' Car,** IW or FW..	**£20-30**
16m	-	**Mercedes-Benz 220 SE** 'POLIZEI' Car. Impy wheels.............	**£20-30**
17	66	**Mercedes-Benz 220 SE,** IW or FW..	**£20-30**

No 18 Motorway 'Police' Car - white, red interior, blue roof light, No 25 Alfa Romeo Spider - red, green seats and No 30 Turntable Fire Engine - red, grey, silver.

18	66	**Ford Corsair**, IW or FW	**£20-30**
19	67	**Volvo 1800 S**, IW or FW.....................	**£20-30**
20	67	**VW Ambulance**, IW or FW	**£20-30**
21	67	**Fiat 2300 S Coupé**, IW or FW	**£20-30**
22	67	**Rolls-Royce Silver Cloud III** Convertible. IW or FW	**£20-30**
23	67	**Alfa Romeo Giulia 1600 Spider** IW or FW..	**£20-30**
24	67	**Foden Tilt-cab 8w Tipper** black plastic or HSW..........................	**£20-30**
25	67	**International Harvester Tractor Shovel**	**£20-30**
26	67	**Foden Tilt-cab Petrol Tanker**	

		'MOBIL', BPW or HSW.........................	**£20-30**
27	67	**Ford Taunus 12M**, IW or FW..............	**£20-30**
28	67	**Peugeot 404 Saloon**, IW or FW.........	**£20-30**
29	-	**Cement Mixer Lorry**, not issued	**NPP**

No 124 Foden Tipping Truck - blue cab, black chassis, grey back and No 129 Express Freight Truck - blue cab, red chassis, grey back.

29	71	**Foden Tilt-cab Box Van,** 'LUCAS', BPW or HSW	**£15-20**
29	72	**Foden Tilt-cab Box Van,** BPW, 'EXPRESS FREIGHT' labels.................	**£25-35**
30	67	**AEC Merryweather Fire Engine** black plastic or Hi-Speed wheels........	**£20-30**
31	67	**Ford Transit Breakdown Lorry** 'ESSO', BPW or HSW........................	**£20-30**
32	68	**'FIRE CHIEF' Car** Ford Corsair, red, IW or FW	**£20-30**
32	-	**'FEUERWEHR' Car** Ford Corsair, red, Impy wheels.............	**£20-30**
33	68	**Austin-Western Mobile Crane** elevating jib	**£20-30**
34	68	**Euclid Crawler Tractor,** rubber tracks	**£20-30**
35	-	**Articulated Flat Truck**, not issued	**NPP**
36	69	**Lotus Europa**, Flyers wheels	**£20-35**
37	-	**Ford GT**, not issued	**NPP**
38	71	**Chevrolet Corvette Stingray,** Flyers wheels	**£20-35**
39	71	**Ford Mustang**, Flyers wheels..............	**£20-35**
40	73	**Cadillac Eldorado**, FW	**£20-35**
41	72	**Leyland Builders Supply Lorry** 4 girders, 8 HSW..............................	**£20-35**
41	73	**Leyland Builders Supply Lorry** 4 girders, 6 HSW..............................	**£20-35**
41	73	**Foden Half-cab Builders Supply Lorry** 4 girders,6 HSW..............................	**£20-35**
42	72	**Foden Half-cab Tipper** 'TILCON' labels, 8 HSW	**£20-35**
43	73	**Leyland Flat Lorry with Pipes** 6 HSW £20-35	
43	73	**Foden Half-cab Flat Lorry** with Pipes. 6 HSW	**£20-35**
44	72	**Leyland Marine Transport Lorry** Speedboat, 8 HSW..............................	**£20-35**
44	73	**Leyland Marine Transport Lorry** Speedboat, 6 HSW..............................	**£20-35**
44	73	**Foden Half-cab Marine Transport Lorry** Speedboat, 6 HSW..............................	**£20-35**
46	73	**Leyland Dropside Lorry** 6 Hi-Speed wheels..............................	**£20-35**
47	73	**Leyland High-Side Lorry** 6 Hi-Speed wheels..............................	**£20-35**
47	73	**Foden High-Side Lorry** Half-cab, 6 HSW..............................	**£20-35**
48	73	**Leyland Hopper Lorry**, 6 HSW.........	**£20-35**

48	73	**Foden Half-cab Hopper Lorry** 6 HSW	**£20-35**
49	73	**Foden Half-cab Tipper**, 6 HSW	**£20-35**

Impy gift sets

301	67	**Six-piece Gift Set**	**£100-150**
302	67	**Six-piece Gift Set**	**£100-150**
303	68	**'MOBIL' Gift Set**	**£100-150**
304	68	**Five-piece Commercial Vehicle Set**	**£100-150**
309	68	**Twelve-piece Gift Set**	**£200-300**

Impy accessories

401	67	**Car Lifting Ramp**	**£10-20**
402	67	**Lock-Up Garage** (plastic)	**£10-20**
403	-	**Service Station** (not issued)............	**NPP**
404	68	**'MOBIL' Petrol Pump Island** Canopy, Forecourt Sign................	**£10-20**
406	-	**Fire House** (not issued)..................	**NPP**

Impy two-packs

422	**VW Ambulance** (20) and **Mercedes-Benz 'Polizei'** (16M)........	**£30-40**
423	**Fiat 2300S** (21) and **Breakdown Lorry** (31)......................	**£30-40**
424	**Foden Tanker (26)** and **Ford Taunus** (27)............................	**£30-40**
425	**Ford Zodiac** (14) and **Tractor** (25)	**£30-40**
427	**Alfa Romeo** (23) and **'MOBIL' Petrol Pumps** (404).............	**£30-40**
431	**Chevrolet Corvette** (11) and **Fiat 2300S** (21)	**£30-40**
432	**Fire Engine** (30) and **Ford Corsair 'FEUERWEHR'** (32)	**£30-40**

Impy series, post-1976

The Market Price Range is shown as £5 - £10 but as yet there is little collectors' interest in these recent models.

50	**Six-wheel Tipper**..................	**£10-20**
51	**Six-wheel High Side Lorry**	**£10-20**
52	**Six-wheel Flat Lorry with Crane** ...	**£10-20**
53	**Six-wheel Flat Lorry with Speedboat**.	**£10-20**
54	**Six-wheel Cement Mixer**..................	**£10-20**
55	**Six-wheel Luton Van**	**£10-20**
56	**Six-wheel Dropside Lorry**	**£10-20**
57	**Six-wheel Flat Lorry with Water Tank**	**£10-20**
58	**Six-wheel Hopper Lorry**	**£10-20**
59	**Six-wheel Flat Lorry with Pipes**........	**£10-20**
60	**Six-wheel Flat Lorry with Planks**	**£10-20**
61	**Six-wheel Petrol Tanker**	**£10-20**
71	**Range Rover**	**£10-20**
72	**Cadillac Eldorado**	**£10-20**
73	**Chevrolet Corvette Stingray**.............	**£10-20**
74	**Toyota 2000 GT**	**£10-20**
75	**Range Rover Police Car**	**£10-20**
76	**Chevrolet Corvette Stingray 'GT Rally'**	**£10-20**
77	**Jaguar Mk.X**	**£10-20**
78	**Maserati Mistral**	**£10-20**
79	**Ford Mustang**	**£10-20**
80	**Lotus Europa**	**£10-20**
81	**Volvo Coupé**	**£10-20**
82	**Mercedes-Benz**	**£10-20**
181	**Articulated Flat Lorry with Crane**..	**£10-20**
182	**Articulated Petrol Tanker**..................	**£10-20**

183	Articulated Low Loader with Tuf-Tots car	£10-20
184	Articulated Flat Lorry with Pipes and water tank	£10-20
185	Cadillac Eldorado with Tuf-Tots Speedboat on trailer	£10-20
185	Range Rover with Tuf-Tots Speedboat on trailer	£10-20
185	Range Rover 'RNLI' with boat on trailer	£10-20
185	Jaguar Mk.X with Cabin Cruiser on trailer	£10-20
186	Crane Lorry (no.52) with Impy car	£10-20
187	Luton Van (no.55) with Trailer	£10-20
188	Articulated Low Loader with Cabin Cruiser	£10-20
189	Articulated Flat Lorry with Planks	£10-20
190	Petrol Tanker (no.61) with Trailer	£10-20
191	High Side Lorry (no.51) with Trailer	£10-20
192	Cement Mixer (no.54) with Flat Trailer	£10-20
1251	Articulated Car Transporter	£10-20
1252	AEC Merryweather HTTL Fire Engine (re-packed no.30)	£10-20
1256	Car Transporter (no.1251) with four Impy cars	£65-75

Lone star sets

'International Peace Force Vehicles' Set
(made 1974) contains:
1271 Small Tank, 1272 Searchlight on Trailer, 1273 Mortar Launcher, 1274 Radar Detector Unit, 1275 Ack-Ack Gun, 1276 Silver Small Canon, 1277 All Blue Military Jeep **£300-400**

'Gulliver county' series.

Boxed set of three Coaches.
White card box with scene depicting a coach, fire engine, articulated lorry and two cars.
i)   Mid-Green Coach, Grey wheels, 'SCHOOL BUS' logo on sides
ii) Cream Coach, Grey wheels, 'SCHOOL BUS' logo on sides
iii) Mid-Green Coach, Grey wheels, 'GREENLINE' logo on sides **£150-200**

'War in the Desert' Set
includes 3 German and 3 US military

vehicles **£200-250**
Miscellaneous items
1259 Routemaster Bus. Made 1972-89, paper adverts 'SEE LONDON BY BUS' and 'BUY LONE STAR'.
Route is '29 VICTORIA', Plastic wheels **£15-20**
RAC Land Rover and Caravan - no details.... **NGPP**

'Aircraft of the World' Series
(boxed, spare transfers, 1:250 scale)
'Scandinavian Airlines' Caravelle **£60-70**
'Pan American' Boeing 707 .... **£60-70**
'BOAC' De Havilland Comet 4c **£60-70**
'BOAC' Bristol Brittania **£60-70**
'British and Commonwealth' Bristol Brittania **£60-70**
'Aer Lingus' Vickers Viscount **£60-70**
'Modern Army' Series
'Lorry', 'Bren Gun Carrier' and 'Jeep' .... each: **£20-35**
'Small Mobile Fighting Unit' .... **NGPP**
'Farm' Series, 'Jeep' **£20-30**

Above: 8 Lone Star Tuf-Tots diecasts: 601, 603, 604, 2x 607, 610 and 2x 611.

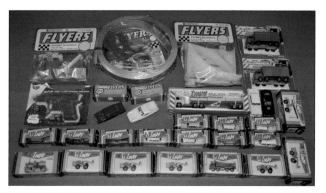

Right: Lone Star diecasts: Lone Star Flyers 412 F Gate, Loop Assy, Flyway 315 Strip Set, 18 Ford Corsair and 36 Lotus Europa GT; carded Lone Star 'spud gun'; 2 carded Lone Star Commercials.

Lonestar Impy Major Series pair of No 184 Pipe Line Transporters - red, black, green and No 51 Bulk Carrier - turquoise, yellow, blue.

Lone Star Ford Sunliner Convertible - white, red interior, plated hubs, front and rear bumpers, black tyres.

Lone Star Cadillac 62 Sedan - mid blue, cream roof, plated plastic bumpers, wheels, black tyres.

Notes

Matchbox Toys

The company was founded in 1947 by the unrelated Leslie and Rodney Smith, who combined their names to form 'Lesney' Products Ltd. They were soon joined by Jack Odell – a recognised diecasting expert.

The most famous of the various early products was the 'Coronation Coach'. During the 1950s the company developed the highly successful Matchbox 1-75 and Models of Yesteryear ranges. Today, certain models in the 1-75 series are highly sought after and fetch very high prices at auction.

Following a difficult trading period Lesney Products Ltd was bought in 1982 by the Universal Toy Co of Hong Kong. Models issued subsequently fall outside the scope of this publication.

New information in the 12th edition included shop display items, card layouts and vinyl collectors' cases. Additionally, many new model variations were listed.

In previous editions, the catalogue's listings of the 1-75 variations have been greatly improved by Trevor Bannister and Nigel Cooper. The 'Models of Yesteryear' listings have similarly benefited from revisions provided by Horace Dunkley. Thanks to Alwyn Brice for further updates in this edition and to Vectis Auctions and Graham Hamilton for use of photographs.

'Moko' Products

'Moko Products' was a toy distribution firm founded by Moses Kohnstam who came to Britain from Nuremburg, Germany around 1900.

Moko provided the distribution and storage facilities and, irrespective of the supplier, all toys were marketed as Moko products. The early issues after the WWII were housed in plain cardboard boxes with 'tuck in' ends. These usually had only single colour printing that did not include a picture of the model. During the early 1950s the packaging became much more attractive with brightly coloured boxes displaying a picture of the model inside. Moko will best be remembered for its distribution of the early Matchbox 1-75 toys under the name of 'Moko-Lesney'. Moses Kohnstam was succeeded by Richard Kohnstam in 1953.

The following listing of Moko items constitutes all the information available to publish at present. Additional information would be welcomed by the editor.

Moko presentation box

RAF Refueller

---   **Railway Timekeeper's Watch** with slide to house matches inside casing... **£250-350**

c1948-53 **Mechanical Tractor** Probably early Lesney. Orange body, Green rubber tracks, Black wheels, Green/Black driver, (early issue in plain box).......................... **£1,500-1,800**

1950-55 **Mechanical Tractor** As previous model but with Orange wheels, (later issue in picture box).......... .... **£300-400**

1947-50 **Excavator** (with open cab) Orange body and jib, Brown digger and chassis, Green rubber tracks, Orange crank handle. Early card box has 'Moko TOYS OF DISTINCTION' logo...... .... **£300-400**

1950-55 **'RUSTON BUCYRUS' Excavator** Yellow over Red body with Black '10 RB' logo. Black or Dark Green chassis, jib, digger, crank wheel and rubber tracks. Later box with full colour picture **£200-250**

1950-55 **Builder's Crane** All Blue crane base and jib with unpainted metal hook. Later card box with full colour picture **£400-500**

1947-50 **Crawler Bulldozer** Red body and dozer blade (possibly early Lesney). In card box (plain at first, later with colour picture)........ **£250-300**

1947-50 **Farm Tractor and Rake** Blue / Orange, with two Brown or Grey figures.................................... **£750-1,000**

1947-50 **Farm Tractor and Wagon** Blue driver **£600-700**

1950-55 **'Pop-Pop Series' Motor Scooter** Blue, Green or Dark Red scooter, Black seat. Female figure has blonde hair, blue sweater, red or blue trousers. Later box has full colour picture **£450-550**

1950-55 **Drummer Boy** (Mechanical) Red body, Gold trim, Black busby. Cream/Yellow drum, Gold drumsticks **£1,000-1,250**

1947-50 **Hayrake** Yellow/Green body or Orange body........ .... **£100-150**

1947-50 **Merry-go-Round** Blue/Red base and centre column,

Maroon or Green/Blue roof, 2 Red and 2 Blue seated figures. Plain card box..............................**£1,000-1,500**

1947-50 **Mechanical Mouse** Brown or Grey body with Red eyes, curling tail. Early plain card box **£600-800**

c1950 **Peregrine Puppet**................... **£600-700**

c1950 **'Jumbo, the Walking Elephant'.** Mechanical / tinplate. With diagonal printing...... **£1,000-1,250** With horizontal printing... **£1,000-1,250**

c1950 **0-4-0 Tank Engine** Light Metallic Green, bare metal wheels **£125-150**

Early Moko vehicles

Moko 'Farmette' series

Miniature size models packed in end-flap type boxes with colour picture of the model. The diecast horses have dark brown bodies and white feet. **NB** These are delicate models; check for metal deterioration.

No.1 50-53 **Timber Trailer with two Horses** Green body, four Red wheels, timber load **£150-200**

No.2 50-53 **Farm Cart (4 wheels) with two Horses** Mid or Dark Blue, Red or Yellow raves, Red 12-spoke wheels............................... **£150-200**

No.3 50-53 **Bull Wagon with two Horses (in tandem)** Green wagon, Brown metal bull, four Red 12-spoke wheels.**£150-200**

Moko 'Treasure Chest' Series

Packed in Brown 'chests' with yellow 'strapping'.
NB These are delicate models; check for metal deterioration.

No.10 50-53 **Hay Cart**
Orange body, 2 Green raves, 2 Green wheels, one horse **£35-50**

No.11 50-53 **Millers Cart**
Blue body, 2 Red or Orange wheels, 3 White sacks, one horse **£35-50**

No.12 50-53 **Water Cart**
Green/Red cart, 2 Red wheels, one horse **£35-50**

The early 'Lesney' toys

Lesney Products issued its first diecast toys in 1948. Whilst production ceased during the Korean war period (1950-52), the models produced formed the basis from which the 1-75 series was launched in 1953. They were sold in boxes under the name of 'MoKo' who were ultimately to also market all the early 1-75 series models.

NB Models were sold boxed.

Road Roller
All Green (shades) body and flywheel, unpainted wheels **£600-800**
As previous but with Red roller wheels and Yellow flywheel **£600-800**
With a driver but without a flywheel **£250-300**
Without a driver and without flywheel. **£250-300**
Greyish-Brown, driver, Red metal rollers, no flywheel, rear canopy supports without cross brace, unboxed **£600-750**

Cement Mixer
All Green or All-Blue body,
Red wheels **£250-300**
Pale Green body, Red or Yellow drum and wheels **£250-300**
Dark Green body, Red or Yellow drum and wheels **£250-300**
Red body, Green drum and wheels **£250-300**
Orange engine cover, Black drum, Yellow wheels **£250-300**
Light Green, Orange barrel and handle, black wheels.......................... **£800-1,000**

Caterpillar Tractor
Orange or Yellow body, Red roller wheels, Black rubber tracks **£300-400**
Orange body and roller wheels **£400-500**

Caterpillar Bulldozer
Green, Orange or Red body, Black tracks **£400-500**

All-Orange body **£600-700**
Yellow body, Red dozer blade and wheels **£200-300**

Prime Mover 'BRITISH ROAD SERVICES'
Orange tractor (Green engine on some), Blue trailer, Red/Yellow dozer.............. **£500-600**
As previous but with Beige trailer **£750-1,000**

'MASSEY-HARRIS 745' Tractor
Red body, Cream hubs, Black rubber tyres **£500-650**
Bright Red variation **£600-800**
Bright Red, Beige wheels **£700-750**

Horse-drawn Milk Float
Orange body, White driver and six crates, Black or Brown horse, Black or Grey wheels, 'PASTEURISED MILK' cast-in **£500-650**
Same but with Dark Blue body **£900-1,200**

Soap-Box Racer
Brown box, Grey wheels (16 + 9 spokes), Brown or Dark Blue boy with Pink face.. **£2,500-3,500**

Quarry Truck 'LAING'
Yellow body, Black tyres.
Only one known .... **NGPP**

Covered Wagon with Barrels
Green body, White cover, two Red barrels, six Mid-Brown horses (with White tails), with postilion rider and wagon driver .. **£125-175**

Covered Wagon
Same model but with Chocolate Brown horses and no barrels **£100-150**

'RAG & BONE MERCHANTS' Cart
Yellow body, Red wheels, Black or Tan or Grey horse, Brown or Cream driver, with 7 pieces of 'junk': mangle-wheel, bike frame, bedhead, bath, bucket, box, cistern.
.... **£450-550**
Green body, Red wheels. **£1,500-2,000**

Coronation Coach (large)

Gold coach with King and Queen, eight White horses, Gold/Red trappings, four Red riders. 200 issued **£500-600**
Modified version: Gold, Silver or Gilt coach with just the Queen inside. Horses and riders as for previous model................. **£225-275**

Coronation Coach (small)
Gold coach, eight White horses, Red/Gold trappings, four Red riders, 'A MOKO TOY BY LESNEY' cast into horsebar **£350-450**
Same but Silver coach........................... **£80-120**
NB 1,000,000 of the small Coach were sold. The Silver to Gold finish ratio is approx. 50:1.

'Muffin The Mule'
White body, Red/Gold harness, Black trim **£300-400**

Excavator
Digger and chassis are Dark Brown...... **£250-300**
Yellow, Red and Green version **£250-300**

Breadbait Press (for anglers)
1st type: Red body, unpainted 'butterfly' press. **£150-175**
2nd type:
As 1st type but with Green press........... **£150-175**
3rd type: As 2nd type but with 'MILBRO' cast onto Red body............... **£150-175**

Rag & bone merchant's cart

Matchbox '1-75' Series Box Types

'1 - 75' Series Regular Wheels Box Types and their abbreviations used in these listings

1. Moko 'A' type Script box
Abbreviation used in listings: **M(A)S box**
Box Design:
• A line picture of the model facing left to right in Black/Red.
• 'A Moko LESNEY 'Product' in Yellow on a Black banner with 'Moko' in Script.
• 'MATCHBOX SERIES' in Red letters. The box end flaps are blank.
• 'MADE IN ENGLAND' in Red plus the Model Number in Black.

2. Moko 'B' type box
Abbreviation used in the listings: **M(B) box**
Box Design:
• Same as 1. above but 'MOKO' now in CAPITALS.
• 'MADE IN ENGLAND' not shown on all examples of this type.
• 'REGD' (Registered) shown in Black on front. The box end flaps are blank.

3. Enlarged Moko 'B' type box
Abbreviation used in the listings: **EM(B) box**
Box Design:
• Same as 2. above with 'MADE IN ENGLAND' shown on all issues.
• 'REGD US PAT OFF.' has been added.
NB The box end flaps display the model number and name in black on a white background.

4. Lesney 'C' type box
Abbreviation used in the listings: **L(C) box**
Box Design:
A line picture of the model in Black/Red with 'MATCHBOX SERIES' in Red CAPITALS.
• 'A LESNEY' is shown in Yellow on a Black banner. On a banner beneath is the word 'PRODUCT'.
• 'MATCHBOX' SERIES in Red capitals. The model number is shown in Black.
• 'REGD US PAT OFF' and 'REGD' are shown to the side beneath the banner.
NB The box end flaps display the model number in Blue on a White circle plus the model name.
Box variation: A Lesney 'C' type box was issued with 'New Model' displayed in White on the box flaps. The abbreviation of this variation is: NM L(C) box.

5. Lesney 'D' type box
Abbreviation used in the listings: **L(D) box**
Box Design:
• A colour picture of the model facing left to right
• 'MATCHBOX Series' in Red across the top
• 'A LESNEY PRODUCT' and the model number in Black letters.
• 'MATCHBOX REGD. T.M. G.B. AND ABROAD' in Red
• 'REGD US PAT OFF' and 'MARCA REGISTRADA' in Red.'

NB The box end flaps display the model number and name in White on the blue background.
Box variation: A Lesney type 'D' box was issued with 'NEW MODEL' on the box end flaps.

6. Lesney 'E' type box
Abbreviation used in the listings: **L(E) box**
Box Design:
• A colour picture of the model facing right to left
• 'MATCHBOX' with 'Series' beneath it in Red
• 'A LESNEY PRODUCT' and the model number in Black
• 'REGD US PAT. OFF' and
  'MATCHBOX REGD'. T.M G.M.AND ABROAD.
  NB Box end flaps display a colour model picture plus the model number in Yellow and the model name in White.

Box variation: A Lesney type 'E' box was issued with 'NEW MODEL' on the end flap; the abbreviation for this variation is: NM L(E) box.

7. Lesney 'F' type box
Abbreviation used in the listings: **L(F) box**
Box Design:
• A large colour picture of the model facing right to left
• Red 'MATCHBOX'Æ with 'Series' below the right side
• The model number is shown in White on a Blue square background
• 'A LESNEY PRODUCT' is shown in Black
• Model features are shown, e.g., 'AUTO-STEER'.
  NB The box end flaps display a colour picture of the model, 'MATCHBOX' is in Red and the model number in Blue.
  A variation exists with 'NEW' on the end flap.

Matchbox '1-75' Pre-Production Models

One of the most fascinating areas of collecting the Lesney 1-75 series is that of the pre-production trials. Not much is known about these models but there seems to be a steady trickle of these vehicles into the marketplace every year. We have not priced the variants listed here simply because in many cases they are one-offs: moreover, some are boxed whilst others have turned up loose. Expect to pay a premium for most of these.

No.4c Triumph T110 Motorcycle with Sidecar finished in metallic blue but with silver trim to engine and exhaust, lights and handle bars

No.8e Ford Mustang finished in white body, off-white interior with black base, wire wheels with black tyres, without silver trim, patent pending base, with tow guides, recessed keyhole, type B rear square vents, with type E4 colour picture box

No.9b Dennis Fire Engine finished in red, gold trim, small 11mm escape wheels, metal wheels with flat crimped axles with type B1 Moko box

No.11d Mercedes Scaffolding Truck finished in yellow, grey plastic base and grille, clear windows, black plastic wheels

No.12c Land Rover Safari "Service Departemental de Secours" in red, black plastic base and interior, blue roof-light, black plastic wheels

No.12c Land Rover Safari, bare metal finish, grey interior, bright red luggage
No.14d Iso Grifo finished with a red metallic body, pale blue interior, type B patent base, chrome hubs with black plastic tyres

No.14d Iso Grifo, finished with a metallic green body, pale blue interior, type B patent base, chrome hubs with black plastic tyres

No.14d Iso Grifo, finished in dull light metallic gold, with pale blue interior, type C patent base, chrome hubs with black plastic tyres

No.14d Iso Grifo, finished in metallic gold, with pale blue interior, type A patent base, chrome hubs with black plastic tyres

No.20c Chevrolet Impala finished in green, with cream interior, unpainted base

No.22c Pontiac GP Coupe finished in blue, grey interior, rear patent number base, without tow guides with type E2 "New Model" colour picture box showing blue illustration

No.23c Bluebird Dauphine Caravan finished in metallic mauve, dark maroon base, black opening door, without tow brace, grey plastic wheels, with standard issue colour picture box

No.28d Mack Dump Truck with orange body and tipper, red plastic clip, clear windows without text to base and tipper, red plastic hubs with black tyres, with E4 "New Model" colour picture box

No.28d Mack Dump Truck with blue body and tipper, clear windows, red plastic hubs with black tyres, No.2 tipper without cast A to base

No.30c 8-wheel Crane Truck, bare metal finish body and jib, grey plastic hook, with unspun base

No.38c Honda Motorcycle finished in dark metallic green, wire wheels with black plastic tyres

No.42c Iron Fairey Crane finished in yellow including boom, red plastic base, interior and hook, black plastic wheels

No.44c GMC Refrigerator Truck finished with a green cab and chassis, silver back, white plastic rear door bumper and grille, black plastic wheels with type E4 colour picture box showing correct colour illustration

No.44c GMC Refrigerator Truck with red cab, chassis and back, grey plastic door, base and grille, black plastic wheels

No.46b Guy "Beales-Bealesons" Removals Van with pale green body, fine tread black plastic wheels, with silver trim

No.46c Mercedes 300SE Coupe with metallic silver body, black plastic wheels

No.48c Dodge Truck finished in orange with short chrome base and grille, unpainted rear chassis, black plastic wheels with small Matchbox brass screws to base

No.50c Ford Kennel Truck finished in yellow, clear plastic canopy, green tinted windows, unpainted base and grille, black plastic wheels

No.50c Ford Kennel Truck finished in metallic aqua, white plastic canopy, chrome grille, black base and plastic wheels, dark green tinted windows

No.56 BMC silver, silver hubs, cream interior

No.61b Alvis Stalwart with ribbed loadbed, metallic green body, black chassis, yellow plastic canopy, mid green plastic hubs with rubber tyres with type E picture box

No.66 Harley Davidson Motorcycle with sidecar, finished in metallic bronze, wire wheels with black tyres, with brown seats, painted engine and handlebars, with type D colour picture box

Matchbox '1-75' Series, 'Regular Wheels' issues, 1953–1969

Matchbox model identification

Model Number is always cast into the base, chassis or body. Obvious exceptions are the early models which were not numbered. 'Lesney' is cast into all issues between 1953 and 1982.
'Matchbox' or **'Matchbox Series'** is shown on the base or chassis of all issues after 1965. All issues after 1957 had the model name on the base or chassis. Exceptions include those

without a base (e.g. No 24 Excavator).

Suspension and **windows.** Car models were fitted with windows after 1961 and suspension after 1965.

Baseplates are metal castings until the late 1970s when plastic bases introduced. From 1983 they are marked 'Made in Macau.'

Wheels were metal castings on early models and were gradually changed to grey, silver or

black plastic. **Superfast wheels** introduced in late 1960s and issues from 1968-69 may be found with either type. Novelties such as **'Laser Wheels'** introduced in the late 1980s. **'Rolamatics'** were introduced in the 1970s having working parts that were operated by pushing (see the Superfast section for these). **Model descriptions.** This catalogue tries to give original maker's description of model names and colours but early Matchbox listings are known to be inaccurate graphically. Maker's catalogue photographs are often taken of mock-ups months before production starts while model designs become changed before release.

Dimensions refer to the greatest overall measurement (usually the length).

Superfast issues are listed separately elsewhere in this Matchbox section.

Model and details	MPR

MB 1

1a 53 **Diesel Road Roller** (Aveling Barford)
Red metal roller wheels, Tan driver cast-in, no number, crimped axles, 49mm.
Type 1: curved lower canopy ends and thin braces above canopy supports,
Type 2: straight ends and thick braces above supports, brace extension.
Dark Green body, Type 1 ....**£150-200**
Dark Green body, Type 2 ....**£75-100**
Light Green body, Type 2 ....**£100-150**

1b 56 **Diesel Road Roller** (Aveling Barford)
Light Green body, Red metal roller wheels, Lt. or Dk. Tan driver, high peaked canopy, no number, hook, 57mm........................**£70-90**

1c 58 **Diesel Road Roller** (Aveling Barford)
Light Green body and metal roller wheels, number cast-in, high peaked canopy, hook, 62mm **£100-150**
Dark Green body...............................**£45-60**

1d 62 **Diesel Road Roller** (Aveling Barford)
Green body and driver, twin-rivet baseplate, Red plastic rollers, 67mm..................**£150-200**

1e 67 **Mercedes Truck**
Turquoise body, Orange canopy, BPW...**£10-12**

Selection of heavy goods vehicle models.

MB 2

2a 53 **Muir Hill Site Dumper**
Dark Green body, Red dumper, Green painted MW, 42mm **£150-200**
Same but with unpainted MW..............**£40-50**

2b 57 **Muir Hill Site Dumper.** Same but:
Tan driver, metal wheels, 46 mm...........**£40-50**
Same but GPW, crimped axles..............**£50-60**
Same but GPW, rounded axles **£50-60**

2c 62 **Muir Hill Dumper Truck**
Red body, Green dumper, 'LAING', Black plastic wheels, 54 mm **£40-60**
Same but 'MUIR HILL' logo and picture-box (72 only known) **£120-140**

2d 67 **Mercedes Trailer.** Turquoise body, Orange top, wide braces to tailboard, BPW...**£30-35**

MB 3

3a 53 **Cement Mixer**
Orange MW, Blue main body **£30-40**
GPW, crimped axles **£80-100**
GPW, rounded axles **£80-100**

3b 61 **Bedford Tipper Truck**
(All have Grey body and chassis)
Maroon back, GPW, 24 treads **£400-450**
Maroon back, GPW, 45 treads **£200-250**
Maroon back, BPW.............................**£30-80**
Red cab and chassis, Tan back, MW.......**£20-40**
Red cab and chassis, Tan back, GPW....**£60-80**
Red dump, GPW **£90-110**
Red dump, BPW **£25-35**

3c 67 **Mercedes Ambulance**
Cream or off-White body **£40-70**

MB 4

4a 54 **Massey Harris Tractor**
(with mudguards over rear wheels), Red body, Gold or Yellow rear hubs, Tan driver, open engine with Lesney or England on mudguards **£60-90**

4b 57 **Massey Harris Tractor**
(without mudguards over rear wheels), MW, Gold or Yellow rear hubs...........**£125-150**
Grey plastic wheels............................**£90-110**

4c 60 **Triumph T110 Motor Cycle**
Steel Blue bike/sidecar, Silver spoked wheels, KBPT **£90-130**
Same but Copper body (beware of fakes)......................... **£2,000-3,000**

4d 66 **Dodge Stake Truck**
Yellow cab, Blue stake body, BPW.........**£50-70**
Yellow cab, Green body, correct box picture................................**£20-25**
In Lesney 'F' box showing picture of Orange model **£175-200**

MB 5

5a 54 **London Bus (52 mm)**
Red body, 'Buy Matchbox Series' on paper label **£70-100**
Type B upper deck window **£200-250**
Green body, MW, Gold radiator, White/Green 'Buy Matchbox Series' paper labels.
Australian issue in Moko 'B' box **£5,000-7,500**

5b 57 **1957 London Bus (57mm)**
'Buy Matchbox Series' decal, MW, Moko 'B' box..............................**£40-50**
'Buy Matchbox Series' decal, GPW **£60-70**
'Players Please' decal, GPW, Moko 'B' box....................................**£140-160**
'BP Visco Static'................................**£400-420**

5c 60 **Routemaster (66mm)**
'Players Please decal, GPW, Lesney 'C' box **£110-140**
'Peardrax', GPW or BPW, Lesney 'C' box **£600-700**
'Baron of Beef' BPW **£200-220**
'Baron of Beef' GPW **£600-700**
'BP Visco-Static' decal, KBPW, box 'D'...**£60-70**
'BP Visco-Static' decal, GPW, box 'D'...**£40-50**

5d 65 **Routemaster (70mm)**
'BP Longlife' decal, box 'D' **£20-25**
'BP Visco-Static' decal or label, box 'E'...**£15-20**
'BP Visco-Static' decal, BPW, box 'F'...**£100-150**
'Baron of Beef' decal, BPW, box 'D'..**£400-500**
'Baron of Beef' decal BPW box 'E' **£500-600**
'Pegram Shopfitters' decal, BPW, box 'E'..**£600-800**
'Pegram Shopfitters' decal, BPW, box 'F'..**£900-1,000**
'News of the World' BPW **£750-850**

MB 6

6a 54 **Quarry Truck 55mm**
Orange body, Grey tipper with six ribs, MW................................**£60-80**
Same, but GPW, domed/crimped axles **£4,000-5,000**
(Unboxed example) **£1,400-1,600**

6b 59 **'Euclid' Quarry Truck**
Yellow body, four ribs, six BPW **£40-50**
Knobbly GPW, domed axles **£3,000-4,000**

6c 63 **Euclid Dump Truck**

Six Black wheels (rear double wheels are one piece)....................................**£20-30**
Ten Black wheels (rear wheels are normal double wheels) **£10-20**

6d 68 **Ford Pick Up**
Red body, White canopy, chrome grille **£25-35**
Same but White grille **£10-20**

MB 7

7a 54 **Horse Drawn Milk Float**
Dark Orange body, White driver, crates and logo, metal wheels...............**£70-80**
As previous but with GPW **£110-140**
Pale Orange body, metal wheels **£70-80**
Pale Orange body and logo, White hat and crates, GPW **£50-100**
Pale Orange body, Silver driver and crates, GPW (beware fakes)........**£400-450**

7b 61 **Ford Anglia**
Light Blue, Green windows, KGPW, Lesney 'F' box.................................**£50-80**
With Silver plastic wheels **£50-100**
With Black plastic wheels....................**£40-50**

7c 67 **Refuse Truck**. Orange-Red body, Grey and Silver dumper **£10-20**
Same but with grooved toe **£70-100**

MB 8

8a 55 **Caterpillar Tractor (42 mm)**
Yellow body and rollers, Red driver, Green tracks, open engine **£250-400**
Same but with unpainted rollers...........**£50-65**
Orange body and driver, Gold or Silver grille, Green tracks **£80-100**
Yellow body/driver, Silver or Yellow grille, Green or Grey tracks **£35-70**

8b 58 **Caterpillar Tractor (42mm)**
Yellow body and driver, no.'8' cast-in, Green rubber tracks..........................**£40-70**

8c 61 **Caterpillar Tractor (48mm)**
Yellow body, metal rollers, Green tracks ..**£40-55**
If box shows correct model picture.....**£125-175**
Same but Silver plastic rollers...........**£150-175**
Same but Black plastic rollers...............**£15-45**

8d 64 **Caterpillar Tractor (51mm)**
Yellow body, no driver, Green rubber tracks, Black rollers, engine filled in **£80-110**
Same but with engine not filled in **£25-55**

8e 66 **Ford Mustang**
White body, BPW with Silver hubcaps..**£25-35**
White body, Chrome wheels with BPT .**£25-35**
Burnt Orange body, Red interior, chrome hubs, BPT, 'F' box **£300-550**

MB 9

9a 55 **Dennis Fire Escape (57mm)**
Red body, no front bumper, MW, crimped axles **£60-80**
With small diameter escape ladder wheels **£125-150**

9b 58 **Dennis Fire Escape (58mm)**
Red body, with front bumper, MW, number cast underneath.......................**£50-80**
Same but with GPW **£250-350**

9c 59 **Merryweather Marquis**
Series III Fire Engine
Red body with Tan ladder, GPW, crimped axles, 64 mm................**£50-75**
Same but with rounded axles **£40-90**
Same but with Gold ladder **£40-50**
With Gold ladder and BPW **£30-40**
Same, ladder has 17 rungs **£50-60**

With Silver ladder, BPW £90-110
With Tan ladder, BPW...........................£150-170

9d 66 Boat and Trailer (76mm, 77mm)
Blue/White boat, Blue trailer, BPW £15-20

MB 10

10a 57 Scammell Mechanical Horse
Red cab, Gold trim, Grey trailer,
crimped axles, MW, 56mm £35-60

10b 57 Scammell Mechanical Horse
Red Cab, Brown trailer,
crimped axles, MW, 75mm £50-60
Red cab, Gold trim, Light Brown
trailer, Grey plastic wheels £100-150
Red cab, Silver trim, Light Brown
trailer, Grey plastic wheels £100-150
If in rare enlarged type 'B' Moko box..£150-200

10c 60 Foden 8-wheel Sugar Container
Dark Blue body, with crown on rear
decal, Grey wheels £60-70
Without crown, Grey wheels.................£50-60
Without crown, Silver wheels £60-80
Without crown, Black wheels £30-40

10d 66 Leyland Pipe Truck
Red body, 6 or 7 Grey pipes,
Silver base and grille...............................£15-20
Same but with White base and grille £40-50

MB 11

11a 55 E.R.F. Road Tanker. All with metal wheels.
Green body, Gold trim, 'B' box £600-700
Dark Yellow body, Silver trim £170-250
Light Yellow body, Silver trim £85-100
Red body, Gold trim, small
'ESSO' decal on rear of tank £120-140
Same but large 'ESSO' decal £75-85
Same but two small 'ESSO'
decals on tank sides........................ £800-1,000
Same but two large 'ESSO'
decals on tank sides........................ £800-1,000
Same but 3 side labels £750-1,000
Same but Orangey Red, with
large end decal...................................£500-600

11b 58 'ESSO' Petrol Tanker (E.R.F.)
All have red body and 'ESSO' decal at rear.
Metal wheels, Gold trim £350-450
Metal wheels, Silver trim......................£50-60
Grey plastic wheels £80-110
Silver plastic wheels £1,000-1,100
Black plastic wheels...........................£110-160

11c 65 Jumbo Crane
Yellow body and weight box, single
or double arm hook £25-30
Yellow body, Red weight box £20-35

11d 69 Mercedes Scaffolding Truck
Silver, Yellow plastic scaffolds, BPW £10-15

MB 12 Land Rover

MB 12

12a 55 Land Rover
Green body, Silver trim on some,
Tan driver, domed or crimped axles,
MW, 43 mm £35-50

12b 59 Land Rover Series II

Green body, BPW, crimped axles..........£50-60
BPW, rounded axles £35-45
GPW £250-350

12c 65 Land Rover Safari
Green body, Brown luggage, BPW £20-45
Blue body, Brown luggage, BPW £25-40
Blue, Red-Brown luggage, BPW............£20-30
Metallic Gold body, BPW,
(beware of fakes).........................£1,200-1,500

MB 13

13a 55 (Bedford) Wreck Truck (51mm)
Tan body, Red crane/hook,
MW, crimped axles £40-55

13b 58 (Ford Thames) Wreck Truck (54mm)
Light Brown body, Red crane and
hook, '13' cast-in, MW............................£40-60
Same but with KGPW £70-130

13c 60 Thames Trader Wreck Truck
All models with Red body and crane.
Yellow side decals, knobbly Grey MW
(24 treads), Red hook............................£45-80
Grey wheels (45 treads), Grey hook,
closed lattice jib, 'D' box £275-325
BPW, Silver or Grey hook £40-60
Same with open lattice jib £80-110

13d 65 Dodge Wreck Truck
Green cab, Yellow body,
Grey hook, 'BP' decal £3,800-4,800
NB Fakes from 1970 have red hooks,
'BP' labels, crimped axles and the thick
crane casting. Only the original Green
cab version (from the Lesney factory)
has a thin crane. But these fakes (only 24
were produced) are now sought after by
some collectors £600-800
Yellow cab, Green body, Grey hook £20-30
Same but with Red hook £20-25
Same but with Yellow hook..................£75-100

MB 14

14a 55 Ambulance (Daimler) (49mm)
Cream body, Silver trim, some with Red Cross
on roof, MW on crimped or domed/crimped
axles, no number, 'Ambulance' cast
on sides £50-60

14b 58 Daimler Ambulance (59mm)
All have a 'Red Cross' on roof.
Cream body, metal wheels....................£40-50
Cream body, KGPW................................£70-90
Off-White body, metal wheels £150-170
Off-White body, GPW £40-60
Off-White body, BPW........................£300-400

14c 62 Bedford Lomas Ambulance
All models with 'Red Cross' and
'LCC Ambulance' on sides.
White body, BPW £250-350
White body, KGPW £90-110
Same but with roof block
and guides £900-1,000
White body, SPW £300-400
Off-White body, SPW........................£120-150
Off-White body, locating marks
for Red Cross cast into roof,
Silver grille, SPW £300-400
Off-White body, GPW £300-350
Off-White body, BPW £30-40

14d 68 Iso Grifo
Metallic Blue body, Blue interior...........£25-30
Dark Metallic Blue, Blue interior...........£30-35
Dark Blue, White interior,
narrow wheels £400-450
Mid Blue, White interior, wide wheels..£15-20
Light Metallic Blue,
Blue interior, 'F' box £90-110

MB 15

15a 55 Diamond T Prime Mover
Yellow body, six MW, hook,
no number, 55mm £1,200-1,500
Orange body, six MW £40-60
Same but with ten GPW £200-300

15b 59 Rotinoff Super Atlantic Tractor
Orange body, Black base, hook,
BPW, 67 mm..£80-110
Orange body, knobbly GPW £2,900-3,400

MB15c Refuse Collector

15c 63 Tippax Refuse Collector
All models have Blue body.
Grey container, Black knobbly
24-tread wheels, decal............................£35-50
Same but without vent hole £180-200
With fine tread wheels,
'Cleansing Service' decal or label..........£20-25

15d 68 Volkswagen 1500 Rally Car
Off-White or Cream,
'137' decals on doors £80-100
Same but '137' labels on doors.............£50-60
'Herbie' film promotional,
Off-White, '53' decals, stripes £700-900

MB 16

16a 55 Transporter Trailer. Tan body,
Six MW (CA, or domed/ CA) £25-35

16b 60 Super Atlantic Trailer
Beige body, GPW £60-100
Orange body, GPW £950-1,100
Bright Orange body, KBPW.................£110-150
Orange, BPW,
Black or Orange drawbar £80-130

16c 63 Scammell Snow Plough
Grey body, Orange tipper, Red/White
or Orange/White decal,
base hole, GPW..................................£110-140
With Black plastic wheels,
no base hole £25-35
Same, but with base hole £50-60

16d 69 Case Bulldozer Tractor
Red/Yellow body, Green rubber
tracks, hook, 64mm £20-35

MB 17

17a 55 Bedford Removals Van. All models with
'MATCHBOX REMOVALS SERVICE'
decals and metal wheels.
Light Blue body, Silver trim £150-220
Maroon body, Silver trim £150-250
Maroon body, Gold trim £150-250
Light or Dark Green body,
Silver trim, crimped axles £50-70
Same but with domed axles £130-150

17b 58 Bedford Removals Van
Green body, MW, decal with or
without Black outline £80-150
Green body, GPW, outlined decal.......£75-110
Dark Green, GPW, outlined decal £200-300

17c 60 Austin FX3 Taxi
Maroon body, Mid-Grey interior,
Tan driver, GPW £45-55
Same but SPW, mid-Grey interior......£100-120
With Pale Grey interior and SPW £150-175

17d 64 Foden Tipper
Red chassis, Orange tipper,
'HOVERINGHAM,' Black base...............£25-35
Same but with Red base £15-20

17e 69 Horse Box Red cab, dark Green box.
Grey door, chrome base, two
White horses £15-20
Same but with Brown door ....NGPP

MB 18

18a 55 Caterpillar Bulldozer (46mm)
Yellow with Red blade, Green tracks.....**£40-50**

18b 58 Caterpillar Bulldozer (50mm)
Light Yellow body and blade,
Green tracks **£35-50**
Bright Yellow body, Light Yellow
blade, Green tracks, 'C' box **£100-150**
Same but with Grey tracks **£70-80**

18c 61 Caterpillar Bulldozer (58mm)
Light Yellow body and blade,
Green tracks, metal rollers **£40-50**
Same but Silver plastic rollers.........**£100-150**
Same but Black plastic rollers...............**£25-30**

18d 64 Caterpillar Bulldozer (62mm)
Yellow body and blade, no driver,
Green tracks, Silver plastic rollers **£100-200**
Same with Green tracks, Black
plastic rollers **£20-25**
Same with large smoke stack **£40-50**

18e 69 Field Car
Yellow body, Red-Brown roof,
Red hubs, Black base.........................**£50-60**
Same but unpainted base **£10-15**
Same but with Green hubs.................**£500-600**

Some Moko era lorries

MB 19

19a 56 MG Midget TD
Cream body, Brown driver, Red seats,
MW, no number, 51mm **£80-130**
Off-White body, metal wheels **£120-140**

19b 58 MG 'MGA' Sports Car
All models with Off-White body,
Red seats and Tan driver.
Metal wheels, Gold trim **£300-400**
Metal wheels, Silver trim....................**£80-120**
Grey plastic wheels, Silver trim **£160-180**
Silver plastic wheels...........................**£400-550**

19c 62 Aston Martin DBR5
All models with Metallic Green body,
'wire' wheels, Grey or White driver,
No. '19', 'New Model' 'C' box.............**£100-130**
No. '3'...**£300-400**
No. '41'...**£260-280**
No. '52'...**£175-220**
No. '5', 'D' type box............................**£200-260**

19d 65 Lotus Racing Car
Dark Green body, Yellow wheels,
White driver, RN '3' decal or label........**£15-35**
Same but with RN '19' **£200-300**
Orange body, RN '3'.............................**£30-45**

MB 20

20a 56 E.R.F. Stake Truck
Light Green, Silver trim, MW **£2,000-3,000**
Maroon, Gold trim, MW, 'B' box **£250-300**
Maroon body, Silver trim, MW **£35-45**
Lighter Maroon body, Silver trim,
Grey PW, 'B' box.................................**£200-300**
Dark Red body, metal wheels **£45-55**
Dark Red body, GPW...........................**£200-250**

20b 59 E.R.F. 68G Truck
All have Dark Blue body and 'EVER
READY' decals on sides. Early decals
with Orange outline, later with Red.
GPW, crimped axles **£80-120**
GPW, rounded axles **£80-120**
Silver plastic wheels...........................**£130-150**
Black plastic wheels............................**£60-100**

20c 65 Chevrolet Impala Taxi
Orange-Yellow body, Cream interior,
GPW, Taxi decal **£1,250-1,500**
Orange-Yellow body, Cream interior, BPW,
Silver base, Taxi decal **£30-40**
Same but with unpainted base **£30-40**
Same but with Red interior **£25-60**
Yellow, Cream interior,
Taxi label...**£400-420**
Same but with Red interior **£30-45**

MB 21

1a 56 Bedford Coach (57mm)
Green body and base,
'LONDON-GLASGOW', MW **£40-60**

21b 58 Bedford Coach (68mm)
All have Black base and
'LONDON TO GLASGOW' decals.
Green body, MW, 'B' type box.........**£100-120**
Light green body, MW **£60-70**
Light Green, GPW, 'B' type box **£80-90**
Dark Green, GPW, 'B' type box..........**£100-110**
Dark Green, SPW **£5,000-6,000**

21c 61 Commer Bottle Float
All models with Pale Green body and
Black base. On early models the bottles
are Cream, later ones are White
Bottle on door, SPW, CW...................**£190-260**
Bottle on door, SPW, GW....................**£70-80**
Same but with light tan crates **£50-70**
Cow on door, SPW **£50-60**
Cow on door, GPW..............................**£175-200**
Cow on door, BPW **£25-30**

21d 68 Foden Concrete Truck
Yellow body, Red chassis,
Black wheels, 'E' & 'F' boxes **£30-50**

MB 22

22a 56 Vauxhall Cresta
Body colours and shades from Dark Red
to Maroon, roof White to Cream **£35-45**

22b 58 Vauxhall Cresta
Pale Pink or Cream body,
without windows, metal wheels **£600-650**
Same but Grey plastic wheels **£120-140**
Same but with windows........................**£175-200**
Pale Pink body, GW, KGPW **£100-125**
Pale Pink body, Blue-Green side
panels, Grey plastic wheels **£2,000-2,600**
Light Metallic Brown body,
Blue-Green side panels, GPW............**£150-170**
Same but with dark metallic
Brown body **£140-170**
Light Grey body, Lilac side panels,
Grey or Silver plastic wheels **£80-140**
Light Gold body, Grey or SPW **£150-170**
Metallic Dark Gold body, SPW **£150-170**
Dark or light Metallic Copper body,
Grey, Silver & Black wheels...............**£110-160**

22c 65 Pontiac GP Sports Coupé
Red body, Pale Grey interior,
BPW, 'E' box **£25-35**
Same but in 'F' type box.......................**£500-700**

MB 23

23a 56 Berkeley Cavalier Caravan
Pale Blue, 'On Tow MBS 23', MW, 65mm..**£40-60**

23b 57 Berkeley Cavalier Caravan
All have 'ON TOW' rear decal.
Pale Blue, metal wheels........................**£40-60**
Lime-Green, metal wheels.................**£110-130**
Lime-Green, GPW.................................**£60-80**
Metallic Lime-Green, GPW.........**£1,200-1,500**
Metallic Green, GPW......................**£3,000-3,600**

23c 60 Bluebird Dauphine Caravan
All models without windows and
with 'ON TOW' rear decal.
Metallic Lime-Green, GPW................**£600-750**
Same, but with Mauve base **£500-550**
Metallic Mauve body, Maroon base..**£600-800**
Metallic Mauve body & base, GPW **£40-50**
Metallic Mauve body & base, 24 tread SPW **£30-40**

Same but with 20 tread SPW.............**£100-130**
Metallic Mauve body & base, BPW....**£800-900**
NB A few issues of 23c are known
with plastic windows

23d 65 Trailer Caravan
Yellow body, 18 tread GPW.........**£1,600-1,900**
Yellow body, KGPW...............................**£12-15**
Yellow body, fine-tread BPW **£30-70**
Pink body, KBGW.................................**£30-40**
Pink body, smooth BPW 'E3' box.........**£50-60**
Same with 'E4' Box **£20-25**
Same with 'F2' Box **£40-50**

MB 24

24a 56 'Hydraulic' Excavator
Orange-Yellow body, metal wheels,
'WEATHERILL', 58mm **£30-40**
Same but Yellow body.........................**£50-70**

24b 59 'Hydraulic' Excavator
Orange-Yellow, GPW, 'C' type box
with 1st type model illustration.........**£150-175**
Same but 2nd type model illustration **£150-200**
Orange-Yellow body, GPW,
rounded axles....................................**£30-40**
Orange-Yellow body, BPW....................**£25-35**

24c 67 Rolls-Royce Silver Shadow
All models with Metallic Red body
and Black base.
Black wheels with
Silver hubcaps.....................................**£20-45**
Silver wheels with Black tyres...............**£15-18**

MB 25

25a 56 Bedford 12 cwt Van
Dark Blue body, Black base,
'DUNLOP' decals, MW **£40-50**
Grey plastic wheels **£40-70**
Black plastic wheels.....................**£3,000-3,400**

25b 60 Volkswagen 1200
Metallic Silver-Blue body,
KGPW, clear windows **£120-140**
Same, Green tinted windows.............**£120-140**
Same but with fine-tread GPW **£160-200**
Same but with SPW.............................**£100-130**
Metallic Silver-Blue, Green windows,
SBPW, 'D' type box **£1,200-1,500**

25c 64 Bedford Petrol Tanker
Yellow cab, Green chassis,
White tank, 'BP', BPW **£20-35**
Same but smooth GPW **£500-1,100**
German issue: Dark Blue cab and
chassis, White tank, 'ARAL', BPW **£200-250**

25d 68 Ford Cortina Mk.II
Metallic Light or Dark Brown body,
BPW...**£20-25**
Gift Set issue:
Same but with Yellow roof rack **£25-30**
Blue body, Silver base, BPW **£800-1,100**

MB 26

26a 56 E.R.F. Cement Mixer (45mm)
Orange body, Gold trim, MW, CA **£275-300**
Same but with Silver trim.....................**£35-50**
With GPW, Silver trim **£80-120**
With SPW, Silver trim, late box..........**£700-800**

26b 61 Foden Cement Mixer (66mm)
Orange body, Dark Grey barrel,
small knobbly GPW............................**£700-900**
Same but with Light Grey barrel........**£400-450**
Orange body, Orange barrel,
Grey or Black plastic wheels **£100-130**
Orange body, Orange barrel, SPW **£800-900**

26c 68 G.M.C. Tipper Truck
Red cab, Green chassis,
Silver tipper, BPW, 67mm **£15-20**
Same but without windows **£50-60**

MB 27

27a 56 Bedford Low Loader (78mm)
Pale Blue cab, Dark Blue trailer,
six metal wheels, crimped axles **£700-900**
Pale Green cab, Tan trailer **£90-110**

27b 58 Bedford Low Loader (95mm)
Pale Green cab, Tan trailer, MW £80-90
Same but with GPW...........................£120-140
Dark Green cab, Light Brown
trailer, Grey plastic wheels £300-350

27c 60 Cadillac Sixty Special
Metallic Pale Green, Cream roof,
Crimson base, SPW, Moko box..........£500-600
Silver-Grey body,
Off-White roof, SPW 'B' box £250-280
Same with 'C' box £180-200
Same but with pale Pink roof, 'C' box .£140-160
Metallic Lilac body, Pink roof,
Crimson base, GPW or SPW £50-100
Same model but with Black base £80-100
Same but Black base and BPW £70-100
Same but Blue base £250-350
Apple-Green body, Red interior .£2,500-3,500

27d 66 Mercedes 230 SL
White body, Red interior.......................£35-45

MB 28

28a 56 Bedford Compressor
Orange/Yellow body, MW, 47 mm £25-50
Yellow body, MW, domed CA £50-60

28b 59 Ford Thames Compressor Truck
Yellow body, Black wheels, CA £40-50
Yellow body, KBPW, rounded axles £60-70
Yellow body, Grey wheels £900-1,100

28c 64 Jaguar Mk.10
Pale Metallic Brown, Cream seats,
BPW, 74 mm £30-40
With 'Matchbox' lapel badge £50-60
With Grey plastic wheels and
without 'Matchbox Series' on base
....£1,700-2,000

28d 68 Mack Dump Truck
Orange body, Red wheels......................£20-45
Orange body, Yellow PH,
blister pack £150-175

MB 29

29a 56 Bedford Milk Delivery Van
Light Brown body, White bottle load,
metal wheels, 57mm..............................£35-45
Same but GPW, White or
Cream bottles £20-50
Same but with smaller wheels £70-90

29b 61 Austin A55 Cambridge
Two-tone Green body,
Green tinted windows, GPW.............£100-130
Same but SPW,
clear or tinted windows 'C' box £50-80
Same but with 'D' box £60-90
Same but with BPW £20-25
Same but with KBPW.............................£40-50

29c 66 Fire Pumper Truck
Red body, with or without
'Denver' decal, recessed door panel,
'E4' box £15-20
Same but with raised door panel £45-60

MB 30

30a 56 Ford Prefect
Grey-Brown body, Red and
Silver trim, metal wheels, domed
crimped axles 58mm £45-50
Same but with crimped axles................£30-45
Same but with GPW, rounded axles....£70-100
Same but Light Blue body, KGPW,
type 'C' Lesney box £350-450
Same but GPW, type 'B4' Moko box..£250-300
Same but with MW, domed
crimped axles, type 'B3' Moko box....£350-400

30b 61 Magirus-Deutz Crane Lorry
Light Brown body, Red or
Orange crane, GPW £4,000-4,500
Silver body, Orange jib and hook,
Grey or Silver wheels £60-70
Silver body, Orange jib, Grey or Silver
plastic hook, GPW £200-250
Same but with BPW £15-20

Same but with long metal hook, KBPW £40-50
Same but with new model
'type C' box £100-120
Same but with KSPW £30-50
Same but with short metal hook, KBPW ..£60-70
Same but with KSPW.............................£30-40

MB 30b Magirus-Deutz crane lorry

30c 65 8 Wheel Crane Truck
Green body, Orange jib £20-45
Turquoise body, Orange jib, BPW **£2,000-2,400**

Early cars without interior detail

MB 31

31a 57 Ford Station Wagon
Yellow body, metal wheels, 66mm £40-45
Yellow body, Grey plastic wheels £45-65
Yellow body, Black base, BPW £500-600

31b 60 Ford Fairlane Station Wagon
Yellow body, Black base, GPW..........£300-350
Yellow body, Black base, SPW £900-970
Yellow body, Crimson base,
clear or Green windows, SPW...........£650-700
Same but no windows £200-240
Metallic Green body, Pink roof,
Crimson base, Green windows,
GPW or SPW £60-80
Same but with clear windows £100-130
Same but with Black base, SPW.........£90-130
Same but with Black base, GPW.......£100-120
Same but with Black base, BPW £500-550

31c 64 Lincoln Continental
Metallic Dark Blue body, BPW,
'New Model', 'E' type box showing
red model £45-55
Metallic Light or Dark Blue body, BPW,
'E' type box showing correct
colour model £25-45
Sea Green body, BPW, 'E' type box
with single-line text to end flaps............£15-25
Same but two-line text to end flaps...£150-200
Metallic Lime Green, BPW......... **£1,200-1,500**

MB 32

32a 57 Jaguar XK-140
Off-White body, Black base,
MW, 60mm £25-35
Same but with GPW...............................£60-100
Light Red body, GPW £60-80
Red body, metal wheels £80-100
Bright Orange-Red, KGPW,
'C' type box £120-160
Same but with 'B5' Moko box £130-150
Dark Red, Black base, GPW £100-110

32b 62 Jaguar E-type
Metallic Red body, Green windows,
Grey tyres, 66mm £90-160
Metallic Red, clear windows,
Grey tyres £45-60
Metallic Red, clear windows,
Black tyres £40-60
Metallic Bronze Red, clear windows,
black tyres £100-120

32c 68 Leyland Tanker (All have a White tank).
Green chassis, Silver base and grille,
'BP' decal £60-80
Green chassis, Silver base and grille,
'BP' label £15-25
Green chassis, White base and grille,
'BP' label £30-40
Blue chassis, Silver base and grille,
'ARAL' label £100-140
Blue chassis, White base and grille,
'ARAL' label £220-260

MB 33

33a 57 Ford Zodiac
Dark Green body, hook, no windows,
metal wheels, 68mm £50-100
58 Dark Blue, hook, no windows,
metal wheels £700-875
58 Sea-Green, hook, no windows,
metal wheels £100-120
Same but with GPW.............................£50-100
59 Metallic Mauve body, Orange
panels, no windows, GPW £190-230
60 Same but with Green tinted
windows, SPW 'type D' box..............£500-550
Same but with 'type C' box £200-260
Same but with GPW £100-150

33b 63 Ford Zephyr 6
Sea-Green body, GPW, 67mm £80-140
same but with SPW £35-50
same but with BPW £20-35

MB 33c Ever-popular Lambourghini Mivra

33c 68 Lamborghini Miura
Yellow body, cream interior
71mm. BPW..£15-20
Yellow body, clear engine cover,
Chrome hubs £400-550
Same but with red interior £20-30
Same but with frosted engine cover £180-220
Metallic Gold or light Gold body,
frosted engine cover, Chrome hubs ..£250-350

MB 34

34a 57 Volkswagen 15cwt Van
All have Blue body; 'MATCHBOX' decals.
With metal wheels £50-70
With Grey plastic wheels.....................£75-100
With Silver plastic wheels £300-400
With KBPW, domed axles £4,000-4,500

34b 62 Volkswagen Caravanette
All have Pale Green body;
Green interior. Silver wheels....... £1,500-1,600
KGPW (24 treads)................................£50-75
With KBPW £50-80
Fine-tread Grey wheels (45 treads) ...£120-150
SBPW, type 'E' box...........................£500-600
Same but with type 'D' box £70-90

MB 34c VW camper van

34c 67 Volkswagen Camper
Silver body, with high roof
(7 windows)..£40-60

Same but lower roof (1 window),
box 'F'..£50-100
Pale Green body, Dark Green base
and interior, SPW £1,500-1,750

MB 35

35a 57 **E.R.F. Marshall Horse Box**
Red cab, Beige back, MW, 52mm £35-45
Same but with Grey plastic wheels,
domed rounded axles £80-90
Same but with domed crimped axles ...£30-50
With Silver plastic wheels £125-150
With Black plastic wheels....................£70-100
35b 64 **Snow-Trac.** Red body, Silver
base, White tracks, 'Snow Trac' cast
on sides..£25-30
Same but with 'Snow Trac' decals
on sides..£20-35
Same but without 'Snow Trac'..............£15-20
35c 68 **Merryweather Fire Engine**
Silver body, boxed.........................£4,500-5,500
NB This was one of the extremely rare
Regular Wheels models released during
the transition to Superfast in 1968/69.

Off-road and farm vehicles

MB 36

36a 57 **Austin A50 Cambridge**
Blue-Green body, Black base,
roof brace MW.......................................£40-45
Same but no roof brace £70-90
Same but with GPW.............................£30-50
Pale Blue body, GPW.............................£60-90
36b 61 **Lambretta and Sidecar**
Metallic Silver Green, KBPW,
'New Model', 'C' type box with
1st type model picture £60-120
Same but 2nd type model on box..........£50-65
Same but in 'D' type colour
picture box £90-110
Metallic Dark Green, KBPW,
'D' type colour picture box £150-175
36c 66 **Opel Diplomat**
Metallic Gold body, chrome engine, BPW,
no tow slot, 'New Model', 'E' type
box showing Dark Green model........£200-250
Same but box shows
Light Green model £25-40
With correct colour model on box £20-30
Met. Gold, Grey engine, tow slot,
'F' type box £40-50

MB 37

37a 57 **Karrier Bantam Lorry** (open base)
All models with 'COCA-COLA' side
and rear decals. Orange-Yellow body,
uneven load, MW...............................£60-100
Yellow body, uneven load, MW £240-260
Orange-Yellow, even load, MW............£55-75
Orange-Yellow, even load, GPW...........£90-110
Yellow body, even load, MW.................£60-80
Yellow body, even load, GPW.............£100-150
37b 60 **Karrier Bantam Lorry** (Black baseplate)
All models with 'COCA-COLA'
side and rear decals, yellow body
Grey plastic wheels, CA.....................£100-120
Grey plastic wheels, rounded axles £40-60
Silver plastic wheels....................£1,500-1,750

Black plastic wheels...............................£70-80
With orange body, GPW, domed
rounded axles £800-900
37c 66 **Dodge Cattle Truck**
Yellow body, Grey cattle box,
2 White bulls, Silver plastic base £20-45
With unpainted metal base...................£15-25

MB 38

38a 57 **Karrier Refuse Collector**
All models with
'Cleansing Department' side decals.
Grey-Brown body, MW......................£250-450
Grey body, metal wheels £40-50
Grey body, GPW, crimped axles............£40-60
Grey body, rounded axles......................£40-60
Metallic Silver, with rear ridge
casting, MW, CA.................................£400-500
Silver body, Grey plastic wheels £70-90
Silver body, Silver plastic wheels.......£600-700
38b 63 **Vauxhall Victor Estate**
Primrose body, Red interior, GPW £200-300
Same but with Silver wheels £45-60
Same but with SBPW...........................£100-120
Yellow body, Green interior, SGPW.....£80-100
Same but with KGPW.............................£60-80
Same but with Silver wheels £30-60
Same but with Black wheels £20-25
38c **Honda Motorcycle and Trailer**
Metallic Green bike,
Orange trailer without decals £30-40
Orange trailer with 'Honda' decals £80-120
Yellow trailer, small 'Honda' decals
or labels £40-50
Same but large decals/ labels £20-35

MB 39

39a 57 **Ford Zodiac Convertible**
Pale Peach body, Light Brown
base/interior/driver, MW..................£350-400
With Light Green base and
interior, MW £50-80
Same but with Light Green
base, GPW £60-70
Pale Peach body, SPW.........................£200-250
Dark Peach body, Blue-Green
base and interior, KGPW...................£300-350
Dark Peach body, Blue-Green base
and interior, SPW..............................£120-150
Dark Peach body with Sea-Green
base, Grey plastic wheels £75-85
39b 62 **Pontiac Bonneville Convertible**
Metallic Purple body, Crimson
base, Red steering wheel, SPW...........£80-100
Same but with Grey wheels...............£750-950
Lemon body, Crimson base, Red
steering wheel, SPW or GPW £65-75
Same but Cream steering wheel...........£25-35
Lemon body, Black base, SPW...............£70-90
Same but with Grey wheels...................£45-80
Same but with Black wheels £40-60
Lemon body, black base,
no silver trim, BPW £100-150
39c 67 **Ford Tractor**
Blue body, Yellow engine cover,
Black plastic tyres, 55mm....................£15-30
Light Blue body and cover,
Yellow hubs £25-50
All-Orange body, Yellow hubs £35-45

MB 40

40a 57 **Bedford 7 Ton Tipper, 53mm**
Red body, Brown tipper, MW...............£35-45
Same but with GPW, domed CA £60-80
With GPW on rivetted axles £30-50
40b 61 **Leyland Tiger Coach**
Steel Blue body, GPW...........................£30-50
Silver plastic wheels.............................£25-35
Fine tread plastic wheels.......................£20-35
Same with KBPW.................................£15-20
40c 67 **Hay Trailer.** Blue body, Yellow

plastic hay racks and wheels, BPT.........£15-25
NB No. 40c deleted in 1972 but appeared
in Two-Packs between 1976-1981.

Minibus, coach and crane lorry

MB 41

41a 57 **Jaguar 'D'-Type (55mm)**
Green body, MW, No. '41' £70-80
Green body, MW, No. '52',
'B' type box £600-750
Green body, GPW, No '41' £90-120
41b 60 **Jaguar 'D'-Type (62mm)**
All have Green body and Black base.
Grey plastic wheels, CA, No. '41' £70-80
Same but MW domed crimped axles £100-120
Same but with crimped axles £70-90
Same but with No. '52'......................£600-700
Wire hubs with Black tyres, No. '41' ..£300-400
same but with No. '5' or '6' £100-150
Red hubs, Black tyres, No.'41' £400-500
41c 65 **Ford GT Racer**
All have the racing number '6' or '9'.
White body, Red hubs and
interior, BPT £300-400
White body, Yellow hubs, BPT..............£25-35
Yellow body, Yellow hubs, BPT,
RN '6' (US set) £80-100
White, spoked wheels, BPT £2,000-2,200

MB 42

42a 57 **Evening News Van**
Yellow body, 'EVENING NEWS'
decals, metal wheels, 57mm £35-40
Grey plastic wheels with 24 treads £50-70
GPW or BPW with 45 treads..............£300-400
BPW with 24 treads..........................£150-170
42b 65 **Studebaker Lark Wagonaire**
(with hunter and dog figures).
Blue body, sliding rear roof
painted as body...............................£100-150
Same but rear roof is Light Blue £25-40
Light Blue body and sliding roof,
no tow guide, BPW............................£180-220
42c 69 **Iron Fairy Crane**
Red body, Yellow boom, BPW £20-25
First casting, hydraulic arm pin.........£500-600

MB 43

43a 58 **Hillman Minx**
Apple Green body, Silver/Red trim,
metal wheels, hook.........................£200-350
Blue/Grey body, Pale Grey roof,
metal wheels £50-90
Same but with Grey plastic wheels £60-70
Turquoise body, Cream roof, GPW £60-80
43b 62 **A.B. Tractor Shovel**
Yellow body, driver and shovel..........£250-300
Yellow body / shovel,
Red driver and base £20-25
Yellow body, driver and base,
Red shovel £40-45
Yellow body, Red driver,
base / shovel......................................£250-300
43c 68 **Pony Trailer**
Yellow body, Grey ramp,
Light Brown base, BPW £20-25
Same but with Dark Green base...........£20-25

MB 44

44a 58 **Rolls-Royce Silver Cloud**
Metallic Silver-Blue body, Red trim,
metal wheels, 67mm...............................**£30-35**
60 Same but with Grey plastic wheels ..**£50-60**
Same but with Silver plastic wheels **£60-90**
Pale Silver Blue, MW,
domed crimped axles...........................**£120-140**

44b 64 **Rolls-Royce Phantom V**
Metallic Mauve body, BPW...................**£25-30**
Same but with GPW.............................**£140-160**
Same but with SPW.............................**£300-400**
Light metallic Mauve, KBPW   ..**£140-170**
Same but with fine tread BPW............... **NGPP**
Same but with SPW **£280-300**
Same but with GPW **£100-120**
Metallic Silver-Grey, BPW...................**£150-175**
Same but with SPW **£400-600**
Silver body, fine tread BPW **£60-80**

44c 67 **GMC Refrigerator Truck**
Red body, Sea-Green container,
Black wheels, 76mm **£15-20**

MB 45

45a 58 **Vauxhall Victor**
Red body, no dashboard casting
bar, MW, 'B' type Moko box **£3,000-4,000**
Yellow or Lemon body, MW...................**£35-45**
Yellow body, metal wheels,
no dashboard casting bar....................**£400-500**
Yellow or Lemon body, Grey plastic
wheels, no window glazing **£40-45**
Same but with clear windows,
8x18 tread **£70-100**
Same but with 7.5x18 tread................**£180-200**
Same but with Green windows, 8x18t....**£50-60**
Lemon, Green windows, SPW **£80-90**
Yellow body, BPW.............................**£120-150**
Same but with SPW **£80-100**
Same but GPW **£50-70**

45b 65 **Ford Corsair with Boat**
Cream body, Red interior, Black
wheels, Silver painted base **£40-45**
Same but with unpainted base **£25-30**
Same but with Grey wheels...................**£80-100**
Models with White interior are
pre-productions **£600-800**

MB 46a Old Faithful Morris Minor

MB 46

46a 58 **Morris Minor 1000**
Tan body, no windows, MW **£2,500-3,500**
Dark Green body, Black base,
metal wheels, domed crimped axles.....**£45-75**
Dark Blue/Green body, MW **£70-80**
Same but with GPW.............................**£100-125**
Blue body, Grey plastic wheels.........**£150-250**

46b 60 **'PICKFORDS' Removals Van**
Dark Blue, GPW, three line decal **£50-80**
Dark Blue, SPW, three line decal.........**£140-180**
Dark Blue, GPW, two line decal........**£120-170**
Dark Blue, SPW, two line decal **£250-300**
Same but 'D' box shows green van .**£650-750**
Green body, GPW, three line decal **£80-110**
Green body, SPW, three line decal........**£60-80**
Green, SBPW, three line decal..............**£30-60**
'BEALES BEALESONS' Van
Light Brown body, 'Beales Bealesons'
decal, BPW, without box **£500-600**
Same but in special White box with
'sun' and 'It's A Pleasure' decal.......**£700-800**

46c 68 **Mercedes-Benz 300 SE**

Green body...**£20-40**
69 Metallic Blue body...........................**£20-35**

MB47

47a 48 **Trojan Van**
Red body, 'BROOKE BOND TEA'
decals, metal wheels, 58 mm **£35-45**
Same but with KGPW, 'B' type box **£50-60**
In 'D' type colour picture box............**£600-700**

47b 63 **Commer Ice Cream Van 'LYONS MAID',**
Metallic Blue body, BPW...................**£120-160**
Same but with Blue body **£50-80**
Blue body, KGPW, 'D' type box **£400-500**
Blue body, BPW, White side decals......**£40-50**
Cream body, 'LYONS MAID'................**£300-350**
Cream body, White side decals **£60-70**
'LORD NIELSENS ICE CREAM',
Cream body, Red/White labels,
Black base, Black plastic wheels...........**£70-90**
Blue body, Black plastic wheels, 'D' box
with cream van illustration................**£50-100**

47c 68 **DAF Container Truck**
Sea Green body, Grey roof,
Yellow container, BPW **£25-35**
Silver body, Grey or Silver roof,
Yellow container, BPW **£10-15**

MB 48

48a 58 **Meteor Sports Boat and Trailer**
Black trailer, Light or dark Brown boat,
Blue hull, metal wheels **£30-40**
With Grey plastic wheels.......................**£50-60**
With SPW, 'B' type Moko box **£175-200**

48b 61 **Sports Boat and Trailer**
Boat with Cream and White deck and
Red hull or with Red deck and
Cream or White hull, silver or gold motor
Dark Blue trailer, BPW........................**£25-40**
Dark Blue trailer, Grey PW **£170-240**
Light Blue trailer, BPW **£40-50**

48c 66 **Dodge Dumper Truck**
Red body, Silver trim, wide or narrow
Black plastic wheels, 76mm **£20-50**

MB 49

49a 58 **M3 Personnel Carrier**
Military Green, White bonnet star on
some, metal wheels and rollers **£25-30**
Grey plastic wheels, metal rollers.........**£35-70**
GPW and Grey plastic rollers............**£350-400**
Grey plastic wheels, Silver rollers......**£120-140**
BPW and rollers, Grey tracks **£30-50**
BPW and rollers, Green tracks.............**£30-40**

MB 49a M3 Personnel Carrier

49b 67 **Mercedes Unimog**
Light Brown body,
Sea-Green base, 61mm **£20-25**
Light Brown body,
Red base (factory error?)....................**£700-800**
Light Blue body, Red base.....................**£20-40**

MB 50

50a 58 **Commer Pick-Up**
Pale Brown body, MW, 64mm **£30-50**
Pale or Light Brown body, GPW...........**£35-45**
Light Brown body, SPW.....................**£150-180**

Dark Tan body, KGPW...........................**£60-70**
Same but with KSPW.........................**£90-110**
Red and White body, SPW **£700-900**
Red / White, KGPW,
'D' type box **£1,500-1,800**
Red and Grey body, SPW **£150-170**
Red and Grey, KGPW,
'D' type box **£180-200**
'B' type box **£80-100**
Red and Grey body, BPW, 'D'
type box **£110-130**

50b 64 **John Deere Lanz Tractor**
Green body, Yellow hubs,
Grey tyres, 50mm **£20-30**
Same but Black tyres.............................**£20-30**

50c 69 **Ford Kennel Truck**
Metallic Green body, White grille,
smooth kennel floor **£30-40**
Same but textured kennel floor
White/or Silver grille **£20-30**

Later cars with interior detail

MB 51

51a 58 **Albion Chieftain**
All models with Yellow body,
Tan or Light Beige load.
'PORTLAND CEMENT' decals, MW **£40-55**
With 'BLUE CIRCLE PORTLAND
CEMENT' decals, MW **£25-40**
Same but with GPW.............................**£40-55**
Same but with SPW, 'D' type box **£200-230**
Same with 'B' type box **£40-60**
Same with 'C' type box **£90-110**
Same but with knobbly BPW **£100-150**

51b 64 **Tipping Trailer**
Green body, three Yellow barrels,
Yellow hubs, Grey tyres **£10-15**
With Yellow hubs, Black tyres **£12-15**

51c 69 **AEC Mammoth Major 8 Wheel Tipper**
Orange body, Silver tipper,
'DOUGLAS', White base grille..............**£90-110**
Same but chrome base **£40-50**
Yellow body, Silver tipper,
'DOUGLAS' **£60-80**
Yellow body, Silver tipper,
'POINTER' **£25-35**

MB 52

52a 58 **1948 Maserati 4 CLT**
Red body, Cream driver, no decal,
Black plastic wheels, 61mm **£40-50**
Same with racing number '52'..............**£35-45**
Red body, racing number '52',
wire wheels, BPW................................**£200-300**
Lemon body, wire wheels, '52' **£60-800**
Same but number '3', '5' or '30'.........**£120-140**

52b 65 **B.R.M. Racing Car**
Blue body, Yellow hubs, BPT, '5'.........**£15-20**
Same but with racing number '3' **£100-140**
Dark Blue (Ultramarine) body, RN '5' . **£150-200**
Gift Set model: Red body,
Yellow hubs with Black tyres...............**£70-80**
Dark Cherry Red body,
Yellow hubs, racing number '5' **£100-120**

MB 53

53a 58 **Aston Martin DB2-4 Mk.I**
Metallic Green body, MW, 65mm **£40-50**
Same but with Grey plastic wheels **£60-80**

Met. Red, KGPW, 'C' type box............**£350-450**
Met. Red, KBPW, 'D' type box **£200-260**
Same but 'C' type box....................**£200-240**
Same but 'B' type box........................**£80-110**

53b 63 **Mercedes-Benz 220SE**
Maroon body, Silver plastic wheels.......**£30-40**
Maroon body, Grey plastic wheels.........**£30-40**
Maroon body, Black plastic wheels.......**£60-80**
Dark Red body, GPW.........................**£200-250**
Dark Red body, BPW.........................**£20-25**
Dark Red, SBPW, no rear trim,
'D' type box with Mercedes
promotional card **£500-600**

53c 68 **Ford Zodiac Mk.IV**
Light Metallic Blue body, BPW.............**£20-25**
Same but with violet interior **£700-800**
Light Metallic Green body, BPW **£3,000-3,500**

MB 54

54a 58 **Saracen Personnel Carrier**
Olive Green body, six BPW, CA **£25-35**
Same but with rounded axles **£20-40**

54b 65 **Cadillac Ambulance**
White, Red cross label or decal and
roof lights, BPW.....................................**£10-20**

MB 55

55a 58 **DUKW Amphibian**
Olive Green body, metal wheels............**£20-25**
Same but GPW **£40-50**
Same but with KBPW , 'B' type box.......**£25-40**
Same but KBPW, 'D' type box
with Green model picture
(normally Red picture).......................**£500-600**

55b 63 **Ford Fairlane 'POLICE' Car**
Non-metallic Dark Blue, BPW.............**£80-120**
Metallic Blue, knobbly BPW **£400-500**
Metallic Blue, BPW **£50-60**
Metallic Blue, GPW **£900-1,200**
Metallic Blue, SPW..........................**£450-500**

55c 66 **Ford Galaxie 'POLICE' Car**
White body, 'Police & Shield'
decal, Blue roof light....................**£180-220**
Same but with Red roof light **£15-20**

55d 68 **Mercury 'POLICE' Car**
White body, 'Police & Shield'
labels, Red roof light...........................**£350-380**
Same but with Blue roof light **£25-50**

MB 56

56a 58 **London Trolley Bus 'Drink Peardrax'**
All with Red body and destination decals.
Black poles, MW, (beware of fakes) ..**£250-300**
Black poles, GPW, (beware of fakes).**£300-400**
Red poles, metal wheels.........................**£45-60**
Red poles, GPW..................................**£100-150**
Red poles, BPW....................................**£45-55**
Red poles, SPW **£190-240**
'BP Visco-Static', KBPW,
red poles, 'D' type box.......................**£750-850**

56b 65 **Fiat 1500** (all have BPW)
Sea-Green body, Brown luggage **£15-20**
Same but with Red-Brown luggage.......**£10-15**
Gift Set version:
Red body, Red-Brown luggage **£70-80**

MB 57

57a 58 **Wolseley 1500**
Pale Green body, Grey plastic
wheels, Gold trim, 55mm...................**£220-250**
Same but with Silver trim......................**£35-60**

57b 61 **Chevrolet Impala**
All versions have Metallic Blue body
and Pale Blue roof,
Clear windows, Black base, SPW.......**£110-130**
Same but with tinted windows **£40-50**
CW, Dark Blue base, SPW,
'C' type box.....................................**£140-160**
GW, Dark Blue base, SPW **£40-50**
GW, Dark Blue base, SPW **£50-60**
GW, Pale or Light Blue base,
Silver plastic wheels.........................**£120-140**

Black base, GPW **£75-100**
Black base, SPW **£70-80**
Black base, BPW **£60-80**

57c 66 **Land Rover Fire Truck**
Red body, 'KENT FIRE BRIGADE',
Black plastic wheels, 64mm **£25-30**
Same but with GPW........................**£400-650**

MB 58

58a 58 **AEC Coach 'BEA'**
Dark Blue body, White letters,
Grey wheels, 65mm **£50-60**
Dark Blue body, Black letters on
White ground, Grey plastic wheels........**£40-70**
Same but with SPW **£70-90**
Same but with KBPW, 'D' type box **£100-1600**

58b 62 **Drott Excavator**
Red body, Silver base,
Black rollers, Green tracks **£20-45**
Same but with Silver rollers **£100-120**
Orange body, Silver base,
Black rollers..**£25-30**
Same but with silver rollers...................**£35-55**
Orange body and base, Black rollers.....**£15-20**

58c 68 **DAF Girder Truck**
White body, Red base and 12 girders,
6 Black plastic wheels, 75mm **£10-15**

MB 59

59a 58 **Ford Thames Van 'SINGER'**
Pale Green body, Grey plastic wheels...**£35-55**
Same but SPW, rivetted axles **£200-250**
Dark Green body, KGPW,
rounded axles **£250-300**
Same but with crimped axles................**£35-55**
Dark Green body, SPW,
rivetted axles **£250-300**

59b 63 **Ford Fairlane Fire Chief**
All models with Red body and 'FIRE
CHIEF' decals on doors and bonnet,
SBPW...**£150-175**
With Grey plastic wheels...................**£110-150**
With Silver plastic wheels **£250-300**
With shield decals on doors.............**£200-250**

59c 66 **Ford Galaxie Fire Chief**
Red body, Blue dome light,
'FIRE CHIEF', BPW **£20-25**
Same but with Red dome light **£250-350**

MB 60

60a 58 **Morris J2 Pick Up**
All with Light Blue body and
'BUILDERS SUPPLY COMPANY' decals.
'Supply Company' in Black,
Grey plastic wheels **£50-60**
'SUPPLY COMPANY' in White,
with rear window, GPW or BPW...........**£30-35**
Same but with SPW **£40-50**
Without rear window, GPW **£180-200**
Without rear window, BPW **£30-40**

60b 66 **Site Hut Truck**
Blue body, Yellow and Green plastic
building, Black plastic wheels...............**£20-25**

MB 61

61a 59 **Ferret Scout Car**
Olive Green body, Tan driver,
BPW, 57mm...**£15-20**

61b 66 **Alvis Stalwart 'BP'**
White body, Green wheels with BPT,
smooth carrier bed **£30-40**
Same but with ribbed carrier bed **£15-20**
White body, Yellow wheels, BPT **£15-25**
Two-Pack version: Military Olive Green
body, Black wheels **£20-30**

MB 62

62a 59 **AEC General Service Lorry**
Olive Green, tow hook, six BPW **£75-100**
Same but KBPW, rounded axles.............**£20-25**

62b 63 **Commer TV Service Van**
All have Cream body, Red plastic ladder,

aerial and 3 TVs. 'RENTASET',
knobbly Grey wheels (24 treads) **£300-400**
'RENTASET', SBPW and KBPW **£30-50**
'RENTASET',
45-tread Grey wheels **£100-130**
'RADIO RENTALS', BPW **£50-60**
'RADIO RENTALS',
fine tread Grey wheels **£450-550**

62c 68 **Mercury Cougar**
Cream body, White interior,
Chrome hubs. **£4,000-4,500**
Metallic Lime Green, Red interior.........**£10-20**

MB 63a Service Ambulance

MB 63

63a 59 **Service Ambulance (Ford)**
Olive Green body, Red crosses,
KBPW, CA..**£45-65**
Same but with fine tread BPW..............**£20-30**
Same but with rounded axles **£25-30**
Same but in rare type 'D' box with
colour picture **£100-125**

63b 63 **Alvis Foamite Crash Tender**
Red body, Silver nozzle,
six BPW, 63mm **£40-50**
With Gold hose nozzle **£60-80**

63c 68 **Dodge Crane Truck**
Yellow body, Red hook, 76mm **£10-15**
Yellow body, Yellow hook.....................**£15-20**
Same but in Spec T blister pack **£140-170**

MB 64

64a 59 **Scammell Breakdown Truck**
Olive Green body, metal or plastic
hook, Black plastic wheels, 64 mm........**£25-35**

64b 66 **MG 1100**
Green body, White seats, driver,
dog, Black plastic tyres, 67mm **£15-20**
Same but on Spec T blister pack **£110-140**

MB 65

65a 59 **Jaguar 3.4 litre**
Blue body, Silver rear no. plate, GPW ...**£40-60**
Same but with Blue rear no. plate **£35-50**
Dark Blue body, KGPW, CA **£100-125**
Same but with GPW............................**£80-100**
Met. Blue body & no. plate, GPW **£100-125**
Metallic Blue body, KGPW **£50-90**

65b 62 **Jaguar 3.4 Sedan**
Metallic Red body, Silver base,
Silver plastic wheels, 68mm **£120-140**
Red body, Grey plastic wheels..............**£50-60**
Red body, Black plastic wheels.............**£50-70**
Same but with SPW **£50-80**

65c 67 **Claas Combine Harvester**
Red body, Yellow blades and front
hubs, no hole in base.........................**£150-250**
Same but with hole in base **£10-12**
Red body, Yellow blades and hubs
with open ladder...............................**£200-240**

MB 66

66a 59 **Citroen DS 19**
Yellow body, Silver trim, GPW.............**£50-60**
Same but with SPW **£70-110**

66b 62 **Harley-Davidson Motor Cycle**
Metallic Bronze bike and sidecar,
spoked wheels, BPT **£70-90**

66c 66 **'GREYHOUND' Coach**
Silver-Grey body, CW, BPW **£60-80**
Silver-Grey body, AW, BPW **£10-15**
Same but on blister.................................. **£50-80**

MB 67

67a 59 **Saladin Armoured Car**
Olive Green body, six SBPW, CA,
'C' box **£35-45**
Same but with rounded axles,
'D' type box **£25-30**
Same but in 'E' type box......................... **£70-90**

67b 67 **Volkswagen 1600 TL**
Red body, Black wheels,
Silver hubcaps.. **£35-55**
Red body, Silver wheels with
black tyres... **£18-20**
Gift Set version:
Red body, Maroon plastic roof rack **£80-90**
Met. Purple, Chrome hubs, BPT........ **£300-400**

MB 68

68a 59 **Austin Radio Truck Mk.II**
Olive Green, KBPW, CA,
'B' type box.. **£30-35**
Same but with rounded axles **£40-60**
Same but in 'E' type box........................ **£100-125**
Green Grey body, fine tread BPW,
'D' box.. **£90-130**

68b 65 **Mercedes Coach** (all have BPW)
Turquoise/White body, US issue **£70-110**
Orange/White body.................................. **£20-30**

MB 69

69a 59 **Commer Van 'NESTLES'**
Maroon body, driver, Yellow logo,
Grey plastic wheels, 56mm **£45-55**
Same but with KBPW............................. **£40-60**
Red body, GPW with 20 treads **£70-100**
Red body, GPW with 36 treads **£200-250**

69b 65 **Hatra Tractor Shovel**
Orange body, Orange wheels,
Grey tyres, 78mm **£65-75**
With Red hubs, Grey tyres..................... **£30-40**
With Red hubs, Black tyres........ **No recent sale**
With Yellow hubs, Black tyres **£20-25**
Yellow body, Yellow hubs...................... **£20-30**
Yellow body, Red hubs **£100-120**
Orange body, Yellow shovel,
Yellow hubs, 'E' box **£1,700-1,900**

MB 70

70a 59 **Ford Thames Estate Car**
Turquoise and Yellow body,
Grey wheels, no windows...................... **£25-45**
Grey wheels, clear windows.................. **£40-50**
Grey wheels, Green windows................ **£25-30**

Silver wheels, clear windows **£40-60**
Silver or Black wheels, GW.................... **£35-40**

70b 66 **Ford Grit Spreader**
Red body, Primrose Yellow
container, Black slide, BPW **£25-30**
Red body, Lemon Yellow
container, Grey slide, BPW............... **£150-175**
Same but on Spec T blister pack **£90-120**

MB 71

71a 59 **200 gallon Austin Water Truck**
(with Collectors Badge)
Olive Green, BPW, with first
'Matchbox Collectors' badge **£50-100**
Same, but without badge **£50-70**
Same in type 'D' box with
colour picture **£300-400**

71b 64 **Jeep Gladiator Pick-Up**
Red body, Green int., BPW, 66mm....... **£30-40**
Red body, White interior........................ **£15-25**

71c 69 **Ford Heavy Wreck Truck** (all BPW)
Red and White body, Amber
windows, smooth loadbed................. **£400-500**
Same but with ribbed loadbed **£200-260**
Same but with Green windows.............. **£20-25**
Military Green body................................ **£20-25**

MB 72

72a 59 **Fordson Major Tractor**
All models with Blue body, 50mm.
Grey front wheels, Orange rear hubs, GPT. **£30-50**
Black front wheels,
Orange rear hubs, BPT **£35-45**
Orange hubs front/rear, Grey tyres........ **£40-45**
Orange hubs front/rear, BPT................. **£40-70**
Yellow hubs front/rear, GPT or BPT **£600-700**
Yellow rear hubs, Grey plastic
front wheels, type 'D' box............ **£2,000-2,500**

72b 66 **Jeep CJ5**
Orange-Yellow body, Yellow
hubs, White interior........................ **£800-1,000**
Yellow body and hubs, Red interior **£15-20**

MB 73

73a 59 **Leyland R.A.F. 10 ton Refueller**
Airforce-Blue, roundel, six GPW **£80-90**
Same but with KBPW.................. **£1,500-2,000**

73b 62 **Ferrari F1 Racing Car**
Red body, Grey or White driver,
RN '73', 'spoked' metal hubs, BPT.......... **£25-35**
In type 'D' box... **£60-80**

73c 68 **Mercury Commuter Station Wagon**
Met. Lime Green, Silver hubs, BPT **£10-15**

MB 74

74a 59 **Mobile 'REFRESHMENTS' Bar**
White body, Pale Blue base,
Blue interior, KGPW............................ **£250-300**
Cream body, Lt. Blue base, GPW......**£130-160**
Cream body, Blue base, GPW **£300-350**
Pinkish Cream body, Light Blue
base, Grey plastic wheels **£900-1,000**
Silver body, Lt. Blue base, GPW.......... **£50-100**
Same but with SPW **£130-160**
Silver body, Turquoise base, SPW **£250-300**
Silver body, Mid-Blue base,
KBPW **£800-1,000**
Same with SPW **£30-40**
Silver body, Sea Green or
Dark Blue base **£100-120**

74b 66 **Daimler Fleetline Bus**
Cream body, 'ESSO' decals **£15-20**
Cream body, 'ESSO' labels.................... **£30-35**
Green body, 'ESSO' labels 'F' box **£25-30**
Red body, 'ESSO' labels **£30-35**
Green, White interior,
'Esso Extra petrol', BPW, blister pack **£40-60**

MB 75

75a 60 **Ford Thunderbird** All have Cream
body and Peach side panels.
Blue base, SPW, Lesney 'C' box **£200-250**
Dark Blue base, SPW **£130-160**
Blue-Green base, SPW.......................**£200-300**
Black base, SPW **£70-80**
Black base, GPW **£120-150**
Black base, SBPW **£250-350**

75b 65 **Ferrari Berlinetta**
Metallic Green body, Silver base,
wire wheels, 'New Model' on
'E' type box **£300-400**
Same but unpainted base **£20-25**
Met.Green body, Silver wheels, BPT **£15-20**
Red body, chrome hubs with BPT.....**£200-300**
Red body, wire wheels.......................**£600-650**

Farm and breakdown models

Matchbox '1-75' Series Early Accessory Packs

A1   1957 **Service Ramp** Gold/Red, pictorial window box **£50-60**
A1a   1957 **'ESSO' Petrol Pump Set** Red pumps, White figure **£30-70**
A1b   1963 **'BP' Petrol Pump Set** White pumps **£25-45**

No 2 Accessory Pack and MB 32b 'E-type' Jaguar

A2   1957 **Car Transporter**
            Box type 1: Dark Blue/Yellow front and back
            'MOKO - LESNEY' line-drawing box.
            Box type 2: Yellow front/back, Blue end tabs,
            'LESNEY MATCHBOX SERIES' logo.
            1: Pale blue body, Dark Blue logo 'MATCHBOX
            CAR TRANSPORTER', metal wheels on tractor and
            trailer, 1st box **£60-70**
            2: Pale Blue body, Red 'CAR COLLECTION Ltd CAR
            TRANSPORTER', KBPW on tractor and trailer,
            1st type box **£80-120**
            3: Pale Blue body, Red 'CAR COLLECTION Ltd CAR
            TRANSPORTER', GPW on tractor and trailer,

            1st type box **£45-60**
            Same but with black lettering **£80-100**
            4: Red cab and lower deck, Grey upper deck and sides,
            BPW, Red logo: 'CAR COLLECTION Ltd' on
            Pale Yellow background, 2nd box **£300-350**
            Same but with 'CAR COLLECTION Ltd CAR TRANSPORTER' ......
            .... **£200-260**
A3   1957 **Garage** Yellow/Green/Red, opening doors,
            all metal with metal connecting clip, Moko box **£30-40**
            In late Lesney picture box **£40-50**

A4   1960 **Road Signs Set** Eight Red/White/Black signs,
            'Lesney' on base. Moko Lesney box **£30-50**
A5   1960 **'HOME STORES' Shop** Food shop with window
            display and opening door, Lesney box **£40-45**
MG1a 1959 **Service Station and Showroom** 'MATCHBOX GARAGE',
            Yellow base and roof sign, Red building, Moko box **£100-125**
            Red base and roof sign, Yellow building, Moko box **£50-60**
MG1b 1961 **'ESSO' Sales and Service Station** Red base,
            Yellow building, White/Red 'MATCHBOX SALES and
            SERVICE' plus clock. Lesney box **£190-220**
MG1b 1961 **'BP' Sales and Service Station** Green base, White building,
            Yellow/Green 'MATCHBOX SALES and SERVICE'.
            Lesney picture box with no background scene **£100-150**
MG1b 1961 **'BP' Sales and Service Station** As previous item,
            but late issue with roof sign labels instead of decals.
            Lesney detailed picture box with background scene
            (houses, cars, etc.) **£150-175**
MG1c 1968 **'BP' Service Station with forecourt pumps.** White
            building, 'BP AUTO SHOP', 'BP SELF-SERVICE CAFE',
            'MATCHBOX' decal in yellow/red **£40-60**
MF1a 1963 **Fire Station** White with Green roof,
            'MATCHBOX FIRE STATION' **£90-140**
            White with Red roof, wording on a Red background **£160-190**
            White with Red roof, wording on Brown background **£160-190**

Major Packs Series

M1 58 **Caterpillar Earthmover**
        Yellow body, MW, CA or RA **£35-45**
M1 63 **'BP' Petrol Tanker**
        Green/Yellow/White body,
        KBPW, Moko box......................... **£75-100**
        Smooth BPW, Lesney box............ **£30-40**
M2 58 **Bedford Articulated Truck**
        'WALLS ICE CREAM'
        All have a Light Blue tractor cab,
        101mm.
        Cream trailer, MW, Moko box **£60-80**
    59 Cream trailer, GPW, Moko box.... **£40-60**
    59-61 White trailer, GPW, Moko box **£75-85**
M2 61 **Bedford Tractor and York Trailer**
        'DAVIES TYRES'
        Orange cab, Silver trailer,
        clear windows, KBPW **£150-200**
        Green tinted windows, KBPW **£40-60**
        Green tinted windows, GPW ... **£125-150**
        Same but with KGPW, ... **£200-250**
        Black fine tread wheels
        (45 treads) **£45-65**
        Grey fine tread wheels
        (45 treads) **£200-250**
        Silver cab, Dark Red trailer,
        Black base................................ **£225-250**
M2 64 **Bedford Tractor and York Trailer**
        'LEP INTERNATIONAL'
        Silver cab, Maroon trailer,
        Dark Red base, SBPW.............. **£150-200**
        Silver cab, Dark Red trailer,
        Black base.................................... **£60-80**
M3 59 **Mighty Antar Tank Transporter**
        and Centurion Tank
        Both models in Military Green,
        Transporter has KBPW,
        tank has metal rollers.................. **£70-80**
        Transporter has SBPW,
        tank has metal rollers.................. **£70-80**

Transporter has SBPW,
tank has GPR............................. **£100-130**
Transporter has SBPW,
tank has BPR **£130-160**
M4 59 **Ruston Bucyrus Excavator**
        Maroon cab, Yellow shovel arms,
        Black base, Red decals 'Taylor
        Woodrow', Green or Grey tracks,
        Moko box.................................... **£75-100**
        Same but Yellow decals,
        'A Lesney Product' box.............. **£60-80**
        Same but the 2nd type of the
        'Lesney' box shows the model
        operating on the slew **£80-110**

Quarry vehicle models

M4 65 **'FREUHOF' Hopper Train**
        Maroon tractor, two Silver
        trailers, Red hubs, BPT **£60-80**
        With Red PH and GPT............. **£175-200**
M5 59 **'MASSEY FERGUSON 780'**
        Combine Harvester
        All with Red body, Yellow blades,
        driver.
        Red metal SW, SPW front,

KBPW rear, SRAB, Moko box **£70-90**
Same but bare metal SW,
in 'A Lesney Product' box............. **£70-90**
Same but Yellow plastic hubs,
in detailed colour picture box . **£200-250**
With bare metal SW, Orange PH on
front, SBPW rear, RACO **£75-100**
Same but Yellow plastic SW....... **£75-100**
With Yellow PSW, Orange PH
front/rear, RACO, late issue
detailed box.............................. **£125-150**
With Silver PH and Grey tyres
(front), rear KGPW, Red PSW,
straight rear axle bar.......... **£1,500-2,000**
M6 60 **Scammell Transporter**
        'PICKFORDS'
        Dark Blue tractor and drawbar,
        Maroon loadbed, KBPW,
        Moko box.................................... **£45-65**
        Dark Blue tractor, Red loadbed,
        Black drawbar, KBPW, in 'A
        Lesney Product' picture box.... **£250-300**
        Bright Blue tractor, Red loadbed,
        Black drawbar, KBPW,
        in 'A Lesney Product' box........... **£70-90**
        Same but with SBPW, in late
        issue detailed 'Lesney' box **£250-300**
M6 66 **Racing Car Transporter 'BP'**
        Green body, Silver ramp/rear door,
        Red hubs with BPT, 'Monza/Le
        Mans/Sebring/Nurburgring'
        on sides.................................... **£300-350**
        With 'Le Mans/Sebring/Silverstone/
        Nurburgring' on sides **£25-35**
M7 60 **Thames Trader Cattle Truck**
        'JENNINGS', Dark Red cab,
        Light Tan box trailer, KGPW......... **£60-70**
        With Dark Tan trailer, Red rear
        lamp, knobbly GPW **£70-100**

Same but with knobbly BPW **£50-70**
Same but Grey
45-tread wheels......................... **£130-150**
Same but Black
45-tread wheels......................... **£160-190**
Light Blue cab, base and rear ramp,
Metallic Copper back,
GPW.....................................**£2,000-3,000**

M8 61 'MOBILGAS' Petrol Tanker
Red body, White 'MOBILGAS'
logo, knobbly GPW.................... **£80-110**
With KBPW (24 treads) **£800-1,000**
With 45-tread BPW, in 'A Lesney
Product' late issue box **£1,000-1,250**
Same but in Moko box **£600-700**

M8 64 Guy Warrior Car Transporter
Blue-Green cab, Orange trailer, Orange
wheels with Grey tyres, 209 mm.
'FARNBOROUGH-MEASHAM'
in Black, White outline................. **£75-85**
'FARNBOROUGH-MEASHAM' in
White, Black outline **£50-60**

M9 62 Inter-State Double Freighter
'COOPER-JARRETT'.
Blue cab/central bogey, Grey trailers
and rear doors, Yellow decals,
detailed BPW,
1st type colour picture box **£140-170**
Blue cab/central bogey, Silver trailers,
Blue doors, Yellow decals,

2nd type picture box................. **£140-170**
Blue cab, bare metal central bogey,
Silver trailers and rear doors, SBPW,
detailed colour picture box...... **£140-170**
Same but with Orange decals...... **£60-80**

M10 62 Whitlock Dinkum Dumper
All have Yellow body.
With Bright Red PSW, bare
metal hubs, 'Lesney' box **£50-60**
With small Maroon PSW,
Red PH... **£35-50**
With large Maroon PSW,
Red PH... **£50-60**

Matchbox Presentation and Gift Sets

Presentation sets

The first presentation set was sold in the USA in 1957 and consisted of an enlarged normal 'Matchbox' containing eight of the 64 models that Lesney manufactured at that time. The first sets were not sold in the UK until 1959.

Ref	Year(s)	Set name and details	MPR
PS 1	1957	**Matchbox Presentation Set** Contains models 1 - 8 (only available in USA).	**£6,000-7,000**
PS 1	1959	**Private Owner Set** 19 MGA, 43 Hillman Minx, 45 Vauxhall Victor, A-3 Garage..............	**£750-1,000**
PS 2	1957	**Matchbox Presentation Set** Contains models 9 - 16 (only available in USA)	**£5,000-6,000**
PS 2	1959	**Transporter and 4 Cars Set** Contains 30 Ford, 31 Ford Station Wagon, 33 Ford Zodiac, 36 Austin A50, and an A-2 Transporter....	**£750-1,000**
PS 3	1957	**Matchbox Presentation Set** Contains models 17 - 24 (only available in USA).	**£5,000-6,000**
PS 3	1959	**Transporter and 6 Cars Set** 22 Vauxhall Cresta, 32 Jaguar XK, 33 Ford Zodiac, 43 Hillman Minx, 44 Rolls-Royce Silver Cloud, 45 Vauxhall Victor and an A-2 Transporter........	**£1,000-1,250**
PS 4	1957	**Matchbox Presentation Set** Contains models 25 - 32 (only available in USA).	**£5,000-6,000**
PS 4	1959	**Commercial Vehicle Set** Contains No.5 Bus, 11 Petrol Tanker, 21 Long Distance Coach, 25 'Dunlop' Van, 35 Horse Box, 40 Bedford Tipper, 47 'Brooke Bond' Van and 60 Morris Pickup	**£750-1,000**
PS 4	1959	**Lastwagen und Omnibuse** German version of PS4; same contents as British issue	**£750-1,000**
PS 5	1957	**Matchbox Presentation Set** Contains models 33 - 40 (only available in USA).	**£5,000-6,000**

Ref	Year(s)	Set name and details	MPR
PS 5	1959	**Army Personnel Carrier Set** M3 Personnel Carrier, 54 Saracen, 55 DUKW, 61 Ferret, 62 General Service Lorry, 63 Ambulance, M-3 Tank Transporter	**£450-550**
PS 6	1957	**Matchbox Presentation Set** Contains models 41 - 48 (only available in USA).	**£5,000-6,000**
PS 7	1957	**Matchbox Presentation Set** Contains models 49 - 56 (only available in USA).	**£5,000-6,000**
PS 8	1957	**Matchbox Presentation Set** Contains models 57 - 64 (only available in USA).	**£5,000-6,000**

Gift sets

The packaging for the first UK issued sets consisted of a frail blue box with a yellow lid panel on which were displayed (in red) the models making up the set. Sets in similar packaging were issued for the German market. Note however that contents may vary within the same type of box (the G4 Farm set listed below is an example). Please advise us of any other different model combinations you may have. NB - Sets containg rare variations will sell for higher prices than the MPR shown here. Each set needs to be priced on its contents.

Ref	Year(s)	Set name and details	MPR
GS 1	c1960	**Garage Set 'C'** 'MATCHBOX' Sales and Service Station (Red/Yellow), Roadway Layout, Accessories Pack No.1 (Esso petrol pumps), Accessory Pack No.2 (Car Transporter, Blue/Red lettering), Major Pack No.6 ('Pickfords' Transporter), 1-75 series models (5c, 29b, 31b, 42a, 45a, 46b, 57b, 74a). All models are individually boxed and housed in larger display box printed with 'MATCHBOX SERIES' and pictures of the garage and models, etc.	**£2,000-2,500**
G 1	60-61	**Commercial Motor Set** Contains: 5b 'Players Please', 20b, 37a (even load), 47a, 51a, 59a, 60a and 69a. (All models in G 1 had Grey plastic wheels)	**£550-600**
G 1	62-63	Commercial Vehicle Set 5c 'Visco-Static', 10c, 12b, 13c, 14c, 21c, 46b, 74a.......	**£350-450**
G 1	1965	**Motorway Set** 6, 10, 13, 33, 34, 38, 48, 55, 71 and R-1 layout.............	**£600-800**
G 1	1967	**Service Station Set** A1 Service Station and 'BP' Pump Set, 31c or 32c, 13d and 64b (or 56b) in pictorial display case....	**£150-200**
G 2	60-61	**Car Transporter Set** A-2 Transporter (metal wheels) and cars 22b, 25b, 33b, 39a, 57b and 75a	**£500-700**
G 2	60-61	**2nd issue:** A-2 Transporter (with Grey plastic wheels to tractor and Black plastic wheels to trailer), plus cars 7b, 22b, 25c, 27c, 57b and 75a......................	**£500-700**
G 2	62-63	**Car Transporter Set** Models 25b, 30b, 31b, 39b, 48b, 65b plus Accessory Pack No.2	**£500-600**
G 2	1965	**Car Transporter Set** (Mail Order issue) Contains 22c, 28c, 36c, 75b and Major Pack 8b	**£300-350**
G2	196?	**Car Transporter Set** Contains M8 Guy Warrior, turquoise cab, orange back/ hubs, grey tyres with 28c metallic Brown, 32b metallic Red, 44b metallic Mauve, 46c metallic Blue	**£300-350**
G 2	196?	As above but 28c metallic Bronze, 32b metallic Red, 44b metallic Mauve, 53b dark Red	**£400-450**
G 2	1967	**Transporter Set** Contains K8 Transporter, 14d, 24c, 31c and 53c	**£160-250**
G 3	60-61	**Building Constructors Set** Contains 2, 6, 15, 16, 18, 24, 28 and M-1	**£300-350**
G 3	62-63	**Constructional Plant Set** Contains 2, 6, 15, 16, 18, 24, 28 and M-1	**£240-280**
G 3	1965	**Vacation Set** Contains 12c, 23d, 27d, 42b, 45b, 56b, 68b, and Sports Boat on Trailer. Artwork on box	**£250-300**

G 3	1965	**Farming Set** (King-Size and Major Models)	Same but in plain white box with red lettering.........**£150-200**

G 3 | 1965 | **Farming Set** (King-Size and Major Models)
1st issue (with rare components):
Detailed picture box with transit card contains:
M5 Combine Harvester (SPH, KBPW on rear axle),
M7 Thames Trader with KBPW, K3 Caterpillar Tractor
with bare metal rollers, K11 Tractor and Trailer.
Orange metal hubs to both **£500-600**
2nd issue (with common components):
M5 Combine Harvester (Orange PH, SBPW on rear axle),
M7 Thames Trader with SBPW,
K3 Caterpillar Tractor with Red plastic rollers,
K11 Tractor and Trailer. Orange plastic hubs **£400-550**

G 3 | 1968 | **Farm Set**
Contains 4d, 12c, 37d, 40c, 39c, 43c, 65c and 72b......**£400-500**

G3 | 196? | Contains 4d, 12c, 37c, 40c, 43, 49c, 65c and 72b............**£80120**

G 4 | 60-61 | **Farm Set**
(1st issue) M-7 Cattle Truck (GPW), 12b Land Rover (BPW),
23b Berkeley Caravan (Lime Green, GPW),
31b Ford (Met.Green/Pink/Maroon/Yellow, SPW), 35a
Horse Box (MW), 50a Commer (Lt.Brown, SPW),
72a Fordson (Orange rear hubs, GPW) **£250-350**
(2nd issue) M-7 Cattle Truck (GPW), 12b Land Rover (BPW),
23c Bluebird Dauphine Caravan (Metallic Mauve, SPW),
31b Ford (Yellow, Maroon base, clear windows, SPW),
35a Horse Box (SPW), 50a Commer (SPW),
72a Fordson (Orange rear hubs, GPW) **£350-400**

G 4 | 1963 | **Grand Prix Set**
Contains 13c, 14c, 19c, 41b, 47b, 52a, 32b, 73b and
Major Pack No.1, R-4 Racetrack, instructions **£400-500**

G 4 | 1965 | **Grand Prix Racetrack Set**
13d, 19d Green, 19d Orange, 41c White, 41c Yellow,
52b Blue, 52b Red, 54b, Major Pack M-6 29c,
'BP Motor Racing' leaflet **£600-700**

G 4 | 1968 | **Race 'n' Rally Set**
19d Orange, 19d Green, 52b Blue, 52b Red, 29d,
3c, 41c, 67b, 25d, 8e **£250-300**

G 5 | 60-61 | **Military Vehicles**
Contains 54, 62, 63, 64, 67, 68 and M-3....................... **£250-300**

G 5 | 1963 | **Army Gift Set**
Contains 54a, 62a, 63a, 67a, 68a, 64a and

		Major Pack No.3 .... **£100-150**	

G 5 | 1965 | **Army Gift Set**
12, 49, 54, 61, 64, 67 and M-3 (picture box) **£250-300**

G 5 | 1965 | **Fire Station Set**
Contains MG1 Fire Station, 29c, 54b and 59c **£900-1,200**

G 6 | 1965 | **Commercial Trucks Set**
Usual contents (may vary): 6, 15, 16, 17, 26, 30,
58 and 62 ....**£600-700**

G 6 | 1966 | **Truck Set** 16c, 17d, 25c, 26b, 30c, 69b, 70b, 71b **£200-250**

G 9 | 1963 | **Major Series Set**
Contains Major Packs 1, 2, 4 and 6........................**£250-350**

G9 | ? | **Commercial Vehicles Gift Set.** M1 - BPW, Silver rear trim,
M2 - 'Davies Tyres' - Orange unit/rear doors, SBPW or KBPW,
M4 Excavator - Yellow side decals, metal rollers,
M6 Scammell - Maroon loadbed, colour picture box **£200-300**

G 9 | 1965 | **Service Station Set**
Contains 13, 33, 71, A-1, MG-1 ....**£300-350**

G 10 | 1963 | **Service Station Set**
Service Station, 13c, 25b, 31b + Accessory Pack No 1 ....**£500-600**

G 10 | 1965 | **Fire Station Set**
Contains MF-1, 14, 59, 2 of No 9..............................**£300-400**

FB 5 | 1969 | **Matchbox Traffic Game**
Contains two cars (No.45 Ford Corsair and
No.56 Fiat 1500) plus game board, etc......................**£175-200**

? | ? | **'GAF' Racing Car Game**
Belgian game set contains four 24d 'TEAM MATCHBOX'
racing cars including the rare Metallic Blue and Yellow
variants. Set issued by 'GAF', not by Matchbox. **£300-400**

TG 7037 | | **Gift Pack** (US issue)
MG1 'BP' Service Station (1st issue); R1 Layout;
3c Ambulance; 5d Bus ('BP' labels); 9d Cabin Cruiser;
'BP' Wreck Truck; 14d Iso Grifo; 23d Caravan; 29c Fire
Pumper; 36c Opel; 'BP' Tanker; 34c VW Camper; 44c GMC
Truck; Red and Yellow square 'GIFT PACK' box **£500-600**

? | ? | **Display Set** (US issue for the Fred Bronner Corporation)
Contents: 26c GMC Tipper Truck; Leyland 'BP' Tanker;
45b Ford Corsair; 46c Mercedes 300SE Coupé; 68b Mercedes
Coach. Contained in interlocking 'see-thru' display case,
shrink-wrapped 'DISPLAY SET' box **£400-500**

? | 1969 | **Display Set** (US issue)
12c, 24c, 30c, 46c, 47c. In plastic display case **£300-400**

'King-Size' gift sets

--- | 1963 | **King-Size Set** K1-1, K2-1, K3-1, K5-1, K6-1 .... **£300-350**
--- | 1965 | **Construction Set** K16-1, K7-1, K10-1,K13-1,K14-1 .. **£200-300**
G 3 | 1965 | **Farming Set** (King-Size and Major Models)
1st issue (with rare components): Detailed picture box with
transit card contains: M5 Combine Harvester (SPH, KBPW on
rear axle), M7 Thames Trader with KBPW, K3 Caterpillar
Tractor with bare metal rollers, K11 Tractor and Trailer.
Orange metal hubs to both **£1,200-1,500**
2nd issue (with common components): M5 Combine
Harvester (Orange PH, SBPW on rear axle), M7 Thames
Trader with SBPW, K3 Caterpillar Tractor with Red plastic

		rollers, K11 Tractor and Trailer. Orange plastic hubs **£400-500**	

G8 | 1965 | **Commercials Set**
K1 Tipper, K11-1 Tractor, K12-1 BP Truck, K15-1 ...... **£200-250**

G8 | 1965 | **Construction Set**
K1 Tipper, K7 Rear Dumper, K10 Shovel,
K13 'Readymix', K14 .... **£150-220**

G8 | 19?? | **King Size Models**
K-71 Rear Dumper, K-101 Tractor Shovel,
K13-1 Concrete Truck, K14-1 Jumbo Crane and
K1-2 Tipper Truck 'Hoveringham' **£225-275**

--- | 1966 | **King-Size Set** K11-1, K12-1, K15-1, K16-1 .... **£200-300**

Matchbox 'King-Size' Series 1960–1970

Following successful sales of Major Models, Lesney Products decided to further develop the range by introducing a larger scale toy. The name chosen was 'King-Size'. In 1966 the popular Major Models were discontinued in name but were themselves built into the King-Size range.

Model and details	MPR	Model and details	MPR	Model and details	MPR
K1-1 60 **Hydraulic Shovel** Yellow body, GPW, 'WEATHERILL. '**£40-45**				K2-2 64 **Dumper Truck** Yellow body, 'KW DART' logo, 6 Red wheels, BPT..........................**£40-50**	
K1-2 63 **Foden Tipper Truck** Red cab and chassis, Orange tipper, 'HOVERINGHAM', Green suspension .... **£80-100** White suspension .... **£80-100** **NB** 'HOVERINGHAM GRAVELS LTD' issued models in their own outer box to their customers................ **£300-400**				K2-3 68 **Scammell Wreck Truck** White body, Red jib and wheels, Grey hook, 'ESSO' ....**£35-45** 71 Gold body version...........................**£70-80**	
K1-3 71 **'O & K' Excavator** Red body, Silver shovel, TW, BPT . **£35-45**				K3-1 60 **Caterpillar Bulldozer** Yellow body, Red engine, bare metal rollers ....**£30-50** Same but Red metal rollers............**£70-80** Same but Yellow metal rollers........**£70-80** Same but Red plastic rollers **£70-100**	
K2-1 60 **Dumper Truck** Red body, 'MUIR HILL 14B', Black or Green MW........................ **£40-50**				K3-2 65 **'HATRA' Tractor Shovel** Orange body, Red wheels...............**£50-60** K3-3 70 **'MASSEY FERGUSON'**	

K-13 Concrete mixer truck

Tractor and Trailer
Red body, Yellow trim £60-70
K4-1 60 **'McCORMICK**
      INTERNATIONAL' Tractor
      Red body, Green wheels £50-60
      Same but Red plastic hubs........... £50-60
      Large hook, Orange PH £150-175
K4-2 67 **GMC Tractor and Hoppers**
      'FREUHOF'
      Dark Red cab, 2 Silver hoppers,
      BPT, slide-tray box £40-50
      GPT, window box £100-120
K4-3 69 **Leyland Tipper 'W. WATES'**
      Maroon cab, Silver tipper.............. £30-40
      Same but Yellow/Green £750-1,000
      Red cab, Green tipper.................... £50-60
      Orange cab, Lime Green tipper £80-90
      Same but Met. Green tipper......... £80-90
      Lime Green cab and tipper £300-400
      Blue cab, Silver tipper, 'Miner'...... £60-70
      With 'LE TRANSPORT' label.......... £30-40
K5-1 61 **Foden Dump Truck**
      Orange Yellow body and tipper, Red
      wheels, 'FODEN' logo................ £100-125
      Dark yellow cab,
      Light yellow tipper £120-140
      Yellow cab, yellow tipper............... £30-40
K5-2 67 **Racing Car Transporter**
      Green body, Silver drop down
      rear door, Red wheels £55-65
K5-3 70 **Tractor and Trailer 'MUIR HILL'**
      Yellow body, Red chassis............... £35-40
K6-1 61 **Earth Scraper**
      'ALLIS CHALMERS'
      Orange body, bare metal hubs £55-65
      Matt Orange, bare metal hubs £55-65
      Bright Orange, bare metal hubs £55-65
      Bright Orange, red hubs £50-60
K6-2 67 **Mercedes Ambulance**
      Off-White body, Red badge,
      ambulance-man, stretcher £25-30
K7-1 61 **Rear Dumper 'CURTISS-WRIGHT'**
      Yellow body, Red engine £45-50
K7-2 67 **S&D Refuse Truck**
      Red, decals, 1st window box £30-40
      Red, labels, 2nd window box £30-40
      72 Blue body version £60-70

K8-1 Prime Mover and Caterpiller Tractor

K8-1 62 **Prime Mover and Transporter**
      with Crawler Tractor 'LAING'
      Orange bodies, thick print 'Laing'
      decals, bare metal hubs. With 'Laing'
      'Civil Engineering Contractors' on
      trailer, square door decals, Tractor
      has bare metal rollers £150-200

Large lettered 'Laing' decals, bare
metal hubs. With 'Laing', without
'Civil Engineering Contractors' on
trailer, rectangular door decals,
Tractor has bare metal rollers,
colour picture box...................... £300-350
With bare metal hubs, thin lettered
'Laing' decals and the Tractor has
red plastic rollers, colour box £120-140
Thin lettered 'Laing' decals, red plastic
hubs and red or orange plastic
rollers £100-120
K8-2 67 **Guy Warrior Transporter**
      'FARNBOROUGH - MEASHAM'
      Turquoise/Orange, Orange PH...... £40-50
      Yellow, Red PH £40-50
      Dark Aqua cab,Yellow trailer...... £100-140
K8-3 70 **'CATERPILLAR TRAXCAVATOR'**
      Yellow body, Orange rams £175-200
      72 Silver body.................................... £50-60
K9-1   **'AVELING BARFORD'**
      Diesel Road Roller Green body,
      Red wheels and Red driver £40-70
      Same, but with Grey driver £90-120
K9-2 67 **'CLAAS' Combine Harvester**
      Red body,
      Yellow blades and wheels £50-50
      Green body, Red blades/wheels.... £30-50
K10-1 63 **'AVELING BARFORD'**
      Tractor Shovel Blue/Green body,
      bare metal hubs, detailed picture
      box with Red end flaps £50-70
      Same but Red plastic hubs, late issue
      box, picture on the end flaps. £60-85
K10-2 66 **Pipe Truck.** Yellow body,
      Red wheels, 6 Grey pipes £45-65
      ('Super-Kings' issue) Purple
      body, Grey or Yellow pipes £25-30
K11-1 63 **'FORDSON SUPER MAJOR'**
      Tractor and Trailer
      Blue tractor, Grey/Blue trailer,
      bare metal steering wheel.............. £40-50
      With Blue metal steering wheel..... £40-50
K11-2 69 **DAF Car Transporter**
      Yellow body, Yellow/Red decks £60-70
      Metallic Blue body, Gold decks £60-70
K12-1 63 **Foden Breakdown Truck**
      Green, Silver grille/headlights,
      'Matchbox Service Station' decal,
      Red plastic hubs, window box £45-55
      Same but Silver grille only,
      colour picture box........................ £80-100
      Silver Grille only, bare metal
      hubs, colour picture box £100-130
K12-2 69 **Scammell Crane Truck**
      Yellow, 'LAING' on crane,
      Red or Black plastic ram £40-50
      71 Silver body.................................... £60-70
K13-1 63 **ERF Concrete Truck 'READYMIX'**
      Orange body and barrel,
      bare metal or Red PH £30-50
      Same but with 'RMC' logo £30-50
K14-1 64 **Jumbo Crane**
      Yellow body and crane,
      'TAYLOR JUMBO CRANE',
      Red or Yellow ballast box £10-25

K15-1 64 **Merryweather Fire Engine**
      Dark or Bright Red body, Silver ladder,
      'KENT FIRE BRIGADE'.................. £40-50
K16-1 66 **Tractor and Twin Tippers**
      Green cab, Yellow tippers,
      'DODGE TRUCKS' in Red £60-80
      Yellow cab, Blue tippers,
      same logo (Superfast).................... £60-65
K17-1 67 **Ford D800 Low Loader / Bulldozer**
      Green cab /trailer, 'LAING', clear
      plastic suspension, Red/Green 'Case'
      Bulldozer (red or green plastic rollers),
      'New Model' window box.............. £50-75
K17-2 71 **Same but 'TAYLOR WOODROW'**
      with screwed baseplate, dozer has
      Yellow plastic rollers. In tall
      window box £60-75
      Same but Light Blue plastic
      suspension, short window box £30-35
      Same but Yellow suspension,
      pictorial window box £65-75
      Same nut White suspension,
      pictorial window box.................. £120-140
K18-1 66 **Kew Fargo Articulated Horse Box**
      'ASCOT STABLES', all versions have Red
      cab, 4 White horses, and were sold in
      window boxes. Cream/Silver Trailer,
      Yellow / Grey trailer interior, cab has
      decals, labels on trailer,
      'New Model' window box.............. £45-55
      Grey or Red trailer interior............ £70-80
      Green or Grey-Green interior £45-55
K19-1 67 **Scammell Tipper**
      Red body, Yellow tipper,
      Clear or Green suspension............. £30-40
K20-1 68 **Ford D800 Tractor Transporter**
      Red body, Yellow or Red tank, 3 Blue/
      Yellow tractors (MB39c),
      Clear or Green suspension......... £60-70
      Same but Orange tractors £120-150
      71 Blue cab £180-200
K21-1 69 **Mercury Cougar**
      Gold body, Cream seats £30-50
      Gold body, Red seats £130-150
K22-1 69 **Dodge Charger**
      Blue body, Yellow or Pale Blue seats £30-40
K23-1 69 **Mercury 'POLICE' Car**
      White, 'HIGHWAY PATROL' £25-35
K24-1 69 **Lamborghini Miura**
      Red body, Cream seats £25-50

Matchbox King Size diecasts: K-5, K-1, K-12 and K-13.

'Super-Kings' and 'Speed-Kings' Series 1971–1980

After 1970 the 'King Size' range developed into the larger 'Super-Kings' Series. They were fitted with extra wide speed slick tyres.
   During the period 1971-79 certain issues were sold as 'SPEED KINGS' and retailed in different coloured packaging. These have been identified in the listings by the abbreviation (SPK).

Market Price Range. In general 'Super-Kings' are not very collectable and most models may be purchased for under £15. However, a little more price information on some of the rarer items has been received since the previous Edition and this is shown where appropriate. We regret we are unable to provide more specific price information on the remainder at this time. Further information on the rare issues and price levels would be welcomed.

K2 77 **'24 HOUR' Recovery** £25-35	K4 74 **Big Tipper,** blue/silver £60-70	K6 74 **Motor Cycle Transporter,** 'HONDA' £30-35
K3 74 **Mod Tractor / Trailer**........................ £25-35	K5 72 **Muir Hill Tractor and Trailer,**	K7 73 **Transporter,** 'TEAM MATCHBOX' ... £30-35
K3 74 **Grain Transporter,**	Yellow £25-30	74 With 'Martini' labels £45-50
Green cab (German)............................ £60-70	Blue (German) £60-70	K9 73 Fire Tender 'DENVER' £30-35
74 Red, 'KELLOGGS' £20-25	K6 76 **Cement Mixer,** blue £20-25	K10 76 **Transporter,** 'AUTO TRANSPORT' .. £30-35

K11 76 **Recovery Truck,**
'SHELL RECOVERY' **£50-60**
76 **Recovery Truck in Red** **£70-80**
K12 75 **Hercules** 'LAING' Crane **£50-60**
K13 71 **Building Transporter,** 'DAF' **£30-35**
K13 76 **Aircraft Transporter** **£20-30**
K14 71 **Scammell Freight** 'LEP' **£30-40**
K14 77 **Breakdown Truck,** 'SHELL' **£20-30**
K15 71 **Merryweather Fire**
Engine, KENT **£70-80**
K15 73 **Londoner Bus issues.**
'HARRODS - ENTER A
DIFFERENT WORLD' **£10-20**
'CARNABY STREET' **£10-20**
'SILVER JUBILEE', ...**£10-20**
'HARRODS - MORE THAN MONEY' **£10-20**
'LONDON DUNGEON' **£10-20**
'HAMLEYS' **£10-20**
'ROYAL WEDDING 81' **£10-20**
'LONDON WIDE TOUR' **£10-20**
'TELEGRAPH&ARGUS' **£10-20**
'MACLEANS' **£10-20**
'HERITAGE OF ENGLAND' **£10-20**
'BUTTERKIST' **£10-20**
'TOURIST LONDON' **£10-20**
'FIRESTONE' **£10-20**
'CHESTERFIELD 1984' **£10-20**
'LONDON PLANETARIUM' **£10-20**
'PETTICOAT LANE' **£10-20**
'NESTLES MILKY BAR' **£10-20**

Matchbox Superkings No K7 Racing Car Transporter group of 3 (1) 'Martini Racing' - white, (2) 'Team Matchbox' - yellow, amber canopy and (3) same as (2) but clear canopy, No K6 'Team Honda' Pick-up Truck - a pair (1) metallic blue, amber windows and roof-light, complete with Motorbike and (2) same as (1) but dark blue with chrome engine.

K16 74 **Ford LTS Tanker,**
'TEXACO', 'CHEMCO', 'LEP', 'ARAL',
'SHELL', 'EXXON', 'TOTAL', 'QUAKER STATE'
'U.S. M/BOX CLUB' **£20-30**
75 With 'BP' labels **£200-300**
K16 **Dodge Tractor,** Yellow/ Blue tippers.**£100-120**
K17 **Container Truck**
'DBP', 'PENGUIN', '7 UP', 'GENTRANSCO' **£30-50**
'TAYLOR WOODROW' **£60-70**
K18 74 **Tipper Truck**
'TARMAC', 'US STEEL', 'HOCH & TIEF' ... **£30-40**
K19 79 **Security Truck**
'GROUP 4', 'FORT KNOX' **£30-40**
K20 73 **Cargo Hauler** **£30-35**
K20 79 **Peterbilt** 'HEAVY DUTY' **£30-35**
K21 71 **Cougar Dragster** (SPK)...................
In Pink, Purple or Crimson **£40-60**
K21 74 **Tractor Transporter** **£30-40**
K21 79 **Ford Transcontinental**
'CONTINENTAL', 'DANZAS',
'POLARA', 'SUNKIST' **£30-35**

K22 71 **Dodge Dragster** (SPK) **£50-60**
K22 74 **Hovercraft,**
'SEASPEED' **£30-40**
'HOVERLLOYD' **£30-40**
All-white **£40-50**
K23 71 **Mercury 'POLICE' Car,** (SPK).........**£40-50**
K23 74 **Low Loader,** 'HOCH & TIEF'.........**£30-40**
K24 71 **Lamborghini Muira** **£20-30**
K24 77 **Scammel Truck**
'LONDON TO GENEVA' **£30-40**
'MICHELIN' **£30-40**
'GENTRANSCO' **£30-40**
'BAUKNECT' **£30-40**

K25 Boat on Trailer - (1) 'Chrysler' - orange, white hull, yellow trailer and (2) same as (1) but 'Seaburst.'

K25 77 **Powerboat and Trailer**
'SEABURST' **£30-35**
'CHRYSLER' **£30-35**
K25 78 **Digger,** 'MUIR HILL' **£20-30**
K26 71 **Mercedes Ambulance** (SPK) **£30-40**
K26 78 **Bedford Cement Truck** 'McALPINE'
'HOCH & TIEF' **£30-40**
K27 71 **Camping Cruiser** **£20-30**
K27 78 **Powerboat Transporter**
'EMBASSY' **£40-50**
'MISS SOLO' **£40-50**
K28 71 **Drag Pack** (SPK) **£50-60**
K28 78 **Bedford Skip Truck**
'HOCH & TIEF' **£25-35**
'HALES' **£25-35**
K29 71 **Muira 'SEABURST' Set,** (SPK).........**£50-60**
K29 77 **Ford Delivery Van,** 'U-HAUL', 'AVIS',
'TAA', 'Mr SOFTY', 'BASSETTS' **£30-35**
K30 72 **Mercedes C111** **£20-30**
K30 78 **Unimog/Compressor** **£20-30**
K31 72 **Bertone Runabout** (SPK) **£20-30**
K31 78 **Peterbilt Refrigeration Truck**
'CHRISTIAN SALVESON', 'BURGER
KING', 'IGLOO', 'GERVAIS GLACE', 'PEPSI',
'DR KOCH'S TRINK',
'DURA PENTA' (S. African) **£30-40**
K32 71 **Shovel Nose** **£20-30**
K33 78 **Cargo Hauler** **£20-30**
K34 72 **Thunderclap** (SPK) **£20-30**
K34 79 **Pallet Truck** **£20-30**
K35 72 **Lightning** (SPK) **£20-30**
Same but with Flameout **£60-70**
K35 79 **Massey Ferguson Tractor**
and Trailer **£50-75**
K36 72 **Bandolero** (SPK) **£20-30**
K36 78 **'LAING' Transporter** **£40-50**
K37 73 **Sandcat** (SPK) **£20-30**
K37 79 **Leyland Tipper** 'LAING' **£30-40**
K38 74 **Gus's Gulpher** (SPK) Green **£30-40**

Same In white **£200-250**
K39 73 **'MILLIGANS MILL'** (SPK) **£30-40**
K40 73 **Blaze Trailer** 'FIRE CHIEF' (SPK) ...**£25-35**
K41 73 **Fuzz Buggy** 'POLICE' (SPK) **£25-35**
K41 78 **Brabham F1** (SPK) **£20-30**
K42 73 **Nissan 270X** (SPK) **£20-30**
K42 79 **Traxcavator Road Ripper** **£20-30**
K43 73 **'CAMBUSTER'** (SPK) **£40-50**
K44 73 **'BAZOOKA'** (SPK) **£40-50**
K44 78 **Surtees F1** **£20-30**
K45 73 **Marauder** (SPK) **£20-30**
K46 74 **Racing Car pack** with K34 and K35..**£35-45**
K47 73 **Easy Rider Trike** (SPK) **£30-40**
K48 74 **Mercedes 350,** (SPK) **£20-30**
K49 73 **Ambulance** (SPK) **£20-30**
K49 74 **'MALTESER' Truck** **£20-30**
K50 74 **Street Rod** (SPK) **£20-30**
K51 73 **Barracuda** (SPK) **£20-30**
K52 73 **Datsun Rally** (SPK) **£20-30**
K53 76 **Hot Fire Engine** (SPK) **£20-30**
K54 76 **AMX Javelin** (SPK) **£20-30**
K55 76 **Corvette 'CAPER CART'** (SPK)........**£40-50**
K56 76 **Maserati Bora** (SPK) **£20-30**
K57 76 **Javelin Drag Racing Set,**
K38 & K39 (SPK) **£30-40**
K58 76 **Corvette Power Boat Set,**
K45 etc. (SPK) **£30-40**
K59 76 **Ford Capri II** (SPK) **£30-40**
K60 76 **Ford Mustang** (SPK) **£20-30**
K61 76 **Mercedes 'POLICE'** (SPK) **£20-30**
78 **Mercedes 'POLIZEI'** (SPK) **£20-30**
K62 77 **Doctors Car** (SPK) **£20-30**
K63 77 **Mercedes 'Binz'**
'AMBULANCE' (SPK) **£20-30**
K64 78 **'FIRE CONTROL'**
Range Rover (SPK) **£20-30**
K65 78 **Plymouth Mountain Rescue**
'EMERGENCY RESUCE' **£50-60**
'BERGRETTUNG WACHT' **£50-60**
K66 79 **Jaguar 'POLICE' Set** **£20-30**
K67 79 **Dodge Monaco** (SPK)
i) 'FIRE CHIEF' **£20-30**
ii) 'HACKENSACK' **£20-30**
K68 78 **Dodge Monaco and Trailer** (SPK) ...**£30-40**
K69 78 **Jaguar XJ12 and Caravan** (SPK).......**£40-50**
K70 79 **Porsche Turbo** **£20-30**
K71 79 **Porsche 'POLIZEI' Set** **£20-30**
K72 79 **Brabham F1,** Red or Green **£20-30**
K73 79 **Surtees F1,**
White or Tan **£20-30**
K74 79 **Volvo Estate** **£20-30**
K75 79 **Airport 'FIRE' Rescue**
'AIRPORT FIRE TENDER' **£20-30**
'FLUGHAFEN-FEURWEHR' **£20-30**
'SECURITE AEROPORT' **£20-30**
K76 79 **Volvo Rally Set** 'CIBIE' **£20-30**
K77 79 **Rescue Vehicle**
'STRASSEN SERVICE' **£20-30**
'SECOURS ROUTIER' **£20-30**
'HIGHWAY RESCUE' **£20-30**
K78 79 **US Police Car,** POLICE',
'POLIZEI' or 'CITY POLICE' **£20-30**
K79 79 **US Taxi** **£20-30**

'Battle-Kings', 1974

Models packed in 'window' boxes. Each has a 'military' theme and includes three plastic soldiers. Expect to pay **£20-25** for any of these items.
K101 **Sherman Tank** ....
K102 **M48 AS Tank** ....
K103 **Chieftain Tank** ....
K104 **King Tiger Tank** ....
K105 **Hover Raider** ....
K106 **Tank Transporter** ....
K107 **155mm Gun** ....
K108 **Half Track** ....
K109 **Sheridan Tank** ....
K110 **Recovery Vehicle** ....
K111 **Missile Launcher** ....

Matchbox Battlekings No K110 Recovery Vehicle

K112 **DAF Ambulance** ....
K113 **Crane Truck** ....
K114 **Army Aircraft Transporter** ....
K115 **Petrol Tanker** ....
K116 **Troop Carrier and Howitzer** ....
K116 **Troop Carrier and Howitzer** ....
K117 **Rocket Launcher** ....
K118 **Army Helicopter** ....

'Sea-Kings', 1976

These models were packed in 'window' boxes. Expect a Market Price of **£12-18** for any of these 'Sea-Kings'.
K301 **Frigate** 'F109' ....
K302 **Corvette** 'C70' ....
K303 **Battleship** '110' ....

Matchbox Seakings (1) No K303 Battleship, (2) No K304 Aircraft Carrier, (3) No K305 Submarine Chaser, (4) No K306 Convoy Escort, (5) No K307 Helicopter and (6) No K308 Guided Missile Destroyer.

K304 **Aircraft Carrier with 4 aircraft '36'** ....
K305 **Submarine Chaser** ....
K306 **Convoy Escort** ....
K307 **Helicopter Carrier** ....
K308 **Missile Destroyer** ....
K309 **Submarine '117'** ....
K310 **Anti Air Carrier** ....

'Big MX', 1972 -74

Special packaging contained models and accessories powered by an 'Activator Gun' which plugged into them and operated the mechanisms.
MX1 Incinerator Site + K7
Refuse Truck.. **£50-70**
BM2 Mechanised Tractor Plant
Transporter (K20-1 Ford), blue/yellow
MB39c Tractors.. **£70-80**

with Orange MB39c Tractors.................. **£175-225**
BM3 Mechanised (K12 Scammell) **Crane Truck** and Building Site........................ **£50-70**
BM4 Mechanised Coal Delivery Hopper and (K4 Leyland) Tipper......................... **£50-70**
BM5 Mechanised Quarry Site and (K8, silver/red) Traxcavator............................ **£40-50**
BM6 Fire Rescue Scene
with mechanised (K15 Merryweather)
Fire Engine plus 4 figures and
scenery **£120-140**

Matchbox Shop Display Items

Item and details	MPR
1956 **Counter Display.** Wood and card, yellow shelves, dark blue/yellow headboard 'MATCHBOX SERIES', '1/8d each' plus red 5a Double-Decker Bus. Will display all 1-75 models	**£700-800**
1960 **Counter Display.** Card, yellow shelves, dark blue headboard, 'MATCHBOX SERIES' in yellow, '1/9d' plus 85a Jaguar 3.4 in red	**£200-250**
1965 **'King-Size' carded Counter Display.** Showing K16 Dodge Tractor model. Yellow/red/white	**£200-300**
1965 **Carded Counter Display Stand.** 'MATCHBOX' King-Size. White shelves, dark blue surround 'Die Cast Metal - Authentic Scale Models'. Holds K1 - K18. (US Fred Bronner issue)	**£200-300**
Late 1960s **'MATCHBOX' Illuminated Display Sign.** Finished in yellow/red/blue (270 x 100 x 120mm)	**£400-500**
1962 **Card Display Stand. Wood frame.** Displays complete Regular Wheels range. Dark blue/yellow headboard with yellow stepped dislay area. 'MATCHBOX SERIES' '1/9'. Features 65b Jaguar 3.8	**£250-350**
1967 **Card Display Stand.** Displays complete Regular Wheels range. 'MATCHBOX NOS. 1 - 75', flyover design	**£200-250**
1967 **Plastic Revolving Display Unit.** Red/Yellow/White. Designed to display all 75 Regular Wheels models	**£200-250**

Fred Bronner Corp. U.S. issues (1-75)

Item and details	MPR
1955 **Card Display Stand.** Pale Blue with Black lettering. Features first 12 models plus Miniature Covered Wagon	**£400-500**
-- **Display Unit.** 1950/60s, holds 75 models at '55c each'	**£800-900**
1961 **Card Display Stand** for 'MATCHBOX SERIES Major Packs and Accessory Packs' which contains models A1 - A4, and M1 - M8. Dark Blue/Yellow/Red headboard features Major Pack 4 Ruston Bucyrus Excavator	**£600-800**
	Stand without the models	**£250-350**
1963 **Card Display Stand.** 'MILITARY MATCHBOX SERIES'. Green/Orange headboard, beige stepped display area containing actual models M3, 12b, 49a, 54a, 61a, 63a, 64a 67a, 68a	**£900-1,100**
	Display stand without the models	**£250-350**
1964 **Aluminium Display Stand.** 'MATCHBOX SERIES' in Red. Features 53b Mercedes 220SE Coupé	**£250-350**
1965 Card Display Stand. 'AUTHENTIC MATCHIES', '49c EACH'	**£200-250**

Item and details	MPR
1966 **Card Display Stand.** 'AUTHENTIC MATCHIES', '55c EACH'	**£200-250**
1967 **Wood Framed Display Stand** to display complete range. Red 'MATCHBOX SERIES', black/white 'NOS. 1-75'	**£200-250**
1968 **Card Display Stand.** Dark blue/red with yellow shelving. Features Red 53b Mercedes 220SE Coupé. 'MATCHLESS MATCHBOX SERIES'	**£350-450**
1968 **Card Dispenser Stand** for 24 models, Red/Yellow/Blue 'MATCHBOX', 'ONLY 55c EACH'	**£200-250**
1968 **Card Display Stand** containing the complete 1 - 75 range. Red/Yellow/Blue with White shelving, 'MATCHLESS MATCHBOX SERIES'	**£1,200-1,400**
	Display Stand without models	**£300-400**
1968 **Card Counter Display.** Holds all 1-75 Regular Wheels issues. 'MATCHLESS MATCHBOX SERIES' on dark blue headboard plus red 85a Jaguar 3.4. Yellow shelves with red surround 'Ask For Free Catalogue', '55c'	**£700-1,000**

Unusual 12 model display set

West German Issues

	MPR
58-60 **Single Model Counter Display.** (German). Yellow/blue/red card stand 'MATCHBOX AUTOS' with 44a Rolls-Royce. 'Neuigkeiten Dieses Monats'	**£400-500**
1960 **Card Counter Display.** 5 tiers, yellow/dark blue 'MATCHBOX SERIES' in yellow, '1 DM'	**£300-400**

Italian Issue

	MPR
1968 **Vac-form Display Stand.** Yellow/Red/Black withwhite shelving 'BARAVELLI MATCHBOX BARAVELLI'	**£150-200**

Models of Yesteryear U.K. issues

	MPR
1965 Wooden Counter Display. Red letters with Yellow shelves designed to display Models of Yesteryear 1 – 16,	

Item and details	MPR
	King Size 1 – 15 and Major Pack models 1 – 6. 'MATCHBOX' in Red plus 'NEW RELEASES'	**£400-500**
56-60 **Card Display Stand.** 'Models of Yesteryear SERIES'. Dark Blue/Red/Yellow headboard, yellow display area designed to display 1st Series models Y1 - Y9 inclusive	**£400-600**
56-60 **Card Display Stand.** 'Models of Yesteryear SERIES'. Dark Blue/Red/Yellow headboard, yellow 'stepped' area to display models Y1 - Y15 inclusive. 'A LESNEY PRODUCT' in red letters	**£500-700**
c.1960 **Card Display Stand.** Red/Yellow/Blue with four shelves designed to display models Y1 - Y16 inclusive. 'MATCHBOX' in red letters	**£250-300**
c1966 **Card Display Stand.** Big Ben and a Packard Landaulet are featured on headboard. Displays Y1-Y16. 'MATCHBOX'	**£200-250**
c1968 **Gold/White Plastic Wall Display Unit** in the shape of a radiator grille - shelves contain Y1-Y16 models, 'MATCHBOX' in black letters	**£275-325**
	Display Unit without models	**£100-125**
1970s **924276 Plastic Display Case** for Y1-Y16 'MATCHBOX MODELS OF YESTERYEAR' in top panel. Gold/cream vac-formed, clear perspex front	**£80-100**

Fred Bronner Corp. U.S. issues (MoY)

	MPR
c1958 **Card Display Stand.** Containing 1st Series models Y1 - Y15. Dark Blue/Yellow/Red headboard design which features a Y13 Sante Fe Locomotive emerging from a 1st type box	**£800-1,000**
	Stand without the models	**£300-400**
c1960 **Card Display Stand** containing 2nd Series models Y1- Y16. Dark Blue surround featuring a Red Y15 Rolls-Royce emerging from a 2nd type box, yellow shelving 'MATCHBOX'	**£450-650**
	Stand without the models	**£200-300**
c1956-60 **Card Display Stand.** Models of Yesteryear SERIES'. Dark Blue/Red/Yellow headboard, yellow display area designed to display 1st Series models Y1 - Y9 inclusive	**£400-600**
c1967 **Card Display Stand** containing models Y1-16. Yellow/Red/ Blue design which features a White Y4 Opel Coupé. 'MATCHBOX' 'START YOUR COLLECTION NOW'	**£300-400**
	Stand without the models	**£150-200**

KING-SIZE Sales Aids
King-Size Shop Display. 1960s showing K16 Dodge Tractor **£250-300**
'Fred Bronner' King-Size. US freestanding unit, No.s K1 - K18.....**£400-500**

Lincoln Industries 'Matchbox Series'

Collectors should be aware that a range of models exists which were made in New Zealand and which at first sight appear to be Matchbox Miniatures. The packaging in particular is strikingly similar to early Lesney Matchbox boxes, even to the extent of having 'MATCHBOX SERIES' printed in a banner as on the Lesney boxes.

It seems that the makers, Lincoln Industries, were so taken with the Lesney idea of 'a model in a matchbox' that they were tempted to capitalise on it by adopting it themselves. 'Lincoln Industries Ltd' and 'Made in New Zealand' are also clearly marked on the boxes so confusion should be avoidable. The models are a little cruder than genuine Matchbox products and all seem to have metal wheels. They are nevertheless collectable and include: a Utility Truck, Breakdown Truck, Large Parcels Van, Ambulance, and a sports car resembling a Jaguar XK120. The editor would welcome more details of these products.

Miscellaneous Matchbox Items

Folded card layouts
contained inside a paper sleeve.
No.1 Roadway Layout 1st issue. In 'A Lesney Moko' picture paper sleeve.................... **£125-150**
R1 Roadway Layout 2nd issue. In 'A Lesney' paper sleeve, b/w illustration **£125-150**
R1 Roadway Layout 3rd issue with flyover picture in 'A Lesney Product' detailed colour picture paper sleeve **£140-160**
R1 Roadway Layout 4th issue. 'New Foldaway Flyover' in detailed colour picture paper sleeve **£75-100**
R2 Roadway Layout 1st issue. 'London' layout in 'A Lesney' paper sleeve **£125-150**

R2 Building Construction Site Early 1st type issue in detailed colour picture sleeve **£75-100**
R2 Building Construction Site Later 2nd type issue in detailed colour picture sleeve with yellow side panel **£75-100**
R3 'London Famous Landmarks' Layout In 'A Lesney' paper sleeve........................ **£50-75**
R3 'Foldaway Farm' Layout In detailed colour picture sleeve **£50-75**
R4 'Racetrack/Speedway' Layout In 'A Lesney' paper sleeve, b/w picture......... **£100-125**
R5 'Grand Prix Race Track' Layout Late issue detailed colour picture paper sleeve **£100-125**

Collector's carrying cases
All are made of vinyl. The US issues were produced on license by the Fred Bronner Corporation.
1965 Has picture of 41c Ford GT40, holds 48 models... **£15-20**
1965 Pictures of 53b Mercedes and 6c Euclid, holds 40 models. US issue........... **£80-100**
1966 Pictures of 19d Lotus and 32b Jaguar, holds 48 models **£60-80**
1966 Garage and Service Station Carrying Case with picture showing boy/E-type/garage. US issue **£60-80**
1967 Has picture of 8e Ford Mustang, holds 18 models. Lesney issue .... NGPP
1968 Has illustration of a green car with red interior, holds 72 models. US issue **£60-80**
1969 Pictures of 14d Iso Grifo, 51c AEC Tipper and 53c Ford Zodiac. Holds 24 models .... NGPP
1969 Pictures of 6d Ford Pickup, 14d Iso Grifo and 62c Mercury Cougar. Holds 24 models. US issue .... NGPP

Matchbox jig-saw puzzles
These jig-saw puzzles each feature a Matchbox model.
29c Fire Pumper **£10-15**
31c Lincoln Continental **£10-15**
34c VW Transporter Camper **£10-15**
35b Snow-Trac **£10-15**
39c and 40c Ford Tractor and Hay Trailer **£10-15**
62c Mercury Cougar (dark green)................ **£10-15**
62c Mercury Cougar (light green)................ **£10-15**
66b Greyhound Bus **£10-15**
72b Standard Jeep....................................... **£10-15**

Matchbox book
Collector's Matchbox Book
'Matchbox 1-75 Regular Wheels'. Collector's ringbound book by Michael Stannard............. NGPP

'Matchbox' series painting books
Four different types of cover and contents numbered 1 to 4. Mint unused set of books .... NGPP

Matchbox Catalogues

Year of intro, publication details	MPR
1957	**Folded Leaflet** Yellow cover has Blue edging and depicts No.1 Diesel Roller. Colour pictures of nos. 1 - 42 of '1-75' series............. **£140-180**
1957	**Folded Leaflet** Blue/Yellow cover featuring MOY No.1 Allchin 7nhp Traction Engine 1st series box. Contents list first nine Yesteryears **£180-200**
1958	**16-page catalogue** Cover shows Rolls-Royce (44) emerging from box. Models 1 - 60 in colour inside, early 'Major Packs' and Accessory Packs **£100-125**
1959	**Leaflet** 'Everyone buys MATCHBOX TOYS by LESNEY'. Blue with line drawings. Gives details of Presentation and Gift Sets **£200-300**
1959	**Folded Leaflet** First 14 Yesteryears in colour **£100-125**
1959	**16-page catalogue** Same cover as 1958 catalogue with '1959 Edition'. Lists 1-75's, Major Packs and accessories. Colour pictures **£40-60**
1959	**24-page catalogue** 'UK' and '2d' on cover with MOY No.9, 1-75 series, No.'43', and Accessory No.'2'. Colour contents show MB 1 - 72 and MoY 1 - 14 plus Accessories

Year of intro, publication details	MPR
	and Major Packs. **£40-60**
1960	**32-page catalogue** 'UK' and '3d' on cover featuring logo 'ALL THE MATCHBOX POCKET TOYS BY LESNEY' plus semi-circle picture of MoY and 1-75's. Contents illustrate all ranges............**£80-100**
1961	32-page catalogue 'International Pocket Catalogue' on cover with picture of 1-75 model No.5 Bus. New style smaller catalogue listing all issues in colour plus International price list **£30-40**

Matchbox catalogue 1963

1962	20-page catalogue '2d', 'International Pocket Catalogue' and

Year of intro, publication details	MPR
	'1962 Edition' on cover. All issues listed, European price list included **£50-60**
1963	**20-page catalogue** No.53 Mercedes-Benz printed on cover with '2d' and '1963 Edition'. Good Gift Set pictures and listings...............**£20-30**
1964	**32-page catalogue** '3d' on cover depicting Blue Mk.10 Jaguar (No.28). '1964 Matchbox Prices' on back cover. Contents include superb Gift Set pictures and listings **£40-50**

Matchbox catalogue 1965

1965	**32-page catalogue** Cover features Motor Racing Cars. '1965 Matchbox Prices' on back cover.

Excellent full colour Gift Set
pictures. (Price 3d) **£10-20**
1965 **US Trade Catalogue.**
Fred Bronner's **£45-65**
1966 **40-page catalogue**
London scene and 'Price 3d' on cover.
Excellent pictures of mid-sixties
Gift Sets plus history of Matchbox **£20-25**
1966 **40-page catalogue**
International issue. **£45-55**
1966 **Sales Promotion Guide**
Multi Language Colour Guide **£125-150**
1967 **40-page catalogue**
Cover shows flags and 1-75 issues,
'Price 3d'. Contents list and
depict Veteran Car Gifts. **£20-25**
1968 **40-page catalogue**
1968 car picture and 'Price 3d' on
cover. Includes details of
manufacturing processes. **£20-25**
1969 **48-page catalogue**
Cover features Motorway scene.
Contents include detailed history of
real cars making up the MoY range ...**£15-30**
2nd edition: The 2nd edition of the 1969
catalogue including first reference to
'Superfast' issues **£12-15**
1969 **'MATCHBOX' Selector Chart.**
Two-sided leaflet with the complete
range of Matchbox products. **£40-50**
1970 **64-page catalogue**
Only drawings of models (no photographs)
throughout. Superfast track featured.
'6d', 'MATCHBOX SUPERFAST'
and a collage of models on cover. **£8-10**
1971 **64-page catalogue**
'24p' on Blue/Red cover with scorpion

design. 'Speed Kings' listed plus
pictures of first Superfast Gift Sets **£8-10**
1972 **72-page catalogue**
Yellow 'MATCHBOX' and '3p' on
cover. Contents feature launch of
'Scream'n Demon' bikes and
excellent Gift Set pictures **£8-10**
1973 **80-page catalogue**
'5p' and '1973' on cover of the largest
Matchbox catalogue produced. Contents
include good 'Super Kings' and
Aircraft Kit listing. **£8-10**
1974 **64-page catalogue**
'2p' and '1974' on cover. Includes
first 'SKYBUSTERS' listing **£5-8**
1975 **64-page catalogue**
'2p' and '1975' on cover. Contents feature
'Rolamatics' and 'Battle Kings' **£5-8**
1976 **64-page catalogue**
'1976' on cover. Feature 'Sea Kings' plus
'Baby Dolls' and 'Disco Girl Dolls'. **£5-8**
1977 **80-page catalogue**
'1977' on cover. Contents list the 'Two
Pack' (TP) range of 1-75's. Good Gift
Set pictures and listings of 1-75's **£5-8**
1978 **64-page catalogue**
'1978' on cover. Good 'SKYBUSTERS'
and 1-75 Gift Set pictures **£5-8**
79-80 **80-page catalogue**
'5p' and '1979-80' on cover. The contents
feature good pictures of Gift Sets G1 - G8.
'900' TP series introduced **£5-8**
80-81 **64-page catalogue**
'5p' on cover. All ranges listed inc. 'Walt
Disney' and 'Power Track' equipment .. **£4-6**
81-82 **64-page catalogue**
'5p' and '1981-82' on cover. 'Adventure

2000' space models pictured. 'Playtrack',
'Popeye' and 'Streak Sets' listed **£4-6**
82-83 **64-page catalogue**
'1982-83' on cover. 'Convoy' series
introduced, good MoY pictures. **£2-4**
1984 **64-page catalogue**
'1984' on cover. 'MATCHBOX SPECIALS'
introduced, 'Burnin' Key Cars', 'Rough
Riders' and 'Lock Ups' **£2-4**
1985 **48-page catalogue**
'1985' and 'chequered flag' design on cover.
All ranges + introduction of 'Trickshifters',
'Power Blasters', 'Matchmates'
and 'Carry Cases'. (Printed in Italy) **£2-4**
1986 **48-page catalogue**
'1986' on cover. 'High Riders',
'Twin-Pack', 'Action Packs' listed
inside. 'Motor City' introduced **£2-4**
1987 **72-page catalogue**
'1987' on cover. Includes 'Superfast
Lasers', 'Pocket Rockets', 'Speed Riders',
'Streak Racing', 'Hot Rod Racers',
'Turbo 2' and 'Demolition Cars'. **£2-4**
1988 **88-page catalogue**
'1988' on cover. Includes Miniatures
Gift Sets pictures, 'Lasers', 'Super GT
Sport' and 'Super Miniatures', 'Team
Convoy', 'Road Blasters', 'Motor City'
and 'Action Matchbox'. Also includes
'MICA' and 'Junior Matchbox Club'
membership details **£2-4**
1989 **80-page catalogue**
'1989' on cover. Include 'Miniatures',
'Twin-Pack', 'Motor City' Gift Sets,
'Dinky Collection', 'Conn-Nect-Ables',
'Flashbacks', 'Super ColourChangers'
and 'Skybusters ColourChangers' **£2-4**

Overseas Catalogue Editions

During the 1960s there were normally six editions of each catalogue:
British, International, USA, German, French and French-Canadian. These
were usually of the same format as UK editions but with the appropriate
language and currency. 'INTERNATIONAL CATALOGUE' was shown
on the front cover together with the edition, e.g. 'EDITION FRANCAISE',
'INTERNATIONAL' or 'U.S.A. EDITION'.
  The 1960 'International Pocket Catalogue' listed the national prices for
every product in Australia, Austria, Belgium, Spain, Denmark, Eire, France,
Germany, Great Britain, Holland, Hong Kong, Italy, Kenya and East Africa,
Singapore and Malaysia, South Africa, Sweden and Switzerland. From 1972 the
country-specific editions only listed the model range available in that country.

Market Price Range Prices are equivalent to those asked for UK editions.

Other Matchbox literature

'Mike and The Modelman' (1st edition 1970), was a childrens' book issued by
Lesney telling the Matchbox story.
A copy in perfect condition should cost between **£50 - £60**.

Trade Catalogues have been published for many years and occasionally
become available for sale. Those before 1970 are scarce and no price
information is possible at present. Those from the 1970-80 period tend to be
in the region of £15-20 while post-1980 editions sell for £5-10 depending on
content and condition.

Matchbox '1-75' Series 'Superfast' issues, 1969–1983

Model and details	MPR

This listing refers to Superfast models produced
between 1969 and 1983. In this period, most
models in the range were presented in picture
boxes with some variations being sold in Twin
Packs and carded 'bubble packs'. The 'cut-off point'
for many collectors of these Matchbox Miniatures
is 1983 when picture boxes ceased. 'See-through'
window boxes sealed at both ends were then
introduced.
  All the models listed have 'Made in England' bases.
Those with 'Macau', 'China', 'Thailand' or elsewhere
are too numerous to mention and are outside the
scope of this listing. There are also many wheel
variations for the models listed, such as 5-spoke, 4-
spoke, 'dot-dash' etc., but again, only specific wheel
variations such as hub colour and colour are noted.
  Due to limitations of space, it has been necessary
to introduce the use of abbreviations into the listing
(see page 7). These have been mainly restricted
to indicate colour of bases and window glazing.
Collectors may come across Twin Pack models that
have been removed from their packaging and put

into empty boxes: this is acceptable since some of the
Twin Pack vehicle issues were never found outside of
this particular type of packaging.

MB 1e   Mercedes Truck

		MPR
70-70	Metallic gold body, yellow or orange canopy, green glass, narrow wheels ..	**£25-35**
76	Military olive drab green body, tan canopy, purple glass, WW, '4TS702K', (TP)......	**£35-40**
76-80	Same but military olive green	**£8-12**
76-80	Red body, yellow or orange canopy, PG, wide wheels, 'Transcontinental' (TP)..	**£8-10**
80-82	Light blue body, light orange canopy, purple glass, WW, 'IMS' (TP)	**£12-15**

MB 1e   Mod Rod

		MPR
71	Yellow body, OG, SE, red wheels, UB or SB, 'spotted cat's head' label	**£30-35**
71-75	Same but with black wheels	**£10-12**
	Black wheels and silver base	**£18-20**
71-75	Same but with 'Wildcat' label............	**£10-12**

		MPR
73	Same but with 'Flower' label..............	**£20-25**
74	Same but with 'Scorpion' label	**£50-60**
78	Striped silver body, BW, UB. (U.S.A. 'Roman Numeral' LE)............	**£25-30**

MB 1g Dodge Challenger 'Revin Rebel'

MB 1g   Dodge Challenger
76-79   Red body, white roof, silver interior ..**£15-20**
76-79   Same but with white interior.............**£15-20**
76-79   Same but with red interior................**£30-35**
80-82   Blue body, white roof, red interior.....**£15-20**
82-83   Orange body, blue roof, black
        interior, UB or SB, 'Revin Rebel'........**£45-50**
82   Same but with white roof..................**£50-65**

MB 2d   Mercedes Trailer
70   Metallic gold body, yellow or orange
        canopy, narrow wheels **£25-30**
76   Military olive drab green body, tan
        canopy, WW, '4TS702K' (TP)'................**£30-35**
76-80   Same but military olive green **£10-12**
76-80   Red body, WW, yellow or orange
        canopy, 'Transcontinental' (TP) **£8-10**
80-82   Light blue body, light orange
        canopy, WW 'IMS' (TP).....................**£10-12**

MB 2e   Jeep Hot Rod
71-75   Light or dark pink body, white or cream
        seats, light or dark green base **£10-15**
        Same but white base **£55-65**
75-76   Red body, white or cream seats, WB..**£12-18**
        Same but green base **£45-50**

MB 2f   Rescue Hovercraft
76-78   Light or dark lime green body, fawn or
        light brown skirt, red or silver air intakes,
        amber or red windows, 'Rescue' **£6-8**
76-79   With Metallic light or dark green body ..**£6-8**
        Same but with red windows **£8-10**
78   Same but black skirt **£8-10**
        Black skirt, red or purple windows **£10-12**
78-80   Pale green body, black skirt, purple
        or AG, '2000' or 'Rescue' **£15-20**

MB 2g   S-2 Jet
81-82   Black/yellow, yellow or red glass **£8-10**
82-83   Metallic light blue and white or grey,
        clear glass, 'Viper' on some **£1-150**

MB 3c   Mercedes 'Binz' Ambulance
70-73   Cream or off-white body, light blue
        glass, NW, opening rear door **£40-50**
        Same but with dark blue glass............**£40-50**
77-80   Cream body, dark blue glass, red cross
        on doors, rear door cast shut (TP) **£20-30**
78-80   Military olive-green body, WW with
        silver hubs, rear door cast shut (TP)..**£60-70**
        Same but with black hubs **£20-30**

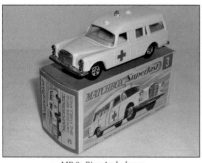

MB 3c Binz Ambulance

MB 3d   Monteverdi Hai
73-78   Orange body, pale yellow interior,
        black or UB, '3' on bonnet.................**£10-15**
        Same but with silver base... ....**£30-40**
        Same but with '16' on bonnet **£35-40**

MB 3e   Porsche Turbo
78-79   Metallic brown body,
        cream interior, clear glass, BB **£10-15**
79-80   Metallic brown body, UB **£14-18**

Silver body, CG, cream or red interior,
black or dark grey base **£8-12**
Tan interior, black or dark grey base .**£12-15**
Tan interior, brown base **£18-20**
Red interior, brown base......................**£8-10**
80-82   Metallic green body, cream interior,
        clear glass, black or dark grey base **£14-18**
        With light or dark yellow interior **£14-18**
        Same but with unpainted base **£14-18**
        Red interior, dark GB or BB **£14-18**
        Red body, tan interior, opaque glass,
        black base, 'Porsche Turbo 90'..........**£14-18**
82-83   Red body, tan or white interior, CG,
        black or dark grey base, 'Porsche Turbo
        90' on some **£14-18**

MB 4d   Stake Truck
70-72   Orange-yellow cab, green stake body,
        Green tinted glass................................**£20-25**
        Same but bright yellow cab **£80-100**

MB 5e Racing Lotus Europa

MB 4e Gruesome Twosome

MB 4e   Gruesome Twosome
71-75   Gold body, SB or UB,
        cream interior, PG **£14-18**
        With white or yellow interior.............**£12-15**
        Gold body, SB, cream interior, AG.**£100-120**
75   Red body, SB or UB, yellow int., PG.**£30-35**
        Same but with cream interior............**£12-15**
        Orange-red body, SB or UB, cream
        interior, purple glass..........................**£35-40**
        Graphite Grey body, PW, yellow
        interior, bare metal base **£225-275**

MB 4f   Pontiac Firebird
75-77   Metallic light blue body, UB, AG........**£15-20**
78-80   Same but metallic dark blue..............**£20-25**

MB 4g   '57 Chevy
80-81   Purple body, silver interior, UB, CG...**£10-15**
82-83   Red, 'Cherry bomb', SB or UB, CG......**£10-15**
        Same but with black base **£20-25**

MB 5e   Lotus Europa
69-70   Dark metallic blue body, ivory
        interior, UB, NW **£40-45**
        Same, no 'Superfast' cast on base..**£200-300**
        Dark metallic blue with '20' and stripe
        labels from G3 racing set **£25-30**
70-75   Pink body, ivory int., SB, NW or WW.**£25-30**
        Same but with unpainted base **£10-12**
        Same, but with UB, NW, '20', and
        stripe decals **£25-30**
77-78   Black body, ivory interior, UB,
        NW, 'JPS' (Japanese issue).................**£30-40**
        Same but without 'JPS' (TP) **£30-40**
        Pre-production model. 1969, red with
        pre-production SF wheels...........**£1,000-1,250**

MB 5f   Seafire Boat
75-79   White deck, blue hull, orange-yellow,
        blue or lemon man, black or red
        exhausts **£6-8**
79-82   Red deck, white hull, orange-yellow
        or lemon man, red exhausts, black
        trailer (TP)...**£7-10**
81   Red deck, blue hull, lemon man,
        red exhausts, black trailer (TP) **£80-100**
81   White deck, brown hull, lemon or
        orange-yellow man, red exhausts **£45-50**
82   Black deck, yellow hull, red man,
        red exhausts, black trailer (TP) **£30-35**
83   Red deck, yellow hull, red man,
        red exhausts, black trailer (TP) **£35-40**

MB 5g   US Mail Truck
78-82   Dark or light blue body, white roof (small
        or large windows), WB, BW, black or
        silver hubs, 'US Mail' on some **£10-12**
        Same but with black base **£10-12**
78   Pale blue body, white roof, 'sleet and
        snow' base, 'US Mail'. US LE **£10-12**

MB 5h Jeep 4 x 4

MB 5h   4x4 Jeep Off-Road
82-83   Metallic light or dark bronze body,
        black base, 'Golden eagle' **£18-22**

MB 6d   Ford Pick-up
70-71   Red body, white roof, white or chrome
grille, NW or WW, black base £30-35
Metallic green or UB £70-80
Green or Grey base £30-35

MB 6e   Mercedes 350sl
74-75   Orange body, black roof, UB, ivory or
pale yellow interior, amber or CG £12-15
75-79   Yellow body, black roof, UB, pale
yellow interior, amber or CG £12-15
77   Silver body, black roof, UB, pale yellow
interior, CG, 'Rennservice'
(German issue) £50-60
Same but without 'Rennservice' £40-50
79   Metallic bronze body, black roof, UB,
pale yellow interior, amber glass........£12-18
79-81   Metallic bronze, white roof, AG,
UB, pale yellow or cream interior £7-10
81-82   Metallic red body, white roof, UB,
pale yellow interior, AG or CG............£30-35
With Cream interior, AG or CG £10-15

MB 6f   Mercedes Convertible
82-83   Metallic blue body, white interior, UB
or SB, silver side stripe on some £8-10
Same but In picture box... ....£40-50
83-84   Maroon body, BB, SB or UB £8-10

MB 7c   Ford Refuse Truck
70-72   Orange or orange-red cab, grey back
WW or NW £20-30

MB 7d   Hairy Hustler
71-74   Metallic bronze body, AG, '5' on yellow
side stripe and bonnet, GB or BB.......£15-20
Same but purple glass.......................£150-160
Metallic bronze body, AG, '5' on blue
side stripe and bonnet, UB or BB......£15-20
Same but green base £20-25
Same but green base, plain sides £20-25
Same but black base, plain sides £15-20
Metallic bronze body, AG, '3' on
side labels, '5' on bonnet, BB £25-30
Met. bronze, AG, '3' or '137' on sides,
'Scorpion' on bonnet, GB or BB £85-100
75-77   White 'Streakers' version, AG, red stripes
with black/white check, GB or BB £10-15
Same but with black base £10-15
78   White body, AG, grey base £25-35
78-79   Yellow body, AG, 'flames', BB,
US 'Roman Numeral' Ltd. Edition £18-20

MB 7e   Volkswagen Golf
76-77   Metallic lime green body, yellow interior,
AG, BB, roof-rack, black surfboards...£15-20
77-81   Same but metallic light green body ...£15-20
77-81   Metallic dark green body, yellow or
lemon interior, AG, BB or GB £15-20
Same but with orange glass £15-20
Red interior, grey base £20-30
77   Yellow body and interior, matt black
base, 'ADAC' , (German issue) £25-30
79-80   Red body, yellow interior, CG or AG,
BB, roof rack, surfboards (TP)...........£12-15
Same but red interior, CG, (TP)........£40-45
81-82   Yellow body, red interior, CG, BB or
GB, roof rack and black surfboards ...£12-16
82-83   Silver body, red interior, CG, BB or
GB, green stripes and 'Golf' £10-14
Same but with tan interior................£15-20
Same but with blue interior £200-240

MB 8e   Ford Mustang
70   White body, red interior, BB, CG WW£275-350
Same but with NW £400-500
70-71   Red body, red interior, BB, CG, WW. £200-250
Same but with ivory interior, WW...£120-140
Orange-red body, red interior, WW £300-400
Same but with ivory interior...........£150-175

MB 8f   Wildcat Dragster
71   Pink body, yellow interior, black
and orange 'Wildcat' labels, BB £40-50
71-75   Same but Orange body, BB...................£40-50
Same but with UB or orange base.....£40-50
With dark or bright yellow base £40-50
Same but with grey base £40-50
Orange body, yellow interior, yellow/
orange 'Wildcat' labels on some, BB .£30-35
Same but grey base £40-50
Same but with UB or green base........£50-60
Orange body, yellow interior,
black base, 'Rat Rod' labels £30-40
Same but with 'Sailboat' labels £100-120

MB 8g   De Tomaso Pantera
75-81   White body, red interior, blue base,
'8' and 'Pantera' labels on some.........£15-20
Same but orange interior....................£10-15
With unpainted base..........................£10-15
White body, orange interior, '9' or
yellow 'Sun' in black or green circle
bonnet label, blue base......................£20-25
81-82   Blue body, black interior, '8' and
'Pantera' labels on some, BB, US issue.£10-15
NB   MB8g can be found with the larger rear
wheels swapped with the smaller front.

MB 8h Rover 3500

MB 8h   Rover 3500
81   Yellow body, red interior, sunroof,
black base, (G1 Gift set) £225-250
Metallic bronze body, white interior,
sunroof, black base.............................£15-20
Same but dark or light tan interior £10-15

MB 8i   Rover 'POLICE' Car
82   White with blue logo/stripe...............£14-18

MB 9d   Boat and Trailer
70-72   White hull, light turquoise deck,
dark blue trailer £30-35
76-83   White hull, light blue deck,
light blue trailer (TP).........................£30-35
82   White hull, black deck,
light or dark blue trailer (TP).............£40-50
Same but with black trailer................£20-25

MB 9e   AMX Javelin
72-78   Metallic lime green body, opening doors,
yellow int., AG, black air intake,
UB or SB, 3rd series box.....................£12-16
Same but with silver air intake...........£50-60
Metallic lime green body, orange interior,
AG, black air intake, UB or SB £25-30
Same but with 5-spoke wheels...........£50-60
Same but white interior, UB £60-70
Same but with blue interior............£125-150
76-78   Metallic light blue body, yellow or
orange-yellow interior, AG, UB or SB ..£8-11
78-81   Metallic dark blue body, cast-in doors,
orange-yellow interior,
AG, UB or SB, (TP)...............................£8-11

80-81   Blue body, cast-in doors, UB or SB,
orange-yellow interior, AG, black
air intake, white '1', (US Ltd.Ed.) £20-25
81-83   Metallic dark green body, cast-in
doors, orange-yellow interior, AG,
UB or SB, black air intake, (TP)..........£20-25
82   Red body, cast-in doors, UB or SB,
orange-yellow interior, AG, (TP) £50-60

MB 9f   Ford Escort RS2000
78-82   White body, tan interior, BB, CG, '9',
'Ford', 'Shell', and 'Dunlop' decals £10-12
Same but with AG... ....£100-120
Same but with grey base £10-12
Same but red interior, black base.....£90-100
White body, tan interior, BB, CG,
'Phantom' decals, (TP) £18-20
80-82   Blue body, tan interior, BB or GB,
CG, 'Phantom' decals, (TP) £10-12
Same but with blue-grey base £20-25
82-84   Green body, tan interior, BB or GB,
CG, 'Phantom' decals (TP) £20-25
Green body, white interior, BB, CG,
'Phantom' decals, (TP) £40-50
Same but with red interior...............£90-100

MB 10d   Leyland Pipe Truck
70   Red body, silver base and grille,
6 grey pipes on sprue £80-100
70-73   Same but orange-red body £20-25
Orange body, silver base and grille,
6 grey or yellow pipes on sprue £20-30
Same but grey base and grille £80-100

MB 10e   Piston Popper
73-80   Metallic blue body, yellow interior,
AG, 'Superfast' on UB.......................£80-100
Same but 'Rola-Matic' on UB £10-15
Same but with silver base £40-45
With CG, 'Rola-Matic' on UB or SB....£18-20
80   White body, yellow interior, AG,
'Rola-Matic' on UB,
(German multi-pack issue) £250-300
80-81   Yellow body (red flames) and interior,
AG, 'Rola-Matic' on UB. US LE...........£15-20

MB 10f   Plymouth Gran Fury Police Car
79-81   White body, black panels, blue or pale
or dark yellow glass, UB, 'Police'....£14-18
82-83   Same but with 'Metro Police Traffic
Control', shield and '012', UB or SB.......£8-11
Same but 'Mercury' base from no 55.£10-15
Same but with PW..............................£50-60

MB 11d   Scaffolding Truck
70-72   Silver body, red base / grille, GG,
yellow scaffold, NW,
'Builders Supply Company'................£25-35

MB 11e VW Flying Bug

MB 11e   Flying Bug
72-77   Red body, SB or UB, grey glass, yellow
exhausts, silver helmet, square cut or

heart-shape bonnet decal..................£25-30
Heart-shape decal, UB, blue glass £70-80
78   Orange body, UB, black glass and
exhausts, flying beetle bonnet decal,
US Ltd. Ed..£25-30
With '4' on bonnet, BB £40-45

MB 11f   Car Transporter
NB   Usually comes with 1 red, 1 blue and
1 yellow car. Other combinations are
common (e.g., 1 blue and 2 yellow) but
this does not affect the price.
77-80   Orange cab, white or beige back, BB
or UB, blue, purple or green glass......£10-15
80-83   Red (later Dark Orange) cab, beige or
grey back, BB, SB or UB,
blue or purple glass.............................£10-15

MB 12c   Safari Land-Rover
70   Blue body, white interior,
UB, NW, brown luggage
(beware of fakes) £1,500-2,000
70-71   Metallic gold body, white interior,
UB, NW, brown luggage......................£20-25

MB 12d   Setra Coach
71   Metallic gold, grey roof, UB, CG.........£20-25
Same but with white roof....................£18-20
72-73   Yellow body, white roof, UB, CG £30-40
Same but with green glass £150-200
73-74   Metallic crimson, UB, CG or GG........£20-25
74-75   Met. purple, UB or PB, CG or GG.......£12-15

MB 12e   Big Bull
75-79   Orange, green shovel, black rollers....£30-40
Same but with yellow rollers £15-20
Same but with orange rollers £10-15

MB 12f   Citroën CX
79-82   Light or dark metallic blue body,
pale yellow or cream or ivory interior,
SB or GB or UB,
clear or blue glass.............................£10-14
Light metallic blue, tan interior £12-16
Dark metallic blue, red interior..........£80-90
82-83   Yellow body, red interior, black base,
dark blue glass, (TP)..........................£12-16
With clear glass, BB, GB or SB, (TP) ..£10-14
Yellow, red interior, BB, CG, 'Team
Matchbox' in black or blue, (TP).......£15-20
83   White body, red interior, BB or UB,
blue glass/lights, 'Ambulance', (TP) £8-10
Same but 'Police', 'Marine Division'
and '8' prints, blue stripes, (TP)...........£8-10

MB 13d   Dodge Wreck Truck
70-71   Yellow (or lighter yellow) cab, green
back, yellow crane, red hook 'B.P.' £50-75

MB 13e   Baja Buggy
71-78   Metallic light green body, orange interior,
UB, black or red exhausts, red or
orange bonnet flower label.................£12-15
With red exhausts, no bonnet label ..£12-15
With red exhausts, 'Police' bonnet
label from 55d....................................£40-45
Same but with red interior..................£40-45
Metallic light green body, orange
interior from 47c, UB, red exhausts,
orange bonnet flower label.............£150-200
78   Metallic dark green body, orange interior,
UB, red exhausts, orange flower label£10-15
Same but 'Sun' label from 47c............£18-20

MB 13f   Simon Snorkel
78-80   Light red body, SB or UB, blue glass,
blue lights, yellow crane and man £10-15
Same but amber glass and lights £25-30
80-82   Dark red body, SB or UB, blue glass,
blue lights, yellow crane and man £10-15
82   Same but white crane and man £8-10

MB 14d Iso Grifo (Japanese issue)

MB 14d   Iso Grifo
69-71   Metallic dark blue body, pale or dark
blue interior, UB, NW..........................£30-40
Same but with white interior.........£250-300
71-75   Lighter metallic blue body, white
interior, UB or SB, NW £18-20
Sky blue, white interior, UB, NW........£18-20
77-78   Lighter powder blue, white interior,
UB, WW, (Japanese issue) £25-30

MB 14e   Mini Ha Ha
75-82   Red body, dark blue glass, UB,
'flesh' coloured man, brown helmet,
4 circle side labels...............................£20-25
Same but with purple man £30-35
'Flesh' man, light blue glass...............£20-25
Purple man, light blue glass £15-20
Pink man, light blue glass £15-20
Red body, light blue glass, 'flesh' or
pink man, 2 circle side labels £30-35

MB 14f   Leyland Tanker
82-83   Red cab, white tank, 'ELF' with red/blue
stripes or orange/turquoise stripes....£10-15
19??   Yellow cab, White tank, 'SHELL' £20-25

MB 15d VW 1500 Monte Carlo

MB 15d   Volkswagen 1500
69-70   Off white or cream body, cream
interior, '137', 'Monte Carlo'...............£35-45
70-72   Metallic red body, cream interior,
'137', 'Monte Carlo' on some..............£30-40
77-78   Off white body, cream interior, '137',
no bumper decal (Japanese issue).....£30-40

MB 15e   Forklift Truck
72-77   Red body, yellow hoist, grey forks, UB,
black steering wheel, 'horse' and
'Lansing Bagnall' labels £10-12
Same but with green or black base £10-12
77-82   Red body, unpainted hoist, yellow forks,
UB, black steering wheel, 'horse' and
'Lansing Bagnall' labels £10-12

Same but with green or black base £10-12
Same but no steering wheel £10-12
Same but with black or grey forks......£10-12
With red forks, no steering wheel £12-15
82-83   Orange body, unpainted hoist, black
forks and roof, UB or SB or BB, no
steering wheel, 'Hi-Lift' labels............£8-10
NB   Models can be found with 'horse' label
facing forwards or backwards and
before or after 'Lansing Bagnall'.

MB 15e Forklift Truck

MB 16d   Case Bulldozer
69-74   Red body, yellow cab, shovel, engine
and base, green rubber tracks............£10-12
Same but with black tracks.................£10-12
77   Military olive drab green body, black
shovel, BB, black tracks (TP) £55-60
Same but olive green body (TP)........£20-25

MB 16e   Badger
74-80   Metallic bronze body, SB, silver radar,
green glass (Rola-Matic) £10-12
Same but BB or SB, cream radar £8-10
Same but with light or dark grey base .£8-10
Dark grey or black base, black radar....£8-10
Same but with purple glass £10-12
Black base, white radar, green glass....£8-10
Same but with dark grey base £8-10
76   Military olive drab green body, light grey
base, cream radar, green glass(TP) ...£35-40
76-78   Same but olive green body (TP)........£18-20

MB 16f   Pontiac Firebird
80-81   Metallic light brown body, red interior,
UB, 'Eagle' bonnet label on most.......£14-18
81-82   Same but metallic light gold body £14-18
Same but metallic dark gold body £14-18
82-83   White body, red interior £23-28

MB 16g   Pontiac T-Roof
1982   Black body, red interior, 'Lesney' base..£15-20

MB 17e   Horse box
70   Red cab, dark green back, grey door,
chrome base, 2 white horses on sprue £55-60
70-71   Same but orange-red cab....................£30-35
Orange-red cab, light grey-white box,
brown door £40-45
Same but orange cab...........................£30-35
Mustard-yellow cab, dark green
box, grey door £30-35

MB 17f   Daimler
'Londoner' Buses
The 'Londoner' bus models are loosely based on
the Daimler Fleetline design of double-decker
buses. Unless otherwise stated all issues have red
bodies and white interiors. Most have metal bases
in gloss or matt black, grey, brown or unpainted.
Before changing to the Titan bus (17g) some were
fitted with plastic bases. Factory issued models are
listed first, then Lesney issued promotional models.

72-74 'Swinging London', 'Carnaby Street' **£8-10**
73 Chrome plated Gift Ware version ..**£150-175**
73 Gold-effect plated Gift Ware version . **£70-80**
73-80 'Berger Paints.' ('Brush' logos may
be at front or rear of label)..................... **£5-7**
73 Same but silver body......................... **£70-80**
73 Same but gold body........................ **£200-300**
Same but orange body **£45-50**
73 Same but cream body, brown roof..... **£60-65**
75 'Esso Extra Petrol'............................ **£65-70**
77 'Silver Jubilee 1952-77.' Silver body
with red interior, special issue box **£12-15**
Same but red body, white interior **£70-80**
78 'Matchbox 1953-78'............................. **£4-6**
Same but orange body **£65-70**
Same but blue body **£45-50**
72 'Preston Guild Merchant' **£75-80**
73 'Impel 73' Trade Fair **£35-40**
'London and Kensington Hilton' **£75-80**
'The Baron of Beef' **£100-120**
'Sellotape Selbstklebebander' **£250-300**
'Sellotape Packaging Systems'........ **£250-300**
'Sellotape Electrical Tapes' **£250-300**
'Barclays Bank' **£80-90**
'Chambourcy Yogurt' **£55-65**
'Interchemicals and Plastics'........ **£200-250**
74 'Typhoo puts the 'T' in Britain' **£80-90**
76 'Impel 76' Trade Fair. Cream body
with brown roof, white interior **£25-30**
'British Airways Busch Gardens'........ **£60-70**
'Ilford HP5 Film'............................ **£150-180**
'A.I.M. Building Fund 1976' **£35-40**
'Selfridges' **£15-20**
'Santa Claus, Aviemore Centre'........ **£35-40**
'Amcel takes you places' **£65-75**
'Eduscho Kaffee' **£140-160**
77 'New! The Museum of London'.......... **£18-20**
'Army and Navy' **£18-20**
'Jacob's the Biscuit Makers'
Red body with white interior............. **£35-40**
Orange body with white interior **£18-20**
78 'Aral-Deutschlands Autopartner'
Blue body with white interior........... **£45-50**
Same but red body **£90-100**
79 'Impel 79' Trade Fair **£25-30**
80 'You can't kid a Bisto kid'.................... **£8-10**
'Borregaard Paper' **£90-100**

MB 17g   Leyland Titan Bus
82 'Berger Paints'.. **£5-8**
'Laker Skytrain'... **£5-8**
82 'Chesterfield Transport Centenary' **£5-8**
'Matchbox No.1, Montepna'
Pale blue/white (Greek issue) **£18-20**
Same but red body **£20-25**

MB 18e   Field Car
70-75 Light yellow body, light brown roof,
white interior, SB, NW or WW **£30-40**
Same but WW, UB **£15-18**
Black roof, UB, WW **£30-40**
76 Military olive drab green body, tan roof,
black interior, BB, 'A' square door
labels, black wide wheels (TP) **£35-45**
76-80 Same but olive green body (TP)......... **£18-20**
Same but 'RA391' bonnet label **£18-20**
With circled star bonnet label (TP)....**£20-25**
77-78 White body, black roof, black interior,
BB, Black/white checked bonnet
label, black wide wheels (TP)........**£200-300**
Same but silver wheel hubs (TP) ...**£200-300**
Orange body, black roof, black interior,
BB, black/white checked bonnet label,
black wide wheels (TP)...................... **£12-15**
Same but silver wheel hubs (TP) **£12-15**
Orange body, black roof, black interior,
SB, black/white checked bonnet label,
black wide wheels (TP) **£30-35**
78-80 Metallic ruby-red body, tan roof, black
interior, SB or BB, '44,' 'Champion' and
'Goodyear' bonnet label (TP)............... **£8-10**

80 Dark orange body, black roof, black
interior, BB or SB, 'AC Filters' and '179
Scout Racing' labels, US Ltd. Ed. **£30-35**
Same but no labels, US Ltd. Ed. **£30-35**
82-83 Dark yellow body, black or tan roof,
black interior, SB, black/white
checked bonnet label, (TP) **£25-30**
Orange, black roof and interior, BB,
black/white checked bonnet, (TP) **£18-20**
Orange body, black or tan roof, white
interior, BB, '44,' 'Champion' and
'Goodyear' bonnet label, (TP)............**£30-35**

MB 18f   Hondarora
74-75 Red body, chrome forks, SE, black
seat, 'Honda' tank labels, WW...........**£18-20**
75-80 Same but no labels or with BW **£15-20**
Red body, black forks, SE, white
seat, 'Honda' tank labels, WW **£85-95**
Same but with black seat **£15-20**
76 Orange body, black forks, SE, black seat,
'Honda' labels, (King Size set 6)........**£20-25**
76 Military olive drab green, black forks,
BE, black seat, no labels, WW (TP) **£25-30**
76-78 Same but military olive green (TP)....**£15-18**
81-82 Metallic green body, black forks,
BE or SE, black seat, no labels, BW **£10-15**
82-83 Yellow body, black forks, SE, black
seat, no tank labels, black wheels **£10-15**
Same but with brown or tan rider......**£10-15**

MB 19d   Lotus Racing Car
70 Metallic purple body, UB, SE, white
driver, round No.'3' side labels **£55-65**

MB 19e   Road Dragster
70-75 Light red body, UB or SB, off-white
interior, '8' labels normal or sideways **£15-20**
Same but with 'Scorpion' labels........**£40-50**
72 Promotional: Fluorescent red body, UB,
off-white interior, 'Wynns' labels ...**£125-150**
Same but smaller 'Wynns' labels ...**£125-150**
75 Metallic purple body, UB, off-white
interior, 'Scorpion' labels...................**£40-50**
Same but '8' labels or no labels .**£15-20**
Metallic red body, UB, off-white
interior, '8' labels as normal **£200-250**

MB 19e Road Dragster

MB 19f   Cement Truck
76-81 Red body, yellow barrel,
red stripes, UB, GG **£6-8**
Same but black stripes or no stripes...... **£6-8**
79 Same but grey barrel with red stripes **£6-8**
Same but with purple glass **£10-12**
81-82 Red body, lemon barrel,
red stripes, UB, GG **£6-8**
Same but black stripes or no stripes **£6-8**
Same but with purple glass **£8-10**

MB 19g   Peterbilt Cement Truck
82-83 Metallic green body, orange barrel,
yellow or white 'Big Pete'.....................**£9-12**
Same but with green body.................**£80-90**

MB 20d Lamborghini Marzal
69 Metallic red body, white interior, UB. **£15-18**
Met. red body, yellow/orange interior ..**£30-35**
70 Same but with 'Avon' and '2' labels
from G3 Racing Specials set **£20-25**
71 Bright pink body, white interior, UB..**£30-40**
Bright pink, silver base......................**£30-40**
Same but with 'Avon' and '2' labels
from G3 Racing Specials set **£20-25**
71-75 Orange or orange-pink body, white
interior, unpainted base......................**£10-12**
72 Yellow body, white interior, UB,
('Brroom Stick' blister pack issue).....**£40-50**
Pre-production model. 1969, metallic
green or yellow, with white interior...
.... **£1,000-1,250**

MB 20e   Police Patrol
75-80 White, UB, orange or red 'Police' stripe,
orange light and interior (Rola-Matic)..**£10-15**
White body, UB or SB, orange 'Police'
stripe, blue or yellow light and interior .**£10-15**
Same but with black base **£8-10**
White body, UB, 'Ambulance' and Red
Cross, orange light and interior..........**£15-18**
76-78 White body, UB, orange 'Site Engineer'
stripes, orange light / interior,
(G3 Consruction Set) **£30-35**
Same but with orange body................**£25-30**
Orange body and 'Police' stripe, orange
light and interior, UB, (G3 Set) **£25-30**
76 Military olive drab green body, UB,
yellow and red 'Police' arrow, orange
light and interior (TP) **£40-50**
Same but 'Ambulance' labels **£40-50**
76-77 Military olive green body, UB, yellow
and red 'Police' arrow, orange light
and interior (TP)................................**£18-20**
Same but with 'Ambulance' labels.....**£18-20**
80 Blue body, UB, yellow 'Paris-Dakar 81'
stripe, (French issue blister pack)......**£40-45**
81 White body, UB, blue 'County Sheriff'
labels, blue light and interior **£12-15**
Same but '017,' 'Sheriff,' blue roof......**£15-18**
81-83 White body, UB, yellow 'Police' and
'shield' stripe above chequered stripe **£10-15**
Same but with black base **£10-15**
White body, UB, black 'Police' on
sides, yellow light and interior **£12-15**
83 Light brown or beige body, UB, yellow
'Securite-Rallye Paris-Dakar 83'........**£24-28**

MB 20f   Desert Dawg
82 US issue. White body, orange canopy ... **£7-9**

MB 21d   Foden Concrete Truck
70-73 Dark yellow cab, yellow barrel, red
body and shute, green base................**£25-30**
Same but bright yellow cab,
green or dark green base **£25-30**

MB 21e   Rod Roller
73-78 Yellow body, black wheels with
metallic red hubs, GB, 'flame' label ..**£30-35**
Same but with matt red hubs **£15-20**
Yellow or darker yellow body, black
wheels, GB or BB, 'flame' or no label **£15-20**

MB 21f   Renault 5TL
78-79 Metallic blue, red interior, BB or SB...**£15-20**
Metallic blue body, tan interior,
black, dark grey or silver base **£8-10**
Yellow body, red interior, BB or SB,
'Le Car' and stripe prints **£12-15**
Yellow body, tan interior, BB or SB
or dark grey base, 'Le Car' prints **£8-10**
79-81 Silver body, red interior, BB or SB,
'A5' and stripe prints **£12-15**
Same but no tampo prints **£8-10**
Silver body, tan interior, SB.............£32-38
81-82 Silver body, red interior, dark grey or

BB or SB, 'Le Car' and stripe prints ...**£10-12**
82-83 White body, tan interior, BB,
'Renault' and '4' on green prints..........**£8-10**
Same but 'Renault' roof prints **£8-10**
White body, white interior, BB,
'Renault' and '4' on green prints..........**£8-10**
White body, tan interior, BB, 'Roloil'
and '21' on yellow prints..................**£8-10**
Same but with orange base **£20-25**
White body, white interior, BB,
'Roloil' and '21' on yellow prints..........**£8-10**
White, Orange interior, 'Roloil' ...**£50-60**
82-83 Red, brown Interior, orange or
black base... ....**£70-80**

MB 22c Pontiac GP

MB 22c   Pontiac GP Sports
70   Red body, grey interior, BB
(beware of fakes) **£3,000-3,200**
Light purple, grey interior, BB **£100-150**
Dark purple, grey interior, BB........**£100-150**
Same with opening doors........**£1,000-1,250**

MB 22d   Freeman Intercity
70-71 Metallic purple body, off-white interior,
UB, yellow arrow labels on some **£15-20**
71-72 Metallic gold body, off-white interior,
UB, yellow arrow labels......................**£30-35**
72-75 Metallic red body, off-white interior,
UB or SB, arrow labels on some **£15-20**

MB 22e   Blaze Buster
75-80 Red body, silver interior, UB,
yellow ladder, 'Fire' labels **£8-10**
Same but with black ladder...............**£42-48**
Same but with white ladder..........**£130-150**
Red body, silver or white interior,
black or dark grey base, yellow ladder. **£8-10**
80-82 Dark red body, white interior, grey or
BB, yellow ladder, 'Fire' labels..............**£8-10**
83   Light red body, white interior, BB, dark
yellow ladder, 'Fire' labels **£8-10**
Same but 'No.32' on yellow labels **£12-15**

MB 22f   Big Foot
1982   Silver body and base,
light or dark blue glass. (US) **£12-15**

MB 23e VW Campervan

MB 23e   VW Camper
70-72 Blue body, orange interior and hinged
roof, UB, CG, rear sailboat side labels
on some, petrol filler cap, NW........**£140-150**
Same but no filler cap **£20-25**
72-75 Orange body, orange interior and hinged
roof, UB, CG, sailboat labels, NW...**£100-120**
Light or dark orange body, white interior,
orange hinged roof, UB, CG, sailboat
labels on some, NW.............................**£30-40**
77-80 Military olive green, no interior, cast roof,
BB, BG, Red Cross labels, WW (TP) ...**£15-18**
80   White body, no interior, cast roof, BB,
GG, 'PizzaVan', WW. US LE **£30-35**

MB 23f   Atlas Truck
75-81 Metallic blue body, orange tipper,
yellow/red arrow labels, chrome
interior, AG, UB.................................. £12-14
Same but without tipper labels **£12-14**
Same but grey interior, CG, UB **£12-14**
Same but grey interior, AG, SB or UB.**£12-14**
With grey interior, CG and SB **£12-14**
81   Metallic blue body, silver tipper, grey
interior, CG, SB **£12-14**
81-82 Same but red body **£12-14**
Same but red body, black interior......**£12-14**

MB 24c Rolls Silver Shadow
70-73 Light metallic red body,
cream interior, BB...............................**£30-40**
Same, but Dark metallic red body **£30-40**
Same but with pink base.....................**£30-40**
Same but SB or grey base...................**£15-18**
Same but with metallic green base **£30-40**
77-78 Light metallic gold body, cream
interior, UB, (Japanese issue) **£30-40**
Same but BB (Japanese issue)............**£25-30**

MB 24d   Team Matchbox
73   Bright yellow body, white man, '4' (or '8')
and 'Team Matchbox' bonnet label . **£200-250**
Metallic blue body, white man,
'1' and 'Team Matchbox' label **£125-175**
With '5' and 'Team Matchbox' **£125-175**
73-75 Metallic green, white man, '5' (or '8'),
'Team Matchbox' label, (G4 set) **£30-50**
73-78 Metallic red body, white man,
'8' and 'Team Matchbox' label **£10-15**
78-80 Metallic ruby-red body, white man,
'44', 'Champion', 'Goodyear',
black trailer (TP)................................**£10-12**
82-83 Same but orange body, yellow man...**£60-70**

MB 24d Racing car 'Team Matchbox'

MB 24e   Diesel Shunter
78   Metallic dark green body, light brown
control panel, 'Railfreight' **£6-8**
Same but with 'D1496-RF' labels..........**£4-6**
78-83 Light or dark yellow body, light brown
control panel (or none), 'D1496-RF'......**£5-8**

MB 25d   Ford Cortina GT
70   Metallic light brown body, off white

interior, unpainted base.................**£180-200**
70-72 Same but metallic light blue body **£25-30**
Same but metallic medium blue body **£40-45**
Same but metallic very dark blue
body..**£200-220**

MB 25e   Mod Tractor
72-78 Metallic purple body, BB, yellow seat,
headlights cast on rear mudguards ...**£40-50**
Without lights on rear mudguards.....**£15-20**
Metallic purple body, BB, red seat.....**£80-90**
Metallic purple, UB, yellow seat........**£15-20**
76-79 Red body, BB, yellow seat (TP) **£15-20**

MB 25f   Flat Car Container
78-80 Light beige container red roof, black flat
car, 'United States Lines' labels...........**£8-10**
Same but with 'N.Y.K.' labels **£4-5**
Same but with 'Sealand' labels **£5-7**
Dark beige container, red roof, black
flat car, 'N.Y.K.' or 'Sealand' labels.......**£4-5**
Same but with 'OCL' labels................**£10-12**
Dark brown container, red roof, black
flat car, 'N.Y.K.' labels.......................**£12-15**

MB 25g   Audi Quattro
82-83 White and black, 'Audi' and '20'........**£10-12**
Same but black and black... ....**£130-150**

MB 26c   GMC Tipper Truck
70-72 Red tipping cab, silver tipper, green
chassis, green glass, wide wheels.......**£20-30**

MB 26d   Big Banger
72-76 Red, UB, 'Big Banger', dk. blue glass ..**£20-25**
Same but with amber glass.................**£18-22**
78   Dark brown, 'Brown Sugar', WB,
amber, black or blue glass (USA) **£25-30**
81-83 White body, BB, 'Cosmic Blues'
clear or blue glass, (US issue)............**£15-20**

MB 26e   Site Dumper
76-78 Yellow body, yellow dumper,
black seats, black base **£5-7**
78-81 Same but with red dumper...................**£4-6**
Same but dark grey base **£8-12**
Same but brown base **£12-15**
81-82 Orange-red body, silver dumper,
white seats, black base **£4-6**
Same but wheels have yellow hubs **£7-10**
Orange-red body, silver dumper, white
seats, dark grey base.............................**£4-6**
Same but wheels have yellow hubs **£7-10**

MB 26f   Cable Truck
82-83 Orange-yellow body, red base, blue
glass, two light grey cable drums **£15-18**
Same but dark grey or BB **£7-10**
83   Bright yellow body,
BB, BG, 2 grey drums **£50-60**
Same but dark red body.....................**£12-15**

MB 27d Mercedes 230SL

MB 27d   Mercedes 230sl
70-71   White body, red interior, CG, UB, NW £40-45
71   Same but yellow body £50-60
71-73   Yellow body, black interior,
         CG, UB, NW or WW £35-40

MB 27e   Lamborghini Countach
73-75   Yellow body, BB, red glass, '3' £14-18
         Same but with amber glass................£10-15
         Same but with purple glass £30-40
         Yellow body, UB, red glass, '3' £10-15
         Same but with purple glass £14-18
75   Orange body, UB, red glass, '3' £70-80
         Same but with amber glass................£70-80
75-81   Lamborghini 'Streakers'. All have
         green/black 'Streaker' prints and a
         red '8' on the bonnet.
         Orange body, chrome interior, BB £20-30
         Same but with amber or green glass...£20-30
         Orange body, grey interior, BB, GG ...£20-30
         Same but with purple glass £20-30
         Orange body, grey interior, UB, GG ...£20-30
         Same but with brown base £20-30
         Orange body, yellow interior, BB or
         dark grey base, green glass £20-30
         Orange, chrome int., UB, GG or AG ...£20-30
         Orange body, grey interior, dark grey
         base, green glass...............................£20-30
         Same but with purple glass £20-30
         Orange, chrome int., red windows.....£45-55
         Orange body, beige interior,
         dark grey base, GG £20-30
         Same but with purple glass £20-30
         Orange body, beige interior, BB, GG .£20-30

MB 27e Lambourghini Countach

MB 27f   Swing Wing
81-83   Red/white, red glass...........................£10-15
         Red/white, dark yellow-orange glass.£10-15
         Red/white, red or black 'Jet Set'........£10-15

MB 28d   Mack Dump Truck
70-73   Metallic lime green body and dumper,
         UB, cab steps cast closed £18-20
         Same but with steps cast open £18-24
77-79   Military olive drab green body/dumper,
         BB, cab steps cast closed (TP)...........£40-50
         Military olive green (TP)....................£20-25

MB 28e   Stoat
73-76   Metallic gold body, UB or BB, dark
         brown man, (Rola-Matic issue)............£5-10
77   Military olive drab green body, BB,
         dark brown man, (TP)........................£40-50
77-79   Military olive green body, BB, dark
         brown man, (TP) £20-25

MB 28f   Lincoln Continental
79   Light red body, white roof,
         beige interior, clear glass, UB £10-15
79-81   Dark red body, beige, dark brown
         or grey interior, clear glass, UB..........£15-20

MB 28g   Formula Racing Car
81-83   Metallic brown-grey body, BB or UB,
         white driver, 'Exxon' and '8' prints £10-12

MB 29c Fire Pumper Truck

MB 29c   Fire Pumper Truck
70   Red body, white back and ladders,
         UB, blue glass, narrow wheels............£35-40
81   Same but 'P1' and 'Los Angeles Fire
         Dept.' wide wheels ('Code Red') £18-20

MB 29d Racing Mini

MB 29d   Racing Mini
70-72   Metallic bronze body, SB or UB,
         off-white interior, '29' on yellow
         labels (orange edges) £30-35
72-76   Orange body, SB or UB, cream or
         off-white interior, '29' on yellow
         labels (orange edges) £12-15
         Same but with green label edges £20-25
76-81   Red body, SB or UB, off-white or
         cream interior, '29' on yellow
         labels (green edges) (TP)....................£35-40
         Red body, SB, cream interior, '3' on
         white circle door labels (TP) £60-70
         Same but with no labels......................£20-25

MB 29e   Tractor Shovel
76-78   Light yellow body, red shovel, silver
         engine and seat, yellow base £8-10
77   Lime green body, yellow shovel and
         base, silver engine and seat,
         (German PS1000 set issue) £60-70
78-81   Yellow body, red shovel, silver or
         black engine and seat, yellow base £6-8
         Same but with cream base....................£8-10
         Same but with black base £6-8
         Yellow body, red shovel, black engine
         and seat, yellow base, yellow hubs £6-8
         Yellow body, black shovel, black engine
         and seat, yellow base............................£6-8
         Same but with cream base....................£8-10
         Same but with black base £6-8
79   Yellow body, black shovel/engine/
         seat/stripes, BB, 'C' prints on some,
         (G5 Set)..£6-8

81   Orange-red body, red shovel, dark grey
         engine and seat, black base................£20-25
82-83   Same but with black shovel £12-15

MB 30c   8-wheel Crane
70   Red body, dark orange crane arm with
         yellow hook, UB(beware of fakes)..£600-800
         Same but with gold crane arm £35-45

MB 30d   Beach Buggy
70-76   Light metallic purple body, yellow
         spots, UB, white interior £40-50
         Same but with orange interior £10-15
         Same but dark metallic purple body .£10-15
NB   The yellow spots on this model can vary
         from only a few spots to almost an
         entire body covering.

MB 30e   Swamp Rat
76-81   Military green deck, light brown hull,
         'Swamp Rat' labels on some.................£9-12

MB 30f   Articulated Truck
81-83   Metallic steel-blue cab, WB,
         red glass, silver trailer £9-12
         Blue cab, WB or YB, silver trailer £9-12
83   Blue cab and trailer, 'Pauls' white labels,
         pale YB or WB, (Ltd. blister-pack
         issue of 900) £35-45
         Blue cab, WB or YB, yellow
         trailer, 'International' labels £8-10
         Red cab, YB and trailer,
         'International' labels £10-12
         Red cab, YB, silver trailer £10-12

MB 30g   Peterbilt Quarry Truck
82   Yellow cab/chassis, grey tipper £12-14

MB 31e Lincoln Continental
70   Sea-green body, white interior,
         unpainted base, CG, NW (beware
         of fakes) £1,000-1,200
         Metallic lime-green body, white
         interior, UB, CG, NW £25-30
         Same but with wide wheels £20-25

MB 31d   Volksdragon
71-77   Red body, PG, UB or SB, yellow or
         cream interior, 'eyes' label on some ..£15-20
         Same but with smooth air scoop... ....£60-70
         Red body, purple glass, UB or SB,
         yellow interior, 'flower' label £40-50
78   Black body, purple glass, UB, yellow
         interior, 'bug'/ 'flames' (US issue) £30-35

MB 31e   Caravan
77-83   White body, off-white, light yellow or
         light brown interior, UB, AG, orange,
         light blue or yellow door, orange stripe
         (white bird labels on some)................£10-15
         Same but light yellow interior £10-15
         Same but dark blue door, blue stripe.£10-15

MB 32c   Leyland Tanker
70-73   Dark green cab and body, BG, 'B.P.'
         labels in centre or front of white tank,
         SB, NW...£18-20
         Dark green cab and body, white tank,
         GB, 'B.P.' labels in centre of tank........£40-50
         Same but with grey grille £80-100
         Blue cab and body, SB, 'Aral' labels
         on white tank, (German,
         'Aral Tankwagen' box) £130-160
         Metallic purple cab and body,
         silver tank, SB, no labels £100-125
         Same but with 'N.A.M.C.' labels.....£250-300
         Red cab and body, white tank,
         SB, 'N.A.M.C.' labels £800-1,000

MB 32d   Maserati Bora
73-78   Metallic crimson body, lime green base,

yellow interior, stripe and '8' label....... **£8-10**
Same but with dark green or UB........ **£10-12**
Same but dark green base, '3' label ...**£15-20**
Same but with no label **£6-8**
79 Metallic gold, SB, yellow interior,
no bonnet label, tow hook, (TP) **£60-75**

MB 32e Field Gun
77-81 Military green body, light or dark brown
base, 2 soldiers and 4 shells on sprue,
black WW **£11-14**
Same but black wheels, silver hubs .**£80-100**
78 Military olive green body, no base,
soldiers or shells, black wheels (TP) **£3-5**

MB 32f Excavator
81-82 Orange-red body, silver-grey tracks.....**£8-10**
82-83 Yellow body, black tracks and
'CAT' prints.......................................**£8-10**
Same but with no 'CAT' print................**£6-8**

MB 33c Lamborghini Miura

MB 33c Lamborghini Miura
69 Yellow body, red interior, UB, NW .**£250-300**
70 Light met. bronze body, red int.,
UB, NW...**£30-40**
Dark met. bronze body, red int.,
UB, NW...**£200-250**
70 -73 Light metallic gold body, off-white
interior, UB, NW **£35-40**
Same but dark metallic gold body **£35-40**
Dark met. gold body, red interior,
UB, NW...**£30-35**
Light met. gold body, off-white interior,
red or pink-red base, NW or WW.......**£30-35**
77-78 Light gold body, off-white interior,
UB or BB, WW (Japanese issue).........**£30-35**

MB 33d Datsun 126X
73-75 Yellow body, orange base, AG **£10-15**
Same but with unpainted base **£30-40**
75-77 Yellow body, orange base, AG,
red/orange or red/black flame prints,
('Streakers' issue).................................**£15-18**
78 Yellow body, BB, AG, red/black flame
prints, (US Roman Numeral issue) **£18-20**
Gold plated body, BB, black glass,
green prints, (US Roman Numeral) ...**£18-20**

MB 33e Police Motorcycle
77-79 White frame, chrome or black engine,
white bars, UW, blue man, white or
black seat and panniers, 'Police'..........**£8-11**
79 White frame and bars, chrome engine,
UW, green man, seat and panniers,
'Polizei' (German) **£15-18**
79 Same but cream frame, man has white
helmet and gloves (KS71 German
Polizei Patrol set)................................**£15-18**
79 All black bike / wheels, dark blue man,
white helmet, seat and panniers.
3 stripes and shield, 'Police',
gold star tank labels (KS 66 set) **£20-25**

79 White frame, bars, helmet, gloves, seat,
and 'Police' labels, black engine/wheels,
blue man **£8-10**
79-81 White frame/bars, BE/wheels, green
man, seat and panniers, 'Polizei' labels
(German)..**£10-12**
79 Same but white helmet and gloves **£12-15**
79-81 Same but white helmet and gloves,
UW, (KS 66 Police Patrol set).............**£20-25**
81 White frame, bars, seat and panniers, green
man, BE/wheels, 'LAPD' labels **£20-25**
81 White frame, seat and panniers,
CE, black bars, black wheels,
no man, 'Police' labels **£10-12**
81-82 Black frame, CE, white bars/seat/panniers,
black wheels, blue man,
'LAPD' (Code Red)............................**£12-15**

MB 34d F-1 Racing Car
71-72 Metallic purple body, UB, CG, yellow
or blue stripe, '16' label, 4 NW **£20-25**
71 Same but yellow stripe, 'Wynns'
labels (Promotional issue).................**£60-70**
72-75 Yellow body, UB, CG, blue bonnet
stripe, '16' label, 4 NW or WW...........**£10-12**
Same but front NW, rear WW **£8-10**
Yellow body/stripe, UB, CG,
'16' label, 4 NW **£8-10**
Yellow body, UB, AG, blue or yellow
stripe, '16' label, 4 WW......................**£12-15**
73-75 Metallic blue body, UB, CG, yellow or blue
stripe, '15' label, 4 WW (or front NW,
rear WW) (G4 set)...............................**£70-80**
Orange body, UB, CG, blue or yellow
stripe, '16', 4 WW (or front NW, rear
WW) (G4 set)......................................**£30-35**
Orange-yellow body, UB, CG, blue
stripe, '16' label, 2 NW, 2 WW **£15-18**

MB 34e Vantastic
75-78 Orange, WB, GG, white int.,
stripes labels **£12-16**
Same but motif instead of stripes **£8-10**
Same but with stripes and UB........**£100-150**
78 Orange body, WB, GG, white interior,
'Jaffa Mobile', (Promotional-but
some doubt over authenticity).......**£200-230**
78 Orange body, WB, GG or CG, white
interior, bonnet 'Sun' label **£25-30**
78-81 Orange body, WB, GG, white interior,
'34', rear stripes labels on some **£10-14**

MB 34f Chevy Pro-Stocker
81-83 White body, UB, blue '34' prints **£8-12**
Same but with no tampo prints **£8-12**
White body, red base, blue '34' **£12-15**
Green and with matching box... ...**£250-300**

MB 35c Merryweather Fire Engine

MB 35c Merryweather Fire Engine
69-71 Metallic red body, GB, white ladder,
'London Fire Service', NW..................**£40-50**

71-75 Red body, GB, white ladder, 'London
Fire Service', NW or WW.....................**£25-30**
Red, GB, 'Flame-Proof Wool'..........**£125-150**
Same but in promotional box..........**£400-500**
Red body, BB, ladder, 'London
Fire Service', wide wheels...................**£25-30**
Same but with tan base **£70-80**
Red body, GB, different style ladder,
'London Fire Service', WW, (TP)........**£20-25**
81 Red body, GB, white ladder and man
from 13f, 'Los Angeles City Fire Dept.'
prints, WW, (Code Red) **£20-25**

MB 35d Fandango
75-77 White body, red interior, red base,
red or silver rear disc, arrow and '35'
bonnet label (Rola-Matic) **£12-16**
White body, red interior, UB, red rear
disc, arrow and '35' bonnet label.......**£25-30**
White body, red interior and base,
silver rear disc, stripe and '6' bonnet
label from 41c **£15-20**
77-82 Red body, red interior, red base,
blue arrow and '35' bonnet label,
blue or silver rear disc......................**£85-100**
Red body, purple windows,
dark blue spinner, UB **£25-30**
Red body, off-white interior, WB,
blue arrow and '35' label, blue,
silver or red rear disc.........................**£10-15**
Red body, off-white or white interior,
UB, blue rear disc, arrow and '35'......**£12-16**
Red body, white interior, UB, blue rear
disc, 'Sun' bonnet label from 47d **£35-40**

MB 35e Zoo Truck
82 Red body, blue cage, light brown
lions, BG, BB **£9-12**
Same but with red base.......................**£25-30**
Same but with grey base **£10-12**
Orange body, blue cage, 5 arch wheels.**£40-45**
83 Red body, silver cage, light or dark
brown lions, blue glass, black base....**£14-18**

MB 36c Opel Diplomat
70 Metallic light gold body,
silver grille, white interior, BB **£70-80**
Metallic dark gold body,
silver grille, white interior, BB **£30-40**
Same but without silver grille.............**£30-40**

MB 36d Hot Rod Draguar

MB 36d Hot Rod Draguar
70-73 Metallic dark red body, off-white or light
yellow interior, silver 'Draguar' label.**£40-50**
Same but with orange interior............**£25-30**
Same but lemon or white interior......**£15-20**
73-75 Metallic pink body, light yellow
interior, silver 'Draguar' label.............**£15-20**
Met. pink body, cream interior,
no boot label **£18-22**
Metallic pink body, light or dark
yellow interior, no boot label..............**£15-20**
Same but with amber glass.................**£15-20**

MB 36e   Formula 5000
75-77   Orange body, blue or yellow man,
'Formula 5000' and orange or yellow '3',
'5000' on rear spoiler............................**£15-20**
77   Same but red body, yellow man.........**£15-20**
77-78   Red body, yellow man, 'Texaco 11' on
bonnet, no spoiler label or 'Marlbro' **£15-20**
78-80   Same but 'Champion' on spoiler **£15-20**

MB 36f   Refuse Truck
80-82   Met. red cab/load, yellow container,
no labels..**£8-10**
Same but no 'Collectomatic' on
container **£50-75**
82-83   Blue cab, yellow or orange container,
black or red load, 'Metro DPW66' on
side labels...**£7-9**
Same but orange container with
yellow opening back, red load.............**£8-10**

MB 37c   Cattle Truck
70-71   Orange-yellow cab and body, grey
back and 2 white cattle **£25-30**
71   Same but orange cab and body..........**£30-40**
Orange cab and body, silver back..**£200-250**
72   Bright-yellow cab/body, grey back **£100-150**

MB 37d   Soopa Coopa
72-75   Metallic light blue body, yellow interior,
AG, unpainted or silver base **£10-15**
75-76   Metallic light purple body, yellow
interior, AG, UB, 'flower' label..........**£12-15**
Same but with red base..................**£150-200**
Purple, yellow interior, UB.................**£25-30**
77   Orange body, yellow interior, AG,
SB, 'Jaffa Mobile' (Promotional) **£100-120**
Orange, yellow interior, UB **£80-90**

MB 37e   Skip Truck
76-81   Red cab, yellow skip,
chrome int., AG, BB.............................**£11-14**
Same but grey interior, clear glass **£8-10**
Same but with brown base **£8-10**
Red cab, yellow skip,
orange int., CG, BB **£10-12**
Red cab, blue skip,
grey interior, CG, BB **£90-100**
77   Orange cab/body, yellow skip, grey
interior, CG, BB (German issue).......**£90-100**
Red skip (German PS1000 set) **£60-70**
81-82   Metallic blue cab, yellow skip,
grey interior, CG, gloss or matt BB ...**£8-10**
Same but with silver base **£10-12**

MB 37f   Matra Rancho
82   Blue body, blue base, black interior **£8-10**
83   Yellow body, yellow base, black
interior, red side stripe prints............**£15-20**

MB 38c Honda Motorcycle and Trailer

MB 38c   Honda Motorcycle
and Trailer
70-71   Metallic blue-green bike,
yellow trailer, 'Honda' labels **£35-40**
71   Same but metallic pink bike **£30-35**

72-73   Same but metallic purple bike **£30-35**
77   Metallic green bike, orange trailer
with 'Honda' labels on some (TP) **£35-40**
82   Same but yellow trailer (TP)..............**£15-18**

MB 38d   Stingeroo
73-76   First issue: Metallic purple body,
purple forks, white horse's head **£15-20**
Later issue with pale blue forks..........**£50-65**
Same but with chrome forks..........**£600-700**

MB 38e   Jeep
76-80   Military green body, gun, BB/seats,
'21*11' or 'star' label **£8-10**
77   Military olive drab green body,
no gun, BB/seats, 'star' label, (TP).....**£55-65**
Same but military olive green body ...**£25-30**
Same but with '21*11' label (TP)........**£20-25**
Yellow body, BB/seats, 'Gliding Club',
(TP with yellow glider trailer)...........**£15-20**
Same but with white base,
(TP with yellow glider trailer)...........**£35-40**
Red body, BB/seats, 'Gliding Club',
(TP with red glider trailer) **£450-550**

MB 38f   Ford Camper
80-82   Orange-red body, green glass, cream
back with AG, UB with no labels....**£90-110**
Same but camper back with no glass ..**£7-10**

MB 38g   Ford Model 'A' Van
The 'collectable cut-off point' for this Catalogue is
generally 1983. However, the MB38g casting was
used well into the 1990s and proved popular as a
promotional item. This section therefore includes
issues up to the end of 1989 but excludes items
likely to be priced below £5.

84   'TOY FAIR 84' (US), roof label **£70-85**
Same but without roof label **£40-50**
84   'PEPSI COLA', 'COME ALIVE' **£8-12**
Same but without 'COME ALIVE' **£8-12**
'PEPSI COLA', 'Matchmates' **£8-12**
84   'BEN FRANKLIN'............................**£250-350**
84   'MATCHBOX USA'..............................**£15-20**
86   'WEET-BIX'/'SANITARIUM' **£8-12**
86   'H.H. BRAIN'...**£8-12**
87   'W.H.SMITH & SON Ltd', Red..............**£8-12**
87   'MICA' 2nd CONVENTION **£100-125**
87   'SILVO 1912-1987 `..............................**£8-12**
87   'This Van Delivers', with phone no......**£8-12**
without phone no **£250-350**
87   'RICE KRISPIES', Dark Blue, (US)........**£8-12**
88   'MICA 3rd CONVENTION' **£8-12**
88   'MICA 1st N.A. CONVENTION' **£8-12**
with black 'island'..........................**£18-22**
88   'W.H. SMITH & SON Ltd', Yellow.........**£8-12**
88   'UNIROYAL' (Canada)..........................**£8-12**
89   'MB US COLLECTORS CLUB' **£18-22**
89   'JACKY MAEDER' (Swiss) **£8-12**
89   'SWARFEGA'...**£8-12**
89   'CAMPERDOWN' (Australia) **£12-15**

MB 39d Clipper

MB 39d   Clipper
73-79   Metallic crimson body, yellow interior,

AG, UB, chrome or white exhausts,
(Rola-Matic).......................................**£20-25**
With green base and amber glass **£10-15**
With green base and clear glass **£12-15**
MB 39e Rolls Silver Shadow
79-81   Silver body, Red interior, SB or UB **£10-12**
81-82   Metallic red body, off-white or yellow
interior, silver or unpainted base **£8-12**
82-83   Metallic gold-brown body, white
interior, silver or unpainted base **£8-10**
Same but with AG.................................**£50-60**
83   Ruby red body, white interior, matt
black or matt silver base **£12-15**

MB 40c   Hay Trailer
67-70   Dark blue body, yellow sides,
BPT with yellow hubs...........................**£8-10**
79-79   Lt. yellow body, no sides, BPT (TP) **£4-6**
Same but with black fixed sides (TP).....**£4-6**
Orange-yellow body, black fixed sides,
black wheels (TP) **£8-10**
79   Same but with light blue body, (TP)..**£10-12**
80   Same but with red body, (TP).............**£10-12**
81   Same but with beige body, (TP)..........**£50-60**

MB 40d Vauxhall Guildsman
71-74   Pink body, GG, cream interior, UB,
blue circle flame bonnet label...........**£15-20**
Same but with silver base **£15-20**
With UB, black circle flame label **£15-20**
Same but with silver base **£15-20**
75   Pink body, GG, cream interior, UB,
blue '40' print (Streakers issue)......**£100-120**
75-76   Red body, AG or GG, cream interior,
UB or SB, blue '40' (Streakers) **£15-20**
76   Red body, GG or AG, cream interior, UB,
Blue circle flame bonnet label, (TP) ..**£30-40**
Red body, AG, UB, cream interior,
no bonnet label, (TP) **£15-20**

MB 40e   Horse Box
77-80   Orange cab, cream horse box, light or dark
brown door, BB, SB, GB or UB...........**£10-12**
Same but red horse box ....**NGPP**
80-83   Light metallic green cab, cream box,
dark brown door, unpainted base......**£10-12**
Same but with white door....................**£10-12**
Dark metallic green cab, cream box,
dark brown door, UB, SB or BB **£10-12**
Same but with lime green door, SB or BB..**£12-15**
83   Dark metallic green cab, dark brown
box, white door, unpainted base........**£12-15**
Yellow cab, dark brown box, lime
green door, black base **£20-25**
Same but with white door...................**£18-20**
Orange cab, dark brown box, lime
green door, BB, SB or UB **£14-18**
Same but with white door...................**£14-18**

MB 41c   Ford GT
69-70   White body, light or dark green or BB,
red interior, '6' on bonnet, NW..........**£25-30**
71-72   Metallic bronze body, dark green or
BB, red interior, '6', NW or WW..........**£30-35**
Same but WW, cream base **£30-35**
Same but WW, grey base **£30-40**
WW, light or dark yellow base **£30-35**
Blue body, Yellow interior **£40-45**
77   White body, red interior, 'Wildcat'
or '6' label, BB, (Japanese issue) **£30-35**
79   Yellow body, red interior, BB, no
bonnet label, MP1 Italian issue**£2,000-2,500**

MB 41d   Siva Spyder
72-75   Metallic red body, cream interior, black
band, unpainted base, clear glass......**£10-14**
Same but with chrome band **£15-18**
Metallic red body, white interior, black
band, unpainted base, clear glass........**£8-10**
75-78   Metallic dark blue body, white or cream
interior, black band, UB, CG, stars &
stripes, '8', (Streakers issue) **£15-20**
77   Light blue body, off-white interior, black

band, UB, black glass or CG, 'Spider'
print, (US Roman Numeral issue)......£20-25

MB 41e   Ambulance
78-81   White body, grey interior, side stripe
with 'Ambulance', red cross labels......£10-12
Same but with yellow interior £12-14
White body, grey interior, side stripe
with 'Emergency Medical Services' ...£10-12
Same but with yellow interior £12-14
White body, grey interior, no stripe -
only 'Ambulance' in grey letters.........£12-15
80   Silver body, grey interior, 'Paris-Dakar
81' (French blistercard issue) £35-40
Same but with white rear doors £35-40
White body, small 'Ambulance' labels £20-25
81   Red body, grey interior, 'Notarzt' and
red cross prints, (German issue)........£25-30
White body, grey interior, side stripe
with 'Ambulance', Blue Cross labels...£10-12
Same but with 'Pacific Ambulance,
Emergency, 101' prints (Code Red) ...£25-30

MB 41f   Kenworth Truck
80   Red body, white canopy.......................£9-12

MB 42c Iron Fairy Crane Truck

MB 42c   Iron Fairy Crane
70   Red body, yellow boom/hook/base £150-175
Light or dark orange-red body, lime
boom, yellow hook, yellow base £45-55
Same but with orange body...............£80-90

MB 42d   Tyre Fryer
72-77   Metallic light blue body,
yellow interior, UB..............................£25-35
Same but with black base £12-16
Met. dark blue body,
orange-yellow int., BB........................£20-25
77   Orange body, yellow interior, BB,
'Jaffa Mobile' (Promotional)...........£100-120

MB42d Tyre Fryer

MB 42e   Mercedes Truck
77   All-yellow body, BG, BB, 'Deutsche

Bundespost' labels (German issue)...£20-25
77-80   Red cab/body, cream container with
red doors and roof, BG, UB,
'Sealand' or 'NYK' labels....................£11-14
Same but with black base £11-14
Same but with UB, 'OCL' labels.........£11-14
81   Same but with 'Confern Mobeltransport-
betriebe' labels, PG (German issue)..£18-20
Dark blue cab and body, blue container
BG, UB, 'Karstadt'(German issue) £20-25
81-82   Red/white, 'Matchbox', BG or PG..........£6-8
Metallic green/yellow, BG or PG,
'Mayflower' and ship labels.................£8-11
Same but with red glass £10-14
Same but red/white body, BG or PG ...£8-11

MB 42   '57 Thunderbird
82-83   Red body, white interior, UB or SB £7-10
Same but with AG £60-70

MB 43c   Pony Trailer
70-71   Yellow body, grey door, light green
base, 2 white horses, NW...................£30-35
Same but with dark green base £25-30
76-79   Orange body, brown door, BB or GB,
2 horses, 'horse head' labels (TP) £25-30
79-83   Same but light brown body £15-20
83   Light brown body, brown door,
BB, 2 horses, 'Silver Shoes' or no
labels (TP) £10-15

MB 43d VW Dragon Wheels

MB 43d   Dragon Wheels
72-77   Dark green, BB, 'Dragon Wheels'.......£12-18
Same but with unpainted base £45-55
Light green, BB, 'Dragon Wheels' £18-20

MB 43e   Steam Locomotive
78-82   Red cab/sides, black engine, '4345' £4-5
Same but with 'NP' labels....................£5-7
81   Green cab/sides, black engine,'4345'...£8-10
81-83   Same but with side 'NP' labels (TP) £7-9
MB 44c Refrigerator Truck
70   Red cab and body, green back, grey
rear door, green glass, UB, NW.......£175-225
70-71   Yellow cab and body, red back, grey
rear door, green glass, UB, WWor NW£20-30

MB 44d   Boss Mustang
72   Yellow body, black bonnet, UB, WW .£20-25
Same but with silver base £20-30
80   Green, UB, 'Cobra', (US Ltd. Ed.).......£15-20
82-83   Dark or light orange body, off-white
interior, UB, 'The Boss' and '5'...........£15-20

MB 44e   Passenger Coach / Caboose
78-83   Red/black, off-white roof, green glass,
red '431 432' side labels £6-8
Same but with clear glass £8-10
Same but with no glass £6-8
Red/black, off-white roof, no glass,
red '5810 6102' side labels £6-8
Same but with cream or tan roof £6-8
Red/black, off-white roof, no glass,
green '5810 6102' side labels £6-8
Red/black, off-white or cream roof,
no glass, green 'GWR' side labels.........£8-10
81-83   Green/black, off-white raised roof, no
glass, green '5810 6102' labels (TP) £6-8

Red/black, off-white raised roof, no
glass, red '431 432' labels (TP) £6-8
Same but red '5810 6102' labels (TP).....£6-8

MB 45c   Ford Group 6
70   Non-metallic green body, white interior
CE, CG, UB, '7' label, NW £600-800
70-71   Dark metallic green body, CE,
CG, UB or BB, '7' label, NW.............£30-35
Same but with AG £200-220
Same but 'Burmah' labels (G3 set) £30-35
Dark metallic green body, CE,
CG, BB or GB,'45' label, NW £20-25
Same but with pink base....................£35-40
71-73   Metallic lime green body, CE,
AG, BB, '45' label, WW £15-20
Same + 'Burmah' labels, (G3 set) £20-25
Metallic lime green body,
grey engine, AG, BB, '45', NW £15-20
Same but grey or CE, GB, WW...........£15-20
73-76   Metallic dark or light purple body,
grey or CE, AG, BB, '45', WW £15-20
Metallic dark purple body, CE, AG,
BB, 'eyes' label from 31d, WW £30-35

MB 45d   BMW 3.0 CSL
76-81   Light or dark orange body, cream
interior, GG, 'BMW' label on some £12-15
Same but with clear glass £18-22
77   White body, cream interior, GG,
'BMW' and 'Manhalter' signature
label, (Austrian 50,000 issue) £30-35
White body, GG, 'Polizei 123', blue
or yellow light, (German issue) £50-60
Same but no light or 'Polizei 123' £50-60
82   Red body, GG, 'BMW' (G15).............£80-100

MB 45e   Kenworth Cabover
82-83   White body, AG, blue/brown stripes .£10-12
With orange/yellow tampos £40-50

MB 46c   Mercedes 300se
70   Metallic blue body, white interior, UB,
opening doors and boot, NW £70-80
70-71   Metallic light or dark gold body,
opening doors and boot, NW £45-50
Metallic light gold body, opening boot
but doors cast shut, NW.....................£30-35
77   Military olive green body, boot and
doors cast shut, 'Staff' labels (TP)....£18-20
81   Silver body, WW, (Multi Pack)...........£70-80

MB 46d   Stretcha Fetcha
72-77   All-white body, red base, BG,
'Ambulance', large Red Cross labels £6-8
Same but no 'Amulance', small RC.....£15-18
All-white body, UB, BG, 'Ambulance'
and large Red Cross labels £8-10
All-white body, red base, 'Ambulance',
large Red Cross labels, AG £15-20
Same but no 'Amulance', small RC.....£20-25
77   All-red body, red base, BG, 'Unfall
Rettung' labels (German issue)..........£40-50
80   Lime green/white, WB or BB, AG,
'Viper Van' prints (US Ltd. Ed.)..........£20-25

MB 46e   Ford Tractor and Harrow
78-81   Blue body, yellow interior, UB, black
wheels, yellow plastic harrow............£9-12
Same but black wheels, yellow hubs ...£9-12
Blue body, white interior, UB, black
wheels, yellow hubs, yellow harrow £9-12
79   Blue body, yellow interior, UB, black
wheels, no harrow (TP)........................£9-12
81   Metallic lime green, yellow interior,
BW, yellow hubs, no harrow (TP) £9-12
81-83   Metallic green body, yellow interior,
BW, yellow hubs, yellow harrow £9-12
83   Blue body, white interior, GB, BW
with gold hubs, no harrow (TP) £9-12

MB 47c   DAF Truck
70-72   Silver cab/body, yellow tipper...........**£20-30**

MB 47d   Beach Hopper
73-78   Blue body with paint spots, pink base,
        orange interior, light brown man,
        clear or no windscreen,
        'Sun' label, wide WW (Rola-Matic)....**£15-18**
        Same but UB, no windscreen **£15-18**
        With light pink base, yellow interior,
        no windscreen, dark brown man.......**£30-35**

MB 47e   Pannier Locomotive
79-82   Dark green and black, BB, 'G.W.R.' **£8-10**
        Same but with unpainted base......**£8-10**
        Same but with brown or grey base.....**£15-20**

MB 47f   Jaguar SS100
82-83   Red body, light brown interior, BB....**£8-10**

MB 48c   Dodge Dumper Truck
69-71   Blue cab and body, yellow tipper,
        chrome base, NW or WW...................**£35-40**

MB 48d Pie-Eyed Piper (Red Rider)

MB 48d   Pie-Eyed Piper
72-77   Metallic blue body, silver engine and
        exhausts, BG, UB, '8' and stars..........**£15-20**
        Same but with amber glass................**£20-25**
        Red body, 'Big Banger', CE and
        exhausts, BG, UB **£150-200**
78   White body, silver/black engine, black
        exhausts, glass and base, orange
        prints, (US Roman Numeral issue)....**£20-25**
81-83   Red body, SE, black exhausts, AG,
        BB, 'Red Rider' prints (USA) **£20-25**

MB 48e   Sambron Jack Lift
77-81   Yellow body, BB, red 'Sambron' **£600-800**
        Same but with no tampo prints **£5-7**
        Yellow body, BB, yellow hubs.................**£6-8**
        Same but with grey or brown base.......**£7-10**
81-83   Yellow body, black forks, BB or GB **£6-8**

MB 49b   Unimog
70   Blue body, red base, GG,
        silver or plain grille..............................**£25-30**
70-71   Same but metallic steel-blue body **£20-25**
71-72   Same but sky blue body, plain grille...**£18-20**
78   Military olive green body, BB, GG,
        tan load, 'A' label in square (TP) **£35-40**
        'Star' circle label,
        tan load on some, (TP).......................**£35-40**

MB 49c   Chop Suey
73-76   Metallic red-purple frame, chrome
        forks, CE, 'bull's head'....................**£400-500**
        Same but with red forks **£8-10**
        With black or orange forks.................**£35-40**

MB 49d   Crane Truck
76-79   Yellow body and crane arm,
        red hook, BB, GG...................................**£6-8**
77   Red body, yellow crane arm, red hook,
        BB, CG (German PS1000 set) **£70-80**

80-82   Same but GG (German PS1000 set)...**£60-70**
        Yellow body, black crane arm, red
        hook, black base, purple or red glass.**£15-18**
        Same but green glass..........................**£15-18**
82-83   Same but 'A1 Crane Service' on arm
        + 'Safety First', 'C', 'Cat' on some **£15-18**

MB 50c   Kennel Truck
70-71   Dark or light metallic green body, BB,
        silver grille, 4 white dogs, NW **£40-50**
        Dark Metallic Green body, Grey base,
        silver grille, 4 white dogs, NW **£40-50**
        Same but with yellow base **£40-50**
72-73   Lime Green body, BB or GB,
        chrome grille, 4 white dogs, WW........**£70-80**
        Same but white grille, BB or GB **£70-80**
        Same but with unpainted base **£70-80**

MB 50c Kennel Truck and Dogs

MB 50d   Articulated Truck
73-79   Yellow cab/body, BB, light blue trailer
        with yellow chevron side labels, yellow
        or orange trailer body, red or PG **£10-15**
        Same but no labels **£8-12**
        Yellow cab/trailer, 'KODAK' logo ....**NGPP**
80   Red cab/body, BB, light blue trailer, no
        labels, red trailer body, PG **£40-45**
        Yellow cab/body/trailer body,
        light blue trailer, no labels, white tow
        hook, purple glass (TP).........................**£8-11**
        Red cab/body, silver trailer (red body),
        white hook on some, PG (TP) **£35-40**
80   Articulated Trailer
        Light blue trailer (yellow body) (TP) **£6-8**
        Silver trailer, red trailer body (TP) **£35-40**

MB 50e   Harley-Davidson
80-82   Light gold frame, black handlebars ...**£13-16**
82-83   Dark bronze frame, black bars **£13-16**
        Light bronze frame, with rider **£13-16**

MB 51c Leyland 8-wheel Tipper
70-71   Yellow cab and body, silver tipper,
        BG, SB, 'POINTER' labels on some....**£30-35**
        Same but with grey base **£80-100**
        Promotional issue: 'Alcon Laboratories Inc.
        Fort Worth, Texas'. Chrome grille,
        plastic bottle, special box................**£250-350**

MB 51d   Citroën SM
72-74   Metallic bronze body,
        cream int., UB, NW.............................**£12-15**
        Same but with orange interior **£120-150**
        Same but with yellow interior **£20-25**
        With cream interior, silver base **£12-15**
75   Metallic blue body,
        yellow int., UB, WW...........................**£30-40**
        Same but with off-white interior, UB.**£50-65**
75-78   Same plus '8', UB (Streakers issue).....**£12-14**
        With '8', UB and off-white or orange
        interior (Streakers issue)...................**£15-18**
79   Metallic blue body, orange interior, UB,
        roof rack, 'Yamaha Shell STP' (TP)....**£15-18**

MB 51e   Combine Harvester
78-81   Red body, yellow blades/arm, BB,
        black 'regular wheels'............................**£8-11**
        Same but with black Superfast wheels.**£8-11**
        Same but with yellow hubs.................**£12-15**
        Red body, yellow blades/arm,
        no base, black Superfast wheels...........**£8-10**
        Same but with yellow hubs.................**£12-14**
        Yellow body, red blades/arm, no base,
        '2' print, Superfast wheels (Gift Set) **£8-10**

MB 51f   Pontiac Firebird SE
82-83   Red body, tan interior, silver base........**£8-10**
        Red body, yellow interior...................**£14-18**

MB 51i Motorcycle Trailer
79-82   Metallic blue body, 3 orange-yellow or
        yellow bikes (TP)..................................**£7-10**
        Same but with 3 red bikes (TP) **£10-12**
82-83   Red body, 3 yellow bikes (TP) **£12-15**

MB 52c Dodge Charger Mk.III
70-71   Metallic light or dark red body,
        black interior......................................**£20-30**
        Same but with '5' labels (G3 set).......**£30-35**
71   Metallic purple body, black interior ..**£20-30**
71-75   Metallic lime green, black interior.....**£20-30**
        Same but with '5' labels (G3 set).......**£25-30**
        Same but with UB (G3 set) **£25-30**

MB 52d   Police Launch
76-80   White deck, light blue hull,
        lt. or dk. BG, orange stripes, 'Police',
        2 light blue men, 2 horns **£10-13**
81   Same but with no roof horns...............**£8-11**
        White deck, red hull, roof and rear, BG,
        'Los Angeles Fire Department',
        2 light blue men (Code Red issue).....**£25-30**
        Same but 2 yellow men (Code Red)...**£18-20**

MB 52e   BMW M1
81-83   Silver body, red interior, BB, CG, black
        stripes and '52' tampo prints.............**£11-14**
        Same but blue-grey base **£10-12**
        With BB, amber glass **£25-30**
        With BB, CG, no tampo prints **£10-12**
        With BB, green glass........................**£120-140**

MB 53c   Ford Zodiac Mk.IV
70   Metallic light blue body, NW.........**£600-700**
70-71   Metallic light green body, NW...........**£50-60**
        Metallic dark green body, NW...........**£35-40**
        Metallic emerald green body.............**£30-40**
72   Lime green body, wide wheels...........**£70-80**

MB 53d Tanzara

MB 53d   Tanzara
72-74   Orange body, SE,
        silver interior, UB, AG **£10-15**
        Same but with green glass **£10-15**
75-76   White body, SE, silver interior, UB,
        AG, blue/orange stripes/stars, '53' **£12-15**

Same but with no tampo prints **£18-20**
With blue/red stripes/stars, '53'.........**£12-15**
Same but with green glass **£18-20**
White body, red engine, red interior,
UB, AG, blue/red stripes/stars, '53' ...**£80-90**

MB 53e   CJ6 Jeep
77-80   Red body, yellow interior,
lt. brown roof, UB, WW **£8-10**
Same but with black interior **£8-10**
With yellow interior, silver base **£8-10**
81-82   Metallic green body, yellow interior,
light brown roof, UB, WW **£8-10**
Same but with black interior **£8-10**
With yellow interior, silver base **£8-10**
Pale yellow body, dark brown roof,
black interior, BB or GB, 'CJ6' print ...**£12-15**

MB 53f   Flareside Pick-up
82-83   Blue body, '326' and 'Baja Bouncer' **£8-10**
Same but with some prints or none.....**£8-10**
Same but with BG **£100-130**

MB 54b Cadillac Ambulance
70   White body, silver grille, red roof lights,
BB, small Red Cross door labels........**£75-85**
Off-white body, plain grille, red roof
lights, BlB, large Red Cross labels **£85-95**

MB 54c   Ford Capri
71   Pink or orange body, black bonnet,
UB, wide wheels **£25-30**
72-75   Metallic crimson body UB or SB **£20-25**
76   Orange body, UB, (TP).......................**£35-40**

MB 54d   Personnel Carrier
76-79   Military green body, black base, green
glass, light brown soldiers on some **£8-10**
Same but with chrome wheels **£20-30**

MB 54e   Mobile Home
80-82   Cream or white body, brown door,
side stripes on some, BB **£9-12**
Same but with grey or brown base.......**£9-12**

MB 54f   NASA Tracking Vehicle
82-83   White/red/black, BB, 'US Space
Shuttle Command Centre', 'NASA' **£15-18**
Same but with grey base **£15-18**

MB 55d Mercury Police Car
70   White body, 2 men, blue roof light,
shields and 'Police' label **£60-70**
Same but with red roof light **£50-60**

MB 55e Mercury Est. Police
71-74   White body, off-white interior, no men,
UB, 2 red roof lights, bonnet shield and
'Police' label and side shield labels ...**£25-30**
Same but UB or SB, bonnet and side
'Police' arrow labels **£15-20**
Same but UB or SB, bonnet 'Police'
arrow label, plain sides **£15-20**

MB 55f Hellraiser

MB 55f   Hellraiser
75-76   White body, red interior, UB,
'Stars and Stripes' bonnet label..........**£10-15**
Yellow body, sun bonnet label
(possible pre-production model)...**£300-350**
Yellow, Red int., bare metal base **£90-110**
77-78   Metallic blue body, red interior, SB,
'Stars and Stripes' bonnet label..........**£12-16**
Metallic blue body, off-white interior,
UB or SB, 'Stars and Stripes') **£10-15**
Metallic blue body, off-white interior,
SB, bonnet stripe and '3' label **£32-38**
Same but with no label **£10-15**

MB 55g   Ford Cortina
79-80   Metallic green body, red interior,
UB, clear glass, opening doors....**£15-18**
Same but with light yellow interior....**£18-22**
81   Metallic red body, light yellow interior,
UB, opening doors..............................**£16-20**
82-83   Metallic light brown body, white interior,
UB or SB, black stripe.........................**£19-24**
Light red body, white interior,
UB or SB, doors cast shut....................**£8-10**
Same but with gloss black base..........**£18-20**
Bright red body, white interior,
UB or SB, opaque glass,
doors cast shut (Gift Set issue) **£27-32**
83   Light red body, light brown interior,
UB or SB, doors cast shut,
black side stripe prints (TP) **£20-25**
Same but white interior (TP).............**£12-15**

MB 56c BMC 1800 Pinifarina
69-70   Metallic gold body, UB, NW **£20-25**
Same, with '17', 'Gulf' (G3 set)...........**£30-35**
71-73   Peach body, UB, NW **£35-40**
Orange body, UB, NW or WW **£12-15**
With '17' and 'Gulf' (G3 set)................**£20-25**
Pre-production model. Colour trial,
Silver or yellow or blue body, baseplate
without 'Superfast', pre-production
Superfast wheels with silver hubs..**£750-950**

MB 56d   Hi-Tailer
74-78   White body, orange/blue stripes, UB,
'MB5 Team Matchbox', yellow man ...**£15-18**
With red labels instead of orange **£75-85**
Same but with silver or red base **£15-18**
Same but with blue man **£15-18**
79   Red base, 'Martini 7' (Gift Set) **£20-25**

MB 56e   Mercedes 450 SEL
79-80   Metallic blue body, red interior **£20-25**
Same but with light brown interior....**£10-12**
81-83   Light brown body, light or medium or dark
brown interior, 'Taxi' sign, UB or SB ...**£16-20**

MB 56f   Peterbilt Tanker
82   US issue: Blue body, white back,
'Milk's the One' **£12-15**
Same but white tampo on doors........**£13-16**

MB 57c Land-Rover Fire Truck
70   Red body, 'Kent Fire Brigade' labels..**£80-90**
Same but with 'Kent Fire Brigade'
labels cut around words...................**£90-110**

MB 57d   Eccles Caravan
70-71   Cream body, orange roof, green
interior, maroon side stripe labels **£15-20**
Same but brown side stripe labels **£18-22**
With brown stripe and flower labels..**£15-20**
72   Pale Yellow body, orange roof, green
interior, brown stripe, flower labels ...**£30-35**
76-78   Yellow body, red-orange roof, white
interior, black stripe, flowers (TP).....**£15-20**
Same but with side red dots label from
K-27 Camping Cruiser set (TP) **£25-30**
79-81   Light brown, red-orange roof, white

interior, black stripe, flowers (TP)......**£12-16**
Same but 'white bird' label (TP) **£20-25**
82   White body, red-orange roof, white
interior, 'Sunset', palm tree (TP).........**£18-22**

MB 57d Eccles Caravan

MB 57e   Wildlife Truck
73-80   Yellow body, clear back, red glass,
'Ranger' (Rola-Matic version) **£10-15**
Same but with amber back **£12-16**
81   White body, clear back, red glass, light
brown lion, black/white camouflage
prints, (Rola-Matic version) **£10-15**
Same but with amber glass.................**£12-16**
Same but with purple glass **£15-20**
Same but tinted detachable back.......**£15-20**

MB 57f   Carmichael Rescue
82   White body, 'Police Rescue' **£15-20**
83   Red body, 'Fire' **£15-20**

MB 58c   DAF Girder Truck
70   Cream or off-white cab and body,
red base (with 'Pat App' on some) .**£125-150**
70-71   Metallic lime green cab and body,
with matching box..............................**£35-40**

MB 58d   Woosh 'n' Push
72-75   Yellow body, red interior, '2' label........**£8-10**
Same but pale yellow interior.............**£25-30**
With red interior, 'flower' label **£12-15**
76   Metallic red body, pale yellow interior,
'2' label on roof **£8-10**
Same but '8' and stars label................**£12-15**

MB 58e   Faun Dump Truck
76-81   Yellow body, yellow tipper.....................**£6-9**
79   Yellow body, red tipper (G5 set).........**£25-30**
82-83   Yellow body, yellow tipper, 'CAT' **£10-12**

MB 59c   Ford Galaxie Fire
70   Red body, white interior, 'Fire Chief'
and side shield labels **£60-75**
Promotional issue 'Lyons Tea', in
promotional blister pack with card
label. Dutch/Belgian market **£750-1,000**

MB 59d   Mercury Fire Chief
71-74   Red body, '59' or '73', 2 men,
yellow 'Fire Chief' on bonnet,
'shield' labels on sides **£20-25**
Same but 'helmet & axes' on sides.....**£15-20**
Same but yellow bonnet 'helmet and
axes' labels, plain sides **£12-16**
Same but yellow 'helmet and axes'
labels on bonnet and sides.................**£12-16**
With nothing or just '59' on base.......**£12-16**
78   Same but with no men (TP) **£12-16**
Red body, CG, 'Fire', shield (TP)........**£12-16**
Same but with purple glass (TP)........**£15-20**
79   White, CG, 'Police', shield (TP) **£20-25**
81   Red body, 'Los Angeles Fire Dept'
tampo prints (Code Red) **£20-25**
White body, CG or BG, 'Los Angeles
Police' tampo prints, (Code Red)......**£20-25**
82   White body, CG, PG or BG, 'Police'

227

and shield, black wing panel prints ...**£20-25**
White body, CG or BG, 'Metro Police',
black wing tampo prints as 10f......**£10-15**
Same but with white wing panels **£12-16**

MB 59e   Planet Scout
75-77   Metallic green and lime green...........**£10-15**
78-80   Metallic red and light brown **£10-15**
77   Avocado/black, PG or AG (Adventure
        2000 K2005 Command Force set) **£25-30**
80   Metallic blue/black, PG,
        (Adventure 2000 set) **£50-60**

MB 59f   Porsche 928
80-81   Light metallic brown body, brown
        interior, black base, clear glass...........**£10-15**
        Same but cream or off-white interior **£10-12**
        With brown interior, amber glass.......**£16-20**
        Dark met. brown, brown interior, BB **£10-15**
        Same but with amber glass................**£16-20**
        Same but with brown glass.................**£10-15**
        With clear glass, brown or grey base **£10-15**
        With AG, brown or grey base.............**£12-15**
81-82   Met. blue body, brown int., CG, BB ...**£10-12**
        Same but with grey or silver base **£10-15**
82-83   Black body, brown interior, 'Porsche' **£12-16**
        Same but with red interior.................**£10-12**

MB 60b Truck and Site Office
70   Blue truck, yellow/green office **£25-30**
        Dark Blue truck, 2-rivet base.............**£40-45**

MB 60c   Lotus Super 7
71-75   Dark orange body, black interior and boot,
        bonnet 'flame' label **£10-15**
        Same but with light orange body **£15-20**
75-76   Same but blue stripe and check design
        + bonnet '60' prints, (Streakers).........**£15-20**

MB 60d   Holden Pick-up
77   Metallic ruby red body, yellow interior,
        AG, yellow bikes, '500' label **£12-15**
77-80   Bright red body, yellow interior,
        AG, yellow bikes, '500' label **£12-15**
        Same but with orange glass **£12-15**
        Bright red body, red interior, orange or
        AG, olive green bikes, '500' label........**£12-15**
        Bright red body, red interior, orange or
        AG, olive green bikes, 'Sun' label........**£35-40**
        Bright red body, yellow interior, AG,
        yellow bikes, 'striped' bonnet label....**£15-18**
80   Metallic ruby red body, yellow interior,
        OG or AG, yellow bikes,
        'Paris-Dakar 81' (French issue).........**£20-25**
81-83   Cream body, red interior, orange or
        AG, red bikes, stripes and Superbike' **£20-25**
        Same but with yellow bikes **£10-14**
        Cream body, red interior, AG,
        red bikes, 'Honda' labels....................**£25-30**

MB 61b   Alvis Stalwart
66-71   White body, yellow detachable top,
        clear glass, 'BP Exploration' labels,
        regular black wheels, yellow hubs **£35-40**
78   Metallic olive green body, fixed top,
        GG, black wide wheels (TP) **£20-25**

MB 61c   Blue Shark
71-77   Metallic blue, UB or SB, CG, '86'........**£15-20**
        Same but with '69' label from 69d **£15-20**
        Metallic blue body, SB, CG or AG,
        'Scorpion' label on bonnet **£50-60**
        Metallic blue body, UB or SB, AG,
        bonnet arrows and '86' label.............**£15-20**
        Same but with '69' label from 69d **£15-20**

MB 61d   Wreck Truck
78-80   Red body, white arms, red hooks,
        BB or GB, AG and 2 roof lights **£10-12**
        With red or white arms, black hooks .**£10-12**
        Red body, red arms, red hooks...........**£10-12**

Red body, white arms, red hooks,
BB, blue glass and 2 roof lights **£25-30**
81   Red body and hooks, off-white arms,
        BB, AG, 'Radio Despatches 24 Hour
        Towing' (TP) **£15-20**
81-82   Light yellow body, red arms, black
        hooks, AG, black or grey base **£10-12**
        Same but with brown base **£10-12**
        Same but with silver base **£10-12**
        With red arms & hooks, BB or GB......**£10-12**
        Light yellow body, white arms, red
        hooks, BB or GB, AG and lights.........**£20-25**
        Light yellow body, green arms, red
        or black hooks, BB or GB, AG lights...**£12-15**
        Dark yellow body, red arms,
        BB/hooks, AG **£10-12**
        Same but with brown base **£8-10**
        Dark yellow body, red arms, red hooks,
        BB or GB, AG and lights.......................**£7-9**
        Dark yellow body, white arms, red
        hooks, BB, AG and lights....................**£20-25**
        Dark yellow body, green arms, red
        or black hooks, BB, AG and lights......**£12-15**
        Same but with grey base **£15-20**

MB 61e   Peterbilt Wrecker
82-83   Red-orange, white 'Eddies Wrecker' ...**£8-11**
        Same but with black tampo prints....**£12-15**
        Blue body, no tampo print, from
        'Highway Express' Gift Set)................**£20-25**
        Blue with no tampos **£150-160**

MB 62c   Mercury Cougar
70   Light metallic gold, red interior **£50-60**
        Metallic green **£50-60**
        Pre-production model. Colours as above
        but with pre-Superfast wheels £800-850

MB 62d Mercury Cougar Dragster
70   Light green body, red interior, UB,
        'Rat Rod' labels **£25-30**
70-73   Same but lime green body.................**£15-20**
        Same but with silver base **£25-35**
        Same but UB, 'Wild Cat' labels..........**£45-55**

MB 62e   Renault 17TL
74-78   Red body, white interior, '9' label **£10-15**
        Red-orange body, white interior, '9' ..**£10-15**
        Same but label reversed to read '6'...**£12-16**
76   Red body, white interior, 'Fire'
        labels, (from G12 Rescue set) **£25-35**

MB 62f Chevrolet Corvette
79-81   Metallic ruby red body, grey interior,
        UB, CG, white bonnet prints **£11-14**
        Same but with black interior **£11-14**
        Same but with white interior **£15-20**
        Same but with black interior **£11-14**
        Same but with grey interior **£11-14**
81-83   Black body, grey interior, UB, CG,
        orange/yellow bonnet stripes **£11-14**
        Same but with silver base **£11-14**
83   Same but UB, opaque glass, (from
        Streak Racing set) **£20-25**
        White body, black stripes, '09'...........**£17-22**

MB 63c Dodge Crane Truck
70-72   Yellow body, yellow crane, arm
        and hook (orange hook on some)......**£25-30**

MB 63d Freeway Gas Tanker
73   Red/black/white, 'Castrol' labels **£60-70**
73-77   Red/black/white, 'Burmah' labels **£10-15**
        Same but with tow hook hole in rear.**£10-15**
76   Military olive drab green and black,
        'Canadian' flag labels (TP).............**£300-400**
        Same but with 'French' flag (TP)........**£70-80**
76-77   Military olive green cab black base,
        '95 High Octane' labels (TP)............**£18-20**
77   Light blue/black/white,
        'Aral' labels (German) **£30-35**
78-79   Red/black/white, 'Chevron' labels,

tow hook hole in rear of tanker **£6-8**
        Same but with white tow hook (TP) **£8-10**
        Red/black/white, 'Burmah' labels,
        cream tow hook (TP).........................**£10-12**
79-80   White/yellow, 'Shell' labels, PG **£10-12**
        Same but with red glass **£12-14**
        Yellow/black/white, 'Shell', PG **£18-22**
80-81   White/yellow, 'Exxon' labels **£18-22**
        White/black, 'Exxon' labels **£18-22**
        White/yellow, 'Shell',
        cream tow hook (TP).........................**£10-15**
        Same but 'Exxon' labels (TP) **£18-22**
81-82   White/black/green, 'BP Super' **£15-20**
        White/yellow, 'BP Super' (TP) **£25-30**

MB 63dx   Freeway Gas Trailer
78-79   White/yellow, 'Chevron' labels (TP).......**£10-15**
        Same but with 'Burmah' labels (TP)..**£10-15**
80-81   White/yellow, 'Shell' labels (TP).......**£10-15**
        White/yellow, 'Exxon' labels (TP)......**£15-18**
81-82   White/yellow, 'BP Super' (TP) **£20-25**

MB 63e   4x4 Open Back Truck
82-83   Orange (shades),
        '24' and 'FWD' or '4x4' UB or SB........**£10-15**

MB 63f Snorkel Fire Engine
82   Red body, white ladder, UB **£18-24**

MB 64b   MG 1100
70   Green body, white interior with man and
        dog, unpainted base, clear glass ...**£300-350**
70-71   Same but metallic light blue body **£45-55**
        Same but metallic dark blue body **£45-55**
        Same but dark blue body, NW **£45-55**

MB 64c Slingshot Dragster
71-72   Metallic pink body, BB, black exhausts,
        bonnet flame and '9' labels **£15-20**
73   Orange body, BB, black exhausts,
        bonnet flame and '9' label.............**£100-120**
        Same but red exhausts **£150-200**
73-75   Metallic blue-green body, UB, red
        exhausts, bonnet flame, '9' label.......**£18-24**
        Same but BB, front NW or WW **£10-15**
        Same but with '3'...............................**£18-20**

MB 64d   Fire Chief Car
76-79   Red body, 'Fire', some yellow shield
        labels have black edging **£8-10**

MB 64e   Caterpillar D-9
79-81   Yellow body, brown roof, yellow shovel,
        black tracks, orange or yellow rollers **£10-15**
82   Yellow body, black roof, yellow shovel,
        'C'on cab, black tracks, yellow rollers **£10-15**
82-83   Same but black shovel, black or silver
        tow hook, 'C' on cab...........................**£10-15**
        Same plus 'CAT' print, (black hook)..**£10-15**

MB 65c Class Combine Harvester
67-72   Red body, yellow cutters, black base,
        black wheels with yellow hubs............**£8-10**

MB 65d Saab Sonnet

MB 65d   Saab Sonnet III
73-76   Metallic blue body, yellow interior,
        UB, AG, grey rear door **£20-25**

79   White body, yellow interior, UB,
AG, grey rear door, (Multi Pack)....**£300-350**

MB 65e   Airport Coach
NB All Airport Coach models have white roofs.
77-81 Metallic blue body, off-white or pale
yellow interior, AG or CG, UB,
'British Airways' **£10-15**
Same but with labels reversed...........**£10-12**
Metallic blue body, off-white interior,
UB, AG, 'American Airlines' labels.....**£10-15**
Same but with clear glass **£12-15**
Same but pale yellow interior, AG......**£10-15**
Same but with clear glass **£12-15**
Metallic blue, off-white or pale yellow
interior, AG, 'Lufthansa' (German) **£10-15**
Same but with clear glass **£12-15**
81   Orange body, pale yellow interior, UB,
AG, 'Schulbus' (German issue) **£25-35**
81-83 Red body, 'TWA' **£9-12**
Red body, 'Qantas' **£9-12**
82   Red body, 'Fly Braniff' **£25-35**
White body, 'Stork SB'(Australian) **£18-20**
Metallic Blue,
'Girobank' (Promotional) **£18-20**
83   Metallic Blue, UB or SB, AG,
'British' labels **£9-12**
Met. Blue, UB or SB, AG,
'Australian' labels **£12-14**
White body, UB or SB, 'Alitalia' **£15-20**
White body, UB or SB, 'Lufthansa'.....**£25-30**

MB 65f   Bandag Bandit
82   Black with green/white stripes.............**£8-11**

MB 66c   Greyhound Coach
70   Silver body, yellow interior, AG, matt
or gloss BB, 'Greyhound,' ' **£30-40**
Same but with yellow or pink base **£60-70**

MB 66d   Mazda RX500
71-74 Orange body, SE, white base, PG **£7-9**
Same but with unpainted base **£15-20**
Orange body, SE, white base, AG........**£12-15**
75-76 Red body, SE, WB, AG, white/green
'77' and stripes (Streakers version)........**£7-9**
Same but with PG (Streakers) **£12-14**
Same but UB, AG (Streakers)..............**£12-14**
Red body, light brown engine, WB,
AG, '77' and stripes (Streakers) **£12-14**
Same but with PG (Streakers) **£15-18**

MB 66e   Ford Transit
77-80 Orange body, green glass, UB,
brown load, green interior.................**£20-25**
Same but light brown interior **£15-20**
Same but light yellow interior **£9-12**
Orange body, amber glass, UB,
beige load, green interior...................**£25-30**
Light brown or light yellow interior ...**£15-20**
81-82 Yellow-orange body, off-white or green
interior, UB, brown load, green glass.**£10-15**
Same but with beige load **£9-12**
Yellow-orange body, green interior, GB,
brown or beige load, green glass........**£10-15**
Same but with black base **£15-20**

MB 66f   Tyrone Malone
82-83 White body, blue/red stripes on some,
'Tyrone Malone' on white aerofoil.......**£8-10**
With plain white or cream aerofoil **£6-8**

MB 67b   Volkswagen 1600TL
70   Dark or light red body,
white interior, UB, CG, NW............**£200-220**
70-71 Metallic purple body (may be dark,
mid or light), white interior,
UB, CG, NW or WW **£40-45**
71-72 Metallic pink body, white interior,
UB, CG, NW or WW **£40-45**
Pre-production model. Colour trial,

Metallic dark blue, no 'Superfast' on
baseplate, pre-production SF wheels
with silver hubs........................ **£1,000-1,300**

MB 67b VW 1600TL

MB 67c   Hot Rocker
73-74 Metallic green-gold body, white interior,
UB, CG (Rola-Matic version)..............**£15-20**
Same but with silver base **£20-30**
Same but metallic green body, UB **£15-20**
Same but with silver base **£20-30**
75-77 Red body, UB, (Rola-Matic version) .**£12-16**
Same but with silver base **£20-30**

MB 67d   Datsun 260Z 2+2
78-80 Metallic crimson body,
white interior, CG, BB..........................**£8-11**
Same but with grey base **£10-12**
79   Metallic blue body, pale yellow
interior, matt black base (TP)............**£15-20**
Same but with red interior (TP) **£30-40**
Metallic blue body, red int.,
brown base (TP) **£40-50**
80   Metallic red body,
pale yellow interior, BB **£15-18**
81-83 Silver body, red interior, black base.....**£8-11**
Same but grey or blue-grey base........**£10-12**
Same but with brown base **£10-12**
Silver body, white interior, GB or BB,
red stripes, black 'Datsun 2+2' (TP)...**£10-12**
Silver body, black interior, BB, blue
stripes, black 'Datsun 2+2' (TP) **£12-15**
83   Black body and interior, BB (TP)........**£20-30**

MB 68c   Porsche 910
70-74 Metallic red body, pale yellow interior,
UB, AG, '68' label on bonnet, NW......**£15-20**
Same + '68' side labels (G3 set)..........**£25-30**
Metallic red body, pale yellow interior,
UB, AG, bonnet '68' label, WW...........**£15-20**
Same but with '45' label from 45c......**£25-30**
Silver body, White interior, UB
(possible pre-production model)...**£140-160**
72   White body, pale yellow interior, UB,
AG, WW ('Brroom Stick' issue) **£60-70**

MB 68d   Cosmobile
75-78 Metallic light blue body, yellow under,
white or silver interior, AG..................**£8-12**
77   Avocado body, black under, white
interior, AG, (Adventure 2000 set)......**£20-25**
Same but with purple glass (set)........**£15-20**
Same but with silver interior (set) **£25-30**
78-79 Metallic red body, beige under,
white or silver interior, AG..................**£8-10**
80   Metallic dark blue, black under, silver
interior, PG (Adventure 2000 set).......**£50-65**

MB 68e   Chevy Van
79-80 Orange body, UB, BG, blue/red or
blue/white stripes **£10-15**
Same but CG, blue/red stripes...........**£12-16**
Same but BG, red/black stripes...........**£10-15**
Same but with green or red glass **£10-15**
80-81 Orange body, 'Matchbox Collectors
Club' labels, BG (Ltd. Edition) **£15-18**
81-82 White body, 'Adidas' (German)..........**£25-30**

White body, 'USA-1' (US issue)..........**£12-15**
Green body, 'Chevy' with brown or
yellow segmented stripes.....................**£9-12**
82-83 Yellow body, 'Collect Exciting
Matchbox' (Australian issue) **£20-25**
Silver body, blue glass, 'Vanpire' **£10-15**

MB 69c Rolls Silver Shadow
69-70 Metallic blue body, brown interior,
tan folded top, BB, AG, NW **£30-40**
Same but dark or light yellow base **£35-40**
71-72 Metallic light gold body, brown interior,
tan folded AG, BB, AG, WW...............**£30-40**
Same but dark or light yellow base **£30-40**
Same but with silver base **£30-40**
With black folded top, BB **£40-45**
Same but with light yellow base........**£30-40**
Same but with silver or grey base **£30-40**
With off-white interior, black folded
top, black base, AG, WW **£40-45**
Same but with grey base **£25-35**
Metallic dark gold, AG, off-white
interior, black folded top, BB, WW **£30-40**
Same but with grey or silver base **£20-25**
Metallic dark gold body, brown interior,
tan folded top, BB, AG, WW...............**£30-40**
Same but with grey or silver base **£25-35**
72-73 Metallic lime gold body, off-white or
brown interior, BB, AG, WW **£40-50**
Same but with grey or silver base **£50-60**

MB 69d   Turbo Fury
73-77 Metallic red body, CG, '69' and
arrows label, (Rola-Matic version).....**£10-15**
Same but AG (Rola-Matic version) **£12-16**
Metallic red body, '86' and arrows
label, (Rola-Matic version) **£25-30**
Same but 'Scorpion' (Rola-Matic)..**£100-120**

MB 69e   Security Truck
78-83 Dark red body, cream roof, UB or SB,
BG, '732 2031', 'Wells Fargo' **£10-12**
Light red body, white roof, SB, CG,
'732 2031' and 'Wells Fargo' **£12-15**
Same but BG, UB or SB **£10-12**
Light red body, white roof, SB, BG,
'QZ 2031' and 'Wells Fargo' **£15-20**
81   Metallic dark green body, SB, BG,
'Dresdner Bank' (German promo) **£25-30**

MB 69f   Willys Street Rod
82   US issue: White, flame-effect tampo..**£10-14**

MB 70b   Grit Spreader TRUCK
70   Red cab and body, dark or pale yellow
grit spreader, UB, GG, 4-spoke NW....**£15-20**
Same but with 5-spoke wheels............**£35-40**

MB 70c Dodge Dragster

MB 70c   Dodge Dragster
71-75 Dark pink body, BG, 'snake' labels.....**£12-16**
With purple, cream, light green, light
yellow, dark yellow or grey base........**£20-25**
With brown or unpainted base **£35-40**

Dark pink body, BB, 'Wild Cat'..........**£40-50**
Dark pink body, 'Rat Rod' labels...**£100-125**
Light pink body, BB, 'snake' labels **£15-18**
Light pink, BB, blue star labels....**£150-175**
Bright pink body, BB, 'snake' labels....**£15-18**
78   Yellow body, red glass, GB or BB,
side prints, (US Roman Numeral)......**£18-20**

MB 70d   S.P. Gun
76-80 Military green body, black or brown
tracks, (Rola-Matic version) **£8-10**

MB 70e   Ferrari 308 GTB
81-83 Red body and base, black stripe, CG .**£10-14**
Red body and base, CG, 'Ferrari' **£10-14**
Same but with AG...............................**£12-15**
83   Red body, silver base, no 'Ferrari'......**£20-25**

MB 71c Ford Wrecker

MB 71c Ford Heavy Wrecker
70-72 Red cab, white body, red crane and
hook, BB, GG, 'Esso' **£55-65**
79   Military olive green, black hook,
BB, GG, '3LGS64' labels (TP).............**£20-25**
81   Dark blue, blue crane, black hook,
BB, GG, no labels (Multi Pack).......**£150-200**

MB 71d   Jumbo Jet
73-75 Metallic blue frame, red elephant head,
dark blue handlebars, black wheels ..**£10-15**
Same but light blue handlebars **£20-25**

MB 71e   Cattle Truck
76-81 Metallic orange-red cab, dark yellow back,
UB or SB, GG or BG, 2 black cattle.....**£10-12**
With AG, PG or orange glass, SB **£10-12**
79-83 Dark red cab, off-white back,
SB, BG, 2 black cattle (TP) **£10-12**
Same but with red or PG (TP) **£10-12**
Dark red cab, dark or light yellow back,
SB, PG, 2 black cattle (TP) **£10-12**
81-83 Metallic light green cab, off-white back,
SB, OG, 2 brown cattle **£8-10**
Metallic light or dark green cab, yellow
back, SB, red or OG, 2 brown cattle **£8-10**
Metallic dark green cab, dark brown
back, SB, red or AG, 2 brown cattle....**£14-18**
83   Yellow cab, brown back, BB, UB or SB,
red or AG, 2 light brown cattle **£8-10**
Same but with black tow hook (TP).....**£8-10**

MB 71ex Cattle Truck Trailer
79-83 Dark red body, off-white or light or dark
yellow back, SB, 2 black cattle (TP) **£5-7**
83   Yellow body, dark yellow back, SB,
2 light brown cattle (TP) **£5-7**

MB 71f   Corvette
82   White, red/yellow tampo **£12-15**

MB 72b   Standard Jeep

70-71 Dull yellow body, red interior, UB......**£35-40**
Bright yellow body, red interior **£75-85**

MB 72c   SRN Hovercraft
72-78 White body, BB, BG, 'R.N.L.I.'................**£6-8**
Same but without glass **£6-8**

MB 72d Bomag Road Roller
79-82 Yellow/red, black roller, 2 wheels **£6-8**
Same but 2 wheels have yellow hubs **£7-9**

MB 72e   Dodge Delivery
All have red cab, white back,
some have 'gold' hubs.
82-83 'Pepsi' **£10-12**
'Kelloggs' **£10-12**
'Smiths Crisps' (Promotional offer) ...**£10-12**

MB 72b Standard Jeep

MB 73c Mercury Commuter
70-71 Metallic lime green body, UB with '59',
'55' or '73', NW **£35-40**
Same but with WW **£80-90**
Metallic lime green, white interior,
with filler cap **£40-50**
71-73 Red body, UB, 'Bull head' label on
bonnet of some, wide wheels.............**£25-30**
Same but with cat's head label on
bonnet **£200-250**

MB 73d   Weasel
74-76 Metallic green body, metallic green and
green base, (Rola-Matic)....................**£10-12**
76   Military olive drab green body,
metallic green and green base,
(Rola-Matic) (TP) **£35-40**
76-79 Same but with military olive green
body (Rola-Matic) (TP).......................**£12-15**
Military olive green body, olive green
and green base, (Rola-Matic) (TP).....**£12-15**
Same but olive green and BB, (TP).....**£12-15**
Met. bronze body, Met. green base**£150-170**

MB 73e Ford Model 'A' Car
79-80 Cream body, dark green wings, GG ...**£10-12**
Same but no spare wheel or glass **£9-11**
80   White body, dark green wings, GG **£10-12**
80-82 Met. green body, dark green wings,
GG or none...**£7-9**
82-83 Lt. brown body, dark brown wings, AG .**£7-9**
Same but with clear glass **£8-10**

MB 74b Daimler Fleetline
70-72 Red body, white interior, 'Esso' **£25-30**
Same but fluorescent pink body **£25-30**
72   Red body, 'Inn on the Park' labels ..**£80-100**
Red body, 'The Baron of Beef' **£80-100**
Red body, 'NAMC', 'The Miniature
Vehicle' labels (Promotional).........**£160-180**
Red body, 'Kensington Hilton' **£100-120**
Red body, 'I.C.P. Interchemicals' ...**£250-300**
Red body, 'Beefeater' **£200-250**
Light red, 'Fly Cyprus Airways'.......**£150-175**
Light red, 'Big T Scotch Whiskies' **£80-100**

MB 74b Daimler Bus (Baron of Beef)

MB 74c   ToW Joe
72-77 Metallic green-gold body, UB, AG and
roof light, green arms, Red hooks **£12-16**
Same but with BB or SB **£12-16**
With UB and black hooks **£15-20**
Metallic green body, BB, AG and
roof light, green arms, red hooks **£10-15**
76-81 Yellow body, BB, SB or UB, AG, red
arms, black hooks (TP) **£10-15**
With matt base, red or black hooks .**£75-100**
Metallic green body, BB, AG,
red arms, black hooks (TP)................**£25-30**
Same, BB or SB, white arms (TP).....**£90-100**
Red body, green arms, red hooks,
BB, AG, (TP)....................................**£150-170**
Red body, green arms, black hooks .**£80-100**
Red body, red arms, black hooks ...**£150-170**
82   Yellow body, UB, AG, red arms, black
hooks, 'Hitch Hiker' labels (TP).....**£100-120**

MB 74d   Cougar Villager
78-81 Metallic light or dark green body,
yellow interior, UB, AG......................**£10-12**
81-82 Metallic blue body, yellow
interior, UB, AG..................................**£15-20**
Same but with orange-yellow Interior **£30-40**

MB 74e   Fiat Abarth
82-83 White body, red interior, 'Matchbox'.**£12-14**
Same but with black interior **£140-180**

MB 75b   Ferrari Berlinetta
70   Metallic green body, off-white interior,
unpainted base, clear glass.............**£300-350**
70-71 Light red body, off-white interior, UB,
CG, silver grille on some **£85-95**
Same but with dark red body **£140-150**

MB 75c   Alfa Carabo
71-75 Metallic Purple body, YB, NW...........**£10-15**
Same but with unpainted base **£50-60**
75   Metallic light pink body, YB, WW **£15-20**
75-76 Metallic light pink or red body, WW,
(Streakers) yellow/black/green prints**£12-16**

MB 75d   Seasprite Helicopter
77-81 White body, Red underside, BG or GG,
black rotors, blue 'Rescue' labels.........**£8-10**
Same but with red glass **£12-15**
Same but with purple glass **£15-20**

MB 75e   Helicopter
82-83 White/orange, black interior, black skids,
AG, 'MBTV News' tampo prints **£8-11**
White/black, black or grey interior, black
skids, AG or CG, 'Police' and '36' **£8-11**
White/black, black or grey interior,
black or grey skids, AG, 'Rescue' **£10-12**

Matchbox 'Superfast' Miscellaneous Sets

G 1	1968	**Service Station Set** 13d, 56b, 32c, and 'BP' Service Station £250-300
G 1	1970	**Service Station Set** 13d, 15d, 32c, and 'BP' Service Station £250-300
	1970	**Magnetic Action Farm Centre** US issue....................£200-250
G 1-8	1981	**Transporter Set** Contains Transporter and 5 Superfast Cars £150-175
G 1-9	1984	**Transporter Set** Contains K10 plus 4 cars £50-60
G 2-7	1970	**Transporter Set** Transporter and 5 Superfast models £100-125
G 2-8	1973	**Transporter Set** Transporter and 5 Superfast models £100-125
G 2-11	1981	**Railway Set** Contains 43e, 2 x 44e, 25f............................£40-50
G 3-7	1970	**Racing Specials Set** Contains 5e, 20c, 45c, 56c, 52c and 68c £50-80
G 3-8	1973	**'WILD ONES' Set.** Contains 5 Superfast Cars.................£30-60
G 3-9	1981	**Racing Car Set** Transporter and 4 Racing Cars............£50-60
G 4-7	1970	**Truck SuperSet** 47c, 63c, 58c, 49b, 16d, 21d, 11d and 51c £100-125
G 4-8	1973	**Team Matchbox Set** Racing Car Transporter + 4 Racing Cars........................£70-90
G 4-9	1981	**Military Assault Landing Craft** + 6 military models £60-90
G 5-9	1981	**Construction Set** Contains 5 construction models £40-50
G 6-6	1970	**Truck Set** 1e, 10d, 21d, 26c, 30c, 60b, 70b and 49b £120-150
G 6-7	1973	**Drag Race Set** Contains 6 Superfast Cars £40-60
G 6-8	1981	**Farm Set** Contains 6 farming models............................ £40-50
G 7-5	1973	**Ferry Boat** With Plastic Boat and 4 Superfast Cars...... £70-100
G 7-8	1978	**Car Ferry Set** 'HERON' Blue hull, white cabin, red deck, four models £50-70
G 7-8	1978	**Car Ferry Set** 'OLYMPUS' Red hull and cabin, yellow deck, four models................ £50-70
G 7-6	1981	**Emergency Set** Contains 5 Rescue models £30-40
G 7-7	1984	**Emergency Set** With models 8, 12, 22, 57 and 75 .... £30-40
G 8-5	1984	**Turbo Charged Set** Turbo Charger plus 7, 9, 52, 60 and 68 .... £35-40
G 9	19??	**Commando Task Force Set** with 2, 3, 16, landing craft.................................... £50-70

G 10-5	1986	**'PAN-AM' Set** Contains 10, 54, 64, 65 + 'Sky-Buster' Boeing £40-45
G 10	19??	**'Thunder Jets' Set** Four SkyBusters.............................. £25-35
G 11-1	1978	**Strike Force Set** Contains 6 Army Vehicles £30-50
G 11-2	1986	**'LUFTHANSA' Set** 30, 54, 59, 65 and 'Sky-Buster' Airbus............................. £20-30
G 12	1978	**Rescue Set** Contains 6 Rescue Vehicles £30-40
G 13	1978	**Construction Set** Contains 6 Construction Vehicles £35-40
G 14	1978	**Grand Prix Set** Transporter and 4 Racing Cars............. £35-40
G 15	1978	**Transporter Set** Transporter and 5 Superfast Cars £35-40
G 16	19??	**'Sky Giants' Set** Four SkyBusters airliners £25-35
G 40	1988	**40 years Set** ('Made in China' cast under models). Aveling-Barford Road Roller, London Bus, Horse Drawn Milk Float, M-H Tractor, Dennis Fire Engine £20-25
C 6		**Emergency Gift Set** All Japanese Set............................. £25-30
C 11		**Airport Gift Set** Japanese Foam Pump, Ikarus Coach + plane £30-35
---	1971	**Matchbox Crash Game** With 4 assorted cars, racetrack, dice and instructions.... £60-75
---		Multi-Pack Gift Set Contains 5 Superfast models £20-25
A1	70-73	**Service Ramp** 'CASTROL' £30-35
A2	1970	**'Superfast Auto Sales'** Plastic kit includes 'MATCHBOX SALES OFFICE', 'STAR VALUE' stand, 3 'M' flagpoles and 4 lampposts, plus pink card base, signs and advert. stickers. 25 items in total £200-300
A2	71-73	**'Matchbox' Sales Park** Pink card sales park + four lampposts £35-40
	1975	**Auto Sales Pitch** no details £75-100
A3	c1971	**'Brroooom Stick'** Blister-packed car with steering control. Contains No.20 Lamborghini Marzal in Yellow and No.68 Porsche in White..£60-70
---	1975	**Military Carry Case Set** with six models....................£150-200
PD1	19??	**Power Driver Set** with No.74 Alfa Carabo £60-80
MG3	19??	**'TEXACO' Garage Set** with unused decals £75-100

Models of YesterYear, 1956–1983

Many variants of Yesteryears have resulted from long production runs which often required renewal or modification of worn dies. Considerable numbers of model variations have thus been issued over the years, some of them quite minor. The objective of this listing is to identify for the Yesteryear collector all those price-significant variations which really do matter. Collectors requiring details of the all the variations issued should contact: The Matchbox International Collectors Association (M.I.C.A.) PO Box 120, Deeside CH5 3HE, UK.

Identification

Common features. Many models have common identifying features and these are shown below to avoid unnecessary repetition in the Features column.

Model name and number. Both 'Models of Yesteryear' and 'Made in England by Lesney' are cast underneath all models issued up to the end of 1982. With the change of ownership this was replaced by 'Matchbox Intl Ltd.' From 1987 'Made in Macau' appears on the base. All models have their 'Y' number shown underneath.

Wheels. All the wheels prior to 1970 were of metal construction. From 1972 (approximately), plastic wheels were used on all models. Nevertheless the models issued at this changeover period are to be found with either metal or plastic wheels.

Scale of models ranges from 1:34 to 1:130. The scale of each model is usually shown on its box.

Logos and designs. The early models had waterslide transfers. Labels have also been used and currently models are tampo printed.

Catalogue listings. Do not place too much reliance on the model colours shown in catalogues. Very often the pictures shown are from mock-ups in colours never actually issued. For example, the 1969 catalogue showed a picture of a blue Y-5 Peugeot that was issued in yellow. Similarly the 1973 catalogue showed a silver Hispano Suiza which was then issued in red.

Bumpers, dashboards, headlights, radiator shells and windscreens. All assumed to be of metal construction prior to 1974 (approx.), after which plastic was increasingly used.

Base plate and chassis are usually of metal construction.

Tyres are of treaded black plastic unless otherwise indicated.

Seats are all made of plastic unless otherwise indicated.

Boxes

1956-57	All card box with just a plain black number shown on box ends. Line drawing of model on the front of box.
1957-60	All card box with line drawing of model used for first 15 models issued, blue number shown on white circle on endflap
1960-61	As first box but with a red number. All card box with coloured picture of the model (3 varieties of this box exist). All card box with model pictures on the box endflaps.
1968-69	Pink and yellow box with clear window.
1968-70	As previous box with hanging display card (developed in the US market and led to blister-pack design).
1969-70	Mauve and yellow box with window.
1974-78	'Woodgrain' window box in various colours
1979-83	'Straw' (light cream), window box.
1984-90	'Red' (maroon), window box.

Model and details	MPR

Y1-1 Allchin Traction Engine
1956-1965. Scale 1:80.
Early issues have rear wheel treads with a straight-across pattern, second type are diagonal; third type has a smooth tread.

With straight-across treads to rear wheels	**£100-125**
Rear wheel treads in Red (as per spokes)	**£40-60**
Brass boiler door, Red angled rear treads, rounded axles	**£70-80**
Rear wheels with no treads (smooth)	**£900-1,100**
Smoke box door in green (as per body)	**£150-200**
Other versions	**£25-50**

Y1-2 1911 Ford Model 'T'
1964-1984. Scale 1:42.
All Y1-2 models have 'brass effect' finish wheels.

Dark Red models with twin brake lever	**£45-70**
Dark Red or White/Red models with Black textured roof)	**£60-75**
Black body, textured roof and seats	**£120-150**
White/Red body, Bright Red textured roof	**£85-120**
Cream body, Red chassis, Dark Red seats, Orange canopy	**£80-100**
Red body and chassis, Black seats, Dark Orange canopy	**£80-100**
Other versions	**£2-10**

Y1-3 1936 Jaguar SS100
1977-1994. Scale 1:38.

With small sidelights (Off-White model only)	**£125-150**
Steel-Grey body and chassis	**£150-175**
Yellow body, Black seats, large lights	**£20-30**

Y2-1 1911 'B'-type London Bus
1956-1961. Scale 1:100.
The diecast driver may be found in any shade of mid or dark blue, sometimes black.

With 4 over 4 side windows	**£60-70**
With Black wheels	**£80-100**
Other versions	**£35-50**

Y2-2 1911 Renault Two-Seater
1963-1968. Scale 1:40.
Note that the red pigment used in the plastic seats is prone to fading in bright light.

All versions	**£15-25**

Y2-3 1914 'Prince Henry' Vauxhall
1970-1979. Scale 1:47.

With Copper petrol tank (Red and Silver issue only)	**£225-275**
Bright Red seats (Blue and Silver issue only)	**£200-300**
Other versions	**£2-8**

Y3-1 1907 'E'-class Tramcar
1956-1965. Scale 1:130. All versions have **a** bright Red body with Yellow 'LONDON TRANSPORT' fleetname and 'NEWS OF THE WORLD' decals.

With thin (Grey) cow-catchers	**£100-125**
Grey base (thin or thick cowcatchers)	**£125-175**
Other versions	**£30-50**

Y3-2 1910 Benz Limousine
1965-1984. Scale 1:54.

Cream body / chassis, Light Yellow roof	**£150-200**
Light Green body / chassis, Dark Green roof	**£150-200**
Light Green body and chassis, Light Yellow roof, separate rear wing supports	**£200-275**
Light Green body and chassis, Black roof	**£60-75**
Dark Metallic Green body and chassis, Light Yellow roof	**£200-250**
As previous model, but no holes in base	**£300-350**
Other versions	**£10-15**

Y3-3 1934 Riley MPH
1974-1979. Scale 1:35.

Dark Purple body and chassis, Black seats and grille	**£100-125**
Ruby Red body / chassis, Black seats / grille	**£100-125**

Model and details	MPR

Other versions	**£2-6**

Y3-4 1912 Ford Model 'T' Tanker
1981-1989. Scale 1:35.

'BP', Green body, Red tank, with 'No. Y12' cast on base	**£40-50**
'BP', other versions	**£2-4**
'ZEROLENE', with 'No. Y12' cast on base	**£40-50**
'ZEROLENE', other versions	**£2-4**
'EXPRESS DAIRY', all versions	**£2-6**

Y4-1 1928 Sentinel Steam Wagon
1956 only. Scale 1:100.
Blue body, 'SAND & GRAVEL SUPPLIES'.

With Black plastic wheels	**£85-100**
With Grey metal wheels	**£35-55**

Y4-2 Shand-Mason Fire Engine

Y4-2 1905 Shand-Mason Fire Engine
1960-1965. Scale 1:63.
Red metal body, two horses, three plastic firemen.

'KENT' Fire Brigade, Pale Grey Horses	**£500-600**
'KENT' Fire Brigade, White Horses	**£85-125**
'LONDON' Fire Brigade, Bronze horses	**£300-400**
'LONDON' Fire Brigade, White or Black horses	**£80-120**
Silver plated, Jack Odell momento	**£1,000-1,250**

Y4-3 1909 Opel Coupé
1967-1984. Scale 1:38.

With Tan textured hood + rear window.....**£175-200**
With Maroon grille and seats **£15-25**
Other versions..**£2-8**

Y4-4 1930 Duesenberg 'J' Town Car
1976-1997. Scale 1:43.
White body, Orange-Red or Red chassis,
    Yellow hood and seats...............**£2,000-2,500**
White body, Orange-red or Red chassis,
    Black hood and seats **£1,500-2,000**
Dark Red body and chassis,
    Maroon hood and seats **£175-200**
Dark Red body and chassis,
    Dark Green hood and seats **£75-100**
Dark Red body and chassis,
    Dark Green hood, Lt. Brown seats.**£100-125**
Metallic all-Red body, White hood **£80-100**
Light Green body and chassis,
    Lime Green side / rear body panels ..**£45-65**
Dark Green, Blue base **£80-100**
Other versions..**£2-5**

Y5-1 1929 Le Mans Bentley
1958-1961. Scale 1:55.
All are finished in British Racing Green.
With Grey folded hood, Silver radiator.......**£85-125**
With Grey folded hood, Gold radiator.........**£80-110**
Other versions..**£35-55**

Y5-2 1929 4½ litre Bentley
1962-1968. Scale 1:52.
Model has Union Jacks and racing numbers on
its sides, folded windscreen and silver 24-spoke
wheels, (spare on nearside).
Metallic Apple Green body,
    Dark Green or Dark Red seats........**£150-200**
Same but with Red seats/tonneau **£100-125**
British Racing Green body, Red RN '6' **£60-70**
Other versions..**£10-15**

Y5-3 1907 Peugeot
1969-1977. Scale 1:43.
Except where noted, the wheels have 12-spokes.
Yellow body and chassis, Black roof, no rib
    on rear edge of front seat side panels **£35-55**
Yellow body/chassis, Black roof,
    clear windows **£85-125**
Yellow body and chassis, Gold roof **£100-150**
Orange-Gold, or Light-Gold body,
    Black chassis and roof **£65-85**
Light Gold body and roof,
    Black chassis, Chrome 12 or 24
    spoke wheels, clear windows **£100-105**
Other versions..**£6-8**

Y5-4 1927 Talbot Van
1978-1988. Scale 1:47.
'LIPTONS TEA' (1978), all versions....................**£2-5**
'CHOCOLAT MENIER' (1978-1979),
    all versions **£2-5**
'TAYSTEE BREAD' (1980), all versions.............**£2-5**
'NESTLES' (1981).
    With Matt Black roof **£100-150**
    With Gloss Black roof **£100-150**
    All other versions..**£2-5**
'CHIVERS' (1982), all versions **£2-5**
'WRIGHTS' (1982),
    with Dark Brown roof......................**£150-180**
    All other versions..**£2-5**
'EVER READY' (1983), all versions **£2-5**

Y6-1 1916 AEC 'Y' type Lorry
1957-1961. Scale 1:100. 'OSRAM LAMPS'
Pale Blue or Mid Blue body,
    Grey metal wheels **£1,250-1,750**
Light Grey body, Grey metal wheels.............**£40-60**
Dark Grey body, Grey metal wheels **£60-100**
Dark Grey body, Black plastic wheels.**£1,300-1,500**

Y6-2 1935 Type 35 Bugatti
1961-1965. Scale1:48. Model has a black baseplate

and gold 8-spoke wheels with a spare on the
nearside. Racing number '6' may be upside-down
and appear as '9'.
Blue body, Grey tyres **£45-65**
Blue body, Blue radiator **£80-100**
Blue body, White dashboard....................**£100-125**
Red body, Red radiator **£80-100**
Red body, Black dashboard......................**£100-150**
Red body, Gold radiator **£125-150**
Other versions...**£15-25**

Y6-3 1913 Cadillac
1968-1975. Scale 1:48.
Gold body, Dark Red textured roof.............**£80-110**
All other Gold body versions..........................**£6-12**
Green body, thin spare tyre carrier...............**£45-65**
Green body with Blue, Pale Green, Metallic Green,
    Beige, Yellow, Pink or Mauve seats **£60-80**
All other Green body versions.........................**£2-6**

Y6-4 1920 Rolls-Royce Fire Engine
1977-1984. Scale 1:48.
Without locating lugs for side label **£75-100**
With red front seats, Brown ladders **£250-350**
All other versions...**£2-8**

*Rare Model of Yesteryear Y7-1 Jacob & Co 1918 Leyland
4-ton van with black plastic wheels*

Y7-1 1918 Leyland 4-ton Van
1957-1960. 'W. & R. Jacob & Co. Ltd.'
    Scale 1:100.
Dark Brown body **£55-75**
Dark Brown body with centre line of
    transfer omitted......................................**£600-800**
Reddish Brown body......................................**£40-60**
Reddish Brown body,
    Black plastic wheels **£1,250-1,500**

Y7-1 Leyland 4-ton Van

Y7-2 1913 Mercer Raceabout type 35J
1961-1965. Scale 1:46.
Lilac body and chassis **£15-20**
Lilac body and chassis, Grey tyres **£60-85**
Yellow body and chassis **£10-15**
Yellow body, chassis and radiator.................**£15-20**

Y7-3 1912 Rolls-Royce
1968-1970. Scale 1:48.
Silver body and bonnet, Dark Red chassis
    and smooth or ribbed roof **£5-10**
Silver body/bonnet, Dark Red chassis and
    smooth roof, Yellow seats / grille ...**£550-800**
Silver body and bonnet, Dark Red chassis,
    Grey ribbed roof **£50-75**
Gold body, Silver bonnet, Dark Red
    chassis and ribbed roof....................**£75-100**

Gold body and bonnet, Dark Red chassis
    and ribbed roof, thin brass
    12-spoke wheels **£50-75**
Gold body / bonnet, Dark Red chassis
    and ribbed roof, wide chrome
    12 or 24-spoke wheels **£5-8**
Gold body and bonnet, Dark Red chassis and
    ribbed roof, wide chrome 12-spoke
    wheels, Dark Green seats / grille ...**£225-275**
Yellow body and bonnet, Red chassis,
    Black ribbed roof **£200-250**
Yellow body and bonnet,
    Black chassis and ribbed roof................**£2-5**

Y8-1 1926 Morris Cowley
1958 only. Scale 1:50.
Tan body, Dark Brown chassis,
    Silver or Light Copper wheels **£40-50**

Y8-2 1914 Sunbeam M/cycle & Sidecar
1962-1967. Scale 1:34
Chrome plated, Black m/cycle seat,
    Dark Green sidecar seat.....................**£25-45**
Chrome plated, Black m/cycle seat,
    Emerald Green sidecar seat...........**£150-250**
Chrome plated, Black m/cycle seat,
    Black sidecar seat **£500-600**
Light Gold plated...**£550-750**

Y8-3 1914 Stutz Roadster
1969-1973. Scale 1:48.
Dark Red body / bonnet, smooth Tan roof **£6-10**
Dark Red body / bonnet, brass petrol tank...**£75-95**
Dark Red body / chassis, textured Tan roof .**£20-25**
Dark Red body / chassis, textured Tan roof,
    Red grille **£30-50**
Dark Red body / chassis, textured Tan roof,
    Pinky-Red seats or Maroon seats....**£50-75**
Metallic Red body, smooth Black roof.........**£80-100**
Metallic Blue body and chassis;
    White, Yellow or Black seats **£80-90**
Blue body and chassis,
    Bright Red seats and grille **£35-45**

Y8-4 1945 MG 'TC'
1978-1984. Scale 1:35.
Green body and chassis **£5-10**
Red body and chassis **£3-5**
Blue body and chassis **£3-5**

Y9-1 1924 Fowler Showman's Engine
1958-1965. Scale 1:80.
'Lesney's Modern Amusements'.
Dark Maroon body **£70-80**
Dark Maroon body, Gold cylinder block.....**£85-125**
Light Purple body, Gold or Light Purple
    cylinder block **£350-400**
Maroon body **£65-75**
Bright Red body **£55-65**
    NB Any of the above with a Black
    nameplate in the base usually
    adds a premium of approximately £10.

Y9-2 1912 Simplex
1968-1988. Scale 1:48.
Lime Green or Mid Green body **£8-15**
Dark Gold body, Dark Red chassis **£10-15**
Dark Gold body, Bright Red chassis **£185-235**
Red body, Yellow seats **£70-80**
Red body, Red or Black chassis........................**£5-10**

Y10-1 1908 'Grand Prix' Mercedes
1958-1959. Scale 1:54.
Off-White/Pale Cream body,
    Light or Mid Green seats....................**£20-50**
Pure White body,
    Light or Mid Green seats...............**£100-150**

Y10-2 1928 Mercedes-Benz 36-220
1963 only. Scale 1:52
White body, Red seats and folded hood,
single or twin spare wheels £10-20
White body, Black seats and folded
hood, twin spare wheels £1,500-1,750

Y10-3 1906 Rolls-Royce Silver Ghost
1969-1983. Scale 1:51.
Lime Green body, Bronze chassis....................£8-12
White body, Purple or Dark Red chassis £4-7
White body, Silver chassis, Black seats......£275-325
Silver body, Purple chassis £275-325
Silver body and chassis, Dark Red seats...........£2-4
Silver body and chassis, Yellow seats............£4-6
Silver body/chassis, White or Ivory seats ..£300-350

Y11-1 1920 Aveling & Porter Steam Roller
1958 only. Scale 1:80.
Mid-Green body/boiler/roof;
Black roof supports £30-50
With Gold maker's plate (front of cylinder
block), Black supports....................£200-250
With Gold maker's plate (front of cylinder
block), Green supports £350-550

Y11-2 1912 Packard Landaulet
1964-1984. Scale 1:50.
Dark Red and Orange-Red versions £8-12
Cream body, only in 1984
'Connoisseur Collection' ....GSP

Y11-3 Lagonda Drophead Coupé

Y11-3 1938 Lagonda Drophead Coupé
1972-1985. Scale 1:43.
Gold body, Purple chassis, Black seats£1,500-2,000
Gold body, Dark Red chassis....................£100-150
Gold body, Strawberry Red chassis £75-85
Gold body, Maroon chassis £15-20
Orange body, Gold chassis,
brass (narrow) 24-spoke wheels £100-125
Orange or Copper body, Gold chassis,
Chrome or Red (wide) wheels.............£4-15
Copper body, Gold chassis, Green or Bright
Red seats, folded hood and grille...£200-250
Copper body, Gold chassis, Black seats £40-50
Orangey-Blood Red body, Gold chassis £65-85
Copper body, Black chassis £175-225
Dark Cream body, Gold chassis £175-225
Dark Cream body, Black chassis £2-8
Maroon body version
(in 1985 'Fathers Day' Set)....................GSP

Y12-1 1899 Horse-drawn Bus
1959 only. Scale 1:100.
Red body and chassis. All versions £35-55

Y12-2 1909 Thomas Flyabout
1967-1975. Scale 1:48.
Blue body / chassis,
Yellow seats and grille £1,000-1,250
Blue body / chassis,
Dark Red seats and grille £5-15
Purple-Red body / chassis,
Off-White seats / grille £4-8

Y12-3 1912 Ford Model 'T' Van
1979-1986. Scale 1:35.
'COCA COLA' (1979)

With 5 vertical Red printed coach lines.....£200-300
With 4 vertical Red printed coach lines.........£40-60
'COLMANS MUSTARD' (1979-1981).
All versions.......................................£2-4
'TAYSTEE' (1980)
Yellow body, Black chassis / roof...£350-500
NB There are known to be fakes which
have the smaller labels as used on the
Y5-4 Talbot Van. Genuine 'Taystee' labels
for the Ford Model 'T' Van measure 29mm
end to end of 'Taystee' oval and 11mm
top to bottom of the oval.
'SUZE' (1980-1981)
With Gloss Black roof,
Red double lines on rear doors £85-125
All other versions................................£2-4
'SMITHS CRISPS' (1981) All versions...............£2-4
'25 YEARS SILVER JUBILEE' (1981)
Silver printed single line
on rear doors...........................£400-475
With Yellow 24-spoke wheels £45-65
All other versions................................£2-4
'BIRDS CUSTARD' (1982)
With Metallic Blue body...................£50-65
All other (plain Blue) versions £2-4
'CEREBOS' (1982)
Light Blue body, Black chassis,
Yellow roof £60-75
All other versions................................£2-4
'ARNOTTS' (1982)
Bright Red body, Black chassis,
Gloss Black roof............................£100-135
Same but with Matt Black roof..........£50-75
'HARRODS' (1982). All versions £2-4
'SUNLIGHT SEIFE' (1983)
Yellow body, Black chassis,
matt Black roof..............................£45-65
NB Models exist with fake labels. Genuine
labels have a clothes line post to the right of
the woman hanging out the washing.
'ROYAL MAIL' (1983)
Bright Red body, Black chassis and
roof, Yellow printed double lines
on rear doors...............................£175-225
All others (cast rear door outline)..........£2-4
'CAPTAIN MORGAN' (1983-1984)
Black body, cast hole in
rear base of body £45-75
All other versions................................£2-4
'HOOVER' (1983).
Blue body, White roof, Black
chassis, Beige seats....................£400-500
All other versions................................£2-4
'MOTOR 100', world globe with blue
land and white oceans £700-800

Y13-1 'Santa Fe' Locomotive (1862)
1959 only. Scale 1:112.
Mid-Green cab and boiler, Dark Red chassis
and smokebox, Gold chimney
rim and condenser tops.............. £900-1,200
Other versions (Dark Green)........................£35-55

Y13-2 1911 Daimler
1966-1967 + 1984. Scale 1:45.
Yellow body, all versions...............................£6-8
Blue body, Powder Blue chassis,
in 1984 'Connoisseur Collection' ....GSP

Y13-3 1918 Crossley Lorry
'RAF' Tender (1975-1976). Scale 1:47.
RAF Blue cab, body and chassis, Black
canopy, no strengthening web between
front mudguards and chassis £300-400
With Dull Dark Red or Green seats.............£75-100
With Olive Green canopy and grille..............£25-35
With Black canopy and grille....................£225-275
All other versions...................................£4-6

Y13-4 1918 Crossley Lorry
'EVANS Bros.' (1979-1982). Scale 1:47.
Red cab and body, with two cast

cleats on body sides £75-125
All other versions...................................£2-4
'CARLSBERG' (1983-1984)
Cream cab / body,
'Matchbox Toys Ltd' base £2-4
With 'Lesney Products' cast on base .£40-50
With Ice Blue canopy and tilt £60-70

Y14-1 'Duke of Connaught' Locomotive
1959 only. Scale 1:130.
Dark Green cab and boiler,
with Gold sand boxes.........................£70-90
With Silver smoke box door....................£75-100
All other versions.................................£35-50

Y14-2 1911 Maxwell Roadster
1965 only (+1984). Scale 1:49.
Turquoise body and chassis,
Copper petrol tank £75-100
Any other versions.....................................£4-8
Cream body, Dark Green chassis,
in 1984 'Connoisseur Collection' ....GSP

Y14-3 1931 Stutz Bearcat
1974-1995. Scale 1:44. All versions.................£2-8

Y15-1 1907 Rolls-Royce Silver Ghost
1960 only. Scale 1:55.
Light Green body and chassis,
Grey knobbly tyres, Silver rear
number plate and Red rear light........£20-35
With Dark Green seats £60-80
Other versions...£4-8

Y15-2 1930 Packard Victoria
1969-1979 (+1984). Scale 1:46.
Lime Gold body, Dark Brown chassis,
wide cast rear coach-line...................£20-30
Lime Gold body, Black chassis,
thin or wide cast rear coach-line ...£235-285
Metallic Lime Gold body, Dark Brown
chassis, Black hood, Brown,
Red or White seats.........................£60-70
Same but with White hood and seats £65-75
Other versions...£2-8

Y16-1 1904 Spyker
1961-1968. Scale 1:45.
Pale Cream body / chassis,
Grey knobbly tyres £275-350
Pale Lemon body / chassis,
Grey knobbly tyres £60-80
With two cast holes in base £45-75
Maroon body and chassis.................. £1,400-1,900
Other versions...£4-8

Y16-2 1928 Mercedes-Benz SS
1972- 1990. Scale 1:45.
Lime Green body, Dark Green chassis,
Black seats.....................................£150-200
Metallic Mid-Green body,
Lime Green chassis £50-60
White body, Black chassis.........................£375-500
Blue body / chassis,
Duck Egg Blue side panels.................£50-60
Blue body and chassis,
Milky White side panels.....................£75-90
Metallic Silver, Metallic Red chassis £55-65
Other versions...£2-8

Y17-1 1938 Hispano-Suiza
1975-1995. Scale 1:48.
Silver body (Powder Blue side panels
on some), Silver or Black chassis,
Yellow seats..................................£135-175
Red/Black body, Red or Black hood £70-80
Other versions...£2-6

Y18-1 1937 Cord 812
1979-1995. Scale 1:48. All versions...................£2-4

Y19-1 1936 Auburn Speedster
1979- 1990. Scale 1:42. All versions.................. **£2-4**

Y20-1 1937 Mercedes-Benz 540K
1981-1995. Scale 1:45. All versions.................. **£2-6**

Y21-1 1930 Ford Model 'A' Woody
1981-1985. Scale 1:40. All versions.................. **£2-6**

Y21-2 1930 Ford Model 'A' Woody
1983-1985. Scale 1:40
'A. & J. BOX'
With Yellow bonnet, 'Lesney' base **£5-10**
All other versions.................................. **£2-6**

Y22-1 1930 Ford Model 'A' Van

1982-1991. Scale 1:41.
'OXO' (1982)
    Red body, seats / interior,
    'Lesney' base...................... **£75-125**
    Red body, Gloss Black van roof......... **£10-15**
    All other versions.................................. **£2-4**

Y23-1 1922 AEC Omnibus
1983-1989. Scale 1:72.
'SCHWEPPES' (1983-1984)
    Red body, with Red lettering on
    advertisement labels **£30-45**
    All other versions..................................... **£2-4**

Y24-1 1928 Bugatti T44

1983-1995. Scale 1:72.
Black and Yellow body with Brown,
    Green or White seats...................... **£175-250**
Black and Yellow body with Black seats........ **£25-45**
Black/Yellow with Grey seats, straw box ...**£100-120**
All other versions.................................. **£2-4**

Y25-1 1910 Renault 'AG' Van
1983-1989. Scale 1:38.
'PERRIER' (1983)
    Green body, Dark Green chassis,
    roof rack with 3 side struts............. **£250-300**
    With closed grab handles **£75-125**
    All other versions.................................. **£2-4**

Models of YesterYear Gift Sets

G 6 1960 **Gift Set** Contains Nos. 1, 2, 5,
    10 and 13. Lesney line-drawing box . **£325-375**
G 7 1960 **Gift Set** Contains Nos 3, 8, 9, 12 and
    14. Lesney line-drawing box................ **£325-375**

No G7 Gift Set 'Veteran & Vintage' - comprising five
models including No 5 Bentley and No 2 Renault

G 6 1962 **Veteran & Vintage Car Set**Contains Nos
    5, 6, 7, 15 and 16. Lesney picture box...**£325-375**
G 7 1962 **Gift Set** Contains Nos 3, 4, 11, 12
    and 13. Lesney picture box................ **£325-375**
G 7 1965 **Veteran & Vintage Set**.............Contains
    Y2, Y5, Y10, Y15 and Y16. Picture box**£250-300**
G 7 1966 **Gift Set** Y1-2 Model T Ford, Y3-2
    Benz, Y11-2 Packard, Y14-2 Maxwell.
    Picture box **£75-100**
G 7 19?? **Gift Set** Y3, Y8, Y9, Y12 and Y14**£200-300**
G 5 1968 **Gift Set** Y4-3 Opel, Y6-3 Cadillac,
    Y9-2 Simplex, Y9-2 Simplex.................. **£40-50**
G 5 1970-72 **Gift Set** Contains Y8-3 Stutz Red,
    Y14 Maxwell, Y16-1 Spyker (Dark Yellow),
    Y7-3 Rolls-Royce Silver and Red. Picture box....
    .... **£45-55**

Y-50 1982 **Gift Set** Contains Y3-4 'BP' Tanker,
    Y5-4 Talbot Van 'Chivers', Y10-3 Rolls
    Royce, Y12-3 Model 'T' Van, Y13-3
    Crossley Coal Lorry...................... **£20-30**

1984 **'Connoisseur Collection'** ....Contains
    Y1-2 Black 1911 Model 'T' Ford, Y4-3
    Red/Beige 1909 Opel, Y3-2 Blue/Black
    1910 Benz Limousine, Y11-2 White/
    Black 1912 Packard Landaulet,
    Y13-2 Blue 1911 Daimler, Y14-2 Beige/
    Black 1911 Maxwell. 30,000 certificated
    and numbered sets issued in beechwood
    display case................................ **£80-100**

Models of YesterYear Plated Souvenirs and Giftware

Models specially plated to adorn giftware (e.g.,
cigarette boxes, ashtrays, penstands, boxes and
pipestands). Non-plated versions of the models
listed will also be found with the two baseplate
holes used for fixing the plated models to the
various items.
Prices (dependent on type of giftware):
Unboxed, not mounted on original giftware......**£2-3**
Unboxed, still mounted on giftware **£5-20**
In original box, still on original giftware **£30-85**

SILVER-EFFECT PLATED MODELS
Y1-2	1911	Model 'T' Ford....................
Y2-2	1911	Renault 2 seater....................
Y2-3	1914	Prince Henry Vauxhall ....
Y3-3	1934	Riley MPH..........................
Y4-3	1909	Opel Coupé ....

Y5-2	1929	4½ Litre Bentley................................
Y6-2	1926	Type 35 Bugatti ....
Y7-2	1913	Mercer Raceabout................................
Y7-3	1912	Rolls-Royce..................................
Y10-2	1928	Mercedes-Benz 36-220 ....
Y10-3	1906	Rolls-Royce..................................
Y12-2	1909	Thomas Flyabout ....
Y13-2	1911	Daimler ....
Y13-3	1918	Crossley ....
Y14-2	1911	Maxwell Roadster ....
Y15-1	1907	Rolls-Royce Silver Ghost ....
Y16-1	1904	Spyker ....

GOLD-EFFECT PLATED MODELS
Y1-2	1911	Model 'T' Ford....................
Y2-3	1914	Prince Henry Vauxhall ....
Y3-2	1910	Benz Limousine ....

Y4-3	1909	Opel Coupé ....
Y5-2	1929	4½ Litre Bentley................................
Y7-2	1913	Mercer Raceabout................................
Y7-3	1912	Rolls-Royce..................................
Y10-2	1928	Mercedes-Benz 36-220 ....
Y10-3	1906	Rolls-Royce..................................
Y12-2	1909	Thomas Flyabout ....
Y13-2	1911	Daimler ....
Y13-3	1918	Crossley ....
Y14-2	1911	Maxwell Roadster ....
Y15-1	1907	Rolls-Royce Silver Ghost ....
Y16-1	1904	Spyker on tray.................... **£130-150**

GOLD PLATED SETS
Golden Veteran Set with 3 models:
Y7-3, Y13-2, Y14-2 .... **£50-65**
Heritage Gifts, 2 models: Y7-3, Y10-3 .... **£35-50**

Selection of popular YesterYear cars

Lesney 'Pub Signs'

A series of plated figurines made for attachment to giftware. The base of each is marked 'Lesney Co. Ltd. 1975'. They have 'spurs' underneath to aid fixing to such items as ashtrays, etc. The Editor would be pleased to receive more details.

'The Cock' ....**£8-10** 'The Unicorn'...............**£8-10** 'The Pig & Whistle' ....**£8-10** 'The Sherlock Holmes' .**£8-10** 'The Mermaid' **£8-10**
'The Lion' ....**£8-10** 'The Bull' ....**£8-10** 'The George & Dragon' **£8-10** 'The Volunteer' ....**£8-10** 'The Royal Standard' **£8-10**
'The Swan' ....**£8-10** 'The Rose & Crown'......**£8-10** 'The Dick Turpin' ....**£8-10** 'The Britannia' **£8-10**

Models of YesterYear 'Codes 1 and 2' special issues

A system of categorising models has evolved among collectors to distinguish between authentic manufacturers' output and acceptable but unauthorised alteration of their models for later resale. The explanation which follows refers to a coding system adopted generally (but not officially) throughout the model collecting fraternity in the UK and elsewhere, and may he applied to models produced by any manufacturer.

CODE 1 Applies to models which have been originated and totally produced by an established manufacturer.

CODE 2 As CODE 1, but labelled or finished outside the factory WITH the manufacturer's permission.

CODE 3 Same as CODE 2, but model re-labelled, altered or re-worked WITHOUT authorisation or permission from the manufacturer.

Y1-2 76 **1911 Ford Model 'T' Car**. Black body, textured roof, grille and seats, Chrome 12-spoke wheels, brass trim, bare windscreen frame. 900 models made for the USA.........**£325-400**

Y5-4 78 **1927 Talbot Van** with 12-spoke wheels and Chrome trim.
'2nd AIM CONVENTION', Dark Green body and wheels, 'Toy Show, Harrisburgh PA May 27/28, 1978' **£75-125**
81 'CRAWLEY SWAPMEET 1981', Royal Blue body, Black roof and chassis, 'Follow Us To Crawley'..............**£125-175**
81 'VARIETY CLUB', 'Sunshine Coach Appeal'
1: Yellow body and chassis, Black roof, Red wheels **£125-165**
2: As 1 but with Black chassis **£150-175**
80 'MERITA BREAD', Yellow body, Red wheels......................**£20-40**
80 'LANGENDORF', Yellow body, Red wheels **£20-40**
80 'TAYSTEE BREAD', Yellow body, Black roof, Red wheels and Pale Yellow 'Taystee' on Red oval...................**£70-80**
81 'IRONBRIDGE' 1: Yellow body, matt Black roof, Red wheels, 'The World's First Iron Bridge'...................**£125-165**
2: As 1 with gloss Black chassis and mudguards............**£140-180**

81 'BEES' 1: Yellow body, Black roof, Red wheels, plain or White-wall tyres, 'Bees Art & Model Service'.............**£100-150**
2: As 1 but Black chassis and mudguards **£90-110**
81 'DUTCH MATCHBOX MEET'.
'lst Matchbox meeting in Holland on 4th October 1981'.
1: Blue and Grey body, Black roof and chassis, 'Stoevclaar', with Certificate **£175-225**
2: Yellow and Red body, Black roof and chassis, 'Stoevclaar', 72 only presented to stallholders **£400-500**
81 LAWRENCE FRASER TOYS', Blue body...........................**£200-250**

Y7-3 82 **1912 Rolls-Royce**. Wedding of Prince Charles and Princess Diana. Bright Yellow and Black, Red wheels, 600 ....**£145-185**

Y12-3 81 **Ford Model 'T' Van**
1: 'BANG & OLUFSEN', White/Red, certificate **£275-325**
2: Without certificate **£165-185**
81 'RAYLEIGH SWAPMEET', Yellow body, Black roof...........**£75-125**
82 'CADA TOYS Have Moved', Yellow/Black, 600................**£180-200**
82 'DEANS of LEEDS', Yellow body, Black roof, Red 'Deans for Toys', telephone no. on some, 800 ....**£125-150**
80 'CAMBERLEY NEWS', Yellow/Black, '75th', 750 ....**£155-185**
83 'HOOVER', Blue body, White roof, Black chassis,
1: With certificate, 500 ....**£500-600**
2: Without certificate, 50 ....**£350-400**

Y13-3 **1918 Crossley**
79 'UK MATCHBOX CLUB', Red/Yellow, 800...........................**£80-90**
81 'ASPECTS and IMAGES', Red/Light Brown **£125-150**
81 'SURREY MODEL FAIR', Red body, 'Tangley Model Workshop' on rear of Grey canopy only, 500.................**£125-150**

Group of Matchbox Models of YesterYear: Y12 Ford Model T 1912 Captain Morgan, Y5 Talbot 1927 Liptons Tea, Y15 Packard Victoria 1930, Y19 Auburn 851 1935, Y18 Cord 812 1937, Y9 Simplex - 50 1912.

Group of Matchbox Models of YesterYear, both standard issue and promotional issue vans: Y22 Ford Model A 1930 Van Maggis Soups, Y12 Ford Model T 1922 Harrods Express Delivery, Y12 Ford Model T 1912 Classic and Collectors Car, Y22 Ford Model A 1930 Auto Sound Incar Electronics, Y5 Talbot 1927 London Model Club.

Matchbox Models of YesterYear No Y12 Ford Model T 1912 Deans of Leeds 75th Anniversary Model.

Group of Matchbox Models of YesterYear including No 5 Bentley, No 7 Rolls Royce, No 4 Opel Coupe, No 1 Ford Model T, plus others.

Matchbox King Size K-8 Tractor and Transporter.

Matchbox Superfast Carry Case, would hold up to 48 models.

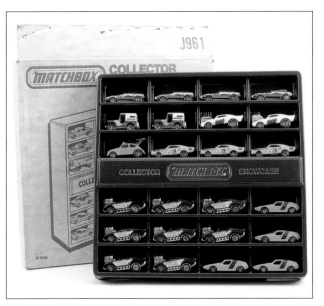

Matchbox Superfast counter/wall mounted Collector 'Matchbox' show case.

Morestone and Modern Products, Budgie Toys and Seerol

The history of these makes is a fascinating story of inter-linked companies, take-overs and bankruptcies reflecting the ups and downs of the toy trade. In the late 1940s Morris & Stone was a toy wholesaler selling the products of many small toy manufacturers including those from Modern Products who had started as die-casters. Morris and Stone decided to have their own exclusive 'Morestone' branded lines and some were made by Modern Products, who increasingly relied on Morestone for the sole marketing and distribution of their toys. Morestone continued to use several suppliers but in 1954 set up a die-casting company jointly with Rodney Smith (one of the founders of Lesney Products).

From the mid-1950s to 1966 the Morestone and Budgie ranges contained models that came either from the in-house factory or from Modern Products. Morestone's production expanded with new ranges of models, such as the 'Noddy' and 'Big-Ears' vehicles in 1956 and the Esso Petrol Pump Series of miniatures, launched at Christmas of that year. In 1958, the 'Trucks of the World International Series' was introduced, but only ran to three models.

Some of the earlier Morestone and Modern Products models were re-issued as part of the Budgie range which was introduced in 1959. Model numbers were allocated in 1960 and new additions to the range continued every year up to 1966. During 1961, Morris & Stone was taken over by S. Guiterman & Co Ltd, who changed the name of their new subsidiary to Budgie Models Ltd. Although the range included many interesting and unusual subjects, they failed to compete with Corgi, Dinky and Matchbox, and losses in Budgie Models Ltd contributed to losses in the Guiterman group. In March 1966 these companies went into voluntary liquidation.

Modern Products was badly hit by this but eventually were able to set up a new company called Budgie Models (Continuation) Ltd and purchase the Budgie trade mark from the receiver. They wanted the Budgie dies as well, but these were destroyed in a fire while negotiations were in progress. The only dies to survive were those in their own factory.

Thus the main range of Budgie commercial vehicles came to an end in 1966. Modern Products continued to produce the Budgie miniatures, mainly for the USA, until 1969 when the stronger competition this time was from Mattel's 'Hot Wheels'. Modern Products direction for the 1970s was to produce models for H. Seener Ltd., distributors of toys and souvenirs to London's tourist shops. The old Budgie Routemaster bus was reintroduced for Seener, followed by a new FX4 Taxi and Rolls-Royce Silver Cloud.

In 1983, following the death of one of the partners in Modern Products, the business was sold to a neighbouring engineering company called Starcourt Ltd (some boxes say Merracroft Ltd - an associated company of Starcourt). The new owners reintroduced several models from the original moulds, starting with the Aveling Barford Road Roller. However, a disagreement developed with Seener who withdrew the dies for the Taxi and Rolls-Royce (which he had paid for), and arranged for these to be made by Corgi together with a completely new Routemaster bus. These 'Seerol' models appeared in 1985 and are still available. Starcourt ceased toy production in 1985.

Some unpainted castings for no.204 Volkswagen Pick-Up and some empty boxes were sold to a Dutch firm and have since appeared in various liveries. These are classed as 'Code 3' models and have not been listed. The die-casting moulds were sold to Autocraft (Dave Gilbert) in 1988, and these include most of the 1950s Modern Products and part of the 1960s Budgie range. Autocraft are now in the process of adapting dies for a range of some 35 various models. Only one model has so far been reintroduced – a run of 1000 of No 258 Daimler Ambulance in kit form.

A complete history of these companies and their products is contained in the book 'Budgie Models' by Robert Newson. This hardback book also has full descriptions of all the models, 58 pages of colour photographs illustrating over 180 models, and reproductions of Budgie leaflets. Sadly the book is now out of print.

Morestone and Modern Products

Ref	Year(s)	Description	MPR
-	c.1946	**Racing Car** Red, Dark Blue, Dark Green or Light Brown. One piece casting including driver. No identification on model. 135 mm	**£50-75**
-	19??	**Monkey Handcarts** Two monkeys on Red handcarts	**£200-250**
-	19??	**Teddy Bears on 'Sociable' Cycle** Brown/Yellow and Brown/Green Teddies on a red cycle	**£500-600**
-	19??	**Clown on Penny Farthing Cycle** Clown and dog on a bicycle	**£400-500**
-	19??	**Tandem Cycling Set** Tandem with sidecar with male and female riders and baby in sidecar	**£100-150**
-	19??	**Boy on Tricycle** Various colours	**£50-70**
-	19??	**Butcher's Deliveryman on bicycle** (no details)	**£50-70**
-	c.1947	**Stage Coach with Four Horses** English mail coach with driver and trunk, Yellow body, Red wheels, 173 mm. 'Ye Olde Coach and Four' on box	**£100-200**

Ref	Year(s)	Description	MPR
-	c.1948-56	**Fire Escape (large)** Brass bell and wheel hubs. Base consists of sump and prop shaft only. Extending wheeled escape ladder. 108 mm. (excluding ladder)	**£250-350**
-	c.1950	**Fire Escape (smaller)** Plain flat base, wheeled escape ladder, 66 mm. (excluding ladder)	**£150-200**
-	c.1948	**Fire Engine** Clockwork motor and bell underneath, 'Morestone Series' cast-in, 135 mm	**£250-350**
-	c.1948-58	**0-6-0 Tank Locomotive** Green or Red, 'British Railways' cast in, re-issued as Budgie 224, 119 mm	**£35-45**

Sam's Snack Bar

Ref	Year(s)	Description	MPR
-	1949-51	**Horse Drawn Snack Bar** 'SAM'S' cast on side below counter, removable roof, separate man, tea urn and two mugs, 117mm. Wide range of colours	**£250-350**
-	1949-59	**Horse Drawn Hansom Cab** Black/Yellow, driver, elastic band for reins, 118 mm. (re-issued as Budgie 100)	**£70-90**
-	1949-?	**Gypsy Caravan** Yellow, Green and Red caravan, step to seat, Grey or Brown horse, Gypsy	**£300-400**
-	c.1948-61	**Horse Drawn Covered Wagon with Four Horses** Green, Red or Orange, driver, cloth canopy plain or printed with 'Thundering Hooves and Blazing Guns on the Western Trail,' or 'Walt Disney's Davy Crockett Frontier Wagon' or 'Last of the Mohicans Chingachgook Hawkeye,' later with two barrels, 'Made in England' cast transversely under, 190 mm. (Budgie 404)	**£100-200**
-	1949	**'Wells Fargo' Stage Coach with two 'Galloping' Horses**	

238

Brown / Yellow, driver and guard, eccentric wheel for 'galloping' effect, some with 'Copyright F.W. Birch & Co.' cast inside, 164 mm... **£100-150**

- c.1950 **'Wells Fargo' Stage Coach**
Various colours, four horses, driver, 172 mm.................. **£100-150**

- 1952-58 **Stage Coach with Two Horses**
Red or Orange (no lettering), Black plastic horses, wheels and figures,165 mm **£100-150**

- 1954-59 **Horse Drawn Covered Wagon with Six Horses**
Red, Yellow wheels, printed cloth canopy 'The Wild West Land of Buffalo and Covered Wagon', driver, two barrels, 'Made in England' cast transversely underneath, 265mm **£100-125**

Mechanical Road Sweeper

- 1950-51 **Mechanical Road Sweeper**
Metallic Green/Black, 'City Cleansing Dept.' cast-in, clockwork motor in some, 91 mm..... **£275-350**
Non clockwork versions .. **£100-150**

- c.1950 **Compressor**
With man and pneumatic drill. No identification cast on model. 76 mm **£40-50**

- 1953 **State with Six Horses**
Coronation souvenir, three figures cast-in. No identification on model. 111 mm **£50-75**

- 1953 **Prime Mover with Trailer**
Red prime mover, 'British Road Services', 'NO 311' and 'MAX 20 MPH' cast-in, Black plastic wheels, 83 mm, Orange plastic trailer, 136 mm **£150-175**

- 1953 **Sleigh with Father Xmas**
One reindeer. No identification on model. About 140 mm **£175-225**

- 1953-55 **RAC Motorcycle and Sidecar**
Cast wheels / tyres and rider, no windscreen, hinged lid on sidecar, 70 mm **£150-175**

- 1954-55 **A.A. Motorcycle and Sidecar**
Cast wheels / tyres and rider, windscreen, non-opening sidecar, separate rails.......................**£75-100**

RAC Motorcycle and Sidecar

- 1956-57 **RAC Motorcycle and Sidecar**
Cast rider, windscreen, separate rails and hinged lid on sidecar, steering front forks, rubber tyres, plain number plates, 82 mm**£75-100**

- 1956-57 **A.A. Motorcycle and Sidecar**
Cast rider, windscreen, separate rails and hinged lid on sidecar, steering front forks, rubber tyres, plain number plates, 82 mm**£75-100**

- 1956-57 **Solo Motorcycle**
Cast rider, steering front forks, rubber tyres, plain number plates, 82 mm. There are four versions: Police Patrol, Despatch Rider, GPO Messenger and TT Rider. Each.......... ....**£75-100**

- ? **Police Motorcycle and Sidecar**
Black machine, Dark Blue sidecar, Black uniformed figures, cast wheels **£75-100**

- 1954-55 **Horse Drawn Gipsy Caravan**
Yellow/Green, tinplate roof and base, separate driver and rear steps, 190 mm **£400-500**

- 1954-56 **Bedford Dormobile**
Red or Green body. 90 mm**£150-200**

- 1955-58 **Leyland Double Deck Bus**
'Finest Petrol - ESSO - in the World', Red or Green, route '7', 103 mm **£100-150**
'ESSO - for Happy Motoring - ESSO', Red body, route '7', 103 mm**£100-150**
'Motor Oil - ESSO - Petrol', Red body, route '7', 103 mm**£100-150**

- 1955-56 **Aveling-Barford Road Roller**
Green, Yellow or Red, with driver, 117 mm. Re-issued as Budgie 701.... ....**£40-50**

- 1955-59 **Wolseley 6/80 Police Car**
Black, loudspeaker, aerial, Bell , 113 mm. No maker's name. (Budgie 246)..................... **£150-175**

1 1955-57 **Foden 8-wheel Petrol Tanker**
Red body, 'Motor Oil Esso Petrol' transfers, leaflet, 136 mm **£100-130**

2 1955-56 **Foden 8-wheel Open Lorry**
Light brown cab and chassis, Red truck body, leaflet, 138 mm**£100-120**

3 1955-56 **Foden Flat Lorry with Chains**
Green cab and 8-wheel chassis, Beige flatbed, brass chain, leaflet, 138 mm **£130-170**

4 1955-57 **Foden 8-wheel Flat Lorry**
Yellow or Orange cab and chassis, Grey flatbed, leaflet, 138 mm **£140-160**

- 1956-57 **Bedford Car Transporter**
Orange cab, Grey trailer, collapsible top deck, two loading ramps, 243mm **£150-180**

- 1956 **Daimler Ambulance**
White or Cream body (no transfers), Silver base, opening rear doors, no maker's name, 110 mm. Re-issued as Budgie 258 .. **£150-200**

- 1955-57 **A.A. Land Rover (large)**
Yellow / Black, 'AA ROAD SERVICE' cast-in, opening rear doors, river, passenger, 108 mm........... **£500-600**

- 1957-58 **A.A. Land Rover (medium)**
Yellow / Black, driver, 79 mm. 'AA ROAD SERVICE' transfers, no rear windows **£150-200**
Same but **'AA ROAD SERVICE'** cast-in, two rear windows **£150-200**

- 1958 **Military Police Land Rover**
Olive Green, driver, 'MP Military Police' and crown cast on sides, 79 mm **£250-350**

- 1958 **Breakdown Service Land Rover**
Red body, driver, 'Breakdown Service Unit' cast on sides, 79 mm **£150-200**

- 1958 **Foden Dump Truck**
Orange cab and chassis, Grey dumper, 108 mm. Re-issued as Budgie 226 .... **£100-130**

Morestone 'Trucks of the World International' Series

- 1958 **Klöckner Side Tipper**
Red cab, Black chassis, Cream tipper, 81 mm. (with 'Driving Licence')................................**£50-70**

- 1958 **Scammell Articulated Tanker**
Orange cab, Cream tank. 'LIQUID IN BULK' cast on sides, 114 mm....... ....**£50-100**

- 1958 **International Articulated Refrigerator Lorry**
Red / Blue cab, Silver trailer, 'COAST to COAST REFRIGERATION' transfers, 153 mm. Re-issued as Budgie 202 ....**£40-50**

'Noddy' items by Morestone and Budgie

301 1956-61 **Noddy and his Car (large)**
Yellow/Red, windscreen, solid rubber wheels, metal or plastic 'Noddy', 98 mm **£150-200**

- 1957-58 **Big Ears on Bicycle (large)**
Red bicycle (64 mm.), metal 'Big Ears' with legs that move as the model is pushed along. No maker's name on model **£100-130**

- c.1959 **Clown on Bicycle (large)**
Metallic Light Brown bicycle (64 mm. as previous model), metal clown figure with moving legs. No maker's name on model**£150-200**

- 1958 **Noddy's Garage Set**
331 Noddy's Car and 'Esso' series nos. 7, 13, 16 and 20. Box folds into garage **£150-200**

303 c.1961 **Noddy and his Car (large) with Big Ears**
As 301 but with additional metal Big Ears Figure **£150-200**

305 1959-61 **Noddy's Gift Box**
Contains numbers 331, 333 and plastic Mr. Plod the Policeman **£600-800**

307 1959-61 **Locomotive and Wagon with Noddy and Big Ears**
Yellow loco with red cab. Red wagon. Plastic figures, 104 mm......... .... **£150-200**

309 c.1961 **Noddy and Locomotive**
As no.307 but without wagon, 57 mm **£100-150**

311 1960-61 **Noddy on Bicycle with Trailer**
Yellow bicycle, red trailer, plastic figure, 81 mm.................... **£150-200**

331 1958-61 **Noddy and his Car (small)**
Yellow car, red base and wheels, plastic figure, 52 mm...........**£80-100**

333 1958-61 **Big Ears on Bicycle (small)**
Red. No maker's name on model, plastic figure, 48 mm........ **£100-130**

Morestone and Budgie Miniatures

Packed in 'Esso' Petrol Pump boxes from 1956 to around 1959, then in Budgie bubble packs (yellow backing card) till 1964, and from 1965 in bubble packs with 'The Esso Petrol Pump Series' blue backing card. In the early 1960s, conventional boxes marked 'Mobile Vehicle Series' or 'Modern Vehicle Series' were also used.

1	1956-58	**A.A. Motorcycle and Sidecar** Yellow/Black motorcycle and sidecar, Blue uniformed rider, 46 mm **£25-50**
2	1956-58	**RAC Motorcycle and Sidecar** Black motorcycle, Mid-Blue sidecar, Dark Blue uniformed rider, 46 mm.... ....**£25-50**
3	1956-58	**A.A. Land Rover** 'AA ROAD SERVICE' cast-in, spare wheel (on bonnet) on some, 54 mm **£25-50**
4	1956-58	**A.A. Bedford Van** AA badge and 'ROAD SERVICE' cast-in, 57 mm **£25-50**

Wolseley 6/80 Police Car

5	1956-70	**Wolseley 6/80 Police Car** Black or green body, 65 mm.**£25-50**
6	1956-58	**Cooper-Bristol Racing Car** Blue or Dark Blue body, Off-White base and driver, 58 mm **£25-50**
7	1956-65	**Mercedes-Benz Racing Car** Silver body, Red base and driver, 60 mm **£25-50**
8	1956-70	**Volkswagen 1200 Saloon** Metallic Light Blue body, 58 mm **£25-50**
9	1956-58	**Maudslay Horse Box** Red body, 'HORSE BOX SERVICE' cast-in, 57 mm **£25-50**
10	1956-58	**Karrier GPO Telephones Van** Dark green body, 57 mm **£25-50**
11	1957-65	**Morris Commercial Van** Red body, 'ROYAL MAIL' and 'E-II-R' cast-in, 58 mm **£25-50**
12	1957-70	**Volkswagen Microbus** .... Light Brown, Pale Blue or Metallic Dark Blue, 61 mm.................**£25-50**
13	1957-64	**Austin FX3 Taxi** Black body, Silver base and driver, 58 mm **£25-50**
14	1957-70	**Packard Convertible** Beige or Metallic Lt.Blue body, Red base/seats, Lt. Brown or Gold driver **£25-50**
15	1957-70	**Austin A95 Westminster Countryman** Blue or Orange, (Silver flash on some); or Metallic Mauve, 66 mm **£25-50**
16	1957-64	**Austin-Healey 100** Red body, Off-White base and driver, 57 mm........................**£25-50**

| 17 | 1957-58 | **Ford Thames 5 cwt. Van** Blue body, 60 mm ....**£25-50** |

Foden Dumper

18	1957-66	**Foden Dumper** Red cab and chassis, Lemon-Yellow or Grey dumper, 60 mm........**£25-50**
19	1957-70	**Rover 105R** Green or Gold body, 65 mm.**£25-50**
20	1957-64	**Plymouth Belvedere Convertible** Pale Pink or White body, Red base and driver, 64 mm **£25-50**
20	1968-70	**Austin A95 Emergency Vehicle** As 15 but White with Orange beacon, 'EMERGENCY' transfer, Red base **£25-50**
21	1963-66.	**Bedford TK Tipper Lorry** Dark Green tipper. Yellow, Off-White or Orange cab, 58 mm **£25-50**
21	1968-70	**Oldsmobile Town Sedan** Gold body, 66 mm.................**£25-50**
22	1963-66	**Bedford TK Crane Lorry** Dark Green cab, Orange crane, Orange or Dark Green platform, 56 mm **£25-50**
22	1968-70	**Cattle Transporter** Adapted from no.58. Light Brown body, Dark Brown rear door, 61 mm **£25-50**
23	1963-66	**Bedford TK Cement Mixer** Off-White mixer. Green, Yellow, Red or Orange cab and chassis, 59 mm **£25-50**
24	1963-66	**Bedford TK Refuse Lorry** Green, Orange, Red or Yellow cab, Silver back, 59 mm **£25-50**
25	1963-66	**Bedford TK Cattle Lorry** Light brown body. Off-White, Orange or Yellow cab, 58 mm**£25-50**
26	1963-66	**Aveling-Barford Road Roller** Similar to Lesney Matchbox no.1c. Green body, Red wheels, 55 mm **£25-50**
27	1963-70	**Wolseley 6/80 Fire Chief Car** Same as no.5 with altered base lettering. Red body, 65 mm ..**£25-50**

Models 50 - 55 were designated the 'Road Tanker Series'.

50	1963-66	**'BP Racing Service' Tanker** Green with White tank, 61 mm **£75-100**
51	1963-66	**'Shell' Tanker** Yellow, 61 mm **£75-100**
52	1963-64	**'Shell BP' Tanker** Green or Yellow; White tank, 61 mm **£75-100**
53	1963-66	**'National' Tanker** Blue with Yellow tank, 61 mm........... ....**£75-100**
54	1963-66	**'BP' Tanker** Green with White tank, 61 mm **£75-100**

55	1963-66	**'Mobil' Tanker** Red body, 61 mm **£75-100**
56	1966-70	**GMC Box Van** 'HERTZ TRUCK RENTAL' transfers and 'TRUCK RENTAL' cast-in. Light Green or Pale Blue body, 61 mm............................**£75-100**
57	1966-70	**International Parcels Van** Green body, sliding door. 'REA EXPRESS' transfers, 67 mm**£75-100**
58	1966-70	**'Modern Removals' Van** 'MODERN REMOVALS' transfers. Light Brown or Metallic Green, 61 mm............................**£75-100**
59	1967-70	**AEC Merryweather Fire Engine** Copied from Lesney Matchbox no.9c. Red body, Gold ladder, 65 mm **£75-100**
60	1966-70	**Rover 105R Squad Car** As no.19 but with altered base lettering. Black or Red body, 65 mm **£75-100**
61	1966-70	**Austin A95 'Q Car'** As no.15 but with altered base lettering. Black or Metallic Dark Blue body **£75-100**

Sets of three vehicles (bubble-packed)

94	1966	**Interpol Set** Intended to contain no.5 Police Car, 60 Squad Car, 61 'Q' Car. Not issued .... **NPP**
95	1966	**Road Haulage Set** Intended to contain 56 Hertz Van, 57 REA Van, 58 Removals Van. Not issued .... **NPP**
96	1965-66	**Road Construction Set** Contains no.18 Dumper, 23 Cement Mixer, 26 Road Roller.......... .... **£125-150**
97	1965-66	**Truck Set** Contains no.21 Tipper, 22 Crane,..... 25 Cattle Lorry **£125-150**
98	1965-66	**Utility Vehicle Set** Contains no.12 VW Microbus, 24 Refuse Lorry, 55 Mobil Tanker **£125-150**
99	1965-66	**Traffic Set** Contains no.8 Volkswagen, 15 Austin, 27 Fire Chief......... **£125-150**
95	1968-70	**Town Set** Contains no.20 Emergency Vehicle, 21 Oldsmobile, 56 Hertz Van **£125-150**
96	1967-70	**Service Set** Contains no.5 Police Car, 19 Rover, 59 Fire Engine **£125-150**
97	1967-70	**Truck Set** Contains no.12 VW Microbus, 57 REA Van, 58 Removals Van........... .... **£125-150**
98	1967-70	**Utility Vehicle Set** Contains no.27 Fire Chief, 60 Squad Car, 61 Q Car **£125-150**
99	1967-70	**Traffic Set** Contains no.8 Volkswagen, 14 Packard, 15 Austin....... **£125-150**

Budgie Toys and Models

100 1972-84 **Horse Drawn Hansom Cab**
With driver, elastic band for reins.
Re-issue of Morestone/Modern
Products model. 'Gold' plated or
Metallic Light Brown, 118 mm ....
....**£25-30**

101 1977-84 **Austin FX4 Taxi**
Also issued as no.703. Re-issued
by Seerol. Black or Maroon.
106 mm **£25-30**

101 1984 **Austin FX4 Taxi**
Silver body, 'LONDON VINTAGE
TAXI ASSOCIATION'. Limited
(1,000) commemorative
marking 25 years of the FX4.
Normal box **£25-30**

102 1981-84 **Rolls-Royce Silver Cloud**
Re-issued by Seerol. Gold (painted
or 'plated'), Black, Silver, Cream,
Red, Blue, Metallic Lt.Blue, Metallic
Turquoise or Metallic Dark Pink,
107 mm **£25-30**

202 1959-66 **International Articulated
Refrigerator Lorry**
Re-issued 'Trucks of the World'
model. Red/Blue or Red cab
(windows later). Silver trailer,
'COAST TO COAST
REFRIGERATION', 153 mm **£60-100**

VW Pick Up

204 1959-64 **Volkswagen Pick-Up**
Blue body, Cream base, cloth tilt
'EXPRESS DELIVERY', 92 mm ....
....**£100-120**

206 1959-64 **Leyland Hippo Coal Lorry**
Green or Orange cab, Light Brown
body, 'COAL AND COKE' cast-in,
coal load, 92 mm **£85-100**

208 1959-61 **RAF Personnel Carrier**
RAF blue, roundels, White tilt.
'A MORESTONE PRODUCT',
104 mm **£90-120**

210 1959-61 **US Army Personnel Carrier**
As 208 but Army brown body
with star, Light Brown tilt,
104 mm **£90-120**

212 1959-61 **British Army Personnel Carrier**
As 208 but Dark Green with Red/
Yellow square, Light Brown tilt ....
....**£90-120**

214 1959-64 **Thornycroft Mobile Crane**
Red cab and chassis, Yellow crane
engine, Light Blue crane, 100 mm ....
....**£50-60**

216 1959-64 **Renault Truck**
Yellow cab, Red body. Cloth tilt,
'FRESH FRUIT DAILY', 103 mm ....
....**£40-50**

218 1959-63 **Seddon 'Jumbo' Mobile Traffic
Control Unit**
Yellow cab and trailer with Black
flash and catwalk. 'AUTOMOBILE

ASSOCIATION' and AA badge
transfers, 168 mm **£100-130**

220 1959-66 **Leyland Hippo Cattle Transporter**
Orange cab, Light Brown body,
Dark Brown base + ramp,
97 mm **£50-60**

222 1959-65 **International Tank Transporter
with Centurion Tank**
Army brown with star transfers.
Cab as no.202. 155 mm. (with
ramps up)........................ **£100-150**

0-6-0 Tank Locomotive

224 1959-66 **0-6-0 Tank Locomotive**
As Modern Products model.
Red, 'BRITISH RAILWAYS' cast-in,
119 mm **£25-35**

224 1971-84 **0-6-0 Tank Locomotive**
Red, Metallic Brown, Black or Dark
Green, 'BRITISH RAILWAYS' on
transfers or labels **£10-15**

226 1959-66 **Foden Dumper**
Re-issue of a Morestone model.
Orange cab and chassis, Grey
dumper. 'BUD 123' number plate
transfers, 108 mm **£80-100**

228 1959-64 **Karrier Bantam Bottle Lorry**
Orange-Yellow, 12 maroon plastic
crates. 'DRINK COCA-COLA'
transfers, 'COMMER LOW LOADER'
cast underneath, 134 mm **£200-250**

230 1959-66 **Seddon Timber Transporter**
Orange cab (no ....windows), or
Green cab (with windows),
Yellow trailer, five 'logs', 178 mm.......
....**£100-150**

232 1960-66 **Seddon Cable Drum Transporter**
Red prime mover (windows later),
Orange trailer, 3 wooden cable
drums 'STANDARD' **£100-150**

234 1960-65 **International Low Loader with
Caterpillar Tractor**
Orange cab, Light Brown trailer,
Orange tractor, 155 mm. (with
ramps up)........................ **£100-150**

LT Routemaster Bus 'Uniflo'

236 1960-66 and
1969-84 **AEC Routemaster Bus**
Also issued as nos.704, 705
and 706. All models have
destination transfers for route
'9' and 'LONDON TRANSPORT'
transfers or labels. They were
available with or without windows.

108 mm.
Red, 'Esso GOLDEN Esso' **£50-75**
Red, 'Esso UNIFLO - the tuned
motor oil'...............................**£50-75**
Red, 'GO ESSO - BUY ESSO -
DRIVE ESSO' **£50-75**
Red, 'UNIFLO sae 10W/50 Motor
Oil' **£50-75**
Red, Green or Gold,
'Houses of Parliament Tower
Bridge' **£50-75**

236 1973 **Promotional issue:** Red body
(with windows),
'Sheraton-Heathrow Hotel' on sides,
'OPENING 1st FEBRUARY 1973'
on roof, Special box.......... **£100-150**

238 1960-63 **Scammell Scarab Van**
Crimson / Cream body. 'BRITISH
RAILWAYS' and 'CADBURYS',
150mm. Note: .... Chocolate Bar
picture may be vertical or
horizontal......................... **£140-170**

238 1964-66 **Yellow cab,** Black chassis,
Yellow trailer. 'Railfreight',
'CADBURYS' **£80-100**

238 1985 **Maroon cab,** Maroon / Cream
trailer. 'BRITISH RAILWAYS' and
'CADBURYS'......................**£25-35**
Yellow cab and trailer. 'Railfreight'
and 'CADBURYS' transfers. Most of
these were issued in original
1960s boxes. 150 mm **£25-35**

240 1960-66 **Scammell Scarab Wagon**
Red/Cream cab, Yellow chassis,
Red trailer, Green cloth tilt,
150 mm **£65-85**

242 1960-66 **Euclid Dumper**
Red cab, Orange chassis and
dumper. 114 mm **£80-100**

244 1961-65 **Morris Breakdown Lorry**
Blue body, Yellow base,
tool box and jib. 'BUDGIE
SERVICE', 120 mm **£80-100**

246 1960-63 **Wolseley 6/80 Police Car**
Re-issued Modern
Products model. Black, loudspeaker,
aerial, 'BUDGIE TOYS' cast under,
'POLICE' transfers on grille
and boot, 113 mm **£40-60**

246 1983 **Wolseley 6/80 Police Car**
Light Blue, 'POLICE' labels,
spotlights and roof sign replace the
loudspeaker and aerial. Trial run
only - did not go into full
production **£80-100**

248 1961 **Stage Coach with Four Horses**
Listed on this number as 'available
later', but issued as no. 434.

250 ------ Pack reference only.
This number was used for packs
of one dozen of the Budgie
miniatures.

252 1961-63 **Austin Articulated Lorry with
Railway Container**
Crimson / Cream cab, windows,
Crimson trailer/container. 'BRITISH
RAILWAYS' transfers **£125-150**

252 1964 Crimson cab/trailer,
windows, Blue container,
'Door to Door' transfers... **£125-150**

254 1961-64 **AEC Merryweather Fire Escape**
Red, windows, Silver extending
turntable ladder. 97 mm.
(excl. ladder).................... **£125-150**

256 1961-64 **Foden Aircraft Refuelling Tanker
'Pluto'**
Red, with windows. 'ESSO
AVIATION PRODUCTS' transfers,
149 mm **£100-125**

258 1961-63 **Daimler Ambulance**
Re-issued Modern Products model. Cream with Red base ('BUDGIE TOYS' cast-in), 'AMBULANCE' and 'EMERGENCY' transfers, 110 mm...............**£80-100**

258 1991 **Daimler Ambulance Kit**
Re-issued as a kit of unpainted castings (by Autocraft)..........**£20-30**

260 1962 **Ruston-Bucyrus Excavator**
Yellow/Red cab, '10-RB', Beige or Olive-Green base and jib, 73 mm **£400-500**

262 1962-64 **Racing Motorcycle**
No maker's name. Unpainted cycle, tinplate fairing in Metallic Blue, Metallic Lilac, Metallic Brown or Lime Green, Black plastic rider, 104 mm **£75-100**

264 1962-64 **Racing Motorcycle and Sidecar**
Cycle as 262, sidecar and fairing in Metallic Blue, Metallic Pinkish-Red, Metallic Green, Metallic Lilac, Metallic Brown or Lime Green. Black plastic rider / passenger, no maker's name, 104 mm .**£75-100**

266 1962-64 **Motorcycle and Delivery Sidecar**
Blue cycle as 262, Red sidecar, 'EXPRESS DELIVERY' cast-in, no maker's name, Black plastic rider. 108 mm **£80-100**

268 1962-64 **A.A. Land Rover**
Different from Morestone AA Land Rovers. Yellow body, Black roof, windows, opening rear doors, 'AA ROAD SERVICE' transfers, 97 mm **£125-150**

270 1962-66 **Leyland Articulated Tanker**
Red, windows, 'ESSO PETROLEUM COMPANY LTD' labels, 132 mm.......
....**£100-125**

272 1962-64 **Supercar From TV series.**
Red/Silver body, Red wings (or colours reversed), clear plastic canopy, 'SUPERCAR' transfers, 122 mm **£150-200**

274 1962-66 **Ford Thames Refuse Lorry**
Blue cab/Silver body, or Yellow cab/Metallic blue body, windows.....
....**£50-70**

276 1962-66 **Bedford LWB Tipper**
Red cab with windows, Yellow tipper, 'HAM RIVER GRIT', 128 mm **£60-80**

278 1963-64 **RAC Land Rover**
Casting as 268, Blue, windows, 'RAC RADIO RESCUE' transfers, 97 mm **£150-175**

280 1963-64 **AEC Super Fueller Tanker**
White cab and trailer, windows, Green base/canopy, 'AIR BP', 219 mm **£400-500**

Euclid Scraper

282 1963-66 **Euclid Scraper**
Yellow or Lime Green, windscreen, 'EUCLID', Black plastic wheels, 163 mm **£100-140**

284 1962 **Euclid Crawler Tractor**
Not issued .... NPP

286 1962 **Euclid Bulldozer**
Not issued .... NPP

288 1963-66 **Leyland Bulk Flour Tanker**
Red cab, windows, Off-White silos, Yellow hoppers, 'BULK FLOUR', 107 mm **£50-70**

290 1963-66 **Bedford Ice Cream Van 'TONIBELL'**
Blue body, pink cow's head on roof, two cows in side transfer . **£150-200**
Same but with three cows in side transfer **£350-450**

292 1963-66 **Leyland Bulk Milk Tanker**
Blue or Red cab, windows, White tank, 'MILK', 107 mm **£50-70**

294 1963-66 **Bedford TK Horse Box**
Off-White cab, windows, Brown body, Light Brown doors. two Brown plastic horses. 'EPSOM STABLE' transfer, 109 mm ..**£80-100**

296 1963-66 **Motorway Express Coach**
Midland Red livery: Red body, Black roof, 'BIRMINGHAM-LONDON MOTORWAY EXPRESS' transfers, windows, 121 mm**£125-150**
USA livery: Light Blue body, Cream roof, 'WASHINGTON D.C.' and 'BLUE LINE SIGHTSEEING CO.' transfers, phone number 'LA9-7755' at rear **£200-250**

298 1963-66 **Alvis Salamander Crash**
Tender Red body, windows, Silver plastic ladder, Yellow engine cover at rear, Black plastic wheels. 'FIRE SERVICE' transfers, 92 mm. ....
....**£100-125**

300 1963-65 **Lewin Sweepmaster**
Blue/Silver, windows, Black plastic wheels, Black sweeping brush ....
....**£75-100**

302 1963-66 **Commer Cabin Service Lift Truck**
Blue cab, windows, Silver body, 'BOAC CABIN SERVICES', 104 mm...
....**£80-100**

304 1964-66 **Bedford TK Glass Transporter**
Off-white cab and chassis, windows, Green body. 'TOWER GLASS CO.' transfers. Four clear plastic 'glass' sheets, 108 mm **£50-70**

306 1964-66 **Fiat Tractor with Shovel**
Orange tractor, Metallic Blue shovel, 108 mm **£100-140**

308 1964-66 **Seddon Pitt Alligator Low Loader**
Green cab, windows, Yellow trailer with Black ramp, 163 mm **£45-55**

310 1964-66 **Leyland Cement Mixer**
Orange cab, windows, Silver mixer, 'INVICTA Construction Co.', 98 mm **£60-80**

312 1964-66 **Bedford Super Tipmaster**
Dark Green cab, windows, Silver tipper. 'SUPER TIP-MASTER', 127mm..................................**£60-80**

314 1965-66 **Fiat Tractor with Dozer Blade**
As 306 but enclosed cab, Orange tractor, Metallic Blue blade, 81 mm..
....**£45-55**

316 1965-66 **Albion Overhead Maintenance Vehicle**
Green body, windows, Silver/Black boom assembly, 107 mm......**£50-70**

318 1965-66 **Euclid Mammoth Articulated Dumper**
Modified from no.242. Green cab, Yellow chassis, Orange tipper, 201 mm **£75-95**

322 1965-66 **Scammell Routeman Pneumajector Transporter**
Light Blue cab, Cream or White tank, 'THE ATLAS CARRIER CO', 111 mm **£60-80**

324 1965-66 **Douglas Prospector Duomatic Tipper**
Tips in two directions. Blue cab

and chassis, windows, Grey tipper, 112 mm **£250-300**

Douglas Prospector Duomatic Tipper

326 1965-66 **Scammell Highwayman Gas Transporter**
Two-tone Green cab, clear windows, Dark Green trailer, Silver plastic hubs, 6 White/Red gas cylinders.......
....**£200-300**

328 1966 **Scammell Handyman Artic.**
Planned but not issued .... NPP

330 1966 **Land Rover**
Modified 268, planned but not issued .... NPP

332 1966 **'Kenning' Breakdown Lorry**
Planned but not issued .... NPP

334 1966 **Austin Gipsy Fire Tender**
Planned but not issued .... NPP

Horsedrawn Covered Wagon with 4 horses

404 1960-61 **Horse Drawn Covered Wagon with Four Horses.**
For details see Morestone and Modern Products entry.

410 1961 **Stage Coach with Four Horses**
Blue or 'Gold' plated coach, no lettering cast on sides but 'WELLS FARGO STAGE COACH' and 'A BUDGIE TOY' cast underneath, plastic horses and driver, bubble-packed, 118 mm **£100-150**

430 1960-61 **Wagon Train Set**
Contains 3 of no. 432 plus two more horses with riders, bubble-packed **£100-130**

432 1960-61 **Horse Drawn Covered Wagon with Two Horses**
Red wagon, ('A BUDGIE TOY' on floor), Grey, White or Lemon metal canopy, 2 barrels, plastic horses, driver, passenger, bubble packed, 82 mm **£35-45**

434 1961 **Stage Coach with Four Horses**
'WELLS FARGO' above windows, 'STAGE LINES' on doors, luggage cast on roof, Red or Blue, plastic horses and driver, 189 mm**£100-150**

452 1958-63 **A.A. Motorcycle and Sidecar**
Initially in Morestone box. Windscreen, plastic rider, integral rails and hinged lid on sidecar, steerable, rubber tyres, plain number plates, 82 mm **£70-90**

452 1964-66 **A.A. Motorcycle and Sidecar**
New design. Sidecar with transfers and 'BUDGIE' underneath, plastic rider, windscreen and leg guards, plain number plates, 84 mm **£70-90**

454 1958-63 **RAC Motorcycle and Sidecar**

Initially in Morestone box. White Windscreen, plastic rider, integral rails and hinged lid on sidecar, steerable, rubber tyres, plain number plates, 82 mm **£70-90**

454 1964-66 **RAC Motorcycle and Sidecar** New design. Sidecar with transfers and 'BUDGIE' underneath, plastic rider, windscreen and leg guards, plain number plates, 84 mm **£70-90**

456 1958-66 **Solo Motorcycle** Initially in Morestone boxes. Two casting versions as 452 and 454 but bikes are 'Silver plated'. Plastic riders:

456 PP **Police Patrol** (Blue uniform an helmet)..................................**£70-90**

456 DR **Despatch Rider** (Light Brown uniform)...........................**£70-90**

456 GPO **GPO Messenger** (Light Blue uniform, Red helmet) **£100-130**

456 TT **'Tourist Trophy' Rider** (White racing overalls, Red helmet) **£50-70**

701 1983 **Aveling-Barford Road Roller** Re-issued Modern Products model. Dark Green body, Silver / Red wheels, Dark Blue driver.......**£10-15**

702 1984-85 **Scammell Scarab Vans** Re-issue of 238. Very Dark Blue cab and trailer, White 'RN' on doors, 'ROYAL NAVY' on tilt .... **£150-250** Very Dark Blue cab and trailer, 'HALLS MENTHO-LYPTUS' labels ... **£25-35**

Scammell Scarab Van Royal Navy

Maroon cab and trailer, 'LMS LIVERPOOL ROAD' transfers.. ....**£25-35** Maroon cab and trailer, 'SPRATTS BONIO' transfers ....**£25-35** Maroon cab and trailer, 'REA EXPRESS' transfers................**£25-35** Grey cab and trailer, white container 'GWR' **£25-35**

703 1984 **Austin FX4 Taxi** As no.101 but in window box. Black, Silver, Met.Dk.Pink, Gold, Dark Green, Grey or White ...**£25-35**

704 1984 **AEC Routemaster Bus** Yellow/Red body with windows, 'SHOP LINKER' labels, casting as 236 ....**£25-35**

705 1984 **AEC Routemaster Bus** Silver body with windows, '25

FAITHFUL YEARS' labels, casting as 236......................................**£25-35**

706 1984 **AEC Routemaster Bus** Yellow / Red with windows, 'Watford FA Cup Final 84' labels, 236 casting **£25-35**

AEC Routemaster Bus Gold with windows London Transport Golden Jubilee 1933-83 ... .**£15-25**

Routemaster Bus Silver Jubilee 25 Faithful Years

Code Three Models AEC Routemaster Bus Red 'Midland Bank' A great British Bank .... NPP Red 'Colour Television with Rediffusion'................................ NPP Red 'GEC Schreiber the Complete Fitted Kitchens............................ NPP Red 'PG Tips /OXO'.................. NPP

Budgie Gift Sets

No. 4 1961 **Gift Set No.4** Contains four models. Price depends on contents which vary **£125-165**

No. 5 1961 **Gift Set No.5** Contains five models. Price depends

No 5A n/a **Gift Set No 5A** Contains six various lorries of which can vary **£300-400**

No.8 1962 **Gift Set No 8** Contains numbers 5, 8, 11, 12, 13, 15,

on contents which vary...... **£300-400**

18 and 19 .... **£200-300**

No 12 1962 **Gift Set No 12** Contains 12 various models of which can vary................... **£160-200**

Seerol Models

Seerol Taxi

- 1985 **Austin FX4 Taxi** Re-issue of Budgie no.101 with amended base lettering and low friction wheels. Black body, 106mm. Still available **£15-25**

- 1985 **Rolls-Royce Silver Cloud** Re-issued Budgie 102, amended lettering, low friction wheels. Black, Silver, White, Yellow, Dark Blue, Pink or Maroon, 107 mm. Still available **£15-25**

- 1985 **AEC Routemaster Bus** New design, 1:76 scale, 108 mm. Was available from London souvenir outlets till the late 1990s. Red, Light Green, or Dark Green, 'Houses of

Parliament Tower Bridge' labels **£15-25**

- Red, 'The Original London Transport Sightseeing Tour' labels **£15-25**

- Red, 'Greetings from London' tampo print ....**£15-25** Red, 'Tower of London' tampo print .. ..**£15-25** Red, 'Petticoat Lane' tampo print **£15-25**

- Red, 'Buckingham Palace' tampo print ....**£15-25** Red 'Cymru Am Byth' 'Big Pit Mining Museum' ....**£15 -25** Red 'J.S.T. Models London' ....**£15-25** White red strip 'DHL'..............**£15-25**

Sales Aids

Shop Display Unit: Five tiers, yellow / blue / red, with 'BUDGIE DIECAST MODELS' plus perching 'Budgie' logo **£200-250**
Shop Display Unit: **'The ESSO Petrol Pump Series':** '1/6d each', 'A MORESTONE PRODUCT'. Features 20 models on four shelves **£200-300**

Budgie Leaflets and Catalogues

A leaflet was included in the box with most Budgie Toys. Dates are not shown on any except the 1963 and 1964 catalogues.

- 1959 **Leaflet** Printed on one side only. 'Budgie Toys Speak for Themselves' at top. **1st version:** Includes the Six-horse Covered Wagon........................**£20-30** **2nd version:** Timber Transporter

replaces the Covered Wagon ..**£20-30**

- 1960 **Leaflet** 'Budgie Toys Speak for Themselves' on front, 'Budgie Toys for Girls and Boys' on reverse **£20-30**

- 1961 **Leaflet** 'Budgie Toys Speak for Themselves' on Black background...............**£20-30**

1961 **Trade catalogue** Fold-out leaflet showing Noddy

items, Wagon Train and Budgie miniatures as well as the main Budgie range. Separate price list marked 'Price List 1961' showing wholesale and retail prices **£40-50**

- 1962 **Leaflet** 'Die-Cast Models by Budgie They Speak for Themselves' on Black background. **1st version:** 268 AA Land Rover on

front, 258 Daimler Ambulance on reverse **£10-15**
2nd version: 214 Mobile Crane on front, 266 Express Delivery Motorcycle on reverse.............**£10-15**

- 1963 **Leaflet**
'Die-Cast Models by Budgie They Speak for Themselves' on Black

background.
1st version: 278 RAC Land Rover on front, 258 Daimler Ambulance on reverse **£10-15**
2nd version: 278 RAC Land Rover on front, 266 Express Delivery Motorcycle on reverse.............**£10-15**

- 1963 **Trade Catalogue (8 pages)**
Landscape format, includes retail price list..................................**£30-40**

- 1964 **Trade Catalogue (8 pages)**
'Budgie Models' on cover (portrait format). Includes retail price list.........
....**£30-40**

The 'River Series'

A trademark owned by M/s Jordan and Lewden of Homerton, London E9. Note that, while 'River Series' models were cast using tools supplied by DCMT, they had no other connection with DCMT. The Jordan and Lewden company started to offer diecast toys to the toy trade from about 1953 and continued to do so for only a few years. Dies were eventually sold to the Habonim firm in Israel and models subsequently appeared in the 'Gamda' series of toys. Some examples are known to have been produced in New Zealand by Lincoln Industries (who were also responsible for some 'lookalike' Matchbox models). Only 'Made in

England' and the car name appear on the diecast base of each model. None of the models acquired window glazing while made as 'River Series' – some did when produced as 'Gamda' toys.

These car models came in various colours and had cast hubs / rubber tyres where friction-motor fitted, otherwise one-piece rubber wheels.
Ford Prefect .... NGPP
American Buick .... NGPP
Daimler Conquest .... NGPP
Austin Somerset.................................. NGPP
Standard Vanguard II Saloon .... NGPP

Standard Vanguard Estate .... NGPP

These larger items were also available in various colours, some have clockwork motor, most have one-piece cast wheels, and some were boxed.
Cattle Truck .... NGPP
Car Carrier .... NGPP
Excavator Truck.................................. NGPP
Tower Wagon .... NGPP
Cattle Truck .... NGPP

The editor would welcome any additional information on the 'River Series'.

Scale Models Ltd (Scamold)

M anufactured between 1939 and 1950 by Scale Models Ltd from whose title the model name was obtained. The models are extremely accurate 1/35 scale diecast models, with their original measurements being taken from the real racing cars at the famous Brooklands race track. Pre-war boxes state 'MANUFACTURED BY SCALE MODELS LTD, BROOKLANDS TRACK, WEYBRIDGE, ENG.' This was dropped after the war. The proprietor of Scale Models Ltd was a Mr Tilley who wound up the business in the 1960s.

The model detail and castings are outstanding, with features such as removeable exhausts, spring suspension, steering wheels and dashboards. In addition the back axle could be exchanged for one

containing a clockwork motor which was wound up by a long starting handle. The wheel axles were crimped and the hubs were either brass (early) or aluminium (later) with black treaded rubber tyres.

Scamold kits were also available. The kit models had detailed features similar to the production issues including a working differential gear. In addition, it was also possible to fit a flywheel type motor which was activated by turning a 'starting handle'.

This information on Scamold models and kits has been kindly provided by Mr R N Eason-Gibson. The editor would welcome additional information on this small but fascinating range.

SCAMOLD PRODUCTION MODELS

101	1939-50	**ERA Racing Car** ....Blue (Light or Dark), Green (Light or Dark), Yellow, White or Black body..	**£150-200**
103	1939-50	**Maserati Racing Car** ....Red, Blue, Green (Mid or Dark), Silver body	**£150-200**
105	1939-50	**Alta Racing Car** ....Green (Mid or Dark), Silver, White or Blue	**£150-200**

SCAMOLD KITS
Austin 7 Single-seater 750cc, Bugatti Type 35, 'E'-type E.R.A. (prototype only), Brooklands Riley, MG (planned type not known), Bentley LeMans Tourer and Maserati Racing Car.

Mobil Midget Fun-Ho! Series

Manufactured and distributed by the Underwood Engineering Co Ltd, Mamaku Street, Inglewood, New Zealand.

Market Price Range. Most small cars and trucks etc. **£20-30**. Exceptions: No.7 BOAC Observation Coach **£40-50**, No.9 VW Beetle **£40-50**, No.11 Morris Mini Minor **£80-90**, No.2 Vauxhall Velox **£30-40**, No.? Morris 1100 **£40-50**, No.17 Austin Mini **£80-90**, No.23 Mark 10 Jaguar **£80-90**, No.25 MG Sports **£80-100**; No.43 E Type Jaguar **£80-90**.Larger Commercials/Emergency vehicles etc.: Nos.18, 21, 22, 27, 31, 35, 36, 40 **£30-40**.

Technical Information. Models from No.10 are 1:80 scale. Early models 1-32 1963-66 were all either chrome or copper plated. Painted finishes were introduced in 1966. Boxed models 1-18 include a folded leaflet in black and white giving details of the first 18 models and all have Black plastic wheels. Similarly the later issues contained leaflets

showing the complete 1-46 model range as per the above leaflet.
'Fun Ho!' Mighty Mover Sets

1 **Army Construction Battalion Kit Set**: Contains six Military models, Bulldozer, Cement Mixer, Road Roller, Earth Mover, JCB, Land Rover, Brown display box **£50-60**

2 **Civilian Road Construction Set**: Yellow/Silver Bulldozer, Red/Silver Bedford Lorry, Green Aveling Road Roller, Blue Earth Mover, Red/Blue Ford Sand Dumper, Yellow JCB, Red window display box **£50-60**

3 **Fire Service Kit Set**: Contains six Red models, 21 Fire Engine, Jeep, Pick Up, Artic Lorry, Rescue Truck, Fire Van with Blue light, Red window display box **£50-60**

Later issues (c.1965?) Window Boxes
48 Ford, Brown/Green, Two-tone Green or Maroon White body **£10-15**
49 Ford Sand Dumper, Red/Blue body **£10-15**, 50 Ford Dumper **£10-15**,
51 Ford Articulated Truck **£15-20**, 52 Sand Dumper Trailer **£5-10**

Shackleton Models

The company was formed by Maurice Shackleton and traded as James Shackleton & Sons Ltd. from 1939 to 1952. They had premises in Cheshire and originally produced wooden toys such as lorries and dolls houses. The toy lorries were only made pre-war and had four wheels, a simple wooden chassis and body with a green name badge on the rear of the cab, and were fitted with a highly detailed aluminium radiator grille. Known models are a Chain Lorry, Breakdown Lorry and a Sided Wagon. Their price today is around £140 each.

In 1948 having expanded its staff to nearly 40 people, the company started to produce diecast constructional models based on the Foden FG six-wheel platform lorry. The models consisted of separate parts all of which were, incredibly, made 'in house', including the clockwork motor, its key, and the wheels and tyres. The models were advertised in the 'Meccano Magazine' with the slogan 'You can dismantle it - Just like the real thing', and they were originally priced at £2/19/6. Eventually the range was extended to include a Dyson Drawbar Trailer and a Foden Tipper. Each model was packed in its own distinctive box which displayed a black and white picture of the model inside.

In 1952, whilst in the midst of producing the David Brown Trackmaster 30¸ Tractor, a shortage of materials coupled with difficult trading conditions brought about the end of the company. Some remaining models from this period were acquired and distributed by Chad Valley. The unique models produced by the Shackleton company are now highly collectable and difficult to find.

Note: It is known that some prototype models of Ploughs and Harrows were made , though it is not known if any were produced for sale.

--	**1948-52 Foden FG 6-wheel Platform Lorry ..** Yellow, Blue, Grey or Green body with Red wings, Grey chassis and Red or Grey fuel tanks, 12½ inches (305 mm.) long, initially in Blue/Yellow box, later in mottled Green box, (20,000 made) .... **£300-500** Same colours as above but with Grey or Black wings and Red chassis **£300-500** Same casting but with Red, Orange or Brown cab.. **£300-500** NB Box difficult to find:Blue box with paper label having picture of chassis.	
---	**1949-52 Dyson 8-ton Drawbar Trailer** Yellow, Blue, Grey or Green body, packed in Red and Yellow box, (15,000) **£80-110**	

---	**1950-52 Foden FG 6-wheel Tipper Lorry** Yellow, Blue, Grey or Green body with Red wings, Grey chassis and Red or Grey fuel tanks, Silver wheels, (5,000)......................... **£400-500** As previous models but with Grey wings and Red chassis .... **£400-500** As previous models but with Blue wings, Grey chassis, Grey wheels ...... **£400-500** Orange or Red body **£400-500**	
---	**1952 David Brown Trackmaster 30 Tractor** Red body, Black rubber tracks, 10 inches long, boxed. Only 50 models thought to exist **£1,500-2,000**	
	1958-60 Foden S21 8-wheel Platform Lorry Dark Blue, Dark Green or Light	

Turquoise fibreglass cab with Red metal chassis and wheels, wooden flatbed, length overall 18½ inches (470 mm), plastic injection moulded springs and axle parts, powered by 'Minimax' electric motor. (250 made as a promotional for Foden) . **£700-1,000**

The information in this listing has been taken from an original article written by John Ormandy in the 'Modellers World' magazine, Volumes 12 and 13, and is used by kind permission of the Editors, Mike and Sue Richardson. Robert Taylor provided additional information. Gary Irwin contributed information on the DB Trackmaster.

Light blue FG6 Tipper. Orange FG6 Flat Truck. Blue FG6 Flat Truck, Green FG6 Flat Truck

Shackleton Foden Tipping Lorry.

Shackleton DB Bulldozer

Shackleton Foden 21T Platform Lorry

Taylor and Barrett

Brothers A R Barrett, S Barrett and F G Taylor founded Taylor and Barrett in 1920. The Barrett Brothers had earlier been employed as casters by William Britain Ltd. Three years later the small business had grown enough to enable them to start producing full time, from premises in Upper Holloway, North London.

Among the first models produced were a large camel, governess cart and pony, two Indians paddling a canoe, a Chinaman and Zulu with rickshaw and a large elephant and howdah. A whole range of horse drawn carts and various military and civilian figures quickly followed these. That in turn forced them to relocate premises to near by East Finchley in 1929 where a range of motor vehicles was first introduced in the mid 1930s.

These were rather crude by comparison with the Dinky Toys of the day as the lead gravity casting process was incapable of working to the fine limits possible with pressure die-casting as used by Meccano Ltd. The majority of the vehicles use a basic chassis incorporating the bonnet and wings. Different bodies are attached to this base unit by tabs and a radiator is plugged into the front. Some versions have the grille cast integrally with the bonnet, and most of these use plain metal wheels instead of having rubber tyres. These vehicles have a tremendous amount of charm as toys while they are only a generic representation of the types of vans and small trucks of the time.

A wide variety of types were made including petrol tankers, a pick-up truck and a couple of mail vans. The breakdown truck is particularly attractive with a working crane on the rear. A range of very nice fire engines came along in the late 1930s with a super turntable ladder appliance as the top of the range. These were longer than the main range and had many parts. To mark the advent of the Home Office Fire Precautions scheme (where fire appliances were made available to local areas by central government), Taylor and Barrett painted their range in grey as well as the more traditional red. These grey models are highly sought after now. Personnel were also available to go with these fire engines. A 'Decontamination Squad' being a particular favourite with their gas masks and chemical-proof overalls. There is also a less impressive fire engine in the short chassis range.

By 1940 the firm was producing a large range of motor vehicles, horse drawn carts, zoo and farm animals, solders and dolls' house furniture a considerable amount of which was being exported. But also in 1940 all production was halted when the factory was bombed out of existence. All salvageable tools, moulds and stock was moved to a new location in North Finchley but production stopped very soon after because of the munitions requirements of the war effort.

During the war the tools were split between the Taylors and the Barretts for safe keeping but they did not join up again afterwards as family problems forced them to become two separate companies, F. G. Taylor & Sons and A. Barrett & Sons, in 1945. One of the features of the split was the share of the Zoo Series moulds of the keepers and accessories that resulted in both the new companies issuing the same items. The main part of the range, the small commercial vehicles and the cars, does not seem to have survived the War, only the trolley buses, which became Barrett's, and the Leyland coach which appeared in one-piece casting form as a Taylor. It is interesting to note that the trolleybus carries a route board '621 Finchley' which probably means that they went past the factory.

The trolley buses came in two sizes. The large one has a separate driver figure (and conductor as well in the T & B version but not the later Barrett), and the body is in two pieces, upper and lower decks. The small one is in one piece and has no driver. Needless to say there is a vast difference in the values of the two sizes.

There are generic cars, roadster, coupé, and saloon, on the short base but there is also quite a good model of the 1935 Singer Airstream saloon. This is also the poor man's Chrysler Airflow but never really caught on, the styling made the car look too tall to be appealing. A rather crude one-piece Austin Seven racer was the final car but this was to a larger scale.

The Meccano Company with their Dinky Toys range were not the only one to make a model of the Air Mail Service Car based on the Morris Commercial chassis. T & B also made one and a nice chunky toy it is too. A couple of aeroplanes, a De Havilland Comet and an airliner, completed the range of powered vehicles. A modified version of the Comet seems to have been made by Barrett later but it differs a lot from the T & B, which is a much better model.

Some of the moulds were still around a few years ago and some attempts were made to make models again. These were fairly unsuccessful as casting techniques had changed and the new metals did not have the same flow characteristics as the early lead. Some models are definitely known to have been re-made so collectors are advised to be wary.

A Barrett & Sons in the 1950s added a range of children's TV characters and hollowcast puppets; they also went on to produce models from Sacul moulds after that company went into liquidation.

A firm called A. Barton & Company later merged with A. Barrett & Sons and the Barrett's production was phased out in favour of dolls' house furniture; Barton then bought out Barretts in 1984 ending 64 years' of production.

The following listing is of models issued by Taylor and Barrett between 1920 and 1939 and post war production which was split between F. G. Taylor & Sons and A. Barrett & Sons, each firm inheriting some moulds and continuing to make some but not all of the models.

(FGT) = produced by F. G. Taylor after 1945, (AB) = produced by A. Barrett after 1945, (-) = date and company not known for certain.

Elephant Ride

10 **Seal Pond. With three Seals**.............. **£250-300**
11 **'Chimpanzee's Tea Party'.**
   Four seated Chimps, a table with plates and a
   Keeper with baby Chimp **£275-325**
13 **Elephant Ride Set with four children.**
   Elephant, howdah etc., Keeper, boxed. **£400-450**
14 **Trotting Pony Racer with jockey,** boxed set of
   three (FGT).. **£200-250**

14 **Trotting Pony Racer.**
   Horse, 2-wheeled cart and Jockey Various
   colours **£65-85**
15 **Turntable Fire Escape and 3 Firemen (AB)** ....
   .... **£200-300**
16 **Fire Engine and Escape Ladder**
   Fire Engine and Two wheeled extending ladder
   5 Firemen (FGT) **£250-300**
17 **Fire Engine and 3 Firemen (FGT)**.... **£200-300**

20 Horse Drawn Water Cart
Green 4-wheeled cart with driver and
white horse with separate road side water pipe
(FGT) **£300-400**

21 Brewery Dray Wagon & Drayman
Horse drawn Brewers dray, brown/red wheels
headboard 'Ale & Stout', six beer barrels ....
.... **£250-£350**

22 Window Cleaner
Figure with ladder and bucket, with green 2-
wheeled handcart with extra ladder . **£150-200**

23 Horse Drawn Baker's Cart (FGT)..... **£100-200**

26 Roman Chariot
Two brown or grey horses Roman figure with
cloak FGT.. **£25-35**

27 Donkey Drawn Coster Cart with Dog and Boy
(FGT) **£100-150**

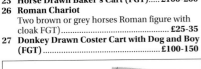

Coster Cart

28 Donkey Drawn Coster Cart, Plants load,
Walking Coster (FGT) **£200-250**

28a Donkey Drawn Coster Cart, Vegetable load,
Walking Coster (FGT) **£200-250**

29 Ice Cream Tricycle, dark blue with rider 'ICE
BRICKS', on side 'Stop Me and Buy One' on the
front (FGT) **£300-400**

32 Tiger Hunt
Elephant with Howdah with hunter aiming
rifle two tigers and two pieces of scrub. ....
.... **£200-300**

33 'Nigger' Jazz Band
Six musicians, with instruments and six
chairs **£500-700**

36 Milk Float and Milkman, 'EXPRESS DAIRY'
(AB)... **£250-350**

41 Miniature Fire Place Set with Accessories
Grate, Fire screen, Fire Surround, Coal scuttle,
with lid, two chairs Brush, tongs and poker.......
.... **£100-150**

42 Fire Escape and Team of Firemen (FGT) ....
.... **£200-300**

43 Air and Land Postal Service Set (-).. **£300-400**

45 Road and Traffic Set (-) Traffic island with
bollards and street lamp, 2 swivelling traffic
lights, school and 30mph signs,
2 Belisha beacons, pavement sections (2
straight, 2 corners). 45mm figures of lady and
gentleman, 2 children (on base),
mounted policeman, traffic policeman. Boxed .
.... **£300-400**

49 Street Cleaner
Figure with brush, green 2 wheeled cart with
silver dustbins **£150-200**

92 Llama Cart
Llama, two wheeled cart, with children, and
guide various colours (FGT) **£100-150**

92a Donkey Cart (FGT)........................... **£100-150**

109 Pony Drawn Governor's Cart (AB)
Two wheeled cart with four seated children,
various colours **£100-150**

109a Pony Drawn Cart (AB) **£75-100**

Saloon Car, Open Car and Petrol/Oil Pumps

111 Saloon Car (-) **£80-100**
112 Transport Lorry (-) **£80-100**
113 'ROYAL MAIL' Van (-) **£150-200**
114 Ambulance
Grey white tyres paper 'Red Cross' 'Ambulance'
cast in side (Wartime civilian) (-)....... **£150-200**
114a Ambulance
Khaki white tyres paper 'Red Cross
Ambulance' cast in side (Army) (-)
.... **£150-200**
115 Sports Car (-) **£100-200**
116 Coupé (-) **£100-200**
117 Ambulance
Cream, with white tyres paper 'Red Cross' on
roof.. **£150 - 200**
119 Racer (AB) **£40-60**
120 Fire Engine (AB).................................. **£60-80**
121 Vacuum Cleaner
Cream with grey handle and black bag**£10 – 15**
123 Atlanta Touring Plane **£100-125**
124 'AIR MAIL' Van .... **£160 -200**
127 Gas Cooker Set.
Cooker with hinged door & grill, Kettle, 3 Pans,
Frying Pan, ... **£70-100**
128 Petrol Tanker
Various colours, two filler caps 'Petrol' cast in
rear of tank with solid wheels or   white rubber
tyres (-) **£90-125**

Breakdown Lorry

129 Breakdown Lorry,
Brown, red or light blue with black roofs, with
crane, silver radiator white tyres (-).... **£80-100**
137 DH 'Comet' Aeroplane
With rotating propellers movable wheel in
RAF camouflage (AB)........................... **£80-100**
138 'AIR MAIL' Streamline Car
Dark blue two-seater with silver radiator
'Royal Air Mail Service' cast in door, white tyres
(Similar to Dinky Toys) **£175-225**
139 Saloon Car
Four door, Lt green, grey mudguards white
tyres **£50-60**
152 Streamline Motor Coach
Based on a Leyland motor coach, green and
cream, white tyres 'London' front destination
board. (-) **£200-250**
163 Streamline Fire Engine
Red, four doors, single ladder, hose at the rear
'Fire Service' cast in side white tyres (-) ....
.... **£200-300**
197 Trolley Bus (small)
Red/black with blue/white paper advert
'Use Dominion Petrol' (AB), ... **£100-150**
204 Trolley Bus (large)
Red/cream blue/white 'Use Dominion Petrol'
advert also issued with cream/black
'Champion's Malt Vinegar' advert (AB),...........
.... **£300-400**
211 First Aid (Stretcher Party)
Two bearers with gas masks with patient on
stretcher .... NGPP
213 'Decontamination Squad' Five Black figures
with protective suits, gas masks, with brooms,
buckets and hoses .... **£400-£500**
214 Stirrup Pump Set, two females, one with
pump in Bucket, other to hold hose, male
figure with two buckets. **£250-300**

224 Refrigerator Set
White fridge on legs, with door, 2 removalable
trays with Chicken, Ham joint, Jellies and 2
milk bottles **£70-100**
302 Horse Drawn Covered Wagon, two horses,
seated Pioneer, wife and outrider (-) **£200-300**
303 Indian and Canoe Set
Yellow canoe with either one or two Indians....
.... NGPP
304 Sledge Dog Team (Small version)
Arctic sledge with driver and four
dogs and two pine trees (FGT) **£100-150**
Arctic Explorers (large version of 304)
Sledge, four huskies, driver, kneeling Explorer
with rifle three Wolves four large and three
small Snow covered Pine Trees........ **£325-£400**
306 Aeroplane Set (Comet, Atlanta and pilots)
(FGT) **£120-150**
307 Fire Brigade Set (-)............................ **£300-400**
310 Rickshaw
Brown/cream two passengers with
Chinese Coolie figure pulling (FGT).. **£250-300**
Similar Model with figure of Zulu warrior
pulling .... **£250-£300**
311 Light Trailer Fire Pump in Action Set
Two firemen two hoses **£150-200**
521 Pixie Tree House and Swing
With owl sitting on branch. Pixies and fences ...
.... **£150-200**
522 Pixie Tea Party (AB)
Four Pixies on toadstools two waiter Pixies
serve the food .... NGPP
Space Ship (AB)
With side panel 'Spacemaster' (understood
that only six produced) (-) .... NGPP
Coronation Coach (small) (AB) **£30-50**
State Landau Coach (FGT)
Two horses with riders red open coach with
Queen and Footman at rear **£40-60**
Farmer's Gig (FGT)............................. **£80-100**
Farm Cart with Trotting Horse (-) **£80-100**
Mobile Animal Laboratory Trailer (FGT
With figure of a vet and a sick cow (-) ....
.... **£600-800**
Racing Car
Red body with 'MG Magnette' cast into side,
110 mm. 'FGT & SONS' **£100-125**
Garage Items
Petrol Pumps and Oil Cabinets Various brand
names and colours **£20-30**
Village Blacksmith Set (FGT)
Contains blacksmith, forge with hood, anvil,
Shire horse. in 2-part card box **£150-175**
Fire Car, Red, with 3 figures............... **£175-200**
Pony drawn Milk Float,
Yellow with red wheels, 'Pure Milk' cast in side
brown pony, milk man, silver milk churn with
tap **£250-300**
Zoo Keeper And Animals Set. In Kay Zoo box
.... **£100-150**
'Visitors to the Zoo Tea Party'.
Waitress, two adults and two children seated
at table **£1,000-1,500**
Ivy and Brumas Polar Bears.
Two white bears, boxed **£275-325**
Dolls House Pieces - Carpet Sweeper,
Fireplace, Oil Heater, Electric Fire **£20-25 each**
Auxiliary Fire Service
three firemen, with gas masks and water pump
trailer **£125-150**
Bakers Covered Handcart
Two-wheeled brown/white cart with bakers
deliveryman with basket **£80-100**
Donkey Ride Set
Two saddled donkeys with child riders,
unsaddled donkey foal, shelter and hitching
rail with notice '2d All the Way' or ''Donkey
Rides' **£150-200**
Windmill
Brown windmill with cream plastic sails. NGPP

Timpo Toys

The name Timpo comes from 'Toy Importers Ltd'. It was only with the outbreak of war in 1939 that Timpo started to manufacture their own lines, when importing became impossible. A few vehicles were made in 1940-41, but the main Timpo range started in 1946. The models were cheap and sturdy, if somewhat crude, and many have survived. Relatively few suffer from metal deterioration. In 1949 Timpo advertised 'faithful replicas of famous delivery services' and introduced several vans with attractive advertising liveries. An AEC Monarch lorry in the livery of Vaux brewery was introduced around 1950, and this was a far better model than the earlier toys.

Sadly it was not the first of a new range – the 1951–2 ban on the use of zinc meant that Timpo discontinued all their diecast vehicles. Some of the dies were subsequently sold to Benbros, including the AEC lorry.

Timpo Toys are very rarely seen in mint condition, and prices are therefore quoted for good original condition. Dates given are the approximate year of introduction.

Thanks to Robert Newson for providing this history and listing of cast metal Timpo motor vehicles.

Intro	Model name and Details	MPR
1940	**MG Record Car** Hollow-cast lead. Red, 'TIMPO TOYS' cast on side, 98 mm	£50-75
1940	**Streamlined Saloon** Separate body and chassis. 'Timpo' in script underneath. 99 mm	£30-40
1940	**Pick-Up Truck** Separate body and chassis. 'Timpo' in script underneath. Re-issued post-war with name blanked out. 97 mm	£30-40
1940	**Four-light Saloon** Possibly re-issue of a Goody Toy	NGPP
1946	**MG Record Car** Zinc diecast. 'TIMPO TOYS' cast at rear on offside. 97 mm	£50-75
1946	**'American Star' Racer** Star transfer on each side, 101 mm	£40-50
1946	**'Timpo Saloon'** Vaguely like a Morris 8. 93 mm	£40-50
1946	**Austin 16 Saloon** Black. 'TIMPO TOYS' underneath. 96 mm	£40-50
	Re-issued by Betal in four versions:	
	1. No name on model, brass hubs	£30-40
	2. 'A BETAL PRODUCT' under roof, tin base with friction motor, brass wheel hubs	£30-40
	3. As 2. but with plastic body	£30-40
	4. As 3. but with clockwork motor and solid metal wheels	£30-40
1946	**MG Midget** Composition wheels. 82 mm	£30-40
1946	**Packard Saloon** Fitted with aluminium baseplate and friction motor from 1948. 113 mm	£30-40
1946	**'Speed of the Wind' Record Car** Similar to the Dinky Toy. 99 mm	£40-50
1946	**No.1 'Arctic' Set** Sledge and dog team, Eskimo with whip, another with rifle, walking stick, 2 penguins, 2 seals, polar bear, snowy hedge and igloo. Boxed	£400-600
1947	**Alvis 14 Saloon** A big four-light saloon. 106 mm	£30-40
1947	**Utility Van** With aluminium baseplate and friction motor from 1948. (Early casting 102mm, later 104mm).	
	1. No transfers, plain colours, without motor	£10-15
	2. Black, 'TYRESOLES SERVICE' transfers, no motor	£200-300
	3. 'HIS MASTER'S VOICE' transfers, pale Yellow, Orange-ellow, pale Blue or Green, motor.in some	£200-300

Intro	Model name and Details	MPR
1947	**Articulated Petrol Tanker** No transfers. Re-issued by Benbros. 149 mm	£30-40
	Red/white body, 'ESSO' logo	£80-120
1947	**Lincoln Convertible** Vaguely like a 1942 Lincoln. Aluminium baseplate and windscreen. Usually single colours. Late version in cream with blue seats. 115 mm	£30-40
1947	**Armstrong-Siddeley Hurricane** Coupé with top up. 105 mm	£30-40
1947	**Streamlined Fire Engine** Red, 2 yellow aluminium ladders. Aluminium baseplate + friction motor from '49. 105 mm	£30-40
1947	**Articulated Box Van** Re-issued by Benbros. 146 mm. Boxed.	
	1. Green, Blue or Red trailer with 'TIMPO TOYS' transfers	£160-190
	2. Black cab and trailer with Grey roof, Red wheel hubs, 'PICKFORDS' transfers	£140-170
	3. Orange cab and trailer, Black roof, 'UNITED DAIRIES' transfers	£140-170
	4. Light Blue cab, Light Blue and Cream trailer, 'WALL'S ICE CREAM' transfers	£140-170
	5. Dark Blue cab and trailer with off-White roof, 'LYONS TEA' transfers	£140-170
	6. Pale Yellow cab and trailer, transfers with 'BISHOPS MOVE' logo and 'BISHOP & SONS DEPOSITORIES LTD. 10-12 BELGRAVE ROAD LONDON, S.W.1'	£140-170
	7. Same, but transfers with 'BISHOPS MOVE' logo and 'JOHN H. LUNN LTD. 6 HOPE CRESCENT EDINBURGH'.	£140-170
1947	**London Taxi** Cast in two parts. 94 mm	£20-25
1947	**Alvis 14 Police Car** Police sign and loudspeakers at front of roof, wire aerial behind. Black. 106 mm	£50-75
1947	**Articulated Low Loader** Re-issued by Benbros. 168 mm	£10-15
1947	**Buick Saloon** Crude model, composition wheels. 99 mm	£10-15
1947	**Pick-Up Truck** With eight cast-in barrels. 104 mm	£15-20
1947	**Forward Control Tipper Lorry** Cream cab and chassis, Red tipper. 101 mm	£15-20
1947	**Forward Control Luton Van** Same chassis as the tipper. 97 mm. boxed.	
	1. No transfers, black lower, light blue upper	£15-20

Intro	Model name and Details	MPR
	2. Dark blue, 'SMITH'S CRISPS' transfers	£120-150
	3. Brown, 'W.D. & H.O. WILLS' transfers	£120-150
1949	**Forward Control Box Van** Same chassis as above. Re-issued by Benbros. Dark blue, 'CHIVERS JELLIES' transfers	£120-150

Timpo group of vehicles.

Intro	Model name and Details	MPR
1949	**Normal Control Box Van** Later models with aluminium baseplate and friction motor. 105 mm. Models were boxed.	
	1. Dark Blue with White roof, 'EVER READY' transfers, motor in some	£150-250
	2. Green, 'GOLDEN SHRED', with motor	£150-250
	3. Green, 'MELTONIAN SHOE CREAM' transfers, with motor	£150-250
1949	**Normal Control Petrol Tanker** Red, 'MOTOR OIL ESSO PETROL' on paper labels, boxed. Re-issued by Benbros	£250-350
1950	**AEC Monarch Brewery Lorry** Red. 'VAUX' cast on headboard behind cab, 'SUNDERLAND' cast on cab sides. Boxed. Brown hollow-cast barrels with 'VAUX' cast on ends. Re-issued by Benbros without the headboard + other changes. 129 mm	£150-250
1940s	**Bomber Station Set** 3 x twin-fuselage aircraft, 2 x twin-engined, single-fuselage aircraft and a single-engined fighter. Box has a pictorial label on its lift-off lid	£150-200
249	**Hopalong Cassidy Series Set** Contains 7 cowboys including Hopalong Cassidy, Lucky, California, etc., 3(?) horses. Boxed	£1,000-1,250
---	**Wild West Set**, boxed. Covered Wagon with Driver	£300-350
---	**'The Ranch' Set**, boxed. Two cowboys playing guitars and two playing accordions, cowboy rider, 2 horses, bench	£350-400
---	**Individual figures** from this group	£15-20 each

Timpo Gift Set including petrol pumps, figures, saloon car and racer.

--- **Petrol Station**
Car plus Pump and Dispenser.
Pictorial box.....................................**£75-100**

--- **Petrol Station No.2 Set**
Saloon Car and Racing Car plus 3 Personnel and 5 Pumps. Pictorial box lid states: 'THE FAMOUS TIMPO CARS' **£150-200**

--- **Petrol Station No.3 Set**
4 Cars, 3 Pumps, 2 Dispensers, Chauffer, 2 Mechanics. Pictorial box has street scene **£150-200**

--- **Car Series No. 1 Set**,
boxed. Green open tourer, pump, oil bin, mechanic **£150-175**

--- **Racing Set**
3 Racing Cars + 3 petrol pumps, 4 mechanics.......................................**£175-200**

--- **Station Figures Set**
Contains Station Master, Porter with trolley, Porter with luggage, Signalman with flag, Signalman with whistle, Railwayman with lamps, Mr Brown, boy hiker, lady with bag, girl in red coat, soldier with kitbag. Box.........
....**£500-750**

--- **Individual figures**
from this group..........................**£15-20 each**

--- **Railway Porter with Luggage**.
Sack barrow, 5 pieces of luggage, boxed........
....**£175-200**

--- **Tiger Hunt Set**
Elephants, howdahs, mahouts, Maharaja, hunter, 2 tigers, 4 bears, natives with spears. Boxed **£900-1,000**

--- **Farm Series Set**
15 piece dairy / poultry set............**£300-350**

Gypsy Organ Grinder with Dancing Bear ...
....**£50-70**

--- **Clown Circus Band**.
Four Clown figures........................**£250-300**

--- **Jaunting Cart**,
boxed. Brown horse and cart with driver ......
....**£500-700**

--- **Domestic Sets**.
A Kitchen Sets, a Washing Set..**£40-50 each**

--- **Coronation Coach**.
Gilt Coach, 8 grey horses, 4 riders **£200-250**

--- **HM Queen Elizabeth II**.
'Trooping the Colours' figure on horse, E in G box...**£75-100**

--- **Timpo figures**.
Knights of the Round Table and Ivanhoe figures. Each **£75-100**
Knights of the Round Table Set. Nine figures, boxed **£500-600**
Policeman, Policewoman, Zoo Keeper, Farm Girls. Each...............................**£15-20**
Super heroes:
Captain Marvel, Mary Marvel, Marvel Junior. Each..**£15-20**

--- **Salesman's 'My Pets' Sample Box**
with 18 dogs...............................**£1,250-1,750**

Timpo commercial vehicles.

That they were produced originally as toys rather than models is evident from the playworn condition of these Timpo vehicles.

Timpo Toys Articulated Cab and Trailer - black cab, silver hubs, blue lowloader trailer.

Timpo Toys Ever Ready Van - blue, white roof, decals to sides, rear and roof, bare metal hubs, black tyres.

Tri-ang Minic Toys

Minic road vehicles and accessories were introduced in June 1935 by the famous English 'Lines Bros', company of, by then, Morden Road, Merton, Surrey. The name 'Minic' had been registered as a trademark a few months earlier and was derived from the words MINIature Clockwork – which accurately described the toys.

Lines Bros Ltd was a British toy manufacturer of the 20th century, operating under the Tri-ang brand name. Lines Bros Ltd, at its peak, was claimed to be the largest toy maker in the world. The brothers George and Joseph Lines, made wooden toys in the Victorian age, their company being G & J lines Ltd. Joseph was the active partner while George went into farming. Joseph (or Joe) had four sons. Three of these formed Lines Bros Ltd soon after WWI. These three were William, Walter and Arthur Edwin Lines. Three Lines making a triangle – hence Tri-ang. Arthur's son, Richard Lines, was largely responsible for the Tri-ang Railways system.

The tinplate material used for the models was always painted and never lithographed as had been the usual method before. Radiator grilles were plated, as were the front wings on many of the models. In a manner similar to the contemporary Dinky Toys, the first issues were not badged as being a model of any particular car or truck, they were just named 'Limousine', 'Tourer', etc. The first car to carry the name of the manufacturer came along in 1936, the Ford £100 Saloon and the Ford Light Van built on the same chassis. These were really delightful little models and over the production run, which continued after 1945, appeared in many colours.

1937 was the year when Minic brought out the named Vauxhall, Rolls-Royce, Bentley and Daimler models. The Vauxhalls were the previous 'Limousine' and others but with the grille and bonnet modified to represent the flutes of the full-size cars. The Rolls, Bentley and Daimler were totally new models and were known as the 'Quality Cars'. These were also offered, with a very few other models, with electric headlights.

Some of the rarest models were produced for only a very short time in 1940-1941 in camouflage colours. Except for one item, these were otherwise normal issue models except for the colouring. The green paint was sprayed all over the assembled model and then the brown shading was brushed on by hand. This of course means that probably no two models are exactly alike. The most desirable is the Balloon Barrage Wagon and Trailer (76) which had a large balloon supplied with it. Once the three pieces of the balloon had been sewn together the toy could not be put back in its box, which has made a boxed version extremely valuable now. Petrol companies were under government control during the war and the petrol was known as 'POOL'. Tri-ang issued both of their petrol tankers, the rigid and the articulated, in grey with 'POOL' on the tanks in white.

At the start of the Second World War, production of children's toys was deemed non-essential by the British Government. As a result, production facilities were converted to weapons manufacture, specifically the Sten Mk III submachine gun. Manufacture of toys resumed shortly after the war ended. At their peak they had 40 companies world-wide, but as a result of losses overseas they were in financial trouble.

When production resumed in 1946 not all of the range was re-introduced. Restrictions on the supply of metal for toys affected all toy factories badly. The colours of paint post-war were generally much harsher in shade – gone were the soft blues, browns, beiges and greys, and in their place were red, green and dark blue. By 1948 over 40 models had been re-issued, but by the middle of 1948 the first plastic Minics had appeared. Plastic of course allowed for more realistic shapes to be made. This applied particularly to private car models as the real car manufacturers had introduced curves into their new models. There were no new tinplate Minic cars after the war.

The generic truck models all featured a 'normal control' cab and bonnet layout left over from the pre-war era until 1950 to 1951. Minic followed the full-size trucks by changing to the more modern looking 'forward control' configuration. This was known in the US as 'cabover', where the driver sat high up alongside the engine rather than behind it. Both the articulated and the rigid trucks were treated this way, but many people feel that Minic trucks lost a lot of their charm at this time. Motors changed from clockwork to 'push and go' about this time also.

Probably the most attractive models of the post-war era were the Delivery Vans (model nos 79–82) painted in the colours of the four independent railway operators. These were only sold from 1947 to 1949 and were correctly coloured and decalled. They also had advertising posters stuck on the van sides. They were replaced by a similar 'British Railways' van (107) in 1950, but this was only sold for one year before being replaced by the short bonnet version. For some unknown reason the G.W.R. and L.M.S. vans are more difficult to find than the other two. The long bonnet B.R. van is also very scarce.

Pre-war Minic also made a wide range of wooden garages, fire stations and other accessories to go with the models. The construction of these was similar to the Tri-ang dolls' houses and other wooden toys.

1936 saw the appearance of the No 1 Construction Set which was supplied in a fitted wooden case with a lovely colour poster on the lid showing six models and a parts list. The models were supplied unpainted and unassembled but with all the necessary axles, wheels, grilles, decals etc., even including small pots of paint. A lovely toy and one which could, and probably did, provide some unusual colour combinations once the children, or more likely, their fathers got at them.

As all Minic vehicles can be carefully disassembled by loosening the tin tabs, many odd variations have appeared over the years. One well known batch of G.W.R. vans appeared on the short bonnet van. These were done openly to use up a batch of old shop stock which had got a bit rusty. When they were sold in about 1978 everyone knew they were repaints, but do all collectors around today, some 25 years later, know this? Remember the Construction Set models as well.

Some cars, taxis and trucks have been very carefully 'restored' by skilful operators and have been seen in collections, sold in auctions and at swapmeets. Just take the usual care and do not jump at a 'yes, it's a rare colour variation' without giving it a very good look.

Minic also illustrated proposed models in their advertising which never went into production. Three of these spring to mind immediately, the Trolley Bus (77M), the Coal Lorry (70M) and the long-bodied Ambulance (75M). Some collectors and artisans have made replicas of these to show what they would have looked like. They are lovely pieces in their own right but just remember they were not made by Tri-ang.

As a very rough guide to dating your Minic collection, it is taken that those with white tyres and a small 'Shell' petrol can on the running board are pre-war, whilst those with black tyres and no petrol can are post-war.

In 1971 Lines Bros Ltd called in the Official Receiver. The Group was broken up and sold off. The name Tri-ang was sold off. As a result the Tri-ang Hornby system took the name Hornby Railways from January 1972.

Tri-ang Minic Toys

Model and details	MPR

Tri-ang Minic 1/20th scale electric Bentley Continental c.1960, maroon, with cream interior, scarce example with rubber tyres, plated parts including lights and numberplates, steerable front wheels

1M **Ford £100 Saloon**
1936-41 Blue, green, beige, grey, red **£150-180**
1MCF 1940-41 Camouflage finish **£200-250**
1M 1946-49 As pre-war civilian version **£75-100**

2M **Ford Light Van**
1936-41 Blue, green, beige, red .. **£100-200**
1946-49 As pre-war version **£100-125**

3M **Ford Royal Mail Van**
1936-41 'Royal Mail' **£120-150**
1946-49 'E.R., later 'G.R.' decals . **£100-125**

4M **Sports Saloon**
1935-41 .... **£150-200**

5M **Limousine**
1935-41 .... **£200-250**

6M **Cabriolet**
1935-40 Pre-war radiator.......... . **£200-225**

7M **Town Coupé**
1935-41 Pre-war with petrol can.**£200-300**
1946-47 Post-war version........... **£100-125**

8M **Open Touring Car**
1935-41 Pre-war with luggage rack or petrol can. **£200-300**
1946-47 Post-war version........... **£100-125**

9M **Streamline Saloon**
1935-41 Pre-war with luggage rack.**£200-225**
1946-51 Post- war version **£100-120**

10M **Delivery Lorry**
1935-41 Pre-war with petrol can **£150-200**
1946-51 Post-war version............. **£90-110**

11M **Tractor**
1935-40 See also 83M................. **£100-150**
11MCF 1940-41 Camouflage finish **£200-250**

12M **Learner's Car**
1936-41 Based on 8M................. **£250-350**
1946-50 Based on 17M **£150-200**

13M **Racing Car**
1936-40 Open cockpit **£150-200**
1947-55 Closed cockit **£50-75**

14M **Streamline Sports**
1935-41 Open version of 9M with luggage rack.. .... **£180-200**
1946-51 With LBL 174 number plate transfer. **£100-150**

15M **Petrol Tank Lorry / Petrol Tanker**
1936-41 Long bonnet cab, 'Shell' or 'B P' decals and petrol can "running man transfer on rear of tanker.. .... **£200-250**
1946-51 Long bonnet cab, 'Shell' or 'B P' decals with "Shell X-100 or Energol transfer on rear of tanker **£120-150**
1950-58 Short bonnet cab, 'Shell' or 'B P' decals..... **£100-120**
NB Some early post-war versions have Tri-ang triangle decal only.

15MCF **Petrol Tanker**
1940-41 Camouflage finish **£400-500**

16M **Caravan**
1936-41 Electric **£150-180**
1947-55 Non-electric..................... **£50-65**

17M **Vauxhall Tourer**
1937-41 Vauxhall grille, bonnet and luggage rack.... .... **£180-250**
1947-55 No luggage rack LBL 174 number plate transfer ... **£120-150**

18M **Vauxhall Town Coupé**
1937-41 Pre-war with luggage rack or petrol can.. .... **£200-250**
1947-55 Post-war version with LBL 174 number plate transfer... **£150-200**

19M **Vauxhall Cabriolet**
1937-41 Pre-war with plated wings and petrol can **£200-300**
19MCF 1940-41 Camouflage finish **£300-400**
19M 1947-55 Post- war version with LBL 174 number plate transfer... . **£100-120**

20M **Light Tank**
1935-41 .... **£200-250**
20MCF 1940-41 Camouflage finish **£200-300**

21M **'TRI-ANG TRANSPORT' Van / Delivery Van**
1935-36 1st series no transfers and no petrol can................. **£300-400**
1936-41 2nd series with petrol can and "Minic Transport" transfer... **£250-300**
1946-50 *Post war version with no petrol can just "Minic Transport" transfer **£100-125**
1946-50 'ATCO' rare version .**£1,000-1,200**
*Replaced by 85M in 1951

21MCF **Delivery Van**
1940-41 Camouflage finish **£500-600**

22M **'Carter Paterson & Co' Van**
1936-41 Pre-war with petrol can **£350-450**
1946-51 Post- war without petrol can **£200-250**
1948-51 Post-war Carter Paterson & Pickfords Van **£120-150**

23M **Tip Lorry**
1935-41 Pre-war with petrol can **£200-250**
1946-51 Post-war with no petrol can.................................. **£100-150**

24M **Luton 'MINIC' Transport Van**
1936-41 Pre-war with petrol can **£300-350**
24MCF 1940-41 Camouflage finish **£500-700**
24M 1946-51 Post-war version with no petrol can...................... **£150-200**

25M **Delivery Lorry with Cases**
All issues came with 6 wooden cases.
1936-41 Pre-war long bonnet cab with petrol can **£200-300**
1946-50 Post- war long bonnet cab with no petrol can.......**£150-200**
1950-56 Short bonnet cab with die cast or plastic wheels........... **£100-120**

26M **Tractor and Trailer with Cases**
1936-41 11M Pre-war Tracked Tractor........................... **£300-400**
1946-51 11M Post-war Tracked Tractor........................... **£150-200**
1951-55 67M Post war Farm Tractor.......... .... **£150-200**

27M, 28M Numbers not allocated.

29M **Traffic Control Car**
1938-41 As 4M, with driver, passenger, single horn loudspeaker on roof and petrol can........ **£250-300**
1947-52 With single horn loudspeaker on roof with no petrol can **£100-150**
With later smaller 2-horn speaker with no petrol can **£100-150**

30M **Mechanical Horse & Pantechnicon**
1935-41 With 2-axle trailer, no decals and no petrol can **£250-300**

1935-41 With 2-axle trailer, "Minic Transport" decals and petrol can **£250-275**
1946-51 With 2-axle trailer, 'Minic Transport' with no petrol can **£150-200**
1951-55 With single-axle trailer, 'Minic Transport' decals, short bonnet cab **£110-120**

'BROCKHURST' promotional **£2,000-2,250**

31M **Mechanical Horse & Fuel Oil Trailer**
(Mechanical Horse & Petrol Trailer)
1936-41 Long bonnet cab, 'Shell BP Fuel Oil'.......... **£300-400**
1946-51 'Shell', 'BP', 'Shell Fuel Oils', or 'BP Fuel Oil'. Long bonnet cab **£150-200**
1951-58 Same, but with short bonnet cab.................... **£150-200**

32M **Dust Cart / Refuse Lorry**
1936-41 Long bonnet with petrol can **£120-150**
1946-50 Long bonnet with no petrol can **£80-100**
1950-56 Short bonnet with no petrol can **£60-100**

33M **Steam Roller**
1935-41 Pre-war with wooden wheels **£120-175**
1946-55 Post-war with plastic wheels **£50-60**

34M **Tourer with Passengers**
1937-40 8M + four lead figures with petrol can **£400-600**

35M **Rolls Tourer**
Post-war numbered '118M'
1937-41 Pre-war with none opening boot **£900-1,000**
1946-52 Post-war with opening boot **£300-500**

36M **Daimler Tourer**
1937-41 Same as 35M with Daimler radiator....................... **£900-1,000**

37M **Bentley Tourer**
Sometimes numbered '39M'
1938-41 Pre-war with electric lights and two seats (57ME)....... **£1,500-1,700**
1938-41 Pre-war without electric lights and four seats **£150-200**

38M **Caravan Set (non-electric)**
1936-40 5M Limousine with non electric pre-war caravan **£500-750**

39M **Taxi / London Taxi**
1938-41 Pre-war with petrol can. (Yellow) **£1,700-2,000**
1938-41 Pre-war with petrol can. (Bright Red) **£1,700-2,000**
1938-41 Pre-war with petrol can. (Light Green) **£1,700-2,000**
1938-41 Pre-war with petrol can, (Pale Blue) **£1,500-2,000**
1938-41 Pre-war with petrol can. (Pale Grey) **£1,700-2,000**
1938-41 Pre-war with petrol can. (Dark Red) **£1,700-2,000**
1938-41 Pre-war with petrol can. (Dark Green) **£1,700-2,000**
1938-41 Pre-war with petrol can, (Dark Blue) **£1,500-2,000**
1946-52 Post-war (35M) no petrol can (Blue) **£200-250**

40M **Mechanical Horse & Trailer with Cases**
1941-41 Long bonnet cab with petrol can, holds 8 cases (very few made) **£300-400**

1946-51 Long bonnet cab without petrol can, holds 6 cases.......... **£150-200**

1951-56 Short bonnet holds 6 cases........... **£100-150**

41ME **Caravan with Electric Light.**
1936-40 16M with light bulb....... **£300-400**

42M **Rolls Sedanca (none electric lights)**
1937-41 With filled in boot
.............................**£1,000-1,500**
1947-52 With opening boot **£750-800**

43M **Daimler Sedanca**
1937-41 With filled in boot
.............................**£1,000-1,500**
1947-52 not released post-war

44M **Traction Engine (without trailer).**
1938-41 With diecast fly wheel... **£200-300**
1946-55 With plastic fly wheel........ **£70-90**

45M **Bentley Sunshine Saloon (sliding sunroof)**
1938-41 With filled in boot or
electric lights **£1,850-2,000**
1946-52 With opening boot only
.... **£750-1,000**

46M **Daimler Sunshine Saloon (sliding sunroof)**
1938-41 With filled in boot or
electric lights **£1,800-2,000**
1946-52 With opening boot only
.... **£700-900**

47M **Rolls Sunshine Saloon (sliding sunroof)**
1938-41 With filled in boot,
no electric lights **£1,250-1,500**
1946-52 With opening boot only
.... **£500-700**

48M **Breakdown Lorry with Mechanical Crane**
1936-41 Long bonnet with petrol can
and triangle symbol transfer
.... **£500-600**
1946-50 Long bonnet without petrol can
and no triangle symbol transfer
.... **£250-300**
1950-56 Short bonnet without petrol can
and plastic or cast wheels
.... **£150-250**

48MCF **Breakdown Lorry**
1940-41 Painted camouflage with painted
wheels **£500-700**

49ME **Searchlight Lorry with Electric Searchlight**
1936-41 With oil can and moveable
searchlight, painted green with
red base......................... **£500-700**

49MECF Searchlight Lorry with Electric Searchlight
1940-41 Camouflage finish, with no oil can
.... **£700-900**

50ME **Rolls Sedanca with Electric Headlamps**
(see also 42M.)
1937-41 With electric headlamps
.................................**£1,000-1,500**
1946-52 Without electric headlamps with
opening boot **£700-1,000**

51ME **Daimler Sedanca with Electric Headlamps**
(see also 43M.)
1937-41 With electric headlamps
.................................**£1,000-1,500**
1946-52 Without electric headlamps with
opening boot **£700-1,000**

52M **Single Deck Bus**
1936-41 Red and stone coloured 'London
Transport' **£350-450**
1946-58 Blue and grey coloured with
blank destination board (diecast
wheels)......................... **£400-450**
1946-58 Red and cream coloured with
blank destination board (diecast
wheels)......................... **£400-450**
1946-58 Green Line with "Dorking"
destination board (diecast
wheels)......................... **£400-450**
1958-60 Green Line with "Dorking"
destination board and
'Routemaster' front grille with
steerable wheels............ **£450-550**

Tri-ang Minic No 53M Greenline Single Deck clockwork
Bus - two tone green, 'Greenline' to sides, 'Dorking'
destination to front, cast hubs, clockwork.

53M **Single Deck Bus**
1936-41 Green Line with 'London
Transport' transfer In two-tone
green............................... **£350-450**

54M **Traction Engine and Trailer with Cases**
All with 6 wooden cases
1939-41 44M and 2-axle Trailer
.... **£150-200**
1946-56 44M and 2-axle Trailer
.... **£125-150**

55ME **Bentley Tourer with Electric Headlamps**
(see also 37M)
1938-40 With electric lights and opening
boot **£1,500-2,000**
1938-40 With opening boot, tin or diecast
wheels **£1,000-1,200**

56ME **Rolls Sunshine Saloon with Electric
headlamps**
1938-41 With opening boot and electric
lights **£1,550-1,700**

57ME **Bentley Sunshine Saloon with Electric
Headlamps**
1938-41 With opening boot
.................................**£1,550-1,700**

58ME **Daimler Sunshine Saloon with Electric
Headlamps**
1938-41 With opening boot
.................................**£1,550-1,700**

59ME **Caravan Set (Tourer with Passengers)**
1937-40 34M with passengers with 41ME
Caravan with Electric Lights
.... **£900-1,100**

60M **Double Deck Bus / London Bus**
1935-41 Red, maroon / stone,
'London Transport'........ **£400-500**
1946-58 All-red, red/cream roof, red
cream-red-cream body with
red roof, red with cream lower
windows, red with cream upper
windows; all with 'London
Transport' decals **£250-300**
Blue / cream **£300-400**
1958-60 Routemaster front, red, London
transport or Tri-ang Transport
decals **£450-500**

61M **Double Deck Bus**
1946-52 In two-tone green.......... **£400-500**

62M **London Fire Engine**
1946-56 With no electric lights with larger
bell................................. **£175-225**

62ME **Fire Engine with Electric Headlamps**
1936-38 With electric lights and smaller
bell................................. **£400-500**

63M **Presentation Set No. 1**
1936-40 Contains 1M, 4M, 5M, 6M
and 8M.....................**£1,000-1,200**

64M **Presentation Set No. 2**
1936-40 Contains 1M, 2M, 5M,13M,
15M, 20M, 21M,22M and 23M. **£1,500-2,000**

65M **Construction Set No. 1**
1936-40 Wooden case containing
unpainted parts to assemble
5M, 6M, 9M, 10M, 11M and21M
models, including paint, various
transfers and tools
.................................**£1,500-2,000**

66M **Six-wheel Army Lorry**
1939-41 Flat back truck in olive green
.... **£300-500**

66MCF 1940-41 Same as 66M but in camouflage
finish............................. **£400-500**

67M **Farm Lorry**
1939-47 Flat back lorry with open cage
like structure on the back not
fitted with petrol can **£600-800**

68M **Builders Lorry**
1939-41 Long bonnet cab, front ladder/
plank rack with petrol can
.... **£350-450**
1946-51 Long bonnet cab, front ladder/
plank rack without petrol can
.... **£150-200**
1951-56 Short bonnet, front ladder/plank
rack............................... **£100-150**

69M **Canvas Tilt Lorry**
1939-41 Same as 66M with permanently
fitted canvas tilt and petrol can
.... **£500-600**

69MCF 1940-41 Same as 66MCF with
permanently fitted canvas tilt
.................................**£800-1,000**

70M **Coal Lorry** Not issued.

71M **Mechanical Horse & Milk Tanker**
1939-41 All-white long bonnet cab, 'Minic
Dairies 3150 Gallons' twin
wheeled tanker............. **£400-500**
1946-51 Long bonnet cab in blue, Minic
Dairies 3150 Gallons' single
wheeled tanker.............. **£200-300**
1951-58 Short bonnet, Minic Dairies 3150
Gallons' single plastic wheeled
tanker **£140-160**

72M **Mechanical Horse & Lorry with Barrrels/
Minic Brewer's Trailer**
1939-41 Long bonnet cab, with petrol can
and 15 small barrels...... **£400-450**
1946-51 Long bonnet cab, with 8 larger
barrels **£200-300**
1951-56 Short bonnet with 8 larger barrels
and plastic wheels......... **£200-250**

73M **Mechanical Horse & Cable Drum
Trailer/Cable Lorry**
1939-41 Although appeared in
catalogue not available pre-war.
1946-51 Long bonnet cab with flat bed
trailer and two cable drums
.... **£250-300**
1951-56 Short bonnet cab with flat bed
trailer and two cable drums
.... **£150-175**

74M **Mechanical Horse & Log Trailer/
Log Lorry**
1939-41 Long bonnet cab with petrol can,
and trailer carrying two logs
£300-350
1946-51 Long bonnet cab with trailer
carrying two logs **£150-200**
1951-56 Short bonnet cab with trailer
carrying two logs **£100-150**

75M **Ambulance**
In 1939 Long bonnet was shown in trade
catalogue but not issued.
1952-56 Short bonnet cab, based on
103M, red cross and'LCC'
decals **£100-150**
1952-56 Short bonnet cab, based on
103M, white cross and'LCC'
decals **£100-150**

76M **Balloon Barrage Wagon and Trailer**
1940-41 As 66MCF with winch, trailer
with 'gas' cylinders, 3-piece
balloon in stiffened fabric in a
picture box..............**£2,000-3,500**

77M **Trolley Bus** In catalogue but not issued.

78M **'POOL' Petrol Tanker**
1940-41 As 15M, grey in colour ,
white 'POOL' decals **£1,000-1,500**

78M **Jeep No 1**
1946-47 Gloss or matt Olive........... **£70-90**

79M **Mechanical Horse & 'POOL' Tanker**
1940-41 As 31M, grey in colour ,
white 'POOL' decals
...............................**£1,000-1,500**

79M **G.W.R. Railway Van**
1946-47 Model as 21M chocolate
brown and cream **£1,000-1,200**

80M **L.M.S. Railway Van**
1947-49 Model as 21M dark plum
and black........................**£500-750**

81M **L.N.E.R. Railway Van**
1947-49 Model as 21M dark blue..**£400-500**

82M **S.R. Railway Van**
1947-49 Model as 21M all green. **£400-500**

83M **Farm Tractor**
1947-56 Main body as 11M...........**£75-100**

84M --- See Plastic Models.

85M **Forward Drive Van**
1951-55 Replaced 21M, short bonnet
version with "Minic Transport"
transfer **£100-120**

86M **Forward Drive Tip Lorry**
1951-56 Replaced 23M....................**£60-55**

87M - 92M --- Numbers not allocated.

93M **'O' Saloon**
1952-56 Small scale car...............**£150-200**

94M - 102M --- See Plastic Models.

103M **Shutter Van**
1951-56 One piece lift-up rear door;
see 75M **£75-80**

104M - 106M See Plastic Models / No.2 Series.

107M **'British Railways' Van**
1950-51 Model as 21M with 'British
Railways' decals.............**£250-300**

1951-55 Model based on 85M **£100-150**
108M - 112M --- See Plastic Models.
113M **Vauxhall Cabriolet and Caravan**
1950-51 19M + 16M **£200-250**
114M **Mechanical Horse & Trailer
with Cruiser**
1950-51 Penguin plastic boat **£150-200**
1951-56 Short bonnet cab,
Penguin plastic boat **£150-200**
119M **Watney's Barrel Lorry**
1952-56 Long bonnet tractor unit with
small plastic red barrel on roof,
wooden barrel artic. trailer; later
models had larger red plastic
barrel **£250-300**
123M **British Road Services Lorry**
1951-56 Short bonnet 25M in red with
B.R.S. decals...................**£220-260**
124M **British Road Services Van**
1952-56 85M in green with B.R.S
decals **£200-220**
145M **Cement Mixer Lorry**
1951-56 Plastic mixer drum on short
bonnet truck chassis/cab **£100-125**
30M base **Mechanical Horse & Pantechnicon**
(promotional model)
1937 'Brockhouse' promotional
based on 30M **£1,500-2,000**
21M base **'Atco Mowers' Van** (promotional model)
1951? Based on 21M **£1,000-1,500**
24M base **'Winstone Tiles' / Furniture Van**
(Promotional model)
1951 New Zealand assembled model,
based on 24M **£800-1000**

Other New Zealand issues
During the post-war period a selection of the Minic range were produced in the Auckland factory from parts supplied unpainted from the UK. They were finished in different colours and packaged in white and blue boxes.

1M **Ford Saloon**
1948-51 Various colours to Include red,
purple and pale blue.....**£200-250**
2M **Ford Van**
1948-51 Various colours to Include red,
purple and pale blue.....**£200-250**
11M **Tractor**
1948-51 Unpainted with rubber tracks.......
......................................**£100-200**
15M **Petrol Tank Lorry 'SHELL'**
1948-51 Red cab / yellow tank....**£500-600**
23M **Tip Lorry**
1948-51 Various colours to Include red,
purple and pale blue **£180-250**
16M **Caravan**
1948-51 Red / white....................**£200-250**
18M **Vauxhall Town Coupé**
1948-51 Purple-grey / red wings other
colours available **£200-250**
19M **Vauxhall Cabriolet**
1948-51 Various colours to Include red,
purple and pale blue **£180-250**

Tri-ang Minic 68M Builders Lorry. post-war version with light green cab and red chassis and body, complete with wood load and key.

Tri-ang Minic 82M Southern Railways Van. Finished in green with white lettering 'Southern Railway' and paper posters for Tri-ang Toys and Pedal Motors to van sides.

Tri-ang Minic No 119M Watney Barrel Lorry. Dark green standard cab, black chassis with wooden barrel-style trailer with a red plastic motif to the cab roof. Cab and trailer front wheels are unusually finished in red in this example.

Tri-ang Minic post-war 42M Rolls Royce Sedanca, finished in dark blue with black mudguards and hood, opening boot, plated tinplate hubs.

Tri-ang Minic Ships

Minic ships are accurately detailed waterline models made between 1958 and 1964 to a scale of 1:1,200 (1in to 100ft).
Six sales catalogues were published which nowadays are quite hard to find. No single catalogue shows the full range.
Minic ships re-introduced in 1976 were fitted with wheels and have 'Hong Kong' on the base.

Ocean Liners

Ref	Model name and details	MPR
M701	RMS 'Caronia' Green body, one plain Red/Black or detailed funnel, one mast, 178 mm. 'Painted in the correct Cunard green she is a most striking vessel'.	£150-175
M702	RMS 'Queen Elizabeth' Black/White, 2 plain Red/Black or detailed funnels, 2 masts, 262 mm. 'The worlds largest ship and the pride of the Cunard fleet'.	£90-110
M703	RMS 'Queen Mary' Black/White, plain Red/Black or detailed funnels, 2 masts, 259 mm. 'Her three funnels make her the most easily recognisable'.	£90-110
M704	SS 'United States' Black/White body, two Red/White/Blue funnels, 252 mm. 'The present holder of the Blue Riband of the Atlantic'.	£100-125
M705	RMS 'Aquitania' Black/White body, four Red/Black funnels, two masts, 231 mm.	£150-200
M706	SS 'Nieuw Amsterdam' Grey/White body, two Yellow funnels, two masts, 192 mm.	£120-140
M707	SS 'France' Black/White, 2 Red/Black funnels, 5 masts, 262 mm. 'The longest ship in the world – 1035ft, being 4ft longer than Queen Elizabeth'.	£125-150
M708	RMS 'Saxonia' Black/White body, one Red/Black or detailed funnel, nine masts, cargo handling gear on stern	£120-140
M708/2	RMS 'Franconia' Green body, one Red/Black funnel, nine Green masts, 155 mm, swimming pool	

Ref	Model name and details	MPR
	on stern.480 made	£500-750
M709	RMS 'Ivernia' Black/White or Green body, 155mm, cargo handling gear on stern	£90-110
M709/2	RMS 'Carmania' Green body, one Red/Black funnel, nine Green masts, 155 mm, swimming pool on stern.480 made	£500-750
M710	RMS 'Sylvania' Black/White, one Red/Black funnel, nine masts, 155 mm.	£120-140
M711	RMS 'Carinthie' Black/White, one Red/Black funnel, nine masts, 155 mm.	£90-110
M712	NS 'Savannah' White, no funnels (nuclear powered), four masts, 149 mm.	£125-150
M713	SS 'Antilles' Black/White, one Red/Black funnel, ten masts, 152 mm.	£125-150
	All White body, one Red/Black funnel, ten masts.	£150-200
M714	'Flandre' Black/White, one Red/Black funnel, ten masts, 152 mm.	£120-140
	All White body, one Red/Black funnel, ten masts.	£90-110
M715	RMS 'Canberra' White body, one Yellow funnel, three masts, 189 mm.	£130-160
M716	MS 'Port Brisbane' Grey/White, one Red/Black funnel, eight masts, 140 mm.	£150-200
M717	SS 'Port Auckland' Grey/White, one Red/Black funnel, seven masts, 140 mm.	£150-175

Ref	Model name and details	MPR
M718	RMS 'Amazon' White, Yellow funnel, 19 masts, 10 lifeboats, 149 mm.	£200-250
M719	RMS 'Arlanza' White, Yellow funnel, 19 masts, 149 mm.	£150-175
M720	RMS 'Aragon' White, Yellow funnel, 19 masts, 149 mm.	£150-175
M721	RMS 'Britannia' The Royal Yacht. Blue/White body, Yellow/Black funnel, 3 masts, 105 mm.	£75-100
M721/H	RMS 'Britannia' Hospital Ship. White body, three masts, 105 mm.	£75-100

Tri-ang Minic Waterline Models: 702 RMS Queen Elizabeth, 706 SS Nieuw Amsterdam, 741 HMS Vanguard, 732 SS Varicella, 751 HMS Bulwark, 752 HMS Centaur, 761 HMS Swiftsure, 762 HMS Superb.

Smaller Craft

Channel islands steamers
(78mm long)

M722	'Isle of Jersey' Black/White, 2 Yellow/Black funnels, 2 masts	£40-50
M723	'Isle of Guernsey' Black/White, 2 Yellow/Black funnels, 2 masts	£40-50
M724	'Isle of Sark' Black/White body, 2 Yellow/Black funnels, 2 masts	£40-50
M726	'PILOTS' Boat Black/White/Yellow, 45 mm	£100-125
M727	Lifeboat Blue body	£40-50

Paddle steamers (all are 78 mm long)

M728	'Britannia' Black/white, 2 funnels (black/blue, red/black or yellow/black), 2 masts	£40-50
M729	'Bristol Queen'	
	Black/white, 2 funnels (black/blue, red/black or yellow/black), 2 masts	£40-50
M730	'Cardiff Queen' Black/White, 2 funnels (Black/Blue, Red/Black or Yellow/Black), 2 masts.	£40-50

Oil tanker

M732	SS 'Varicella' Black/White body, Black/Yellow funnel ('SHELL' logo), 2 masts, 169 mm.	£90-110

Whale factory ships

M733	TSS 'Vikingen' Grey body, six masts, 125 mm.	£100-125
M734	Whale Chaser Grey, Yellow/Black funnel, 39 mm.	£40-50

Tugboats (all except 'Turmoil' are 38mm long)

M731	Tugboat Black/Grey/Red, Red/Black funnel	£15-20
M731	Tugboat	

M731	Tugboat Black/Grey/Red, Yellow/Black funnel	£15-20
M731	Tugboat Black/Blue/Red, Yellow/Black funnel	£15-20
M731	Tugboat Black/Grey/Yellow, Yellow/Black funnel	£15-20
M740	Barge Intended to match M731, but not issued	NPP
M810	Navy Tug HMS 'Turmoil' Black/Blue or Grey, Black funnel, 50 mm.	£40-50

Lightships (all are 33mm long)

M735	'SUNK' Red body, White logo/name	£40-50
M736	'SHAMBLES' Red body, White logo/name	£40-50
M737	'CORK' Red body, White logo/name	£40-50
M738	'VARNE' Red body, White logo/name	£40-50
M739	'St GOWAN' Red body, White logo/name	£40-50

Tri-ang Minic Warships

Battleship
M741   **HMS 'Vanguard'**
Grey or Blue, two masts, 206 mm **£60-80**

Aircraft carriers
M751   **HMS 'Bulwark'**
Grey or Blue, one mast, 186 mm. **£100-125**
M752   **HMS 'Centaur'**
Grey or Blue body with one mast **£100-125**
M753   **HMS 'Albion'**
Grey or Blue body with one mast **£100-125**

Commando ship
M754   **HMS 'Albion'**
Grey ship with 12 Cream or Brown plastic
helicopters. 1,000 models issued and given
to H.M.S. 'Albion' crew members
(Capt. Adams in command)........ **£500-750**

Cruisers
M761   **HMS 'Swiftsure'**
Blue or Grey, one crane, 145 mm **£35-45**
M762   **HMS 'Superb'**
Blue or Grey, one crane, 145 mm **£35-45**

Destroyers, fleet escort, 'Daring' class
M771   **HMS 'Daring'**
Blue or Grey, one mast, 98 mm........**£35-45**
M772   **HMS 'Diana'**
Blue or Grey, one mast, 98 mm........**£35-45**
M773   **HMS 'Dainty'**
Blue or Grey, one mast, 98 mm........**£35-45**
M774   **HMS 'Decoy'**
Blue or Grey, one mast, 98 mm........**£35-45**

Destroyers, fleet, 'Battle' class
M779   **HMS 'Alamein'**
Blue or Grey, one mast, 97 mm........**£35-45**
M780   **HMS 'Jutland'**
Blue or Grey, one mast, 97 mm........**£35-45**
M781   **HMS 'Anzac'**
Blue or Grey, one mast, 97 mm........**£35-45**
M782   **HMS 'Tobruk'**
Blue or Grey, one mast, 97 mm........**£35-45**

Destroyers, guided missile, 'County' class
M783   **HMS 'Hampshire'**
Grey body with two masts, 136 mm **£55-65**
M784   **HMS 'Kent'**
Grey body with two masts, 136 mm **£50-65**
M785   **HMS 'Devonshire'**
Grey body with two masts, 136 mm **£50-65**
M786   **HMS 'London'**
Grey body with two masts, 136 mm **£50-65**

Frigates, fast anti-submarine, 'V' class
M787   **HMS 'Vigilant'**
Blue or Grey, one mast, 92 mm........**£40-50**
M788   **HMS 'Venus'**
Blue or Grey, one mast, 92 mm........**£40-50**
M789   **HMS 'Virago'**
Blue or Grey, one mast, 92 mm........**£40-50**
M790   **HMS 'Volage'**
Blue or Grey, one mast, 92 mm........**£40-50**

Frigates, anti-submarine, 'Whitby' class
M791   **HMS 'Whitby'**
Blue or Grey body, 94 mm...............**£40-50**
M792   **HMS 'Torquay'**
Blue or Grey body, 94 mm...............**£40-50**
M793   **HMS 'Blackpool'**
Blue or Grey body, 94 mm...............**£40-50**
M794   **HMS 'Tenby'**
Blue or Grey body, 94 mm...............**£40-50**

Minesweepers, 'Ton' class
M799   **HMS 'Repton'**
Blue or Grey body...........................**£40-50**
M800   **HMS 'Dufton'**
Blue or Grey body...........................**£40-50**
M801   **HMS 'Ashton'**
Blue or Grey body...........................**£40-50**
M802   **HMS 'Calton'**
Blue or Grey body...........................**£40-50**
M803   **HMS 'Picton'**
Blue or Grey body...........................**£40-50**
M804   **HMS 'Sefton'**
Blue or Grey body...........................**£40-50**
M805   **HMS 'Upton'**
Blue or Grey body...........................**£40-50**
M806   **HMS 'Weston'**
Blue or Grey body...........................**£40-50**

Submarines, 'A' class
M817   **Sub 'A' Class**
Blue or Grey body, 61 mm...............**£15-25**
M818   **Sub Recon**
Blue or Grey body, 61 mm...............**£15-25**

Tri-ang Minic Ships Trade Boxes and Sales Aids

Trade boxes   Note that the MPR refers to full boxes.

M735-M739   **Trade Box for 12 Lightships,**
each in cellophane bag .. **£200-250**
M731   **Trade Box for 12 Tug Boats**
each in cellophane bag .. **£140-160**
M726   **Trade Box for 12 'PILOTS' Boats,**
in cellophane bags.......... **£140-160**
M722 /3/4.   **Trade Box for 12 Paddle Steamers**
.... **£400-450**
M771/2/3/4.   **Trade Box for 12 'Daring' Class Destroyers** **£150-200**

M779, 780/1/2.   **Trade box for 12 'Battle' Class Destroyers** **£150-200**
M786   **Trade box for 3 HMS 'London'** ....
.... **£150-170**
M787/8/9. M790.**Trade box for 12 Anti Sub 'V' Class Frigates** **£150-200**
M791/2/3/4. 7   **Trade box for 12 Anti-Sub 'Whitby' Class Frigates** . **£150-200**
M799, M800-6.   **Trade box for 8 Minesweepers 'Ton' Class** **£300-350**
M810   **Trade box for 12 HMS 'Turmoil' Tugs** **£175-200**

M853   **Trade box for 6 Factory Units**.......
.... **£200-250**
M884   **Trade box for 2 'Statue of Liberty'**........................... **£100-125**

Shop display and sales aids
Shop Display Unit.
Over 40 models/accessories
displayed,
48" x 30".....................**£1,500-2,000**
Shop Display Banner.
Paper, 36" long x 8" deep,
displaying full range **£500-750**

Accessories, Gift Sets, Hong Kong issues and Catalogues

Dockside accessories
M827   **Breakwater Straights**, Grey **£5**
M828/L   **Breakwater Angle**, Left, Grey..............**£1**
M828/R   **Breakwater Angle**, Right, Grey **£1**
M829   **Breakwater End**, Grey **£1**
M836   **Quay Straights**,Tan.............................**£5**
M837   **Crane Units,**
Tan, Brown or Green cargo **£5**
M838   **Storage Tanks,**
Grey/Silver and Red.............................**£5**
M839   **Customs Shed**, Green **£5**
M840   **Warehouse**, Brown............................**£5**
M841   **Ocean Terminal**, White with
Black windows **£10**
M842   **Swing Bridge,**
Red, no description on base **£8**
M843   **Terminal Extension,**
White with Black windows.................**£10**
M844   **Lock Gates** (pair), Brown.....................**£3**
M845   **Landing Stages,**

Cream 'L' shaped, 1in long...................**£3**
M846   **Lift Bridge**, Silver/Tan.......................**£5**
M847   **Pier centre section**, White **£5**
M848   **Pier entrance section**, White.............**£5**
M849   **Pier head**, White...............................**£20**
M850   **Pier Shelter**, Green, 35 mm **£10**
M851   **Pier archways** **£5**
M852   **Pier Building,**
White/Blue/Green, Silver Cupola
'RESTAURANT' plus 'DANCING
TONIGHT' **£20-25**
M853   **Factory Unit,**
Pink and Buff, Black chimneys........**£30-40**
M854   **Tanker Wharf Straight,**
Cream and Red **£65-75**
M855   **Tanker Wharf Berth,**
Red and Green or Cream and
Green, Black plastic pipeline **£5**
M857   **26in Sea**, Blue plastic **£25-35**
M857   **52in Sea**, Blue plastic **£40-50**
M861   **Lifeboat set,**

Grey, Blue shed, one lifeboat........**£60-80**
M878   **Lighthouse**, White............................**£10**
M880   **Whales**, White or plain Grey **£15-20**
M882   **Beacon**, White/Red or Green **£5**
M884   **Statue of Liberty**, Green/Grey.......**£30-40**
M885   **Floating Dock,**
Grey, 4 Black plastic cranes **£50-60**
M -   **Helicopter,**
Cream or Brown plastic.................**£30-35**

Gift sets and special presentation packs
M891   **'Queen Elizabeth'** Gift Set **£250-300**
M892   **'United States'** Gift Set............ **£250-350**
M893   **'Task Force'** Gift Set **£250-300**
M894   **'Royal Yacht Britannia'** Gift Set
containing 'Britannia'
plus two Destroyers strung to green
backing card **£300-350**
M895   **'Nieuw Amsterdam'** Gift Set **£750-1,000**

M702s	**'Queen Elizabeth'**	
	Presentation Set	£200-250
M703s	**'Queen Mary'** Presentation Set	£300-350
M704s	**SS 'United States'**	
	Presentation Set	£250-350
M705s	**RMS 'Aquitania'** Presentation Set	£200-250
M707s	**SS 'France'** Presentation Set ...	£300-350
M741s	**HMS 'Vanguard'** Presentation	
	Set..............................	£180-220

Hong Kong 'blue box' models (1976-80)

These models are slightly larger than original issues, e.g., Canberra is 207mm.
'Queen Mary', 'Queen Elizabeth', 'United States', 'Canberra', HMS 'Vanguard', HMS 'Bulwark', 'Missouri', 'Bismark',
'Scharnhorst', 'Yamato'. Each, boxed..........**£20-30**
RMS 'Canberra', boxed **£30-40**

Hong Kong sets of models

1	**Fleet Anchorage Set,**	
	dockyard entrance scene on lid **£30-40**	
2	**Quay Set** **£30-40**	
3a	**Ocean Terminal,**	
	lid shows stern of RMS 'Queen Mary'	

	....**£50-65**	
3b	**Ocean Terminal,**	
	lid shows bow of RMS 'Queen Mary'	
	....**£40-50**	
4	**Naval Task Force,**	
	with HMS 'Bulwark' and 'Vanguard'.........	
	....**£40-50**	
5	**Naval Task Force,**	
	with 'Bismark' and 'Scharnhorst'. .**£70-90**	

Minic catalogues 1958-64

1st Ed.	**Leaflet**	
	with first Minic Ships listed...... **£100-125**	
2nd Ed.	**Booklet**	
	with first Minic Ships listed...........**£75-80**	
3rd Ed.	**Booklet**	
	with Ships and other Tri-ang products.....	
	....**£60-75**	
4th Ed.	**Booklet**	
	with Minic Ships only **£25-30**	
5th Ed.	**Booklet**	
	with Minic Ships only **£25-30**	
6th Ed.	**Booklet**	
	with Tri-ang range **£30-35**	
M862	**Leaflet**	
	Minic illustrated leaflet **£10-15**	

Tri-ang Minic Ships M.891 RMS Queen Elizabeth Presentation Set.

Tri-ang Minic Ship M716 MS 'Port Brisbane' - grey hull, white superstructure, single red and black funnel.

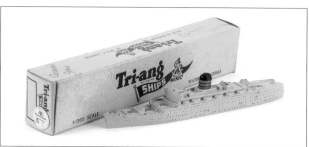

Extremely scarce (only very limited numbers produced) Tri-ang Minic Ships M709 'Carmania' - pale green hull and superstructure, single red and black funnel.

Tri-ang Minic Ships M703 RMS 'Queen Mary' - black hull, white superstructure, three red and black funnels.

Tri-ang Minic Ships, four unboxed ships including – No M714 SS 'Flandre' - black hull, white superstructure, single red and black funnel, masts. M716 SS 'Port Brisbane' pale grey hull, white superstructure, single red and black funnel. M719 RMS 'Arlanza' - white hull and superstructure, single yellow funnel, masts and M733 TSS 'Vikingen' - grey hull and deck, 2 yellow and black funnels, masts.

Picture shows part of a sale lot including Tri-ang Minic Ships and accessories: Quay Straights, Breakwater Straights, Custom Sheds, Warehouse, Statue of Liberty, Pierhead and Pier Building and others. Together with 2nd edition catalogue with price list dated 1962.

Notes

Tri-ang Spot-On Models

Spot-On models were introduced in 1959 by Tri-ang Toys to gain a foothold in the diecast market dominated, at the time, by Dinky Toys and its recently established rivals, Corgi Toys.

Tri-ang realised that it had to offer not only a range of features similar to those of its competitors' products but something more besides. It decided that collectors would appreciate models that were all made to the same precise scale right across the range.

The models would thus look right together and qualify as such rather than toys. Much of the Dinky and Corgi car ranges were made to a scale of around 1:45 (with a few exceptions).

Tri-ang advertised the precise nature of its (larger) chosen scale as being 'spot-on' at 1:42 throughout.

A large modern factory was set up in Belfast, Northern Ireland, to produce the models. A coloured picture of the real vehicle was included in the box of most early issues.

Well over a hundred different models were designed, the range being extended to include scale buildings and road signs. Production continued until the time that Tri-ang bought Dinky Toys in 1967. After the cessation of UK production, some of the Spot-On dies went to New Zealand where some interesting versions were produced for a couple of years.

All Spot-On models are highly collectable today particularly commercial vehicles, buses and the presentation and gift sets.

Spot-On Model Identification

Maker's Name and Trade Mark are clearly marked on base of the model ('SPOT-ON' and 'Models by Tri-ang'). Some New Zealand produced versions have nothing at all on the base.

Model Name is shown on the base (except some New Zealand versions) while the **Model Number** is usually shown on box but not always on the model.

Baseplates can be any of a variety of colours: black, silver, grey - even green has been observed on the base of a maroon version of No. 155 Taxi !

Scale of models is 1:42 (with very few exceptions) and is usually (but not always) shown on the base.

Wheel hubs on cars are usually turned aluminium with a raised 'hub cap'. Truck models usually have diecast and more accurate representations of real hubs. **Tyres** are mostly black rubber (occasionally plastic) on all the vehicle models. Rear twin wheels have special 'double tyres'.

Number plates are represented on most Spot-On models with the exception of those having plastic chassis (such as 266 Bull Nose Morris and 279 MG Midget). A large range of registration numbers were available to factory production staff and were applied randomly to most models. Different number plates are therefore to be expected on different examples of the same model and do not have any effect on the price.

Windscreens and windows are included in all vehicle models.
Other features include seats and steering wheel on most models, suspension on most cars, driver, other figures and lorry loads with some. Very few 'decals' or 'frills' is the norm.
Colours were applied to cars in a random fashion and have no real bearing on their value.
Colour Collector Cards. These were included with all models supplied in all-card boxes until 1963.

Prices shown in the 'Market Price Range' column are for mint models in pristine boxes. These models are rare, hence their high market prices. The condition of models generally encountered tends towards the average and consequently command lower prices.

Spot-On Cars

The cars were produced in a range of various colours with no real variation as to their value

Model and details	MPR

100 Ford Zodiac Saloon Car.

Model and details	MPR
100	Ford Zodiac (without lights) (1959). **£100-130**
100sl	Ford Zodiac (with lights) (1959)....**£110-140**
101	Armstrong Siddeley 236 Sapphire (1959) **£150-200**
102	Bentley Continental 4-door Sports (1959) **£160-200**
103	Rolls Royce Silver Wraith (1959)..**£125-145**
104	M.G. 'MGA' Sports Car (1959) **£120-140**
105	Austin-Healey 100/6 (1959) **£80-100**
107	Jaguar XK-SS (top down) (1960) ...**£160-180**
108	Triumph TR3a Sports (1960) ....**£110-140** NB Two baseplate castings are known with this model. One exposes the axle ends near to the wheels, while the other completely hides the axles.
112	Jensen 541 (1960) **£110-130**
113	Aston-Martin DB3 Saloon (1960).**£100-130**

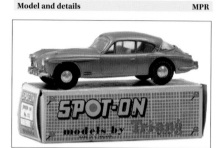

112 Jensen 541 Sport Car.

114	**Jaguar 3.4 Mark 1 Saloon** (1960) ..£120-160	
115	**Bristol 406 Saloon** (1960) £110-140	
118	**BMW Isetta Bubble Car** (1960) £80-100	
119	**Meadows Frisky Sport** (1960) £70-90	
120	**Fiat Multipla Estate** (1960) £90-110	
131	**Goggomobil Super Regent** (1960) ...£50-70	
154	**Austin A40 Farina Saloon** (1961) .£100-120	
	'MAGGI' Promotional (1966),	
	Red body, Cream interior, 'MAGGI'	
	in yellow on front doors. Special	
	red/yellow box with leaflet £250-300	
157	**Rover 3-litre** (without lights) (1963) £120-140	
157sl	**Rover 3-litre** (with lights) (1963)...£130-160	
165/1	**Vauxhall PA Cresta Saloon** (1961)..£80-100	
165/2	**Vauxhall PA Cresta**	
	with roof rack (1961) £100-125	
166	**Renault Floride Convertible** (1962)	
	....£100-120	
183	**Humber Super Snipe Estate** (1963)	
	With driver and passenger, Roof Rack	
	and two cases...................................£150-200	
184	**Austin A60 Cambridge** (1963	
	skis on roof rack, some models have driver	
	and passenger..................................£110-140	
185	**Fiat 500** (1963)................................£70-90	
191	**Sunbeam Alpine Convertible** (1963)£110-140	
191/1	**Sunbeam Alpine Hardtop** (1963).£110-130	
193	**N.S.U. Prinz** (1963) £90-110	
195	**Volkswagen Rally Car** (1963)	
	With roof light, bonnet flags,	
	racing number '6', '9' '11' '13' '15' or '23'.	
	And driver £150-200	
210	**Morris Mini Minor** (1960)	
	Shown in catalogue but not issued........NPP	
211	**Austin Seven** (Mini) (1963)...........£150-200	
213	**Ford Anglia Saloon** (1963)...........£130-150	
215	**Daimler Dart SP250** (1961) £120-150	
216	**Volvo 122s**	
	(with sliding roof) (1963) £100-120	
217	**Jaguar 'E' Type** (1963) £150-175	

218	**Jaguar Mk.10** (1963) £120-150	
219	**Austin-Healey Sprite Mk.III**	
	(with driver figure) (1963) £80-100	
259	**Ford Consul Classic** (1963) £100-125	
260	**Royal Rolls-Royce Phantom V** (1963)	
	Maroon body, Blue interior, two flags on	
	roof, Queen and Prince Philip in rear	
	seats, driver + attendant in front....£400-600	
261	**Volvo P1800** (1963) Two versions	
	of this model exist (no price difference):	
	1: the bonnet and boot can be opened,	
	and a spare wheel is supplied;	
	2: only the bonnet can be opened. £120-150	
262	**Morris 1100** (1963) £80-110	
263	**Bentley 4½ Litre** (Supercharged) (1964)	
	Green body, Union Jack,	
	number '9' '27', '20' '11' or '15' £80-100	
266	**'Bull Nose' Morris 1923**	
	(Scale 1:48) (1965) £70-90	
267	**M.G. 1100 Saloon** (1964)...............£120-150	
268	**Vauxhall PB Cresta. (1965).**	
	Shown in catalogue but not issued	
	under this number, see 280 ....NPP	
270	**Ford Zephyr 6 Mk.III**	
	(with poodle) (1965) £140-160	
274	**Morris 1100 with Blue/Red canoe** (1965)	
	....£125-150	
276	**Jaguar 'S' type** (with 2 figures)(1964) £150-200	
278	**Mercedes-Benz 230 SL**	
	(with 2 figures) (1965) £90-120	
279	**M.G. PB Midget 1935**	
	(scale 1:48) (1965) £80-100	
280	**Vauxhall PB Cresta** (1963)................£60-90	
281	**M.G. Midget Mk.II,**	
	(plus policeman figure) (1966) £80-100	
286	**Austin 1800** (1965).......................£120-150	
287	**Hillman Minx**	
	(with Roof Rack and two brown suitcases)	
	(1965)..£90-120	
	NB This model is also known	

	with the reference '287/1'.	
289	**Morris Minor 1000** (1963) £90-120	

A New Zealand produced model of the Volkswagen Variant Estate Car (NZ115).

304	**VW Variant Estate Car** (1967) £300-450	
306	**Humber Super Snipe Estate** (1964)	
	Same casting as 183 but with	
	roof-rack and two suitcases. £150-200	
307	**Volkswagen Beetle 1200** (1965)....£150-200	
308	**Land Rover and Trailer** (1965)	
	Green (Tan canopy), trailer	
	has Brown plastic body.....................£125-150	
401/1	**VW Variant Estate Car** (1967)	
	with roof rack and skies £300-500	
405	**'BEA' Vauxhall Cresta** (1966)	
	'Crew Car' With red/white British	
	European Airways 'BEA' logo,	
	plus figure of a Pilot......................£200-250	
406	**Hillman Minx with Dinghy** £150-175	
407	**Mercedes-Benz 230 SL** (1966)	
	Brown body, Red interior,	
	boot rack and luggage £70-80	
408	**Renault Caravelle (1966)**	
	Not issued ....NPP	
410	**Austin 1800 and Rowboat**	
	(on roof) and figure (1965) £90-120	

Spot-On Commercial Vehicles

Model and details	MPR

Austin Articulated Flatbed Lorry (106a/0c) with a model of an MGA in the crate.

106a/0c	**Austin Articulated Flatbed Lorry**	
(1960)	**with MGA in Crate**	
	Light Blue, Dark Blue,	
	Red or Orange cab £200-300	
106a/1	**Austin Artic. Dropside Lorry**	
(1959)	Light Blue, Green or	
	Orange cab/body £160-200	
106a/1c	**Austin Artic. Flatbed Lorry**	
	with Crate Load	
(1960)	Light Blue, Light Green or Orange	
	cab, 7 black plastic crates..........£200-250	
	Turquoise or Dark Blue body....£250- 300	
CB106	**Four Wheel Trailer**	
(1961)	Turquoise or Red body...................£60-70	
109/2	**E.R.F. 68g Flatbed Lorry**	
(1960)	Turquoise, Light Grey, or Blue.. £200-260	
	Maroon body.................................£350-400	
109/2p	**E.R.F. 68g Flatbed Lorry with Planks**	
(1960)	Turquoise body	
	(Black cab roof on some) £350-450	
	Yellow body £600-700	
109/3	**E.R.F. 68g Dropside Lorry**	
(1960)	Dk. Blue cab/Pale Blue body £300-400	

Dark Blue cab/Silver body £300-400	
Yellow body (Black or Grey roof)£200-£240	
Light Green body (Green roof)..£160-190	
Blue body (Black roof) £160-190	
Green body (Black roof).............£160-190	
Deep Blue body, Silver chassis ..£250-350	
Orange-Red body,	
Light Green chassis £350-450	
Lemon body, Silver chassis........£400-500	
Pale Green body, Silver chassis .£300-350	
Turquoise body, Silver chassis...£300-350	

109/3b	**E.R.F. Dropside Lorry and Barrel load**	
(1960)	Turquoise, Light Blue or Red	
	body (Silver truck bed on some),	
	ten Brown plastic barrels £360-400	
110/2	**A.E.C. Mammoth Major 8 Flatbed Lorry**	
(1960)	Dark Red (Black roof on some) .£320-400	
	Strawberry Red body £400-500	

A.E.C. Flatbed Lorry (110/2b) 'London Brick Company Ltd' with a load of bricks.

110/2b	**A.E.C. Lorry 'London Brick Co Ltd'**	
(1960)	Red body, Black cab roof,	
	'brick' load, 'Phorpes Bricks' £250-350	
110/3	**A.E.C. Lorry 'British Road Services'**	
(1960)	Red body, Black cab roof on some,	
	Silver chassis/back, barrels........£300-400	

110/3d	**A.E.C. Lorry with Oil Drums Load**	
(1962)	Red body, Black cab roof............£350-450	
	Red with Silver inner back and	
	chassis, Cream seats,	
	Red steering wheel......................£350-450	
	Yellow cab and back, Dark Grey	
	chassis, Cream seats,	
	Black steering wheel...................£650-850	
	Same but Light Grey chassis £500-600	
110/4	**A.E.C. Tanker 'SHELL-BP'**	
(1961)	Green cab, Red tank,	
	Black chassis and catwalk £350-450	
	Yellow cab, White/Yellow tank,	
	Silver chassis/catwalk.................£500-600	

Ford Thames Trader lorry (111a/0g) with a garage kit as a load.

111/a0g	**Ford Thames with Garage Kit**	
(1962)	Orange cab and truck body,	
	Silver chassis £400-500	
	Light Blue cab and truck body,	
	White garage...............................£400-500	
111/a0t	**Ford Thames Trader with**	

Three Log Load
(1961) Dark Blue or Red cab and truck
body, 3 logs................................. **£300-400**
Light Blue cab and truck body... **£300-400**
Light Yellow cab/truck body...... **£300-400**

**111a/1 Ford Thames Trader
'British Railways'**
(1959) Maroon and White body, ... **£300-400**

111a/1 Ford Thames Trader 'R.Hall & Son'
Green body, door logo. Not issued? ...**NPP**

111a/1s Ford Thames with Sack Load
(1960) Light Blue and Silver,
twelve brown plastic sacks......... **£300-400**
Dark Green body, Green inner
back, Black chassis..................... **£500-750**
Two-tone Blue body,
Cream interior............................ **£300-400**
Strawberry and Cream body,
Purple interior........................... **£300-400**
Green with Cream interior and
inner back, black chassis............ **£300-400**

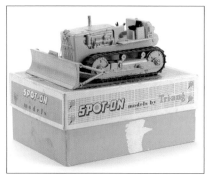

Spot-On Caterpillar D9 Bulldozer (116).

116 'CATERPILLAR' Tractor D9
(1959) Dark Yellow/Silver body,
Black rubber tracks, 'CAT D9',
information leaflet **£1,000-1,200**

117 'JONES' Mobile Crane
(1963) Cream cab and jib,
Red body and wheels,
Black chassis, Grey base............ **£150-200**
Dark Red cab/body, White jib,
Light Grey chassis,
Silver wheels................................ **£150-200**

**122 Milk Float
'UNITED DAIRIES'**
(1961) Red/White body, chains,
'Lada and New Yoghurt'............ **£160-200**

123 Bamford Excavator 'J.C.B.'
(1959) Red/Yellow. Not issued ....**NPP**

137 'MASSEY FERGUSON 65' Tractor
(1962) Red engine cover,

Grey chassis/engine,
Yellow hubs, Black tyres,
plastic seat **£400-500**

*Spot-On Bedford 10 ton petrol tanker (158a/2)
'Shell BP'*

158a/2 Bedford 'S' Type 2000 Gallon
(1961) **'SHELL-BP' Tanker**
Green cab, Red tank,
Black chassis, 'P33A37' **£400-500**
Yellow cab, White tank **£700-1,000**
Dark Metallic Green cab,
Red tank, Black chassis.............. **£500-600**

158a/2C Bedford Low Loader
(1961) Red, with cable drum. Not issued?.....**NPP**

161 Land Rover (long wheel base)
(1961) Grey/White **£125-150**
Light Grey/White **£125-150**
Blue/White **£125-150**

210 Morris Mini Van
(1961) Bright Yellow, seats/steering
wheel, suspension **£160-200**

210/1 Morris Mini Van 'Royal Mail'
(1962) Red body,
Post Office crest, 'E-II-R' **£160-200**

210/2 Mini Van 'P.O. Telephones'
(1962) Olive-Green body, White interior,
Gold crown logo,
'TELEPHONE MANAGER' **£160-200**

258 'R.A.C.' Land Rover
(1963) Dark Blue body,
'RADIO RESCUE' **£100-125**

265 'TONIBELL' Ice Cream Van
(1964) Blue body, thick Red flash,
attendant ....

*Bedford 15cwt Van (265) conversion to an Ice Cream
vendor's vehicle 'Tonibell' Dairy Ice Cream.*

271 'EXPRESS DAIRIES' Milk Float
(1965) Dark Blue/White, 3 wheels,
driver, crates and bottles,
'Drink Express Milk' **£169-200**

273 Commer Van 'SECURITY EXPRESS'
(1965) Green/Gold, driver, seated
guard, coin slot in roof **£150-200**

*Commer Van 'Security Express' (273) acts as a
moneybox with a coin slot in the roof.*

308 Land Rover and Trailer
(1965) Green (Tan plastic canopy),
trailer has Brown plastic body ... **£100-150**

*Commer Van (315) with driver and ladders, with the
company logo Glass & Homes, Window Cleaners.*

315 'GLASS & HOLMES' Commer Van
(1965) Blue/Yellow, 'Window Cleaning
Co. Est 1891', ladder and
figures **£150-200**

402 Crash Service Land Rover
(1966) Orange body, 'MOTORWAYS
CRASH SERVICE' in Blue........... **£100-150**

404 Morris Mini Van
(1966) Yellow body, ladder, figure......... **£300-350**

404/1 Morris Mini Van 'SHELL'
(1966) As previous model but without
ladder and figure........................ **£300-350**

404/2 Morris Mini Van 'AA'
(1966) In 1966 catalogue but never seen ....**NGPP**

Spot-On Miscellaneous Models

Buses, coaches and taxis

*London Transport Routemaster Bus (145) with
Ovaltine advertisement*

145 1963 **Routemaster Bus,**
Red 'London Transport' bus, route '284',
'Ovaltine - The Worlds Best Nightcap'.
1st type has chrome moulded radiator....
.... **£350-450**
2nd type has transfer print on plastic
background **£350-450**

155 1961 **Austin FX4 Taxi,**
Maroon body, Cream steering wheel,
Green base, tin-plate hubcaps.. £500-600
Black body, Red seats, Grey base ....
.... **£100-150**

156 1961 **Mulliner Luxury Coach,**
Pale Blue/Grey, Red flash,
'Tri-ang Tours' rear logo, 213 mm**£400-500**
Yellow/White body, Brown side flash......
.... **£800-1,000**

*Mulliner Luxury Coach (156) with 'Tri-ang Tours'
logo on the rear*

Sea Green/Cream, Red flash **£800-1,000**
Silver/Red/Dark Blue **£600-800**
Sky Blue/White body, Red flash ....
.... **£600-800**

Boats, caravans and scooter

135 1961 **14ft Sailing Dinghy and Trailer,**
Blue/Grey, Dark Blue/Red, Dark Blue / White, or Red/White boat (with or without cover), plastic trailer **£60-80**

135 1964 **14ft GP Sailing Dinghy,**
Brown or Yellow boat on trailer... **£30-60**

139 1960 **Eccles E.16 Caravan,** Blue body, White roof, 146 mm .... **NPP**

Lambretta Scooter (229) with white side panels

229 1966 **Lambretta,** Pale Blue body, Red or White side panels, Black seat ....
.... **£175-225**

264 1962 **Tourist Caravan,** Blue body, White roof, 152 mm **£90-120**
Yellow or Cream body, White roof, Red trim **£90-120**
Tan body, White roof, Red trim . **£90-120**

Emergency vehicles

207 1964 **Wadham Ambulance,**
Cream body, no Red crosses, with stretcher and patient **£300-400**
White body with Red crosses, stretcher and patient **£400-500**

256 1966 **Jaguar 3.4 'POLICE' Car,** White or Black. Very few exist with undamaged aerial or roof sign **£300-450**

258 1963 **'R.A.C.' Land Rover,** Dark Blue body, 'RADIO RESCUE', 108 mm **£100-125**

309 1965 **Police 'Z' Car,**
Ford Zephyr police car from the BBC-TV series 'Z-Cars'.
1st type with aerial and 'POLICE' sign, White body **£160-200**
2nd type with no aerial or police sign. Black body **£300-400**
2nd type (no aerial or police sign), White body **£300-400**

316 1966 **'FIRE DEPT' Land Rover,**
Red body, suspension, two firemen, 112 mm **£120-150**

402 1966 **Land Rover 'MOTORWAYS',**
Orange/Blue body, hook, Blue 'CRASH SERVICE' logo **£150-200**

409 1966 **Leyland 'Black Maria',**
Blue body, 'Police', policeman and villain. Not issued .... **NPP**

415 **Land Rover 'R.A.F. Fire Service'.**
Greyish Blue, Grey interior **£150-200**

Road signs and accessories

L208/B **Road Traffic Signs:**
20 different signs issued, each **£5-10**

L1271/ **Road Direction Signs:**
/1 Portsmouth, /2 Guildford, /3 Bristol, /4 Birmingham, /5 Biggar, /6 Dumfries ...
.... **£10-15**
Road Signs Presentation Set of 18 various signs............................... **£50-100**

L151 **Police Public Call Box** **£75-100**

--- **Bus Stops:** No details available ... **£10-15**

--- **Road sections:** Straights, curves, T-junctions. Each **£6-8**

--- **Plastic Figures:** In groups set on a card. Figures include:
Garage Personnel, Newspaperman/

Milkman/Postman, Doctor/Parson/ Schoolmaster, 2 Policeman and an RAC Man, 3 Schoolboys, 2 Children and a Man (in country clothes), 3 Roadmen and Brazier or 3 Roadmen and Road Drill/Planks/Walls Per card **£5-10**
Retailer's sheet of any six cards of figures
.... **£130-180**

Military models

Land Rover (415) as a Royal Air Force Fire Service vehicle

415 1965 **R.A.F. Land Rover,**
Blue/Grey, R.A.F. roundel, hose/pump/ attendant, 111 mm **£300-400**

Bedford 15cwt Van conversion to a Military Field Kitchen (417)

416 1965 **Leyland Army Ambulance.**
Not issued.......................................**NPP**

417 1965 **Military 'FIELD KITCHEN',**
Olive Green body, squadron markings, suspension, 108 mm................. **£200-250**

418 1965 **Leyland Military Bus, '**
Army Personnel'. Not issued .... **NPP**

419 1965 **Land Rover and Missile Carrier,**
Olive Green body, three White missiles ..
.... **£400-600**

Garages and equipment

L146	'SHELL' lamp standard.................	**£20-25**
L147	'SHELL' sign	**£15-20**
L148	'SHELL' petrol pump..................	**£15-20**
L148	Trade pack, Blue card box of 6 of L148 pumps.............................	**£100-150**
L149	Oil Dispenser Rack	**£10-15**
L159	'BP' Lamp Standard....................	**£20-25**
L162	'BP' or 'SHELL' Filling Station .	**£100-125**
162/1/2/3	Garages, each..........................	**£20-30**
163	'BP' Petrol Pump.........................	**£15-20**
164	'BP' Forecourt Sign.....................	**£15-20**
172a	'SHELL' Garage Set....................	**£75-100**
172b	'BP' Garage Set..........................	**£75-100**
257	Garage Kit.................................	**£150-175**
---	**Spot-On Garage.**	

Cardboard unit with white clock, 'GARAGE' in red, with 'The ONLY complete Highway System', plus 'Number Plates' and 'Windows', plus 'Steering Wheels' and 'Seats' on the 3 floor levels. Red/White/Blue sign on roof 'Tri-ang SPOT-On', 'Scale 1/45'...
....**£3,000-4,000**

'A' **Spot-On No. 'A' Garage.**
Cardboard/metal two-floor Garage ....
.... **£150-200**

'Magicar' series

Plastic bodies, programmable mechanisms. Box has additional accessories.

901 1965 **Jaguar Mk.10,**
Blue or Green body **£70-90**

902 1965 **Rolls-Royce Silver Cloud Mk.III,**
Blue or Red body **£90-120**

903 1965 **Bentley S3 Saloon,**
Blue or Red body **£80-110**

904 **Ferrari Superfast,** Blue or Red **£90-120**

905 1966 **Batmobile,**
Black body with Batman and Robin figures **£250-300**

MG1 **'Magicar Motoring' Set**
503 Bentley S3 and 504 Ferrari Superfast, roadway sections and traffic cones .. **£90-150**

MG2 **'Magicar Motoring' Set**
1966 501 Jaguar Mk.10 and 502 Rolls-Royce, roadway sections and traffic cones **£125-200**

MG3 **'Batman' Magicar Set (904)**
Batmobile with Batman and Robin figures ....
.... **£250-350**

MG4 **Captain Scarlet single car Set**
With three road section on bubble card **NGPP**

MG5 **Captain Scarlet two car set**
Red and Yellow cars with road sections ....
.... **£120-150**

943 **Quick Change Body Shell**
Blue Bentley .... **NGPP**

980 **Shell and Chassis Pack**
Red Rolls Royce, green Jaguar bodies with one clockwork chassis, with sailing dingy on trailer See through window box .... **NGPP**

981 **Shell and Chassis Pack**
Blue Bentley and red Ferrari, one clockwork chassis, Brown and green horse box with horse .... **NGPP**

MG21 - MG22
Packs containing various track parts and accessories **£10-20**

Trik Trak

?	**?**	**Trik-Trak car,** Plastic bodied racing car...........	**£80-110**

TT1 **Road Rally**
Car, 7 track curves, 2 Short Track straights 1 set of press-out colour models .... **NGPP**

TT2 **Dare Devil**
2 cars, 7 track curves, 2 short straights, 3 long straights, 3 track supports, 1 somersault/Wall of Logs, 4 Logs, 1 set of press out colour models .... **NGPP**

TT3 **Crazy Ace**
2 cars, 7 track curves, 2 short straights, 1 long straight 1 track support, 1 Spin-a-round with spare bands, 1 set of press out colour models..................... **NGPP**

TT10 **Stunts Pack**
No car, 1 Somersault/Wall of Logs, 3 long straights, 3 track supports, 4 Logs. ...... **NGPP**

Spares *(only available from the Manufacturer priced 10/6)*

TT51 **3 Short Track straights** .... **NGPP**

TT52 **3 track curves** (right hand) .... **NGPP**

TT 53 **3 track curves** (left hand) .... **NGPP**

Other Accessories
Road Traffic and Destination Signs, Roadway sections, Petrol Filling Station items were available either as single items or in boxes of six boxes **£10-15**
Single items **£1-3**

Tri-ang Spot-On 184 Austin A60 Cambridge with roof rack and skis, together with a 217 Jaguar 'E' Type.

Spot-On Presentation and Gift Sets

Ref./Issued	Set name and details	Market Price Range

Colours of individual items are not listed. It is possible to find virtually any factory colour that was available at the time of manufacture in Spot-On Gift Sets. Early sets should contain Picture Cards, Fleet Owners leaflets and Magazine Club leaflets.

A Presentation Set 'A'
1960   102 Bentley, 108 Triumph TR3, 114 Jaguar 3.4,118 BMW Isetta, 154 Austin A40 .... **£500-750**

No.0   Presentation Set
1960   106a/1 Austin Articulated Dropside Lorry, 100 Ford Zodiac, 103 Rolls-Royce Silver Wraith, 104 MGA,113 Aston Martin .. **£500-750**

Spot-On Presentation Set No 0 with Rolls Royce, MGA, Aston Martin, Ford Zodiac and Austin lorry.

No.1   Presentation Set
1960   100 Ford Zodiac, 101 Armstrong-Siddely, 103 Rolls-Royce and 104 MGA **£800-1,000**

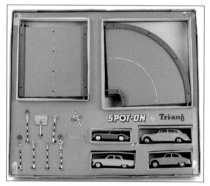

Spot-On Presentation Set No 0 with Rolls Royce, MGA, Armstrong Siddeley and Jaguar 3.4 with sections of roadway and traffic signs

No.2   Presentation Set
1960   109/3 ERF Dropside Lorry, 101 Armstrong-Siddeley, 102 Bentley Continental and 105 Austin-Healey 100/6 .... **£800-1,000**

No2a   Presentation Set
Bedford S Tanker, ERF sided Wagon, Austin FX4 Taxi, Land Rover, Friskysport, Austin Healey, Rover 3ltr, Vauxhall Cresta (2) **£1,200-1,500**

No.3   Presentation Set
1960   Contains 111a/1 Ford Thames Trader, 101 ... Armstrong-Siddely, 104 MGA, 108 Triumph TR3a, 112 Jensen 541,113 Aston Martin, 114 Jaguar 3.4....................................**£800-1,000**

No.4   Presentation Set
1960   106a/1 Austin Articulated Dropside Lorry, 109/3 ERF, 100 Ford Zodiac, 107 Jaguar XK-SS, 112 Jensen 541 .... **£800-1,000**

No.4a   Presentation Set (Sports Cars)
1963   104 MGA, 105 Austin-Healey, 107 Jaguar and 108 Triumph TR3a **£600-700**

No.5   Presentation Set (Pocket Set)
118 BMW Isetta, 119 Meadows Frisky Sport and 131 Goggomobil...................... **£400-600**

No.6   'Miniature' Presentation Set
131 Goggomobil, 185 Fiat 500, 193 NSU Prinz, 211 Austin Seven **£400-600**
Variation with 210/1 'ROYAL MAIL' Van instead of 193 NSU Prinz **£400-600**

No.6a   'Miniature' Presentation Set
131 Goggomobil, 185 Fiat 500, 119 Meadows Frisky and 211 Austin Seven........... **£400-600**

No.7   Rally Presentation Set
166 Renault Floride, 191 Sunbeam Alpine, 211 Austin Seven, 213 Ford Anglia, 215 Daimler Dart, 217 Jaguar 'E'-type .. **£600-800**

No.8   Presentation Set
157 Rover, 191 Sunbeam, 213 Ford Anglia, 216 Volvo, 258 RAC Land Rover, petrol pumps..**£2,500-3,000**

No.9   Presentation Set
122 Milk Float, 145 Routemaster Bus, 193 NSU Prinz, 207 Wadham Ambulance, 211 Austin Seven, 256 Jaguar Police Car .... **NGPP**

No.10   Presentation Set
122 Austin Seven, 145 Routemaster Bus, 157 Rover 3 litre, 158a/2 Bedford Tanker, 185 Fiat 500, 165 Vauxhall, 166 Renault, 211 Austin Seven, 215 Daimler Dart and 262 Morris 1100.. **£500-750**

Set 13   Road Signs Presentation Set
Two direction signs two Belisha Beacons 14 various road signs .... **NGPP**
(Also issued in plastic)

No.14   Presentation Set
211 Austin 7 Mini, 154 Austin A40, 156 Mulliner Coach, 191/1 Sunbeam, 122 Milk Float, 157sl Rover 3 Litre with lights **£600-800**

173   Terrapin Building Set   A constructional set
.... **£35-45**

208/a   Road Construction Set
4 workmen, brazier, hut, poles, road sections

+ 18 other small items **£150-200**

212   Car, Dinghy and Trailer Set
1963   (1) Contains 165 Vauxhall PA Cresta (Red/Cream) and 135 GP Dinghy (Grey/White/Lemon)... **£200-225**
(2) Contains 270 Ford Zephyr 6 (Red) and 135 GP Dinghy (Red/White/Blue) . **£300-400**
NB The price of a set depends on the rarity of the contents.

257   Garage Set   A constructional set....... **£35-45**

269   Ford Zephyr and Caravan
1965   Contains 270 Ford Zephyr 6 (Red) plus 264 Caravan **£400-500**

308   Land Rover and Trailer
1965   Green bodywork, Fawn cover......... **£150-250**

406   Hillman Minx and Dinghy
1966   Contains 287 Hillman Minx and 135 GP Dinghy and trailer **£150-250**

701   'His, Her's, Junior's' Set
219 Austin-Healey Sprite, 267 MG 1100, 280 Vauxhall Cresta, in 'window' box **£400-500**

702   Holiday Gift Set   270 Zephyr Six, 274 Morris 1100 and canoe, 286 Austin 1800 and 135 Dinghy **£250-350**

702(a)Gift Set   195 VW Rally, 217 Jaguar 'S' type, 261 Volvo P1800, 287 Hillman Minx **£600-800**

703   Gift Set 703   Red Zephyr 6, Light Blue Morris 1100 with kayak and paddle, Lemon Humber Super Snipe, Dinghy on Trailer........ .... **£500-750**

Tri-ang Spot-On 119 Meadows Frisky and 113 Aston Martin DB mk 3.

Tri-ang Spot-On 108 Triumph TR3 and 112 Jensen 541.

'Tommy Spot' Gift Sets   *All include a building kit and Tommy Spot figure.*

801   'Home with Tommy Spot'
287 Hillman Minx (with Mr Spot), 270 Ford Zephyr Six with driver, pictorial stand **£450-500**

802   'Cops 'n' Robbers with Tommy Spot'
309 BBC-TV 'Z-Car' with driver and criminal, 276 Jaguar and driver, pictorial stand **£450-500**

803   'Superville Garage with Tommy Spot'
286 Austin 1800 with driver, 279 MG Midget, two garage workers, pictorial stand **£450-500**

804   'Sailing with Tommy Spot'
280 Vauxhall PB Cresta and sailing dinghy with Tommy and Mr Spot, pictorial stand .....

.... **£450-500**

805   'Fire with Tommy Spot'
316 Fire Dept Land Rover and trailer, two firefighters, pictorial stand............. **£700-900**

806   'Royal Occasion with Tommy Spot'
260 Royal Rolls-Royce with chauffeur and royal passengers, 6 guardsmen, pictorial stand **£700-800**

807   'Pit stop with Tommy Spot'
Mercedes-Benz 230 SL and Jaguar 'S', two racing drivers, pictorial stand...**£1,200-1,500**

808   'Motorway Rescue with Tommy Spot'
402 'Crash Service' Land Rover and

mechanic, A.A. van and man, pictorial stand **£600-700**

Spot-On Tommy Spot Gift Set 'Royal Occasion with Tommy Spot' (806) with the Royal Rolls Royce

Spot-On 'Cotswold Village' series

The 'Cotswold Village' items are rare and it is suggested that larger buildings are likely to be in the region of **£100-£130**, while smaller items might be anything from **£80-£100** depending on size, complexity, etc. These price levels can only be applied to pristine items in perfect original boxes.

1	School	£100-130
2a	Haystack, Memorial Stone, Well Set	£80-100
3	'Cornerstones' Cottage	£90-100
4	'Fourways' Cottage	£90-110
4b	'The Cot' Cottage	£100-130
5	Antiques Shop	£100-130
6	General Store	£70-100
7	Bourton Town Hall	£80-100
8	Barn	£90-110
9	'The King's Head' Public House	£80-100
10	'Coach & Horses'	£80-100
10	Farm House	£90-130
11	Manor House	£150-200
12	Post Office	£100-130
13	Church	£80-100
14	Forge	£90-110
15	Stone Bridge	£40-60
16	Water Well	£40-60
16a	Stocks	£40-60
-	Set of Trees	£20-30

Cotswold Village Series model of the Forge (14)

Catalogues, Leaflets and Pictures

Issued	Publication details	Market Price Range

Spot-On 2nd 1960 Edition small landscape format Catalogue

1959 **Early issue** Red cover featuring a Target plus the dividers and diagram of Rolls Royce 'LTP 103'. Wording: '1/42' and 'SPOT-ON MODELS BY TRI-ANG'. Contains 8 pages **£40-50**

1959 **'1st Edition'** Village scene with Spot-On buildings and models, 'Tri-ang' logo in bright red, '6d', 'dividers' mark, 'SCALE 1/42'. Thick numbered pages with superb pictures **£40-50**

1960 **'2nd Edition'** As 1st Edition but 'Tri-ang' logo in maroon and pages not numbered **£25-30**

1961 **'3rd Edition'** '100M/C.P.C./6.61'. Same as 2nd Edition **£25-35**

1963 **'4th Edition'** '5a7383/DP' Royal Rolls-Royce on cover, '3d'. Page 19 shows the new Presentation Sets 5-10 and 14 .... **£20-30**

1964 **'5th Edition'** Blue Austin 1800 (286) on cover, '2d', concertina type leaflet featuring new type of Black/Red window boxes for Gift Sets and single models **£25-30**

1965 **'6th Edition'** Cover again features 286 Austin 1800 plus 289 Morris Minor, '2d', concertina type leaflet which includes 'Tommy Spot' and 'Magicar' listings and pictures **£20-30**

1966 **'7th Edition'** Booklet type featuring 407 Mercedes 230 SL and 287 Hillman Minx, '6d', 'Tommy Spot' featured with 'Royal Occasion' set and Car Spotters guide **£20-30**

Leaflets and model pictures

The early 'blue boxes' for cars and small commercial vehicles and the early card boxes for the large commercial vehicles contained a model picture and a yellow/blue/white leaflet listing the models available.

Prices of model picture cards can vary depending on the rarity of the model itself within a price range from £5 to £25. Spot-On 'Picture wallets' are to be found at **£15-20**.

It should be noted that no 'blue box' model or early large commercial boxed model is complete without the model picture. Leaflets are not uncommon and may be obtained for, say, **£3-5**.

Trade display material

Electric revolving Trade Display Unit **£300-400**

Glass shop-sign with 'SPOT ON MODELS' in red/black/yellow design, 25 inches long **£150-200**

Glass Shop Counter display unit with three internal shelves with heading 'Spot-On models by Tri-ang' **£400-500**

Collector's lapel badge

'Spot-On by Tri-ang', Blue/Gold/Red, 2.5cm **£80-100**

Spot-On New Zealand Issues

When Tri-ang took over the production of Dinky Toys in 1967 they stopped production of Spot-On Models in the United Kingdom. Fourteen models were subsequently produced by the Tri-ang Pedigree company of New Zealand from the original dies sent out from the U.K.

New Zealand production lasted just two years and ceased in 1969/70. The New Zealand model reference numbers were different to their UK counterparts as listed in the Spot-On 7th Edition catalogue. Extras such as roof racks and luggage were not included with NZ issues and the models were housed in New Zealand yellow cellophane 'window' boxes. The following listing first appeared in 'Mini Cars' ('The News Sheet for Caledonian Autominologists'), dated September 1972 and was prepared by Eric Brockie in New Zealand. Thanks are due to James McLachlan (Club Secretary) for his kind permission to reproduce the listing.

UK no.	NZ no.	Model name	Difference from UK version	NZ colour	Market Price Range
289	101	**Morris Minor 1000**	Not issued	-	NPP
219	102	**Austin-Healey Sprite**	Colour only	White body, Red seats	£250-300
281	103	**MG Midget**	No Policeman included	Dark Green or Red, White seats	£250-300
404	104	**Morris Mini Van**	No 'Shell' logo, ladder or mechanism	Yellow	£350-400
267	105	**MG 1100**	Single colour only	Green	£150-200
262	106	**Morris 1100**	Same as UK issue	Blue	£200-250
287/406	107	**Hillman Minx**	No roof rack or dinghy	Green	£150-200
280	108	**Vauxhall Cresta**	Single colour only	Blue	£150-200
276	109	**Jaguar 'S' type**	Same as UK issue	Metallic Blue	£200-250
286	110	**Austin 1800**	No lady driver or schoolboy	Light Brown or Mauve, White seats	£200-250
270	111	**Ford Zephyr 6**	Same as UK issue	White	£200-250
308	112	**Land Rover**	No trailer included	Olive Green body, Pale Green tilt	£200-250
401	115	**Volkswagen Variant**	No roof rack or skis	Dark Blue, Red int., White hatchback	£250-300
279	116	**MG PB Midget**	Same as UK issue	Blue, Black, Red seats	£150-200
265	117	**'TONIBELL' Ice Cream Van**	Same as UK issue	Turquoise	£300-400
402	118	**Crash Service Land Rover**	Same as UK issue	Orange, Blue	£200-300
316	119	**Fire Dept Land Rover**	No Firemen	Red	£200-300
415	120	**RAF Land Rover**	Not issued	-	NPP

Minor Manufacturers

Many toys and models exist about which we know very little. The 1940s in particular saw a proliferation of small manufacturers (often only a one-man operation in a North London shed). In this post-wartime period the established manufacturers were engaged in an export drive that meant shortages of products at home. Not surprisingly, enterprising ex-servicemen and others turned their hands to toy production on a scale that they could manage. Their range was small (sometimes only one product) and they were often in business for only a year or two.

One outcome of this is that some toys and models discovered in attics or at swapmeets present us with a puzzle. Who made the item? When were they in production? Where was the maker's workshop? Very often there is no information at all on the product or simply a statement to the fact that it was 'Made in England'. Identification is sometimes diffcult – but is it impossible?

Since the 12th Edition was published, some very interesting additional information has been obtained and we are delighted to be able to pass on the details below. However, our lists are far from complete and we do still require your help, so if you have any information on any of the manufacturers mentioned, or not mentioned at all, please write to the editor.

Astra Pharos	Denzil Skinner	Louis Marx	Sundaw
Automec	Eaglewall Plastics	Luntoy	Tal Developments
Arbur	Empro	Mafwo	Teddy Toys Industries
Baxtoys	Excella	Millbo	Toby
Betal	Gaiety	Millbro	Toy Products
BHL	Gilco	Milton Toys	Tractoys
BMC	Goody Toys	Minitoy	Trent Products
Bradscars	Johillco	Model Toys	Tremo
Brighton	John Hill & Co.	Moultoys Ltd	True to Type
Bren L Toys	Jolly Roger	Sacul	Tudor Rose
Brimtoy	Kay	Salco	Wardie
Cherilea	Kembo	Scaledown	Wend-al
City Toys	Kemlow	Sentry Box	
Condon	Kitmaster	Skybirds	
Cursor	Knight	Slikka	

Astra Pharos Co
(Shepherds Bush, London)

Model No 17 - 12" Heavy Howitzer, post-war issue, with green painted gun body mounted on 'Garrison' type carriage and working elevating and firing mechanisms.

Heavy 12 inch Howitzer. Military Green, 11" long, 3 wooden shells, green lift-off lid box **£100-125**
Pom Pom Gun. WWII Anti-aircraft style naval/land based weapon, ... **£100-125**
WWII Mobile Unit. Anti-Aircraft Gun + Searchlight Unit on trolley, boxed **£100-125**

Automec

This small Lincoln firm was started by two brothers, Stanley and Basil Clark, in 1956. The catalyst for their already existing enthusiasm was being able to purchase castings from Kemlow of their existing Dinky lookalike military Bedford truck. This they developed quite successfully with two new rear bodies, plus various civilian and military liveries, something Dinky never did.

The first all new product was a Caravan, accurately based on local manufacturer Carlight's Colonial. A Jaguar 2.4 followed but severe early production difficulties were unsurmountable financially and all Automec production was curtailed later in 1960.

Models were sold direct to retailers from the company van within a 100 mile or so radius of Lincoln. They were always individually boxed, at first using the same multi-coloured illustrated ones formerly used by Kemlows, with suitable Automec overlays. Later, an unillustrated white box was introduced.

Kemlow production and boxes did not carry any maker identification, but in theory at least Automec's did. This could be a red Automec sticker on the underside, now often missing, or the tin bases may be suitably embossed. There are considerable variations in detail to be aware of, and a complete list of basic colours of the civilian vehicles is unlikely.

B159 BEDFORD TRUCKS

Only the covered truck was marketed by Kemlow, in army green and assorted civilian colours. Exact attribution of production may not be possible, but all Kemlows (and maybe first Automecs) seem to have the tow hook as a separate casting riveted on. Corgi self adhesive number plates were brought in by Automec to be factory applied, later they had their own "AUT 60" printed.

Cab windows appear on some examples, both military and civil, whilst the latter had the option of double rear wheels. Unpainted wheels are to be found, but many are chassis coloured having been painted at the same time, pre-assembled with the axles and tin base. Coloured wheels and axle ends that look hand painted are just that, but at the factory. Silver can be applied to the front bumper and Bedford badge as well as the headlights, and yellow to the front cab corner indicators.

Automec's best selling and unique Coal Robot, with later plain box design. All three Bedford body styles and various liveries were B159! Note twin rear wheels on example to right which uses the earlier labels with rounded corners.

Military Covered Truck – small round yellow bridge plate sticker front and rear. Army versions with blue/yellow Royal Army Service Corps signs.
    N.A.T.O. – Army green.............................. **£30-40**
    Red Cross – Army green **£40-45**
    8th Army – Sand..................................... **£40-45**
    Royal Air Force – Blue Grey, with RAF roundels and "B/1" signs. **£55-70**
    Royal Navy – Navy blue, four "RN" signs. White bumper. **£55-70**

Civilian Covered Truck – often with Automec" label on rear cover.
Colours – chassis and cab / rear body / cover.
Red/Grey/Grey; Blue/Very Pale Grey/Dark Grey;
Buff Grey/Buff Grey/Dark Grey;
Pale Grey/Very Pale Grey/Dark Grey;
Mid Grey/Mid Grey/Dark Grey. **£40-45**

Flat Bed Truck – Colours – Chassis and Cab/Rear body.
Red/Pale Grey; Mid Blue/Pale Grey; Turquoise Blue/Pinkish Grey; Green/Cream; ....**£40 -45**
Pale Grey/Pinkish Grey; Grey/Pale Grey;
Pale Lemon Yellow/Pale Grey. **£40-45**

Hopper or Spreader Truck – All with self-adhesive labels at rear, sometimes above front windows. Red rear lights often detailed.
Colours – chassis and cab/rear body.
Grit Spreader – usually with Chevron sticker at rear, White or Grey/Red. **£30-40**
Ballast – Orange or Red/Cream................. **£40-50**
Bulk Flour – Pale Green/White. **£30-40**
Coal Robot – with coal load, Black/Black**£55-70**

Carlight Colonial Caravan, same 1:60 scale as the Bedford to which it cannot be attached. Box is original Kemlow with added Automec labels, but the caravan only used a later plain style.

Lime Spreader – Deep Turquoise/Pale Lime Yellow or Pale Blue Grey. **£30-40**
Wessex Spreaders Ltd. – with cab headboard and two rear spinner discs. Promotional.
Bright Green/Light Yellow **£100-150**

T101 Caravan – inscribed tinplate base.
Colours – Main body/Lower side panels.
Cream/Pale Beige (or similar) near prototypical Carlight Colonial colours. **£90-120**
Light Grey/Yellow, Bright Blue, Red, Bright or Dark Green. **£90-120**

C160 Jaguar 2.4. Approx. only 250 produced.
Cream; Metallic Red; Light Blue. ....**NGPP**
Corgi with Automec base, Blue. ....**NGPP**
(Emergency measure to pair with Caravan.)

U-Builtit Assembly Kits, bagged on card.
Bedford – Covered, Flat, or Hopper. **£20-25**
Caravan. **£30-40**

Accessory Packs – in clear cellophane.
Loads (for Bedfords) – Logs (dowels), Planks or Pipes.. **£10-15**
Towbars (for Caravans) – Tin plate and wire to attach to Dinky and Corgi cars. Six types. **£10-15**
Garage Staff – Six figures, three pieces of equipment, a repackaged Wardie (Kemlow) product with Automec header card. **£45-55**
Spare tyres (12)... **£5-10**

Betal

Saloon Car. Clockwork motor in some ... **£15-20**
Large Tinplate Trolleybus. Red, Cream, silver poles, driver, CW, (28 cms).......... **£250-350**
AEC 'Q' type Bus with Lights.
Red/Cream/Silver, balloon tyres **£200-300**

BHL (British Home Life)

First Traffic Set. Motorcycle Policeman and die-cast Road Signs, red box **£60-80**

Bradscars B.M.P. (c.1951-1954)

Bradscars, early 1950s lead OO vehicles. The Austin A30 is just under 50mm long, the Riley (centre) and Morris Six about 60mm each.

OO scale cars produced in the early 1950s by Bradshaws Model Products Ltd. of Hove, a major retailer and distributor. One new introduced each year at Spring London Model Railway Exhibition, the first probably the Morris Six in 1951 but the year dates are not definite. The first three are cast in lead, the Jaguar is plastic. They are not mentioned in Bradshaw's own comprehensive 1955/56 catalogue. No catalogue numbers or individual boxes are known. Delivered to retailers tissue wrapped in trade boxes. Other colours and shades almost certainly exist. Bases are black.

1951 Morris Six – plain or inscribed tin base.
Black, Blue, Fawn, Red, Grey Green.......... **£35-45**
1952 Riley 1½ litre – plain or inscribed tin base.
Black, Green, Red, Grey. **£35-45**
1953 Austin A30 – Cast inscribed base.
Red, Green, Black, Grey. **£40-50**
[1953] Morris Minor – shown in 1953 advert, not issued. **NGPP**
1954 Jaguar Mk.VII – all plastic, inscribed base.
Black, Green, Grey...................................... **£45-55**

Brighton Manufacturing Co.

World's Warships Series Set 12. Fifteen cast ships inc. a Hospital ship, boxed **£75-100**

Brimtoy (diecast issues)

1948-50 Vauxhall Saloon. Yellow body, cast wheels, plain card box with picture **£100-150**

Cherilea

Set 1001 'Spacemen'. With rocket, 3 robots, 6 spacemen, 2 space animals. **£500-600**

Condon

These two based on the same chassis casting:
Dumper Truck, various colours **£20-30**
Site Crane, various colours **£20-30**
Elevator Loader, various colours **£20-30**

Denzil Skinner

Nuffield Universal Tractor. Made for the Morris Motors Agricultural Division **£300-500**

Excella

Three Pigs' Houses, with Pigs. House of Sticks, House of Bricks, House of Straw with Pigs playing Flute, Violin and standing with trowel, indivual boxes ...... **As a set: £5,000-7,000**
Big Bad Wolf and Three Pigs.
Tied in box with lift-off lid **£2,500-3,000**

Gaiety Toys (late 1940s)

Castle Art Products Ltd., Birmingham.
Models may be found painted in various colours, often chromed, sometimes motorised. Models in boxes are rare. Products known:
Morgan 3-wheel Sports Car, 4.75in........ **£70-90**
Racing Car, single driver, 5in. long **£30-40**
Racing Car, driver/co-driver, 4in. long **£30-40**
Racing Car, single driver, 3.25in. long **£20-30**
Fire Engine .... **NGPP**

Gilco

No. 1 Traffic Sign Set. Ten items **£30-40**
No. 3 Traffic Signs Set. Ten signs **£70-90**
No. 4 Traffic Sign Set. Contains 24 items inc. Road Signs, Traffic Lights, Telegraph Poles, 2 Belisha Beacons. Pictorial card box. **£80-100**

John Hill & Co (Johilco)

Roman Gladiator Set: Gold Chariot and Charioteer, 2 horses, 5 Centurion Gladiators + Officer in pale cream toga. Boxed **£125-150**
Roman Chariot: Gold Chariot/Charioteer, 2 horses, 2 Roman Soldiers..................... **£80-100**
Coronation (1935 Jubilee) **Coach Set**, 4 white horses + 2 riders, 6 'Beefeaters', 6 Footmen. The coach is 23cm long and contains figures of King George V and Queen Mary.
Blue box marked 'Jubilee' .... **NGPP**
Jubilee Coach, King George V and Queen Mary in a 'coronation'-style coach with 4 horses, 2 riders, 6 mounted Life Guards, 6 Beefeaters, 6 footmen, blue box .... **NGPP**
Mack Mail Van. Red, Grey wheels **£70-90**
Racing Car. Red **£40-50**
Tank. Light Khaki, rubber tracks........... **£100-125**
Mack Gun Lorry. Khaki / Black **£90-110**
Searchlight Lorry. Khaki / Black **£90-110**
Mack Stake Truck. Green / Yellow.......... **£40-50**
Mack Concrete Truck. Mustard Yellow... **£30-40**
Ford 'T' Truck. Dk. Blue, Gold screen **£60-70**
Fargo Single Deck Coach. Lt. Green **£30-40**
'Millers' Series Set. Windmill, Miller, Labourer with sack, Barrow man, Wheelbarrow, full and half full sacks corn bin, two mice.......................... **£150-200**
Dirt Track Bike and Rider. Pre-war, unpainted bike, Brown/Black rider **£70-90**
Police Motorcycle and Sidecar. Unpainted cycle, Blue sidecar, rider/passenger, white tyres **£100-125**
Street Gas Lamp Set. Gas Lamp, Lamp Cleaner and Ladder, Boxed........ **£175-225**
Father Christmas.
65mm tall figure with toy sack.............. **£100-130**
R.N.L.I. figures. Three lifeboat men plus pincushion Lifeboat **£100-125**

Jolly Roger

Made c1946/7 by Tremo Mouldings, Cardiff.
Racing Car (boxed).................................... **NGPP**
Saloon Car (boxed) (picture opposite) ...... **NGPP**

Kay

'Safety First' Traffic Set, boxed.
Two Petrol Pumps/Attendant, Signs......... **£60-80**

Kembo

Articulated Lorry. Heavy lorry cab (tinplate base), open semi-trailer with curved front board and 'KEMBO TRANSPORT' paper labels. Minic-style tinplate wheels, rubber tyres. **£40-50**
Saloon Car Cast wheels, no base.............. **£20-30**

Kemlow (1950s)

Kemlow promotional model for 'Pickfords Removals' - dark blue body, cream roof, smooth brass hubs.

Kemlow's Diecasting Products Ltd., Wood Green, London. Distributors B.J. Ward Ltd. (trading as 'Wardie Products').
'PICKFORDS' Removal Van, 1:60 .... **NGPP**
Articulated Timber Truck, 1:50 .... **NGPP**
Farm Tractor and Trailer, 1:60 .... **NGPP**
Caravan. 1:43 .... **NGPP**
Ford Zephyr Mk.I, 1:43 .... **NGPP**
Thornycroft Mighty Antar, 1:43 & 1:60 ..... **NGPP**

Flat Truck, 1:50 .... NGPP
Daimler Armoured Car, 1:60 Dinky copy..... NGPP
Field Gun, 1:60 .... NGPP
Mobile Artillery Unit..................................... NGPP

Luntoy (London Toy Co) 1950-54

As well as producing wooden forts and cast knights in armour, Luntoy seized the opportunity offered by early children's television. The items were produced for them by Barrett and Sons and fall into two distinct groups. Sizes are approximate and only the main colours are given.

Sooty

Children's Television Series. All come in a standard shallow box about 60mm square. Each has an individual T.V. "picture" of its contents. Most are single items of a size to nearly fit the box. All are listed on the back, but despite "etc, etc, etc." at the end, no others are thought to have been produced. Boxes are clearly marked Luntoy, but only No.11 of this presumably pocket money range carries markings itself.

    1. **Muffin the Mule.** White **£50–70**
    2. **Prudence Kitten.** Blue, White **£40–50**
    3. **Peregrine Penguin.** Black, White........ **£40–50**
    4. **Mr Turnip.** Red, Green **£30–40**
    5. **Sooty,** Yellow, Blue............................ **£40–50**
    6. **Princess Tai-Lu.** Fawn, Brown............. **£50–70**
    7. **Andy Pandy.** White, Blue **£40–50**
    8. **Flower Pot Man.** One only, no weed!
       Red, Green **£50–70**
    9. **Billy Bean,** White, Green **£50–60**
    10. **Rag, Tag and Bobtail.** Three separate castings 35mm each, White, Grey, Tan **£60–80**
    11. **Hank and Silver King.** Moulded together Fawn, Red **£50–70**

Metal String Puppets
Heavy hollow cast lead puppets, in many ways similar to the well known diecast Moko-Lesney Muffin. Individual illustrated card boxes. Rectangular wire frame to work six strings to move arms, legs, and head.

    Sooty. Knees and elbows not jointed. Separate magic wand can be threaded through either hand. Only box marked Luntoy. Yellow-Brown and Light Blue, 160mm. **£200–250**
    Flowerpot Man (one only). Limbs fully jointed. Only box marked Luntoy. Box size would indicate came with 70-90mm flower pot. Red and Green. 180mm...............................**£350–450**
    Mr Turnip. Limbs fully jointed. Puppet only marked Luntoy. Brown box with label. Red and green. 120mm. **£60–80**

Milton Toys

Made in India from old Corgi dies.
    Routemaster Bus. Red, 'MILTON' logo ... **£35-45**

Minitoy

    Racing Car. Single piece casting includes cast stub axles for the cast wheels. 90mm.......... NGPP

Moultoys Products (Great Britain)

    'RAC' Patrol Cycle and Sidecar.
    Black/Silver cycle, Blue sidecar with 'RAC' cast in sides, patrolman.............. **£100-125**
    'AA' Patrol Cycle and Sidecar.
    Black/Yellow/Silver bike,Yellow sidecar with 'AA' cast into sides **£100-125**
    Sports Motorcycle and Sidecar with Rider.

Red/Yellow/Silver bike, Red/Yellow sidecar, Green/Black rider **£100-125**

Sacul

Knights and ceremonial figures formed a fair part of this firm's production but they are best remembered for their larger than normal scale, and better than normal quality, T.V. and Disney figures. Each item or group were supplied in individually designed lift-off lid style boxes. 'Sacul' and 'England' can also be found on the castings, sometimes with difficulty. The similarity of some items with the smaller Luntoy ones is explained by Barrett and Sons also being involved in the earlier stages. Sizes given are approximate, and only the main colours are listed.

Rob Roy, Hank and Silver King

Andy Pandy, Teddy and Looby Loo. Three separate figures from 50-80mm, Blue, White, Red-Brown. .... **£200 – 300**
Rag, Tag and Bobtail. Three separate figures from 50-90mm. Cream (Hedgehog), Brown (Mouse), White (Rabbit). .... **£200 – 300**
Billy Bean. Single figure, 90mm. White and Green .... **£150 – 200**
Hank and Silver King. Separate Horse and Rider, together 90mm. Off White, Red and Blue.
.... **£200 – 300**
Muffin the Mule. Single figure, moveable legs, 80mm. Tall. White............................... **£200 – 250**
Pluto, Mickey, Minnie, Donald and Goofy. Five separate figures. Pluto with separate collar, both mice with wire tails. 50-80mm. Multi-coloured....
.... **£1500 – 2000**
Peter Pan and Captain Hook (Disney). Separate figures. Peter, Green 60mm. A truly magnificent Captain Hook (? Terry Thomas), 90mm, Deep Red and Grey. .... **£400 – 500**
Bill and Ben, and Little Weed. Three separate figures, 75mm. Red and Green. Includes two clay pots. .... **£300 – 400**
Rob Roy and the Redcoat (Disney). Two separate fighting figures, 75mm plus swords. Red, Green and Black. .... **£400 – 500**

Scaledown Models

    Fordson Major Roadless Halftrack
    Blue body **£100-125**

Sentry Box Series

Three models in individual 'Sentry Box' boxes: Centurion Tank, Big Bedford Military Truck, 25 pdr Field Gun .... **each, £15-20**

Skybirds (1930s)

    Army Truck **£80-100**
    Anti-Aircraft Gun, 4 Gunners, box...... **£400-500**
    Lanchester Armoured Car, box........... **£500-600**
    Tanker, 6 wheels, rubber tyres.................. NGPP
    Military Refuelling Truck.
    Gloss Olive Green, Extending Arm **£100-125**
    3A Civil Airline Personnel Boxed Set plus RFC and other figures (12 in total)...... NGPP
    Sound Locator Unit.................................. NGPP
    '39 Skybird League Challenge Trophy ..... NGPP
    '40 11b Handley Page Hampden, box....... NGPP
    Skybird enamel badges. .... each, NGPP
    Skybird books Vols. 1, 2 and 3, etc.. each, NGPP

Sundaw Products (c1950)

    H130 **Single-deck Motor Bus.** Red body, 'TRANSPORT SERVICES', rubber wheels. Red/white end-flap box (picture)................. **£250-350**

H131 **Double-deck Motor Bus**. Green body, 'TRANSPORT SERVICES', rubber wheels. Green/white end-flap box (picture)................. **£400-600**
NB Similar models were sold by Vectis Auctions Ltd in December 2000 for **£180** (H130) and **£600** (H131).

Tractoys Models

    Ferguson 25 Tractor **£175-200**

True-to-Type Models (similar in

size to Matchbox 1:75s; all have unpainted cast wheels)
    Cable-Layer Truck.
    Green truck, Grey/Cream cable drum...... **£25-35**
    Tip Cart Truck. Red body and tipper....... **£25-35**
    Excavator Truck.
    Green body, Blue back **£25-35**
    NB The three models listed above were sold by Vectis Auctions Ltd in 2000 for **£800**!

Tremo Models See also 'Jolly Roger'.

    Set No.2 'Famous Fighting Ships of the Royal Navy'. Contains 5 ships: 'Resolution', 'Defender', 'Dauntless', Grimsby Escort Veassel + 'Shark' Submarine. Green presentation box / packing......... **£250-300**

Tudor Rose

    Heavy Duty Farm Tractor Red / Yellow / Silver, Green driver, boxed **£100-150**

Wardie Products Ltd

    Oil Cabinets Set, boxed.
    Twelve Oil Bins, 'Castrol', 'Shell', etc. **£200-250**
    Garage Personnel Set, boxed.
    Five various figures plus pumps, etc..... **£300-400**
    'FINA' Petrol Pumps Set, boxed.
    Six blue pumps **£80-90**
    Traffic Signals Set, boxed. Ten signs with Traffic Light and Beacon **£30-40**
    Garage Equipment Set, with 'BP' and National Benzole' signs, boxed. Two Pumps, 'DUNLOP' Tyre Rack', 'Castrol' Oil Cabinet **£200-250**
    Garage Equipment Set, with 'ESSO' and 'OPEN' Signs, boxed. Three 'ESSO' Pumps and an 'Essolube' Oil cabinet. **£50-75**

Wend-al Ltd

    Horse-drawn Farm Vehicles:
    Rake, Grass Cutter, Reaper..................... ea. NGPP
    Tumbrel Cart, Red or Green Cart, dark brown Horse, driver, blue box......... **£75-100**
    Horse-drawn Plough Display Box.
    Plough, Ploughman, white Horse **£200-300**
    Farmyard Display Box. Includes Farmer's Wife, Poultry, Animals............ **£200-300**
    Farm Set with Farmer and Land Girl, plus ten farmyard animals, boxed......... **£125-150**

Unknown Diecast Manufacturer

(possibly Modern Products)
    'Cinderella Coach to the Ball' in lift-off lid box with colour wash line drawing. Early 1950s, Pink Coach and frame, blue spoked wheels, two cast-in footmen, four white horses, 6½' long. Box **£175-225**

Wardie Garage Accessory Series – a group of 12 Oil Bins with various logos to include 'Esso,' 'Castrol' and 'Shell' plus others.

Tudor Rose (UK) clockwork Dump Truck, yellow, black chassis.

Sacul TV Series - The Flowerpot Men, comprising: Bill & Ben with outstretched arms, Little Weed and 2 x Terracotta Flower Pots.

A small collection of Skybirds including 6-wheeled Open Lorry in green, solid black metal wheels, three repainted models including 6-wheeled Army Type Lorry with tilt in two-tone brown, 'Esso' Tanker in green with yellow hubs and another Tanker in blue.

Skybirds (UK) No 36A Lanchester Armoured Car - khaki green, with black tyres including spare.

Wardie Master Models: WH Smith Bookstall, LT Shelter, Police Boxes, Telephone Boxes and diecast figures.

Sundaw Products No H130 - Motorbus - red, 'Transport Services.'

Meccano

Meccano Cars and Constructor Outfits

In 1932, Meccano introduced its 'Motor Car Constructor Outfit'. With its special parts (not compatible with standard Meccano), a small range of very sporty looking car models could be built. A year later, a smaller set, designated 'Motor Car Constructor Outfit No 1' appeared and the first set was given the superior 'No 2' tag. Features abounded: stylishly shaped mudguards and body panels, alternative radiators, working Ackermann steering, a driver; even working brakes! The kits included a powerful clockwork motor as standard and the whole lot could be driven 'at night' with the addition of the Motor Car Lighting Set that came along as early as 1933.

In addition, spare parts were available from Meccano dealers that enabled young builders to achieve different colour schemes. Body sections were available in orange and in yellow, wings in orange and in green, and wheels in orange or yellow.

Ready-built models were available and are listed below. These were made up from parts relevant to the No 1 Outfit. A non-constructional Meccano Sports Car was also marketed at the time, as was a Motor Car Garage to house the vehicles, whether ready-made or owner constructed.

Production quantities of the outfits appear to have been somewhat limited in the latter half of the 1930s, thus surviving items are quite rare nowadays, especially in good and complete condition. All the Car Constructor Outfits were withdrawn from the Meccano Products Catalogue around 1940 and were never reintroduced.

Motor Car Constructor Outfit
Made from 1932 to 1933. No driver figure.
Supplied in a strong green carton with a colourful label on the lid. In 1933, this set was promoted to 'Motor Car Constructor Outfit No 2'. Three colour options were available:
Red main components..............................**£400-500**
Blue main components............................**£400-500**
Green main components.........................**£400-500**

No 1 Car Constructor Outfit

Motor Car Constructor No 1 Outfit
Made from 1933 to 1940. No driver figure.
Supplied in a strong green and yellow carton on the lid of which was a colourful label with an artist's impression of the Road Racer at speed.
Outfits were supplied complete with a powerful clockwork motor. Four colour options were available:
Red and Light Blue main components....**£300-400**
Light Blue and Cream main components**£300-400**
Green and Yellow main components **£300-400**
Cream and Red main components.........**£300-400**

Ready-built models were also available, made up from the No.1 Outfit:
1/1 **Sports Tourer** (with Hood), blue box, instruction sheet...............................**£500-700**
1/2 **Saloon Coupé**, blue box with instruction sheet **£500-700**

1/3 **Road Racer**, blue box with instruction sheet **£500-700**
1/4 **Sports Tourer**, blue box with instruction sheet **£500-700**

Meccano Two-seater Sports Car (non-constructional)
Length 8½". Clockwork motor. Available in three different colours:
Red, patterned green box has lift-off lid with full-colour label **£900-1,100**
Blue, patterned green box has lift-off lid with full-colour label **£900-1,100**
Cream, patterned green box has lift-off lid with full-colour label **£900-1,100**

Unboxed Car Constructor set

Motor Car Constructor No 2 Outfit
Made from 1933 to 1941. Presentation and colours of parts were identical to those of the No.1 Outfit. As this set was developed from the 1932 Outfit, early versions have no driver figure. This enhancement (plus a few other minor modifications) appeared a few months later. The separately available spare parts also came in the same choices as for the No.1 set. However, it is very important to note that parts for the No.1 Outfit were **not compatible** with the No.2 Outfit (nor with standard Meccano parts).
Red and Light Blue main components**£1,000-1,250**
Light Blue and Cream main components **£1,000-1,250**
Green and Yellow main components **£1,000-1,250**
Cream and Red main components....**£1,000-1,250**

Ready-built models were also available, made up from the No.2 Outfit:
2/1 **Sports Tourer** (with Hood), blue box, instruction sheet...............................**£700-900**
2/2 **Saloon Coupé**, blue box with instruction sheet **£700-900**
2/3 **Road Racer**, blue box with instruction sheet **£700-900**
2/4 **Sports Tourer**, blue box with instruction sheet **£700-900**

Meccano No 2/2 Coupé 'ready-built' model

Motor Car Lighting Set
Introduced in 1933. This set enabled the headlights in the No.2 Outfit to be illuminated using a 3 volt battery (not supplied).
Green box with lift-off lid ('M251'), instruction sheet **£150-300**

Meccano Motor Car Garage
designed to accommodate Meccano Motor Cars (or others of a suitable size).
Inside dimensions: H 5in., L 13in., W 7 3/4in. Green box, lift-off lid **£200-400**

Meccano Aeroplane Constructor Outfits

Meccano Aeroplane Constructor Outfits were introduced in October 1931 and were available in two varieties, simply called Outfits No 1 and No 2. Unlike the Car Constructor Outfits, there was compatability between the No 1 and No 2 Aeroplane sets. This allowed the inclusion of a further set - No 1A Accessory Outfit which could convert the smaller one into the larger. Early wheels were actually standard Meccano pulleys painted red. There were a few other conventional Meccano parts in these outfits

(originally sprayed in silver paint) but the major components were specially designed for the purpose.

For the No 1 set, the manual described three bi-planes and three monoplanes that could be constructed. With its extra parts, which included diecast engine and seaplane floats, the No 2 manual suggested 16 additional potential models.

Early in 1932, two clockwork motors were introduced for use with these outfits. The smaller of them just rotated the propeller, while the larger one actually provided sufficient motive power to the landing wheels to cause the model aircraft to taxi along the carpet runway.

A year later, much development work had produced better components. Special wheels complete with stylish spats, for instance, replaced the unsuitable pulley wheels. Wing edges had become realistically rounded and wing tips and fuselages were enamelled in red.

1933 saw the introduction of outfits No OO and No O as cheaper, simpler sets aimed at younger builders, and not interchangeable with Nos 1 and 2. In the same year, the range was enlarged to include No

1 Special Outfit (20 models) and No 2 Special Outfit (44 models). Available in various bright and attractive colours, the special outfits were very well endowed with new purpose-made components such as workable ailerons and rudders, passenger window panels, pilot's cabins, tail elevators, etc. There was even a model pilot for insertion into the open-cockpit model. Both civilian and military liveries were from time to time available in the late 1930s.

As with most Meccano items, the war brought production to a halt around 1940. Aeroplane Constructor Outfits were officially withdrawn in 1941 and sadly were never made again.

No 00 Aeroplane Constructor Outfit
Made from 1932 to 1940. Designed for the younger builder, this set had a one-piece fuselage plus a few simple parts that were not compatible with Outfits No 1 and 2. Supplied in a stout box with a two-colour label on the lid.
Red and cream components. Blue box with instructions **£200-300**
Green and cream components. Blue box with instructions **£200-300**
Blue and white components. Blue box with instructions **£200-300**

No 0 Aeroplane Constructor Outfit
Made from 1932 to 1940. As the No 0 Outfit but with more parts (also not compatible with Outfits No 1 and 2). Supplied in a stout box with a full-colour label on the lid.
Red and cream components. Blue box with instructions **£250-400**
Green and cream components. Blue box with instructions **£250-400**
Blue and white components. Blue box with instructions **£250-400**
Seville Grey components, RAF markings. Blue box + instructions **£250-400**

No 0P Aeroplane Hangar Outfit
Made from 1933 to 1940. The complete range of parts from Outfit No 0, packed into a No 01 Aeroplane Hangar, then into a stout carton.
Red and cream components, blue box with lift-off lid, instructions.. **£350-500**
Green and cream components, blue box with lift-off lid, instructions.. **£350-500**
Blue and white components, blue box with lift-off lid, instructions.. **£350-500**

No 01 Aeroplane Hangar
Made from 1933 to 1940. To house a model aircraft made from Outfits No 00, 0 or 01P. Single door, size (mm): 292(L) x 260(D) x 108(H) .... NGPP

No 02 Aeroplane Hangar
Made from 1933 to 1940. To house two models made from Outfits No 00, 0 or 01P. Single door, size (mm): 546(L) x 279(D) x 159(H) .... NGPP

No 1 Aeroplane Constructor Outfit
Made from 1931 to 1932. Silver coloured components, standard Meccano pulley wheels (red). Wings and tailplanes have 'RAF markings. Manual shows 6 examples of mono and biplanes that can be built. Supplied in a strong carton with a colourful label on the lid...................... **£100-200**

No 1 Aeroplane Constructor Outfit
Made from 1932 to 1940. Purpose-made wheels with enveloping spats replaced the Meccano pulley wheels. Wing and tailplanes edges were more rounded and realistic. Civilian as well as

'Military' models could also be built. Supplied in a strong blue carton with a colourful label on the lid.
Silver components (early production).... **£150-250**
Cream components, RAF roundels **£250-400**
Blue and cream components, RAF roundels **£250-400**
Red and cream components **£250-400**
Green and cream components............... **£250-400**

No 1A Aeroplane Constructor Accessory Outfit
Made from 1931 to 1932. Silver components, sufficient to convert the No 1 Outfit into a No 2. Supplied in a strong carton with a colourful label on the lid **£100-200**

No 1 Aeroplane Constructor Outfit

No 1A Aeroplane Constructor Accessory Outfit
Made from 1932 to 1940. As the earlier set, but in the colours of the main Outfits available at the time Supplied in a strong carton with a colourful label on the lid. **£100-200**

No 2 Aeroplane Constructor Outfit
Made from 1931 to 1932. Silver coloured components, red standard Meccano pulley wheels. Additional parts included seaplane floats and diecast engines. Wings and tailplanes have RAF markings.
Manual shows 22 examples of mono, bi and seaplanes that can be built. Supplied in a strong carton with a colourful label on the lid.
.... **£100-200**

No 2 Aeroplane Constructor Outfit
Made from 1932 to 1940. As with the No 1 Outfit, purpose-made wheels with spats replaced the original pulley wheels. Wing and tailplanes edges were more rounded and realistic. A much larger range of models could be built, including 'planes with 1, 2 or 3 engines, a Racing Seaplane, and a Giant Italian Bomber. Supplied in a strong blue carton with a colourful label on the lid.
Silver and blue components (early production)
.... **£150-250**

Cream components, RAF roundels **£300-400**
Blue and white components, RAF roundels **£500-750**
Red and Cream components.................. **£300-400**
Green and Cream components............... **£300-400**

No 1 Special Aeroplane Constructor Outfit
Made from 1933 to 1940. In addition to the improved parts in the standard Outfits, new components in the 'Special' sets included engine cowlings, a pilot figure, passenger windows, moving ailerons and rudders. The manual (that covered both Outfits 1 and 2) showed 20 example models. Supplied in a strong blue carton with a colourful label on the lid.
Silver components (early production).... **£300-450**
Cream components, RAF roundels **£300-450**
Blue and white components, RAF roundels **£300-450**
Red and Cream components.................. **£300-450**
Green and Cream components........... **£300-450**

No 1AS Special Aeroplane Constructor Accessory Outfit
Made from 1933 to 1940. This set provided sufficient parts to convert the No1 Special Outfit into a No 2. Supplied in a strong blue carton with a colourful label on the lid. **£100-200**

No 2 Special Aeroplane Constructor Outfit
Made from 1933 to 1940. As the No 1 Special Outfit, but with many additional parts that allowed the construction of the 44 models shown in the manual, plus many others. Supplied in a strong blue carton with a colourful label on the lid.
Silver components (early production)
.... **£500-750**
Cream components, RAF roundels **£500-750**
Blue and white components, RAF roundels **£500-750**
Red and Cream components............... **£500-750**
Green and Cream components........... **£500-750**

Meccano Aero Motor No1
Produced from early 1932. Designed to fit in the fuselage component of Outfit Nos 1 or 2, the clockwork motor would 'rotate the propeller at high speed, thus greatly adding to the realism of the model' **£30-40**

Meccano Aero Motor No2
Produced from early 1932. Suitable for use with Outfit Nos 1 or 2, this was a more powerful clockwork motor that would spin the propeller and drive the landing wheels 'making the machines taxi along the floor in a most realistic manner.' An Adjustable Tailwheel was included with Aero Motor No 2 ....**£60-80**

M236 Aeroplane Pilots.
Trade box of six containing 2 red, 2 green and 2 blue... **£200-300**

Hornby Speed Boats

Hornby toy boats were introduced in the summer of 1932, in four basic hulls 21.5cm, 23.5cm, 32cm and 42cm. Although In 1932, only one model was available; it was simply called Speed Boat 'Hornby' 23.5cm, having no reference number. In 1933 Speed Boat No 3 was launched and the first models produced were also named 'Hornby'. The range soon grew with four other boats put into production costing between 2/6 and 17/6 each, depending on their size. The Hornby 'Racer' range followed in late 1934, available in 3 hull lengths from 21.5cm (Racer1), 32cm (Racer 2) and 42cm (Racer 3). Hornby received many letters from female collectors asking for other 'water toys' and in response they launched a now rare 'Clockwork Duck' using a similar hull to Hawk, packaged simply in a Hawk Speedboat box. This, like all the Hornby pre-war boats was operated by a clockwork motor, these were specially geared for higher speed, although they did not travel that

far on a single winding. Hornby claimed that their 'Racer 3' could travel almost 300ft at a single winding, whereas the standard gearing used for both 'Viking' and 'Venture' would travel over 500ft. Also available from retailers were Pennants, Motors, Collectors badges, Propellers and Shafts for the customisation or scratch-building of model boats.

Production of the original tinplate products ceased at the outbreak of war in 1939 and sadly never returned, as Hornby began to focus on their railway customers as the boats were seen to be too expensive to make and sell. 1960 saw a brief reappearance, but only a small new range of plastic boats were launched with extra detail and clockwork motors until 1965. A battery-operated model continued in production up to 1969, the range being dropped by Lines Brothers five years after their acquisition of Meccano.

A boxed pre-war Hornby Speed Boat, a No 3 model 1935/1936 showing extremely little use with pale blue hull and engine cover with cream decking and dark blue accessories. The model retains its original front screen and transfers 'Racer Three', and is in original box together with forward and rear packing pieces and original key contained in original envelope

1932-32	**Speed Boat 'Hornby',** Red, Green or Blue, open cockpit, 16in long **£300-400**
1933-34	**Speed Boat No. 3, 'Hornby',** Red, Green or Blue, open cockpit, 16in long **£350-400**
1934-39	**Speed Boat No.2, 'Condor',** Red/Cream, 16½in long.......... **£350-400**
	Speed Boat No.3, 'Gannet', Blue/White.............................. **£350-400**
	Speed Boat No.3, 'Curlew', Green/Ivory **£350-400**
1934-39	**Speed Boat No.1 'Hawk',** Red/cream, Blue/White or Green/Ivory 9¼in long **£80-100**
1947-50	**Speed Boat No.1 'Gleam',** Green/White, picture box.............. **£90-120**
1947-50	**Speed Boat No.1 'Naval Launch X46',** Grey, picture box..........**£60-80**
1934-39	**Speed Boat No.2 'Swift',** (blue box, full-colour label), Red/Cream, Blue/White or Yellow/White, 12½in long............ **£100-150**
1934-39	**Limousine Boat No.4, 'Venture',** Red/Cream, Blue/White or Green/Ivory, 16½in long **£400-550**
1934-39	**Cabin Cruiser No.5 'Viking',** Red/Cream, Blue/White or Green/

	Ivory, 16½in long **£300-350**
1934-39	**Racing Boat No.1 'Racer I',** Cream/Green, 8½in long **£125-150**
1934-39	**Racing Boat No.2 'Racer II',** Blue/Cream, 12½in long.......... **£150-170**
1934-39	**Racing Boat No.3 'Racer III',** Red/Cream, 16½in long.......... **£350-400**
1934-39	**Hornby Water Toy (Duck),** Superstructure is a tinplate pressing in the shape of a duck fitted to a 'Hawk' hull. 9¼in long **£1,000-1,200**
1960-62	**Speed Boat No.3 River Launch,** Plastic moulding, 10in. long, clockwork motor **£30-45**
1960-62	**Speed Boat No.4, Fast Patrol Launch,** plastic moulding, White hull, 'mahogany' deck, 10in. long, clockwork motor **£30-50**
1960-65	**Speed Boat No.5 RAF Range Safety Launch,** plastic moulding, Black hull, Brown deck, 10in. long, clockwork **£50-60**
1963-69	**Speed Boat,** plastic moulding, battery-operated motor **£30-35**

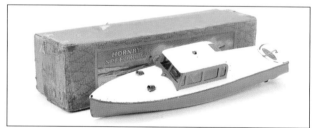

Hornby No 4 Speedboat 'Venture', finished with red hull and white decking with white and red cabin.

ABOVE Meccano/Hornby Speedboat No 2 'SWIFT', finished in two-tone green and cream.

LEFT Sutcliffe Commodore tinplate clockwork Cruiser - red hull, cream deck superstructure, blue engine cover, with deck mounted accessories.

Sutcliffe Model Boats

Sutcliffe Pressings started in 1885 from humble beginnings in Horsforth Leeds, initially repairing old pans and kettles for local residents and factories in the nearby area. In 1905 the company started to produce different size oilcans for the engineering and domestic market, photography exposure plates along with darkroom lights. In 1918 with the scarcity of any toys entering the country Sutcliffe Pressings produced their first 16" Battleship, nobody seems to know the exact reason to move into toys but it is thought that the then director bore a love for the tinplate boats available at the time from Germany. This initial battleship remained un-named. The early battleships were powered by a simple circulation type boiler heated via a basic spirit burning lamp. In 1928 the factory produced their first clockwork powered battleship aptly named Valiant. This was the start of a range of boats that would include tinplate yachts, speedboats, cruisers and in 1934 submarines. Each submarine was tested before it left the factory to make sure when

it got to its proud owner it would dive then resurface. Over the years the company had many partnerships to produce boats, Disney for a Nautilus diving submarine in 1955 to commemorate the launch of 20,000 leagues under the sea, Harry Corbett in 1958 to produce a Sooty Speedboat and a year later a matching Noddy speedboat. Sutcliffe Pressing's also produced a range of three Bluebird speedboats to include a spectacular tri hull version. Around 1960 they produced several plastic boats both clockwork and battery powered, which also included a catamaran called "Typhoon". After 1963 the factory stuck to its more successful tinplate 9" and 12" hulls powered by both clockwork and battery. Over the years Sutcliffe Pressings produced many other toys to include push along cranes and trucks, mini loaf tins, children's dust pan and brush set and in the later years a push along dump truck named "Trojan". In 1984 the factory closed and the then current Director retired, the machinery and presses were sold and the factory demolished to make way for modern flats.

1918 **'Un-named 16" Battleship'.** The first boat produced by Sutcliffe, powered by a single spirit burning lamp .... **£1,500-£1,800**

1920 **'Un-named 12" Battleship'** Single spirit burner powered **£750**

1921 **'Un-named 16" Battleship'** Double spirit burner powered **£900**

1922 **'Un-named 16" Cruiser'** Single spirit burner powered with a copper lift up cabin roof ....**£1,000-£1,100**

1925/26 **'Un-named 8" and 12" Speedboats'** Single spirit burner powered, red and white in colour.. **£600-£650**

1928 **'Valiant 12" Battleship'** clockwork, with moveable gun turrets and mast .... **£600-£650**

1929 **'Nelson 16" Battleship'** clockwork, with moveable gun turrets and mast .... **£800-£1000**

1930 **'Electric Powered 24" Speedboat'** With a slide on copper cabin roof .... **£800-£1,000**

1930 **'Minx 12" Speedboat'** clockwork, with a flip up windscreen and motor stop, mahogany engine cover .... **£600-£750**

1931 **'Meteor 16" Speedboat'** clockwork, with soldered windscreen and mahogany engine cover... **£600-£750**

Early 12v Speedboat

1932 **'12"/16"/20" Sailing yachts'** tinplate with moveable rudder and pinstriped sails ....**£1,000-£1,200**

1932 **'Racer1 9" Speedboat'**clockwork, with slide off engine cover and motor stop .... **£200-£300**

1933 **'Un-named 20" Speedboat'** clockwork, with flip up windscreen, mahogany engine cover and seat to rear .... **£800-£1000**

1933 **'Snappy 9" Sub Chaser'** clockwork, with slide off upper deck with gun turret .... **£450-£500**

1934 **'Swallow 12" Cruiser'** clockwork, with slide off lid to the cabin, well area to rear of boat with handrails.............................. **£750-£800**

1934 **'Unda-Wunda Submarine'** clockwork, with rubber periscope bung, keel is rounded at base with copper wire inserted for ballast, yellow picture box with instructions

.... **£500-£550**

1934 **'Racer1 9" Speedboat'** clockwork, with oval lift off motor cover and metal topped cork stopper, various colours .... **£200-£300**

1935 **'Zip 9" Speedboat'** clockwork, totally enclosed motor with blue and red waterslide transfer to engine cover .... **£300-£350**

1936 **'Commodore 16" Cruiser'** clockwork, with slide off lid to the cabin, well area to rear of boat with handrails.................... **£750-£800**

1936 **'Empress 20" Cruiser'** clockwork, with slide off lid to the cabin, well area to rear of boat with a mahogany seat ....**£1,000-£1,200**

1937 **'Bluebird 1 9" Speedboat'** clockwork, with three single exhaust ports to either side of raised deck, two part windscreen, no forward engine intakes, plain box .... **£500-£600**

1938 **'Grenville Destroyer'** clockwork, with grey upper structure and black below the waterline, picture box labelling every part of the boat, clockwork motor wound via second funnel............................ **£700-£750**

1946 **'Racer1 9" Speedboat'** clockwork, painted red hull, white deck and blue removable engine cover. Picture box.............. **£100-£150**

1947 **'Pull Along 9" Steamer'** no motor or rudder a simple tow eye soldered to the bow to attached string, single funnel to superstructure .... **£500-£550**

1948 **'Unda-Wunda Submarine'** clockwork, with rubber periscope bung, and pre-weighted diving keel .... **£250-£300**

1948 **'Bluebird1 9" Speedboat'** clockwork, with a single orange exhaust port to either side of raised deck, one part windscreen, two forward facing orange engine intakes, plain box... **£450-£500**

1948 **'Grenville Destroyer'** clockwork, with grey upper structure and red below the waterline, picture box labelling every part of the boat, clockwork motor wound via second funnel............................ **£600-£650**

1949 **'Bluebird1 9" Speedboat'** clockwork, with a single gold exhaust port to either side of raised deck, one part windscreen, two forward facing gold engine intakes, white picture box.................................. **£300-£325**

1950 **'Viking 9" Steamer'** clockwork, twin funnel steamer with gold detailed decks .... **£250-£300**

1954 **'Fury 9" Torpedo Boat'** clockwork, large single funnel with gun turrets and torpedo

tubes on deck, white picture box.................
.... **£250-£300**

1955 **'Nautilus Submarine'** clockwork, with rubber periscope bung, pre weighted diving keel, no hole on rudder, in green and purple picture flip up lid box .... **£250-£300**

1955 **'Comet 9" Speedboat'** clockwork, in various colours, made until 1980 ....**£100-£120**

1958 **'Sooty 9" Speedboat'** clockwork, painted cream with Sooty decals to engine cover, included a small plastic Sooty figure, in a Sooty picture box ....**£600-£750**

1958 **'Bluebird II Speedboat'** clockwork, tri- hull design, two gold exhausts to side of the deck, in a picture lift off lid box .... **£350-£450**

Noddy Speedboat

1959 **'Noddy 9" Speedboat'** clockwork, various hull colours with Noddy decals to engine cover, included a small plastic Noddy figure, in a Noddy picture box .... **£700-£750**

1960 **'Zodiac Plastic Speedboat'** battery powered, plastic hull with wooden deck, in brown corrugated box with picture sticker.................................. **£200-£250**

1960 **'Meteor Plastic Speedboat'** clockwork, plastic hull with wooden deck, in brown corrugated box with picture sticker .... **£200-£250**

1960 **'Commodore Plastic Cruiser Kit'** battery powered, self build plastic kit, plastic hull with wooden deck, balsa wood cabin, in a blue box with picture sticker...... **£250-£300**

1960 **'Minx Plastic Speedboat'** clockwork, plastic hull with plastic deck, in brown corrugated box with picture sticker .... **£200-£250**

1961 **'Typhoon Plastic Catamaran'** plastic hull with plastic deck, wooden dagger board, blue sails, in brown corrugated box with picture sticker .... **£200-£250**

1963 **'Sea-Wolf Submarine'** clockwork, cream, pre-weighted diving keel, rubber periscope bung with red plastic coning tower and missile, green and purple picture box

.... **£200-£250**
1963 **'Jupiter 9" Pilot Boat'** clockwork, picture box with mast .... **£80-£100**

View of the factory

1963 **'Merlin 12" Speedboat'** battery powered, control switch situated behind windscreen, lift off engine cover, plastic flag, in picture box .... **£180-£200**
1963 **'Merlin 12" Speedboat'** battery powered, control switch situated on engine cover, plastic flag in picture box .... **£100-£120**
1967 **'Sprite 9" Day Cruiser'** clockwork, in various colours, picture box, produced until 1980 .... **£60-£80**
1968 **'Kestrel 12" Cruiser'** battery powered, control switch situated on the lift off engine cover, plastic flag and radar mast and plastic windscreen, in picture box .... **£90-£120**
1968 **'Hawk 12" Speedboat'** clockwork, finished in yellow with green engine cover only produced in small numbers, lift off engine cover, plastic flag, picture box.... **£180-£200**
1968 **'Hawk 12" Speedboat'** clockwork, finished in green and white, with green lift off engine cover, plastic flag, picture box.... **£180-£200**
1969 **'Sea-Wolf Submarine'** clockwork, yellow, pre-weighted diving keel, rubber periscope bung with red plastic conning tower and missile, cream and red picture box .... **£180-£200**
1969 **'Tiger 9" Speedboat'** clockwork, raised engine cover secured by a screw, picture box... **£120-£150**
1971 **'Victor 9" Torpedo Boat'** clockwork, blue hull, four black plastic torpedo tubes fastened to deck, forward facing gun turret, mast, picture box.......................... **£110-£125**
1976 **'Unda-Wunda Submarine'** clockwork, blue, with rubber periscope bung, and pre weighted diving keel .... **£200-£220**
1976 **'Nautilus Submarine'** clockwork, with rubber periscope bung, pre weighted diving keel, hole drilled in rudder, in red and orange picture lift off lid box...... **£180-£250**
1977 **'Commodore 12" Cruiser'** clockwork, lift off engine cover, plastic flag and radar mast and plastic windscreen, in picture box .... **£90-£120**
1978 **'Jane 9" Speedboat'** clockwork, produced for "The Windermere Steamboat Museum", orange in colour with white adhesive transfer, in yellow picture box (rare) .... **£300-£350**
1978 **'Jane 9" Speedboat'** clockwork, produced for "The Windermere Steamboat Museum", orange in colour with white adhesive transfer, in plain white box or brown corrugated box with information sheet .... **£200-£250**
1978 **'Valiant 12" Battleship'** clockwork reproduction of the earlier version, motor wound between the funnels, metal flag, mast and hull stand included in lift off lid picture box .... **£180-£250**
* Towards the end of production a number of reproduction boats were made to use up old hull parts, these must not be confused with the original models and can be

identified by the later Sutcliffe Boats waterslide transfer, they also all came packed in plain white boxes.
1979* **'Noddy 9" Speedboat'** clockwork, various hull colours with Noddy decals to engine cover, included a small plastic Noddy figure, in a plain white box......... **£550-£600**
1979* **'Bluebird1 9" Speedboat'** clockwork, with a single gold exhaust port to either side of raised deck, one part windscreen, two forward facing gold engine intakes, white plain box.......................................**£180-£250**
1979* **'Fury 9" Torpedo Boat'** clockwork, large single funnel with gun turrets and torpedo tubes on deck, white plain box .... **£170-£190**
1979* **'Viking 9" Steamer'** clockwork, twin funnel steamer with gold detailed decks, in a plain white box .... **£180-£200**
1979* **'Zip 9" Speedboat'** clockwork, totally enclosed motor with blue and red waterslide transfer to engine cover, in a plain white box.......................................**£180-£200**
1979* **'Snappy 9" Sub Chaser'** clockwork with soldered upper deck with gun turrets, in plain white box........................... **£180-£200**
1979* **'Comet 9" Speedboat'** clockwork, in various colours, in a plain white box .... **£100-£120**
1980 **'Minx 12" Speedboat'** clockwork reproduction of the 1930s model with a soldered windscreen and no motor stop, mahogany engine cover, sold in a Hawk Speedboat box with 'Minx' written on the end flaps...................... .... **£180-£200**

Diana Speedboat

1981 **'Diana 12" Cruiser'** clockwork, in blue with a white cabin roof attached to the windscreen, plastic flag, sold in a white corrugated box with picture attached, only 375 made .... **£180-£250**
1981 **'Valiant 12" Battleship'** battery powered reproduction of the earlier version, electric motor switched on between the funnels, metal flag, mast and hull stand included in lift off lid picture box with sticker applied over the word clockwork, only 6 made .... **£700-£800**

Miscellaneous and Other Toys
1905-1980 **Various oil can,** midgets, ¼ pint, ½ pint in various colours............. **£10-£50**
1963-1968 **'Mummy's Help'** a small dust pan and brush set sold in a picture box, various colours .... **£80-£120**

Crane, oil can, baking tins and pull-along truck

1965-1970 **'Junior Pull Along Crane'** tinplate crane, with moveable jib and bucket, boxed in corrugated card with printed picture...................... **£50-£70**
1965-1968 **'Pull Along Truck'** tinplate four wheeled truck with detachable handle, in various colours .... **£50-£70**
1971-1972 **'Mini Loaf Tins'** polished mini loaf tins with folded over edges sold in sets of four............................. **£20-£30**
1970-1972 **'Mamod' branded Oil Can** green in colour with a Mamod Steam waterslide transfer, sold in a clear plastic bag .... **£70-£90**
1972-1975 **'A Gift For Every Man'** included a midget oil can and a tube of lubricating oil in a presentation box .... **£100-£150**

Oil Cans and Dumper

1972-1980 **'Oil Can Display Box'** including 6 midget oil can .... **£180-£200**

Point of Sale Material.
1958-1970 **'Nautilus 3-D Display Stand'** produced from fold out cardboard to display the clockwork submarine........................ **£250-£300**
1958-1970 **'Nautilus Fold Out Stand'** produced to assist sales stating "TV Demonstrated" green in colour .... **£110-£150**
1960-1970 **'Sutcliffe Boat Wire Stand'** produced to hold four 9" boats on display .... **£120-£150**
1969-1975 **' Submarine 3-D Cardboard Stand'** produced to display two submarines for sale, fold out construction to produce an under water scene .... **£300-£350**
1969-1970 **'Sea-Wolf Cardboard Stand'** made from card yellow in colour to hold and display one model by its keel .... **£30-£50**
1969-1970 **'Sutcliffe Boats Best For Performance'** made from card yellow in colour to hold one 9" boat on display .... **£50-£70**
1971-1972 **'Bake a Cake' Display Card** produced to promote the sales of the mini loaf tins .... **£200-£250**
1970-1975 **'Member of the Sutcliffe Boat Club Badge'** a small yellow pin badge purchased from authorised boat retailers .... **£20-£25**

Advertiser's Index

Notes

Notes

Notes